Hofstadter.
Nuclear and nucleon structure.

Date Due

NUCLEA[illegible]ND NUCLEON S[illegible]JCTURE

Frontiers in Physics

A Lecture Note and Reprint Series

DAVID PINES, *Editor*

N. Bloembergen **NUCLEAR MAGNETIC RELAXATION:** *A Reprint Volume*

Geoffrey F. Chew **S-MATRIX THEORY OF STRONG INTERACTIONS:** *A Lecture Note and Reprint Volume*

R. P. Feynman **QUANTUM ELECTRODYNAMICS:** *A Lecture Note and Reprint Volume*

R. P. Feynman **THE THEORY OF FUNDAMENTAL PROCESSES:** *A Lecture Note Volume*

Hans Frauenfelder **THE MÖSSBAUER EFFECT:** *A Collection of Reprints with an Introduction*

Robert Hofstadter **ELECTRON SCATTERING AND NUCLEAR AND NUCLEON STRUCTURE:** *A Collection of Reprints with an Introduction*

Leo P. Kadanoff and Gordon Baym **QUANTUM STATISTICAL MECHANICS:** *A Lecture Note Volume*

George E. Pake **PARAMAGNETIC RESONANCE:** *An Introductory Monograph*

David Pines **THE MANY-BODY PROBLEM:** *A Lecture Note and Reprint Volume*

L. Van Hove, N. M. Hugenholtz, and L. P. Howland **PROBLEMS IN THE QUANTUM THEORY OF MANY-PARTICLE SYSTEMS:** *A Reprint Volume*

ELECTRON SCATTERING AND NUCLEAR AND NUCLEON STRUCTURE

A COLLECTION OF REPRINTS WITH AN INTRODUCTION

*

ROBERT HOFSTADTER
Stanford University

W. A. BENJAMIN, INC. New York 1963

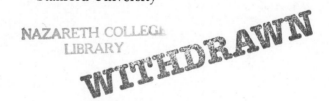

ELECTRON SCATTERING AND
NUCLEAR AND NUCLEON STRUCTURE
A Collection of Reprints with an Introduction

Library of Congress Catalog Card Number 62-17799
Manufactured in the United States of America

*The manuscript was received on September 20, 1962,
and was published March 15, 1963*

W. A. BENJAMIN, INC.
2465 Broadway, New York 25, New York

EDITOR'S FOREWORD

The problem of communicating in a coherent fashion the recent developments in the most exciting and active fields of physics seems particularly pressing today. The enormous growth in the number of physicists has tended to make the familiar channels of communication considerably less effective. It has become increasingly difficult for experts in a given field to keep up with the current literature; the novice can only be confused. What is needed is both a consistent account of a field and the presentation of a definite "point of view" concerning it. Formal monographs cannot meet such a need in a rapidly developing field, and, perhaps more important, the review article seems to have fallen into disfavor. Indeed, it would seem that the people most actively engaged in developing a given field are the people least likely to write at length about it.

"Frontiers in Physics" has been conceived in an effort to improve the situation in several ways. First, to take advantage of the fact that the leading physicists today frequently give a series of lectures, a graduate seminar, or a graduate course in their special fields of interest. Such lectures serve to summarize the present status of a rapidly developing field and may well constitute the only coherent account available at the time. Often, notes on lectures exist (prepared by the lecturer himself, by graduate students, or by postdoctoral fellows) and have been distributed in mimeographed form on a limited basis. One of the principal purposes of the "Frontiers in Physics" series is to make such notes available to a wider audience of physicists.

It should be emphasized that lecture notes are necessarily rough and informal, both in style and content, and those in the series will prove no exception. This is as it should be. The point of the series is to offer new, rapid, more informal, and it is hoped, more effective ways for physicists to teach one another. The point is lost if only elegant notes qualify.

A second way to improve communication in very active fields of physics is by the publication of collections of reprints of recent articles. Such collections are themselves useful to people working in the field. The value of the reprints would, however, seem much enhanced if the collection would be accompanied by an introduction of moderate length, which would serve to tie the collection together and, necessarily, constitute a brief survey of the present status of the field. Again, it is appropriate that such an introduction be informal, in keeping with the active character of the field.

A third possibility for the series might be called an informal monograph, to connote the fact that it represents an intermediate step between lecture notes and formal monographs. It would offer the author an opportunity to present his views of a field that has developed to the point at which a summation might prove extraordinarily fruitful, but for which a formal monograph might not be feasible or desirable.

Fourth, there are the contemporary classics—papers or lectures which constitute a particularly valuable approach to the teaching and learning of physics today. Here one thinks of fields that lie at the heart of much of present-day research, but whose essentials are by now well understood, such as quantum electrodynamics or magnetic resonance. In such fields some of the best pedagogical material is not readily available, either because it consists of papers long out of print or lectures that have never been published.

"Frontiers in Physics" is designed to be flexible in editorial format. Authors are encouraged to use as many of the foregoing approaches as seem desirable for the project at hand. The publishing format for the series is in keeping with its intentions. Photo-offset printing is used throughout, and the books are paperbound, in order to speed publication and reduce costs. It is hoped that the books will thereby be within the financial reach of graduate students in this country and abroad.

Finally, because the series represents something of an experiment on the part of the editor and the publisher, suggestions from interested readers as to format, contributors, and contributions will be most welcome.

DAVID PINES

Urbana, Illinois
August 1961

ACKNOWLEDGMENTS

The publisher wishes to acknowledge the assistance of the following organizations in the preparation of this volume:

The American Physical Society, for permission to reprint the articles from *The Physical Review, Physical Review Letters, Reviews of Modern Physics,* and the *Bulletin of the American Physical Society.*

The Italian Physical Society, for permission to reprint the articles from *Il Nuovo Cimento.*

The Royal Society, for permission to reprint the articles from the *Proceedings of the Royal Society.*

Academic Press, for permission to reprint the articles from the *Annals of Physics.*

CERN, for permission to reprint the article from the *Proceedings of the 1958 Annual International Conference on High Energy Physics at CERN.*

The National Academy of Sciences, for permission to reprint the article from the *Proceedings of the National Academy of Sciences of the United States of America.*

Macmillan & Co., Ltd., for permission to reprint the article from *Nature.*

Springer-Verlag, for permission to reprint the article from *Akademie der Wissenschaften in Wien.*

Saclay, for permission to reprint the article from Vol. II of the *Proceedings of the Aix-en-Provence International Conference on Elementary Particles, 1961.*

Annuals Reviews, Inc., for permission to reprint the article from the *Annual Review of Nuclear Science.*

The Institute of Physics and The Physical Society, for permission to reprint the article from the *Proceedings of the Physical Society.*

CONTENTS

Editor's Foreword v

Acknowledgments vii

Foreword 1

Comments on the Reprints 3

Reprints

1 The Quantum Theory of the Electron, P. A. M. Dirac; *Proc. Roy. Soc. (London)*, **A117**, 610 (1928) 31

2 The Scattering of Fast Electrons by Atomic Nuclei, N. F. Mott; *Proc. Roy. Soc. (London)*, **A124**, 425 (1929) 46

3 Uber die Wechselwirkung zwischen schnellan Elektronen und Atomkernen, E. Guth; *Akad. Wiss. Wien, Math.-Naturw. Kl.*, **24**, 299 (1934) 64

4 Interaction of Neutrons with Electrons in Lead, W. W. Havens, Jr., I. I. Rabi, and L. J. Rainwater; *Phys. Rev.*, **72**, 634 (1947) 72

5 On the Interaction between Neutrons and Electrons, E. Fermi and L. Marshall; *Phys. Rev.*, **72**, 1139 (1947) 75

6 The Charge Distribution in Nuclei and the Scattering of High Energy Electrons, M. E. Rose; *Phys. Rev.*, **73**, 279 (1948) 83

7 High Energy Elastic Scattering of Electrons on Protons, M. N. Rosenbluth; *Phys. Rev.*, **79**, 615 (1950) 89

8 The Effect of Nuclear Structure on the Elastic Scattering of Fast Electrons, L. R. B. Elton; *Proc. Phys. Soc. (London)*, **A63**, 1115 (1950) 94

9 Interaction of Neutrons with Electrons in Liquid Bismuth, W. W. Havens, Jr., L. J. Rainwater, and I. I. Rabi; *Phys. Rev.*, **82**, 345 (1951) 104

10 The Electron-Neutron Interaction, L. L. Foldy; *Phys. Rev.*, **83**, 688 (1951) 105

11 Scattering of 15.7-Mev Electrons by Nuclei, E. M. Lyman, A. O. Hanson, and M. B. Scott; *Phys. Rev.*, **84**, 626 (1951) 106

12 A Measurement of the Electron-Neutron Interaction, M. Hamermesh, G. R. Ringo, and A. Wattenberg; *Phys. Rev.*, **85**, 483 (1952) 115

13 The Neutron-Electron Interaction, J. A. Harvey, D. J. Hughes, and M. D. Goldberg; *Phys. Rev.*, **87**, 220 (1952) 116

14 The Electromagnetic Properties of Dirac Particles, L. L. Foldy; *Phys. Rev.*, **87**, 688 (1952) 117

15 The Electron-Neutron Interaction, L. L. Foldy; *Phys. Rev.*, **87**, 693 (1952) 123

16 The Neutron-Electron Interaction, D. J. Hughes, J. A. Harvey, M. D. Goldberg, and M. J. Stafne; *Phys. Rev.*, **90**, 497 (1953) 127

17 Scattering of High-Energy Electrons and the Method of Nuclear Recoil, R. Hofstadter, H. R. Fechter, and J. A. McIntyre; *Phys. Rev.*, **91**, 422 (1953) 128

18 High-Energy Electron Scattering by Nuclei, R. W. Pidd, C. L. Hammer, and E. C. Raka; *Phys. Rev.*, **92**, 436 (1953) 130

19 Studies of X-Rays from Mu-Mesonic Atoms, V. L. Fitch and J. Rainwater; *Phys. Rev.*, **92**, 789 (1953) 132

20 High-Energy Electron Scattering and Nuclear Structure Determinations, R. Hofstadter, H. R. Fechter, and J. A. McIntyre; *Phys. Rev.*, **92**, 978 (1953) 144

21 Phase-Shift Calculation of High-Energy Electron Scattering by Nuclei, D. R. Yennie, R. N. Wilson, and D. G. Ravenhall; *Phys. Rev.*, **92**, 1325 (1953) 154

22 Inelastic Scattering of 190-Mev Electrons in Beryllium, J. A. McIntyre, B. Hahn, and R. Hofstadter; *Phys. Rev.*, **94**, 1084 (1954) 155

23 Phase-Shift Calculation of High-Energy Electron Scattering, D. R. Yennie, D. G. Ravenhall, and R. N. Wilson; *Phys. Rev.*, **95**, 500 (1954) 156

24 High-Energy Electron Scattering and Nuclear Structure Determinations, II, R. Hofstadter, B. Hahn, A. W. Knudsen, and J. A. McIntyre; *Phys. Rev.*, **95**, 512 (1954) 169

25 Results of a Phase Shift Calculation of High-Energy Electron Scattering, D. G. Ravenhall and D. R. Yennie; *Phys. Rev.*, **96**, 239 (1954) 173

26 Nuclear Multipole Transitions in Inelastic Electron Scattering, L. I. Schiff; *Phys. Rev.*, **96**, 765 (1954) 175

27 Electron Scattering from the Proton, R. Hofstadter and R. W. McAllister; *Phys. Rev.*, **98**, 217 (1955) 183

28 High-Energy Electron Scattering and Nuclear Structure Determinations,

III. Carbon-12 Nucleus, J. H. Fregeau and R. Hofstadter; *Phys. Rev.*, **99,** 1503 (1955) 185

29 High-Energy Electron Scattering and the Charge Distributions of Selected Nuclei, B. Hahn, D. G. Ravenhall, and R. Hofstadter; *Phys. Rev.*, **101,** 1131 (1956) 192

30 Elastic Scattering of 188-Mev Electrons from the Proton and the Alpha Particle, R. W. McAllister and R. Hofstadter; *Phys. Rev.*, **102,** 851 (1956) 204

31 Coherent Neutron Scattering Amplitudes of Krypton and Xenon, and the Electron-Neutron Interaction, M. F. Crouch, V. E. Krohn, and G. R. Ringo; *Phys. Rev.*, **102,** 1321 (1956) 210

32 Calculation of Electron-Deuteron Scattering Cross Sections, V. Z. Jankus; *Phys. Rev.*, **102,** 1586 (1956) 214

33 Electron Scattering and Nuclear Structure, R. Hofstadter; *Rev. Mod. Phys.*, **28,** 214 (1956) 220

34 Structure of the Proton, E. E. Chambers and R. Hofstadter; *Phys. Rev.*, **103,** 1454 (1956) 261

35 Electron Scattering from the Deuteron, J. A. McIntyre; *Phys. Rev.*, **103,** 1464 (1956) 271

36 On the Scattering of High Energy Electrons by Protons, E. Clementel and C. Villi; *Nuovo Cimento,* [**X**]**4,** 1207 (1956) 279

37 Inelastic and Elastic Scattering of 187-Mev Electrons from Selected Even-Even Nuclei, R. H. Helm; *Phys. Rev.*, **104,** 1466 (1956) 284

38 Absolute Cross Section for Electron Scattering from Protons, R. W. McAllister; *Phys. Rev.*, **104,** 1494 (1956) 294

39 Electromagnetic Structure of Nucleons, D. R. Yennie, M. M. Lévy, and D. G. Ravenhall; *Rev. Mod. Phys.*, **29,** 144 (1957) 295

40 Electron Scattering from Nonspherical Nuclei, B. W. Downs, D. G. Ravenhall, and D. R. Yennie; *Phys. Rev.*, **106,** 1285 (1957) 309

41 Possible Existence of a Heavy Neutral Meson, Y. Nambu; *Phys. Rev.*, **106,** 1366 (1957) 314

42 Nuclear and Nucleon Scattering of High-Energy Electrons, R. Hofstadter; *Ann. Rev. Nucl. Sci.*, **7,** 231 (1957) 315

43 Magnetic Form Factor of the Neutron, M. R. Yearian and R. Hofstadter; *Phys. Rev.*, **110,** 552 (1958) 401

44 Incoherent Electron Scattering from the Nucleons in Beryllium and Carbon and the Magnetic Size of the Neutron, H. F. Ehrenberg and R. Hofstadter; *Phys. Rev.*, **110,** 544 (1958) 414

45 Electromagnetic Structure of the Neutron, L. I. Schiff; *Rev. Mod. Phys.*, **30,** 462 (1958) 421

46 Electromagnetic Structure of the Proton and Neutron, R. Hofstadter, F. Bumiller, and M. R. Yearian; *Rev. Mod. Phys.*, **30,** 482 (1958) 424

47 Electromagnetic Structure of the Nucleon in Local-Field Theory, G. F. Chew, R. Karplus, S. Gasiorowicz, and F. Zachariasen; *Phys. Rev.*, **110,** 265 (1958) 440

48 Form Factor of the Photopion Matrix Element at Resonance, W. K. H. Panofsky and E. A. Allton; *Phys. Rev.*, **110,** 1155 (1958) 452

49 Electron-Deuteron Scattering by the Impulse Approximation, A. Goldberg; *Phys. Rev.*, **112,** 618 (1958) 463

50 Electromagnetic Structure of the Nucleon, P. Federbush, M. L. Goldberger, and S. B. Treiman; *Phys. Rev.*, **112,** 642 (1958) 468

51 Nucleon Structure (I and II), S. D. Drell; *Proc. 1958 Ann. Intern. Conf. High Energy Phys. at CERN,* pp. 20-24, 27-33 492

52 High-Energy Electron Scattering and the Charge Distribution of Carbon-12 and Oxygen-16, H. F. Ehrenberg, R. Hofstadter, U. Meyer-Berkhout, D. G. Ravenhall, and S. S. Sobottka; *Phys. Rev.*, **113,** 666 (1959) 504

53 Effect of a Pion-Pion Scattering Resonance on Nucleon Structure, W. R. Frazer and J. R. Fulco; *Phys. Rev. Letters,* **2,** 365 (1959) 513

54 Experimental Determination of the Nonmagnetic Neutron-Electron Interaction, E. Melkonian, B. M. Rustad, and W. W. Havens, Jr.; *Phys. Rev.*, **114,** 1571 (1959) 517

55 Charge Distributions of Nuclei of the 1*p* Shell, U. Meyer-Berkhout, K. W. Ford, and A. E. S. Green; *Ann Phys. (N. Y.),* **8,** 119 (1959) 523

56 Experimental Evidence for the Pion-Pion Interaction at 1 Gev, I. Derado; *Nuovo Cimento,* **[X]15,** 853 (1960) 524

57 Neutron Form Factors from High-Energy Inelastic Electron-Deuteron Scattering, S. Sobottka; *Phys. Rev.*, **118,** 831 (1960) 527

58 The Nucleon-Nucleon Spin-Orbit Potential, G. Breit; *Proc. Natl. Acad. Sci. U.S.*, **46,** 746 (1960) 535

59 Effect of a Pion-Pion Scattering Resonance on Low Energy Pion-Nucleon Scattering, J. Bowcock, W. N. Cottingham, and D. Lurié; *Nuovo Cimento,* **[X]16,** 918 (1960) 543

60 Theory of Strong Interaction, J. J. Sakurai; *Ann. Phys. (N. Y.)*, **11**, 1 (1960) 564

61 Electron Scattering from the Proton, F. Bumiller, M. Croissiaux, and R. Hofstadter; *Phys. Rev. Letters*, **5**, 261 (1960) 567

62 Splitting of the Proton Form Factors and Diffraction in the Proton, R. Hofstadter, F. Bumiller, and M. Croissiaux; *Phys. Rev. Letters*, **5**, 263 (1960) 570

63 Scattering of High-Energy Electrons by Protons, R. R. Wilson, K. Berkelman, J. M. Cassels, and D. N. Olson; *Nature*, **188**, 94 (1960) 573

64 Electromagnetic Properties of the Proton and Neutron, D. N. Olson, H. F. Schopper, and R. R. Wilson; *Phys. Rev. Letters*, **6**, 286 (1961) 583

65 Dirac and Pauli Form Factors of the Neutron, R. Hofstadter, C. de Vries, and R. Herman; *Phys. Rev. Letters*, **6**, 290 (1961) 588

66 Electric and Magnetic Structure of the Proton and Neutron, R. Hofstadter and R. Herman; *Phys. Rev. Letters*, **6**, 293 (1961) 592

67 Experimental Results on the π-π Cross Section, J. A. Anderson, V. X. Bang, P. G. Burke, D. D. Carmony, and N. Schmitz; *Phys. Rev. Letters*, **6**, 365 (1961) 596

68 Electromagnetic Form Factors of the Nucleon and Pion-Pion Interaction, S. Bergia, A. Stanghellini, S. Fubini, and C. Villi; *Phys. Rev. Letters*, **6**, 367 (1961) 599

69 Pion-Pion Interaction in Pion Production by π^+-p Collisions, D. Stonehill, C. Baltay, H. Courant, W. Fickinger, E. C. Fowler, H. Kraybill, J. Sandweiss, J. Sanford, and H. Taft; *Phys. Rev. Letters*, **6**, 624 (1961) 604

70 Evidence for a π-π Resonance in the $I=1, J=1$ State, A. R. Erwin, R. March, W. D. Walker, and E. West; *Phys. Rev. Letters*, **6**, 628 (1961) 606

71 Inelastic Electron-Deuteron Scattering and the Electromagnetic Structure of the Neutron, L. Durand, III; *Phys. Rev. Letters*, **6**, 631 (1961) 609

72 Radiative Corrections to Electron-Proton Scattering, Yung-Su Tsai; *Phys. Rev.*, **122**, 1898 (1961) 613

73 Scattering of Bev Electrons by Hydrogen and Deuterium, R. M. Littauer, H. F. Schopper, and R. R. Wilson; *Phys. Rev. Letters*, **7**, 141 (1961) 623

74 Structure of the Proton and Neutron, R. M. Littauer, H. F. Schopper, and R. R. Wilson; *Phys. Rev. Letters*, **7**, 144 (1961) 626

75 Evidence for a $T=0$ Three-Pion Resonance, B. C. Maglíc, L. W. Alvarez, A. H. Rosenfeld, and M. L. Stevenson; *Phys. Rev. Letters*, **7**, 178 (1961) 630

76 π–π Resonance in $\pi^- - p$ Interactions at 1.25 Bev, E. Pickup, D. K. Robinson, and E. O. Salant; *Phys. Rev. Letters*, **7**, 192 (1961) 635

77 Electromagnetic Form Factors of the Proton, F. Bumiller, M. Croissiaux, E. Dally, and R. Hofstadter; *Phys. Rev.*, **124**, 1623 (1961) 639

78 Evidence for a Three-Pion Resonance Near 550 Mev, A. Pevsner, R. Kraemer, M. Nussbaum, C. Richardson, P. Schlein, R. Strand, T. Toohig, M. Block, A. Engler, R. Gessaroli, and C. Meltzer; *Phys. Rev. Letters*, **7**, 421 (1961) 648

79 Electromagnetic Structure of Pions and Nucleons, S. Fubini; *Proc. Aix-en-Provence Intern. Conf. Elementary Particles*, Vol. II, pp. 33-55, 1961 651

80 Scalar Nucleon Form Factor $F_1^n + F_1^p$, N. K. Glendenning and G. Kramer; *Phys. Rev. Letters*, **7**, 471 (1961) 674

81 Neutron Form Factors and Nucleon Structure, C. de Vries, R. Hofstadter, and R. Herman; *Phys. Rev. Letters*, **8**, 381 (1962) 676

82 Mu-Mesonic X-Ray Energies, C. S. Johnson, E. P. Hincks, and H. L. Anderson; *Bull. Am. Phys. Soc.*, **[II]7**, 340 (1962) 681

83 Mu-Mesonic Atom Studies of Ti, Fe, Co, Zn, Tl, Pb, and Bi, W. Frati and J. Rainwater 682

Corrections and Addenda 683

Name Index 688

FOREWORD

There is much to be gained by reading original articles in physics. I was, therefore, very pleased to have the opportunity of preparing a reprint volume on the subject of electron scattering and nuclear and nucleon structure. In collecting this particular set of reprints I have been guided by a number of criteria. Among these the most important ones have been novelty, historical interest, importance of the subject matter, usefulness, and clarity of exposition. Evidently very few published articles can lay claim to all these desirable characteristics, and I have been forced to make compromises in choosing among possible papers. It will be clear to the reader that my own particular selection of papers does not necessarily correspond to what some other investigator in this field might choose as his "best" set. My views and interests in the subject of this book are colored by the set of experiments carried out at Stanford University during the past decade and by my contact with theoretical physicists at that university. I have included many samples of work done at other institutions, but the reader will undoubtedly note evidence of bias toward the work done "close to home."

Many important papers have not been reproduced here simply because of limitations of space. My original set of selections totaled about twice the number of pages appearing in this book. For example, I have been unable to reprint several significant papers on dispersion relations and their connection with nucleon structure. Also, I have not been able to include some interesting papers on deuteron theory, on radiative effects, on excitation of nuclear levels by inelastic scattering of electrons, on absolute cross sections of heavy nuclei, on checks of the Rosenbluth formula, or on many other interesting subjects. It has not been possible to reprint a summary of results on the intrinsic neutron-electron interaction. Where possible, however, I have tried to include in the comments on related papers references to those articles I have been forced to omit.

I have included two of my own lengthy, summary-type articles (Papers 33 and 42) because they were written from an introductory point of view. As far as I know they still serve in this capacity.

It would be very pleasing indeed if the covers of this book could contain a complete story providing final results on nuclear and nucleon structure. This is, of course, very far from being true. Results in physics, and particularly in a branch of physics in process of evolution, are produced in a series of successive approximations to the truth. In the present subject we can see this most clearly in following the course of the papers on nucleon structure. Even now we do not know the form factors of the nucleons over a large range of momentum transfer with an accuracy better than, hopefully, plus or minus 5 per cent--particularly in the case of the neutron. And yet the most important facts concerning nucleon structure are probably wrapped up in the 5 per cent we do not yet know. Thus if there is ever a later edition of this material, there will be cause for dropping some of the papers reproduced here and, of course, reason for adding new ones.

The initial uncertainty and the partial step-by-step working out of the details in the subject of nucleon structure have given me a dramatic picture of a developing field in physics. In passing on these reprints to the reader I hope that he can share some of the stimulation and excitement that my colleagues and I have enjoyed over the last decade.

I have attempted to present all the articles in chronological order. This is the way the subject developed and it seems most natural to present the reprints in this manner. In almost all cases the articles have been presented in the order in which they actually *appeared* as published material. Where publication dates were the same, we have relied upon dates of receipt. Sometimes because dates of receipt of the manuscript are not given, it has been difficult to know which paper came first--in a precise sense—and I have had to be guided by the knowledge of events I had at the time in question. Such cases are rare, and I am glad that any possible errors of this kind will be few in number.

I have prepared brief comments associated with each paper. The comments are given solely for the purpose of helping to orient the reader. I hope they will be useful, but they must, of course, be regarded merely as expressing personal views. In any important sense the papers really speak for themselves!

Some of the most important errata are included in a separate list at the end of the volume.

I wish to thank the following individuals for helpful advice I have received in choosing some of the papers in this book: Professors G. F. Chew, W. R. Frazer, S. Glashow, M. M. Lévy, L. I. Schiff, J. D. Walecka, and M. R. Yearian. I wish also to thank Mrs. M. Lochner and Miss J. M. Rabbinowitz for their assistance in getting the manuscript together.

COMMENTS ON THE REPRINTS

Paper 1 (page 31)
THE QUANTUM THEORY OF THE ELECTRON, by P. A. M. Dirac
Proc. Roy. Soc. (London), **A117**, 610 (1928)

The theory of the electron given in this paper has been of fundamental importance in the development of modern physics. A relativistic quantum theory of the electron in agreement with experiment was developed by Dirac in this article; it explained in a natural way the effects of electron spin postulated earlier by Goudsmit and Uhlenbeck. The Dirac theory of the electron remains to this day the foundation on which many high-energy phenomena, such as electron scattering, can be explained. The theory is also used as a tool in the development of electron-scattering analyses of nuclear and nucleon structure.

Paper 2 (page 46)
THE SCATTERING OF FAST ELECTRONS BY ATOMIC NUCLEI, by N. F. Mott
Proc. Roy. Soc. (London), **A124**, 425 (1929)

In this paper Mott gave for the first time a quantum mechanical formula for the scattering of unpolarized fast electrons against massive atomic nuclei. This formula for "Mott scattering" differed from the famous result of Rutherford in containing, as $v \rightarrow c$, a factor $\cos^2 \theta/2$, which includes the effect of electron spin. Application of the results was made to *point* nuclei. This paper also deals with the question of calculating intensities of polarized beams of scattered electrons, a subject of considerable importance in some branches of nuclear physics. The mathematical series given by Mott in this work has been summed by many authors in subsequent analyses of electron scattering. [See, for example, the work of J. H. Bartlett and E. E. Watson, *Proc. Am. Acad. Arts Sci.*, **74**, 53 (1940), and the paper of W. A. McKinley, Jr., and H. Feshbach, *Phys. Rev.*, **74**, 1759 (1948).] Asymmetries to be expected in double scattering of electrons from gold targets are calculated in a second paper of Mott [*Proc. Roy. Soc. (London)*, **A135**, 429 (1932)].

Paper 3 (page 64)
ÜBER DIE WECHSELWIRKUNG ZWISCHEN SCHNELLEN ELEKTRONEN UND ATOMKERNEN, by Eugene Guth
Anz. Akad. Wiss. Wien, Math.-Naturw. Kl., **24**, 299 (1934)

The effects of deviations from the point Coulomb interaction in the scattering of relativistic electrons are given in this paper (Eq. 6) for cases when the Born approximation applies. For fast electrons the results apply to light nuclei. This work foreshadows the use of electron scattering in investigations of nuclear size.

Paper 4 (page 72)
INTERACTION OF NEUTRONS WITH ELECTRONS IN LEAD, by W. W. Havens, Jr., I. I. Rabi, and L. J. Rainwater
Phys. Rev., **72**, 634 (1947)

A positive result on the neutron-electron interaction was obtained in this paper, and numerical values of the effective interaction potential are deduced. The intrinsic structure of the neutron was probed for the first time in this experiment.

Paper 5 (page 75)
ON THE INTERACTION BETWEEN NEUTRONS AND ELECTRONS, by E. Fermi and L. Marshall
Phys. Rev., **72**, 1139 (1947)

An independent attempt was made to study the short-range neutron-electron potential by scattering neutrons from xenon gas. This paper and the preceding one by Havens, Rabi, and Rainwater were the pioneering experiments in investigations of the electromagnetic properties of neutrons. Earlier discussions of this subject were made by P. I. Dee [*Proc. Roy. Soc. (London)*, **A136**, 727 (1932)] and by E. U. Condon [*Phys. Rev.*, **49**, 459 (1936)].

Paper 6 (page 83)
THE CHARGE DISTRIBUTION IN NUCLEI AND THE SCATTERING OF HIGH ENERGY ELECTRONS, by M. E. Rose
Phys. Rev., **73**, 279 (1948)

The fact that nuclear charge distributions and nuclear sizes could be obtained from experiments with high-energy electrons was pointed out very clearly by Rose in this paper giving Born approximation results. An unpublished paper by L. I. Schiff [Microwave Laboratory, Stanford University, Report 102 (1949)] also showed that electron scattering could be used to investigate proton and nuclear structure. Other interesting and relatively early papers on the same subject are those of E. Amaldi, G. Fidecaro, and J. Mariani [*Nuovo cimento*, **7**, 553 (1950); *ibid.*, 757] and H. Feshbach [Symposium Electron Phys., Natl. Bur. Standards, Washington (Oct. 1951)]. Later papers on the Born approximation were written by L. I. Schiff [*Phys. Rev.*, **92**, 988 (1953)] and by J. H. Smith [*Phys. Rev.*, **95**, 271 (1954)]. Smith's thesis "The Scattering of High Energy Electrons by Heavy Nuclei" [Cornell University (1951)] is also relevant.

Paper 7 (page 89)
HIGH ENERGY ELASTIC SCATTERING OF ELECTRONS ON PROTONS, by M. N. Rosenbluth
Phys. Rev., **79**, 615 (1950)

Rosenbluth's work provided the first explicit elastic scattering formula for electrons on protons. The "Rosenbluth formula" is a first-order calculation and allows for Dirac magnetic scattering as well as charge scattering and also takes account of the Pauli scattering from the anomalous magnetic moment of the proton. The influence of form factors on the scattering was introduced by employing "effective" values of the charge and magnetic moment. The Rosenbluth formula was subsequently also applied to the neutron by many authors. Tables of numerical values of point-proton and point-neutron cross sections will be found in the book "High-Energy Electron Scattering Tables," by R. Herman and R. Hofstadter (Stanford Univ. Press, Stanford, Calif., 1960).

Possible corrections to the Rosenbluth formula due to two-photon exchange have been considered by S. Drell and M. Ruderman [*Phys. Rev.*, **106**, 561 (1957)] and by S. Drell and S. Fubini [*Phys. Rev.*, **113**, 741 (1959)]. The influence of an electron dipole moment on the Rosenbluth formula has been determined by B. Margolis, S. Rosendorff, and A. Sirlin [*Phys. Rev.*, **114**, 1530 (1959)] and experiments searching for such an effect were carried out by G. R. Burleson and H. W. Kendall [*Nucl. Phys.*, **19**, 68 (1960) and J. Goldemberg and Y. Torizuka [*Phys. Rev.* (to be published)], who found no deviation from the Rosenbluth result. See also the theoretical considerations of G. V. Avakov and K. A. Ter-Martirosyan [*Nucl. Phys.*, 13, 685 (1959)].

Paper 8 (page 94)
THE EFFECT OF NUCLEAR STRUCTURE ON THE ELASTIC SCATTERING OF FAST ELECTRONS, by L. R. B. Elton
Proc. Phys. Soc. (London), **A63**, 1115 (1950)

Exact calculations of the effects of finite size of a nucleus on the elastic scattering of high-energy electrons were first made by Elton in this paper. The differential cross section was computed explicitly for gold at about 20 Mev. Different nuclear charge distributions were considered.

Paper 9 (page 104)
INTERACTION OF NEUTRONS WITH ELECTRONS IN LIQUID BISMUTH, by W. W. Havens, Jr., L. J. Rainwater, and I. I. Rabi
Phys. Rev., **82**, 345 (1951)

An accurate determination of the neutron-electron interaction was given in this short paper.

Paper 10 (page 105)
THE ELECTRON-NEUTRON INTERACTION, by L. L. Foldy
Phys. Rev., **83**, 688 (1951)

This important paper recognized that the neutron-electron interaction found experimentally was at least partly due to the presence of the neutron's anomalous magnetic moment. The question of whether there was a residual or "intrinsic" neutron-electron interaction was therefore raised again by this result. The fact that the neutron-electron interaction is represented to a large extent by the anomalous magnetic moment is known as the "Foldy effect." Foldy's observation appears in more modern guise in the form of the "charge" form factor $F_{\mathrm{ch}} = F_1 - (q^2/4M^2)KF_2$. (See the note under Paper 39, by Yennie, Lévy, and Ravenhall.)

Paper 11 (page 106)
SCATTERING OF 15.7-MEV ELECTRONS BY NUCLEI, by E. M. Lyman, A. O. Hanson, and M. B. Scott
Phys. Rev., **84**, 626 (1951)

In this work the authors first showed that the effects of nuclear size could be seen experimentally in electron scattering. The measurement of nuclear size by this method was in approximate agreement with size determinations made by earlier methods, although the observations showed a tendency toward smaller radii in gold and silver.

Paper 12 (page 115)
A MEASUREMENT OF THE ELECTRON-NEUTRON INTERACTION, by M. Hamermesh, G. R. Ringo, and A. Wattenberg
Phys. Rev., **85**, 483 (1952)

This work provided a refined measurement of the Fermi-Marshall type, and a more accurate value of the depth of the "potential well" was obtained, agreeing with Havens et al. (Paper 9).

Paper 13 (page 116)
THE NEUTRON-ELECTRON INTERACTION, by J. A. Harvey, D. J. Hughes, and M. D. Goldberg
Phys. Rev., **87**, 220 (1952)

A balanced technique, more sensitive than used heretofore, was developed for measuring the neutron-electron interaction. The nuclear effect in neutron scattering could be eliminated almost entirely by using a bismuth mirror covered with liquid oxygen to reflect the neutrons. When the Foldy effect was allowed for, the resultant electron-neutron interaction was observed to be very small.

Paper 14 (page 117)
THE ELECTROMAGNETIC PROPERTIES OF DIRAC PARTICLES, by L. L. Foldy
Phys. Rev., **87**, 688 (1952)

A phenomenological description representing the various moments of the charge and current distributions in the nucleons is given in this work. This paper offers a theoretical foundation for the understanding of the principal neutron-electron interaction term. Foldy also shows in the Appendix that under certain assumptions the nucleon charge-current density of a Dirac particle must have the phenomenological form associated with the vertex operator $\gamma_\mu F_1 + (\kappa/2M)\sigma_{\mu\nu}q_\nu F_2$ in the notation of Paper 39. The works of G. Salzman [*Phys. Rev.*, **99**, 973 (1955)] and A. C. Zemach [*Phys. Rev.*, **104**, 1771 (1956)] also bear on this important problem.

Paper 15 (page 123)
THE ELECTRON-NEUTRON INTERACTION, by L. L. Foldy
Phys. Rev., **87**, 693 (1952)

This is a companion to the preceding paper. This work also makes a comparison of the experimental value of the intrinsic neutron-electron interaction with the results of weak-coupling meson theories and shows that a discrepancy between theory and experiment exists. This discrepancy persisted in the literature for many years and perhaps may now be on the verge of resolution in terms of the strong resonances among pions. For an early discussion of this question see the paper of G. Salzman [*Phys. Rev.*, **99**, 973 (1955)].

Paper 16 (page 127)
THE NEUTRON-ELECTRON INTERACTION, by D. J. Hughes, J. A. Harvey, M. D. Goldberg, and M. J. Stafne
Phys. Rev., **90**, 497 (1953)

A precise determination of the intrinsic neutron-electron interaction was made in this experiment, which showed that the well depth, assuming the usual well radius (classical electron radius), was no more than a few hundred volts.

Paper 17 (page 128)
SCATTERING OF HIGH-ENERGY ELECTRONS AND THE METHOD OF NUCLEAR RECOIL, by R. Hofstadter, H. R. Fechter, and J. A. McIntyre
Phys. Rev., **91**, 422 (1953)

This paper is the earliest communication on high-energy electron scattering at energies above 100 Mev. Among other cases, the nucleus of gold was investigated and it was suggested that its nuclear boundary was not sharp. Electron-proton peaks were observed also for the first time.

Paper 18 (page 130)
HIGH-ENERGY ELECTRON SCATTERING BY NUCLEI, by R. W. Pidd, C. L. Hammer, and E. C. Raka
Phys. Rev., **92**, 436 (1953)

This paper represents the first known example of the use of an electron synchrotron for studies of electron scattering. A similar technique was employed many years later at Cornell University to study electron-nucleon scattering. The present paper indicated quite small values for the nuclear radii of tungsten and tin, assuming uniform charge distributions, and was among the first investigations of nuclear size by electron scattering methods.

Paper 19 (page 132)
STUDIES OF X-RAYS FROM MU-MESONIC ATOMS, by Val L. Fitch and James Rainwater
Phys. Rev., **92**, 789 (1953)

This is the first and classic paper on mu-mesonic X-rays. It was demonstrated experimentally that large shifts in the X-ray energies could be observed and were associated with the finite size of nuclei as predicted by J. A. Wheeler [*Rev. Mod. Phys.*, **21**, 133 (1949)]. Various nuclear radii were measured and the values were found to correspond to $r_o \cong 1.19 \times 10^{-13}$ cm. in the relationship $R = r_o A^{1/3}$, where R is the radius of a uniform distribution of protons in a nucleus of mass number A. See also Paper 83.

Paper 20 (page 144)
HIGH-ENERGY ELECTRON SCATTERING AND NUCLEAR STRUCTURE DETERMINATIONS, by R. Hofstadter, H. R. Fechter, and J. A. McIntyre
Phys. Rev., **92**, 978 (1953)

A detailed report is given in this paper of results presented briefly at an earlier time (Paper 17). Extension of the measurements to 150 Mev was also made. Gold, lead, tantalum, beryllium, deuterium, and hydrogen were studied at various energies. Inelastic level-scattering effects were first seen in the case of beryllium. Effects of the finite size of nuclei were shown to be very large in electron-scattering studies. The absence of sharp diffraction minima in heavy elements was noted. Tentative conclusions based on the Born approximation concerning nuclear charge distributions were presented.

Paper 21 (page 154)
PHASE-SHIFT CALCULATION OF HIGH-ENERGY ELECTRON SCATTERING BY NUCLEI, by D. R. Yennie, R. N. Wilson, and D. G. Ravenhall
Phys. Rev., **92**, 1325 (1953)

Accurate phase-shift calculations were made by the authors for gold and copper and the results were compared with the Born approximation results, as well as with Stanford experimental results. The fact that the diffraction features were considerably washed-out, as found by experiment, was satisfactorily explained in terms of nuclear models with uniform charge distributions and small electromagnetic radii. See also the work of Elizabeth U. Baranger [*Phys. Rev.*, **93**, 1127 (1954)].

Paper 22 (page 155)
INELASTIC SCATTERING OF 190-MEV ELECTRONS IN BERYLLIUM, by J. A. McIntyre, B. Hahn, and R. Hofstadter
Phys. Rev., **94**, 1084 (1954)

This paper gave the first clear, quantitative example of inelastic level scattering of electrons observed in any nucleus.

Paper 23 (page 156)
PHASE-SHIFT CALCULATION OF HIGH-ENERGY ELECTRON SCATTERING, by D. R. Yennie, D. G. Ravenhall, and R. N. Wilson
Phys. Rev., **95**, 500 (1954)

This paper gives a detailed description of the phase-shift type of calculation and explores the angular distribution of scattered electrons resulting from various models of nuclear charge distributions. Models with small radii and smooth drop-off at the edge of the nucleus appeared to give the best fit with experiment. Subsequently the results of experiment and theory confirmed these conclusions. A similar and independent study was made by S. Brenner, G. E. Brown, and L. R. B. Elton [*Phil. Mag.*, **45**, 524 (1954)].

Paper 24 (page 169)
HIGH-ENERGY ELECTRON SCATTERING AND NUCLEAR STRUCTURE DETERMINATIONS, II, by R. Hofstadter, B. Hahn, A. W. Knudsen, and J. A. McIntyre
Phys. Rev., **95**, 512 (1954)

The results in this paper were designed to furnish experimental data on elastic scattering in gold and lead at various energies. The use of several energies permitted a more definite selection of the type of nuclear model best fitting all the data and gave smaller-than-usual values for the electromagnetic radii of these nuclei.

Paper 25 (page 173)
RESULTS OF A PHASE SHIFT CALCULATION OF HIGH-ENERGY ELECTRON SCATTERING, by D. G. Ravenhall and D. R. Yennie
Phys. Rev., **96**, 239 (1954)

The authors give a detailed study of the fit between experimental electron-scattering angular distribution and the theoretical results corresponding to various assumed charge distributions in the nucleus of gold. It was shown that two parameters in the theoretical form of the charge distribution are adequate to describe the observed results. Similar results were obtained also by G. E. Brown and L. R. B. Elton [*Phil. Mag.*, **46**, 164 (1955)].

Paper 26 (page 175)
NUCLEAR MULTIPOLE TRANSITIONS IN INELASTIC ELECTRON SCATTERING, by L. I. Schiff
Phys. Rev., **96**, 765 (1954)

This paper laid the basis for many subsequent experimental determinations of the behavior of inelastic scattering cross sections of high-energy electrons. The effects of various types of multipole transitions were investigated by treating the charge, current, and magnetization densities in a semiclassical way. Special attention was given to electric monopole and electric quadrupole excitations. First-order perturbation theory was used in the analysis.

Paper 27 (page 183)

ELECTRON SCATTERING FROM THE PROTON, by Robert Hofstadter and Robert W. McAllister

Phys. Rev., **98**, 217 (1955)

This paper represents the first observation of structure effects in the proton. A value of the root-mean-square charge radius was determined which lies close to present determinations of this quantity. The effects of magnetic scattering were observed.

Paper 28 (page 185)

HIGH-ENERGY ELECTRON SCATTERING AND NUCLEAR STRUCTURE DETERMINATIONS. III. CARBON-12 NUCLEUS, by Jerome H. Fregeau and Robert Hofstadter

Phys. Rev., **99**, 1503 (1955)

The important nucleus C^{12} was investigated in detail in this experiment. Elastic electron scattering was studied at energies up to 187 Mev and numerous quantitative features of the inelastic level scattering were reported, including details of quadrupole scattering in connection with the 4.43-Mev state. The size and shape of the carbon nucleus were determined.

Paper 29 (page 192)

HIGH-ENERGY ELECTRON SCATTERING AND THE CHARGE DISTRIBUTIONS OF SELECTED NUCLEI, by Beat Hahn, D. G. Ravenhall, and Robert Hofstadter

Phys. Rev., **101**, 1131 (1956)

The main contribution of this paper was the establishment of a general scheme based on experiment for determining the charge distribution in any stable, spherically symmetric nucleus with $Z \geqq 20$. Two nuclear parameters were introduced: the radial distance to the half-density point c and the skin thickness t. Rules for the behavior of c and t were suggested. Subsequent investigation has confirmed these rules. Experimental angular distributions of scattered electrons were also given for nuclei known to be distorted from the spherical shape.

Paper 30 (page 204)

ELASTIC SCATTERING OF 188-MEV ELECTRONS FROM THE PROTON AND THE ALPHA PARTICLE, by R. W. McAllister and R. Hofstadter

Phys. Rev., **102**, 851 (1956)

This work confirmed an earlier investigation of the proton structure and for the first time determined the size and shape of the alpha particle.

Paper 31 (page 210)
COHERENT NEUTRON SCATTERING AMPLITUDES OF KRYPTON AND XENON, AND THE ELECTRON-NEUTRON INTERACTION, by M. F. Crouch, V. E. Krohn, and G. R. Ringo
Phys. Rev., **102**, 1321 (1956)

The accurate measurement of the coherent neutron scattering amplitudes in krypton and xenon permitted a more exact evaluation of the intrinsic neutron-electron interaction, which was based on the earlier results of Hamermesh, Ringo, and Wattenberg (Paper 12). Results were obtained in agreement with other independent methods of measuring the neutron-electron interaction.

Paper 32 (page 214)
CALCULATION OF ELECTRON-DEUTERON SCATTERING CROSS SECTIONS, by V. Z. Jankus
Phys. Rev., **102**, 1586 (1956)

Early calculations on the scattering of high-energy electrons by the deuteron were made by M. E. Rose [*Phys. Rev.*, **73**, 279 (1948)]; by J. A. Thie, C. J. Mullin, and E. Guth [*Phys. Rev.*, **87**, 962 (1952)]; by L. I. Schiff [*Phys. Rev.*, **92**, 988 (1953)]; and by J. H. Smith [Ph.D. thesis, Cornell Univ. (1951)]. Other references to early literature are given in the paper by Thie et al. V. Z. Jankus made the first Born approximation calculations of inelastic high-energy electron cross sections of the deuteron extending to large momentum transfers and to higher multipoles. He also investigated the elastic scattering cross sections in great detail. The effects of the spherically symmetric part of the charge distribution, the influence of the quadrupole moment, and the behavior of magnetic scattering were evaluated in this paper. Furthermore, very important theoretical results were obtained for the inelastic "break-up" cross sections of the deuteron. These calculations were subsequently used by other authors to determine the approximate form factors of the neutron (see Paper 43, by M. R. Yearian and Robert Hofstadter). The detailed shape of the deuteron inelastic peak was also given for the first time by Jankus in this paper. Estimates of corrections to the shape of the inelastic curve due to final state interaction were made by the same author. The effects of finite size of the nucleons were considered briefly. This paper provided much stimulation to experimentalists in the electron-scattering field, for it gave a theoretical basis for understanding the details of the experiments on the deuteron. Subsequent simplifications and improvements on Jankus' theory are given in papers by A. Goldberg (Paper 49) and by L. Durand, III [*Phys. Rev.*, **115**, 1020 (1959), and *Phys. Rev.*, **123**, 1393 (1961)]. A recent paper concerned with elastic scattering of electrons on deuterons by H. F. Jones of Imperial College, London, "Dispersion Theory of the Deuteron Form Factor and Elastic *e-d* Scattering" (to be published), should also be consulted.

Paper 33 (page 220)
ELECTRON SCATTERING AND NUCLEAR STRUCTURE, by Robert Hofstadter
Rev. Mod. Phys., **28**, 214 (1956)

A review was given in this paper of the principal phenomena observed in high-energy electron scattering and the results obtained in nuclear structure by use of the method. The method of investigating neutron structure by means of electron-deuteron inelastic scattering was first suggested in this paper. Results were also given on the structure effects in the proton and neutron as they were known at the time of publication. Nuclear charge distributions were also summarized by K. W. Ford and D. L. Hill [*Ann. Rev. Nucl. Sci.*, **5**, 25 (1955)]. A more recent summary of all types of nuclear size determinations will be found in the book by L. R. B. Elton, "Nuclear Sizes" (Oxford Univ. Press, New York, 1961).

Paper 34 (page 261)
STRUCTURE OF THE PROTON, by E. E. Chambers and R. Hofstadter
Phys. Rev., **103**, 1454 (1956)

New measurements were reported in this paper on the form factors of the proton up to values of $q^2 = 15f^{-2}$ (500 Mev, 135°). The measurements confirmed earlier results on the structure of the proton and gave an rms radius of 0.77×10^{-13} cm for the Dirac charge cloud and Pauli magnetic moment cloud. In this early work it was assumed that $F_{1p} \cong F_{2p}$ within experimental error, although at $q^2 = 4.0 f^{-2}$ it was determined experimentally that $F_{1p}/F_{2p} = 1.1 \pm 0.2$.

Paper 35 (page 271)
ELECTRON SCATTERING FROM THE DEUTERON, by John A. McIntyre
Phys. Rev., **103**, 1464 (1956)

This early experiment on elastic scattering of electrons on the deuteron showed that a finite proton size was consistent with the observed experimental results and with a conventional theory of the deuteron based on experiments in low-energy nuclear physics. Other work on the deuteron was carried out by J. A. McIntyre and R. Hofstadter [*Phys. Rev.*, **98**, 158 (1955)]; J. A. McIntyre and S. Dhar [*Phys. Rev.*, **106**, 1074 (1957)]; J. A. McIntyre and G. Burleson [*Phys. Rev.*, **112**, 2077 (1958)]; and J. I. Friedman, H. W. Kendall, and P. A. M. Gram [*Phys. Rev.*, **120**, 992 (1960)]. See also Paper 80 by Glendenning and Kramer, and an article to be published by D. J. Drickey and L. N. Hand.

Paper 36 (page 279)
ON THE SCATTERING OF HIGH ENERGY ELECTRONS BY PROTONS, by E. Clementel and C. Villi
Nuovo cimento, [X] **4**, 1207 (1956)

The Clementel-Villi form factor was first introduced in this paper. Application was made to the proton charge distribution.

Paper 37 (page 284)
INELASTIC AND ELASTIC SCATTERING OF 187-MEV ELECTRONS FROM SELECTED EVEN-EVEN NUCLEI, by Richard H. Helm
Phys. Rev., **104**, 1466 (1956)

In this paper Helm made the first systematic investigation by means of electron scattering of the ground states and lower excited states of several even-even nuclei. The useful idea of a folded charge distribution—*gU* model—was also introduced for the ground state. Helm employed Schiff's (Paper 26) analysis of multipole excitation to derive values of the transition matrix elements in the case of several excited states of the even-even nuclei. Later work on this subject was carried out by H. Crannell, R. Helm, H. Kendall, J. Oeser, and M. Yearian [*Phys. Rev.*, **123**, 923 (1961)]. The work of W. C. Barber, F. Berthold, G. Fricke, and F. E. Gudden [*Phys. Rev.*, **120**, 2081 (1960)] is also related to this same topic. An earlier summary of inelastic electron scattering work will be found in the article by R. Huby, "Electromagnetic Excitation of Nuclei by Nuclear Projectiles and Electrons," *Rept. Progr. Phys.* (The Physical Society of London, 1958). An interesting article on various types of excitation of nuclei by high-energy particles was written by L. I. Schiff, "Low-Energy Physics from a High-Energy Standpoint" [*Science*, **121**, 881 (1955)].

Paper 38 (page 294)
ABSOLUTE CROSS SECTION FOR ELECTRON SCATTERING FROM PROTONS, by Robert W. McAllister
Phys. Rev., **104**, 1494 (1956)

This is the first relatively accurate determination of an absolute cross section in electron-proton scattering. Other less accurate absolute determinations had been made earlier by Chambers and Hofstadter (Paper 34).

Paper 39 (page 295)

ELECTROMAGNETIC STRUCTURE OF NUCLEONS, by D. R. Yennie, M. M. Lévy, and D. G. Ravenhall

Rev. Mod. Phys., **29**, 144 (1957)

This important paper discusses many of the fundamental aspects of the nucleon structure problem. Several significant results are presented in the appendix of this paper, including the introduction of the "charge" form factor, $F_{ch} = F_1 - (q^2/4M^2)KF_2$, and "magnetic moment" form factor, $F_{mag} = F_1 + KF_2$—form factors of the nucleon now employed by many authors. In this connection, see, e.g., the important contribution to this subject made by J. D. Walecka [*Nuovo cimento*, **11**, 821 (1959)]. The paper by F. J. Ernst, R. G. Sachs, and K. C. Wali [*Phys. Rev.*, **119**, 1105 (1960)] is important because the "new" form factors are discussed in detail and their physical interpretation is also considered. See also R. G. Sachs [*Phys. Rev.*, **126**, 2256 (1962)] and K. J. Barnes [*Physics Letters*, **1**, 166 (1962)]. A paper by L. N. Hand, D. G. Miller, and R. Wilson [*Phys. Rev. Letters*, **8**, 110 (1962)] has recently employed the new form factors. Extension of the phenomenological form factor approach to a general spin one-half particle is demonstrated in the appendix of the Yennie et al. paper. Many investigators in the nucleon structure field were greatly stimulated by the appearance of this publication by Yennie, Levy, and Ravenhall.

Paper 40 (page 309)

ELECTRON SCATTERING FROM NONSPHERICAL NUCLEI, by B. W. Downs, D. G. Ravenhall, and D. R. Yennie

Phys. Rev., **106**, 1285 (1957)

An approximate theory and explanation were first given in this paper of the smooth, rather featureless behavior of the angular distributions of the elastic (and inelastic) scattering of high-energy electrons from nonspherical nuclei.

Paper 41 (page 314)

POSSIBLE EXISTENCE OF A HEAVY NEUTRAL MESON, by Yoichiro Nambu

Phys. Rev., **106**, 1366 (1957)

In this article Nambu postulated the existence of a heavy neutral meson to account for the proton and neutron form factors found by electron scattering methods. Although Nambu called his meson a "ρ_0" particle, this meson is now called by the name of "ω_0" or simply "ω." The ω-meson was discovered experimentally recently (Paper 75), but has a mass about a factor of two larger than first supposed by Nambu. Nambu also wrote down a spectral representation for the form factor of the nucleon, one of the first known uses of this representation. Early suggestions of the existence of a vector meson were made by G. Breit [*Phys. Rev.*, **51**, 248 (1937); *ibid.*, **53**, 153 (1938); and Paper 58] in connection with theoretical work on the repulsive core and spin-orbit interaction. See also the suggestion of a neutral meson by M. H. Johnson and E. Teller [*Phys. Rev.*, **98**, 783 (1955)].

Paper 42 (page 315)
NUCLEAR AND NUCLEON SCATTERING OF HIGH-ENERGY ELECTRONS, by Robert Hofstadter
Ann. Rev. Nucl. Sci., 7, 231 (1957)

This paper was written with the intention of clarifying and systematizing many of the ideas involved in the electron scattering experiments. It also served as a summary of work done in this field up to the middle of 1957.

Paper 43 (page 401)
MAGNETIC FORM FACTOR OF THE NEUTRON, by M. R. Yearian and Robert Hofstadter
Phys. Rev., **110**, 552 (1958)

The research reported in this paper gave the first detailed experimental proof that the neutron could not be represented by a point-like structure. [Earlier intimations of this result by Blankenbecler, Hofstadter, and Yearian are reported in the review article by R. Hofstadter (Paper 33; see p. 246 of that article).] In the paper of Yearian and Hofstadter both the "area" method and the "peak" method were employed to find the neutron form factors. The Jankus theory of the deuteron, modified by the authors, was used as a starting point in analyzing the peak data. The final results reported in this paper are surprisingly close to the most recent data on the neutron form factors, and the value $F_{1n} = 0$, used in the analysis is quite close, if not exactly equal to, the values employed most recently. Subsequent work on the deuteron was carried out by M. R. Yearian and R. Hofstadter [*Phys. Rev.*, **111**, 934 (1958)] and by J. I. Friedman, H. W. Kendall, and P. A. M. Gram [*Phys. Rev.*, **120**, 992 (1960)].

Paper 44 (page 414)
INCOHERENT ELECTRON SCATTERING FROM THE NUCLEONS IN BERYLLIUM AND CARBON AND THE MAGNETIC SIZE OF THE NEUTRON, by Hans F. Ehrenberg and Robert Hofstadter
Phys. Rev., **110**, 544 (1958)

In this work a first attempt was made to discover the cross section for electron scattering of the average nucleon and, in particular, the cross section of the neutron bound in a light nucleus. Rough information about the form factors of a bound neutron could be found in this way. A later experiment designed to measure bound neutron cross sections was made by U. Meyer-Berkhout [*Phys. Rev.*, **115**, 1300 (1959)].

Paper 45 (page 421)
ELECTROMAGNETIC STRUCTURE OF THE NEUTRON, by L. I. Schiff
Rev. Mod. Phys., **30**, 462 (1958)

An attempt was made in this paper by Schiff to understand the charge structure in the neutron on the basis of experimental information on nucleon form factors. Schiff's conclusions appear to be remarkably up to date.

Paper 46 (page 424)
ELECTROMAGNETIC STRUCTURE OF THE PROTON AND NEUTRON, by R. Hofstadter, F. Bumiller, and M. R. Yearian
Rev. Mod. Phys., **30**, 482 (1958)

A review of the findings on the electromagnetic form factors of the proton and neutron was given in this paper. The Clementel-Villi formula for the proton form factors was employed in this article. The "peak" and "area" methods of determining neutron structure were discussed in relation to the neutron form factor problem. A value of zero for F_{1n} of the neutron was employed in this work and this value was consistent with all the known deuteron data. Information on the shape of the deuteron inelastic electron scattering peaks was summarized. In this paper the proton form factors, F_{1p} and F_{2p}, were still assumed to be approximately equal to each other. A book by S. D. Drell and F. Zachariasen, "Electromagnetic Structure of Nucleons" (Oxford Univ. Press, New York, 1961) covers theoretical considerations on this subject.

Paper 47 (page 440)
ELECTROMAGNETIC STRUCTURE OF THE NUCLEON IN LOCAL-FIELD THEORY, by Geoffrey F. Chew, Robert Karplus, Stephen Gasiorowicz, and Frederik Zachariasen
Phys. Rev., **110**, 265 (1958)

This is one of the early and influential papers on the use of the mass-spectral representations (weight functions in the dispersion-theory approach to the nucleon structure problem) in the problem of the electromagnetic form factors of the nucleons. This paper showed the advantage of using this method of calculation over the older, often-tried, and rather unsuccessful methods of perturbation theory. The technique employed did not amount to an expansion in powers of the coupling constant but rather represented a sum in terms of the mass of the intermediate states, and in particular showed the importance of intermediate states with the lightest mass. The possible large effect of the three-pion state in the consideration of nucleon charge structure is emphasized. The independent work of P. Federbush, M. L. Goldberger, and S. B. Treiman (Paper 50) came to many of the same conclusions and proposed essentially the same method of calculating nucleon form factors.

Paper 48 (page 452)
FORM FACTOR OF THE PHOTOPION MATRIX ELEMENT AT RESONANCE, by W. K. H. Panofsky and E. A. Allton
Phys. Rev., **110**, 1155 (1958)

Electron production of pions from the proton was studied in this work. Application to the neutron form factors could be made since the theory of the experiment involved an expression containing the difference between the magnetic form factors of neutron and proton. The suggestion that this process involves the nucleon form factors is due to S. Fubini, Y. Nambu, and V. Wataghin [*Phys. Rev.*, **111**, 329 (1958)]. By employing the known values of the proton form factors information on the neutron form factors could be obtained. Values determined in this way were in reasonable agreement with other methods of finding such form factors. This paper provided for the first time an approach to the neutron problem without the complications introduced by deuteron theory. On the other hand, the use of meson theory involved various theoretical uncertainties. A subsequent investigation of the electron-pion production problem in hydrogen and deuterium was made by G. Ohlsen [*Phys. Rev.*, **120**, 584 (1960)].

Paper 49 (page 463)
ELECTRON-DEUTERON SCATTERING BY THE IMPULSE APPROXIMATION, by A. Goldberg
Phys. Rev., **112**, 618 (1958)

Impulse approximation calculations were made by Goldberg corresponding to the electro-disintegration of the deuteron, i.e., inelastic scattering of electrons on the deuteron involving break-up. Goldberg showed that, to a good approximation, the Rosenbluth neutron and proton cross sections add together in a simple way to give the deuteron inelastic peak cross section. This was an important result and was later verified by more detailed calculations of Durand [*Phys. Rev.*, **123**, 1393 (1961)].

Paper 50 **(page 468)**
ELECTROMAGNETIC STRUCTURE OF THE NUCLEON, by P. Federbush, M. L. Goldberger, and S. B. Treiman
Phys. Rev., **112**, 642 (1958)

This paper and Paper 47, by Chew et al., represent the two early and basic works on the use of dispersion theory relations in making a modern theory of the electromagnetic structure of the nucleon. Many of the remarks in Paper 47 are applicable here. The conclusions on page 660 of the Federbush et al. paper are especially interesting in view of the subsequent development of the subject in theory and experiment. A summary of later work on this subject and on related material will be found in the article by W. R. Frazer in the book

"Dispersion Relations" [Oliver & Boyd, Edinburgh; Interscience, New York, 1961, G. R. Screaton (ed.)].

Paper 51 (page 492)

NUCLEON STRUCTURE (I AND II), by S. D. Drell

Proc. 1958 Ann. Intern. Conf. High Energy Phys. at CERN (CERN, Geneva, 1958), ed. by B. Ferretti, pp. 20-24, 27-33

This paper presented a timely review of the theoretical understanding of the form factors of the nucleon, and showed that it was difficult to explain the electromagnetic form factors without introducing the possibility of a strong pion-pion interaction. Considerable attention was devoted in this summary to the important paper of P. Federbush et al. (Paper 50). Subsequently the strong pion-pion interaction was employed by W. R. Frazer and J. R. Fulco [*Phys. Rev.*, **117**, 1609 (1960)] to explain the nucleon form factors.

Paper 52 (page 504)

HIGH-ENERGY ELECTRON SCATTERING AND THE CHARGE DISTRIBUTION OF CARBON-12 AND OXYGEN-16, by Hans F. Ehrenberg, Robert Hofstadter, Ulrich Meyer-Berkhout, D. G. Ravenhall, and Stanley S. Sobottka

Phys. Rev., **113**, 666 (1959)

The first extension of electron-scattering methods to energies high enough to observe the pronounced diffraction features of light elements was reported in this paper. A theoretical phase-shift analysis for harmonic-well models of C^{12} and O^{16} was made, and reasonable fits with the experimental data were obtained.

Paper 53 (page 513)

EFFECT OF A PION-PION SCATTERING RESONANCE ON NUCLEON STRUCTURE, by William R. Frazer and José R. Fulco

Phys. Rev. Letters, **2**, 365 (1959)

By using a dispersion-relation treatment the authors of this paper showed in detail how the isotopic vector features of the electromagnetic form factors of the nucleons and the static values of the nucleon magnetic moments could be explained simultaneously by taking into account a strong pion-pion resonance interaction. An interaction of this type had been proposed previously, in particular at an early date by W. G. Holladay and R. G. Sachs [*Phys. Rev.*, **98**, 1155 (1955)] and W. G. Holladay [*Phys. Rev.*, **101**, 1198 (1956)] to explain the static values of the anomalous moments of the nucleons. The Frazer-Fulco paper provided considerable impetus in stimulating further work on the understanding of nucleon structure. The present paper was followed by two other investigations by the same authors bearing on the electromagnetic form factor problem, viz.: "Partial Wave Dispersion Relations for the Process $\pi + \pi \rightarrow N + \bar{N}$" [*Phys. Rev.*, **117**, 1603 (1960)]; and "Effect of a Pion-Pion Scattering Resonance on Nucleon Structure, II" [*Phys. Rev.*, **117**, 1609 (1960)]. In the latter paper the details of fitting the theoretical form factor curves to the experimental ones are given. Only the resonance in the $J = 1$, $I = 1$ state of the two-pion system is discussed. The paper shows the resonance to be near $12m_\pi^2$, a value now known to be on the low side. However, the fitting procedure employed by the authors was unable to give an accurate measure of the resonance value.

Paper 54 (page 517)
EXPERIMENTAL DETERMINATION OF NONMAGNETIC NEUTRON-ELECTRON INTERACTION, by E. Melkonian, B. M. Rustad, and W. W. Havens, Jr.
Phys. Rev., **114**, 1571 (1959)

The work reported in this paper gives a precise determination of the intrinsic neutron-electron interaction. The result was in agreement with earlier work and gave a very small attractive interaction, although the experimental error was still large enough to allow a value of zero for the intrinsic interaction.

Paper 55 (page 523)
CHARGE DISTRIBUTION OF NUCLEI OF THE 1*p* SHELL, by Ulrich Meyer-Berkhout, Kenneth W. Ford, and Alex E. S. Green
Ann. Phys. (N.Y.), **8**, 119 (1959)

This paper provides a useful summary of electron-scattering results for nuclei of the first *p*-shell. Of great interest is the work reported on B^{11} and N^{14}, in which effects of quadrupole scattering are observed. Methods of using Born approximation form factors in finding nuclear charge distributions are discussed in detail. Only the abstract of this lengthy paper is reproduced in this book.

Paper 56 (page 524)
EXPERIMENTAL EVIDENCE FOR THE PION-PION INTERACTION AT 1 GEV, by I. Derado
Nuovo cimento, [X]**15**, 853 (1960)

Examination of the proton spectrum resulting from the production of neutral pions by negative pions of 1 Bev energy showed a peak consistent with the existence of a strong pion-pion resonance at $22m_\pi^2$. The correct value of the resonance is now known to be $\sim 28m_\pi^2$ and this type of experiment foreshadowed the discovery of the ρ-meson. Subsequently E. Pickup, F. Ayer, and E. O. Salant [*Phys. Rev. Letters*, **5**, 161 (1960)] also obtained evidence suggestive of a π-π interaction in the state of isotopic spin $I = 1$, at a value of about $19\,m_{\pi}^2$. Of interest also is the paper of F. Bonsignori and F. Selleri [*Nuovo cimento*, **15**, 465 (1960)]. These authors made theoretical calculations of the production of neutral pions in collisions of negative pions with protons and pointed out the probable existence of a pion-pion interaction. The work of P. Carruthers and H. A. Bethe [*Phys. Rev. Letters*, **4**, 536 (1960)] also relates to this pion-pion interaction and the paper by J. G. Rushbrooke and D. Radojicic [*Phys. Rev. Letters*, **5**, 567 (1960)] has an historical interest concerning the question of the pion-pion interaction.

Paper 57 (page 527)

NEUTRON FORM FACTORS FROM HIGH-ENERGY INELASTIC ELECTRON-DEUTERON SCATTERING, by S. Sobottka

Phys. Rev., **118**, 831 (1960)

Inelastic electron scattering from the deuteron was studied in this paper and the Goldberg approximation to the peak cross section was used to analyze the data. Sobottka also developed a simple approximate correction factor for evaluating radiative effects in electron-proton and electron-deuteron scattering. An earlier paper by R. Hofstadter [Proc. Ninth Intern. Ann. Conf. High Energy Physics (Academy of Science, USSR, Moscow, 1960), Vol. I, p. 355] introduced the "method of intersecting ellipses" to find the proton and neutron Dirac and Pauli form factors separately. Other methods of obtaining these results have been developed subsequently.

Paper 58 (page 535)

THE NUCLEON-NUCLEON SPIN-ORBIT POTENTIAL, by Gregory Breit

Proc. Natl. Acad. Sci. U.S., **46**, 746 (1960)

The suggestion of a neutral vector meson field is made in this paper as an explanation of the nucleon-nucleon spin-orbit potential. The effect of such a heavy meson on the electromagnetic form factors is also considered briefly.

Paper 59 (page 543)

EFFECT OF A PION-PION SCATTERING RESONANCE ON LOW ENERGY PION-NUCLEON SCATTERING, by J. Bowcock, W. N. Cottingham, and D. Lurié

Nuovo cimento, [X]**16**, 918 (1960)

The idea of using a pion-pion resonance ($J = 1$, $I = 1$) to explain low-energy pion-nucleon scattering by dispersion theory was developed in this investigation.

The same resonance also gave agreement with the electromagnetic form factors of the nucleon and the value chosen to fit all the data was $22.4 m_\pi^2$. This value is in good agreement with recent determinations of nucleon form factors by electron scattering, but differs from the actual experimental value of the ρ-meson resonance ($\sim 28 m_\pi^2$). Similar work was carried out by S. C. Frautschi and J. D. Walecka [*Phys. Rev.*, **120**, 1486 (1960)] and by S. C. Frautschi [*Phys. Rev. Letters*, 5, 159 (1960)]. More general techniques for making studies of this type were suggested by M. Gell-Mann and F. Zachariasen [Phys. Rev., **124**, 953 (1961)].

Paper 60 (page 564)
THEORY OF STRONG INTERACTIONS, by J. J. Sakurai
Ann. Phys. (N.Y.), **11**, 1 (1960)

Only the abstract of this lengthy paper is reproduced herewith. In his paper Sakurai predicts and uses the existence of the two-pion (ρ) and three-pion (ω, η) resonances in a vector theory of strong interactions. See also later papers by Sakurai [*Phys. Rev. Letters*, **7**, 355 (1961); *ibid.*, 426].

Paper 61 (page 567)
ELECTRON SCATTERING FROM THE PROTON, by F. Bumiller, M. Croissiaux, and R. Hofstadter
Phys. Rev. Letters, **5**, 261 (1960)

This paper and its companion (Paper 62) presented detailed results on proton cross sections and on the splitting of the proton form factors. This paper described the method of finding the experimental cross sections and gave values of the differential cross sections in the range of incident energies 597 to 900 Mev and over an angular interval of 60 to 145° for the scattered electron. The same data were presented at a Rochester conference [*Proc. 1960 Ann. Intern. Conf. High Energy Physics at Rochester* (Interscience, New York, 1960), pp. 762-766].

Paper 62 (page 570)
SPLITTING OF THE PROTON FORM FACTORS AND DIFFRACTION IN THE PROTON, by R. Hofstadter, F. Bumiller, and M. Croissiaux
Phys. Rev. Letters, **5**, 263 (1960)

The results obtained in the companion paper (Paper 61) were analyzed in this article by the method of intersecting ellipses, and values of F_{1p} and F_{2p} were found which departed considerably from each other at large values of q^2.

It was pointed out in the paper under discussion that the split proton form factors would yield new information on F_1 of the neutron when the data on inelastic electron scattering on the deuteron could be combined with these results. A speculative attempt to make such evaluations of F_{1n} was carried out by R. Herman and R. Hofstadter [*Proc. 1960 Ann. Intern. Conf. High Energy Physics at Rochester* (Interscience, New York, 1960), pp. 767-768].

Paper 63 (page 573)

SCATTERING OF HIGH-ENERGY ELECTRONS BY PROTONS, by R. R. Wilson, K. Berkelman, J. M. Cassels, and D. N. Olson

Nature, **188**, 94 (1960)

In this paper an independent evaluation of the proton form factors was made by using the Cornell synchrotron as the source of high-energy electrons. Evidence was presented that the values of F_1 and F_2 for the proton were not equal at large values of q^2. At $q^2 = 20 f^{-2}$ the ratio of F_2/F_1 was given as $0.37 \begin{Bmatrix} +0.17 \\ -0.14 \end{Bmatrix}$. An earlier report of these results is contained in *Proc. 1960 Ann. Intern. Conf. High Energy Physics at Rochester* (Interscience, New York, 1960), pp. 757-761.

Paper 64 (page 583)

ELECTROMAGNETIC PROPERTIES OF THE PROTON AND NEUTRON, by D. N. Olson, H. F. Schopper, and R. R. Wilson

Phys. Rev. Letters, **6**, 286 (1961)

Proton and neutron cross sections were measured in this work and values of the nucleon isotopic form factors were deduced. Proton and neutron charge clouds were then approximated by various analyses which suggested a positive core for both proton and neutron, consisting of about 30 per cent (of a proton charge) in each case and a radius of dimensions of approximately one nucleon Compton wavelength. A positive shell on the outside of the neutron was also a conclusion of these workers.

Although at the present time it is not known whether final conclusions on proton and neutron charge clouds will substantiate these results (see Paper 81), one of the principal points about this paper was that an attempt was made in it to fit both the proton and neutron into a consistent scheme by using the concept of isotopic spin as a guide.

Paper 65 (page 588)

DIRAC AND PAULI FORM FACTORS OF THE NEUTRON, by R. Hofstadter, C. de Vries, and Robert Herman

Phys. Rev. Letters, **6**, 290 (1961)

An independent investigation of the electron scattering differential cross section of the deuteron at the peak of the inelastic continuum was made in this paper and neutron form factors, F_{1n}, F_{2n}, were deduced from the data by use of a modified Jankus theory of electrodisintegration of the deuteron. Isotopic form factors of the nucleon were then found from the experimental data. The companion paper (Paper 66) gave the analysis of these results. The use of the modified Jankus theory resulted in positive values of F_{1n} if the "right-hand" choice of intersections in the method of intersecting ellipses was employed. It was subsequently shown by Durand (Paper 71) that application of an improved theory gave values of F_{1n} closer to zero.

Paper 66 (page 592)

ELECTRIC AND MAGNETIC STRUCTURE OF THE PROTON AND NEUTRON, by Robert Hofstadter and Robert Herman

Phys. Rev. Letters, **6**, 293 (1961)

This paper attempted to present a unified interpretation of the experimental electromagnetic form factors of the proton and neutron and uses, for this purpose, experimental data found in the companion paper (Paper 65). Isotopic form factors of the nucleon were found, and an interpretation of these results was given in terms of the Clementel-Villi form factors. These results yielded qualitative conclusions about the charge clouds and magnetic moment clouds in both the proton and neutron in terms of delta-function cores and Yukawa clouds. Radii of the proton and neutron clouds were also found and the question of the anomalous behavior of the neutron's small charge radius and normal magnetic radius was explained in terms of two opposite charge clouds and magnetic moment clouds. Although an ambiguity in the sign of F_{1n} could not be resolved, the positive choice of values of F_{1n} was made in this interpretation.

The results in this paper were based on the neutron form factors found in the companion paper (No. 65), which were in turn dependent on the use of a modified Jankus theory of electrodisintegration of the deuteron. Subsequently Durand (Paper 71) gave a better approximation to the peak differential cross section of the deuteron and pointed out that the positive values of F_{1n} were reduced to nearly zero when the improved theory was employed. Although the numerical values of the parameters in the paper of Hofstadter and Herman have been modified by these corrections, the qualitative ideas and modes of expression of the form factors (Eqs. 9 to 12) still seem to be correct. Improved values of the proton and neutron form factors are given in the work of C. de Vries, R. Hofstadter, and Robert Herman (Paper 81).

The connection between the Clementel-Villi form factors and the postulated existence of heavy pion resonance (ρ and ω) was first made by S. Bergia, A. Stanghellini, S. Fubini, and C. Villi (Paper 68). The outline of such a theory was given earlier by Y. Nambu (Paper 41).

Paper 67 (page 596)

EXPERIMENTAL RESULTS ON THE π-π CROSS SECTION, by Jerry A. Anderson, Vo X. Bang, Philip G. Burke, D. Duane Carmony, and Norbert Schmitz
Phys. Rev. Letters, **6**, 365 (1961)

These authors studied the inelastic scattering of negative pions of momentum 1.03 Bev/c in a liquid hydrogen bubble chamber and employed the Chew-Low extrapolation scheme to show experimentally that their data were consistent with a π-π resonance at a value near $20 m_\pi^2$ and implied a value of $J = 1$. Thus this paper pointed to the existence of a ρ-meson.

Paper 68 (page 599)

ELECTROMAGNETIC FORM FACTORS OF THE NUCLEON AND PION-PION INTERACTION, by S. Bergia, A. Stanghellini, S. Fubini, and C. Villi
Phys. Rev. Letters, **6**, 367 (1961)

By writing the dispersion-theoretic expression for the nucleon form factors in terms of an integral of the strength function $g(-q^2) = g(t)$ and assuming that the strength function has a strong resonance, these authors showed that a simple argument gave the appearance of a Clementel-Villi function to the nucleon form factor. This Clementel-Villi function had already been shown to fit the experimental data (Papers 45 and 46). The paper of Bergia et al. called attention to the possibility that the existence of two resonances could explain the experimental situation with respect to nucleon form factors, as well as the pion-nucleon phase shifts deduced from low-energy pion scattering. The numerical values of the parameters selected in this paper have been superseded, but at this moment the main idea of the paper under discussion still appears to be correct. Further work on this subject has been reported by S. Bergia and A. Stanghellini [*Nuovo cimento*, **21**, 155 (1961)].

Paper 69 (page 604)

PION-PION INTERACTION IN PION PRODUCTION BY $\pi^+ - p$ COLLISIONS, by D. Stonehill, C. Baltay, H. Courant, W. Fickinger, E. C. Fowler, H. Kraybill, J. Sandweiss, J. Sanford, and H. Taft
Phys. Rev. Letters, **6**, 624 (1961)

In this paper $\pi^+ - p$ collisions were investigated at three different energies of the pion, and evidence was obtained for the existence of a unique pion-pion resonance, now also called the ρ-meson, with energy 700 to 770 Mev (25 to $30 m_\pi^2$) and full width at half-maximum of ~ 90 MeV. See also the later communications of C. Alff, D. Berley, D. Colley, N. Gelfand, U. Nauenberg, D. Miller, J. Schultz, J. Steinberger, T. H. Tan, H. Brugger, P. Kramer, and R. Plano [*Phys. Rev. Letters*, **9**, 322 (1962); *ibid.*, p. 325].

Paper 70 (page 606)
EVIDENCE FOR A π-π RESONANCE IN THE $I = 1$, $J = 1$ STATE, by A. R. Erwin, R. March, W. D. Walker, and E. West
Phys. Rev. Letters, **6**, 628 (1961)

This was one of the first papers to give a clear-cut and positive experimental proof of the existence of a ρ-meson. The value of the resonance was found to be close to 750 Mev with a width of 150 to 200 Mev at half-maximum for the π-π cross-section curve. The magnitude of the π-π cross section indicated a value of $J = 1$ for the resonant state.

Paper 71 (page 609)
INELASTIC ELECTRON-DEUTERON SCATTERING AND THE ELECTROMAGNETIC STRUCTURE OF THE NEUTRON, by Loyal Durand, III
Phys. Rev. Letters, **6**, 631 (1961)

By correcting the modified-Jankus electrodisintegration cross section of the deuteron used previously by Hofstadter, de Vries, and Herman (Paper 65), Durand showed that the F_1 values of the neutron were lower than found in that work and that they were probably near zero. The complete discussion of Durand will be found in an article published subsequently [Phys. Rev., **123**, 1393 (1961)], in which final-state interactions and relativistic corrections are considered in detail. See also the work of B. Bosco [*Nuovo cimento*, **23**, 1028 (1962)].

Paper 72 (page 613)
RADIATIVE CORRECTIONS TO ELECTRON-PROTON SCATTERING, by Yung-Su Tsai
Phys. Rev., **122**, 1898 (1961)

When the proton recoil is taken into account the radiative corrections to electron-proton scattering undergo a correction. This paper reports the magnitude of the correction for cases realized in practice. Numerical values of the Tsai correction have been obtained by R. Herman (private communication). Corresponding radiative corrections when the relativistic proton alone is detected have been calculated, first by L. I. Schiff [*Phys. Rev.*, **87**, 750 (1952)] and more recently by A. S. Krass [*Phys. Rev.*, **125**, 2172 (1962)]. An early experiment on this subject was made by G. W. Tautfest and W. K. H. Panofsky [*Phys. Rev.*, **105**, 1356 (1957)].

Paper 73 (page 623)

SCATTERING OF BEV ELECTRONS BY HYDROGEN AND DEUTERIUM, by R. M. Littauer, H. F. Schopper, and R. R. Wilson

Phys. Rev. Letters, **7**, 141 (1961)

This paper provided proton and neutron differential cross sections in the scattering of high-energy electrons up to an energy of 1.16 Bev and extending to laboratory angles of 135°. The results of a Goldberg-analysis of the data gave values of proton and neutron form factors in detailed agreement with earlier work (Papers 65 and 66).

Paper 74 (page 626)

STRUCTURE OF THE PROTON AND NEUTRON, by R. M. Littauer, H. F. Schopper, and R. R. Wilson

Phys. Rev. Letters, 7, 144 (1961)

An analysis was made in this work of the experimental proton and neutron form factors found in the preceding paper. The data were analyzed in terms of isotopic form factors. Core models with exponential density distributions were found that gave a good fit to the data. Clementel-Villi fits to the data were also made and the parameters determined in this way agreed in detail with a similar analysis made by Hofstadter and Herman (Paper 66). These data indicated a positive fringe of charge on the outside of the neutron. See, however, the differences between these data and subsequent data of C. de Vries, R. Hofstadter, and Robert Herman (Paper 81).

Paper 75 (page 630)

EVIDENCE FOR A $T = 0$ THREE-PION RESONANCE, by B. C. Maglić, L. W. Alvarez, A. H. Rosenfeld, and M. L. Stevenson

Phys. Rev. Letters, 7, 178 (1961)

This important paper proved the experimental existence of a new heavy meson (ω) with isotopic spin $T = 0$ and $J = 1^-$. Although the vector ρ-meson of spin $T = 1$ had already been found, no direct evidence of the scalar particle (ω) had been observed previously. The theoretical prediction by Nambu (Paper 41) and others from the knowledge of the electromagnetic form factors of proton and neutron was thus justified. By studying the effective mass distributions of pion triplets in antiproton-proton annihilations in a bubble chamber, dramatic evidence of a sharp peak in the "missing mass" distributions was observed. The ω-meson thus discovered had a mass value near 787 Mev ($\sim 32 m_\pi^2$) and a full width at half-maximum of less than 30 Mev. The width was so small that it might have been of instrumental origin. Thus the ω-resonance was surprisingly sharp. Dalitz plots of the data showed that it was very likely that the spin of the ω-meson was 1^- and therefore that the

ω-meson would contribute in an important way to the understanding of the nucleon form factors.

Paper 76 (page 635)

π-π RESONANCE IN π^- - p INTERACTIONS AT 1.25 BEV, by E. Pickup, D. K. Robinson, and E. O. Salant

Phys. Rev. Letters, **7**, 192 (1961)

Further work on a pion-pion resonance of the ρ-meson type is reported in this paper, and improved statistics made it possible to calculate the shape of the π-π resonance curve (Fig. 3).

Paper 77 (page 639)

ELECTROMAGNETIC FORM FACTORS OF THE PROTON, by F. Bumiller, M. Croissiaux, E. Dally, and R. Hofstadter

Phys. Rev., **124**, 1623 (1961)

This paper presented a summary of Stanford work on the proton form factors up to the time of publication. A table of electron-proton elastic scattering cross sections is presented and a final set of results of proton form factors is calculated (Fig. 11). Recent Stanford results, as yet unpublished, appear to confirm the general character of the cross sections and form factors of this paper. The flattened behavior of the cross sections at the very highest values of q^2 (at 145°) in this paper are being restudied at Stanford (T. Janssens et al., to be published.)

Other recent data on proton form factors at low values of q^2 are given by P. Lehmann, R. Taylor, and Richard Wilson [*Phys. Rev.*, **126**, 1183 (1962)].

Paper 78 (page 648)

EVIDENCE FOR A THREE-PION RESONANCE NEAR 550 MEV, by A. Pevsner, R. Kraemer, M. Nussbaum, C. Richardson, P. Schlein, R. Strand, T. Toohig, M. Block, A. Engler, R. Gessaroli, and C. Meltzer

Phys. Rev. Letters, **7**, 421 (1961)

Although subsequent events seem to show that the new meson (η-meson) discovered in this paper has an angular momentum of zero, and hence is not involved in the nucleon electromagnetic form factors, the importance of this sharp new resonance is great and will undoubtedly affect nucleon structure in some way. See the paper of P. L. Bastien, J. Peter Berge, O. I. Dahl, M. Ferro-Luzzi, D. H. Miller, J. J. Murray, A. H. Rosenfeld, and M. B. Watson [*Phys. Rev. Letters*, **8**, 114, 302E (1962)] for the information on the spin of the η-meson, as well as that of D. D. Carmony, A. H. Rosenfeld, and R. T. Van de Walle [*Phys. Rev. Letters*, **8**, 117 (1962)]. The possible existence of a second $T = 1$ resonance (ζ-meson) is discussed by R. Barloutoud,

J. Heughebaert, A. Leveque, J. Meyer, and R. Omnes [*Phys. Rev. Letters*, **8**, 32 (1962)]. The nature of such a resonance is still uncertain.

Paper 79 (page 651)

ELECTROMAGNETIC STRUCTURE OF PIONS AND NUCLEONS, by S. Fubini

Proc. Aix-en-Provence Intern. Conf. Elementary Particles (Saclay, France, 1961), vol. II, pp. 33-55, 1961

A clear summary was given in this paper of the theoretical status of nucleon structure problems up to the middle of 1961. The dispersion-theory treatment of form factors is explained in a simple way. Experimental determination of the neutron form factors from deuteron data is also discussed. Isotopic form factors are presented, and fits to experimental form factors using the pion resonances are made. It appears likely that the numerical fits of the data will be superseded.

Paper 80 (page 674)

SCALAR NUCLEON FORM FACTOR $F_1^n + F_1^p$, by Norman K. Glendenning and Gustav Kramer

Phys. Rev. Letters, **7**, 471 (1961)

The isotopic scalar form factor $F_{1S} = F_1^p + F_1^n$ is calculated from the elastic electron-deuteron scattering data of Friedman, Kendall, and Gram [*Phys. Rev.*, **120**, 992 (1960)]. The values of F_{1S} reported in this paper are in agreement with the trend of the data given in the following paper by de Vries, Hofstadter, and Herman (Paper 81). A recent investigation by H. F. Jones (see the comment under Paper 32) is relevant to the elastic electron-deuteron problem. Very recent work by D. J. Drickey and L. N. Hand (to be published) on the charge form factor of the neutron is related to the same problem.

Paper 81 (page 676)

NEUTRON FORM FACTORS AND NUCLEON STRUCTURE, by C. de Vries, R. Hofstadter, and Robert Herman

Phys. Rev. Letters, **8**, 381 (1962)

In this paper the corrected deuteron formula of Durand and Goldberg was used to interpret old and new Stanford data on the peak deuteron inelastic-scattering cross sections. The experimental data support a neutron form factor F_{1n}, close to zero as found earlier by Durand [Paper 71 and *Phys. Rev.*, **123**, 1393 (1961)] (see also Paper 45 by L. I. Schiff). Analysis of the isotopic form factors in terms of Clementel-Villi expressions can be carried out in terms of two "effective" meson masses. The best values are found to lie in the neighborhood of $18 m_\pi^2$ for the ρ'-meson and $23 m_\pi^2$ for the ω'-meson. The symbols ρ' and ω' are meant to indicate that the effective masses found from this analysis differ from those of the real ρ- and ω-mesons, namely, ~28 and $32\,m_\pi^2$, respectively.

The quantitative conclusions of this paper differ from those of earlier Stanford publications (Papers 65 and 66) and also from those of the Cornell publications (Papers 64 and 73). The theoretical model introduced in the reference of Hofstadter and Herman (Paper 66) and also by Bergia et al. (Paper 68) is still thought to be approximately correct and was used in the analysis of the paper under discussion.

For an expression of the form factors in terms of "charge" and "magnetic moment" varieties see the paper of L. N. Hand, D. G. Miller, and R. Wilson [*Phys. Rev. Letters*, **8**, 110 (1962)], in which the authors use some preliminary values of the form factors.

Paper 82 (page 681)

MU-MESONIC X-RAY ENERGIES, by C. S. Johnson, E. P. Hincks, and H. L. Anderson

Bull. Am. Phys. Soc., [II] **7**, 340 (1962).

Precise investigation of the X-rays resulting from muon transitions in the nuclei between $Z = 12$ and $Z = 50$ are reported in this abstract. These studies indicate good agreement of the final results with nuclear charge distributions obtained by electron-scattering methods. In this connection the paper [*Phys. Rev.*, **125**, 2102 (1962)] by the same authors should be consulted, especially for the note added in proof (p. 2109). The investigation of H. Crannell, R. Helm, H. Kendall, J. Oeser, and M. Yearian [*Phys. Rev.*, **121**, 283 (1961)] is also of interest, since it is related to the interpretation of the results of Johnson et al. See also the work of P. Brix, R. Engfer, U. Hegel, D. Quitmann, G. Backenstoss, K. Goebel, and B. Stadler [*Physics Letters*, **1**, 56 (1962)].

Paper 83 (page 682)

MU-MESONIC ATOM STUDIES OF Ti, Fe, Co, Zn, Tl, Pb, Bi, by W. Frati and J. Rainwater

To be published in *Phys. Rev.* See also *Bull. Am. Phys. Soc.*, [II] **7**, 340 (1962).

This report by Frati and Rainwater is a summary of results to be presented at greater length in the *Physical Review*. The work represents the culmination of nearly a 10-year effort to improve the original data of Fitch and Rainwater (Paper 19). Remarkable improvements are described in this brief report and resulted in the possibility of measuring the separations of the $2p_{3/2}$ and $2p_{1/2}$ levels, as well as observing the transitions between higher levels ($3d_{5/2} - 2p_{3/2}$), etc. Good agreement is found with electron-scattering results on nuclear charge distribution.

I wish to thank Professor J. Rainwater for his kind permission to present these results in advance of publication.

PAPER 1*

The Quantum Theory of the Electron.

By P. A. M. Dirac, St. John's College, Cambridge.

(Communicated by R. H. Fowler, F.R.S.—Received January 2, 1928.)

The new quantum mechanics, when applied to the problem of the structure of the atom with point-charge electrons, does not give results in agreement with experiment. The discrepancies consist of "duplexity" phenomena, the observed number of stationary states for an electron in an atom being twice the number given by the theory. To meet the difficulty, Goudsmit and Uhlenbeck have introduced the idea of an electron with a spin angular momentum of half a quantum and a magnetic moment of one Bohr magneton. This model for the electron has been fitted into the new mechanics by Pauli,* and Darwin,† working with an equivalent theory, has shown that it gives results in agreement with experiment for hydrogen-like spectra to the first order of accuracy.

The question remains as to why Nature should have chosen this particular model for the electron instead of being satisfied with the point-charge. One would like to find some incompleteness in the previous methods of applying quantum mechanics to the point-charge electron such that, when removed, the whole of the duplexity phenomena follow without arbitrary assumptions. In the present paper it is shown that this is the case, the incompleteness of the previous theories lying in their disagreement with relativity, or, alternatetively, with the general transformation theory of quantum mechanics. It appears that the simplest Hamiltonian for a point-charge electron satisfying the requirements of both relativity and the general transformation theory leads to an explanation of all duplexity phenomena without further assumption. All the same there is a great deal of truth in the spinning electron model, at least as a first approximation. The most important failure of the model seems to be that the magnitude of the resultant orbital angular momentum of an electron moving in an orbit in a central field of force is not a constant, as the model leads one to expect.

* Pauli, 'Z. f. Physik,' vol. 43, p. 601 (1927).

† Darwin, 'Roy. Soc. Proc.,' A, vol. 116, p. 227 (1927).

See page 683 of this volume for corrections and addenda.

§ 1. *Previous Relativity Treatments.*

The relativity Hamiltonian according to the classical theory for a point electron moving in an arbitrary electro-magnetic field with scalar potential A_0 and vector potential $\mathbf{A}$ is

$$F \equiv \left(\frac{W}{c} + \frac{e}{c} A_0\right)^2 + \left(\mathbf{p} + \frac{e}{c}\mathbf{A}\right)^2 + m^2c^2,$$

where $\mathbf{p}$ is the momentum vector. It has been suggested by Gordon* that the operator of the wave equation of the quantum theory should be obtained from this F by the same procedure as in non-relativity theory, namely, by putting

$$W = ih\frac{\partial}{\partial t},$$

$$p_r = -ih\frac{\partial}{\partial x_r}, \qquad r = 1, 2, 3,$$

in it. This gives the wave equation

$$F\psi \equiv \left[\left(ih\frac{\partial}{c\,\partial t} + \frac{e}{c}A_0\right)^2 + \Sigma_r\left(-ih\frac{\partial}{\partial x_r} + \frac{e}{c}A_r\right)^2 + m^2c^2\right]\psi = 0, \qquad (1)$$

the wave function ψ being a function of x_1, x_2, x_3, t. This gives rise to two difficulties.

The first is in connection with the physical interpretation of ψ. Gordon, and also independently Klein,† from considerations of the conservation theorems, make the assumption that if ψ_m, ψ_n are two solutions

$$\rho_{mn} = -\frac{e}{2mc^2}\left\{ih\left(\psi_m\frac{\partial\bar{\psi}_n}{\partial t} - \bar{\psi}_n\frac{\partial\psi_m}{\partial t}\right) + 2eA_0\psi_m\bar{\psi}_n\right\}$$

and

$$\mathbf{I}_{mn} = -\frac{e}{2m}\left\{-ih\left(\psi_m \operatorname{grad}\bar{\psi}_n - \bar{\psi}_n \operatorname{grad}\psi_m\right) + 2\frac{e}{c}\mathbf{A}_m\psi_m\bar{\psi}_n\right\}$$

are to be interpreted as the charge and current associated with the transition $m \to n$. This appears to be satisfactory so far as emission and absorption of radiation are concerned, but is not so general as the interpretation of the non-relativity quantum mechanics, which has been developed‡ sufficiently to enable one to answer the question: What is the probability of any dynamical variable

* Gordon, 'Z. f. Physik,' vol. 40, p. 117 (1926).

† Klein, 'Z. f. Physik,' vol. 41, p. 407 (1927).

‡ Jordan, 'Z. f. Physik,' vol. 40, p. 809 (1927); Dirac, 'Roy. Soc. Proc.,' A, vol. 113, p. 621 (1927).

at any specified time having a value lying between any specified limits, when the system is represented by a given wave function ψ_n? The Gordon-Klein interpretation can answer such questions if they refer to the position of the electron (by the use of ρ_{nn}), but not if they refer to its momentum, or angular momentum or any other dynamical variable. We should expect the interpretation of the relativity theory to be just as general as that of the non-relativity theory.

The general interpretation of non-relativity quantum mechanics is based on the transformation theory, and is made possible by the wave equation being of the form

$$(\mathrm{H} - \mathrm{W}) \psi = 0, \tag{2}$$

i.e., being linear in W or $\partial/\partial t$, so that the wave function at any time determines the wave function at any later time. The wave equation of the relativity theory must also be linear in W if the general interpretation is to be possible.

The second difficulty in Gordon's interpretation arises from the fact that if one takes the conjugate imaginary of equation (1), one gets

$$\left[\left(-\frac{\mathrm{W}}{c} + \frac{e}{c}\mathrm{A}_0\right)^2 + \left(-\mathbf{p} + \frac{e}{c}\mathbf{A}\right)^2 + m^2c^2\right]\psi = 0,$$

which is the same as one would get if one put $-e$ for e. The wave equation (1) thus refers equally well to an electron with charge e as to one with charge $-e$. If one considers for definiteness the limiting case of large quantum numbers one would find that some of the solutions of the wave equation are wave packets moving in the way a particle of charge $-e$ would move on the classical theory, while others are wave packets moving in the way a particle of charge e would move classically. For this second class of solutions W has a negative value. One gets over the difficulty on the classical theory by arbitrarily excluding those solutions that have a negative W. One cannot do this on the quantum theory, since in general a perturbation will cause transitions from states with W positive to states with W negative. Such a transition would appear experimentally as the electron suddenly changing its charge from $-e$ to e, a phenomenon which has not been observed. The true relativity wave equation should thus be such that its solutions split up into two non-combining sets, referring respectively to the charge $-e$ and the charge e.

In the present paper we shall be concerned only with the removal of the first of these two difficulties. The resulting theory is therefore still only an approximation, but it appears to be good enough to account for all the duplexity phenomena without arbitrary assumptions.

§ 2. *The Hamiltonian for No Field.*

Our problem is to obtain a wave equation of the form (2) which shall be invariant under a Lorentz transformation and shall be equivalent to (1) in the limit of large quantum numbers. We shall consider first the case of no field, when equation (1) reduces to

$$(-p_0{}^2 + \mathbf{p}^2 + m^2c^2)\,\psi = 0 \tag{3}$$

if one puts

$$p_0 = \frac{W}{c} = ih\frac{\partial}{c\,\partial t}.$$

The symmetry between p_0 and p_1, p_2, p_3 required by relativity shows that, since the Hamiltonian we want is linear in p_0, it must also be linear in p_1, p_2 and p_3. Our wave equation is therefore of the form

$$(p_0 + \alpha_1 p_1 + \alpha_2 p_2 + \alpha_3 p_3 + \beta)\,\psi = 0, \tag{4}$$

where for the present all that is known about the dynamical variables or operators $\alpha_1, \alpha_2, \alpha_3, \beta$ is that they are independent of p_0, p_1, p_2, p_3, *i.e.*, that they commute with t, x_1, x_2, x_3. Since we are considering the case of a particle moving in empty space, so that all points in space are equivalent, we should expect the Hamiltonian not to involve t, x_1, x_2, x_3. This means that $\alpha_1, \alpha_2, \alpha_3, \beta$ are independent of t, x_1, x_2, x_3, *i.e.*, that they commute with p_0, p_1, p_2, p_3. We are therefore obliged to have other dynamical variables besides the co-ordinates and momenta of the electron, in order that $\alpha_1, \alpha_2, \alpha_3, \beta$ may be functions of them. The wave function ψ must then involve more variables than merely x_1, x_2, x_3, t.

Equation (4) leads to

$$\begin{aligned} 0 &= (-p_0 + \alpha_1 p_1 + \alpha_2 p_2 + \alpha_3 p_3 + \beta)(p_0 + \alpha_1 p_1 + \alpha_2 p_2 + \alpha_3 p_3 + \beta)\,\psi \\ &= [-p_0{}^2 + \Sigma\,\alpha_1{}^2 p_1{}^2 + \Sigma\,(\alpha_1\alpha_2 + \alpha_2\alpha_1)\,p_1 p_2 + \beta^2 + \Sigma\,(\alpha_1\beta + \beta\alpha_1)\,p_1]\,\psi, \end{aligned} \tag{5}$$

where the Σ refers to cyclic permutation of the suffixes 1, 2, 3. This agrees with (3) if

$$\left.\begin{aligned} &\alpha_r{}^2 = 1, \qquad \alpha_r\alpha_s + \alpha_s\alpha_r = 0 \quad (r \neq s) \\ &\beta^2 = m^2c^2, \qquad \alpha_r\beta + \beta\alpha_r = 0 \end{aligned}\right\} \quad r, s = 1, 2, 3.$$

If we put $\beta = \alpha_4 mc$, these conditions become

$$\alpha_\mu{}^2 = 1 \qquad \alpha_\mu\alpha_\nu + \alpha_\nu\alpha_\mu = 0 \;(\mu \neq \nu) \qquad \mu, \nu = 1, 2, 3, 4. \tag{6}$$

We can suppose the α_μ's to be expressed as matrices in some matrix scheme, the matrix elements of α_μ being, say, $\alpha_\mu(\zeta'\,\zeta'')$. The wave function ψ must now be a function of ζ as well as x_1, x_2, x_3, t. The result of α_μ multiplied into ψ will be a function $(\alpha_\mu \psi)$ of x_1, x_2, x_3, t, ζ defined by

$$(\alpha_\mu \psi)(x, t, \zeta) = \Sigma_{\zeta'} \alpha_\mu (\zeta \zeta') \psi (x, t, \zeta').$$

We must now find four matrices α_μ to satisfy the conditions (6). We make use of the matrices

$$\sigma_1 = \begin{pmatrix} 0 & 1 \\ 1 & 0 \end{pmatrix} \qquad \sigma_2 = \begin{pmatrix} 0 & -i \\ i & 0 \end{pmatrix} \qquad \sigma_3 = \begin{pmatrix} 1 & 0 \\ 0 & -1 \end{pmatrix}$$

which Pauli introduced* to describe the three components of spin angular momentum. These matrices have just the properties

$$\sigma_r^2 = 1 \qquad \sigma_r \sigma_s + \sigma_s \sigma_r = 0, \qquad (r \neq s), \tag{7}$$

that we require for our α's. We cannot, however, just take the σ's to be three of our α's, because then it would not be possible to find the fourth. We must extend the σ's in a diagonal manner to bring in two more rows and columns, so that we can introduce three more matrices ρ_1, ρ_2, ρ_3 of the same form as σ_1, σ_2, σ_3, but referring to different rows and columns, thus :—

$$\sigma_1 = \begin{Bmatrix} 0 & 1 & 0 & 0 \\ 1 & 0 & 0 & 0 \\ 0 & 0 & 0 & 1 \\ 0 & 0 & 1 & 0 \end{Bmatrix} \quad \sigma_2 = \begin{Bmatrix} 0 & -i & 0 & 0 \\ i & 0 & 0 & 0 \\ 0 & 0 & 0 & -i \\ 0 & 0 & i & 0 \end{Bmatrix} \quad \sigma_3 = \begin{Bmatrix} 1 & 0 & 0 & 0 \\ 0 & -1 & 0 & 0 \\ 0 & 0 & 1 & 0 \\ 0 & 0 & 0 & -1 \end{Bmatrix},$$

$$\rho_1 = \begin{Bmatrix} 0 & 0 & 1 & 0 \\ 0 & 0 & 0 & 1 \\ 1 & 0 & 0 & 0 \\ 0 & 1 & 0 & 0 \end{Bmatrix} \quad \rho_2 = \begin{Bmatrix} 0 & 0 & -i & 0 \\ 0 & 0 & 0 & -i \\ i & 0 & 0 & 0 \\ 0 & i & 0 & 0 \end{Bmatrix} \quad \rho_3 = \begin{Bmatrix} 1 & 0 & 0 & 0 \\ 0 & 1 & 0 & 0 \\ 0 & 0 & -1 & 0 \\ 0 & 0 & 0 & -1 \end{Bmatrix}.$$

The ρ's are obtained from the σ's by interchanging the second and third rows, and the second and third columns. We now have, in addition to equations (7)

and also
$$\left.\begin{aligned} &\rho_r^2 = 1 \qquad \rho_r \rho_s + \rho_s \rho_r = 0 \qquad (r \neq s), \\ &\rho_r \sigma_t = \sigma_t \rho_r. \end{aligned}\right\} \tag{7'}$$

* Pauli, *loc. cit.*

If we now take

$$\alpha_1 = \rho_1\sigma_1, \quad \alpha_2 = \rho_1\sigma_2, \quad \alpha_3 = \rho_1\sigma_3, \quad \alpha_4 = \rho_3,$$

all the conditions (6) are satisfied, *e.g.*,

$$\alpha_1^2 = \rho_1\sigma_1\rho_1\sigma_1 = \rho_1^2\sigma_1^2 = 1$$

$$\alpha_1\alpha_2 = \rho_1\sigma_1\rho_1\sigma_2 = \rho_1^2\sigma_1\sigma_2 = -\rho_1^2\sigma_2\sigma_1 = -\alpha_2\alpha_1.$$

The following equations are to be noted for later reference

$$\left.\begin{aligned}\rho_1\rho_2 = i\rho_3 = -\rho_2\rho_1\\ \sigma_1\sigma_2 = i\sigma_3 = -\sigma_2\sigma_1\end{aligned}\right\}, \tag{8}$$

together with the equations obtained by cyclic permutation of the suffixes.

The wave equation (4) now takes the form

$$[p_0 + \rho_1(\boldsymbol{\sigma}, \mathbf{p}) + \rho_3 mc]\,\psi = 0, \tag{9}$$

where $\boldsymbol{\sigma}$ denotes the vector $(\sigma_1, \sigma_2, \sigma_3)$.

§ 3. *Proof of Invariance under a Lorentz Transformation.*

Multiply equation (9) by ρ_3 on the left-hand side. It becomes, with the help of (8),

$$[\rho_3 p_0 + i\rho_2(\sigma_1 p_1 + \sigma_2 p_2 + \sigma_3 p_3) + mc]\,\psi = 0.$$

Putting

$$p_0 = ip_4,$$

$$\rho_3 = \gamma_4, \quad \rho_2\sigma_r = \gamma_r, \quad r = 1, 2, 3, \tag{10}$$

we have

$$[i\Sigma\gamma_\mu p_\mu + mc]\,\psi = 0, \quad \mu = 1, 2, 3, 4. \tag{11}$$

The p_μ transform under a Lorentz transformation according to the law

$$p_\mu' = \Sigma_\nu a_{\mu\nu} p_\nu,$$

where the coefficients $a_{\mu\nu}$ are c-numbers satisfying

$$\Sigma_\mu a_{\mu\nu} a_{\mu\tau} = \delta_{\nu\tau}, \quad \Sigma_\tau a_{\mu\tau} a_{\nu\tau} = \delta_{\mu\nu}.$$

The wave equation therefore transforms into

$$[i\Sigma\gamma_\mu' p_\mu' + mc]\,\psi = 0, \tag{12}$$

where

$$\gamma_\mu' = \Sigma_\nu a_{\mu\nu}\gamma_\nu.$$

Now the γ_μ, like the α_μ, satisfy

$$\gamma_\mu^2 = 1, \quad \gamma_\mu\gamma_\nu + \gamma_\nu\gamma_\mu = 0, \quad (\mu \neq \nu).$$

These relations can be summed up in the single equation

$$\gamma_\mu \gamma_\nu + \gamma_\nu \gamma_\mu = 2\delta_{\mu\nu}.$$

We have

$$\begin{aligned}\gamma_\mu' \gamma_\nu' + \gamma_\nu' \gamma_\mu' &= \Sigma_{\tau\lambda}\, a_{\mu\tau}\, a_{\nu\lambda}\, (\gamma_\tau \gamma_\lambda + \gamma_\lambda \gamma_\tau) \\ &= 2\Sigma_{\tau\lambda}\, a_{\mu\tau}\, a_{\nu\lambda}\, \delta_{\tau\lambda} \\ &= 2\Sigma_\tau\, a_{\mu\tau}\, a_{\nu\tau} = 2\delta_{\mu\nu}.\end{aligned}$$

Thus the γ_μ' satisfy the same relations as the γ_μ. Thus we can put, analogously to (10)

$$\gamma_4' = \rho_3' \qquad \gamma_r' = \rho_2' \sigma_r'$$

where the ρ''s and σ''s are easily verified to satisfy the relations corresponding to (7), (7′) and (8), if ρ_2' and ρ_1' are defined by $\rho_2' = -i\gamma_1'\gamma_2'\gamma_3'$, $\rho_1' = -i\rho_2'\rho_3'$.

We shall now show that, by a canonical transformation, the ρ''s and σ''s may be brought into the form of the ρ's and σ's. From the equation $\rho_3'^2 = 1$, it follows that the only possible characteristic values for ρ_3' are ± 1. If one applies to ρ_3' a canonical transformation with the transformation function ρ_1', the result is

$$\rho_1' \rho_3' (\rho_1')^{-1} = -\rho_3' \rho_1' (\rho_1')^{-1} = -\rho_3'.$$

Since characteristic values are not changed by a canonical transformation ρ_3' must have the same characteristic values as $-\rho_3'$. Hence the characteristic values of ρ_3' are $+1$ twice and -1 twice. The same argument applies to each of the other ρ''s, and to each of the σ''s.

Since ρ_3' and σ_3' commute, they can be brought simultaneously to the diagonal form by a canonical transformation. They will then have for their diagonal elements each $+1$ twice and -1 twice. Thus, by suitably rearranging the rows and columns, they can be brought into the form ρ_3 and σ_3 respectively. (The possibility $\rho_3' = \pm \sigma_3'$ is excluded by the existence of matrices that commute with one but not with the other.)

Any matrix containing four rows and columns can be expressed as

$$c + \Sigma_r c_r \sigma_r + \Sigma_r c_r' \rho_r + \Sigma_{rs} c_{rs} \rho_r \sigma_s \tag{13}$$

where the sixteen coefficients c, c_r, c_r', c_{rs} are c-numbers. By expressing σ_1' in this way, we see, from the fact that it commutes with $\rho_3' = \rho_3$ and anti-commutes* with $\sigma_3' = \sigma_3$, that it must be of the form

$$\sigma_1' = c_1\sigma_1 + c_2\sigma_2 + c_{31}\rho_3\sigma_1 + c_{32}\rho_3\sigma_2,$$

* We say that a anticommutes with b when $ab = -ba$.

i.e., of the form

$$\sigma_1' = \begin{Bmatrix} 0 & a_{12} & 0 & 0 \\ a_{21} & 0 & 0 & 0 \\ 0 & 0 & 0 & a_{34} \\ 0 & 0 & a_{43} & 0 \end{Bmatrix}$$

The condition $\sigma_1'^2 = 1$ shows that $a_{12}a_{21} = 1$, $a_{34}a_{43} = 1$. If we now apply the canonical transformation: first row to be multiplied by $(a_{21}/a_{12})^{\frac{1}{2}}$ and third row to be multiplied by $(a_{43}/a_{34})^{\frac{1}{2}}$, and first and third columns to be divided by the same expressions, σ_1' will be brought into the form of σ_1, and the diagonal matrices σ_3' and ρ_3' will not be changed.

If we now express ρ_1' in the form (13) and use the conditions that it commutes with $\sigma_1' = \sigma_1$ and $\sigma_3' = \sigma_3$ and anticommutes with $\rho_3' = \rho_3$, we see that it must be of the form

$$\rho_1' = c_1'\rho_1 + c_2'\rho_2.$$

The condition $\rho_1'^2 = 1$ shows that $c_1'^2 + c_2'^2 = 1$, or $c_1' = \cos\theta$, $c_2' = \sin\theta$. Hence ρ_1' is of the form

$$\rho_1' = \begin{Bmatrix} 0 & 0 & e^{-i\theta} & 0 \\ 0 & 0 & 0 & e^{-i\theta} \\ e^{i\theta} & 0 & 0 & 0 \\ 0 & e^{i\theta} & 0 & 0 \end{Bmatrix}$$

If we now apply the canonical transformation: first and second rows to be multiplied by $e^{i\theta}$ and first and second columns to be divided by the same expression, ρ_1' will be brought into the form ρ_1, and σ_1, σ_3, ρ_3 will not be altered. ρ_2' and σ_2' must now be of the form ρ_2 and σ_2, on account of the relations $i\rho_2' = \rho_3'\rho_1'$, $i\sigma_2' = \sigma_3'\sigma_1'$.

Thus by a succession of canonical transformations, which can be combined to form a single canonical transformation, the ρ''s and σ''s can be brought into the form of the ρ's and σ's. The new wave equation (12) can in this way be brought back into the form of the original wave equation (11) or (9), so that the results that follow from this original wave equation must be independent of the frame of reference used.

§ 4. *The Hamiltonian for an Arbitrary Field.*

To obtain the Hamiltonian for an electron in an electromagnetic field with scalar potential A_0 and vector potential $\mathbf{A}$, we adopt the usual procedure of substituting $p_0 + e/c \, . \, A_0$ for p_0 and $\mathbf{p} + e/c \, . \, \mathbf{A}$ for $\mathbf{p}$ in the Hamiltonian for no field. From equation (9) we thus obtain

$$\left[p_0 + \frac{e}{c} A_0 + \rho_1 \left(\boldsymbol{\sigma}, \mathbf{p} + \frac{e}{c} \mathbf{A} \right) + \rho_3 mc \right] \psi = 0. \tag{14}$$

This wave equation appears to be sufficient to account for all the duplexity phenomena. On account of the matrices ρ and σ containing four rows and columns, it will have four times as many solutions as the non-relativity wave equation, and twice as many as the previous relativity wave equation (1). Since half the solutions must be rejected as referring to the charge $+ e$ on the electron, the correct number will be left to account for duplexity phenomena. The proof given in the preceding section of invariance under a Lorentz transformation applies equally well to the more general wave equation (14).

We can obtain a rough idea of how (14) differs from the previous relativity wave equation (1) by multiplying it up analogously to (5). This gives, if we write e' for e/c

$$\begin{aligned} 0 &= [-(p_0 + e'A_0) + \rho_1 (\boldsymbol{\sigma}, \mathbf{p} + e'\mathbf{A}) + \rho_3 mc] \\ &\qquad \times [(p_0 + e'A_0) + \rho_1 (\boldsymbol{\sigma}, \mathbf{p} + e'\mathbf{A}) + \rho_3 mc] \, \psi \\ &= [-(p_0 + e'A_0)^2 + (\boldsymbol{\sigma}, \mathbf{p} + e'\mathbf{A})^2 + m^2c^2 \\ &\qquad + \rho_1 \{(\boldsymbol{\sigma}, \mathbf{p} + e'\mathbf{A})(p_0 + e'A_0) - (p_0 + e'A_0)(\boldsymbol{\sigma}, \mathbf{p} + e'\mathbf{A})\}] \, \psi. \end{aligned} \tag{15}$$

We now use the general formula, that if $\mathbf{B}$ and $\mathbf{C}$ are any two vectors that commute with $\boldsymbol{\sigma}$

$$\begin{aligned} (\boldsymbol{\sigma}, \mathbf{B})(\boldsymbol{\sigma}, \mathbf{C}) &= \Sigma \, \sigma_1^2 B_1C_1 + \Sigma \, (\sigma_1\sigma_2 B_1C_2 + \sigma_2\sigma_1 B_2C_1) \\ &= (\mathbf{B}, \mathbf{C}) + i \, \Sigma \, \sigma_3 (B_1C_2 - B_2C_1) \\ &= (\mathbf{B}, \mathbf{C}) + i \, (\boldsymbol{\sigma}, \mathbf{B} \times \mathbf{C}). \end{aligned} \tag{16}$$

Taking $\mathbf{B} = \mathbf{C} = \mathbf{p} + e'\mathbf{A}$, we find

$$\begin{aligned} (\boldsymbol{\sigma}, \mathbf{p} + e'\mathbf{A})^2 &= (\mathbf{p} + e'\mathbf{A})^2 + i \, \Sigma \, \sigma_3 \\ &\qquad [(p_1 + e'A_1)(p_2 + e'A_2) - (p_2 + e'A_2)(p_1 + e'A_1)] \\ &= (\mathbf{p} + e'\mathbf{A})^2 + he' (\boldsymbol{\sigma}, \operatorname{curl} \mathbf{A}). \end{aligned}$$

Thus (15) becomes

$$0 = \Big[-(p_0 + e'A_0)^2 + (\mathbf{p} + e'\mathbf{A})^2 + m^2c^2 + e'h(\boldsymbol{\sigma}, \text{curl } \mathbf{A}) - ie'h\rho_1\Big(\boldsymbol{\sigma}, \text{grad } A_0 + \frac{1}{c}\frac{\partial \mathbf{A}}{\partial t}\Big)\Big]\psi$$

$$= [-(p_0 + e'A_0)^2 + (\mathbf{p} + e'\mathbf{A})^2 + m^2c^2 + e'h(\boldsymbol{\sigma}, \mathbf{H}) + ie'h\rho_1(\boldsymbol{\sigma}, \mathbf{E})]\,\psi,$$

where **E** and **H** are the electric and magnetic vectors of the field.

This differs from (1) by the two extra terms

$$\frac{eh}{c}(\boldsymbol{\sigma}, \mathbf{H}) + \frac{ieh}{c}\rho_1(\boldsymbol{\sigma}, \mathbf{E})$$

in F. These two terms, when divided by the factor $2m$, can be regarded as the additional potential energy of the electron due to its new degree of freedom. The electron will therefore behave as though it has a magnetic moment $eh/2mc \,.\, \boldsymbol{\sigma}$ and an electric moment $ieh/2mc \,.\, \rho_1\boldsymbol{\sigma}$. This magnetic moment is just that assumed in the spinning electron model. The electric moment, being a pure imaginary, we should not expect to appear in the model. It is doubtful whether the electric moment has any physical meaning, since the Hamiltonian in (14) that we started from is real, and the imaginary part only appeared when we multiplied it up in an artificial way in order to make it resemble the Hamiltonian of previous theories.

§ 5. *The Angular Momentum Integrals for Motion in a Central Field.*

We shall consider in greater detail the motion of an electron in a central field of force. We put $\mathbf{A} = 0$ and $e'A_0 = V(r)$, an arbitrary function of the radius r, so that the Hamiltonian in (14) becomes

$$F \equiv p_0 + V + \rho_1(\boldsymbol{\sigma}, \mathbf{p}) + \rho_3 mc.$$

We shall determine the periodic solutions of the wave equation $F\psi = 0$, which means that p_0 is to be counted as a parameter instead of an operator; it is, in fact, just $1/c$ times the energy level.

We shall first find the angular momentum integrals of the motion. The orbital angular momentum **m** is defined by

$$\mathbf{m} = \mathbf{x} \times \mathbf{p},$$

and satisfies the following " Vertauschungs " relations

$$\left.\begin{aligned} m_1x_1 - x_1m_1 &= 0, & m_1x_2 - x_2m_1 &= ihx_3 \\ m_1p_1 - p_1m_1 &= 0, & m_1p_2 - p_2m_1 &= ihp_3 \\ \mathbf{m} \times \mathbf{m} &= ih\mathbf{m}, & \mathbf{m}^2m_1 - m_1\mathbf{m}^2 &= 0, \end{aligned}\right\}, \qquad (17)$$

together with similar relations obtained by permuting the suffixes. Also **m** commutes with r, and with p_r, the momentum canonically conjugate to r.

We have

$$m_1 \mathrm{F} - \mathrm{F} m_1 = \rho_1 \{ m_1 (\boldsymbol{\sigma}, \mathbf{p}) - (\boldsymbol{\sigma}, \mathbf{p}) m_1 \}$$
$$= \rho_1 (\boldsymbol{\sigma}, m_1 \mathbf{p} - \mathbf{p} m_1)$$
$$= ih\rho_1 (\sigma_2 p_3 - \sigma_3 p_2),$$

and so

$$\mathbf{m}\mathrm{F} - \mathrm{F}\mathbf{m} = ih\rho_1 \, \boldsymbol{\sigma} \times \mathbf{p}. \tag{18}$$

Thus **m** is not a constant of the motion. We have further

$$\sigma_1 \mathrm{F} - \mathrm{F} \sigma_1 = \rho_1 \{ \sigma_1 (\boldsymbol{\sigma}, \mathbf{p}) - (\boldsymbol{\sigma}, \mathbf{p}) \sigma_1 \}$$
$$= \rho_1 (\sigma_1 \boldsymbol{\sigma} - \boldsymbol{\sigma} \sigma_1, \mathbf{p})$$
$$= 2i\rho_1 (\sigma_3 p_2 - \sigma_2 p_3),$$

with the help of (8), and so

$$\boldsymbol{\sigma} \mathrm{F} - \mathrm{F} \boldsymbol{\sigma} = - 2i\rho_1 \, \boldsymbol{\sigma} \times \mathbf{p}.$$

Hence

$$(\mathbf{m} + \tfrac{1}{2} h \boldsymbol{\sigma}) \mathrm{F} - \mathrm{F} (\mathbf{m} + \tfrac{1}{2} h \boldsymbol{\sigma}) = 0.$$

Thus $\mathbf{m} + \frac{1}{2} h \boldsymbol{\sigma}$ (= **M** say) is a constant of the motion. We can interpret this result by saying that the electron has a spin angular momentum of $\frac{1}{2} h \boldsymbol{\sigma}$, which, added to the orbital angular momentum **m**, gives the total angular momentum **M**, which is a constant of the motion.

The Vertauschungs relations (17) all hold when M's are written for the m's. In particular

$$\mathbf{M} \times \mathbf{M} = ih\mathbf{M} \quad \text{and} \quad \mathbf{M}^2 \mathrm{M}_3 = \mathrm{M}_3 \mathbf{M}^2.$$

M_3 will be an action variable of the system. Since the characteristic values of m_3 must be integral multiples of h in order that the wave function may be single-valued, the characteristic values of M_3 must be half odd integral multiples of h. If we put

$$\mathbf{M}^2 = (j^2 - \tfrac{1}{4}) h^2, \tag{19}$$

j will be another quantum number, and the characteristic values of M_3 will extend from $(j - \frac{1}{2}) h$ to $(-j + \frac{1}{2}) h$.* Thus j takes integral values.

One easily verifies from (18) that $\mathbf{m}^2$ does not commute with F, and is thus not a constant of the motion. This makes a difference between the present theory and the previous spinning electron theory, in which $\mathbf{m}^2$ is constant, and defines the azimuthal quantum number k by a relation similar to (19). We shall find that our j plays the same part as the k of the previous theory.

* See 'Roy. Soc. Proc.,' A, vol. 111, p. 281 (1926).

§ 6. *The Energy Levels for Motion in a Central Field.*

We shall now obtain the wave equation as a differential equation in r, with the variables that specify the orientation of the whole system removed. We can do this by the use only of elementary non-commutative algebra in the following way.

In formula (16) take $\mathbf{B} = \mathbf{C} = \mathbf{m}$. This gives

$$(\boldsymbol{\sigma}, \mathbf{m})^2 = \mathbf{m}^2 + i(\boldsymbol{\sigma}, \mathbf{m} \times \mathbf{m}) \tag{20}$$
$$= (\mathbf{m} + \tfrac{1}{2}h\boldsymbol{\sigma})^2 - h(\boldsymbol{\sigma}, \mathbf{m}) - \tfrac{1}{4}h^2\boldsymbol{\sigma}^2 - h(\boldsymbol{\sigma}, \mathbf{m})$$
$$= \mathbf{M}^2 - 2h(\boldsymbol{\sigma}, \mathbf{m}) - \tfrac{3}{4}h^2.$$

Hence

$$\{(\boldsymbol{\sigma}, \mathbf{m}) + h\}^2 = \mathbf{M}^2 + \tfrac{1}{4}h^2 = j^2h^2.$$

Up to the present we have defined j only through j^2, so that we could now, if we liked, take jh equal to $(\boldsymbol{\sigma}, \mathbf{m}) + h$. This would not be convenient since we want j to be a constant of the motion while $(\boldsymbol{\sigma}, \mathbf{m}) + h$ is not, although its square is. We have, in fact, by another application of (16),

$$(\boldsymbol{\sigma}, \mathbf{m})(\boldsymbol{\sigma}, \mathbf{p}) = i(\boldsymbol{\sigma}, \mathbf{m} \times \mathbf{p})$$

since $(\mathbf{m}, \mathbf{p}) = 0$, and similarly

$$(\boldsymbol{\sigma}, \mathbf{p})(\boldsymbol{\sigma}, \mathbf{m}) = i(\boldsymbol{\sigma}, \mathbf{p} \times \mathbf{m}),$$

so that

$$(\boldsymbol{\sigma}, \mathbf{m})(\boldsymbol{\sigma}, \mathbf{p}) + (\boldsymbol{\sigma}, \mathbf{p})(\boldsymbol{\sigma}, \mathbf{m}) = i\Sigma\sigma_1(m_2p_3 - m_3p_2 + p_2m_3 - p_3m_2)$$
$$= i\Sigma\sigma_1 \, . \, 2ihp_1 = -2h(\boldsymbol{\sigma}, \mathbf{p}),$$

or

$$\{(\boldsymbol{\sigma}, \mathbf{m}) + h\}(\boldsymbol{\sigma}, \mathbf{p}) + (\boldsymbol{\sigma}, \mathbf{p})\{(\boldsymbol{\sigma}, \mathbf{m}) + h\} = 0.$$

Thus $(\boldsymbol{\sigma}, \mathbf{m}) + h$ anticommutes with one of the terms in F, namely, $\rho_1(\boldsymbol{\sigma}, \mathbf{p})$, and commutes with the other three. Hence $\rho_3\{(\boldsymbol{\sigma}, \mathbf{m}) + h\}$ commutes with all four, and is therefore a constant of the motion. But the square of $\rho_3\{(\boldsymbol{\sigma}, \mathbf{m}) + h\}$ must also equal j^2h^2. We therefore take

$$jh = \rho_3\{(\boldsymbol{\sigma}, \mathbf{m}) + h\}. \tag{21}$$

We have, by a further application of (16)

$$(\boldsymbol{\sigma}, \mathbf{x})(\boldsymbol{\sigma}, \mathbf{p}) = (\mathbf{x}, \mathbf{p}) + i(\boldsymbol{\sigma}, \mathbf{m}).$$

Now a permissible definition of p_r is

$$(\mathbf{x}, \mathbf{p}) = rp_r + ih,$$

and from (21)

$$(\boldsymbol{\sigma}, \mathbf{m}) = \rho_3 jh - h.$$

Hence

$$(\boldsymbol{\sigma}, \mathbf{x})(\boldsymbol{\sigma}, \mathbf{p}) = rp_r + i\rho_3 jh. \tag{22}$$

Introduce the quantity ε defined by

$$r\varepsilon = \rho_1 (\boldsymbol{\sigma}, \mathbf{x}). \tag{23}$$

Since r commutes with ρ_1 and with $(\boldsymbol{\sigma}, \mathbf{x})$, it must commute with ε. We thus have

$$r^2\varepsilon^2 = [\rho_1 (\boldsymbol{\sigma}, \mathbf{x})]^2 = (\boldsymbol{\sigma}, \mathbf{x})^2 = \mathbf{x}^2 = r^2$$

or

$$\varepsilon^2 = 1.$$

Since there is symmetry between $\mathbf{x}$ and $\mathbf{p}$ so far as angular momentum is concerned, $\rho_1 (\boldsymbol{\sigma}, \mathbf{x})$, like $\rho_1 (\boldsymbol{\sigma}, \mathbf{p})$, must commute with $\mathbf{M}$ and j. Hence ε commutes with $\mathbf{M}$ and j. Further, ε must commute with p_r, since we have

$$(\boldsymbol{\sigma}, \mathbf{x})(\mathbf{x}, \mathbf{p}) - (\mathbf{x}, \mathbf{p})(\boldsymbol{\sigma}, \mathbf{x}) = ih (\boldsymbol{\sigma}, \mathbf{x}),$$

which gives

$$r\varepsilon (rp_r + ih) - (rp_r + ih) r\varepsilon = ihr\varepsilon,$$

which reduces to

$$\varepsilon p_r - p_r\varepsilon = 0.$$

From (22) and (23) we now have

$$r\varepsilon\rho_1 (\boldsymbol{\sigma}, \mathbf{p}) = rp_r + i\rho_3 jh$$

or

$$\rho_1 (\boldsymbol{\sigma}, \mathbf{p}) = \varepsilon p_r + i\varepsilon\rho_3 jh/r.$$

Thus

$$\mathrm{F} = p_0 + \mathrm{V} + \varepsilon p_r + i\varepsilon\rho_3 jh/r + \rho_3 mc. \tag{24}$$

Equation (23) shows that ε anticommutes with ρ_3. We can therefore by a canonical transformation (involving perhaps the x's and p's as well as the σ's and ρ's) bring ε into the form of the ρ_2 of § 2 without changing ρ_3, and without changing any of the other variables occurring on the right-hand side of (24), since these other variables all commute with ε. $i\varepsilon\rho_3$ will now be of the form $i\rho_2\rho_3 = -\rho_1$, so that the wave equation takes the form

$$\mathrm{F}\psi \equiv [p_0 + \mathrm{V} + \rho_2 p_r - \rho_1 jh/r + \rho_3 mc]\,\psi = 0.$$

If we write this equation out in full, calling the components of ψ referring to the first and third rows (or columns) of the matrices ψ_α and ψ_β respectively, we get

$$(\mathrm{F}\psi)_\alpha \equiv (p_0 + \mathrm{V})\,\psi_\alpha - h\frac{\partial}{\partial r}\psi_\beta - \frac{jh}{r}\psi_\beta + mc\psi_\alpha = 0,$$

$$(\mathrm{F}\psi)_\beta \equiv (p_0 + \mathrm{V})\,\psi_\beta + h\frac{\partial}{\partial r}\psi_\alpha - \frac{jh}{r}\psi_\alpha - mc\psi_\beta = 0.$$

The second and fourth components give just a repetition of these two equations. We shall now eliminate ψ_α. If we write $h\mathrm{B}$ for $p_0 + \mathrm{V} + mc$, the first equation becomes

$$\left(\frac{\partial}{\partial r} + \frac{j}{r}\right)\psi_\beta = \mathrm{B}\psi_\alpha,$$

which gives on differentiating

$$\frac{\partial^2}{\partial r^2}\psi_\beta + \frac{j}{r}\frac{\partial}{\partial r}\psi_\beta - \frac{j}{r^2}\psi_\beta = \mathrm{B}\frac{\partial}{\partial r}\psi_\alpha + \frac{\partial \mathrm{B}}{\partial r}\psi_\alpha$$

$$= \frac{\mathrm{B}}{h}\left[-(p_0 + \mathrm{V} - mc)\psi_\beta + \frac{jh}{r}\psi_\alpha\right] + \frac{1}{h}\frac{\partial \mathrm{V}}{\partial r}\psi_\alpha$$

$$= -\frac{(p_0 + \mathrm{V})^2 - m^2c^2}{h^2}\psi_\beta + \left(\frac{j}{r} + \frac{1}{\mathrm{B}h}\frac{\partial \mathrm{V}}{\partial r}\right)\left(\frac{\partial}{\partial r} + \frac{j}{r}\right)\psi_\beta.$$

This reduces to

$$\frac{\partial^2}{\partial r^2}\psi_\beta + \left[\frac{(p_0 + \mathrm{V})^2 - m^2c^2}{h^2} - \frac{j(j+1)}{r^2}\right]\psi_\beta - \frac{1}{\mathrm{B}h}\frac{\partial \mathrm{V}}{\partial r}\left(\frac{\partial}{\partial r} + \frac{j}{r}\right)\psi_\beta = 0. \quad (25)$$

The values of the parameter p_0 for which this equation has a solution finite at $r = 0$ and $r = \infty$ are $1/c$ times the energy levels of the system. To compare this equation with those of previous theories, we put $\psi_\beta = r\chi$, so that

$$\frac{\partial^2}{\partial r^2}\chi + \frac{2}{r}\frac{\partial}{\partial r}\chi + \left[\frac{(p_0 + \mathrm{V})^2 - m^2c^2}{h^2} - \frac{j(j+1)}{r^2}\right]\chi - \frac{1}{\mathrm{B}h}\frac{\partial \mathrm{V}}{\partial r}\left(\frac{\partial}{\partial r} + \frac{j+1}{r}\right)\chi = 0. \quad (26)$$

If one neglects the last term, which is small on account of B being large, this equation becomes the same as the ordinary Schroedinger equation for the system, with relativity correction included. Since j has, from its definition, both positive and negative integral characteristic values, our equation will give twice as many energy levels when the last term is not neglected.

We shall now compare the last term of (26), which is of the same order of magnitude as the relativity correction, with the spin correction given by Darwin and Pauli. To do this we must eliminate the $\partial\chi/\partial r$ term by a further transformation of the wave function. We put

$$\chi = \mathrm{B}^{-\frac{1}{2}}\chi_1,$$

which gives

$$\frac{\partial^2}{\partial r^2}\chi_1 + \frac{2}{r}\frac{\partial}{\partial r}\chi_1 + \left[\frac{(p_0 + \mathrm{V})^2 - m^2c^2}{h^2} - \frac{j(j+1)}{r^2}\right]\chi_1$$

$$+ \left[\frac{1}{\mathrm{B}h}\frac{j}{r}\frac{\partial \mathrm{V}}{\partial r} - \frac{1}{2}\frac{1}{\mathrm{B}h}\frac{\partial^2 \mathrm{V}}{\partial r^2} + \frac{1}{4}\frac{1}{\mathrm{B}^2h^2}\left(\frac{\partial \mathrm{V}}{\partial r}\right)^2\right]\chi_1 = 0. \quad (27)$$

2 U 2

The correction is now, to the first order of accuracy

$$\frac{1}{Bh}\left(\frac{j}{r}\frac{\partial V}{\partial r} - \frac{1}{2}\frac{\partial^2 V}{\partial r^2}\right),$$

where $Bh = 2mc$ (provided p_0 is positive). For the hydrogen atom we must put $V = e^2/cr$. The first order correction now becomes

$$-\frac{e^2}{2mc^2r^3}(j+1). \tag{28}$$

If we write $-j$ for $j+1$ in (27), we do not alter the terms representing the unperturbed system, so

$$\frac{e^2}{2mc^2r^3}\,j \tag{28'}$$

will give a second possible correction for the same unperturbed term.

In the theory of Pauli and Darwin, the corresponding correcting term is

$$\frac{e^2}{2mhc^2r^3}(\boldsymbol{\sigma}, \mathbf{m})$$

when the Thomas factor $\frac{1}{2}$ is included. We must remember that in the Pauli-Darwin theory, the resultant orbital angular momentum k plays the part of our j. We must define k by

$$\mathbf{m}^2 = k\,(k+1)\,h^2$$

instead of by the exact analogue of (19), in order that it may have integral characteristic values, like j. We have from (20)

$$(\boldsymbol{\sigma}, \mathbf{m})^2 = k\,(k+1)\,h^2 - h\,(\boldsymbol{\sigma}, \mathbf{m})$$

or

$$\{(\boldsymbol{\sigma}, \mathbf{m}) + \tfrac{1}{2}h\}^2 = (k + \tfrac{1}{2})^2h^2,$$

hence

$$(\boldsymbol{\sigma}, \mathbf{m}) = kh \text{ or } -(k+1)\,h.$$

The correction thus becomes

$$\frac{e^2}{2mc^2r^3}k \quad \text{or} \quad -\frac{e^2}{2mc^2r^3}(k+1),$$

which agrees with (28) and (28'). The present theory will thus, in the first approximation, lead to the same energy levels as those obtained by Darwin, which are in agreement with experiment.

PAPER 2

The Scattering of Fast Electrons by Atomic Nuclei.

By N. F. Mott, B.A., St. John's College, Cambridge.

(Communicated by N. Bohr, For. Mem. R.S.—Received April 25, 1929.)

Section 1.—The hypothesis that the electron has a magnetic moment was, as is well known, first introduced to account for the duplexity phenomena of atomic spectra. More recently, however, Dirac has succeeded in accounting for these same phenomena by the introduction of a modified wave equation, which conforms both to the principle of relativity and to the general transformation theory. Formally, at least, on the new theory also, the electron has a magnetic moment of $\varepsilon h/mc$, but when the electron is in an atom we cannot observe this magnetic moment directly; we can only observe the moment of the whole atom, or, of course, the splitting of the spectral lines, which we may say is "caused" by this moment. The question arises, has the *free* electron "really" got a magnetic moment, a magnetic moment that we can by any conceivable experiment observe? The question is not so simple as it might seem, because a magnetic moment $\varepsilon h/mc$ can never be observed directly, *e.g.*, with a magnetometer; there is always an uncertainty in the external electromagnetic field, due to the uncertainty in the position and velocity of the electron, and this uncertainty is greater than the effect of the electron magnet which we are trying to observe.* Our only hope of observing the moment of a free electron is to obtain a "polarised" beam, in which all the spin axes are pointing in the same direction, or at any rate more in one direction than another. The obvious method of obtaining such a polarised beam is a Stern-Gerlach experiment, but here again the Uncertainty Principle shows that this is impossible*; in fact, it appears certain that no experiment based on the classical idea of an electron magnet can ever detect the magnetic moment of the electron.

We are, however, unwilling to give up altogether the idea of the direction of the spin axis of the free electron, because of the form that the solution of the wave equation has for this case. Whether we consider an infinite plane wave, or a wave packet, there are, in the solution, two arbitrary constants A, B, which are just enough to determine a "spin" direction. Further, it has been shown by Darwin† that the electromagnetic field due to a wave packet can be separated formally into two parts, the one due to the charge and current, and the other due to the magnetic moment of the electron, which points in a definite direction and is determined by A, B. As we have pointed out, this second part cannot be observed, because it is less than the uncertainty in the first; but nevertheless, we can associate formally a direction of the spin axis with any given solution of the wave equation.

Now, have these constants A, B, this direction of the spin axis, any physical meaning? Suppose, for example, a wave packet were to fall on a nucleus; would the scattered intensity depend on the A and B of the initial wave packet? This can only be decided by a mathematical investigation, to which the greater part of this paper is devoted. If the scattered intensity does not depend on A, B, that would be very satisfactory; we should consider A and B to be constants used in the mathematics, but with no physical meaning, and the spin of a free electron to be something non-existent. However, we shall find that the scattered intensity does depend on A and B, so that the spin direction has some meaning after all. Suppose an electron, about whose spin direction we know nothing, falls on a nucleus and is scattered through a given angle; we now know that its spin axis is more likely to be in one direction than another. Suppose an unpolarised beam, in which the spin axes are pointing in all directions at random, falls on a target and is scattered; the scattered beam is partly polarised; more spin axes point in one direction than another; and this

* These arguments are due to Prof. Niels Bohr, and are discussed further in an appendix.

† C. G. Darwin, 'Roy. Soc. Proc.,' A, vol. 120, p. 631 (1928).

polarisation could be detected by letting the scattered beam fall on a second target. Since the beam is polarised it will not be scattered in the same way as an unpolarised beam; actually we shall find that the scattering is asymmetrical about the direction in which the beam falls on the second target, and this could be detected experimentally.

In this paper we shall investigate the scattering of fast electrons by atomic nuclei, using the wave equation of Dirac. As well as investigating the polarisation, we shall obtain a formula* for the scattering of an unpolarised beam, which is to replace the Rutherford formula for fast electrons. In Section 2 we shall obtain certain general results for scattering by a field of force $V(r)$. In Section 3 we shall investigate the scattering by a Coulombian field of force, and determine the scattering law and the polarisation to be expected. The mathematics can be interpreted without difficulty, since the energy is an integral of the equations of motion, and we are not troubled by transitions to negative energy. We may emphasise once again that we do not want to know how the spin axis is turned when the electron is deflected, so much as how the direction of the spin axis affects the probability of the electron being scattered in a given direction, as it is this last that will be observable experimentally.

Section 2.—We consider the scattering of an infinite plane wave by a centre of force $V(r)$. If we were working with Schrödinger electrons, the wave equation would be

$$\nabla^2\psi + \frac{8\pi^2 m}{h^2}(W + V)\psi = 0, \tag{1}$$

and we should have to find a solution ψ, such that for large r

$$\psi \sim I + S \,.\, u(\theta\,\phi), \tag{1.1}$$

where I is written for $\exp(2\pi ipz/h)$ and represents the incident wave, and S for $\exp(2\pi ipr/h)/r$ to represent the scattered wave. Then, if a beam of electrons were to fall on a foil, say, of thickness t and containing n nuclei per unit volume, the proportion of the original beam scattered in a given solid angle will be

$$nt\,|u(\theta\,\phi)|^2 \sin\theta\, d\theta\, d\phi.$$

With Dirac electrons, we have, of course, four components of the wave function, $\psi_1, \psi_2, \psi_3, \psi_4$. The wave equation is the familiar wave equation of Dirac.†

$$[p_0 + V(r)/c - 2\pi ih(\sigma, \text{grad}) + \rho_3 mc]\,\psi = 0, \tag{2}$$

* This formula, of course, includes "Relativity correction" as well as "spin correction," but does not include the effect of radiative force.

† 'Roy. Soc. Proc.,' A, vol. 117, p. 610 (1928).

and, as before, we want a solution representing an incident plane wave falling on the nucleus and a scattered wave—a solution ψ therefore, such that, for large r

$$\psi \sim a_\lambda \mathrm{I} + \mathrm{S} u_\lambda (\theta\phi). \tag{3}$$

The a_λ are constants, but not all arbitrary constants, for if any two are given, the other two are known.† We set

$$a_3 = \mathrm{A}, \qquad a_4 = \mathrm{B},$$

where A and B are arbitrary complex constants. Then we have

$$a_1 = -\mathrm{A}p/(p_0 + mc), \qquad a_2 = \mathrm{B}p/(p_0 + mc).$$

The current represented by the incident wave is equal to $\sum_{\lambda=1}^{4} |a_\lambda|^2$, which is proportional to $\mathrm{AA}^* + \mathrm{BB}^*$. In the same way, the current scattered depends on u_3, u_4 only.

To interpret our formulæ, therefore, we choose A, B in such a way that

$$\mathrm{AA}^* + \mathrm{BB}^* = 1.$$

Then, if $nt\,\mathrm{P} \sin\theta\, d\theta\, d\phi$ is the proportion of the original beam scattered in a given solid angle, we have

$$\mathrm{P} = |u_3(\theta\phi)|^2 + |u_4(\theta\phi)|^2. \tag{4}$$

The constants A, B determine also the polarisation, or direction of the spin axis, of the incident electrons. When we speak of the direction of the spin, we shall mean the direction referred to axes with respect to which the electron is at rest; it is this that will be distributed equally in all directions in an unpolarised beam. If χ, ω are the spherical polar angles of the spin direction, then‡

$$-\frac{\mathrm{B}}{\mathrm{A}} = \cot \tfrac{1}{2}\chi \,.\, e^{i\omega}. \tag{5}$$

In the same way, u_4/u_3 will determine the polarisation of the electrons scattered in any direction. To determine the proportion scattered from an unpolarised beam, we must average P of equation (4) over all values of χ, ω.

If we find ψ_3 and ψ_4 for the two cases $\mathrm{A} = 1$, $\mathrm{B} = 0$ and $\mathrm{A} = 0$, $\mathrm{B} = 1$,

† Darwin, 'Roy. Soc. Proc.,' A, vol. 118, p. 654 (1928).
‡ Darwin, 'Roy. Soc. Proc.,' A, vol. 120, p. 631 (1928).

then we can form the general solution (3) by superposition of these two. We shall show in the next section that these two solutions are of the form

$$\left.\begin{aligned} \psi_3 &\sim \mathrm{I} + \mathrm{S}f(\theta) \\ \psi_4 &\sim \quad\quad \mathrm{S}g(\theta)\, e^{i\phi} \end{aligned}\right\}, \tag{6.1}$$

and

$$\left.\begin{aligned} \psi_3 &\sim \quad - \mathrm{S}g(\theta)\, e^{-i\phi} \\ \psi_4 &\sim \mathrm{I} + \mathrm{S}f(\theta) \end{aligned}\right\}, \tag{6.2}$$

where $f(\theta)$, $g(\theta)$ are functions of θ (not ϕ) which depend on the form of $V(r)$.

By superposition of these two, we have at once the general solution of the form (3), with

$$u_3(\theta\phi) = \mathrm{A}f - \mathrm{B}g\, e^{-i\phi},$$
$$u_4(\theta\phi) = \mathrm{B}f + \mathrm{A}g\, e^{i\phi}.$$

Hence we have

$$|u_3|^2 + |u_4|^2 = (|\mathrm{A}|^2 + |\mathrm{B}|^2)(|f|^2 + |g|^2) + (fg^* - f^*g)(-\mathrm{AB}^* e^{i\phi} + \mathrm{A}^*\mathrm{B}e^{-i\phi}), \tag{7}$$

so, if $nt\,\mathrm{P}\sin\theta\, d\theta\, d\phi$ is the proportion of the beam scattered in the solid angle $\sin\theta\, d\theta\, d\phi$, then we see from (4), (5) that

$$\mathrm{P} = |f|^2 + |g|^2 + \mathrm{D}\sin\chi\sin(\omega - \phi), \tag{8}$$

where

$$\mathrm{D}(\theta) = i(fg^* - f^*g)$$

and χ, ω determine the direction of the spin axis of the incident electrons.

To obtain the number $\overline{\mathrm{P}}$ scattered from an unpolarised beam, we must average over all directions of the spin axis ; we obtain

$$\overline{\mathrm{P}} = |f|^2 + |g|^2. \tag{9}$$

Unless, however, $\mathrm{D}(\theta) = 0$ for the angle of scattering considered, the function P will depend on the polarisation of the incident beam ; and if the incident beam is unpolarised, the scattered beam will not be. We shall be able to detect this polarisation by scattering the beam again by a second nucleus.

Before considering this double scattering in detail, it will be well to point out an obvious trap. On the old Quantum Theory, one used to say that a magnet, such as an electron magnet, must orientate itself either parallel or anti-parallel to a magnetic field. Such an assumption would in our case lead to inconsistent results. For from equation (8) we see that electrons whose spin axes lie parallel and anti-parallel to the direction of motion are scattered in the same way as an unpolarised beam. Suppose then we always had a weak magnetic field in the direction of motion, before and after scattering; then the scattering would always be normal, and the double scattering experiment would give a null result, which is contrary to the result of the following calculation. The fallacy is probably this, that we must not think of the axes of the electron magnets as lying parallel and anti-parallel to the field, but as precessing round it.

We shall now consider the double scattering experiment. A beam of electrons LT_1 falls on a target T_1 and is scattered. A second target is placed at T_2 so that the electrons scattered through an angle θ_1 in the plane of the paper (for which $\phi = 0$) undergo a second scattering. We observe the number of electrons scattered by T_2 at a given angle θ_2. If the beam T_1T_2 is polarised, the second scattering will not be symmetrical about T_1T_2; the number scattered in the directions T_2M, T_2M' will not be the same.

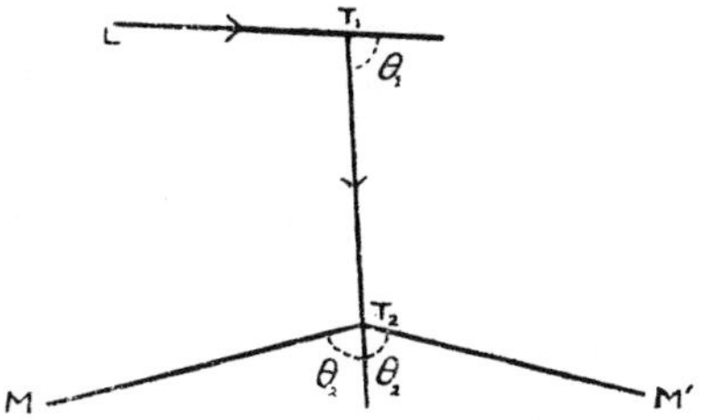

Fig. 1.

Suppose we represent the initial beam LT_1 by

$$\psi_3 = AI \qquad \psi_4 = BI.$$

We shall, of course, have to average over all spin directions later. The direction of the spin axis of the scattered beam T_1T_2 is determined, according to (5), by the ratio of the amplitudes of the two components of the wave function of the scattered beam, namely*

$$Af_1 - Bg_1, \qquad Ag_1 + Bf_1.$$

We now rotate our axes through an angle θ_1 so that T_1T_2 becomes the axis of z and we can represent the beam of electrons T_1T_2 by

$$\psi_3 = A_1I \qquad \psi_4 = B_1I$$

with†

$$A_1 = (Af_1 - Bg_1)\cos\tfrac{1}{2}\theta_1 + (Ag_1 + Bf_1)\sin\tfrac{1}{2}\theta_1$$
$$B_1 = (Ag_1 + Bf_1)\cos\tfrac{1}{2}\theta_1 - (Af_1 - Bg_1)\sin\tfrac{1}{2}\theta_1.$$

We can now obtain the number of electrons scattered by the second target T_2 in a given direction $\theta_2\phi_2$; we must insert these values of A_1, B_1 for A, B,

* f_1 is written for $f(\theta_1)$, etc.

† Darwin, 'Roy. Soc. Proc.,' A, vol. 118, p. 654 (1928).

in (7) and average over all directions of the spin axis of the initial beam LT_1. We are interested primarily in the asymmetry in the scattering about the line T_1T_2. For given θ_1, θ_2, therefore, but variable ϕ_2, a straightforward calculation shows that the number scattered per unit solid angle is proportional to

$$1 - \delta \cos \phi_2, \tag{10}$$

where

$$\delta = 2 \frac{(f_1 g_1^* - f_1^* g_1)(f_2 g_2^* - f_2^* g_2)}{(f_1 f_1^* + g_1 g_1^*)(f_2 f_2^* + g_2 g_2^*)}.$$

The greatest asymmetry, therefore, will be found in the directions TM, TM′, in the plane of the paper. In the plane through T_1T_2 perpendicular to the plane of the paper, the scattering *is* symmetrical about T_1T_2. It was in this plane that asymmetry was looked for by Cox, McIlwraith and Kurrelmeyer,‡ and the asymmetry found by them must be due to some other cause.

We must now show that we can obtain solutions of the wave equation of the form (6.1), (6.2), and obtain expressions for f and g. We shall first consider Schrödinger electrons.§ The general solution of (1) is

$$\Sigma\, a_k \mathrm{P}_k (\cos \theta)\, \mathrm{L}_k (r)$$

where L_k is the bounded solution of

$$\frac{d^2\mathrm{L}}{dr^2} + \frac{2}{r}\frac{d\mathrm{L}}{dr} + \left[\frac{8\pi^2 m}{h^2}(\mathrm{E} + \mathrm{V}) - \frac{k(k+1)}{r^2}\right]\mathrm{L} = 0. \tag{11}$$

For large r, L_k has the form

$$\mathrm{L}_k \sim r^{-1} \cos (2\pi pr/h + \eta_k{}^0).$$

Remembering that

$$e^{ir\cos\theta} = \left(\frac{\pi}{2r}\right)^{\frac{1}{2}} \sum_{k=0}^{\infty} (2k+1)\, i^k\, \mathrm{P}_k (\cos \theta)\, \mathrm{J}_{k+\frac{1}{2}} (r)$$

we see that the solution of (1) of the form (2) is

$$i \sum_{k=0}^{\infty} (2k+1)\, e^{i\eta_k{}^0 + ik\pi}\, \mathrm{P}_k (\cos \theta)\, \mathrm{L}_k (r)$$

with

$$u(\theta\,\phi) = \frac{h}{2\pi p} \sum_{k=0}^{\infty} (k + \tfrac{1}{2}) \left[e^{2i\eta_k{}^0 + \frac{2k+1}{2}\pi i} + 1 \right] \mathrm{P}_k (\cos \theta).$$

The general solution in spherical harmonics of Dirac's wave equation (2)

† 'Proc. Nat. Ac. Sci.,' vol. 14, p. 545 (1928).

‡ *Cf.* Faxen and Holtmark, 'Z. Physik,' vol. 45, p. 307 (1927); Mott, 'Roy. Soc. Proc.,' A, vol. 118, p. 542 (1928); Gordon, 'Z. Physik,' vol. 48, p. 187 (1928).

has been given by Darwin for the case of discrete energy values, and his analysis is immediately applicable to our case. A set of solutions are :—

$$(\alpha)\quad \psi_3 = (k+1)\,P_k G_k \qquad \psi_4 = -\,G_k P_k^1$$
$$(\beta)\quad \psi_3 = k\,P_k G_{-k-1} \qquad \psi_4 = G_{-k-1}\,P_k^1$$
$$(\gamma)\quad \psi_3 = P_k^1 G_k \qquad \psi_4 = (k+1)\,G_k P_k$$
$$(\delta)\quad \psi_3 = -\,G_{-k-1}\,P_k^1 \qquad \psi_4 = G_{-k-1}\,P_k.$$

Here P_k is the ordinary Legendre coefficient $P_k(\cos\theta)$ (not Darwin's notation) and P_k^1 is $\sin\theta \dfrac{d}{d(\cos\theta)} P_k(\cos\theta)\,e^{i\phi}$. $G_k(r)$ is the bounded solution of the pair of equations

$$\left.\begin{aligned} \frac{2\pi}{h}\left(p_0 + \frac{\varepsilon V}{c} + mc\right)F + \frac{dG}{dr} - \frac{k}{r}\,G = 0. \\ -\frac{2\pi}{h}\left(p_0 + \frac{\varepsilon V}{c} - mc\right)G + \frac{dF}{dr} + \frac{k+2}{r}\,G = 0. \end{aligned}\right\} \qquad (13)$$

Now, G_k has the asymptotic form

$$G_k \sim r^{-1}\cos(2\pi pr/h + \eta_k) \qquad (14)$$

Hence, in the same way as for Schrödinger electrons, we can form a solution representing an incident wave and a scattered wave. From (α) and (β) we see that a solution with the asymptotic form (6.1) is

$$\left.\begin{aligned} \psi_3 &= i\sum_{k=0}^{\infty}\{(k+1)\,e^{i\eta_k}\,G_k + k e^{i\eta_{-k-1}}\,G_{-k-1}\}\,(-)^k\,P_k(\cos\theta) \\ \psi_4 &= i\sum_{k=0}^{\infty}\{-\,e^{i\eta_k}\,G_k + e^{i\eta_{-k-1}}\,G_{-k-1}\}\,(-)^k\,P_k^1(\cos\theta)\,e^{i\phi}, \end{aligned}\right\} (15)$$

and that

$$\left.\begin{aligned} f(\theta) &= \frac{h}{2\pi p}\cdot\tfrac{1}{2}\sum_0^\infty i\,\{(k+1)(e^{2i\eta_k+ki\pi}+1) + k\,(e^{2i\eta_{-k-1}+ki\pi}+1)\}\,P_k(\cos\theta) \\ g(\theta) &= \frac{h}{2\pi p}\,\tfrac{1}{2}\sum_0^\infty i\,\{-\,(e^{2i\eta_k+ki\pi}-1) + (e^{2i\eta_{-k-1}+ki\pi}-1)\}\,P_k^1(\cos\theta) \end{aligned}\right\}$$
$$(16)$$

In an exactly similar way from (γ) and (δ), we can construct a solution of the form (6.2), with the same f and g.

There is no difficulty in justifying these processes mathematically, provided that the series (12), (16) converge absolutely. And they do converge absolutely, if $V(r) \to 0$ faster than $1/r^2$, as may be seen by solving equation (11) for very large k, when V may be considered as a perturbation. We shall consider the case of a Coulombian field in the next section.

Section 3.—We shall now consider the case that is of greatest interest, namely, the scattering by an atomic nucleus with inverse square law field, such that

$$V(r) = Z\varepsilon^2/r.$$

We know that, for Schrödinger electrons, with neglect of relativity and spin, the scattering obeys the Rutherford law. It is interesting to compare the second order wave equation for Dirac electrons* with the Schrödinger equation, and to see what are the order of the deviations to be expected from Rutherford scattering. This second order equation is

$$\left[-\left(p_0 + \frac{Z\varepsilon^2}{cr}\right)^2 - 4\pi^2h^2\nabla^2 + m^2c^2 + \frac{2\pi i\varepsilon^2 h}{cr^3}\rho_1(\sigma\, r)\right]\psi = 0,$$

where cp_0 is equal to the energy E of the electron, including the rest mass.

The order of magnitude of the various terms is best seen if we take for our unit of length $1/2\pi$ times the de Broglie wave-length in free space, namely

$$h/2\pi p = h/2\pi\,(p_0{}^2 - m^2c^2)^{\frac{1}{2}} = \frac{h}{2\pi m V}\left(1 - \frac{v^2}{c^2}\right)^{\frac{1}{2}}.$$

The wave equation then becomes

$$\left[\nabla^2 + 1 + \frac{2\mu\alpha}{r} + \frac{\alpha^2}{r^2} - i\frac{\alpha}{r^3}\rho_1(\sigma r)\right]\psi = 0, \qquad (17)$$

where

$$\alpha = \frac{2\pi Z\varepsilon^2}{hc} = \frac{Z}{137}, \quad \mu = \frac{p_0}{\sqrt{p_0{}^2 - m^2c^2}} = \frac{c}{v}.$$

The last three terms inside the square bracket may be said to "cause" the scattering. For small velocities of the incident electron, it is clear that the term $2\mu\alpha/r$ is much larger than the other terms, and therefore the scattering is approximately inverse square. But for velocities comparable with the velocity of light, μ tend to unity, and so the effect of the "spin" term, $i\alpha/r^3 \,.\, \rho_1(\sigma r)$, will be of the same order as the effect of the inverse square law term. For light nuclei, α is very much smaller than unity, and therefore the "relativity" term α^2/r^2, which is "responsible" for the fine structure of atomic spectral lines, has only a small effect on the scattering.

We can obtain a solution of equation (17) of the form (6.1) by the method of Born† and Wentzel.‡ The method yields a solution of the form

$$\psi^{(0)} + \alpha\psi^{(1)} + \alpha^2\psi^{(2)} + \dots,$$

* Dirac, 'Roy. Soc. Proc.,' vol. 117, p. 610 (1928).

† 'Z. Physik,' vol. 38, p. 803 (1926).

‡ 'Z. Physik,' vol. 40, p. 590 (1927). We should have to use an 'Abschirmungsfeld.'

with $\psi^{(0)}$ representing the incident wave, and the other terms the scattered wave. Such a method is only convenient for the evaluation of $\psi^{(1)}$; the author has actually evaluated $\psi^{(1)}$ by this method, and the calculation provides a useful check upon the subsequent work. For light nuclei, for which α is small, this first approximation would probably be sufficient; but the interest of $\psi^{(2)}$ lies in this, that to the first order of approximation f and g turn out to be real, and there is therefore no polarisation to this order. We shall therefore return to formula (15) and from it evaluate ψ as far as $\psi^{(2)}$.

In our subsequent work we shall take the unit of length to be $h/2\pi p$.

The equations (13) have been solved for F_k and G_k by Darwin, and by Gordon*; for continuous energy values Gordon's solution is more suitable. We introduce the following notation

$$q = \frac{\alpha E/mc^2}{\sqrt{(E/mc^2)^2 - 1}} = \frac{2\pi\varepsilon^2}{hv},$$

$$q' = \frac{\alpha}{\sqrt{(E/mc^2)^2 - 1}} = \frac{2\pi\varepsilon^2}{hv}\left(1 - \frac{v^2}{c^2}\right)^{\frac{1}{2}}$$

$$\rho = \sqrt{k^2 - \alpha^2}, \qquad \alpha = \frac{2\pi Z\varepsilon^2}{hc},$$

v is the classical "velocity" of the particle defined by

$$E = mc^2\left(1 - \frac{v^2}{c^2}\right)^{-\frac{1}{2}}. \tag{18}$$

With the usual notation for generalised hypergeometric series, we write

$$F(\alpha;\ \beta;\ x) = 1 + \frac{\alpha}{1!\ \beta}x + \frac{\alpha(\alpha+1)}{2!\ \beta(\beta+1)}x^2 + \dots.$$

The asymptotic expansion of this function for large x is well known.† We require the first term only; for pure imaginary x we have

$$\left.\begin{array}{ll} F(\alpha;\ \beta;\ x) \sim \dfrac{\Gamma(\beta)}{\Gamma(\beta-\alpha)}(-x)^{-\alpha}, & \\ \text{or} & \\ F(\alpha;\ \beta;\ x) \sim \dfrac{\Gamma(\beta)}{\Gamma(\alpha)}e^{x}\,x^{\alpha-\beta} & \\ |\arg(-x)| < \pi \qquad |\arg x| < \pi & \end{array}\right\}, \tag{19}$$

according as the real part of $-2\alpha + \beta$ is greater or less than zero.

* Darwin, 'Roy. Soc. Proc.,' A, vol. 118, p. 654 (1928); Gordon, 'Z. Physik,' vol. 48, p. 11 (1928).

† *Cf.* for example, Gordon, 'Z. Physik,' vol. 48, p. 187 (1928).

With this notation we have* for G_k,

$$G_{-k-1} = N\left[\frac{e^{-\frac{1}{2}\pi i\rho}\, c_k\zeta_k}{\Gamma(\rho+1+iq)} + \frac{e^{+\frac{1}{2}\pi i\rho}\, c_k'\zeta_k'}{\Gamma(\rho+1-iq)}\right],$$

where

$$\zeta_k = \frac{\Gamma(\rho+1+iq)}{\Gamma(2\rho+1)}\, e^{+\frac{\pi i\rho}{2}+\frac{q}{2}}\, F(\rho+1+iq\,;\ 2\rho+1\,;\ 2ir)\tfrac{1}{2}\,(2r)^{\rho}\, e^{-ir}/r,$$

$$\zeta_k' = \frac{\Gamma(\rho+1-iq)}{\Gamma(2\rho+1)}\, e^{-\frac{\pi i\rho}{2}+\frac{q}{2}}\, F(\rho+iq\,;\ 2\rho+1\,;\ 2ir)\,\tfrac{1}{2}\,(2r)^{\rho}\, e^{-ir}/r,$$

and

$$c_k/c_k' = -\,(k-iq')/(\rho-iq)$$

and N is a normalising factor.

From formulæ (19) we have at once

$$\zeta_k \backsim \tfrac{1}{2}\,(2r)^{iq}\,.\,e^{ir}/r,$$

$$\zeta'_k \backsim \tfrac{1}{2}(2r)^{-iq}\,.\,e^{-ir}/r,$$

and

$$G_{-k-1} \backsim r^{-1}\cos\,(r + q\log 2r + \eta_{-k-1})$$

with η_k given by

$$e^{2i\eta_{-k-1}} = -\,\frac{k-iq'}{\rho-iq}\, e^{-\pi i\rho}\, \frac{\Gamma(\rho+1-iq)}{\Gamma(\rho+1+iq)}$$

$$= B_k \quad \text{say.}$$

The asymptotic expansion of G_k is not quite of the form (14), differing from it by the logarithmic term ; as has been pointed out by various authors, for an inverse square law field the incident wave is not quite plane. We can, however, construct the solution of the form (6.1) without difficulty. This solution is

$$\left.\begin{aligned} \psi_3 &= i\sum_{k=0}^{\infty}\,[(2k+1)\,\zeta_k' + \{kB_k + (k+1)\,B_{-k-1}\}\,\zeta_k]\,(-)^k\,P_k(\cos\theta) \\ \psi_4 &= i\sum_{k=0}^{\infty}\,[B_k - B_{-k-1}]\,\zeta_k\,(-)^k\,P_k^1(\cos\theta)\,e^{i\varphi} \end{aligned}\right\}. \quad (21)$$

These series converge absolutely for given r. A method previously given by the present author† can be used to prove that, for large r

$$i\sum_{k=0}^{\infty}\,(2k+1)\,\zeta'_k(r)\,(-)^k\,P_k(\cos\theta) \backsim e^{ir\cos\theta - iq\log r\,(1-\cos\theta)}.$$

This represents the incident wave. The remaining terms represent outgoing

* Gordon, *loc. cit.*, p. 13, equation (10). If we put Gordon's j' equal to our k, then his ψ_2 is equal to our $r\,G_{-k-1}$.

† Mott, 'Roy. Soc. Proc.,' A, vol. 118, p. 543.

waves only. We cannot, however, obtain the form of the wave for large r by inserting the asymptotic solution (20) for ζ_k, because the series so obtained do not converge. They can, however, be summed as the limit of a power series on its radius of convergence.* If we express the functions ζ_k as the contour integrals from which the asymptotic expansion is obtained, it is easy to see that these sums do in fact give the asymptotic form of (21). The method is the same as that used in the author's previous paper. We see, therefore, that (21) is a solution of the wave equation with the asymptotic form (6.1) with

$$I = e^{ir\cos\theta - iq\log r(1-\cos\theta)},$$

$$S = e^{ir + iq\log 2r}/r,$$

and

$$f(\theta) = \tfrac{1}{2}i\,\Sigma\,[k\mathrm{B}_k + (k+1)\,\mathrm{B}_{-k-1}](-)^k\,\mathrm{P}_k(\cos\theta)$$

$$g(\theta) = \tfrac{1}{2}i\,\Sigma\,[\mathrm{B}_k - \mathrm{B}_{-k-1}]\,(-)^k\,\mathrm{P}_k^1(\cos\theta),$$

the summation of each series being carried out as the limit of a power series on its radius of convergence.

We can express f and g in terms of series which do not contain q'. If we write

$$c_k = -\,e^{-i\pi\rho}\,\Gamma(\rho - iq)/\Gamma(1+\rho+iq)$$

and

$$\mathrm{F}(\theta) = \tfrac{1}{2}i\sum_0^\infty(-)^k\,\{k\mathrm{C}_k + (k+1)\,\mathrm{C}_{k+1}\}\,\mathrm{P}_k(\cos\theta),$$

$$\mathrm{G}(\theta) = \tfrac{1}{2}i\sum_0^\infty(-)^k\,\{k^2\mathrm{C}_k - (k+1)^2\,\mathrm{C}_{k+1}\}\,\mathrm{P}_k(\cos\theta),$$

we obtain

$$\left.\begin{aligned} f &= -\,iq'\mathrm{F} + \mathrm{G} \\ g &= [iq'(1+\cos\theta)\,\mathrm{F} + (1-\cos\theta)\,\mathrm{G}]/\sin\theta \end{aligned}\right\}. \tag{23}$$

F and G are functions of θ, α^2 and q. It has not been found possible to sum the series in terms of known functions; we can, however, write $q = \alpha\mu$ and expand F and G as power series in α. We shall obtain the first two terms of the expansion. α has, of course, any value from 1/137 for hydrogen up to about 3/4 for the heavy nuclei; and for fast electrons μ will be about 3, though for slow electrons it will be greater. *Our approximation is best, therefore, for fast electrons and for light nuclei.*

* Whittaker and Watson, 'Modern Analysis,' p. 155.

If we refer to the series (22), and put $q = q'$ and $\alpha^2 = 0$, we obtain

$$\left.\begin{aligned} f(\theta) &= -\tfrac{1}{2}i\,\Sigma\,(2k+1)\,\frac{\Gamma(k+1-iq)}{\Gamma(k+1+iq)}\,P_k(\cos\theta) \\ g(\theta) &= 0 \end{aligned}\right\}. \tag{24}$$

This corresponds to a neglect of relativity and spin. Since $g = 0$ we see that the direction of the spin axis is unchanged on collision. The series (24) occurs in the investigation of the scattering of Schrödinger electrons; it can be summed by the method of the author's previous paper,* the sum being

$$R \operatorname{cosec}^2 \frac{\theta}{2},$$

where

$$R = \tfrac{1}{2}q \exp\left[2iq \log \sin\frac{\theta}{2} + \frac{\Gamma(1-iq)}{\Gamma(1+iq)} + i\pi\right].$$

The scattering is therefore classical, as it should be.

Now, α occurs in F and G only as α^2, so that as a first approximation we can neglect α altogether. Let F_0, G_0 be the values of F and G to this approximation. Since we know f_0 and g_0 when $q = q'$, and q' does not occur in F and G, we have at once from (23)

$$iq\,F_0 = -R,$$
$$G_0 = R \cot^2 \frac{\theta}{2}.$$

Hence

$$\left.\begin{aligned} f_0 &= \left(\frac{q'}{q} - 1 + \operatorname{cosec}^2\frac{\theta}{2}\right) R \\ g_0 &= -\left(\frac{q'}{q} - 1\right) R \cot\frac{\theta}{2} \end{aligned}\right\}. \tag{24}$$

These are the first order scattering formula that we should obtain by the Born method. The ratio of f_0 and g_0 is real; it follows that to this order there is no polarisation. It is therefore of interest to evaluate f and g to the next power of α, q.

Expanding C_k in powers of α we have

$$C_k = \frac{(-)^k\,\Gamma(k-iq)}{\Gamma(1+k+iq)} + \frac{\alpha^2}{2k^2}(-)^k\left[i\pi + \frac{1}{k}\right]. \qquad k \neq 0$$
$$+ \text{ terms } \alpha^2 q, \text{ etc.}$$

* Mott, 'Roy. Soc. Proc.,' vol. 118, p. 543 (1928). The result given there can be simplified to that given above. *Cf.* Whittaker and Watson, p. 240.

Neglecting terms of the order $\alpha^2 q$ we obtain†

$$iq\mathrm{F} = iq\mathrm{F}_0,$$

$$\mathrm{G} = \mathrm{G}_0 + \frac{\alpha^2}{4}\left[\pi \operatorname{cosec}^2 \frac{\theta}{2} - i \log \operatorname{cosec}^2 \frac{\theta}{2}\right],$$

whence from (23), (24) we can obtain at once formulæ for f and g.

To this order, we find that f/g is not real; we have therefore some polarisation on a collision; the constant that determines the polarisation is

$$fg^* - f^*g = \frac{i\alpha^2 q'}{4} \operatorname{cosec}\theta \log \operatorname{cosec}\frac{\theta}{2} + \text{terms of order } \alpha^4.$$

To the same order

$$|f|^2 + |g|^2$$

$$= \tfrac{1}{4}\left[q^2 \operatorname{cosec}^4\frac{\theta}{2} + \frac{q'^2 - q^2}{4}\operatorname{cosec}^2\frac{\theta}{2} + \frac{\pi q \alpha^2}{4}\frac{\cos^2\frac{\theta}{2}}{\sin^3\frac{\theta}{2}} + \text{terms of order } \alpha^4\right].$$

We shall now return to the ordinary unit of length; our formulæ are most conveniently expressed in terms of v, the velocity of the electron, defined by (18). We have then

$$|f|^2 + |g|^2 = \frac{\mathrm{Z}^2\varepsilon^4}{4m^2v^4}\left(1 - \frac{v^2}{c^2}\right)\left[\operatorname{cosec}^4\frac{\theta}{2} - \frac{v^2}{c^2}\operatorname{cosec}^2\frac{\theta}{2} + \frac{v}{c}\pi\frac{2\pi\mathrm{Z}\varepsilon^2}{hc}\frac{\cos^2\frac{\theta}{2}}{\sin^3\frac{\theta}{2}} + \text{terms of order } \alpha^2\right], \quad (25)$$

and

$$fg^* - f^*g = \frac{\mathrm{Z}^2\varepsilon^4}{4m^2v^4}\left(1 - \frac{v^2}{c^2}\right)^{3/2}\frac{v}{c}\, 4i\alpha \operatorname{cosec}\theta \log\operatorname{cosec}\frac{\theta}{2}. \quad (26)$$

The formulæ (25) and (26) determine the total scattering and the polarisation of the scattered beam. They are, of course, calculated with neglect of radiative

† We use the formulæ

$$\sum_0^\infty \frac{\mathrm{P}_k(\cos\theta)}{k+1} = \int_0^1 \frac{dx}{\sqrt{1 - 2x\cos\theta + x^2}} = \log\left(1 + \operatorname{cosec}\frac{\theta}{2}\right)$$

$$\sum_1^\infty \frac{\mathrm{P}_k(\cos\theta)}{k} = \int_0^1 \left(\frac{1}{x\sqrt{1 - 2x\cos\theta + x^2}} - \frac{1}{x}\right)dx = \log\frac{\operatorname{cosec}^2\frac{\theta}{2}}{1 + \operatorname{cosec}\frac{\theta}{2}}.$$

forces, which, for fast electrons, is a serious matter. An electron deflected through 90° by a nucleus of charge $Z\varepsilon$ would, on the classical theory, lose an amount of energy equal to *

$$\frac{1}{Z}\frac{4}{3}(2\pi + 3)\,\tfrac{1}{2}mv^2\,\frac{v^3}{c^3}.$$

This formula is calculated with neglect of relativity, but it shows that for light nuclei, an electron with a velocity approaching that of light is acted on by forces comparable with the electrostatic field of the nucleus. For heavy nuclei, however, the radiative forces are less important, but for heavy nuclei our approximations are less good—though there would be no difficulty in pushing them to any degree of accuracy required. The author hopes, in a later paper, to consider in greater detail the effect of radiative forces on the scattering.

From (25) and (26) we can see the order of magnitude of the effect that may be expected in the double scattering experiment considered in Section 2. In equation (10), we suppose that both θ_1 and θ_2 are 90°; then we have approximately

$$\delta = 11\cdot 2 \times \frac{(1 - v^2/c^2)\, v^2/c^2}{2 - v^2/c^2}\alpha^2,$$

δ has a maximum when $v/c = 0\cdot 764$ so there is an optimum value of the velocity of the incident electrons. With this value of v/c we have

$$\delta = (Z/96)^2,$$

Z being the atomic number of scattering nucleus.

For light elements, therefore, the effect is very small, and, indeed, may not exist, since the radiative forces are so considerable. For heavy elements, however, the effect of the radiative forces falls off inversely as the atomic number, whereas the polarisation effect increases with Z^2, and so it seems certain that the Dirac theory of the electron does predict a polarisation on collision. Whether the effect could be observed experimentally is more doubtful; the K electrons of heavy atoms have themselves velocities of the order of $0\cdot 7\,c$, and would interfere with the nuclear scattering.

The proportion of an unpolarised beam scattered in a given solid angle is given by (9), so that for the scattering of fast electrons (25) is to replace Rutherford's formula $Z^2\varepsilon^4/4m^2v^2 \operatorname{cosec}^4\frac{\theta}{2}$. Our formula bears no resemblance

* Kramers, 'Phil. Mag.,' vol. 46, p. 845 (1923).

to Darwin's* classical relativity correction; this is not surprising in view of the fact that we are dealing with a case where the wave-length is long compared to the classical distance of closest approach. There is therefore no possibility of forming a wave packet that must follow the classical orbit.

Nothing occurs in the wave mechanics at all analogous to the spiral orbits of the classical theory.

The formula does not agree very well with the available experimental evidence, giving in all cases too little scattering. Chadwick and Mercier, for instance, have investigated the scattering of β particles from Ra C by aluminium. At angles from 10°–20° our formula gives 2/3 of the observed scattering. It is possible that the radiative forces may be sufficient to account for this divergence. Without a fuller investigation nothing can be said on this point.

In conclusion, the author would like to express his thanks to Prof. Niels Bohr for the opportunity to work at his Institute, and for constant help and discussion.

Summary.

The scattering of a beam of fast electrons by an atomic nucleus is investigated, using the wave equation of Dirac. A scattering formula is obtained, and it is found that the scattered beam is polarised. A method by which this polarisation could be detected is discussed.

Appendix.

Suppose we wish to observe the spin of a free electron directly, with a magnetometer. We will suppose the electron to be at a distance R from the magnetometer, so that the order of magnitude of the magnetic field due to the spin is

$$\frac{eh}{mc} \cdot \frac{1}{\mathrm{R}^3}. \tag{1}$$

Now, there may also be a magnetic field due to the motion of the electron; the order of magnitude of this field is

$$\frac{ev}{c} \cdot \frac{1}{\mathrm{R}^2}. \tag{2}$$

Now, by the Uncertainty Principle, R and v cannot both be known at the same time; if $\Delta\mathrm{R}$, Δv are the uncertainties in our knowledge of R and v, then

$$\Delta\mathrm{R} \,.\, \Delta v > h/m. \tag{3}$$

* C. G. Darwin, 'Phil. Mag.,' vol. 25, p. 201 (1925).

Now, in order that (1), the effect of the spin, shall be observable, it must be greater than the uncertainty in (2). That is to say

$$\frac{h}{m} \cdot \frac{1}{R} > \Delta v.$$

Hence from (3)

$$\Delta R > R.$$

The experiment will therefore be impossible, since the uncertainty in the position of the electron would have to be greater than the distance of the electron from the magnetometer; the uncertainty in (1) would be greater than the field (1) that we want to measure.

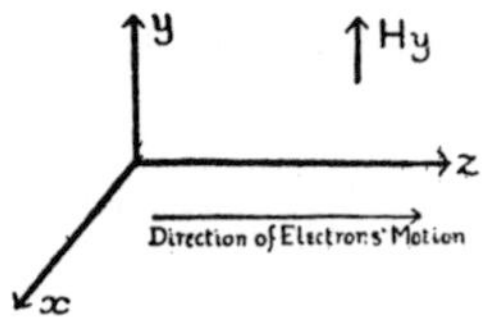

FIG. 2.

Stern Gerlach Experiment.—A beam of electrons travels along the z axis with velocity v_z in an unhomogeneous magnetic field **H**. We shall suppose that H_z is everywhere zero, and that in the plane Oyx H_x is also zero. The force on the electron magnets tending to split the beam is

$$\frac{eh}{mc}\frac{\partial H_y}{\partial y},$$

and in the plane Oyz this is the only force in y direction. However, the beam must be of finite breadth, and since

$$\frac{\partial H_y}{\partial y} = -\frac{\partial H_x}{\partial x}, \tag{2}$$

it is clear that H_x is only zero in the plane Oyz. In general

$$H_x = \int_0^x \frac{\partial H_x}{\partial x}\,dx$$

$$= \int_0^x \frac{\partial H_y}{\partial y}\,dx. \qquad \text{by (2)}$$

Electrons, therefore, travelling at a distance Δx from the plane Oyz will be subject to a force

$$\frac{ev_z H_x}{c} \tag{3}$$

in the direction Oy due to their motion through the field, and we see that (3) is equal to

$$\frac{ev_z}{c}\frac{\partial H_y}{\partial y}\Delta x. \tag{4}$$

This force is in different directions according as Δx is positive or negative, and will therefore cause a spreading of the beam, which will mask the Stern-Gerlach splitting, unless (4) is less than (1), *i.e.*, unless

$$mv_z \, \Delta x < h. \tag{5}$$

Now the uncertainty principle states that

$$\Delta v_x \, . \, m \, \Delta x \backsim h. \tag{6}$$

That is to say, that the slit that we use to limit our beam to the dimensions of Δx will introduce an uncertainty in the velocity Δv_x, given by (6). Inequality (5) therefore leads to the inequality

$$\Delta v_x > v_z.$$

That is to say, the slit must be so narrow (of the order of the de Broglie wave-length) that we have not got a beam at all, but a cylindrical wave emerging from it.

PAPER 3

Sitzung der mathematisch-naturwissenschaftlichen Klasse vom 22. November 1934

(Sonderabdruck aus dem Akademischen Anzeiger Nr. 24)

Das korr. Mitglied H. Mark übersendet folgende Mitteilung:

»Über die Wechselwirkung zwischen schnellen Elektronen und Atomkernen« von Eugen Guth.

Die heutige Atomphysik entwickelte sich zunächst im wesentlichen als eine Physik des Elektrons. Bald nach seiner Entdeckung wurde gezeigt, daß das Elektron in makroskopischen, elektrischen und magnetischen Feldern sich gemäß der klassischen Mechanik verhält, sofern seine Geschwindigkeit klein gegenüber der Lichtgeschwindigkeit ist. Bei größeren Geschwindigkeiten ergab sich eine Abhängigkeit der Masse von der Geschwindigkeit, im Einklang mit der inzwischen aufgestellten Relativitätsmechanik. Zur Beschreibung der Bewegung der Elektronen in den mikroskopischen Feldern der Atomkerne wurde sodann zur klassischen Mechanik (und bald auch zur Relativitätsmechanik) die Quantentheorie, zunächst in ihrer älteren halbklassischen Form, herangezogen. Schließlich entstand dann die heutige Quantenmechanik, die gleichfalls relativistisch ausgebaut wurde.

1. Bei all dem wurde für die Wechselwirkung die ausnahmslose Gültigkeit des Coulomb'schen Gesetzes — extrapoliert aus Erfahrungen über die Wechselwirkung makroskopischer Ladungen — angenommen.

Gegen die Gültigkeit des Coulomb'schen Gesetzes bei den kleinsten Distanzen (zwischen Elektron und Kern) gibt es schwerwiegende theoretische und — allerdings noch nicht völlig sichergestellte — experimentelle Argumente.

Einerseits führt nämlich das Coulomb-Feld als Punktladung bekanntlich zu einer unendlich großen elektromagnetischen Energie und daher entsprechend der grundlegenden Einstein'schen Gleichung: $E = mc^2$ auch zu einer äquivalenten unendlich großen elektromagnetischen Masse. Dieser Umstand tritt bekanntlich in der Quantenelektrodynamik als »Selbstenergiekatastrophe« in Erscheinung und bewirkt — zusammen mit einer analogen Schwierigkeit für Lichtquanten — den unbefriedigenden Zustand jenes Gebietes.

Anderseits gibt es eine Reihe von Unstimmigkeiten zwischen den Folgerungen aus den Dirac'schen Gleichungen und der Erfahrung, die allerdings zum Teil sehr klein sind, und allesamt noch genauerer Untersuchungen bedürfen. Solche neuen Versuche zu veranlassen, ist übrigens einer der Zwecke dieser und einiger folgenden Mitteilungen.[1]

Bei den periodischen Vorgängen gibt es Abweichungen bei der Wasserstofffeinstruktur.[2] Die Dubletts sind um mehrere Prozente schmäler als nach der Theorie.

Ferner sei noch auf die Isotopenverschiebungen bei den Hyperfeinstrukturen und weiter auf die abweichenden Ergebnisse für die magnetischen Momente von Proton und Deuton, nach der Methode von Stern einerseits, der von Rabi anderseits, hingewiesen (vgl. weiter unten).

Bei den unperiodischen Vorgängen erwähnen wir besonders die allerdings äußerst spärlichen Versuche über die einmalige Streuung von Elektronen an Atomkernen,[3] ferner die (allerdings negativen) Versuche zur Auffindung einer Polarisation von Elektronenwellen.[4] Hieher gehören schließlich die Unstimmigkeiten bei der Bremsstrahlung sehr schneller Elektronen.[5]

2. In Analogie zu den Verhältnissen bei der Wechselwirkung zwischen Atomkernen und schweren geladenen Teilchen, wo Anomalien bekanntlich auf Abweichungen vom Coulomb-Feld zurückgeführt werden konnten, soll hier und in folgenden Mitteilungen

---

[1] Die Experimentatoren haben sich nämlich gegenwärtig vornehmlich auf die Beschleunigung (positiver) schwerer Ladungen konzentriert. Methoden zur Herstellung sehr schneller Elektronen scheinen kaum vorzuliegen. In der neueren Literatur scheinen als einzige Beams und Trotter, Phys. Rev., *45*, 849, 1934, Vorversuche hierüber ausgeführt zu haben. Siehe auch A. Brasch, Naturw., *21*, 82, 1933.

[2] Spedding, Shane und Grace, Phys. Rev., *44*, 58, 1933; Houston und Hsie, ebenda, *45*, 263, 1934; Williams und Gibbs, ebenda, p. 475; Heydenburg, ebenda, p. 759, versucht die von Houston und Hsie gefundenen Abweichungen auf einen Starkeffekt, hervorgerufen durch das Feld der in der Entladungsröhre eventuell vorhandenen Ionen zurückzuführen. Für H_ε gelingt dies ihm jedoch nicht restlos.

[3] Neher, Phys. Rev., *38*, 1321, 1931, fand bei der Streuung von Elektronen (56 bis 145 KV.) an Al, Ag, Au eine um etwa 30% größere Streuintensität als die Dirac'sche Gleichung (mit Coulomb-Potential) es verlangt. Vgl. auch Klemperer, Ann. d. Phys., *3*, 849, 1929. Die früheren Versuche von Chadwick und Mercier, Phil. Mag., *50*, 208, 1925, sowie Schonland, Proc. Roy. Soc., *113*, 87, 1927, arbeiten mit stark inhomogenen β-Strahlen Die Resultate sind daher etwas unsicher. Dymond, Proc. Roy. Soc., *145*, 657, 1934, l. c. p. 665—666, erhält für die an Au zweimal unter 90° gestreute Intensität angenäherte Übereinstimmung mit der Theorie, sagt aber selbst: »Owing to the corrections too much reliance must not be placed on the experimental result, . . .«.

Unabhängig von den folgenden theoretischen Erörterungen wäre es sehr wünschenswert, zunächst die bei (einmaliger) Streuung auftretenden Diskrepanzen zu klären, bevor man Polarisationsversuche (zweimalige Streuung) unternimmt.

[4] Die letzten Versuche sind die von Dymond, Anm. 3, dieser Seite; Rupp, Zeitschr. f. Phys., *79*, 647, 1932; *88*, 242, 1934, findet eine Asymmetrie, die von der von Mott berechneten abweicht. Vgl. auch Rupp, Zeitschr. f. Phys., *90*, 166, 1934 (Polarisation im Magnetfeld).

[5] Vgl. Bethe und Heitler, Proc. Roy. Soc., *146*, 83, 1934. Diese Abweichungen sind allerdings viel plausibler, als die oben erwähnten, da es sich hiebei um Elektronenenergien größer als 137 mc^2 (Versuche von Anderson) handelt, so daß die de-Broglie-Wellenlänge der Elektronen bereits kleiner ist als der klassische Elektronenradius: e^2/mc^2. Siehe hiezu auch E. Guth, Naturwiss., *20*, 470, 490, 1932.

durchdiskutiert werden, welche Konsequenzen Abweichungen vom Coulomb-Feld bei der Wechselwirkung zwischen leichten Teilchen (Elektronen, Positronen) untereinander und insbesondere mit Atomkernen auf die unter 1. genannten und überhaupt auf alle jene Erscheinungen haben, bei denen das Coulomb-Feld direkt oder indirekt (Coulomb-Eigenfunktionen!) eine Rolle spielt.

Die Abweichungen vom Coulomb-Feld sollen hiebei zunächst in ähnlicher Weise phänomenologisch schematisiert werden, wie dies im Falle der Wechselwirkung zwischen schweren Teilchen und Atomkernen zu geschehen pflegt, ohne auf das wesentlich tiefer liegende Problem des Zustandekommens solcher Abweichungen einzugehen. Einen derartigen Versuch unternahm kürzlich Born.[1] Nun gibt aber seine Theorie — selbst ihre Richtigkeit vorausgesetzt — zunächst nur eine Modifikation des Coulomb'schen Feldes des Elektrons allein, während man schon bei der Wechselwirkung von Elektronen mit den einfachsten Kernen, den Protonen, das Feld letzterer kennen müßte.[2] Beim Proton ist aber bisher noch nicht einmal die Gültigkeit der Relativitätsmechanik (Abhängigkeit der Masse von der Geschwindigkeit) verifiziert. Auch wissen wir, daß das Proton der Dirac'schen Gleichung nicht genügt.[3]

Im folgenden ist die Gültigkeit der Dirac-Gleichung für die Beschreibung des Gebarens eines Elektrons im modifizierten (abgebrochenen Coulomb-Feld) vorausgesetzt. Ohne diese Voraussetzung könnten wir nichts aussagen. Die korrekte quantitative Formulierung der Abweichungen, die z. B. aus einer Theorie vom Typus der Born'schen folgen würden, und durch die Dirac-Gleichung samt abgebrochenem Coulomb-Feld nicht vollständig erfaßt werden könnten, ist heute nicht bekannt. Dasselbe gilt auch für den aus der Positronentheorie von Dirac, von Dirac selbst. Oppenheimer und Furry sowie Peierls gefolgerten Umstand, daß die effektive Ladung eines bei Distanzen kleiner als die Compton-Wellenlänge beobachteten Elektrons etwas verschieden ist von dem Ladungswert, den man durch Versuche bei größeren Distanzen erhalten würde. Ferner ist auch die Rückwirkung der Ausstrahlung auf die Be-

---

1 Born, Nature, *132*, p. 282; 970, 2004 (mit Infeld), 1933; *133*, 63, 1934. Proc. Roy. Soc., *143*, 410; *144*, 425 (mit Infeld), 1934; International conference on Physics, London, Okt. 1934; vgl. auch Watson, Trans. Roy. Soc., Canada, III., *28*, 1934. Bateman, Phys. Rev., *45*, 727, 1934. Frenkel, Proc. Roy. Soc., *146*, 930, 1934.

2 Die Folgerung der klassischen elektromagnetischen Theorie der Masse, das Proton sei etwa zweitausendmal kleiner als das Elektron, ist aller Wahrscheinlichkeit nach, nicht zutreffend. Vielmehr dürften die Abmessungen des Protons von derselben Größenordnung wie die des Elektrons sein.

3 Frisch und Stern, Zeitschr. f. Physik, *85*, 4; Estermann und Stern, ebenda, *85* 17, 1933, erhielten für das Protonenmoment 2·5 Protonenmagnetonen. Rabi, Kellogg und Zacharias, Phys. Rev., *46*, 157, 1934, erhielten 3·25. Auf die theoretischen Voraussetzungen bei der Auswertung dieser Versuche kommen wir noch zurück. — Die Dimensionen des Protons, genauer: die Wechselwirkung zwischen 2 Protonen kann durch Streuung schneller Protonen an Protonen abgetastet werden, wie an anderer Stelle gezeigt wird.

wegung des Elektrons ungeklärt. Daher müssen wir damit rechnen, daß ein Teil der durch das Abbrechen des Coulomb-Feldes bewirkten Abweichungen von den obigen Effekten maskiert oder verstärkt wird.

3. Wir schematisieren die Abweichungen vom Coulomb-Feld, wie schon erwähnt, durch ein Abbrechen derselben und Annahme eines konstanten Potentials im Kerninneren ($Z =$ Kernladungszahl, $e =$ Elektronenladung, $r =$ Radiusvektor, $\gamma =$ Zahlenfaktor).

$$\left.\begin{aligned} V_a &= -\frac{Ze^2}{r}; \quad \text{für } r > r_0 \\ V_i &= -\gamma \cdot \frac{Ze^2}{r_0}; \quad \text{für } r \leqq r_0. \end{aligned}\right\} \tag{1}$$

Ein abstoßendes Coulomb-Feld im Kerninneren:

$$V_i = +\frac{Ze^2}{r_0} \quad \text{für } r \leqq r_0; \quad V_a \text{ wie in (1)} \tag{2}$$

gibt ähnliche Ergebnisse wie der Spezialfall $\gamma = 1$ in (1), d. h. wie ein einparametriges (r_0) Feld im Inneren, wie unten gezeigt werden soll. Die Kernradien, die man durch Vergleich von experimentellen Abweichungen von der (unter Zugrundelegung des Coulomb-Feldes) entwickelten Theorie mit Rechnungen, die die beiden zuletzt genannten (einparametrigen) Potentiale verwenden, erhält, sind somit nicht bündig. Denn aus (1) ist evident, daß z. B. statt eines zu großen r_0 und $\gamma \sim 1$ auch ein kleineres r_0 mit $\gamma \gg 1$ genommen werden kann, wie wir sogleich sehen werden.

Es sollen nun für zwei Fälle, nämlich I. im Falle periodischer Prozesse für die Störung des s-Niveaus eines (insbesondere) H-ähnlichen Atoms, und II. im Falle aperiodischer Prozesse für die (einmalige) Streuung von Elektronen an Kernen auf Grund der Dirac'schen Gleichung und der obigen Potentialansätze [(1) und (2)] einige provisorische quantitative Angaben gemacht werden, provisorisch auch deshalb, weil für die Potentiale (1) und (2) die Dirac-Gleichung durch Zusammenstückelung exakt gelöst werden kann, während wir uns hier jeweils auf die erste Näherung von Störungsrechnungen beschränken werden, die ja in vielen Fällen ausreichen.

I. Für die Störung eines s-Niveaus durch die Abweichung eines Feldes vom Typus (1), beziehungsweise (2) vom reinen Coulomb-Feld ergibt die Störungsrechnung auf Grund der Dirac'schen Gleichungen in erster Näherung:

$$-\Delta E = 4\pi \int_0^{r_0} (V_a - V_i)\, \rho\, r^{2\sigma}\, dr. \tag{3}$$

ρ bezeichnet hiebei die Ladungsdichte, für die wegen der Kleinheit von r_0 ($\leqq 10^{-12}\, cm$) ihr Wert im Ursprung genommen werden darf, ist somit durch das Dirac'sche Analogon des nichtrelativistischen $\psi^2(0)$, nämlich:

$$\rho = -\frac{8\pi mc}{h}\int_0^\infty \frac{\psi_1\psi_2}{r^2}.dr \qquad (3a)$$

gegeben, wo ψ_1, ψ_2 die von Gordon[1] so bezeichneten Eigenfunktionen bedeuten. ρ tritt bekanntlich in der Theorie der Hyperfeinstrukturen in der Kopplungskonstante a für die Aufspaltung des s-Terms als Faktor auf:

$$a = \frac{16\pi}{3}\frac{1}{I}\mu\mu_0\rho \qquad (3b)$$

($\mu_0 = eh/4\pi mc$: Bohr'sches Magneton; μ: magnetisches Moment des Kerns). Der Quotient $\rho/\psi^2(0)$ erscheint in der Theorie der Hyperfeinstrukturen als Relativitätskorrektur[2] und werden für ρ in diesem Zusammenhang Näherungsformeln angegeben. So z. B. die folgende:[3]

$$\rho = \frac{2(1+\sigma)\psi^2(0)}{[\Gamma(2\sigma+1)]^2}\cdot\left(\frac{2Z}{a_0}\right)^{2\sigma-2}; \quad a_0 = \frac{h^2}{4\pi me^2}. \qquad (3c)$$

σ ist gegeben durch:

$$\sigma = \sqrt{1-\alpha^2 Z^2}; \quad \alpha = \frac{2\pi e^2}{hc}. \qquad (3d)$$

Mit dem Potentialverlauf (1) ergibt (3) bei Verwendung von (3c)

$$-\Delta E = \rho . Ze^2 . r_0^{2\sigma}\frac{1+2\sigma(1-\gamma)}{2\sigma(2\sigma+1)}. \qquad (4)$$

Nimmt man nun an, daß die Isotopenverschiebung der Hyperfeinstrukturen zum Teil auf die Verschiedenheit der Felder [vom Typus (1)] der Isotopen im Kerninnern zurückführbar ist, so erhält man für diese Verschiebung aus (4) beim gleichzeitigen Übergang zu Termen:

$$\delta\Delta T = -\frac{1}{hc}\left(\frac{\partial\Delta E}{\partial r_0}\delta r_0 + \frac{\partial\Delta E}{\partial\gamma}\delta\gamma\right) =$$

$$= \frac{2\sigma}{r_0}\Delta T.\delta r_0 + 2\sigma\,(\Delta T)_{\gamma=1}\,\delta\gamma. \qquad (5)$$

Für $\gamma = 1$ ($\delta\gamma = 0$) geht (5) in eine von Racah[4] angegebene Formel über.

---

1 Gordon, Zeitschr. f. Physik, *48*, 11, 1928. Die Gordon'schen Eigenfunktionen hängen mit den von Darwin, Proc. Roy. Soc., *118*, 654, 1928, eingeführten F und G durch die Relationen $\psi_1 = -rF$; $\psi_2 = rG$ zusammen.

2 Vgl. Breit, Phys. Rev., *38*, 463, 1931; Racah, Zeitschr. f. Physik, *71*, 431, 1931.

3 Vgl. Racah, Nature, *129*, 723, 1932. Sein ρ bezeichnen wir durch σ.

4 Racah, l. c.

Bei der Anwendung von Formel (5) wurde gewöhnlich $\delta\gamma = 0$ implizite vorausgesetzt. Unter der Annahme $r_0 \sim \sqrt[3]{\text{Atomgew.}}$ ergaben[1] sich dann nur bei den schwersten Elementen (Hg, Pb, Tl) $\delta\Delta T$-Werte von der ungefähren Größe der beobachteten Verschiebungen. Für die leichten Elemente resultieren viel kleinere $\delta\Delta T$-Werte als die beobachteten, welch letztere hier auf die Kernmitbewegung (unter Berücksichtigung des Elektronenaustausches) allein zurückgeführt werden.[2] Wegen den, allerdings nur schwer vermeidbaren Approximationen in der Berechnung der Kernmitbewegung bei Mehrelektronensystemen einerseits, der Voraussetzung $\delta\gamma = 0$ anderseits, scheint jedoch noch nicht ausgeschlossen zu sein, daß die Kernmitbewegung auch bei schweren Elementen[3] sowie die eventuellen Abweichungen vom Coulomb-Feld auch bei leichten Elementen zu den beobachteten Isotopenverschiebungen[4] praktisch beitragen. Prinzipiell sind natürlich beide Einflüsse stets vorhanden. Auch die Berechtigung der Störungsrechnung zur Herleitung von (5) scheint noch nicht hinreichend geklärt zu sein.[5]

a) Für den wasserstoffähnlichen Fall gilt:

$$\psi^2(0) = \frac{1}{8\pi}\left(\frac{2Z}{na_0}\right)^3. \qquad (3c')$$

Dieser läge vor bei einer eventuellen Hyperfeinaufspaltung im Röntgengebiet, sei es zufolge eines Kernmoments[6] oder des Vorhandenseins von Isotopen. Beobachtungen hierüber gibt es bisher noch nicht. Ob bei den Röntgen(K-)termen,[7] beziehungsweise den Röntgen(L-)dubletts selbst Abweichungen vom Coulomb-Feld sich bemerkbar machen, kann wohl erst dann entschieden werden, wenn die Abschirmung theoretisch ermittelbar wird.

b) Für das Wasserstoffatom selbst sind die Relativitätskorrekturen $[\sim \alpha^2 \sim (1/_{137})^2]$ vernachlässigbar. Mit $(3c)$ und $(3c')$ gibt (4):

$$-\Delta E = \frac{2e^4}{n^3 a_0^3} r_0^2 (1 - 2/_3 \cdot \gamma). \qquad (4')$$

---

[1] Breit, Phys. Rev., *42*, 348, 1932; *44*, 418, 1933. Erster Vorschlag auf Zurückführung eines Teiles der beobachteten Isotopenverschiebungen auf Verschiedenheit der elektrischen Felder der Isotope: Pauling und Goudsmit, The Structure of Line Spectra, McGraw-Hill, New York, 1930; l. c., p. 202. Siehe auch Bartlett, Nature, *128*, 408, 1931; Racah, l. c., Anm. 3 auf p. 5; Rosenthal und Breit, Phys. Rev., *41*, 459, 1931.

[2] Hughes und Eckart, Phys. Rev., *36*, 694, 1930 (Li); Bartlett-Gibbons, Phys. Rev., *44*, 538, 1933 (Ne).

[3] Vgl. Dickinson, Phys. Rev., *46*, 598, 1934 (Pb).

[4] Siehe die Zusammenstellung bei Schüler und Schmidt, Zeitschr. f. Physik, *92*, 148, 1934.

[5] Hierauf kommen wir in Zusammenhang mit der strengen Behandlung periodischer und aperiodischer Prozesse unter Annahme des Potentials (1) noch zurück.

[6] Vgl. hiezu Breit, Phys. Rev., *35*, 1447, 1930.

[7] Nach (4), $(3c)$ und $(3c')$ ist $\Delta E \sim Z^{2\sigma+2}$, während die Röntgen(Grob)-terme $\sim Z^2$ sind. Allerdings ist die Abhängigkeit der Parameter r_0 und γ von Z nicht geklärt.

Der Potentialverlauf (2) anstatt (1) liefert statt (4'):

$$-\Delta E = \frac{4\,e^2}{n^3\,a_0^3}\,r_0^2. \tag{4''}$$

Setzt man in (4') $\gamma = 1$, so unterscheiden sich (4') und (4'') bloß um einen Faktor 6.

(4') mit der impliziten Annahme $\gamma = 1$, ferner (4'') ziehen Kemble und Present[1] zur Deutung der unter 1. angeführten Diskrepanzen bei der H-Feinstruktur heran. Hiebei müssen sie $r_0 = 5 . 10^{-12}$ *cm* annehmen. Nun wissen wir zwar nichts Sicheres über den »Kernradius gegenüber Elektronen«, man möchte aber erwarten, daß er von derselben Größenordnung ist, wie der »Kernradius gegenüber den schweren (positiven) Teilchen«. Diese Erwartung wird auch durch die Kleinheit der beobachteten Isotopenverschiebungen bei den schweren Elementen nahegelegt oder zumindest nicht widerlegt. Ferner ist auch kaum anzunehmen, daß die unter 2. am Schluß erwähnten, heute einer konsequenten Behandlung noch kaum zugänglichen Effekte eine so erhebliche scheinbare Vergrößerung des Kernradius bewirken könnten. Wegen dem zweiparametrigem (r_0, γ) Charakter des Potentials (1) können wir jedoch ein ΔE, zu dem Kemble und Present mit $\gamma = 1$ einen Kernradius $r_0 = 5 . 10^{-12}$ *cm* benötigten, auch mit $\gamma = -2 \cdot 5 . 10^2$ und $r_0 = 2 \cdot 3 . 10^{-13}$ *cm* erhalten.[2]

c) Eine Hyperfeinstruktur des *H*-Spektrums konnte bisher wegen ihrer Kleinheit direkt noch nicht beobachtet werden. Indirekt geht sie ein in die Auswertung der Atomstrahlversuche von Rabi, Kellog und Zacharias[3] zur Messung des magnetischen Moments des Protons. Man könnte in diesem Zusammenhang daran denken, das unterschiedliche Ergebnis von Rabi, Kellog und Zacharias einerseits, Estermann, Frisch und Stern[4] anderseits auf eine Modifikation von $\psi^2(0)$ in $(3c')$ durch das Abbrechen des Coulomb-Berges[5] zurückzuführen. Die erste Näherung der Störungsrechnung ergibt in der Tat eine Vergrößerung von $\psi^2(0)$ und damit eine Verkleinerung des magmatischen Moments des Kerns μ [vgl. $(3b)$], jedoch in zu geringem Ausmaß.

d) In diesem Zusammenhang sei auf die Untersuchungen der Feinstruktur von D^2 hingewiesen.[6] Danach ist das D^2_α-Dublett um

---

[1] Kemble und Present, Phys. Rev., *44*, 1031, 1933. Herrn Prof. Kemble danke ich bestens für eine Diskussion des Gegenstandes.

[2] Die Zahlenwerte kommen bei einer strengen Rechnung etwas anders heraus.

[3] Rabi, Kellog und Zacharias, l. c., Anm. 3 auf p. 301.

[4] Estermann, Frisch und Stern, l. c., Anm. 3 auf p. 3. Bei diesen (Molekularstrahl-)Versuchen werde die von einem inhomogenen Magnetfeld auf das magnetische Moment des Protons ausgeübte Kraft direkt gemessen.

[5] Diese Modifikation wäre eigentlich auch bei der Ermittlung der magnetischen Momente der übrigen Kerne aus der Kopplungskonstante a [vgl. $(3b)$] zu berücksichtigen. Die hiezu benötigten $\psi^2(0)$ wurden nämlich bisher entweder unter Voraussetzung der ausnahmslosen Gültigkeit des Coulomb'schen Gesetzes berechnet oder halbempirisch der Grobstruktur entnommen.

[6] Williams und Gibbs, Phys. Rev., *45*, 475, 1934; siehe auch Kopfermann, Naturwiss., *22*, 218, 1934.

$0 \cdot 013\,cm^{-1}$ größer als das H^1_α-Dublett (aber noch immer um $0 \cdot 006$ bis $0 \cdot 007\,cm^{-1}$ kleiner als die theoretische Aufspaltung). Man könnte hier auf einen Isotopenverschiebungseffekt wie bei den schweren Elementen denken.[1]

II. Für den aperiodischen Fall des Stoßes von schnellen Elektronen gegen Kerne ergibt die erste Näherung[2] der Born'schen Methode auf Grund der Dirac'schen Gleichung bei vorausgesetzter Kugelsymmetrie des Potentials: $V(x, y, z) = V(r)$ zwischen Elektron und Kern für das Verhältnis der beobachteten und der mittels des Coulomb'schen Gesetzes berechneten Streuintensitäten:

$$\frac{J}{J_R} = \frac{\left|\int_0^\infty V(r) \sin \eta r . r dr\right|^2}{(Ze^2/\eta)^2} \tag{6}$$

mit

$$\eta = 2k \sin\frac{\vartheta}{2}; \quad k = \frac{2\pi}{h}\frac{mv}{\sqrt{1-\beta^2}}; \quad \beta = \frac{v}{c}; \quad \vartheta: \text{Streuwinkel.} \tag{6a}$$

Das Potential (1) liefert:

$$\frac{J}{J_R} = \left[(1-\gamma)\cos \eta r_0 + \gamma \frac{\sin \eta r_0}{\eta r_0}\right]^2. \tag{6'}$$

Für $\gamma \sim 1$ und beliebigem β, ferner für $\gamma \gg 1$ und $\beta \ll 1$ kann man sin und cos in (6') entwickeln. Wir erhalten:

$$\frac{J}{J_R} = 1 - \eta^2 . r_0^2 (1 - {}^2/_3 \cdot \gamma), \tag{6''}$$

also in dieser Näherung dieselbe Abhängigkeit von r_0 und γ wie in (4'). Mit $r_0 = 5 . 10^{-12}\,cm$, $\gamma = 1$, beziehungsweise mit $r_0 = 2 \cdot 3 . 10^{-13}\,cm$, $\gamma = -2 \cdot 5 . 10^2$ ergeben sich bei $\beta \sim 0 \cdot 5$ Abweichungen von bloß einigen Promillen.

Die von Neher gefundenen Abweichungen lassen sich somit nicht mit einem Feld von ähnlichen Dimensionen deuten, wie die Diskrepanzen bei der *H*-Feinstruktur, was wegen der Größe der ersteren von vornherein zu erwarten war.

a) Bezüglich der Bremsstrahlung schneller Elektronen sei bloß bemerkt, daß ein Potential vom Typus (1) schon genügt, um den theoretischen Wert den experimentellen Resultaten von Anderson anzupassen.

b) Abweichungen vom Coulomb-Feld dürften auch bei der Erscheinung der sogenannten »internal conversion« eine Rolle spielen.

[1] Allerdings könnte der Unterschied teilweise oder auch ganz durch die Verminderung der Dopplerbreite beim Übergang von H^1 zu D^2 bedingt sein. Jedenfalls wäre eine erneute Untersuchung der Feinstruktur von He^+, wo die Dopplerbreite noch geringer als bei D^2 ist und man bisher (Paschen) Übereinstimmung mit der Theorie fand, sehr wünschenswert.

[2] Der Entwicklungsparameter ist $\frac{\alpha Z}{\beta}$. — In der 1. Näherung kann eine Art »Fourieranalyse des Kernfeldes« gegeben werden.

PAPER 4

Interaction of Neutrons with Electrons in Lead*

W. W. Havens, Jr., I. I. Rabi, and L. J. Rainwater
Department of Physics, Columbia University, New York, New York

(Received August 11, 1947)

About ten years ago Condon[1] showed that Dee's[2] estimate of the upper limit for the neutron-electron interaction could be greatly reduced by considering the interaction of slow neutrons with atoms.

These considerations can be greatly extended by considering the interference of the wave scattered by the nucleus with the wave scattered by all of the electrons in the atom as first introduced by Bloch[3] in connection with the magnetic scattering of neutrons. In this case the scattered amplitude consists of the sum of terms due to the nucleus and to the electron

$$\psi=\psi_N+\psi_e+\cdots, \qquad (1)$$

and the atomic cross section becomes, to a close approximation,

$$\sigma=\sigma_N+2Z\bar{f}(\sigma_e\cdot\sigma_N)^{\frac{1}{2}}+Z^2(f^2)_{Av}\sigma_e, \qquad (2)$$

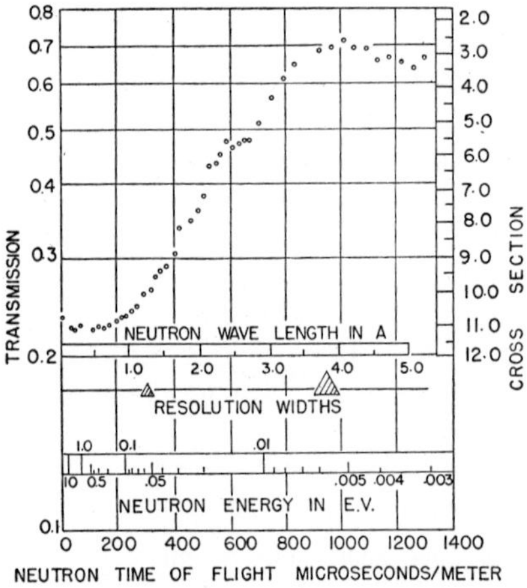

Fig. 1. The slow-neutron transmission of 46.51 g/cm² of solid lead.

where σ_N is the nuclear cross section, σ_e is the cross section per bound electron, $\bar{f}$ is the integrated form factor for the amplitude, and $(f^2)_{Av}$ for the square of the amplitude of the wave scattered by the bound electrons. For $\sigma_e \ll \sigma_N$ the main contribution to $\Delta\sigma\equiv(\sigma-\sigma_N)$ is from the cross term $2Z\bar{f}(\sigma_N\sigma_e)^{\frac{1}{2}}$. For $Z\bar{f}\sim 40$ it is seen that $\sigma_e=6\times10^{-8}\sigma_N$ will give a 2 percent shift in the total cross section. The last term in Eq. (2) can be neglected for subsequent considerations.

The effect here described is not a spin-spin interaction since the total electronic spin of the atom is zero and the effect is thus different from the paramagnetic and ferromagnetic scattering of neutrons.

To study this effect we have measured the total cross section of solid and molten lead as a function of the wave-length of the incident neutrons using the neutron spectrometer.[4] Lead was chosen because of its large value of $Z(Z=82)$ and its small absorption for slow neutrons ($\sigma=0.1\lambda$ in units of 10^{-24} cm²/atom where λ is given in angstrom units). The change of the atomic form factor $\bar{f}$ for the electrons as λ changes from 0.2A to 1.7A, is used for the observation of the effect. The nuclear form factor remains constant and equal to unity since the nuclear scattering is isotropic. The atomic form factor is given sufficiently well for this purpose by the Fermi-Thomas atom model.

The experimental points are given in Figs. 1 and 2. Figure 1 is for the solid and shows the characteristic increase in transparency with λ as is expected for crystalline materials. Figure 2 shows the results for liquid lead at about 350°C and 500°C. A disk of lead metal was used for the solid sample. A sample holder, in which the lead could be poured in and out of the sample position without altering the position of the container in the beam, was used for the liquid sample. The thicknesses (g/cm²) of the liquid samples were

* This document is based on work performed under Contract AT-30-1-GEN-72 with the Atomic Energy Commission at Columbia University.

[1] E. U. Condon, Phys. Rev. **49**, 459 (1936).
[2] P. I. Dee, Proc. Roy. Soc. **A136**, 727 (1932).
[3] F. Bloch, Phys. Rev. **50**, 529 (1936).

[4] Rainwater, Havens, Wu, and Dunning, Phys. Rev. **71**, 65 (1947).

not known accurately so the cross sections were adjusted to be equal to that of the solid in the region above thermal energies. In any event, it is the *shape* rather than the absolute value of the curve which is of greatest importance. A minimum of uncertainty in the shape of the curve was obtained by the fact that all 16 points on a given curve were taken simultaneously.

The general flatness of the curve shows that the diffraction effects due to the liquid structure are not very important at these neutron wave-lengths. Nevertheless, a correction can be made for this effect by the use of the theory of liquid scattering.[5]

From this theory the contribution to $\Delta\sigma$ due to the liquid molecular structure is $(\lambda^2/\lambda_0^2)\Delta\sigma(\lambda_0)$, when λ_0 is taken at some point where the liquid form factor deviates imperceptibly from the atomic form factor. X-ray results indicate that this is true for most monatomic liquids at $\lambda \sim 1.6$A. Since the nuclear scattering is isotropic, the nuclear form factor is always unity, therefore the cross section would be constant with respect to λ in the energy region investigated except for a small correction for the temperature agitation. This correction is under 1 percent in the region in which we are interested from 0.2A to 1.7A and is parabolic in form, therefore this correction can be lumped with the parabolic correction for the liquid-diffraction effect.

In our analysis we have assumed that all of the isotopes of lead scatter with the same phase and approximately the same amplitude, because the capture cross section is small and the scattering cross section is very nearly $4\pi R^2$.[6] However, the recent results of Fermi and Marshall[7] suggest that one isotope has opposite phase and therefore the effective scattering length of lead of normal isotopic composition is about $\frac{1}{2}$ of the expected value. This would reduce the sensitivity of our measurement of the electron-interaction amplitude by a factor of two.

To obtain the true variation of the total atomic scattering (nuclear+electron), we have to subtract the liquid interference effect together with

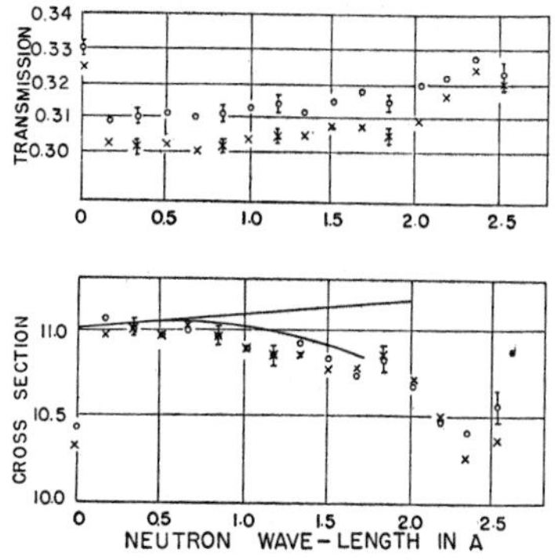

FIG. 2. The slow-neutron transmission and cross section of molten lead as a function of the neutron wave-length. O—temperature ~500°C, X—temperature ~350°C.

the 1/v change in cross section which is due to absorption.

In addition it should be noted that we assume the incoherent scattering to be constant and small over the region because of the great mass of the lead atom and because the temperature of the lead is from 7 to 9 times the characteristic temperature Θ which is 88°K for solid lead; furthermore, the two curves agree closely although one is close to the melting point and the other is about 150°C higher, indicating no great effect because of liquid aggregation. We also neglect spin-orbit interaction which gives an effect which is orders of magnitude less than observable in our experiment.

The net result is given in Fig. 3. The 1/v capture line and the parabolic correction are indicated in Fig. 2. The values of the ordinates of the points in Fig. 3 correspond to the distance of the points from the correction curve in Fig. 2. The magnitude of the parabolic correction is closely

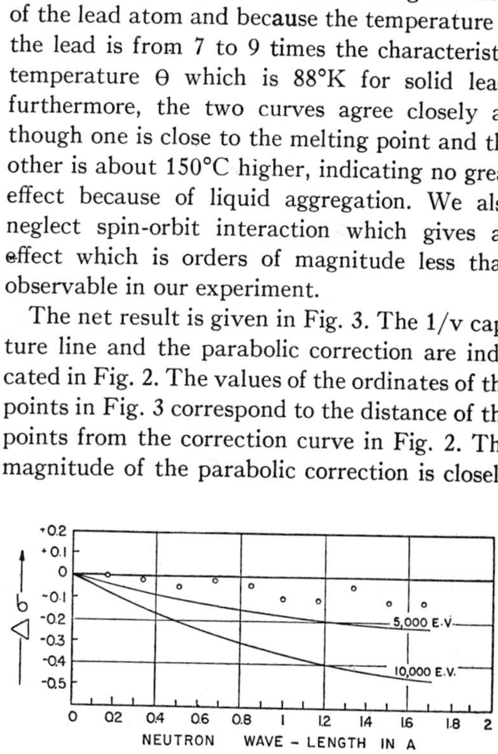

FIG. 3. Comparison of the corrected experimental points with the theoretical electron-neutron interaction curve for two different interaction potentials.

---

[5] N. S. Gingrich, Rev. Mod. Phys. **15**, 90 (1943).
[6] H. Feshbach, D. Peaslee, and V. F. Weisskopf, Phys. Rev. **71**, 145 (1947).
[7] E. Fermi and L. Marshall, Phys. Rev. **71**, 666 (1947).

determined by comparing the *shape* of the first part of the curve (0.2 to 1A) and the total deviation of the latter part of the curve near 1.7A. The points shown in Fig. 3 are the averages of the values for the two temperatures.

From the Born approximation

$$\Delta\sigma = 2\pi^{\frac{1}{2}}(2M/\hbar^2)(KZ/4\pi)\bar{f}(4\pi/\lambda). \quad (3)$$

K is the interaction function which we take as $4/3\pi a^3 V$ where a is the electron radius e^2/mc, M is the mass of the neutron, and $\bar{f}(4\pi/\lambda)$ is the integrated atomic form factor for the given wave-length which can be evaluated from the curve on page 148 of Compton and Allison.[8]

The two solid lines show what form this curve would take for a potential well of 10,000 ev and of 5000 ev. It is clear that the experimental points are well within the 5000-ev curve which can be taken as a fairly safe upper limit. Perhaps 2500 ev would be a closer fit to the present status of this experiment. At 5000 ev σ_e per bound electron is 4×10^{-31} cm^2. If the effective scattering length of lead is $\frac{1}{2}$ the assumed value,[7] the magnitude of all the interaction potentials given here should be doubled.

The experimental results seem to indicate that the electronic interaction causes a diminution of the scattering cross section. This would mean that the interaction is that of an attraction rather than a repulsion. If, as is supposed in some meson theories of neutron structure, the neutron is part of the time a proton plus a negative meson at a distance of the Compton wave-length of the meson, this would correspond to an attraction.

Experiments of this type can yield exact information which should provide a severe test of the validity of such theories of the structure of the elementary nuclear particles.

[8] A. H. Compton and S. K. Allison, *X-rays in Theory and Experiment* (D. Van Nostrand and Company, Inc., New York, 1935).

PAPER 5

On the Interaction Between Neutrons and Electrons*

E. FERMI AND L. MARSHALL
Argonne National Laboratory and Institute for Nuclear Studies, University of Chicago, Chicago, Illinois
(Received September 2, 1947)

The possible existence of a potential interaction between neutron and electron has been investigated by examining the asymmetry of thermal neutron scattering from xenon. It has been found that the scattering in the center-of-gravity system shows exceedingly little asymmetry. By assuming an interaction of a range equal to the classical electron radius, the depth of the potential well has been found to be 300 ± 5000 ev. This result is compared with estimates based on the mesotron theory according to which the depth should be 12000 ev. It is concluded that the interaction is not larger than that expected from the mesotron theory; that, however, no definite contradiction of the mesotron theory can be drawn at present, partly because of the possibility that the experimental error may have been underestimated, and partly because of the indefiniteness of the theories which makes the theoretical estimate uncertain.

INTRODUCTION

THE purpose of this paper is to investigate an interaction between neutrons and electrons due to the possible existence of a short range potential between the two particles. If such a short range force should exist, one would expect some evidence of it in the scattering of neutrons by atoms. The scattering of neutrons by an atom is mostly due to an interaction of the neutrons with the nucleus. In addition, there is a somewhat smaller interaction of neutrons and the electron system which has been observed by Bloch and his co-workers in their work on polarization of neutrons. This interaction is due to the magnetic field produced by the electronic currents within the atom acting on the magnetic moment of the neutron and will be referred to as magnetic interaction. Except for negligible higher order perturbations that will be discussed later, the magnetic interaction should not exist for atoms in which the electrons are bound in closed shells. In the present work, noble gases have been used in order to eliminate perturbations due to this magnetic interaction.

Besides the magnetic interaction, one might expect also the existence of a spin independent potential energy between neutron and electron. Such an interaction could be expected, for example, according to the current mesotron theories of nuclear forces. According to these theories, proton and neutron are basically two states of the same particle, the nucleon. A neutron can transform into a proton according to the reaction:

$$N = P + \bar{\mu}. \qquad (1)$$

(N = neutron, P = proton, $\bar{\mu}$ = negative mesotron)

Actually, a neutron will spend a fraction of its time as neutron proper (left-hand side of Eq. (1)) and a fraction of its time in a state that can be described as a proton with a negative mesotron nearby, (right-hand side of Eq. (1)). The system oscillates with extremely high frequency between these two forms and the fraction of the time spent in either of them is different depending on the specific form of mesotron theory.

According to the estimate given in Section 4, the neutron may spend 20 percent of the time as proton and negative mesotron and 80 percent of the time as neutron proper.

If these views are correct, in the immediate vicinity of a neutron one would expect an electric field of a strength equal to that produced by a charge $0.2e$, e being the proton charge. Of course, this field would extend only to a very small distance, because it would be screened by the negative charge of the mesotron, which is present whenever the nucleon is in the proton form. Indeed, the range of this electric force would be of the order of magnitude of the distances of the negative mesotron from the nucleon, that is about 10^{-13} cm. This force should be attractive and could be represented as a potential hole of

* Footnote added in proof: Havens, Rabi and Rainwater (Phys. Rev. **72**, 634 (1947)) have published results similar to the present ones obtained by a somewhat different method. Their results are in essential agreement with those of the present work.

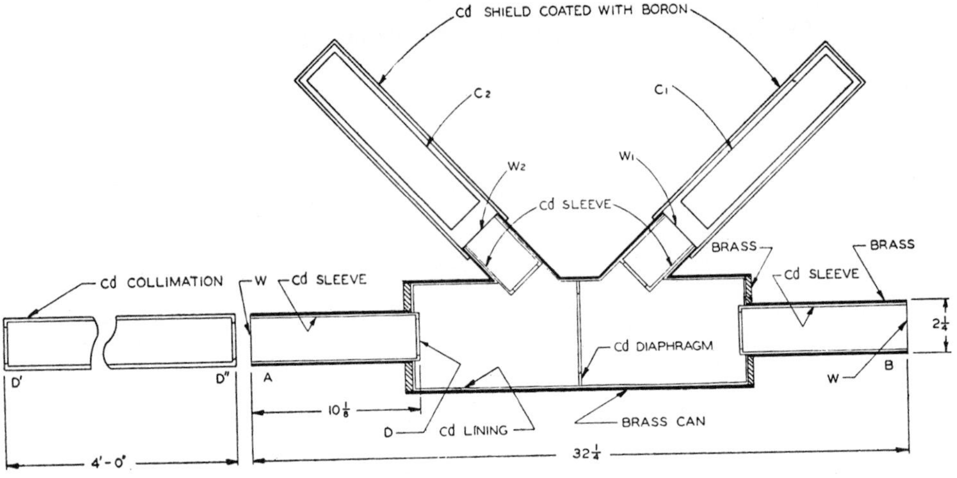

FIG. 1. Diagram of apparatus.

extremely small diameter. In the present paper, an attempt to detect an interaction of this type between neutrons and electrons is described.

If the scattering of neutrons were due only to nuclear interaction, one would expect the scattering to be spherically symmetrical in the center-of-gravity system whenever the wave-length of the neutron is large compared with nuclear dimensions. This last condition is very amply fulfilled for thermal neutrons which have a wave-length of the order of 2×10^{-8} cm, about 20,000 times larger than the nuclear dimensions. One would expect, therefore, that thermal neutrons should be scattered by nuclei in spherically symmetrical waves in the center-of-gravity system.

Deviations from the spherical symmetry can be due to several causes. The scattering atoms may be paramagnetic, in which case there is the magnetic interaction already discussed. A second reason for possible asymmetries in the scattering is interference of the waves scattered by different atoms. Such interference will be expected, both in solid and liquid elements and in gases with more than one atom in the molecule. Finally, asymmetric scattering could be due to a short range potential interaction whose investigation is the main object of this paper.

In order to eliminate the first two types of asymmetry, the experiments to be described were performed on xenon at pressures of the order of one atmosphere. An attempt was made to detect deviations from the spherical symmetry in the scattering of slow neutrons by this element.

If a short range potential interaction between neutron and electron should actually exist, one would expect the scattered waves to result from the interference of a spherically symmetrical wave scattered by the nucleus and a non-symmetrical wave scattered by the electrons. This last wave is expected to be non-symmetrical because the electrons are spread through a region of dimensions of the order of 10^{-8} cm, comparable to the wave-length of the neutrons. The interference of these two waves should make the intensity of the scattered beam a function of the scattering angle, as will be discussed in detail in Section 3.

SECTION 1. EXPERIMENTAL PROCEDURE

The apparatus used for the experiment is shown in Fig. 1. It consists of a tank of the dimensions and shape indicated in the figure, lined with cadmium as indicated, except for the four windows A, B, W_1, W_2. A beam of thermal neutrons from the thermal column of the heavy water pile at the Argonne National Laboratory was allowed to pass along the axis of this tank. The beam was collimated by the cadmium diaphragms D, D'', D' $1\frac{1}{2}$ inches in diameter. The tank was filled with xenon at the pressure of about one atmosphere and the neutrons scattered by the gas were recorded by the 2 BF_3-counters

C_1 and C_2. The counter C_1 records the neutrons scattered at an angle of about 45° with the direction of the primary beam and the counter C_2 records neutrons scattered at an angle of 135°. In order to correct unavoidable differences in sensitivity and geometry between the two counters, all the apparatus can be turned around, so that the neutrons enter through window B instead of entering through window A. Cadmium screens could be inserted in front of the windows W_1 and W_2. In all measurements Cd differences were taken.

Each run of the experiment consisted of four measurements, each of which was a cadmium difference. Two of them were taken with the apparatus in the position indicated in the figure (position A) and two with the apparatus turned around (position B). With the apparatus in position A, one takes first the number of counts in C_1 and C_2 with xenon inside the tank. The counts so observed must be corrected for a background. This is obtained by taking a second series of counts while the xenon is frozen out of the tank into a liquid air trap, not shown in the figure. Let n_{1a} and n_{2a} be the net number of counts per minute in the two counters. The same two measurements are performed successively with the whole tank in position B. Let n_{1b} and n_{2b} be the net number of counts observed in the counters C_1 and C_2 on this second measurement. The expression

$$\rho=[(n_{1a}/n_{2a})(n_{2b}/n_{1b})]^{\frac{1}{2}} \qquad (2)$$

gives the ratio of the scattering in the two directions at 45° and 135° corrected for the possible differences in sensitivity of the two counters.

The numbers from a typical run are given in Table I.

Two series of measurements were made, with two different pairs of counters. In each series, ten complete measurements like the one given above were taken. The consistency of the two series may be seen in Table II.

The result is

$$\rho=1.0235\pm0.0085. \qquad (3)$$

The errors indicated are mean square errors obtained by a statistical study of the consistency of the various runs. They are only slightly larger than the statistical errors calculated from the actual number of counts.

SECTION 2. CORRECTIONS

Some corrections must be applied to the results (3) in order to arrive at the true ratio of the intensities scattered in the center-of-gravity system for scattering angles 45° and 135°.

Although xenon is rather heavy, one cannot altogether neglect the fact that the center of gravity of the neutron-atom system does not coincide with the center of the atom. In computing the correction due to this effect one must also take into account the fact that the scattering atoms are in thermal agitation at room temperature. There is, in addition, a geometrical correction. Although the beam going through the tank is rather well collimated, it still diverges a little while going through the tank. This introduces an asymmetry which is not eliminated by switching the tank from position A to position B and must be, therefore, corrected by calculation. Here is a brief outline of the methods used for calculating these corrections.

TABLE I. Data of a typical run.

Position	Counter	Cd	Xe	c/min	c/min cadmium difference	Net
A	C_1	no	yes	720		
					434	
		yes	yes	286		
						$448=n_{1a}$
		no	no	276		
					−14	
		yes	no	290		
A	C_2	no	yes	690		
					429	
		yes	yes	261		
						$421=n_{2a}$
		no	no	262		
					8	
		yes	no	254		
B	C_1	no	yes	726		
					414	
		yes	yes	312		
						$406=n_{1b}$
		no	no	311		
					8	
		yes	no	303		
B	C_2	no	yes	635		
					400	
		yes	yes	235		
						$392=n_{2b}$
		no	no	227		
					8	
		yes	no	219		

TABLE II. Comparison of data from two pairs of counters.

	n_{1a}/n_{2a}	n_{2b}/n_{1b}
First pair of counters	1.064	0.916
	1.064	0.975
	0.986	1.030
	1.017	0.920
	1.035	0.966
	1.104	1.019
	1.110	0.919
	1.155	1.019
	1.127	0.964
	—	0.955
Average	1.074±0.018	0.968±0.014
	$\rho=\left(\frac{n_{1a}n_{2b}}{n_{2a}n_{1b}}\right)^{\frac{1}{2}}=1.020\pm0.012$	
Second pair of counters	0.943	1.031
	1.000	1.091
	0.892	1.047
	1.059	1.074
	0.884	1.116
	1.035	1.109
	1.020	1.028
	0.932	1.044
	0.971	1.100
	1.005	1.183
	—	1.093
Average	0.974±0.019	1.083±0.014
	$\rho=\left(\frac{n_{1a}n_{2b}}{n_{2a}n_{1b}}\right)^{\frac{1}{2}}=1.027\pm0.012$	
Combined result: $\rho=1.0235\pm0.0085$.		

a. Doppler Effect Correction

We consider an infinitely collimated beam of monochromatic neutrons being scattered by a gas, whose atoms move with a Maxwell distribution of velocity. The scattered neutrons are observed in a direction forming an angle θ with the direction of the primary beam and are observed with a counter covering a small solid angle $\Delta\omega$ Two alternative assumptions are made as to the sensitivity of this counter: (1) the counter is a "thin" detector, in which case the sensitivity follows the $1/v$-law; (2) the counter is a "thick" detector, in which case the sensitivity is independent of the velocity of the neutron. If one assumes that the scattering of the neutrons is spherically symmetrical in the center-of-gravity system, one can calculate in a straightforward way the dependence upon θ of the number of counts recorded. One finds that the angular dependence is represented by the following factors:

For assumption 1,

$$1+\frac{\cos\theta}{A}\left(1+\frac{KT}{MV^2}\right), \tag{4}$$

and for assumption 2,

$$1+\frac{1}{A}\left(2\cos\theta-1+\frac{KT}{MV^2}\right). \tag{5}$$

A is the atomic weight of the scattering atoms, M and V are mass and velocity of the neutrons. In both formulae, terms of the order of $1/A^2$ have been neglected.

In the actual case, the neutrons used were not monochromatic, but had approximately a Maxwellian distribution corresponding to room temperature. The correction factors (4) and (5) must, therefore, be averaged for such a distribution. The correction factors so averaged are for assumption 1,

$$1+(2\cos\theta/A), \tag{6}$$

and for assumption 2,

$$1+(2\cos\theta-\tfrac{1}{2})/A. \tag{7}$$

In the actual cases, θ has the two values 45° and 135°, and we are interested in the ratio of the correction factors for these two values. Within our approximation, this ratio is the same for assumptions (1) and (2) and equal in both cases to:

$$1+\frac{2\sqrt{2}}{A}=1.022 \quad \text{for} \quad \text{Xe}(A=130). \tag{8}$$

b. Other Geometrical Corrections

The experimental results must also be corrected for another reason. The beam entering the tank is collimated by an opening of 1.5 in. diameter at D and an opening of equal diameter at D', the distance between the two being 178 cm. The beam that passes through these two diaphragms is slightly spread and is, therefore, surrounded by a penumbra which increases with the distance from D. Consequently the two counters C_1 and C_2 see a beam of slightly different shape. As already pointed out, this difference between the two counters is not corrected by inversion of the tank.

In order to correct for this effect, the following procedure was adopted. An auxiliary experiment was carried out in order to determine the sensitivity of the counters to thermal neutrons originating at different places. A counter was surrounded with cadmium, shaped as in Fig. 2, and was mounted on the tool holder of a lathe so that it was possible to move it parallel to itself into any desired position. A small source of thermal neutrons was obtained by exposing a small copper plate weighing about one gram to a beam of thermal neutrons. The neutrons scattered by this copper plate were recorded for a number of positions of the counter. In all cases the average of the readings obtained with the counter at two positions symmetrical with respect to a plane perpendicular to the neutron beam and passing through the copper scatter was taken. This procedure corrects for the asymmetries of the source. In this way, the sensitivity of the counter surrounded by its cadmium shield was mapped as a function of the relative position of the source of scattered neutrons with respect to the counter.

The geometric corrections were calculated by dividing the volume of the beam seen by either of the counters C_1 or C_2 in about 200 parts. For each such section, the intensity of the radiation scattered into each counter was computed using the previously described calibration of the counter sensitivity and all the results were added. In this calculation, the Doppler correction and the correction due to the absorption of the beam were included. This rather lengthy calculation gave the following result.

If the scattering were symmetrical in the center-of-gravity system, the front counter C_1 would record a slightly larger number of counts than the back counter C_2. The ratio of the number of counts would be $\rho = 1.024$ in the case of Xe. It should be noticed that this number is quite close to the corresponding number (8) obtained by applying only the Doppler correction and assuming that otherwise the geometry is ideally well collimated. This indicates that the error due to lack of collimation is a minor one. The calculated values of ρ should be compared with the observed value (3). The difference can be attributed to a deviation of the scattering from the spherical symmetry in the center-of-gravity system.

The observed relative difference between forward and backward scattering, with all corrections, is therefore

$$-0.0005 \pm 0.0085. \tag{9}$$

SECTION 3. CALCULATION OF AN UPPER LIMIT FOR THE ELECTRON-NEUTRON INTERACTION

Both the sign and magnitude of the interaction between neutrons and electrons can be calculated from the ratio of the scattering intensities for the scattering angles 45° and 135°.

A short-range interaction between the neutron and other particles such as the nucleus or the electrons can always be represented in the Hamiltonian by terms proportional to the δ-function of the vector leading from the other particle to the neutron. Accordingly, the interaction of the neutron with the nucleus shall be represented by:

$$a\delta(\vec{r}), \tag{10}$$

and the interaction with each electron by terms of the form,

$$b\delta(\vec{r}-\vec{r}_e), \tag{11}$$

where $\vec{r}$ is the radius vector from the nucleus to the neutron, and $\vec{r}_e$ is the radius vector from the nucleus to one of the electrons. The constants a and b give a measure of the interactions of the neutron with the nucleus and with one electron. They have the dimensions of energy times volume. Indeed, when the interaction is weak, as is

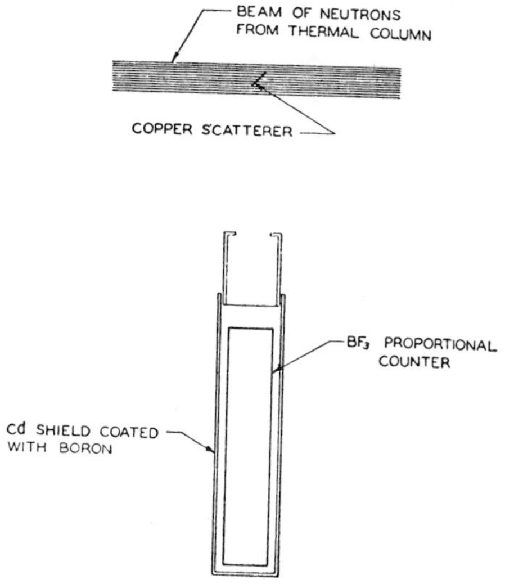

FIG. 2. Arrangement used to make geometrical corrections.

the case for the neutron-electron interaction, the coefficient b is simply equal to the volume integral of the potential energy between the two particles. If the potential energy between electron and neutron is a function $U(r)$ of the distance r between the two particles, then

$$b=4\pi\int_0^\infty U(r)r^2dr. \quad (12)$$

We can now apply the Born approximation in order to find out the scattering in the various directions due to the interactions (10) and (11). A straightforward calculation, based on the Born approximation gives the following differential cross section for scattering within the element of solid angle $d\omega$:

$$d\sigma=\frac{M^2d\omega}{4\pi^2\hbar^4}(a+bZ\mathfrak{F}(\theta))^2. \quad (13)$$

$\mathfrak{F}(\theta)$ represents the form factor of the electron distribution. A simple expression for the form factor has been given by Bethe.[1] By means of his results, the form factors at 45° and 135° can be calculated for Xe ($Z=54$). One finds

$$\mathfrak{F}(45°)=0.776,$$
$$\mathfrak{F}(135°)=0.515.$$

The difference of the form factor for the two scattering angles is responsible for the asymmetry in the scattering.

In the parenthesis of formula (13), the second term is very small compared with the first and one can neglect terms containing b^2. It follows that the ratio of the intensity scattered in two directions at 45° and 135° is given by:

$$1+2Z[\mathfrak{F}(45°)-\mathfrak{F}(135°)]\frac{b}{a}=1+28.2\frac{b}{a}. \quad (14)$$

Comparison of these values with the experimental result (9) allows one to determine the ratio b/a between the interaction constants for neutron-electron and neutron-xenon nucleus. One finds

$$b/a=-0.00002\pm0.00030. \quad (15)$$

In order to obtain b, we calculate the nuclear interaction constant a from the scattering cross section.

The scattering cross section of xenon was determined by comparison of the scattered intensity (average of the net counts in the two counters C_1 and C_2) when the tank was filled with xenon or nitrogen. The scattering cross section of the molecule N_2 was assumed to be 20×10^{-24}. It was found in this way that the scattering cross section of xenon is 4.4×10^{-24}. Disregarding the very small correction due to the electron interaction term b, it follows from (13) that the scattering cross section is given by

$$M^2a^2/\pi\hbar^4. \quad (16)$$

From this formula one finds

$$a=2.46\times10^{-42}\text{ ergs}\times\text{cm}^3 \quad \text{for Xe.} \quad (17)$$

The sign of a is almost certainly positive. This choice is justified by the fact that nuclear interaction constants have been found to be positive for almost all nuclei.[2]

From (15) and (17) the value of b can be calculated. One finds

$$b=(-5\pm74)\times10^{-47}\text{ ergs}\times\text{cm}^3. \quad (18)$$

As previously stated, the experimental error is a mean square error computed from the coherence of the various sets of measurements and it is only slightly in excess of the statistical error. In spite of that, one cannot guarantee that the actual value of b will lie within the limits as indicated in formula (18). It should be noted that the interaction constant b is found to be of the order of 10,000 times smaller than the constant of the interaction between a neutron and a proton or even smaller.

If the constant b should ultimately turn out to be negative it would mean that the potential between neutron and electron is negative (attractive force).

According to (12), b is the volume integral of the potential hole. Experiments of the type here discussed do not allow an independent determination of the depth and volume of the potential hole. If one assumes arbitrarily, that the potential hole has a volume equal to the classical volume of the electron,

$$V_{el}=(4\pi/3)(e^2/mc^2)^3=0.94\times10^{-37}\text{ cm}^3, \quad (19)$$

one finds from (18) the depth of the attractive

[1] H. A. Bethe, Ann. d. Physik 5, 385 (1930).

[2] E. Fermi and L. Marshall, Phys. Rev. 71, 666 (1947).

potential to be

$$\overline{U(r)} = b/V_{el} = (-6\pm 79)\times 10^{-10} \text{ ergs} = -300\pm 5000 \text{ ev.} \quad (20)$$

Before concluding this section, the effect of two possible perturbations should be discussed. It has been stated in the introduction that for atoms in which the electrons are bound in closed shells, no magnetic interaction between the neutron-electron system is to be expected. While this is certainly true in first approximation, one might, in reality, expect a small perturbation of this type to appear in second approximation, through the interaction of the magnetic moment of the neutron with currents in virtual excited states of the noble gas electron system. A closer discussion shows, however, that the contribution of the second order effect is quite negligible. By applying the conventional methods of quantum mechanics, one can readily estimate the interaction constant corresponding to this perturbation. This constant is found to be of the order of magnitude

$$(e\hbar/2Mc)^2 e^2 \lambdabar^2/mc^2R^3 \approx 10^{-48} \text{ ergs}\times\text{cm}^3. \quad (21)$$

In this formula $e\hbar/(2Mc)$ is the nuclear magneton, $\lambdabar$ is its wave length divided by 2π, R is the average radius of the electronic orbit.

It is seen that the correction (21) is entirely negligible compared with the value (18) of b.

There is a second possible interaction between neutron and atom that could lead to an asymmetric scattering. When the neutron passes by the atom and penetrates the electronic system, it is exposed to an electric field due to the unscreened part of the nuclear charge. Since the neutron is moving, this electric field in the frame of reference of the neutron gives rise to an apparent magnetic field. This last interacts with the magnetic moment of the neutron, giving rise to a mutual energy, which might be capable of contributing a scattering asymmetry. A closer discussion shows that the error introduced by neglecting this effect is negligible. The main reason is that scattering due to the interaction just mentioned is always connected with a change in the spin direction of the neutron. There can be, therefore, no strengthening of this effect by interference with the large nuclear scattering, since in the latter case, change of the spin direction of the neutron on scattering is always coupled with a change in the spin state of the nucleus.

SECTION 4. COMPARISON WITH THE MESOTRON THEORY

The results (18) or (20) should be compared with the expectations of the mesotron theory.

From the qualitative discussion already given in the introduction it is clear that, according to the mesotron theory, a short-range attractive potential between neutron and electron should be expected. On the other hand, because of the indefiniteness of the mesotron theories, it is not feasible to predict in a precise way the strength of the interaction to be expected. Indeed, most mesotron theories require elimination of divergences by cutting off the field at a distance from the nucleon of the order of 10^{-13} cm, which is just the expected range of the electric field surrounding the neutron.

A second point that should be mentioned in this connection is the influence on the neutron-electron interaction of the size of the electron. If we take the classical picture of the electron as a small sphere throughout whose volume negative electricity is spread, and we assume also, in a purely classical way, that the neutron is surrounded by a short range electric field, one would expect that the range of the interaction is of the order of magnitude of the largest of the two lengths, radius of the electron and range of the electric field surrounding the neutron. If the radius of the electron is larger than the range of the electric field, the interaction will extend, therefore, to a distance of the order of the electron radius. In this sense, the size of the electron influences the expected potential hole in that if the radius of the electron is taken larger, the potential hole becomes shallower and wider. Actually, one can determine on this classical model that the interaction constant, namely, the volume integral over the potential hole, is not influenced by the size of the electron. We can, therefore, in these estimates, regard the electron as a point-charge.

One possible approach to a semi-quantitative estimate of the interaction to be expected, according to the mesotron theory, is the following.

According to the most simple forms of mesotron theory, the wave function describing the mesotrons in the vicinity of the nucleus is of the form

$$(e^{-\mu cr/\hbar})/r, \tag{22}$$

where μ is the mesotron mass. To this wave function there corresponds a density distribution of the mesotrons proportional to the square of (22); namely, to

$$\frac{\exp[-2\mu cr/\hbar]}{r^2}. \tag{23}$$

One can then calculate in an elementary way the electric field E at a distance r from the center of the neutron,

$$E = \frac{ze}{r^2}\exp[-2\mu cr/\hbar], \tag{24}$$

where z is the fraction of the time that the neutron spends in the state represented by the right-hand side of Eq. (1) (proton and negative mesotron).

From (24) one can immediately calculate the potential energy for an electron in the electric field surrounding the neutron. One finds

$$U = -e\int_r^\infty Edr$$

$$= -ze^2\int_r^\infty (dr/r^2)\exp[-2\mu cr/\hbar]. \tag{25}$$

From (25) and (12) we obtain finally the interaction constant

$$b = -(\pi/3)(ze^2\hbar/\mu^2c^2)^2. \tag{26}$$

A simple procedure for estimating the value of z is given here. One of the objectives of the mesotron theory is to explain the neutron magnetic moment as the magnetic moment of the virtual mesotron field surrounding the neutron. If such an interpretation is correct and if we assume further that each mesotron bears a magnetic moment equal to $e\hbar/2\mu c$, we are led to the estimate that the average number of mesotrons near a neutron is 0.2. Therefore, in calculating the numerical value of (26), we shall use $z=0.2$. Assuming a mesotron mass 200 times larger than the electron mass, we find from (26)

$$b = -1.8\times 10^{-45}. \tag{27}$$

If we spread the interaction over the potential hole having the volume (19) we find that the depth of the potential hole is 12,000 ev.

SECTION 5. CONCLUSIONS

The comparison of the last result with the experimentally found depth of -300 ± 5000 ev indicates an experimental value appreciably less than the theoretical estimate. This does not necessarily mean that this experiment decisively contradicts the mesotron theory. On one hand, the experimental error may be somewhat larger than has been indicated. On the other hand, the theory outlined is obviously exceedingly crude. It may very well be that some mesotron theory eventually will lead to a lower estimate of the depth of the well. It would seem that the experimental result is sufficiently conclusive to exclude the so-called strong coupling theories according to which $z=0.5$ and the depth is therefore about 30,000 ev which appears to be well outside of our experimental error.

A final conclusion one might draw from these experiments is that no interaction of an order of magnitude larger than that predicted by the mesotron theory exists between neutron and electron.

Our thanks are due to Dr. A. Wattenberg for help in this experiment.

PAPER 6

The Charge Distribution in Nuclei and the Scattering of High Energy Electrons

M. E. Rose
Clinton National Laboratory, Oak Ridge, Tennessee
(Received November 3, 1947)

It is pointed out that the finite size of the nucleus will give rise to large deviations from Mott scattering when the change in wave-length of the electrons is of order of the nuclear dimensions. This deviation from Mott scattering at large scattering angles therefore provides a possibility for determination of the shape of the charge distribution and size of nuclei. In the case of a spherically symmetric charge distribution the nuclear charge density is immediately obtained from the observed angular distribution by a Fourier transform. The effects of competing processes, inelastic collisions with nuclear excitation or disintegration, atomic excitation or ionization and bremstrahlung are considered. It is shown that the first two competing effects may be disregarded if the electron energy is in the neighborhood of 50 Mev, the angle of scattering large (but not near π) and if the scattered electron has an energy equal to or nearly equal to the primary energy. With the latter condition fulfilled the bremstrahlung is reduced by the same factor as the elastic scattering and the two processes are indistinguishable.

I. INTRODUCTION

RECENT developments in the direction of obtaining high energy electron beams, as in the betatron and synchrotron, raise the question of using these high energy electrons in scattering experiments to obtain some information regarding nuclear structure. It will be readily recognized that for large angle scattering of electrons of several Mev ($\sim$50 Mev) the intensity of the scattering will depend strongly on the interaction between charges at very small distances. Specifically, the scattering nucleus cannot be regarded as a point charge but must be represented by an extended charge distribution whose shape can be explored by the scattering of electrons which penetrate inside the nucleus. Thus, even if the electrostatic interaction between charged elements is Coulombian down to essentially zero separation, the angular distribution of the scattered electrons will deviate markedly from the so-called Mott scattering.[1]

Actually there are two questions of considerable importance which are involved in the interpretation of scattering experiments of the kind under discussion. These concern (1) the nature of the (electric) interaction between charged particles at very small distances of separation and (2) the charge distribution and size of nuclei. Clearly, at least in principle, one may obtain information as to either question if the answer to the other is known. Unfortunately there is no case in which the nuclear charge distribution is known sufficiently well to allow a determination of possible deviations from the Coulomb interaction. However it should be possible to obtain evidence on this point from the scattering of high energy electrons by protons. It is plausible that deviations from Coulomb interaction, if such exist, are too small to be significant from the point of view of the accuracy obtainable in scattering measurements and we omit consideration of such deviations in the following.

With the assumption of an electrostatic Coulomb interaction between charges[2] it is possible to determine the charge density explicitly in terms of the nuclear form factor or observed scattering intensity. Applications to two important cases are immediately apparent: (1) Scattering in deuterium from which one may hope to obtain, for the first time, detailed information as to the deuteron wave function thereby establishing a criterion for the validity of nuclear force models. Here the effect of the non-central forces are unimportant unless the electron energy is several hundred Mev; i.e., the square of the reduced deBroglie wave-length is about equal to the quadrupole moment of the deuteron. (2) Scattering in heavier nuclei. Here the charge density is uniform, or nearly so, so that the

[1] E.g., see H. A. Bethe, *Handbuch der Physik*, XXIV/1, p. 495f.

[2] Effects of magnetic interaction with the nuclear spin are negligible.

primary information to be obtained is a measurement of nuclear radii.[3]

In the following these considerations are given quantitative formulation. Results for the angular distribution in the cases mentioned above are given as an indication of the magnitude of the effect. Finally, consideration of the feasibility of the measurements from the point of view of competing processes is presented.

II. ELASTIC SCATTERING BY EXTENDED CHARGE DISTRIBUTIONS

In the following the electron energy is sufficiently large to make the effect of nuclear penetration important, which implies extreme relativistic energies, but not so large that magnetic effects from nuclear recoil need be considered. For this reason and because of the considerations presented below our considerations are restricted to electron energies of order 50 Mev. The differential cross section for scattering electrons of total energy W into solid angle $d\Omega$ is

$$\sigma d\Omega = \frac{d\Omega}{4\pi^2}\frac{W^2}{(\hbar c)^4}|V_{if}|^2 \quad (1)$$

where

$$V_{if} = Ze^2 \int\int d\tau_e d\tau_p \Psi^*(\mathbf{r}_p)\psi_f^*(\mathbf{r}_e) \times V(|\mathbf{r}_e - \mathbf{r}_p|)\Psi(\mathbf{r}_p)\psi_i(\mathbf{r}_e). \quad (2)$$

Here $\mathbf{r}_e$ and $\mathbf{r}_p$ are vectors defining the position of the electron and a volume element of protonic charge while the interaction energy between the electron and unit charge of the latter is represented by eV. The charge density in the nucleus is

$$\rho(\mathbf{r}_p) = |\Psi(\mathbf{r}_p)|^2$$

which is normalized to unity

$$\int \rho(\mathbf{r}_p)d\tau_p = 1. \quad (3)$$

The subscripts i and f on the electron wave functions refer to initial and final states and are taken to be plane waves. Thus

$$\psi_i = a_i(\mathbf{P}) \exp(i\mathbf{P}\cdot\mathbf{r}_e/\hbar),$$

$$\psi_f = a_f(\mathbf{P}') \exp(i\mathbf{P}'\cdot\mathbf{r}_e/\hbar),$$

where $\mathbf{P}$ and $\mathbf{P}'$ are the initial and final momenta while a_i and a_f are Dirac amplitudes for the plane wave.

We allow for non-central fields (quadrupole moment!) by writing

$$\int V(|\mathbf{r}-\mathbf{r}_p|)\rho(\mathbf{r}_p)d\tau_p = \sum_0^\infty (2l+1)v_l(r)P_l(\cos\beta) \quad (4)$$

in which the subscript e has been dropped. In (4) the polar axis ($\beta=0$) is the direction of quantization for the nuclear spin. We introduce

$$\psi_f^*\psi_i = a_f^*a_i e^{i\mathbf{q}\cdot\mathbf{r}} = a_f^*a_i \sum_0^\infty (2l+1)j_l(qr)P_l(\cos\Theta), \quad (5)$$

$$j_l = i^l(\pi/2qr)^{\frac{1}{2}}J_{l+\frac{1}{2}}(qr) \quad (5a)$$

where Θ is the angle between $\mathbf{q}$ and $\mathbf{r}$, J is the Bessel function and $\hbar\mathbf{q}$ is the change of momentum. In terms of the scattering angle ϑ we have

$$q = 2P/\hbar \sin\vartheta/2.$$

After integration over the angular coordinates, the matrix element becomes

$$V_{if} = 4\pi Ze^2(a_f^*a_i)\sum_0^\infty (2l+1)K_l(q)P_l(\cos\theta)$$

where

$$K_l = \int_0^\infty v_l(r)j_l(qr)r^2dr \quad (6)$$

and θ is the angle between $\mathbf{q}$ and the spin axis. Averaging over all directions of the nuclear spin, we get

$$|V_{if}|^2 = 16\pi^2Z^2e^4|a_f^*a_i|^2 \sum_0^\infty (2l+1)K_l^2. \quad (7)$$

Summing over final spin states of the electron and averaging over initial spin states we obtain

$$|a_f^*a_i|^2_{\text{Av}} = c^2/W^2(m^2c^2 + P^2\cos^2\vartheta/2). \quad (8)$$

From (1), (7) and (8) the angular distribution is

$$\sigma(\vartheta) = \left(\frac{Ze^2m}{2P^2\sin^2\theta/2}\right)^2 \times (1 + (P/mc)^2\cos^2\vartheta/2)\sum_0^\infty (2l+1)f_l^2 \quad (9)$$

[3] Such deviations from the uniform distribution as may arise from the electrostatic repulsion between the protons are sufficiently small to be ignored.

where

$$f_l(q) = q^2 K_l(q). \tag{9a}$$

The ratio of expected scattering to Mott scattering[4] is, therefore,

$$\sigma/\sigma_M = \sum_0^\infty (2l+1) f_l^2. \tag{10}$$

It may be noted that the small angle scattering is determined chiefly by the isotropic term in (10) and for $q \approx 0$ the scattering is unchanged. Therefore the total cross section for scattering will be affected very slightly, in agreement with observations of cascade showers in the cosmic radiation, whereas the large angle scattering will be materially reduced by the penetration effect.

a. Scattering by Central Fields

It is clear that deviations from central symmetry make a non-vanishing contribution to the scattering so that in principle one might use such measurements for the determination of nuclear quadrupole moments. However, at energies for which such quadrupole contributions are appreciable the penetration effect arising from the spherically symmetric part of the charge distribution would be important and the two effects would have to be disentangled. For the sake of simplicity we consider only those cases wherein deviations from central symmetry produce negligible or vanishing effects; that is, the quadrupole moment may vanish or be small compared to 10^{-24} cm^2, or the electron energy may have some intermediate value for which the monopole effect is appreciable and the quadrupole effect is very small.[5]

For the monopole term we have from (6) and (5a)

$$K_0 = f_0/q^2 = \int_0^\infty \frac{\sin qr}{qr} v_0(r) r^2 dr$$

so that K_0 is proportional to the Fourier transform of v_0. Inverting we get

$$v_0 = \frac{2}{\pi}\int_0^\infty f_0(q)\frac{\sin qr}{qr} dq.$$

For the Coulomb interaction the charge density in the nucleus is given by

$$\rho(r) = -\frac{1}{4\pi r^2}\frac{d}{dr} r^2 \frac{dv_0}{dr}$$

$$= \frac{1}{2\pi^2 r}\int_0^\infty f_0(q) q \sin qr dq. \tag{11}$$

Since f_0 is real and for a point charge

$$f_0(q) = 1$$

it follows that

$$f_0(q) = (\sigma/\sigma_M)^{\frac{1}{2}}$$

and

$$\rho(r) = \frac{1}{2\pi^2 r}\int_0^\infty (\sigma/\sigma_M)^{\frac{1}{2}} q \sin qr dq. \tag{12}$$

Alternatively the deviation from a point charge distribution is expressed by

$$\rho(r) - \frac{\delta(r)}{4\pi r^2} = \frac{1}{2\pi^2 r}\int_0^\infty [(\sigma/\sigma_M)^{\frac{1}{2}} - 1] q \sin qr dq. \tag{13}$$

Either (12) or (13) permit the determination of the shape of nuclear charge distributions directly from experimental data.

b. Scattering by Deuterium Nuclei

For the purpose of illustration we consider the example of electron scattering by a relatively extended nuclear charge distribution, viz: the deuteron for which a reasonable estimate of the nuclear wave function can be made. From (11) we find in general

$$f_0 = 4\pi \int_0^\infty \rho(r) \frac{\sin qr}{qr} r^2 dr. \tag{14}$$

For not too large q this may be written

$$f_0 = 1 - \frac{1}{3!} q^2 (r^2)_{\text{Av}} + \frac{1}{5!} q^4 (r^4)_{\text{Av}} - \cdots \tag{14a}$$

Appreciable penetration effects may therefore be expected for scattering angles as small as $\hbar/PR$

[4] The first two factors in (9) give, of course, the Born approximation to the scattering by a point charge. A first order correction to the Born approximation consists in replacing the second factor by

$$1 + (P/mc)^2 \cos^2\vartheta/2 + (\pi e^2 Z P W/\hbar m^2 c^4) \sin\vartheta/2,$$

cf. P. Urban, Zeits. f. Physik **119**, 67 (1942).

[5] For small q it follows from (6) that

$$f_l \approx \delta_{l0} + \text{const.}(qR)^{l+2}$$

where R is a length of order of nuclear dimensions, δ_{l0} is the Kronecker symbol.

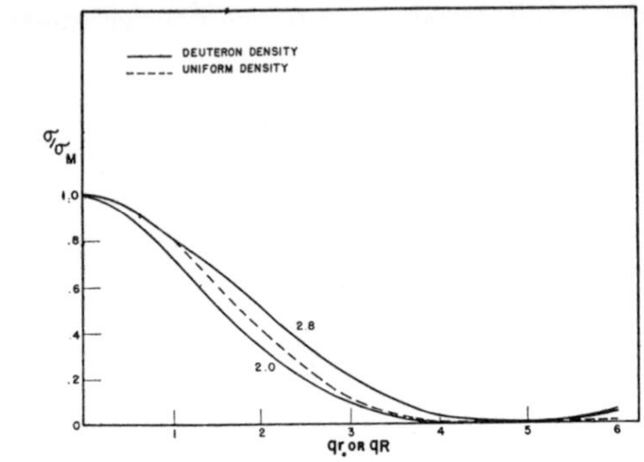

FIG. 1. Full curves give the ratio of expected elastic scattering to Mott scattering in deuterium as a function of qr_0 with $\hbar q$ the change in momentum and r_0 the range for a central square well. Numbers affixed to the curves give r_0 in units 10^{-13} cm. The dashed curve shows the same scattering ratio for a nucleus with constant charge density and radius R as a function of qR.

where again R is of order of nuclear dimensions. For 50 Mev electrons this is an angle of about 10°.

Using the wave function of the deuteron corresponding to a central square well potential of range r_0 and depth V_0 the scattering can be easily calculated from (14). We find

$$f_0=\frac{\cos^2 b}{1+a}\cos\frac{\xi}{2}+\frac{a}{1+a}\left\{4e^{2a}(G/\xi)\sin^2 b+\frac{2}{\xi}Si\left(\frac{\xi}{2}\right)+\frac{1}{\xi}\left[Si(2b-\tfrac{1}{2}\xi)-Si(2b+\tfrac{1}{2}\xi)\right]+\frac{1}{2}\left(1-\frac{\xi}{b}\right)\frac{\sin(2b-\frac{1}{2}\xi)}{2b-\frac{1}{2}\xi}+\frac{1}{2}\left(1+\frac{\xi}{b}\right)\frac{\sin(2b+\frac{1}{2}\xi)}{2b+\frac{1}{2}\xi}\right\} \quad (15)$$

where

$$Si(y)=\int_0^y \sin t\,dt/t,\quad \xi=qr_0,$$
$$a=(M\epsilon)^{\frac{1}{2}}r_0/\hbar,\quad b=[M(V_0-\epsilon)]^{\frac{1}{2}}r_0/\hbar \quad (15a)$$

and ϵ is the binding energy = 2.17 Mev. The quantity

$$G=\int_{\frac{1}{2}}^{\infty} e^{-4ax}\sin\xi x\,dx/x=\arctan\xi/4a-\int_0^{\frac{1}{2}} e^{-4ax}\sin\xi x\,dx/x$$

is computed numerically.

The ratio to Mott scattering, that is, f_0^2, is given as the full curves in Fig. 1 for ranges $r_0=2.0$ and 2.8×10^{-13} cm. For the scattering of 50 Mev electrons at $\vartheta=\pi/2$ the scattering is reduced to 23 percent of the Mott scattering in the case of the larger range. At a larger scattering angle, say $\vartheta=\pi$ the deviation from Mott scattering is, of course, even more striking; but of course the cross section becomes smaller and the measurements more difficult (cf. further Section IIIa and b below).

c. Scattering by Heavier Nuclei

As a second example we consider heavier nuclei for which it is reasonable to assume a constant charge density. We find directly from (14)

$$f_0=\frac{3}{\eta^2}\left(\frac{\sin\eta}{\eta}-\cos\eta\right) \quad (16)$$

where $\eta=qR$ and R is the nuclear radius. The scattering ratio f_0^2 is given as the dashed curve in Fig. 1. For typical values of the nuclear radius the large angle scattering is again reduced from the Mott value by a large amount.

III. COMPETING PROCESSES

In order to form some idea as to the feasibility of the proposed scattering experiments we consider what might be expected from concomitant processes. These are (1) excitation and disintegration of the nucleus, (2) inelastic scattering involving atomic excitation and ionization, and (3) bremsstrahlung.

a. Nuclear Excitation and Disintegration

While it is rather difficult to make a quantitative estimate of the angular distribution of scattering with nuclear excitation or disintegration, the total cross section for this process may be evaluated with sufficient accuracy. Since the collision considered takes place mainly through the virtual quanta emitted by the deflected electron and the consequent photo-effect of these quanta, the angular distribution of the scattered electrons will show a strong forward peak very much like that exhibited by the elastic scattering. Therefore, under conditions which make the total cross section for scattering with nuclear excitation small compared to the total elastic scattering cross section, the former may be disregarded.

The total cross section for nuclear disintegration may be calculated by the Williams-Weiszäcker method.[6] For the ejection of a single particle from the nucleus the total cross section is approximately

$$\sigma_{\rm dis} \sim \frac{\pi e^4}{Mc^2 E_0} \log \frac{MW}{mE_0} \tag{17}$$

where E_0 is the threshold energy and M the mass of the ejected particle. In (17) some numerical factors of order unity have been omitted.[7] For the ejection of a single particle (neutron, or proton) with $E_0 = 6$ Mev and $W = 50$ Mev we have $\sigma_{\rm dis} \sim 10^{-4}$ barn. The total elastic scattering cross section can be evaluated quite easily. Since the major contribution comes from small angles we have for the differential cross section at high energies (cf. reference 9)

$$\sigma_{\rm el}(\vartheta) = \left(\frac{Ze^2 \cos\vartheta/2}{2cP \sin^2\vartheta/2} \right)^2 (1-F)^2 \tag{18}$$

where F is the atomic form factor arising from the scattering by orbital electrons.[8] We find for the total elastic scattering cross section

$$\sigma_{\rm el} \approx 6Z^{4/3}(\hbar/Mc)^2 \tag{19}$$

which is enormously greater than $\sigma_{\rm dis}$. While (19) includes essentially unobservable scattering at $\vartheta = 0$ the same is true of the cross section for disintegration, Eq. (17).

In order to be more certain that the disintegration cross section is also negligible at large scattering angles a comparison of the angular distributions for elastic scattering and inelastic scattering with disintegration may be made in the one case where the latter can be readily calculated, *viz*; disintegration of the deuteron.[9] The differential cross section for high energy electrons is approximately

$$\sigma_{\rm dis}(\vartheta) = \frac{8}{3\pi} \frac{m}{M} \left(\frac{e^2}{Mc^2} \right)^2 \epsilon^{\frac{1}{2}} \int_0^{W-mc^2-\epsilon} \frac{dE E^{\frac{3}{2}}}{(E+\epsilon)^4} \times \left[\frac{W^2 + W'^2}{(\hbar c q)^2 - (W-W')^2} - \frac{1}{2} \right] \tag{20}$$

where W and W' are the initial and final electron energies and $E = W - W' - \epsilon$ is the kinetic energy of the nucleons. The evaluation of (20) to give the angular distribution leads to the following conclusions: (1) The comparison of total cross sections as given above is somewhat too optimistic insofar as the decrease of $\sigma_{\rm dis}(\vartheta)$ with the angle of deflection is not nearly so rapid as is the decrease of the elastic differential cross section $\sigma_{\rm el}(\vartheta)$. (2) Since $\sigma_{\rm dis}(\vartheta)$ varies only slowly with energy (cf. Eq. (17)), and the differential cross section $\sigma_{\rm el}(\vartheta)$ varies as W^{-2} (except in the backward direction), the disintegration effect can be neglected only if the electron energy is not greatly in excess of 50 Mev. (3) The scattering angle at which the electrons are observed should not be too near π since in this case elastic scattering is very much reduced (because of factor $P^2 \cos^2\vartheta/2$) and will be considerably larger than $\sigma_{\rm dis}(\vartheta)$ only for energies so low that the effect of electron penetration into the nucleus is negligible. With $W = 50$ Mev and $\vartheta = \pi/2$, which values represent favorable conditions, $\sigma_{\rm dis} = 6 \times 10^{-7}$ barn and $\sigma_{\rm el} = 1.6 \times 10^{-5}$ barn.

b. Ionizing Collisions

The cross section for inelastic collisions with the orbital electrons is not negligible compared to the elastic scattering. However, competition due to such collisions is unimportant if it is arranged to observe electrons which have energies equal or nearly equal to the primary energy and are scattered through angles other than 0 or π. This follows from simple energy and momentum considerations which show that the primary electron scattered through an angle $\mu = \arccos\vartheta$ or a secondary traveling in the same direction has a total energy given by

$$\frac{W'}{mc^2} = \frac{W + mc^2 + \mu^2(W - mc^2)}{W + mc^2 - \mu^2(W - mc^2)}. \tag{21}$$

Here the binding of the secondary in the initial state is neglected. Therefore, for $W \gg mc^2$ the secondary energy W' cannot be large unless $\mu^2 \approx 1$. Therefore, under the conditions $W \gg mc^2$ and ϑ in the range $\pi/2 \pm \pi/4$ say, there will be no fast electrons which were not elastically scattered. These conditions are the same as those providing a large ratio of elastic scattering to nuclear disintegration.

[6] E. J. Williams, K. Danske Vidensk. Selskab. **13**, no. 17 (1934–36).

[7] For energies such that $\hbar c/W$ is larger than nuclear dimensions the argument of the *log* in (17) is multiplied by W/Mc^2 which reduces the cross section. Cf. further reference 9.

[8] Cf. H. A. Bethe, Ann. d. Physik **5**, 325 (1930).

[9] H. A. Bethe and R. Peierls, Proc. Roy. Soc. **148**, 146 (1935).

c. Bremsstrahlung

The bremsstrahlung competes with the elastic scattering in a way which would make interpretation of measurements ambiguous except when the deflected electrons have energies about equal to the primary energy. In this case, the quanta emitted are soft and, as is well known, the angular distribution of the scattered electrons is precisely the same as the distribution of elastically scattered electrons.[10] Obviously the bremsstrahlung will also be reduced by the same factor f_0^2 due to nuclear penetration and thus, under the conditions cited, one need not distinguish between elastic scattering and bremstrahlung.

[10] F. Bloch and A. Nordsieck, Phys. Rev. **52**, 54 (1937).

IV. ACKNOWLEDGMENT

It is a pleasure to thank Professor H. A. Bethe for interesting discussions. This document is based on work performed under Contract No. W-35-058-eng. 71 for the Manhattan Project at the Clinton Laboratories.

PAPER 7

High Energy Elastic Scattering of Electrons on Protons

M. N. Rosenbluth
Stanford University, Stanford, California

(Received March 28, 1950)

The theory of the elastic scattering of electrons on protons at very high energies is discussed in detail. A formula is given for the cross section. This formula contains certain parameters which depend on the action of the virtual photon and meson fields. In particular, curves have been calculated on the assumption of scalar and pseudoscalar meson theory. While these perturbation theory calculations are not very trustworthy, and the results depend on the choice of coupling constants, it is felt that qualitative features can be checked with experiment. It is concluded that at low relativistic energies ($E<50$ Mev) the experiment provides a valuable check on quantum electrodynamics. At higher energies it should yield data on the nature of the meson cloud of the proton.

I. INTRODUCTION

The Stanford linear electron accelerator program is expected to make available large currents of relativistic electrons with various energies ranging from 6 to 1000 Mev. Among the experiments of considerable interest which may then be performed is the elastic scattering of electrons on protons. This may be done on a hydrogen gas or liquid target. Despite the smallness of the cross section at high energies, the expected large intensity of the beam should render the experiments possible.

It is the purpose of this paper to show that, at appropriate energies and angles, the experiment should give considerable information both about the validity of the "quantum electrodynamical radiative corrections" to scattering, and about the structure of the meson cloud associated with the proton.

Processes competing with electron-proton elastic scattering can be grouped into two classes: (a) those arising from electron-electron interactions; (b) other electron-proton processes. The electron-electron interactions have a much larger cross section at high energies than the electron-proton interactions. Background from the electron-electron interactions may be eliminated by (1) angular coincidences between the scattered particles, (2) energy selection of the scattered electron at a given angle [or a combination of (1) and (2)], or (3) direct observation of the recoil protons by photographic plates.

The competing electron-proton processes are bremsstrahlung and meson production. They will have cross sections comparable to the corrections to the elastic scattering which are discussed below. Methods (1) and (2), discussed above, would also eliminate background from these processes. If the proton is observed directly a determination of its energy by grain counting and a correlation of energy and angle could be used to eliminate these processes. At very high energies it may prove experimentally impossible to separate the different electron-proton processes, in which case the bremsstrahlung and meson production must be added to the elastic scattering which is calculated in this paper.

II. ELASTIC SCATTERING OF AN ELECTRON AND PROTON

The elastic scattering of an electron and a proton can be represented schematically on a Feynman[1] diagram as in Fig. 1.

Figure 1 shows a proton of 4-momentum $\mathbf{p}_1$ and an electron of 4-momentum $\mathbf{p}_2$ exchanging a virtual quantum of 4-momentum $\mathbf{q}=\mathbf{p}_3-\mathbf{p}_1=\mathbf{p}_2-\mathbf{p}_4$ and being scattered to momenta $\mathbf{p}_3$ and $\mathbf{p}_4$, respectively. Here M is the proton rest-mass, e'' is the effective charge of the electron, e' the effective charge of the proton, and $\kappa' e'/2M$ its effective anomalous magnetic moment. The effective charges and magnetic moments are functions of $q^2=q_4^2-q_3^2-q_2-q_1^2$ as discussed below. The notation of a German letter, $\mathfrak{q}$, means $q_4\gamma_4-q_3\gamma_3-q_2\gamma_2-q_1\gamma_1$, where the γ's are given in terms of the usual Dirac matrices by $(\boldsymbol{\gamma}, \gamma_4)=(\beta\boldsymbol{\alpha}, \beta)$.

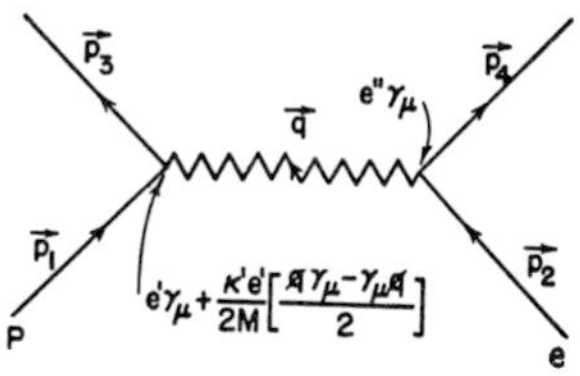

FIG. 1. Diagram for the elastic scattering of a physical proton and a physical electron. (The letter "q" with the bar through it in this figure is the same as the German letter, $\mathfrak{q}$, used in the text.)

The cross section for this process is computed by standard spur techniques to be

$$\sigma d\Omega=\left(\frac{e'e''}{2E}\right)^2 \operatorname{ctn}^2\frac{\theta}{2}\csc^2\frac{\theta}{2}\left\{\frac{1+2(E/M)\sin^2(\theta/2)+(E^2/M^2)[2(1+\kappa')^2\tan^2(\theta/2)\sin^2(\theta/2)+\kappa'^2\sin^2(\theta/2)]}{[1+(2E/M)\sin^2(\theta/2)]^2}\right\}d\Omega. \quad (1)$$

[1] R. P. Feynman, Phys. Rev. **76**, 749 and 769 (1949). The methods of calculation and the notation used in this paper are just those of Feynman unless otherwise indicated. We also use natural units, $\hbar=c=1$.

Here E is the energy of the incident electron and θ the angle through which it is scattered, both as measured in the system where the proton is initially at rest. The rest-mass of the electron has been neglected compared to its energy. We also introduce the useful parameter

$$q^2 = \frac{-4E^2 \sin^2(\theta/2)}{1+2(E/M)\sin^2(\theta/2)}. \quad (2)$$

For electron energies small compared to the proton rest-mass Eq. (1) reduces just to the usual Mott-Rutherford formula for scattering of an electron by a fixed electrostatic potential. Since κ', the effective anomalous proton magnetic moment, may be larger than 1 (for $\mathbf{q}=0$, $\kappa'=\kappa_0=1.79$) the magnetic moment

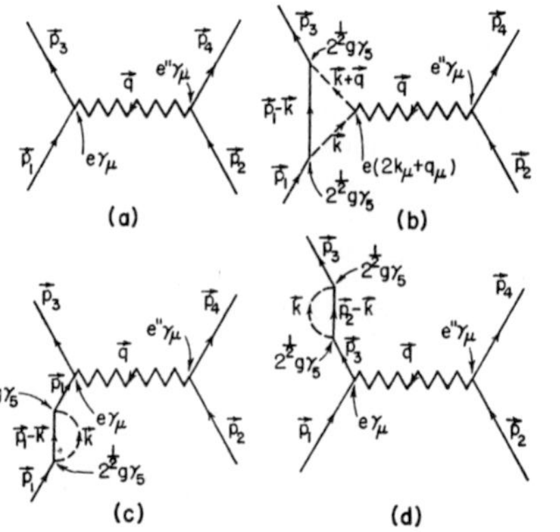

FIG. 2. Diagram showing the effect of a virtual charged pseudoscalar meson on electron-proton scattering.

will play an important role in the very high energy region.

That the effective electron charge e'' differs from its "natural" value e is due to the so-called radiative correction to scattering,[2] i.e., to the possibility that the electron may emit and reabsorb a virtual quantum, or emit a low energy real quantum, during the scattering process. This modification has been treated extensively by Schwinger.[3] His formula is valid under the assumption that the proton acts as a fixed electrostatic potential. This is the case in the low energy region in which this is the most important correction term. At higher electron energies, the more exact expression could be derived by a modification of the radiative correction to Møller scattering, which has been calculated at Cornell.[4] Here we restrict ourselves to the remark that the Schwinger correction is a slowly varying function of angle and energy and corresponds to a decrease of the order of magnitude of five percent in the effective electron charge for the region of interest.

[2] Strictly speaking, we should also give the electron an anomalous magnetic moment, but this is quite small and decreases rapidly at high energy.

[3] J. Schwinger, Phys. Rev. **76**, 813 (1949). In our notation $(e''/e)^2 = e^{-\delta}$ where δ is given by Schwinger in his Eq. (2.105).

[4] R. P. Feynman (private communication).

III. MESON FIELD CORRECTIONS TO ELECTRON-PROTON SCATTERING

The modification of the proton charge and anomalous magnetic moment is here assumed to be caused by the action of a virtual meson field. At electron energies small compared with the meson rest-mass these modifications will be small. Thus, at low energies the scattering will give us information concerning chiefly the radiative corrections to scattering; at higher energies we may expect to learn something of the nature of the meson cloud which surrounds the proton.

The action of a scalar meson field in modifying the effective proton charge and magnetic moment can be understood qualitatively by assuming that during a fraction R of the time the proton exists as a neutron and a positive meson. Its charge and anomalous moment then will be spread out like $e^{-2\mu}/r^2$ (the square of the meson wave function) where μ is the mass of the meson. Thus a high energy electron is able to penetrate the meson cloud and hence see a smaller effective charge and magnetic moment. Under these assumptions Schiff[5] has given the effective charge and magnetic moment to be

$$(e'/e) = [(1-R) + R2\mu/(-q^2)^{\frac{1}{2}} \tan(-q^2)^{\frac{1}{2}}/2\mu], \quad (3)$$
$$(\kappa' e'/\kappa_0 e) = 2\mu/(-q^2)^{\frac{1}{2}} \tan^{-1}(-q^2)^{\frac{1}{2}}/2\mu,$$

where q^2 is given by Eq. (2).

We will here calculate in the covariant manner of Feynman the effective charge and magnetic moment of the proton as given by four theories: Neutral and charged scalar mesons with scalar-coupling, neutral and charged pseudoscalar mesons with pseudoscalar coupling. The results for symmetrical theories may be obtained simply by adding the results for charged and neutral theories. Other meson theories lead to divergent results.

To illustrate the method, we will discuss briefly the case of charged pseudoscalar theory. The effect of the virtual mesons on the scattering is shown in Fig. 2.

Figure 2(a) shows the usual electromagnetic interaction between two Dirac-type particles of charge e and e''. Figure 2(b) shows the proton emitting a positive meson which absorbs the virtual photon and is then reabsorbed by the neutron. Figure 2(c) shows the meson being emitted and reabsorbed before the scattering takes place. Figure 2(d) shows the virtual emission and reabsorption taking place after the scattering. Here g is the meso-nuclear coupling constant; $\gamma_5 = i\gamma_1\gamma_2\gamma_3\gamma_4$; the factor 2 is inserted for simplicity in later discussing symmetrical theory; and the $2k_\mu + q_\mu$ at the meson-quantum vertex reflects the fact that a Klein-Gordon particle interacts with the electromagnetic field through the terms $i\partial(A_\mu\psi)/\partial x_\mu + iA_\mu\partial\psi/\partial x_\mu$ where ψ is the meson wave function, and A_μ the electromagnetic potential.

We endeavor to show that adding the diagrams 2(a) to 2(d) produces a situation like that in Fig. 1, and to

[5] L. I. Schiff, Stanford Microwave Laboratory Report No. 102, p. 8 (1949).

deduce the values of e' and κ'. For the case of $\mathbf{q}$, the photon momentum, equal to zero, diagrams (b), (c), and (d) are found to add to zero as might be expected, since there is then no scattering process. (There are non-essential mass renormalization terms but they do not concern us.) Moreover, the value of $\mathbf{q}$ does not affect the proton-meson parts of diagrams (c) and (d). Therefore we can obtain the final proton-meson portion of the amplitude by adding the proton-meson parts of diagrams (a) and (b) and subtracting off the value of diagram (b) for $\mathbf{q}=0$.

The proton-meson amplitude matrix from diagram (a) is simply $e\gamma_\mu$, that from diagram (b) can be written:[6]

$$e\frac{2g^2}{\pi i}\int d^4\mathbf{k}\frac{\gamma_5(\mathfrak{p}_1-\mathfrak{k}+M)\gamma_5(2k_\mu+q_\mu)}{[(\mathbf{p}_1+\mathbf{k})^2-M^2][k^2-\mu^2][(\mathbf{k}+\mathbf{q})^2-\mu^2]}.$$

Here μ is the meson rest-mass; the integration is to be performed over all virtual mesons; and we are interested in the element between initial and final proton states of this matrix.

After the integral over the virtual mesons is performed, and the amplitudes from diagrams (a) and (b) added, with the $\mathbf{q}=0$ value of diagram (b) subtracted, we obtain as final amplitude:

$$e\gamma_\mu\left\{1-\frac{g^2}{2\pi}\int_0^1 dx\int_0^1 dy\left[\frac{1}{2}\ln\left(1+\frac{u}{a}\right)-\frac{u[3y^3-(5-(a/2))y^4+2y^5]}{[(1-y)^2+uy^2+ay][(1-y)^2+ay]}\right]\right\}$$
$$+\frac{e}{2M}\left[\frac{\mathfrak{q}\gamma_\mu-\gamma_\mu\mathfrak{q}}{2}\right]\frac{g^2}{\pi}\int_0^1 dx\int_0^1 dy\left(\frac{y(1-y)^2}{(1-y)^2+uy^2+ay}\right). \quad (4)$$

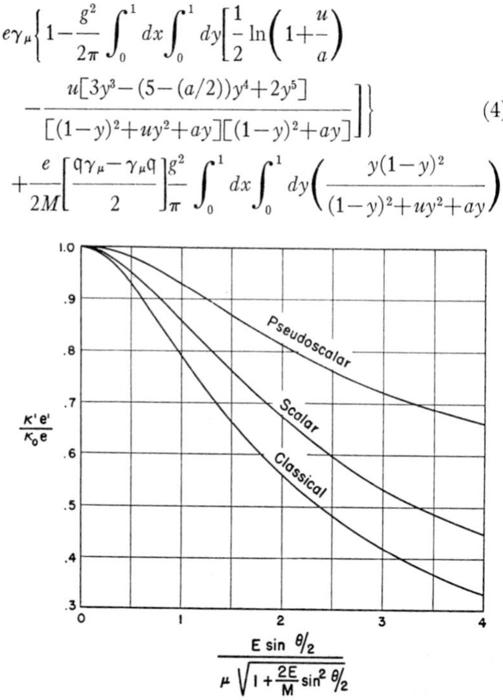

FIG. 3. Ratio of effective anomalous proton magnetic moment to its zero-energy value for charged meson theories.

[6] See Feynman, reference 1, for a full discussion of the method notation, and calculation techniques. In particular, the Appendix, p. 785, gives a full discussion of the evaluation of the radiative correction to scattering integral which is very analogous to our case.

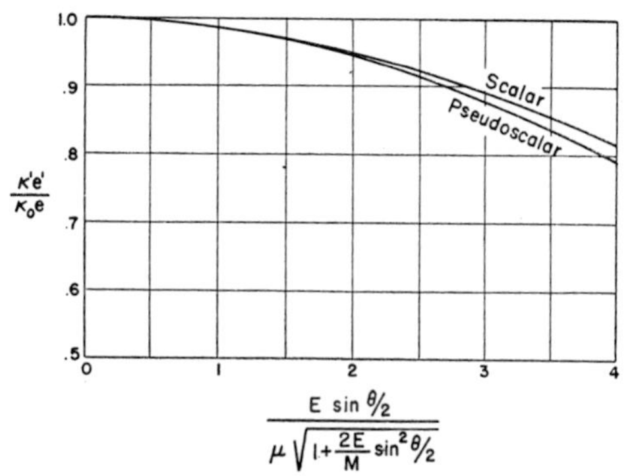

FIG. 4. Ratio of effective anomalous proton magnetic moment to its zero-energy value for neutral meson theories.

Here x and y are integration parameters, $a=\mu^2/M^2$; $u=q^2(x^2-x)/M^2$. The first term here represents the effective charge of the proton, the second its anomalous magnetic moment. For $u=0$ this term gives just the value for the anomalous moment previously derived by Case.[7]

For the case $u\neq 0$ the integrals are very complicated. The integral on y can be performed analytically. The remaining integral on x then depends on the parameters q^2/μ^2 and q^2/M^2. If q^2 is of comparable order of magnitude to μ^2, but much smaller than M^2, a region of considerable interest, the integral may be expanded to first order in the parameter q^2/M^2 and then performed analytically. For larger values of q^2 it must be carried out numerically. The other meson theories require the same type of calculation.

Figures 3, 4, 5, and 6 give the results of these integrations.

Figures 3 and 4 are graphs of $\kappa'e'/\kappa_0 e$, the ratio of the effective anomalous magnetic moment to the zero-energy anomalous moment. On Fig. 3 we have also plotted the "classical" formula (3). We have assumed in all calculations that μ, the meson mass, is 276 electron masses, consistent with experimental values for the π-meson. These ratios are independent of the coupling constant, which will determine only the magnitude of the zero-energy moment. It should be noted, however, that the scalar charged and pseudoscalar neutral theories predict the wrong sign for the proton moment.

Figures 5 and 6 are graphs of the effective proton charge. For reasons discussed below, we have plotted $e'/e=e^{-\delta}$, rather than $e'/e=1-\delta$ as obtained directly from (4). As can be seen from (4), δ is directly proportional to g^2. We have plotted $e^{-\delta}$ for those values of g^2 necessary to predict the correct value for the magnitude of the zero-energy proton moment. These values are given in Table I.

To illustrate the use of the graphs, and to show how they may be adapted to symmetrical theory, let us

[7] K. Case, Phys. Rev. 76, 6 (1949).

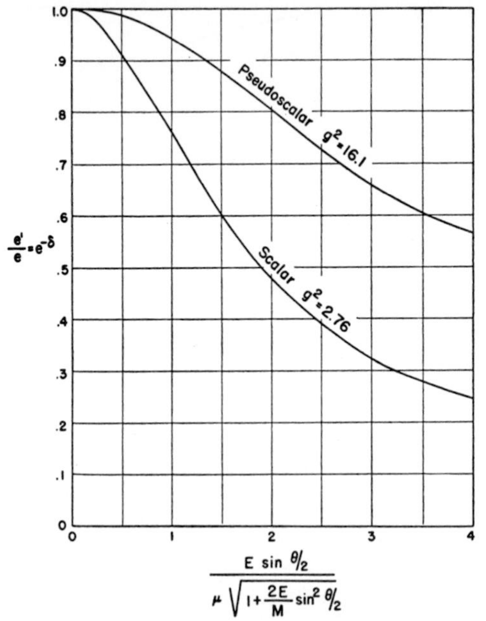

FIG. 5. Effective proton charge for charged meson theories with coupling constants chosen to fit the magnitude of the observed proton anomalous magnetic moment.

calculate the effective charge and magnetic moment for a 500-Mev electron scattered through 90° on the basis of symmetrical pseudoscalar theory with coupling constant 57.2. The abscissa

$$\left(E\sin\frac{\theta}{2}\right)\Big/\mu\left(1+\frac{2E}{M}\sin^2\frac{\theta}{2}\right)^{\frac{1}{2}}=(-q^2)^{\frac{1}{2}}/2\mu$$

in this case is equal to 2.03. Since the neutral and charged theories give opposite signs for the magnetic moment:

$$(\kappa'e')_s=(\kappa'e')_c-(\kappa'e')_n.$$

Using Table I and Figs. 3 and 4,

$$(\kappa'e'/\kappa_0 e)_s=0.81(57.2/16.1)-0.94(57.2/22.4)=0.48.$$

To obtain the effective charge:

$$\delta_s=\delta_c+\delta_n=0.22(57.2/16.1)+0.15(57.2/22.4)=1.16,$$
$$(e'/e)_s=\exp(-\delta_s)=0.31.$$

To obtain the final cross section these values for e' and κ', and Schwinger's[3] value for e'' are substituted in (1).

It will be noted that symmetrical theory predicts a rapid dropping off of magnetic moment and charge due to the large coupling constant.

IV. CONCLUSIONS

It will be noted at once that the values of g^2 listed in Table I are so large as to throw grave doubts on the use of second-order perturbation theory. This is especially true for the pseudoscalar case where we expect second-order terms to be small compared to higher order terms. In this connection it may be noted that the values of g^2 listed in Table I do not give the correct neutron moment. Some justification for the perturbation theory procedure may be found in the fact that experimental results on photo-meson production do seem to agree with the qualitative predictions of second-order pseudoscalar perturbation theory.[8] (There has been no effort to measure the absolute cross section so that no experimental value of g^2 is obtained.) It is because of doubt of the adequacy of the second-order theory that we have plotted $e'/e=\exp(-\delta)$, thus considering at least some of the higher order terms.

It will be noted that even though the meson clouds are more tightly bound than a naive picture would predict (see Fig. 3), there is nonetheless a very sizeable decrease in proton charge and magnetic moment to be expected at high energies. This is especially true if we assume the large values of coupling constant necessary to predict the proper proton moment. Even if only the qualitative features of these curves are dependable the experimental results should at least indicate (1) if the proton magnetic moment is really due to the π-meson

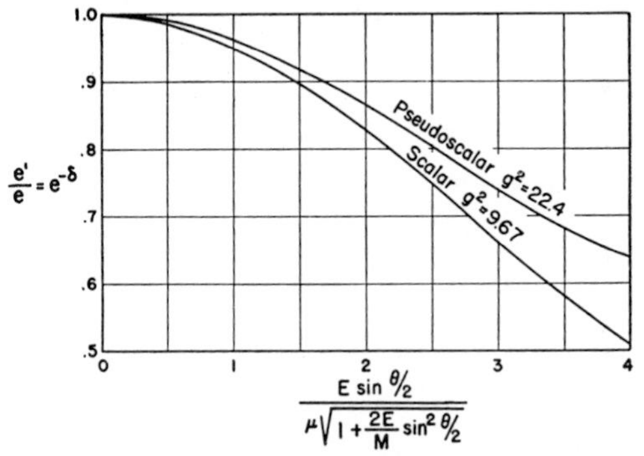

FIG. 6. Effective proton charge for neutral meson theories with coupling constants chosen to fit the magnitude of the observed proton anomalous magnetic moment.

TABLE I. Coupling constants necessary for correct magnitude of proton magnetic moment.

Theory	Scalar charged	Scalar neutral	Scalar symmetrical	Pseudo-scalar charged	Pseudo-scalar neutral	Pseudo-scalar symmetrical
g^2	2.76*	9.67	3.86*	16.1	22.4*	57.2

* Indicates wrong sign for magnetic moment.

[8] J. Steinberger, experiments performed at Berkeley and not yet published.

field, (2) whether a loose-bound scalar type theory or a tight-bound pseudoscalar-type theory is preferable, and (3) how much faith can be placed in the "quantum electrodynamical radiative corrections" to scattering and in the far more dubious second-order meson corrections to scattering.

I would like to thank Professor L. I. Schiff for many helpful discussions and suggestions. I would like to express my gratitude also to Dr. Ross Thompson of Cornell University who has performed most of these calculations independently, and who very kindly checked, and improved upon one of, my results.

PAPER 8*

The Effect of Nuclear Structure on the Elastic Scattering of Fast Electrons

By L. R. B. ELTON
University College, London

Communicated by H. S. W. Massey; MS. received 8th March 1950

ABSTRACT. The cross section for the scattering of electrons by atomic nuclei is investigated at energies for which the nuclei can no longer be treated as point charges. Two simple nuclear models are used. A general expression is obtained using Born's approximation, and an exact numerical calculation is carried through for 20 Mev. electrons scattered by gold nuclei. It is concluded that at this energy considerable deviations from the formulae which treat the nucleus as a point charge should be expected, and that these should furnish some information about the charge distribution within the nucleus.

§ 1. INTRODUCTION

The elastic scattering of fast electrons by atomic nuclei has been investigated theoretically by Mott (1929, 1932), and calculations by Bartlett and Watson (1940) and McKinley and Feshbach (1948) based on Mott's formulae agree well with the experimental results of Van de Graaff *et al.* (1946, 1947) and Sigrist (1943). In these calculations the scattering nucleus was taken to be a point charge, and the agreement with the experimental results shows that at the energies considered (up to 3 Mev.) this approximation was justified. At higher energies, however, the electron wavelength becomes comparable with and even smaller than the diameter of the nucleus, and scattering experiments at such energies should give information about the charge distribution within the nucleus. The present investigation is concerned with (*a*) estimating by means of Born's approximation at what energies effects due to the finite extent of the

* *See page 683 of this volume for corrections and addenda.*

nucleus would first become measurable and (*b*) carrying through a numerical calculation at one energy for gold. Three nuclear models were used:

A. Point charge.
B. Uniform spherical charge distribution of radius R.
C. Uniform spherical shell charge distribution of radius R.

These will hereafter be referred to as cases A, B and C respectively. These letters will also appear as affixes to distinguish corresponding quantities for the three cases. The nuclear radius is taken, as given by Wheeler (1949), to be

$$R=\frac{\mathbf{e}^2}{2\mathbf{m}\mathbf{c}^2}A^{1/3},$$

where $\mathbf{m}$ and $\mathbf{e}$ are the mass and charge of the electron, $\mathbf{c}$ the velocity of light and A the mass number of the nucleus.*

§ 2. DIFFERENTIAL CROSS SECTION BY BORN'S APPROXIMATION

The differential cross section for a Dirac particle in the Born approximation is given by Mott and Massey (1949 b) as

$$I(\theta)=\frac{1-\beta^2\sin^2\theta/2}{1-\beta^2}|f(\theta)|^2,$$

where

$$f(\theta)=-\frac{2\mathbf{m}}{\hbar^2}\int_0^\infty \frac{\sin Kr}{Kr}V(r)r^2\,dr.$$

Here

$$K=2k\sin\theta/2,\quad k^2=\frac{W^2-\mathbf{m}^2\mathbf{c}^4}{\hbar^2\mathbf{c}^2}=\frac{\mathbf{m}^2v^2}{\hbar^2(1-\beta^2)},\qquad \beta=\frac{v}{\mathbf{c}},$$

and W, v and m are the total energy, the velocity and the rest mass of the particle respectively. This formula is now applied to the three types of nuclei under consideration. The integrals which occur are not convergent, because of the slow falling-off of the Coulomb field, but if each integrand is multiplied by $\exp(-\mu r)$, the limit as $\mu\to 0$ exists and is taken to be the value of the integral. Similar formulae have already been given by Rose (1948).

Case A.

$$V(r)=-\frac{Z\mathbf{e}^2}{r}.$$

Therefore

$$f_A(\theta)=\frac{Z\mathbf{e}^2(1-\beta^2)}{2\mathbf{m}v^2}\operatorname{cosec}^2\frac{\theta}{2}.$$

Case B.

$$V(r)=\begin{cases}-\dfrac{Z\mathbf{e}^2}{R}\left(\dfrac{3}{2}-\dfrac{r^2}{2R^2}\right), & r<R.\\[2ex] -\dfrac{Z\mathbf{e}^2}{r}, & r\geqslant R.\end{cases}$$

Therefore

$$f_B(\theta)=\frac{2\mathbf{m}Z\mathbf{e}^2}{K\hbar^2}\left\{\int_0^R\frac{1}{R}\left(\frac{3}{2}-\frac{r^2}{2R^2}\right)r\sin Kr\,dr+\int_R^\infty \sin Kr\,dr\right\}$$
$$=\frac{3}{K^3R^3}(\sin KR-KR\cos KR)f_A(\theta).$$

* Since these calculations were completed, Lu (1950) has advocated a radius of $r_0A^{1/3}$, where $r_0=1\cdot47\times10^{-13}$ cm. for case B and $r_0=1\cdot34\times10^{-13}$ cm. for case C, as against the value $r_0=\mathbf{e}^2/2\mathbf{m}\mathbf{c}^2=1\cdot41\times10^{-13}$ cm. which has been used for both cases in the present calculation. Clearly, if his values are used, any effects due to the finite extent of the nucleus will be slightly increased in case B and slightly decreased in case C.

Case C.
$$V(r)=\begin{cases}-\dfrac{Ze^2}{R}, & r<R.\\[2mm] -\dfrac{Ze^2}{r}, & r\geqslant R.\end{cases}$$

Therefore

$$f_{\rm C}(\theta)=\frac{2mZe^2}{K\hbar^2}\left\{\int_0^R\frac{r}{R}\sin Kr\,dr+\int_R^\infty\sin Kr\,dr\right\}$$

$$=\frac{\sin KR}{KR}f_{\rm A}(\theta).$$

That the Born approximation is invalid for any but the lightest nuclei ($Z\lesssim15$) can be seen from the calculations of McKinley and Feshbach (1948). Nevertheless, it gives a useful indication as to the magnitude of the effects to be expected even for heavy nuclei, though it will underestimate them. From Table 1 it is clear that observable effects can hardly be expected for energies below 20 Mev. for heavy nuclei and for energies below 40 Mev. for light nuclei, particularly since scattering at large angles is difficult to measure because of the small intensity at these angles.

Table 1. $I_{\rm B,\,C}(\theta)/I_{\rm A}(\theta)$

Ratio of the differential cross sections for the two cases of the extended nucleus to that for the case of the point nucleus, for electrons of energy Wmc^2 being scattered by aluminium and gold nuclei, using Born's approximation.

	Aluminium : $Z=13$, $A=27$				Gold : $Z=79$, $A=197$			
θ	30°		150°		30°		150°	
	B	C	B	C	B	C	B	C
$W/mc^2=$ 5	1·00	1·00	1·00	1·00	1·00	1·00	1·00	0·99
10	1·00	1·00	1·00	0·99	1·00	1·00	0·97	0·95
20	1·00	1·00	0·96	0·94	1·00	0·98	0·87	0·79
40	1·00	0·98	0·86	0·78	0·96	0·94	0·57	0·37
80	0·96	0·94	0·55	0·35				

§ 3. EXACT CALCULATION OF THE DIFFERENTIAL CROSS SECTION

This calculation will be carried out for gold nuclei and electrons of energy $40mc^2$ ($\simeq$20 Mev.). For gold, $Z=79$ and $R=8{\cdot}196\times10^{-13}$ cm. The theory of the scattering of electrons by a centre of force can be found in Mott and Massey (1949 a) and their notation will be largely followed here.

(i) *The Differential Cross Section*

The differential cross section is

$$I(\theta)=|f(\theta)|^2+|g(\theta)|^2, \qquad \ldots\ldots(1)$$

where

$$\left.\begin{aligned} f(\theta)&=\frac{1}{2ik}\Sigma\{(n+1)(\exp[2i\eta_n]-1)+n(\exp[2i\eta_{-n-1}]-1)\}P_n(\cos\theta),\\ g(\theta)&=\frac{1}{2ik}\Sigma\{-\exp[2i\eta_n]+\exp[2i\eta_{-n-1}]\}P_n'(\cos\theta),\end{aligned}\right\} \qquad \ldots\ldots(2)$$

and η_n, η_{-n-1} are the phases. Now it will be shown below that the phases for the cases of the extended nucleus and of the point nucleus differ significantly only for $n=0$ and $n=-2$. Hence the differential cross section for case B can be written

$$I_B(\theta)=|f_B(\theta)|^2+|g_B(\theta)|^2, \qquad \ldots\ldots(3)$$

where

$$\left.\begin{aligned} f_B(\theta)&=f_A(\theta)+\frac{1}{2ik}\{(\exp[2i\eta_0^B]-\exp[2i\eta_0^A])P_0(\cos\theta)\\ &\qquad+(\exp[2i\eta_{-2}^B]-\exp[2i\eta_{-2}^A])P_1(\cos\theta)\},\\ g_B(\theta)&=g_A(\theta)+\frac{1}{2ik}(\exp[2i\eta_{-2}^B]-\exp[2i\eta_{-2}^A])P_1'(\cos\theta),\\ f_A(\theta)&=\frac{1}{2ik}\Sigma\{(n+1)(\exp[2i\eta_n^A]-1)+n(\exp[2i\eta_{-n-1}^A]-1)\}P_n(\cos\theta),\\ g_A(\theta)&=\frac{1}{2ik}\Sigma(-\exp[2i\eta_n^A]+\exp[2i\eta_{-n-1}^A])P_n'(\cos\theta), \end{aligned}\right\} \qquad \ldots\ldots(4)$$

and similarly for C. f_A and g_A are calculated from the formulae

$$\left.\begin{aligned} kf_A=i\gamma'F+G,\qquad kg_A&=\{i\gamma'(1+\cos\theta)F+(1-\cos\theta)G\}\operatorname{cosec}\theta,\\ \gamma'&=\frac{Ze^2}{\hbar v}\sqrt{(1-\beta^2)}, \end{aligned}\right\} \qquad \ldots\ldots(5)$$

where F and G are found by extrapolation to the higher energy from the tables of Bartlett and Watson (1940). These have actually been calculated for the case of Hg, but there will be no significant difference for the case of Au.

(ii) *Method of Calculation of the Phase Shifts*

To find the phase shifts we have to fit the regular solutions of the two radial equations inside the nucleus to the regular and irregular solutions of the radial equations outside the nucleus. This is equivalent to the condition of continuity of charge and current.

The radial equations are

$$\left.\begin{aligned} \frac{1}{\hbar}\left(\frac{W}{c}-\frac{V}{c}+mc\right)R_n+\frac{dS_n}{dr}-\frac{n}{r}S_n&=0,\\ -\frac{1}{\hbar}\left(\frac{W}{c}-\frac{V}{c}-mc\right)S_n+\frac{dR_n}{dr}+\frac{n+2}{r}R_n&=0, \end{aligned}\right\} \qquad \ldots\ldots(6)$$

where W is the energy of the electron. By elimination of R_n we have

$$\frac{d^2S_n}{dr^2}+\left(\frac{2}{r}-\frac{\alpha'}{\alpha}\right)\frac{dS_n}{dr}+\left\{k^2-\frac{2WV}{\hbar^2c^2}+\frac{V^2}{\hbar^2c^2}-\frac{n(n+1)}{r^2}+\frac{n}{r}\frac{\alpha'}{\alpha}\right\}S_n=0, \qquad \ldots\ldots(7)$$

where $\qquad \alpha=\frac{1}{\hbar}\left(\frac{W}{c}-\frac{V}{c}+mc\right), \qquad k^2=\frac{W^2-m^2c^4}{\hbar^2c^2},$

or, putting
$$S_n = r^{-1}\alpha^{1/2}\mathscr{S}_n,$$

$$\frac{d^2\mathscr{S}_n}{dr^2} - f_n(r)\mathscr{S}_n = 0, \qquad \ldots\ldots(8)$$

where
$$f_n(r) = -k^2 + \frac{n(n+1)}{r^2} + \frac{2WV}{\hbar^2\mathbf{c}^2} - \frac{V^2}{\hbar^2\mathbf{c}^2} - \frac{n+1}{r}\frac{\alpha'}{\alpha} + \frac{3}{4}\frac{\alpha'^2}{\alpha^2} - \frac{1}{2}\frac{\alpha''}{\alpha}.$$

Similarly for $\mathscr{R}_n = r\alpha^{-1/2}R_n$.

Corresponding to $\mathscr{R}_n$ and $\mathscr{S}_n$ let the regular solutions inside the nucleus be $\mathscr{D}_n$ and $\mathscr{K}_n$, the regular solutions outside the nucleus $\mathscr{F}_n$ and $\mathscr{G}_n$, and the irregular solutions outside the nucleus $\mathscr{E}_n$ and $\mathscr{H}_n$ respectively. Similarly D_n, K_n, F_n, G_n, E_n, H_n correspond to R_n, S_n. Then for $r = R$,

$$\left.\begin{aligned} \mathscr{K}_n &= A_n\mathscr{G}_n + B_n\mathscr{H}_n, \\ \mathscr{D}_n &= A_n\mathscr{F}_n + B_n\,\mathscr{E}_n. \end{aligned}\right\} \qquad \ldots\ldots(9)$$

Now asymptotically, in the usual notation,

$$\left.\begin{aligned} \mathscr{G}_{n,-n-1} &\sim \mu^{-1/2}\sin(kr + \gamma\ln 2kr - \tfrac{1}{2}n\pi + \eta_{n,-n-1}), \\ \mathscr{H}_{n,-n-1} &\sim \mu^{-1/2}\sin(kr + \gamma\ln 2kr - \tfrac{1}{2}n\pi + \eta_{n,-n-1} + \theta_{n,-n-1}), \end{aligned}\right\} \qquad \ldots\ldots(10)$$

where $\mu = (W + \mathbf{mc}^2)/\hbar\mathbf{c}$, $\gamma = Z\mathbf{e}^2/\hbar v$, and the phase $\theta_{n,-n-1}$ depends on the particular irregular solution used. The required phase shift $\zeta_{n,-n-1}$ is then given by

$$\begin{aligned} &A_{n,-n-1}\mathscr{G}_{n,-n-1} + B_{n,-n-1}\mathscr{H}_{n,-n-1} \\ &\qquad \sim C_{n,-n-1}\sin(kr + \gamma\ln 2kr - \tfrac{1}{2}n\pi + \eta_{n,-n-1} + \zeta_{n,-n-1}). \end{aligned} \qquad \ldots\ldots(11)$$

From (10) and (11),
$$\zeta_n = \tan^{-1}\frac{B_n\sin\theta_n}{A_n + B_n\cos\theta_n}. \qquad \ldots\ldots(12)$$

(iii) *Solution outside the Nucleus*

If $V = -Z\mathbf{e}^2/r$ in (3), then, for positive and negative n, the regular solution is given by Mott and Massey (1949 a) as

$$\begin{aligned} \mathscr{G}_n = \alpha^{-1/2}N_n(2kr)^{\rho_{n+1}}e^{-ikr}\{&(n+1+i\gamma')F(i\gamma+\rho_{n+1}+1, 2\rho_{n+1}+1, 2ikr) \\ &+ (\rho_{n+1} - i\gamma)F(\rho_{n+1}+i\gamma, 2\rho_{n+1}+1, 2ikr)\}, \end{aligned} \qquad \ldots\ldots(13)$$

where
$$N_n = \frac{1}{2}\frac{|\Gamma(\rho_{n+1}+1+i\gamma)|}{\Gamma(2\rho_{n+1}+1)}e^{\frac{1}{2}\pi\gamma}\{(i\gamma'+n+1)(\rho_{n+1}-i\gamma)\}^{-1/2},$$

and
$$\rho_n = \sqrt{(n^2 - \lambda^2)}, \qquad \lambda = Z\mathbf{e}^2/\hbar\mathbf{c}.$$

The corresponding phase is given by

$$\left.\begin{aligned} \exp(2i\eta_n) &= \frac{n+1+i\gamma'}{\rho_{n+1}-i\gamma}\frac{\Gamma(\rho_{n+1}+1-i\gamma)}{\Gamma(\rho_{n+1}+1+i\gamma)}\exp\{-\pi i(\rho_{n+1}-n-1)\}, \qquad n \geqslant 0. \\ \exp(2i\eta_{-n-1}) &= \frac{n-i\gamma'}{\rho_n - i\gamma}\frac{\Gamma(\rho_n+1-i\gamma)}{\Gamma(\rho_n+1+i\gamma)}\exp\{-\pi i(\rho_n - n)\}, \qquad n > 0. \end{aligned}\right\} \qquad \ldots\ldots(14)$$

Thus if
$$\mathscr{G}_n=\alpha^{-1/2}r^{\varrho_n+1}(a_{n0}+a_{n1}r+\ldots), \qquad \ldots\ldots(15)$$
then
$$a_{n0}=N_n(2k)^{\varrho_n+1}\{n+1+\rho_{n+1}+i(\gamma'-\gamma)\}. \qquad \ldots\ldots(16)$$
As ρ_{n+1} is not an integer, we obtain an independent irregular solution $\mathscr{H}_n$ by replacing ρ_{n+1} by $-\rho_{n+1}$ throughout. Hence
$$\mathscr{H}_n=\alpha^{-1/2}r^{-\varrho_n+1}(b_{n0}+b_{n1}r+\ldots), \qquad \ldots\ldots(17)$$
where
$$b_{n0}=M_n(2k)^{-\varrho_n+1}\{n+1-\rho_{n+1}+i(\gamma'-\gamma)\}, \qquad \ldots\ldots(18)$$
and M_n is obtained from N_n by replacing ρ_{n+1} by $-\rho_{n+1}$. Also
$$\exp 2i(\eta_n+\theta_n)=\frac{n+1+i\gamma'}{-\rho_{n+1}-i\gamma}\,\frac{\Gamma(-\rho_{n+1}+1-i\gamma)}{\Gamma(-\rho_{n+1}+1+i\gamma)}\exp\{-\pi i(-\rho_{n+1}-n-1)\}, \quad n\geqslant 0,$$
and hence
$$\exp 2i\theta_n=\frac{\rho_{n+1}-i\gamma}{-\rho_{n+1}-i\gamma}\,\frac{\Gamma(-\rho_{n+1}+1-i\gamma)}{\Gamma(-\rho_{n+1}+1+i\gamma)}\,\frac{\Gamma(\rho_{n+1}+1+i\gamma)}{\Gamma(\rho_{n+1}+1-i\gamma)}\exp 2\pi i\rho_{n+1}. \qquad \ldots\ldots(19)$$
This is clearly true for negative as well as positive n.

The analytical expressions for $\mathscr{G}_n$ and $\mathscr{H}_n$ are very unsuitable for numerical calculation. Hence equation (7) was solved directly by a numerical method (Mott and Massey 1949 c). Putting $V=-Ze^2/r$, (7) can be written
$$\left(\mu+\frac{\lambda}{r}\right)\frac{d^2S_n}{dr^2}+\left(\frac{2\mu}{r}+\frac{3\lambda}{r^2}\right)\frac{dS_n}{dr}$$
$$+\left\{\mu^2\nu+\frac{\lambda\mu(\mu+2\nu)}{r}+\frac{\lambda^2(2\mu+\nu)-n(n+1)\mu}{r^2}+\frac{\lambda^3-n(n+2)\lambda}{r^3}\right\}S_n=0, \qquad \ldots\ldots(20)$$
where $\mu=(W+\mathbf{m}\mathbf{c}^2)/\hbar\mathbf{c}$, $\nu=(W-\mathbf{m}\mathbf{c}^2)/\hbar\mathbf{c}$. The initial integration by the method of Frobenius gives
$$G_n=r^{-1+\varrho_n+1}\sum_{m=0}^{\infty}a_{nm}r^m, \qquad H_n=r^{-1-\varrho_n+1}\sum_{m=0}^{\infty}b_{nm}r^m, \qquad \ldots\ldots(21)$$
where the coefficients satisfy the recurrence relation
$$\mu^2\nu a_{nm}+\lambda\mu(\mu+2\nu)a_{n,m+1}+\{\lambda^2(\mu+\nu)+\mu(3+3\rho_{n+1}+n)+\mu(3+2\rho_{n+1})m$$
$$+\mu m^2\}a_{n,m+2}+\lambda\{9+6\rho_{n+1}+(6+2\rho_{n+1})m+m^2\}a_{n,m+3}=0. \qquad \ldots\ldots(22)$$
A similar relation holds for b_{nm}, if ρ_{n+1} is replaced by $-\rho_{n+1}$. The forward integration is then carried out on equation (8). This method checks itself very satisfactorily.

In calculating a_{n0} and b_{n0} the common factor $2^{-1/2}\exp(\frac{1}{2}\pi\gamma)$ can be omitted since (12) only contains the ratio A_n/B_n. Thus
$$a_{n0}=\frac{|\Gamma(\rho_{n+1}+1+i\gamma)|}{\sqrt{2}\Gamma(2\rho_{n+1}+1)}(2k)^{\varrho_n+1}\frac{n+1+\rho_{n+1}+i(\gamma'-\gamma)}{\{(n+1+i\gamma')(\rho_{n+1}-i\gamma)\}^{1/2}}$$
$$=\frac{|\Gamma(\rho_{n+1}+1+i\gamma)|}{\Gamma(2\rho_{n+1}+1)}(2k)^{\varrho_n+1}\left\{1+\frac{(n+1)\rho_{n+1}-\gamma\gamma'}{\rho_{n+1}^2+\gamma^2}\right\}^{1/2}, \qquad \ldots\ldots(23)$$
if numerator and denominator are multiplied by $n+1+\rho_{n+1}-i(\gamma'-\gamma)$, and similarly for b_{n0}.

Lastly, from (14) and (19),

$$\left.\begin{aligned}\eta_n=&\frac{\pi}{2}(n+1-\rho_{n+1})+\tfrac{1}{2}\arg(\rho_{n+1}+i\gamma)-\arg\Gamma(\rho_{n+1}+1+i\gamma)\\&+\tfrac{1}{2}\arg(n+1+i\gamma'),\qquad n\geqslant 0,\\ \eta_{-n-1}=&\frac{\pi}{2}(n-\rho_n)+\tfrac{1}{2}\arg(\rho_n+i\gamma)-\arg\Gamma(\rho_n+1+i\gamma)\\&-\tfrac{1}{2}\arg(n+i\gamma'),\qquad n>0,\end{aligned}\right\}\quad\ldots\ldots(24)$$

$$\theta_n=\pi(\rho_{n+1}+\tfrac{1}{2})-\arg(\rho_{n+1}+i\gamma)+\arg\Gamma(\rho_{n+1}+1+i\gamma)-\arg\Gamma(-\rho_{n+1}+1+i\gamma).\quad\ldots\ldots(25)$$

(iv) *Solution inside the Nucleus*

For the solutions inside the nucleus the different expressions for the potential for cases B and C must be substituted in (7).

Case B. $$V=-\frac{Ze^2}{R}\left(\frac{3}{2}-\frac{r^2}{2R^2}\right).$$

If the variable is changed to $\sigma=r^2/R^2$, equation (7) can be written

$$2(A\sigma^2-\lambda\sigma^3)\frac{d^2S_n}{d\sigma^2}+(3A\sigma-\lambda\sigma^2)\frac{dS_n}{d\sigma}$$
$$+\{-\tfrac{1}{2}An(n+1)+[\tfrac{1}{2}\lambda n(n-1)+B]\sigma+C\sigma^2+D\sigma^3+E\sigma^4\}S_n=0,\quad\ldots\ldots(26)$$

where

$$A=2\mu R+3\lambda,$$
$$B=\tfrac{1}{8}A\{4\mu\nu R^2+6\lambda R(\mu+\nu)+9\lambda^2\},$$
$$C=-\tfrac{1}{4}A\lambda\{R(\mu+\nu)+3\lambda\}-\tfrac{1}{8}\lambda\{4\mu\nu R^2+6\lambda R(\mu+\nu)+9\lambda^2\},$$
$$D=\tfrac{1}{8}A\lambda^2+\tfrac{1}{4}\lambda^2\{R(\mu+\nu)+3\lambda\},$$
$$E=-\tfrac{1}{8}\lambda^3.$$

The initial integration gives for the regular solution

$$K_n^{\mathrm{B}}=\sigma^{n/2}\sum_{m=0}^{\infty}c_{nm}\sigma^m,\quad n\geqslant 0,\qquad K_n^{\mathrm{B}}=\sigma^{-(n+1)/2}\sum_{m=0}^{\infty}c_{nm}\sigma^m,\quad n<0,\quad\ldots\ldots(27)$$

where

$$\left.\begin{aligned}&Am(2m+2n+1)c_{nm}+[B-\lambda(m-1)(2m+2n-3)]c_{n,m-1}+Cc_{n,m-2}+Dc_{n,m-3}\\&\qquad+Ec_{n,m-4}=0,\qquad n\geqslant 0,\\&Am(2m-2n-1)c_{nm}+[B-\lambda(m-2)(2m-2n-3)]c_{n,m-1}+Cc_{n,m-2}+Dc_{n,m-3}\\&\qquad+Ec_{n,m-4}=0,\qquad n<0.\end{aligned}\right\}\quad\ldots\ldots(28)$$

It is found that for the energy considered the series are sufficiently rapidly convergent for a forward integration to be unnecessary. Thus for $\sigma=1$,

$$\left.\begin{aligned} \mathscr{K}_n^{\mathrm{B}} &= R\left(\frac{R}{\mu R+\lambda}\right)^{1/2} K_n^{\mathrm{B}}, \\ \frac{d\mathscr{K}_n^{\mathrm{B}}}{dr} &= \left(\frac{R}{\mu R+\lambda}\right)^{1/2}\left\{\left[1+\frac{\lambda}{2(\mu R+\lambda)}\right]K_n^{\mathrm{B}}+2\frac{dK_n^{\mathrm{B}}}{d\sigma}\right\}, \\ \frac{d^2\mathscr{K}_n^{\mathrm{B}}}{dr^2} &= \frac{1}{R}\left(\frac{R}{\mu R+\lambda}\right)^{1/2} \\ &\times\left\{\left[\frac{3\lambda}{2(\mu R+\lambda)}+\frac{3\lambda^2}{4(\mu R+\lambda)^2}\right]K_n+\left(6+\frac{2\lambda}{\mu R+\lambda}\right)\frac{dK_n}{d\sigma}+4\frac{d^2K_n}{d\sigma^2}\right\}. \end{aligned}\right\} \qquad \ldots\ldots(29)$$

A check was carried out by substitution in equation (8).

Case C. $$V=-\frac{Ze^2}{R}.$$

Equation (7) becomes

$$\frac{d^2S_n}{dr^2}+\frac{2}{r}\frac{dS_n}{dr}+\left\{\kappa^2-\frac{n(n+1)}{r^2}\right\}S_n=0, \qquad \ldots\ldots(30)$$

where $\kappa^2=(\mu+\lambda/R)(\nu+\lambda/R)$. The regular solution of the equation is

$$K_n^{\mathrm{C}}=\left(\frac{\pi}{2\kappa r}\right)^{1/2}J_{n+\frac{1}{2}}(\kappa r),\quad n\geqslant 0;\qquad K_n^{\mathrm{C}}=\left(\frac{\pi}{2\kappa r}\right)^{1/2}J_{-n-\frac{1}{2}}(\kappa r),\quad n<0. \qquad \ldots\ldots(31)$$

Neglecting a constant factor,

$$\mathscr{K}_n^{\mathrm{C}}=rK_n^{\mathrm{C}}. \qquad \ldots\ldots(32)$$

(v) *The Second Radial Equation*

From equation (6), $$\alpha R_n=\frac{n}{r}S_n-\frac{dS_n}{dr}.$$

Therefore $$\mathscr{R}_n=r\alpha^{-1/2}R_n=\frac{1}{\alpha}\left(\frac{n+1}{r}\mathscr{S}_n-\frac{1}{2}\frac{\alpha'}{\alpha}\mathscr{S}_n-\frac{d\mathscr{S}_n}{dr}\right).$$

Thus for $r=R$,

$$R\alpha\mathscr{F}_n=\left\{n+1+\frac{\lambda}{2(\mu R+\lambda)}\right\}\mathscr{G}_n-R\frac{d\mathscr{G}_n}{dr}. \qquad \ldots\ldots(33)$$

The same relation holds for $\mathscr{E}_n$, $\mathscr{H}_n$ and for $\mathscr{D}_n^{\mathrm{B}}$, $\mathscr{K}_n^{\mathrm{B}}$ respectively. However, in case C,

$$R\alpha\mathscr{D}_n^{\mathrm{C}}=(n+1)\mathscr{K}_n^{\mathrm{C}}-R\frac{d\mathscr{K}_n^{\mathrm{C}}}{dr}. \qquad \ldots\ldots(33')$$

(vi) *Numerical Results*

The phase shifts ζ_n were calculated for $n=0, -2, 1, -3$, and it was found that, at the energy considered, only the first two phase shifts were significant. The differential cross sections were then calculated using (3) and (4). The results of the calculations are summarized in Tables 2 and 3 and also in the Figure, where $I_B(\theta)/I_A(\theta)$ and $I_C(\theta)/I_A(\theta)$ are plotted against θ.

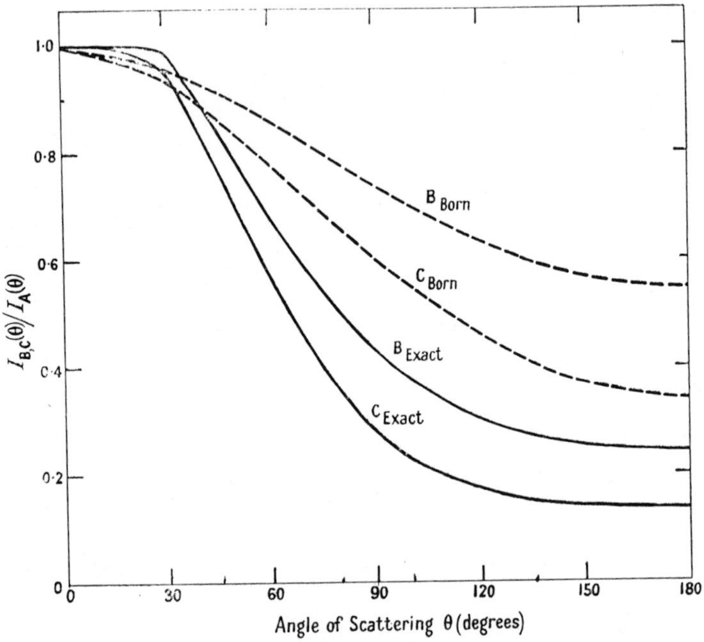

Angular distribution of the ratio of the differential cross sections for the two cases of the extended nucleus to that for the case of the point nucleus, for electrons of energy 40 mc^2 being scattered by gold nuclei.

(Full line —— exact calculation, dotted line - - - Born approximation.)

Table 2

Phases η_n^A for the case of the point nucleus, and phase shifts $\zeta_n^{B,C}$ for the difference in phase between the case of the point and that of the extended nucleus, for electrons of energy 40 mc^2 being scattered by gold nuclei.

n	η_n^A	$\zeta_n^B = \eta_n^B - \eta_n^A$	$\zeta = \eta_n^C - \eta_n^A$
0	0·415	−0·196	−0·271
−2	0·400	−0·195	−0·268
1	−0·234	−0·002	−0·004
−3	−0·242	−0·001	−0·004

Table 3

Differential cross sections for the case of the point nucleus and the two cases of the extended nucleus, for electrons of energy 40 mc^2 being scattered by gold nuclei.

θ (deg.)	30	45	60	90	120	150	180
$k^2 I_A(\theta)$	25·608	6·489	2·543	0·638	0·186	0·0377	0·00015
$k^2 I_B(\theta)$	25·268	5·463	1·735	0·277	0·056	0·0096	0·00005
$k^2 I_C(\theta)$	24·707	5·019	1·450	0·178	0·031	0·0052	0·000018

§4. CONCLUSION

The investigation has shown that, if 20 MeV. electrons are scattered elastically by gold nuclei, considerable deviations from calculations based on the Mott formulae should occur for angles greater than about 45°, showing up most clearly in the ratio of large to small angle scattering. These deviations should give some information about the charge distribution within the nucleus. For that purpose the models used in the present calculation have been chosen so that cases A and C are extreme possibilities, while case B is intermediary. However, because of the electrostatic repulsion of the charges inside the nucleus, the charge density is likely to increase with the radius, and so the true distribution is likely to be somewhere between models B and C. The deviations should therefore not be larger than those found for case C, and are unlikely to be smaller than those found for case B. Similar but probably slightly smaller effects are to be expected for light nuclei at about 40 MeV.

Note added in proof. Recently published preliminary experimental results by Lyman, Hanson and Scott (1950) on the scattering of 16·5 MeV. electrons by Be, C, Al, Cu, Ag, Au nuclei agree quite satisfactorily with the above calculations, when these have been adjusted to the lower energy (Elton 1950). The adjustment has been made more accurately since, and the results for gold and aluminium are given in Table 4, where the ratio $R_{B,C}=I_{B,C}(\theta)/I_A(\theta)$ is compared with the most recent experimental ratio $R_{exp}=I_{exp}(\theta)/I_A(\theta)$.

Table 4

θ (degrees)		30			90			150		
	Z	R_B	R_C	R_{exp}	R_B	R_C	R_{exp}	R_B	R_C	R_{exp}
Al	13	1·00	0·99	0·91	0·97	0·95	0·89	0·89	0·84	1·06
Au	79	0·99	0·97	0·87	0·52	0·35	0·59	0·41	0·32	0·43

ACKNOWLEDGMENTS

The author wishes to express his sincere thanks to Professor H. S. W. Massey for his suggestion of this problem and general guidance of the work.

REFERENCES

Bartlett, J. H., and Watson, R. E., 1940, *Proc. Amer. Acad. Arts Sci.*, **74**, 53.
Elton, L. R. B., 1950, *Phys. Rev.*, **79**, 412.
Lu, H., 1950, *Phys. Rev.*, **77**, 416.
Lyman, M., Hanson, A. O., Scott, M. B., 1950, *Bull. Amer. Phys. Soc.*, **25**, 3, and private communication.
McKinley, W. A., Jr., and Feshbach, H., 1948, *Phys. Rev.*, **74**, 1759.
Mott, N. F., 1929, *Proc. Roy. Soc.* A, **124**, 426; 1932, *Ibid.*, **135**, 429.
Mott, N. F., and Massey, H. S. W., 1949, *The Theory of Atomic Collisions*, 2nd edition (Oxford : University Press), (*a*) Chapter IV, §4; (*b*) Chapter VII, §3, (*c*) Chapter VII, §6.
Rose, M. E., 1948, *Phys. Rev.*, **73**, 279.
Sigrist, W., 1943, *Helv. Phys. Acta*, **16**, 471.
Van de Graaff, R. J., *et al.*, 1946, *Phys. Rev.*, **69**, 452; 1947, *Ibid.*, **72**, 678.
Wheeler, J. A., 1949, *Rev. Mod. Phys.*, **21**, 133.

PAPER 9

Z7. Interaction of Neutrons with Electrons in Liquid Bismuth. W. W. HAVENS, JR., L. J. RAINWATER, AND I. I. RABI, *Columbia University*.—The neutron electron interaction has been determined by measuring the cross section of liquid bismuth as a function of neutron wavelength. This cross section decreases by 3 percent between 0.33A and 1.33A. The change in cross section is caused by (a) neutron capture, (b) liquid scattering, (c) relative velocity effect, (d) neutron electron interaction. The spin dependent scattering is small because the total cross section of solid Bi is less than 0.5 barn at 5.5A. The capture cross section of this Bi is 0.035 barn at 0.026 ev, determined by the pile oscillator. The relative velocity correction is $0.011\lambda^2$. The liquid effect was investigated by Placzek, Nyboer, and Van Hove, who proved that the type of structure did not alter the liquid effect a great deal. The liquid correction used was $0.095\lambda^2$. After applying these corrections the residual change was attributed to the neutron electron interaction. The neutron electron cross section can be expressed in terms of the Born approximation by giving an interaction potential V acting over a volume τ. Assuming τ a spherical volume of radius 2.8×10^{-13} cm, V is (5300 ± 1000) ev. An uncertainty of 650 ev is due to statistical consideration, the additional uncertainty being due to the uncertainty in the corrections applied.

PAPER 10

The Electron-Neutron Interaction*

L. L. Foldy

Case Institute of Technology, Cleveland, Ohio

(Received June 18, 1951)

THE existence of a weak attractive interaction between electrons and neutrons has recently been reported by two groups of workers.[1,2] It was immediately recognized that such an interaction is to be expected on the basis of current meson theories of nuclear forces as a consequence of the partial dissociation of a neutron into a proton and virtual negative meson. Explicit calculations[3] have shown that an electron-neutron interaction of the required character and order of magnitude is indeed obtained on the basis of this assumption.

We wish to show first that an electron-neutron interaction of the desired character and magnitude can also be obtained as a direct consequence of attributing to a neutron an anomalous magnetic moment in the manner suggested by Pauli[4] without any further assumptions. The relativistic (one-particle) hamiltonian for such a neutron in an external electromagnetic field is

$$H=\beta M+\boldsymbol{\alpha}\cdot\mathbf{p}-\mu_N(e/2M)[\beta\boldsymbol{\sigma}\cdot\mathbf{H}-i\beta\boldsymbol{\alpha}\cdot\mathbf{E}],$$

where μ_N is the magnetic moment of the neutron measured in nuclear magnetons. On reducing this by a canonical transformation to the corresponding nonrelativistic hamiltonian by the method of Foldy and Wouthuysen[5] one obtains

$$H=\beta M+(\beta p^2/2M)-\mu_N(e/4M^2)\beta\,\mathrm{div}\mathbf{E}+\mu_N(e/4M^2)\beta\boldsymbol{\sigma}\cdot[\mathbf{p}\times\mathbf{E}-\mathbf{E}\times\mathbf{p}],$$

where we have retained terms up to order $(1/M)^2$. For the coulomb field of an electron located at the point $\mathbf{x}_e$, the above hamiltonian becomes

$$H=\beta M+(\beta p^2/2M)+4\pi\mu_N(e^2\beta/4M^2)\delta(\mathbf{x}-\mathbf{x}_e)+\cdots.$$

The term[6] containing the delta-function $\delta(\mathbf{x}-\mathbf{x}_e)$ is exactly of the form of the electron-neutron interaction. Expressing the interaction in terms of the well-depth V_0 of an equivalent[7] square well of radius e^2/mc^2, one obtains for V_0

$$V_0=\pi\mu_N(e^2/M^2)[(4\pi/3)(e^2/mc^2)^3]^{-1}=\tfrac{3}{4}\mu_N(\hbar c/e^2)^2(m/M)^2\,mc^2=3900\text{ ev},$$

where we have taken $\mu_N=-1.9$ nuclear magnetons. The above figure is to be compared with the experimental value:[2] $V_0=5300\pm1000$ ev.

We do not wish to imply that this is the correct explanation of the interaction, but we do wish to point out an important bearing of the above result on meson-theory calculations of the interaction. When one calculates the electromagnetic properties of nucleons according to meson theory by canonical transformations which remove the coupling of the mesons to the nucleon to any given order in the meson coupling constants, one obtains interaction terms representing the anomalous magnetic moment of the nucleon interacting with the magnetic field, together with its relativistic complement expressing the interaction of an electric dipole moment for the nucleon with the electric field, plus an additional term which gives rise to a direct electron-neutron interaction. In the calculations employing this method (Case, and Borowitz and Kohn) only the last term has been compared with the experimental interaction. Actually, the electric dipole moment term gives in second order an additional contribution which is exactly that found above[8] and which must be added to the direct term before the comparison with experiment is made. In the calculations performed by direct computation of neutron scattering by an external coulomb field (Slotnick and Heitler, and Dancoff and Drell) the extra term is automatically included in the computation. We believe that this extra term may account for the discrepancy between the results of Slotnick and Heitler and of Borowitz and Kohn which was noted in a footnote to the paper of the latter authors.

* Supported by the AEC.

[1] E. Fermi and L. Marshall, Phys. Rev. **72**, 1139 (1947).

[2] Rainwater, Rabi, and Havens, Phys. Rev. **72**, 634 (1947); Phys. Rev. **75**, 1295 (1949). Quoted experimental value taken from L. Wilets and L. C. Bradley, III, Phys. Rev. **82**, 285 (1951).

[3] M. Slotnick and W. Heitler, Phys. Rev. **75**, 1645 (1949); K. M. Case, Phys. Rev. **76**, 1 (1949); S. M. Dancoff and S. D. Drell, Phys. Rev. **76**, 205 (1949); S. Borowitz and W. Kohn, Phys. Rev. **76**, 818 (1949).

[4] W. Pauli, Revs. Modern Phys. **13**, 203 (1941).

[5] L. L. Foldy and S. A. Wouthuysen, Phys. Rev. **78**, 29 (1950).

[6] Note the similarity of origin of this term with the "Darwin" term for the hydrogen atom as derived in reference 5.

[7] By the equivalent square well is meant here one having the same volume integral for the potential and consequently giving the same scattering cross section in the Born approximation at very low energies.

[8] In this respect we disagree with the remarks of K. M. Case given at the beginning of Sec. VI of his paper referred to in footnote 3 above. A careful investigation is necessary before discarding terms proportional to the Dirac matrix $\boldsymbol{\alpha}$ on the grounds that they are velocity proportional, since they may give rise to velocity independent contributions in higher order.

PAPER 11

Scattering of 15.7-Mev Electrons by Nuclei*

E. M. Lyman, A. O. Hanson, and M. B. Scott†
Department of Physics, University of Illinois, Urbana, Illinois

(Received July 3, 1951)

Electrons removed from the 20-Mev betatron are focused to a 0.08-inch spot about 10 feet from the betatron by a magnetic lens. The electrons impinge on thin foils at the center of a highly evacuated scattering chamber having a diameter of 20 inches. Elastically scattered electrons, selected by a $\frac{3}{8}$ inch$\times$2 inch aperture, are focused by means of a 75° magnetic analyzer with 3 percent energy resolution and are detected by coincidence Geiger counters. Corrections are applied for multiple scattering and for energy losses which remove the electrons from the range of energies accepted by the detector arrangement. The scattering cross section for gold at 150° is found to be about 2.6 times that given by Mott's formula in the Born approximation and about one-half of that expected for the scattering by a point nucleus. This result is in good agreement with the calculations for electrons of this energy if the nuclear charge is assumed to be distributed uniformly throughout the nuclear volume.

The results for the scattering from C, Al, Cu, and Ag are also in agreement with the assumption of a uniformly distributed nuclear charge within the uncertainties involved in the theory and the experimental results.

INTRODUCTION

THE scattering of fast electrons by nuclei has been the subject of a large number of researches. The previous work in the energy range above 10 Mev has been done primarily with cloud chambers. The results are quite divergent but could be considered to be in qualitative agreement with theoretical calculations.[1]

At lower energies some accurate measurements have been made using electrons accelerated by an electrostatic generator to energies up to 2.25 Mev. These results, reported by Van de Graaff, Buechner, and Feshbach, for several elements and for a number of angles up to 50° are in good agreement with calculations.[2] The more recent work of Champion and Roy and that of Sigrist[3] indicate that the scattering at larger angles is also in agreement with calculations, although others report divergent results.[4]

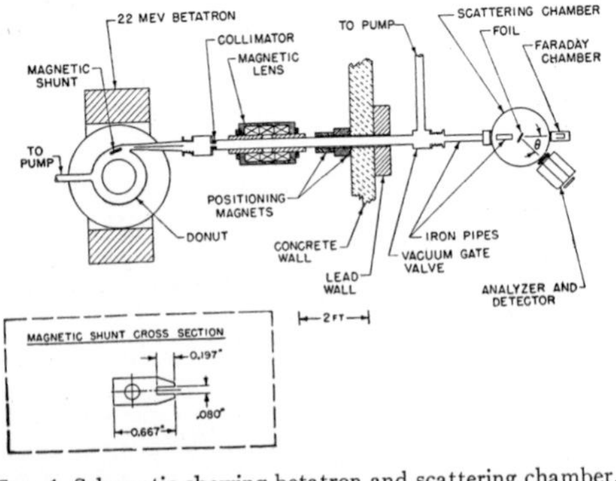

Fig. 1. Schematic showing betatron and scattering chamber.

It appears that the remaining discrepancies at these energies are due to experimental difficulties, and it will be assumed in this work that the scattering of electrons having energies up to 3 Mev are described by complete calculations[5,6] based on Mott's formulas for the scattering by a point charge.

At sufficiently high energies, Rose, and more recently Elton, have shown that the scattering of electrons by nuclei would be considerably modified by the fact that the size of the nuclear charge distribution is no longer small compared to the electron wavelength.[7]

An experimental investigation of the scattering of high energy electrons was made feasible by the successful extraction of the electron beam from the 20-Mev betatron. Preliminary results have been reported briefly[8] and have been compared with the accurate calculations by Elton.[9]

I. APPARATUS AND EXPERIMENTAL METHOD

Production, Extraction, and Focusing of the Electron Beam

The experimental arrangement is shown schematically in Fig. 1. When electrons accelerated in the betatron donut reach 15.7 Mev, as determined by a flux

* Supported by the joint program of ONR and AEC.

† Now at Massachusetts Institute of Technology, Cambridge 39, Massachusetts.

[1] Randels, Chao, and Crane, Phys. Rev. **68**, 64 (1945). See also reference 18, p. 83.

[2] Van de Graaff, Buechner, and Feshbach, Phys. Rev. **69**, 452 (1946); Buechner, Van de Graaff, Sperduto, Burrill, and Feshbach, Phys. Rev. **72**, 678 (1947).

[3] F. C. Champion and R. R. Roy, Proc. Phys. Soc. (London) **61**, 532 (1948); W. Sigrist, Helv. Phys. Acta **16**, 471 (1943).

[4] Alichanian, Alichanow, and Weissenberg, J. Phys. (USSR) **9**, 280 (1945); W. Bothe, Z. Naturforsch. **4a**, 88 (1949).

Note added in proof:—Paul and Reich have recently reported general agreement with theory at 2.2 Mev except for somewhat low values for gold at 90° and 120°. (Private communication. Work to appear in *Zeitschrift für Physik*.)

[5] J. H. Bartlett and R. E. Watson, Proc. Am. Acad. Arts Sci. **74**, 53 (1940).

[6] W. A. McKinley and H. Feshbach, Phys. Rev. **74**, 1759 (1948).

[7] M. E. Rose, Phys. Rev. **73**, 279 (1948).

[8] Lyman, Hanson, and Scott, Phys. Rev. **79**, 228 (1950); Phys. Rev. **81**, 309 (1951).

[9] L. R. B. Elton, Phys. Rev. **79**, 412 (1950); Proc. Phys. Soc. (London) **A63**, 1115 (1950).

integrating circuit,[10,11] an expansion pulse causes their orbit to spiral outward and enter a magnetic shunt, or field free region,[12] from which they are able to escape the betatron guide field. The shape of the iron laminations comprising the shunt is shown by the inset in Fig. 1. The laminations are separated by mica spacers and the stack, 3.5 in. long, is located tangentially, at a radius of 8.6 in. from the center of the donut. The injector is at a radius of 8.75 in. and the equilibrium orbit at 7.6 in. The radial position of the magnetic shunt is rather critical; if it is located at too large a radius, the electron beam fails to enter the slot in the shunt; while if it is at too small a radius, the orbit expands into the shunt prematurely before the electrons have reached full energy. The proper orientation of the shunt is accomplished by selsyn remote control while the betatron is in operation.

The spray of electrons emerging from the magnetic shunt is about 1° high and 6° wide. The most intense portion of this beam is selected by a collimator subtending 1°, and passed down the axis of a magnetic lens which focuses it into a spot 0.08 in. in diameter at a point about 10 feet from the betatron. Positioning electromagnets provide a means of fine adjustment of the vertical and horizontal position of the focal spot.

Scattering Chamber, Energy Analyzer, and Detectors

The electron beam enters the scattering chamber shown in Fig. 2 through one of the port holes spaced at intervals of 30° in the cylindrical wall and comes to a focus on the target foil at the center. A thick aluminum faraday chamber diametrically opposite the beam entrance port is connected to a vibrating reed electrometer and serves to measure the charge incident upon the foil. The scattered beam of electrons is selected by a rectangular aperture $\frac{3}{8}$ in. wide and 2 in. high, located in the chamber wall 10 inches from the scattering foil. After passing through the aperture they enter the magnetic analyzer which focuses them upon a group of Geiger counters in coincidence.

The chamber, defining aperture, magnetic analyzer, counters and their shielding are all mounted on a rotating platform with its axis of rotation at the center of the target foil. The angle of scattering is changed by detaching the entrance tube and faraday chamber, rotating the table to the new position, then reconnecting the tube and faraday chamber. During this process, the chamber is isolated from the betatron and diffusion pumps by a system of vacuum gates. While operating, there are no foils or windows anywhere in the path of the incident beam.

Target selection is accomplished remotely by a selsyn system which drives the target holder through 0-ring

[10] McElhinney, Hanson, Becker, Duffield, and Diven, Phys. Rev. **75**, 542 (1949).

[11] Katz, McNamara, Forsyth, Halsam, and Johns, Can. J. Research **A28**, 113 (1950).

[12] Skaggs, Almy, Kerst, and Lanzl, Radiology **50**, 167 (1948).

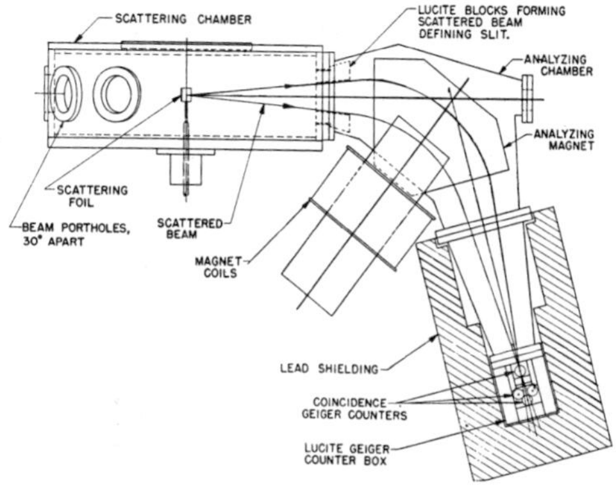

FIG. 2. Scattering chamber.

seals. The target holder has spaces for 10 target foils, a space for a piece of fluorescent x-ray screen used for observation of the beam position and focus, a blank space for transmitting the incident beam directly to the faraday chamber without intervening scattering material, and a 20-mil vertical tungsten wire used for alignment purposes. The scattering angle is read from a vernier scale attached to the stationary part of the framework supporting the rotating platform.

The magnetic analyzer focuses the elastically scattered electrons from the 0.08-inch beam incident on the scattering foils to a line about $\frac{1}{4}$ in. wide and 2 in. long. This beam is more than covered by the Geiger counter which has a diameter of $\frac{3}{4}$ in. and an active length of about 3 inches. The $\frac{3}{4}$-inch width of the Geiger counter corresponds to an energy range of 3 percent. Hence the maximum count obtained by varying the magnetic field will include all electrons which have lost less than 3 percent of the initial energy.

The field of the analyzer magnet is controlled to 0.1 percent by a servo system which derives its error signal by comparing the voltages developed in two rotating flip coils, one in the magnetic field and the other in a permanent magnet reference field. The position and nature of the focus of the analyzer magnet and its $H\rho$ calibration were determined by the well-known "hot-wire" method using No. 44 copper wire carrying about 1 ampere.

To eliminate serious interaction between the field of the analyzer magnet and the incident beam at large scattering angles, it was found to be necessary to shield the incident beam with iron pipe duct, both outside and inside the chamber.

Experimental Procedure

During the initial stages of extraction of the electron beam and alignment of the apparatus, a telescope, mirrors, and a piece of fluorescent x-ray screen were used to observe the beam position and intensity at various points in its path. First, the orientation of the magnetic shunt was adjusted to produce a small in-

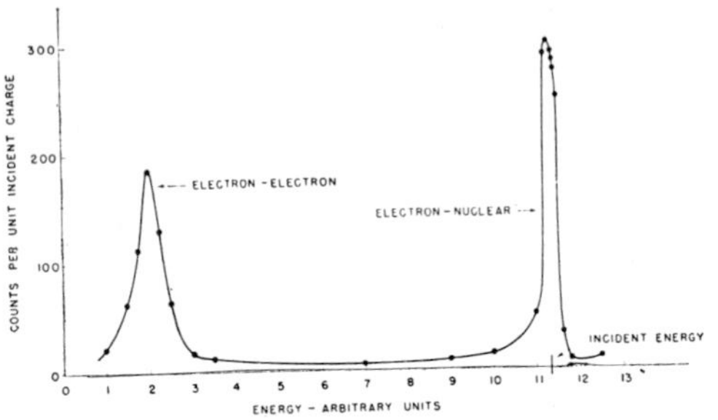

FIG. 3. Energy spectrum of 15.7-Mev electrons scattered at 30° by polystyrene (carbon). The ordinate represents the observed count as a function of the analyzer magnetic field, and does not represent the number of electrons per unit energy interval. The counters have a 3 percent resolution in energy.

tense spot at the exit port of the donut. Next, the duct leading to the scattering chamber was attached, evacuated, and oriented until maximum intensity was obtained at the chamber end. Further fine adjustment was continued with the magnetic lens current turned on, until a small, focused spot was formed centrally at the end of the duct and remained stationary upon reversal of the magnetic lens current, indicating coincidence of source, focal spot and axis of the lens. Under these conditions, the position of the beam was stable for slight variations in energy and magnetic lens current.

The final step in alignment consisted of locating the framework supporting the rotating platform and chamber so that the beam came to focus precisely at the center of the chamber. After careful visual alignment, exact centering was accomplished by placing the 20-mil vertical tungsten wire at the center of the chamber and measuring the beam scattered from it by an auxiliary ionization chamber at 30°. The position of the incident electron beam was then adjusted by the horizontal positioning electromagnet until the scattering was a maximum. It was necessary to repeat the centering adjustment at each scattering angle because of the slight interaction between analyzer field and incident beam.

The vernier dial reading corresponding to zero angle of scattering was determined by adjusting the chamber position until the beam passed centrally through the defining aperture into the detectors. Other scattering angles were read to 0.03° with reference to this position.

The shape and magnitude of the peak due to nuclear scattering and the background were determined for each foil at each angle of scattering. A typical complete spectrum is shown in Fig. 3.

Each point of the spectrum is the number of counts recorded (adjusted for counting-rate losses) while a given charge was being collected by the faraday chamber directly behind the foil. The faraday chamber was connected to a vibrating reed electrometer whose instrumental capacitance was increased by a calibrated polystyrene condenser connected between the input and inverse feedback terminals. With this connection, the charge was simply the product of voltage change and the capacitance, the effect of all other capacitances being degenerated to insignificance by the feedback.[13] The charge incident upon the foil was obtained from the charge measured by the faraday chamber and the foil transmission factor. The latter was determined by a series of measurements of the time required to collect a given charge, with the foil present and then absent, at constant beam intensity.

Shielding of the counter system from the x-ray background produced by the betatron was not difficult for scattering at 30°, but at 150° a foot-thick concrete wall and 6 inches of lead surrounding the counters were required.

II. TREATMENT OF DATA

The number of counts corresponding to the maximum of the approximately flat-topped elastic scattering peak for a given incident charge is a measure of the cross section for scattering at any particular angle. The fact that electrons were incident upon the foil in microsecond bursts 180 times per second, made it necessary to correct for the number of counts which correspond to more than one electron passing through the Geiger counters. This correction is given with sufficient accuracy by [14]

$$C = C_{obs}(1 + C_{obs}/360t), \tag{1}$$

where C_{obs} is the number of counts recorded in t seconds. This correction was applied individually to every observation. In taking the data the counting rate was kept sufficiently low so that this correction did not exceed 10 percent.

A cross section can be obtained from the usual relation

$$\sigma_{obs} = C/nN\Omega, \tag{2}$$

where C is the count corrected for the above losses minus the count with the scattering foil absent; n is the number of electrons incident on the foil as determined by the charge collected in the faraday chamber and the transmission ratio; N is the number of atoms/cm² in the path of the beam as determined by the weight of the foils and the angle between the normal to the foils and the direction of the incident beam; and Ω is the solid angle determined by the aperture defining the scattered beam.

In comparing experimental cross sections with theory, it was found to be convenient to adjust the observed cross section to take account of (1) the small range of scattering angle of the electrons admitted to the detectors because of the finite size of the defining aperture and the size and angle of convergence of the incident beam, (2) effects due to the finite thickness of the scat-

[13] Palevsky, Swank, and Grenchick, Rev. Sci. Instr. **18**, 298 (1947).
[14] C. H. Westcott, Proc. Roy. Soc. (London) **A194**, 508 (1948).

tering foils, and (3) the effect of radiation associated with the single scattering process itself.

In calculating the geometrical corrections, it is sufficient to assume that the angular dependence of the scattering cross section is given by the Mott formula (Born approximation),

$$\sigma_M(\theta)=(Ze^2/2mv^2)^2(\csc^4\tfrac{1}{2}\theta-\beta^2\csc^2\tfrac{1}{2}\theta). \quad (3)$$

It can be shown from spherical trigonometry that an electron which enters the defining aperture making an angle θ_x, θ_y with respect to the line connecting the center of the foil with the center of the aperture has been scattered through an angle

$$\theta=\theta_0+\theta_x+\tfrac{1}{2}\theta_y^2\cot\theta_0, \quad (4)$$

where θ_0 is the scattering angle to the center of the aperture. The average intensity (I_{Av}) over the aperture is then given by

$$I_{\text{Av}}=I_0\left(1+\frac{\sigma'}{\sigma}\frac{h^2}{24}\cot\theta_0+\frac{\sigma''}{\sigma}\frac{W^2}{24}\right), \quad (5)$$

where I_0 is the intensity at θ_0. W and h represent the angular width and height of the aperture and σ' and σ'' represent derivatives of Eq. (3) with respect to θ. The correction to the observed cross section calculated from this equation resulted in an increase of 1.8 percent at 30° and a decrease of 1.3 percent at 150°, for example. The corrections for the width and angular divergence of the incident beam are negligible when superimposed on the aperture correction.

Multiple scattering of electrons in the foil results in a correction very similar to the aperture correction. Chase and Cox[15] have shown that the combination of single scattering superimposed upon the multiple scattering results in an additional averaging over the multiple scattering distribution such that the average intensity at θ_0 is

$$I=I_0[1+\tfrac{1}{4}\epsilon^2(\sigma'\cot\theta_0+\sigma'')/\sigma], \quad (6)$$

where ϵ represents the rms value of the multiple scattering distribution (the $1/e$ width, if the distribution is gaussian). In the angular range where the cross section varies as $1/\theta^4$ the above correction agrees with the first order term of the expression given by Butler.[16]

At scattering angles exceeding 90°, the scattered electrons must emerge from the same side of the foil as they enter. The probability of a double large angle scattering becomes important because of the increased path length for electrons scattered into the plane of the foil.[17] For example, for scattering at 150° from a foil with its plane perpendicular to the incident beam, the ratio of intensity I to the intensity I_0 due to single scattering alone may be estimated as

$$I/I_0\approx 1+[\sigma(90°)\sigma(60°)N\pi/\sigma(150°)]. \quad (7)$$

Since the correction is proportional to the thickness of the foil, it may be determined experimentally by comparing the scattering from thick and thin foils of the same element. For the thin Au foil, the experimentally determined correction was 1.8±1.0 percent while that determined from Eq. (7) was 0.3 percent. The discrepancy between the experimental and calculated correction is in qualitative agreement with that observed by Shull, Chase, and Myers.[18]

The correction for loss of electrons from the peak due to energy degradation in electron-electron collisions is found by determining the fraction that lose more than 3 percent of their energy in traversing the foil. The effective cross section for loss of energy between E and $E+dE$ in a single small angle electron-electron collision is[19]

$$pdE\simeq(2\pi e^4/mv^2)(dE/E^2). \quad (8)$$

The cross section for the loss of more than 3 percent of the energy of a 15.7-Mev electron obtained by integrating Eq. (8) is found to be 0.542 barn per electron in the foil.

In addition to the correction for energy losses due to single electron-electron collisions, a small correction is included to account for the effect of double collisions in which the energy loss per collision is less than 3 percent.

The correction for loss of electrons from the peak due to energy degradation by radiation in small-angle nuclear collisions is found by calculating the number of photons produced whose energies exceed $0.03E_0$. For 15.7-Mev electrons, the number of such photons produced per Mev radiation loss by an electron is found from the bremsstrahlung spectrum to be 0.291 photon, where the total radiation loss is given by Heitler.[20] The fraction of electrons which lose 3 percent or more of their energy, and will therefore escape detection is approximately equal to 0.291 times the total radiation loss in the foil.

Superimposed on the energy losses of electrons in penetrating a foil, which are in all cases proportional to the thickness of the foil, is another radiative loss associated with the single large angle scattering being observed. This energy loss has a distribution qualitatively similar to the average bremsstrahlung spectrum radiated by electrons. There will therefore be no electrons which are scattered strictly elastically. Most will be scattered with small radiative losses and a certain number will fall out of the energy range ΔE accepted by the counters. This correction can be obtained from a calculation by Schwinger[21] which includes the reduction in cross section associated with the energy

[15] C. T. Chase and R. T. Cox, Phys. Rev. **58**, 246 (1940).
[16] S. T. Butler, Proc. Phys. Soc. (London) **A63**, 599 (1950).
[17] G. Goertzel and R. T. Cox, Phys. Rev. **63**, 37 (1943).
[18] Shull, Chase, and Myers, Phys. Rev. **63**, 29 (1943).
[19] Mott and Massey, *Theory of Atomic Collisions* (Oxford University Press, London, 1949), second edition, p. 369.
[20] Heitler, *Quantum Theory of Radiation* (Oxford University Press, London, 1945), second edition, p. 191.
[21] J. Schwinger, Phys. Rev. **76**, 790 (1949); see also reference 19, p. 379.

TABLE I. Typical corrections. Percent corrections added to observed cross sections for thin and thick gold foils.

	30°		60°		90°		120°		150°	
	Thin	Thick	Thin	Thick	Thin	Thick	Thin	Thick	Thin	Thick
Multiple scattering	−1.0	−5.9	−0.3	−1.8	−0.2	−1.3	−0.2	−1.0	−0.3	−1.8
Radiation straggling	0.4	1.7	0.4	1.9	0.5	2.3	0.4	1.9	0.4	1.7
Electron-electron straggling	0.1	0.3	0.1	0.4	0.1	0.5	0.1	0.4	0.1	0.3
Double scattering	0	0	0	0	0	0	−0.5	−2.9	−1.7	−10.1
Schwinger formula (9)	5.4	5.4	7.0	7.0	7.9	7.9	8.5	8.5	9.1	9.1
Aperture size	1.8	1.8	0.3	0.3	−0.1	−0.1	−0.3	−0.3	−1.3	−1.3

loss ΔE as well as the effect of the more complete treatment of the interaction of the electron with the radiation field. This reduction in the cross section is given by the equation

$$\delta=\frac{4}{137\pi}\left[\left(\ln\frac{E}{\Delta E}-\frac{13}{12}\right)\left(\ln\left[\frac{2p_0\sin\frac{1}{2}\theta}{K}\right]-\frac{1}{2}\right)+\frac{17}{72}+\tfrac{1}{2}\sin^2\tfrac{1}{2}\theta F(\theta)\right], \quad (9)$$

where, for this work, $F(\theta)$ may be taken as unity, $\Delta E/E=0.03$, and $p_0/K=31.7$. The large part of this correction can be seen to be associated with the radiative losses. In order to put the observed results in a form which is independent of the energy band ΔE, accepted by the detectors the observed cross sections have been increased by the factor $1/(1-\delta)$. Values of δ for various angles are given in Table I. These values are taken as the same for all materials, although the calculation is not expected to be accurate for high Z materials.

The magnitudes of the corrections applied to the observed scattering cross sections for a typical element at various angles are summarized in Table I. This table is also representative of the other foils, since they were chosen to have approximately the same NZ^2. It can be seen that the effect of multiple scattering and energy straggling is small, especially for the thin foil. The corrections for the radiation loss associated with large angle scattering (δ) and the aperture correction are independent of the scattering material. The effect of double scattering is appreciable only at 120° and 150°. As mentioned previously, the magnitude of this correction was estimated from the variation of the observed scattering from two foils of the same material having different thicknesses, and is rather uncertain. Since these corrections are considerably larger than those calculated for this effect the increased scattering attributed here to double scattering may in part have some other interpretation.

It should be pointed out that the data from the thicker foils were not considered as reliable as those from the thinner foils and were used primarily to check or to determine the corrections which were applied to the thin target data.

III. EXPERIMENTAL RESULTS

The scattering cross sections measured for C, Al, Cu, Ag, and Au at scattering angles ranging from 30° to 150° are given in Table II. The numbers of atoms/cm² of the scattering foils are listed in column 2. In column 3, row a, are the observed, unadjusted scattering cross sections at 30° in barns per unit solid angle while in column 3, row b, are the same cross sections corrected for the effects listed in Table I, except for the correction calculated from the Schwinger formula. (This correction is not a function of foil thickness.) In column 4, the estimated standard error is given for the cases of the thin foils. Similar data for the other angles are given in columns 5 to 12.

The results listed in Table II were obtained from the last of a series of 5 runs, taken over a period of a year, during which a great effort was made to decrease random errors and eliminate all sources of systematic error.

The estimated standard errors shown in Table II are based solely upon the sources of random error in the experiment. For the majority of the points, the error due to counting statistics is about 1.2 percent, but at 150° due to low count and large background, it is about 3 percent on the average. In the case of polystyrene, which gave the lowest ratio of counts to background, the error is 10 percent. The estimated error in reading the meter which measured the charge incident upon the foil is 1 percent, in determining the foil transmission factor, 1 percent, and in measurement of the scattering angle (because of the uncertainty in locating the exact position of the incident beam), 1 percent. The total random errors for most of the points are then estimated to be of the order of 2 percent.

The number of atoms/cm² in the foils was determined by weighing an accurately cut area of the foil. Most foils were uniform to within 1 percent. The thinnest gold foil (10^{-4} inch) exhibited a thickness variation of 2 percent over the region struck by the incident beam.

The solid angle of the scattered beam admitted to the detector was the same for all angles and any error in it would affect all data equally. Two types of material for defining the aperture were tried; Lucite, 3 inches thick with sides curved to match the electron trajectories and gold, $\frac{1}{16}$ inch thick, backed by lead. The scattering cross sections observed with the two types of apertures were identical to within 1 percent.

TABLE II. Observed and adjusted scattering cross sections.

		30°		60°		90°		120°		150°	
Element	$N/cm^2 \times 10^{20}$	σ	%	$\sigma \times 10^{+1}$	%	$\sigma \times 10^{+2}$	%	$\sigma \times 10^{+3}$	%	$\sigma \times 10^{+4}$	%
C	11.18 [a]	0.1501		0.08305		0.1230		0.2881		0.4500	
Polystyrene	[b]	0.1502	2.4	0.08340	2.0	0.1238	2.4	0.2887	3.4	0.4476	10
Al	3.050 [a]	0.7078		0.3940		0.6447		...		...	
	15.21 [a]	0.7126		0.3881		0.6571		1.455		2.652	
	3.050 [b]	0.7065	2.2	0.3951	2.0	0.6477	1.8	...		...	
	15.21 [b]	0.7017		0.3932		0.6713		1.455	2.1	2.510	4.5
Cu	2.339 [a]	3.663		2.271		3.860		8.680		14.00	
	6.895 [a]	3.785		2.311		3.737		8.685		15.68	
	2.339 [b]	3.615	2.2	2.283	1.9	3.899	1.8	8.651	2	13.48	3.9
	6.895 [b]	3.596		2.339		3.835		8.529		13.57	
Ag	0.3889 [a]	10.82		7.045		12.31		28.28		...	
	1.143 [a]	10.93		7.105		12.67		28.60		51.30	
	0.3889 [b]	10.78	2.3	7.057	2	12.36	1.8	28.27	2.2	...	
	1.143 [b]	10.74		7.165		12.79		28.43		48.83	3.2
Au	0.1726 [a]	33.67		25.30		49.65		134.2		323.5	
	0.7814 [a]	35.63		28.71		51.11		124.3		247.9	
	0.1726 [b]	33.49	2.2	25.36	2.0	49.87	2.1	133.9	2	228.8	3.8
	0.7814 [b]	34.25		28.84		51.87		122.2		223.5	

[a] Observed.
[b] Corrected for geometry, multiple scattering, $e-e$ collisions, double scattering at large angles, and radiation in small-angle collisions.

Other tests indicated that the counting rates were proportional to the area of the aperture.

The ability of the thick-walled aluminum faraday chamber to retain all of the electron charge collected by it was tested by placing a lead disk at the bottom of the chamber to increase the scattering and the number of x-rays produced by the incident beam. It was found that the total charge retained by the chamber was 3 percent less with the lead bottom than with the usual all-aluminum chamber. From this it was estimated that the loss of charge by the standard aluminum chamber was about 1 percent.

IV. THEORY

In order to discuss the observed results it is convenient to display the ratio of the observed scattering cross sections to that calculated from the simple Mott formula. This formula has already been given as Eq. (3) and accounts for the very large variations in the cross sections. It is expected to represent the observed scattering at small angles for all values of Z and the scattering at all angles for very low Z.

McKinley and Feshbach[6] have given another formula which is essentially a first-order correction to the simple Mott formula. By their relation the ratio of the coulomb scattering to that given by Eq. (3) is

$$\frac{\sigma}{\sigma_M} = 1 + \frac{\pi Z\beta \sin\theta/2[1-\sin(\theta/2)]}{137[1-\beta^2 \sin^2(\theta/2)]}. \qquad (10)$$

McKinley and Feshbach also obtained an expression involving terms to the fourth power of α, where $\alpha = Z/137$. These results, which will be referred to as the α^4 approximation, should be reliable for higher values of Z but are not good for the heavy elements where α is not small compared to unity.

The accurate evaluation of Mott's theory for the scattering of electrons by a heavy element is a difficult task and has been carried out in detail for ($Z=80$) by Bartlett and Watson using numerical methods,[5] and only recently for $Z=47$.[22]

The calculated values of σ_M and σ_c/σ_M for 15.7-Mev electrons are given in Table III. The values of σ_c/σ_M for carbon were calculated from Eq. (10). The values for copper are based on the α^4 approximation for $\beta=1$ as calculated by Acheson.[23] The values for silver are those given by Feshbach[22] and those for gold are obtained by a small extrapolation of the results of Bartlett and Watson to $Z=79$ and to $\beta=1$.[24]

A rough experimental check on the reliability of the calculations was made by reducing the energy of the electrons to 4.6 Mev during one of the runs at 150 degrees. Although the multiple and double scattering corrections were large the relative values were still fairly good for those foils where the corrections were about the same. The ratio of the scattering from gold and silver to that from aluminum was found to be in good agreement with the calculated ratio. The accuracy of these relative measurements was not high but the results lend support to the conclusion that the scatter-

[22] Private communication from H. Feshbach giving F and G. values for high energy electrons on silver.

[23] L. K. Acheson Jr., Phys. Rev. 82, 488 (1951). We are indebted to Professor Feshbach for informing us of these calculations before publication.

[24] We are indebted to Professor Bartlett for assistance in extrapolating the calculations so as to be applicable to gold at these energies.

TABLE III. Calculated values for scattering from a point charge. (σ_M in barns per steradian).

Z	$\beta^2=0.999$ 30°		60°		$E=31.72$ mc² 90°		Kinetic energy $=15.7$ Mev 120°		150°	
	σ_M	σ_c/σ_M	$\sigma_M\times10^2$	σ_c/σ_M	$\sigma_M\times10^2$	σ_c/σ_M	$\sigma_M\times10^4$	σ_c/σ_M	$\sigma_M\times10^4$	σ_c/σ_M
6	0.1481	1.029	0.855	1.045	0.1425	1.057	3.17	1.063	0.566	1.067
13	0.6950	1.069	4.01	1.112	0.6692	1.143	14.9	1.154	2.608	1.154
29	3.459	1.165	19.97	1.300	3.330	1.387	74.1	1.444	12.98	1.437
47	9.085	1.300	52.44	1.630	8.747	1.852	194.6	2.126	34.09	2.211
79	25.67	1.456	148.2	2.482	24.71	3.795	550	4.828	96.3	5.54

ing theory, when completely evaluated, is sufficient to describe the observed results at lower energies.

Since the wavelength for 15.7-Mev electrons is comparable with nuclear dimensions, the observed scattering is reduced somewhat from that expected for the scattering by a point charge.

For light nuclei where the Born approximation expresses the scattering with reasonable accuracy, the ratio of scattering from a uniform charge distribution of radius R to that from a point charge can be expressed by the relation,[7,9]

$$\sigma/\sigma_c=[(3/K^3R^3)(\sin KR-KR\cos KR)]^2 \quad (11)$$

where K is the change in wave number associated with the angle of scattering as expressed by the relation $K=(2p/\hbar)\sin\frac{1}{2}\theta=(1.64\times10^{12}\sin\frac{1}{2}\theta\ \text{cm}^{-1})$. Although this relation is not accurate for any but the lightest nuclei, it is useful in estimating the magnitude of the effect and the manner in which the cross section depends on the nuclear radius.

Elton and Acheson have treated the size effect in more detail and have derived expressions for the reduction in the cross sections which should be quite reliable. In particular, Acheson[23] has shown that the effect of the finite distribution of the nuclear charge can be expressed in terms of the change in a single phase shift δ_1 in what corresponds to the S wave. According to Acheson the ratio can be written

$$\frac{\sigma}{\sigma_c}=1+\frac{4\cos^2\frac{1}{2}\theta}{|G|^2}\mathrm{Re}\left[Ge^{-2i\chi_1}\left(\frac{e^{2i\delta_1}-1}{2i}\right)^*\right]+\frac{4\cos^4\frac{1}{2}\theta}{|G|^2}\sin^2\delta_1, \quad (12)$$

where G is the complex function determining the coulomb scattering in the approximation that $\beta=1$, χ_1 is the first-order phase shift for the scattering by a coulomb field, and $\delta_1=\eta_1-\chi_1$ is the change in the phase shift for the given charge distribution.

It may be pointed out that the ratio σ/σ_c is not independent of σ_c since $\sigma_c=\lambda\!\!\!^{-2}|G|^2\sec^2\frac{1}{2}\theta$. Therefore, a calculation which gives too small a value for σ_c will at the same time predict too large a decrease in the ratio σ/σ_c for any given charge distribution. The experimental values for σ/σ_c for a given element as a function of angle are sufficient to determine only one constant, namely, δ_1. It is, therefore, not possible to use these results to determine the nuclear radius as well as the charge distribution.

Since there are several methods of measuring nuclear radii the values of the phase shifts determined from the present experiments may be used to distinguish between various possible nuclear charge distributions. For a given nuclear radius the phase shift for the case where the nuclear charge is distributed over the surface of the nuclear volume will be about 50 percent larger than that for the charge distributed uniformly throughout the nuclear volume. The deviations from coulomb scattering [Eq. (12)] will also be different by about 50 percent for these two cases. The difference for the heaviest elements is large enough to be experimentally distinguishable at this energy.

Recent determinations of nuclear radii as obtained from the scattering of fast neutrons indicate that on the average the radii are given by the relation $R=1.37A^{\frac{1}{3}}\times10^{-13}$.[25] This radius does not include the range of nuclear forces and should represent the effective radius

TABLE IV. Theoretical and experimental ratios of the scattering to that from a point charge. (σ/σ_c).

		U	30°	S	U	60°	S	U	90°	S	U	120°	S	U	150°	S
C	Theory	0.996		0.993	0.984		0.976	0.972		0.952	0.956		0.928	0.927		0.910
	exp't		1.003			1.004			0.878			0.935			0.833	
Al	Theory	0.992		0.986	0.971		0.948	0.942		0.897	0.915		0.864	0.890		0.823
	exp't		1.006			0.952			0.920			0.925			0.917	
Cu	Theory	0.981		0.969	0.928		0.880	0.872		0.760	0.794		0.654	0.744		0.574
	exp't		0.948			0.945			0.916			0.884			0.795	
Ag	Theory	0.962		0.945	0.863		0.806	0.754		0.656	0.685		0.567	0.636		0.512
	exp't		0.966			0.887			0.828			0.747			0.712	
Au	Theory	0.991		0.973	0.77		0.672	0.57		0.425	0.45		0.292	0.39		0.262
	exp't		0.978			0.741			0.577			0.551			0.472	

[25] Cook, McMillan, Petersen, and Sewell, Phys. Rev. **75**, 7 (1949); J. DeJuren and N. Knable, Phys. Rev. **77**, 606 (1950); H. Lu, Phys. Rev. **77**, 416 (1950).

containing all nuclear particles. It does not necessarily follow that the nuclear protons are distributed over this entire volume but this is the simplest assumption.

The values for σ/σ_c as based on the work of Acheson are given in Table IV for cases of uniform and surface distributions.

V. DISCUSSION OF RESULTS

Before comparing the experimental results with the calculations of the previous section it is necessary to make the adjustment discussed previously for the effect of radiative losses associated with the observed scattering. The experimental arrangement used was not designed to check this effect accurately and hence there is only indirect experimental evidence that the correction as calculated by Schwinger and shown in Table I is correct. The agreement of the results with theory, however, is better when the radiative correction is applied. This is particularly true in the case of polystyrene and aluminum scatterers. A systematic error, such as an error in the energy of the incident beam or an error in measuring the charge incident on the foil, which could change all the observed cross sections uniformly might be wrongly interpreted in terms of a larger or smaller radiative correction. The tabulated values of δ are not expected to be accurate for high values of Z, but are used here since there are no better calculations available.

The experimental cross sections, therefore, have been adjusted for the radiative losses, δ, and are presented as ratios to the point charge scattering in Table IV. The adjusted data are shown in Fig. 4 as ratios to the simple Mott formula. This plot shows very clearly the way the scattering deviates from the simple formula. The adjusted data are presented as ratios to coulomb scattering in Fig. 5. The solid lines in this figure represent the theoretical values for a uniform nuclear charge distribution over a radius given by $1.45A^{\frac{1}{3}}\cdot 10^{-13}$ cm as used by Acheson.

Upon comparing the experimental results with the calculated values the following conclusions might be drawn. In the case of gold where the decrease in the scattering is the greatest, the results agree fairly well with the assumption that the charge is distributed uniformly over the usually accepted nuclear volume. It is apparent that the agreement would be somewhat better if a radius about 20 percent smaller than that shown in the figure is used. This indicates that the proton distribution might be more densely packed toward the center of the nucleus as suggested by Born and Yang.[26]

If it is assumed that the charge density is distributed uniformly over the surface of the nuclear volume, it is found that the observed phase shift would give a nuclear radius for gold almost a factor of two smaller than that usually accepted. Although there are reasons to expect a charge distribution which has the greatest density toward the outside of the nucleus, the present measurements seem to exclude this distribution. The decrease in the cross section for silver can also be explained in terms of a uniform distribution of charge over a 20 percent smaller radius.

It is difficult to say much about nuclear size in the cases of C, Al, and Cu since the reduction from coulomb scattering is small and of the same order of magnitude as the uncertainties in the measurements. The over-all

[26] M. Born and L. M. Yang, Nature **166**, 399 (1950).

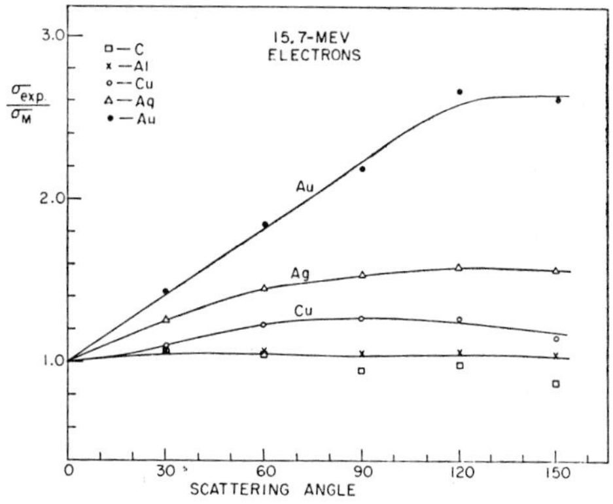

FIG. 4. Experimental results after correcting for counting losses due to radiation. The results are shown here as ratios to the simple Mott formula, Eq. (3). The solid lines sketched in are used merely to connect the experimental data and have no theoretical significance.

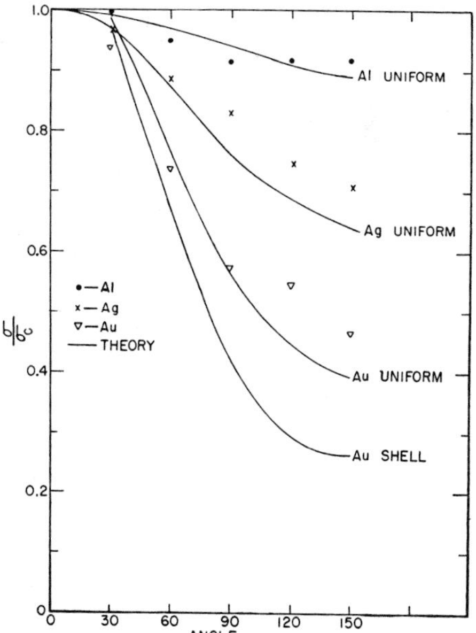

FIG. 5. Experimental results, as in Fig. 4, shown as ratios to coulomb scattering. The solid lines represent the calculated reduction in scattering for nuclear radii given by $R=1.45A^{\frac{1}{3}}\times 10^{-13}$. Calculated curves are shown only for a uniform distribution of charge except for gold where the curve for a surface charge distribution is also shown.

data, however, agree better with the calculations for a uniform charge distribution than for the surface charge distribution.

VI. SUMMARY

The observed scattering of 15.7-Mev electrons by nuclei is compared with the calculations of Elton and of Acheson on the assumption that the radiation correction as calculated by Schwinger is valid. The observed deviations from coulomb scattering are consistent with the picture of a nuclear charge whose radius is given by the neutron experiments and whose density distribution is uniform or possibly slightly greater at the center of the nucleus.

We wish to express our appreciation to S. M. Dancoff and S. Drell for preliminary discussions, to M. E. Rose and L. R. B. Elton for communications regarding the earlier results, and to J. H. Bartlett and J. M. Blatt for discussions regarding the calculations and the interpretation of the results. We are particularly indebted to H. Feshbach for his kind cooperation in sending us the results of pertinent calculations in advance of publication.

The valuable assistance of D. E. Riesen, J. R. Leiss, A. J. Petersen, A. R. Olson, F. Schroeder, K. Hiroshige, and B. A. Smith in building some of the equipment and carrying out the measurements is gratefully acknowledged.

PAPER 12

A Measurement of the Electron-Neutron Interaction

M. Hamermesh, G. R. Ringo, and A. Wattenberg*
Argonne National Laboratory, Chicago, Illinois
(Received December 10, 1951)

We have remeasured the electron-neutron interaction, using the method developed by Fermi and Marshall.[1] In this method the ratio of intensities of scattered thermal neutrons at 45° and 135° is measured. This ratio is given by,

$$\frac{d\sigma(45°)}{d\sigma(135°)}=1+\frac{2ba}{(\sigma_s/4\pi)}\left[\left(\int nFd\lambda\right)_{45°}-\left(\int nFd\lambda\right)_{135°}\right], \quad (1)$$

where b is the electron-neutron scattering amplitude, a is the coherent nuclear scattering amplitude, σ_s is the total nuclear scattering cross section, F is the atomic form factor of the monatomic scattering gas, and n is the wavelength distribution of the neutrons. If one describes the interaction in terms of a rectangular potential well whose radius is the classical electron radius, the measured b determines the depth V of this well. Fermi and Marshall obtained $V=300\pm5000$ ev.

Our experiment differed from the original experiment in the following ways:

1. Instead of one counter at 45° and one at 135° to the beam, two were used at each angle, placed symmetrically with respect to the beam. This has the effect of canceling small errors in the alignment of the apparatus.

2. The scattering was measured in krypton as well as xenon in order to check on systematic errors, and in argon to check on the correction for center-of-gravity motion.

3. The statistical accuracy was improved by using longer counts and higher neutron fluxes. Counting rates were between 500 and 5000 per minute.

4. The effect of angular spread of the beam on the measured 45°/135° ratio was eliminated by reducing the angular beam spread until the ratio approached a constant value. This can be seen in the data on Kr given in Table I. In the case of Xe, where the statistics are not so good, the second change is in the opposite direction to the first, indicating that we are not dealing with a geometrical effect since the geometrical correction is a monotonic function of the beam divergence.

In order to calculate b, it is necessary to know the value of the coherent amplitude a. Since a has never been measured for Kr and Xe, we assumed $a=0.90(\sigma_s/4\pi)^{\frac{1}{2}}$. For 90 percent of the elements with several important isotopes for which a has been measured,[2] this estimate is within 12 percent of the measured value. In addition, in the case of Kr, where nearly 75 percent of the material is in the form of even-even isotopes of small thermal neutron capture cross section, it is almost certain that the assumption is within 12 percent of correct, since all such isotopes show small incoherence.

Table I. Observed and calculated data.

Gas	Run	Average 45°/135°	Center-of-gravity motion factor[a]	Width of beam at center of chamber, inches	Angular spread of incident beam	$e-n$ scattering amplitude, cm	$e-n$ well depth, ev	
Argon	1	1.0781±0.0038	1.0705	3.32	±2.04°			
	2	1.0610±0.0019		3.32	±2.04°			
Krypton	1	1.0218±0.0005	1.0335	3.32	±2.04°			
	2	1.0294±0.0008		2.35	±1.28°	-1.87×10^{-16} (runs 2, 3)	5020 (±13%)	4100 (±10%) (Kr and Xe)
	3	1.0293±0.0012		1.40	±0.60°			
Xenon	1	1.0095±0.0003	1.0213	3.32	±2.04°			
	2[b]	1.0103±0.0012		3.32	±2.04°			
	3	1.0185±0.0012		2.10	±0.91°	-1.06×10^{-16} (runs 3, 4)	2860 (±16%)	
	4	1.0124±0.0021		1.40	±0.60°			

[a] Gas temperature = 27°C, neutron temperature = 36°C.
[b] Gas pressure ½ atmosphere.

The errors given in Table I are those obtained from the fluctuations in the ratios in the series of five to ten measurements in each run. They are not much larger than the statistical errors to be expected from the total number of counts. Our value for the potential well depth is $V=4100\pm1000$ ev, where about 500 ev of the uncertainty is the result of statistics and the remainder is our estimate of systematic errors caused mainly by our uncertainty about the coherent amplitude. This value is in reasonable agreement with the value $V=5300\pm1000$ ev obtained by Havens, Rainwater, and Rabi.[3] An attempt will be made to improve our statistical accuracy and to measure the coherent amplitudes involved.

We are indebted to T. R. Robillard and D. Meneghetti for help in constructing the equipment and taking the data.

* Now at Laboratory of Nuclear Science and Engineering, Massachusetts Institute of Technology, Cambridge, Massachusetts.
[1] E. Fermi and L. Marshall, Phys. Rev. 72, 1139 (1947).
[2] C. G. Shull and E. O. Wollan, Phys. Rev. 81, 527 (1951).
[3] Havens, Rainwater, and Rabi, Phys. Rev. 82, 345 (1951).

PAPER 13

S10. The Neutron-Electron Interaction.* J. A. Harvey, D. J. Hughes, and M. D. Goldberg, *Brookhaven National Laboratory.*—The electrostatic neutron-electron interaction, caused by the dissociation of the neutron into a proton and a meson, has been measured by a mirror experiment. A well-collimated beam of neutrons was totally internally reflected from a bismuth mirror covered with liquid oxygen. From the critical angle for total reflection for graphite filtered neutrons and the coherent scattering amplitudes of bismuth and oxygen we determine the neutron-electron interaction. The liquid oxygen is used since it balances the nuclear scattering of bismuth almost completely, with the result that the critical angle is very sensitive to neutron-electron scattering. The free atom cross sections of bismuth and liquid oxygen were determined from transmission measurements with pile neutrons filtered through various thicknesses of cadmium and boron. Since the incoherent scattering cross sections of bismuth and oxygen are small, the coherent amplitudes follow directly from the free atom cross sections. The neutron-electron interaction can be represented by a potential well equal to the radius of electron and a depth only a few hundred volts greater than the magnetic interaction of 3900 volts. This difference, which is the electrostatic interaction between the neutron and the electron, is smaller than the predictions of meson theory.

* Research carried out under contract with the AEC.

PAPER 14

The Electromagnetic Properties of Dirac Particles*

L. L. Foldy
Case Institute of Technology, Cleveland, Ohio
(Received April 30, 1952)

A framework for describing those electromagnetic properties of Dirac (spin-$\frac{1}{2}$) particles which determine their behavior when moving with low momentum through weak, slowly varying, external electromagnetic fields is developed by finding the most general interaction terms which may be added to the Dirac equation for the particle subject to appropriate conditions. The interaction terms found form an infinite series involving arbitrarily high derivatives of the electromagnetic potentials evaluated at the position of the particle. The series of coefficients of these terms then characterize the properties to be described and can be interpreted as a series of moments of the charge and current distribution associated with the Dirac particle. The first coefficient represents the charge of the particle, the second its anomalous magnetic moment. The third is a measure of the spatial extent of the particle's charge distribution, and the corresponding term describes a direct interaction of the particle and the charge distribution responsible for the external electromagnetic field. Higher terms in the series describe direct interactions of the particle with various derivatives of the external charge and current distribution. The correct physical interpretation of the terms is examined by transforming to the Foldy-Wouthuysen (nonrelativistic) representation of the Dirac equation. The consistency of the framework developed with field theoretical results is discussed. Limitations of the characterization derived here and the possibilities of broadening the assumptions on which it is based are examined. The results are applied in the succeeding paper to the interpretation of the electromagnetic properties of nucleons with particular reference to the electron-neutron interaction.

INTRODUCTION

The present paper represents an attempt to characterize those electromagnetic properties of Dirac (spin-$\frac{1}{2}$) particles which determine their behavior when moving with low momentum through weak, slowly varying, external (classically describable) electromagnetic fields. For this purpose we assume that the particle satisfies a Dirac equation with terms representing the interaction with the electromagnetic field. The nature of the interaction terms which are included is determined by the following restrictions:

(a) that the equation be Lorentz covariant and gauge invariant;

(b) that the interaction be linear in the electromagnetic potentials (the assumption of weak fields);

(c) that the terms do not vanish in the limit of vanishing momentum of the Dirac particle;

(d) that the charge and current distribution associated with the Dirac particle be sufficiently localized that its interaction with slowly varying electromagnetic fields may be expressed, through an expansion in "moments," in terms of the electromagnetic potentials and arbitrarily high derivatives of these potentials evaluated at the position of the particle.

It is found that an infinite series of interaction terms can be found satisfying these restrictions. The coefficients of these terms then characterize the electromagnetic properties of the particle which we set out to describe and represent "moments" of various order of the charge and current distribution associated with the Dirac particle. The first two coefficients can be identified with the charge and anomalous (intrinsic) magnetic moment of the particle. The next term represents a direct interaction between the Dirac particle and the charge distribution which produces the external electromagnetic field. In the case of the neutron, the coefficient of this term characterizes the "intrinsic" electron-neutron interaction, that is, the part of the electron-neutron interaction which is not associated with the anomalous magnetic moment of the neutron.[1] Higher terms in the series describe the interaction of the particle with various derivatives of the charge and current distribution responsible for the electromagnetic field.

While the characterization of the electromagnetic properties of a Dirac particle by the series of coefficients mentioned above is based on the assumption that the particle satisfies the Dirac equation, it is believed that this characterization actually has greater validity and applies under more general assumptions. The S-matrix formalism provides a more general domain in which this problem may be examined, and the author hopes to investigate this more general problem in the future.

Although from the point of view of Lorentz covariance it is convenient to deal with the problem posed above in the usual Dirac representation of the Dirac equation, the physical interpretation of the interaction terms is facilitated by passing to the Foldy-Wouthuysen (nonrelativistic) representation of the Dirac equation.[2] The coefficients defining the interaction take different forms in the two representations and in describing an electromagnetic property of a Dirac particle it is necessary to specify the representation which is being employed in order to avoid ambiguity. The confusion concerning the electron-neutron interaction stems primarily from a confusion of representations, and it is hoped that the discussion given below will clarify this point. The results derived herein are applied in the subsequent paper to an analysis of the significance of

* The research was supported by the AEC. Some of the results contained herein were presented at the Columbus, Ohio, meeting of the American Physical Society, March 20–22, 1952.

[1] L. L. Foldy, Phys. Rev. **83**, 688 (1951).
[2] L. L. Foldy and S. A. Wouthuysen, Phys. Rev. **78**, 29 (1950).

the experimental results on the electron-neutron interaction.

ELECTROMAGNETIC INTERACTIONS OF DIRAC PARTICLES

The Dirac equation for a free particle can be written in the form

$$H\psi=\{\beta mc^2+c\boldsymbol{\alpha}\cdot\mathbf{p}\}\psi=i\hbar\partial\psi/\partial t, \quad (1)$$

where $\mathbf{p}=-i\hbar\nabla$, $\mathbf{x}$ is the position vector of the particle, β and $\boldsymbol{\alpha}$ are the familiar Dirac matrices, and m, c, and $\hbar$ are, as usual, the rest mass of the particle, the velocity of light, and Planck's constant (divided by 2π), respectively. It is convenient for our purposes to write Eq. (1) in manifestly covariant form:

$$\gamma_\mu\partial\psi/\partial x_\mu+(mc/\hbar)\psi=0, \quad (2)$$

by the use of the relations

$$x_\mu=(\mathbf{x},\, ict), \quad \gamma_\mu=(-i\beta\boldsymbol{\alpha},\, \beta),$$

with the usual summation convention applying in expressions involving repeated Greek indices.

If the particle has a charge e and interacts with an electromagnetic field specified by the four-vector potential $A_\mu(x)$, then Eq. (2) must be modified to read

$$\gamma_\mu\partial\psi/\partial x_\mu+(mc/\hbar)\psi-i(e/\hbar c)\gamma_\mu A_\mu\psi=0. \quad (3)$$

Although the addition of this term appears to imply that the Dirac particle has only a point charge, it is well known that in its interactions the particle behaves as if it also had a magnetic moment of one Bohr magnetron. Pauli[3] showed that Eq. (3) can be still further modified so as to represent a particle having an arbitrary magnetic moment by adding to the left side the term $-(i\mu/\hbar c)\gamma_\mu\gamma_\nu(\partial A_\mu/\partial x_\nu-\partial A_\nu/\partial x_\mu)$, whereupon the particle behaves as if it had an "anomalous" moment μ in addition to its "normal" moment.

One may inquire as to the degree to which one can add further interaction terms to Eq. (3) without destroying its relativistic covariance and gauge invariance. One easily finds that a great variety of terms may be added. If one restricts oneself to such terms as satisfy the conditions specified in the introduction, namely, terms which are linear in the electromagnetic potentials, which depend on these potentials and their derivatives evaluated only at the position of the particle, and which do not vanish in the limit of vanishing momentum of the particle (quasi-static interactions) and hence do not involve derivatives of the wave function, then one can easily construct all possible terms. This calculation is given in the appendix; the result for the most general equation is[4]

$$\gamma_\mu\frac{\partial\psi}{\partial x_\mu}+\frac{mc}{\hbar}\psi-\frac{i}{\hbar c}\sum_{n=0}^{\infty}\left[\epsilon_n\square^n\gamma_\mu A_\mu+\mu_n\square^n\gamma_\mu\gamma_\nu\left(\frac{\partial A_\mu}{\partial x_\nu}-\frac{\partial A_\nu}{\partial x_\mu}\right)\right]\psi=0, \quad (4)$$

where $\square$ stands for the d'Alembertian operator:

$$\square=\partial^2/\partial x_\sigma\partial x_\sigma=\nabla^2-\partial^2/c^2\partial t^2.$$

The coefficients ϵ_n and μ_n are constants characterizing the interactions, of which ϵ_0 may immediately be identified as the electric charge of the Dirac particle and μ_0 as its anomalous magnetic moment. The higher terms in the series represent a direct interaction between the Dirac particle and the charge and current distribution which produces the external electromagnetic field as may be seen by employing the equations

$$\square A_\mu=-4\pi j_\mu, \quad F_{\nu\mu}=\partial A_\mu/\partial x_\nu-\partial A_\nu/\partial x_\mu, \quad (5)$$

with

$$j_\mu=(\mathbf{j},\, i\rho), \quad F_{\nu\mu}=(\mathbf{H},\, i\mathbf{E}),$$

to rewrite Eq. (4) in the form

$$\gamma_\mu\frac{\partial\psi}{\partial x_\mu}+\frac{mc}{\hbar}\psi-\frac{i}{\hbar c}\left\{\epsilon_0\gamma_\mu A_\mu+\mu_0\gamma_\mu\gamma_\nu F_{\nu\mu}-4\pi\sum_{n=1}^{\infty}\left[\epsilon_n\square^{n-1}\gamma_\mu j_\mu+\mu_n\square^{n-1}\gamma_\mu\gamma_\nu\left(\frac{\partial j_\mu}{\partial x_\nu}-\frac{\partial j_\nu}{\partial x_\mu}\right)\right]\right\}\psi=0. \quad (6)$$

The remainder of this paper is concerned with a more direct physical interpretation of these interaction terms.

However, before proceeding with this aspect of the problem, we wish to comment briefly on the domain of validity of an equation of the type (4). It is very unlikely that there exist any real particles which satisfy an equation of this type rigorously. However, it is not necessary that the equation be satisfied rigorously for the characterization of the electromagnetic structure of the particle by the coefficients ϵ_n and μ_n to be valid. In fact we may assume that the interaction terms in (4) must be treated only by first-order perturbation theory (Born approximation) since we have limited ourselves to the case of terms linear in the electromagnetic field. In this case, Eq. (4) may be used to calculate the S-matrix in the Born approximation for the elastic scattering of the Dirac particle in an external electromagnetic field, and the elements of the S-matrix will then depend on the coefficients ϵ_n and μ_n in a definite way. Equation (4) may then be considered as reduced to playing the role of an equation which gives the same S-matrix for weak electromagnetic fields as will be yielded by some more elaborate and fundamental theory. That Eq. (4) can actually play such a role is demonstrated by the usual treatment of the problem of

[3] W. Pauli, Revs. Modern Phys. **13**, 203 (1941).

[4] That the meson theory expression for the modification of the convection current of a nucleon due to interaction with mesons can be put into the form of the term in ϵ_1 in Eq. (4) was pointed out to the author by Professor F. Villars in a private communication.

the modification of the interaction of a nucleon with an electromagnetic field due to the interaction of the nucleon with a meson field. In this case an equation of the form (4) can be written down with determined values of the coefficients which will yield the same result in the Born approximation for the elastic scattering part of the S-matrix as is yielded by the more fundamental methods of field theory. The characterization by the coefficients ϵ_n and μ_n of certain of the electromagnetic properties of a Dirac particle may thus have a domain of validity much wider than would be indicated by the basis on which it was derived. This is the reason for our earlier remark that it would be of interest to reinvestigate this problem directly from the point of view of the S-matrix and its invariance properties rather than from a wave equation.

PHYSICAL INTERPRETATION OF THE DIRAC EQUATION

The physical interpretation of the interaction terms contained in Eq. (4) requires considerable care; that this is the case can already be seen in the special case represented by Eq. (3), for an examination of this equation itself would lead one to the conclusion that the interaction of the Dirac particle with the electromagnetic field is simply that of a point electric charge. Actually, as mentioned above, it is well known that the Dirac particle described by this equation exhibits in its electromagnetic interactions not only the properties of a point charge but also more complex properties, ordinarily characteristic of a particle possessing an extended charge and current distribution, as, for example, a magnetic moment.

As has been demonstrated in a previous publication,[2] the electromagnetic properties of a Dirac particle may be exhibited in a very direct way by transforming the Dirac equation into a new representation in which states of positive and negative energy for the particle are separately represented by two-component wave functions. The unitary transformation which generates the new representation leads to the introduction of a new position operator (the Newton-Wigner position operator[5]) for the particle which can more readily be identified with the conventional position operator for a particle. The modification in form of the electromagnetic interaction of the particle can then be traced directly to the fact that the interaction in the new representation is expressed in terms of the electromagnetic potentials and their derivatives evaluated at this new position which is displaced by a finite distance from the Dirac position which occurs in the usual representation of the Dirac equation. Actually, in the presence of interaction, the generating function for the transformation to the new representation can only be obtained as a series expansion in powers of the Compton wavelength of the particle and consequently the Hamiltonian occurring in the new form of the Dirac equation is also obtained as a power series in the same parameter. Details of the transformation are given in the reference quoted and hence will not be discussed here. If the transformation is carried out on Eq. (3), the Dirac equation takes the form[6]

$$\left\{\beta mc^2+\frac{\beta}{2m}\left(\mathbf{p}-\frac{e}{c}\mathbf{A}\right)^2+e\varphi-\frac{e\hbar}{2mc}\beta\boldsymbol{\sigma}\cdot\mathbf{H}+\frac{e\hbar}{8m^2c^2}\left[\boldsymbol{\sigma}\cdot\left(\mathbf{p}-\frac{e}{c}\mathbf{A}\right)\times\mathbf{E}-\boldsymbol{\sigma}\cdot\mathbf{E}\times\left(\mathbf{p}-\frac{e}{c}\mathbf{A}\right)\right]-\frac{e\hbar^2}{8m^2c^2}\operatorname{div}\mathbf{E}+\cdots\right\}\psi=i\hbar\frac{\partial\psi}{\partial t}, \quad (7)$$

where we have retained terms to order $(\hbar/mc)^2$ relative to the rest energy of the particle. It will be noted that the electromagnetic interaction is now expressed in a relatively complicated way but that one may immediately recognize the physical significance of the various terms:

(a) The term

$$e\varphi-(e\beta/2mc)[(\mathbf{p}-e\mathbf{A}/c)\cdot\mathbf{A}+\mathbf{A}\cdot(\mathbf{p}-e\mathbf{A}/c)]$$

represents the interaction of a point charge e with the electromagnetic field.

(b) The term $-(e\hbar/2mc)\beta\boldsymbol{\sigma}\cdot\mathbf{H}$ expresses the interaction of a magnetic moment of one Bohr magneton with the magnetic field.

(c) The term

$$(e\hbar/8m^2c^2)[\boldsymbol{\sigma}\cdot(\mathbf{p}-e\mathbf{A}/c)\times\mathbf{E}-\boldsymbol{\sigma}\cdot\mathbf{E}\times(\mathbf{p}-e\mathbf{A}/c)]$$

represents the "spin-orbit" coupling associated with this magnetic moment; it arises from the fact that the motion of the magnetic moment gives rise to an electric moment for the particle which interacts with the electric field.

(d) The term $-(e\hbar^2/8m^2c^2)\operatorname{div}\mathbf{E}$ (the so-called "Darwin" term)[7] can be interpreted in the following way: if the charge of the particle is not concentrated at a point but is spread out over a small spherical volume, then the first-order correction to the point charge interaction is represented by this term. Since $\operatorname{div}\mathbf{E}=4\pi\rho$, where ρ is the density of charge giving rise to the external electromagnetic field, this term expresses a direct interaction of the Dirac particle with the charge distribution generating the external electromagnetic field.

(e) Higher order terms in the series which have not been written down describe interaction terms depending

[5] T. D. Newton and E. P. Wigner, Revs. Modern Phys. **21**, 400 (1949).

[6] The last section of the paper quoted in reference 2 contains a number of errors and misprints in its equations. The correct form of Eq. (36) of that reference is given in Eq. (7) of the present paper.

[7] C. G. Darwin, Proc. Roy. Soc. (London) **A118**, 654 (1928). The term we call the Darwin term is not identical with that introduced by Darwin in this reference. The difference is due to the fact that Darwin does not write his spin-orbit coupling term as a Hermitian operator.

on higher derivatives of the electromagnetic fields evaluated at the Newton-Wigner position of the particle. All such terms can be written as for (d) above directly in terms of the charge and current distributions which generate the external electromagnetic field. For example, the next term in the series is proportional to $\beta\boldsymbol{\sigma}\,\text{curl}\,\mathbf{j}$, where $\mathbf{j}$ is the current density generating the external electromagnetic field.

The direct physical interpretation of the various terms occurring in the Hamiltonian is possible since the wave function for the Dirac particle in a state of definite energy is just the usual Pauli wave function with well-known properties.

We can then interpret physically the interaction terms in our more general equation (4) by transforming it into the same representation. The methods given in the reference quoted above are directly applicable here, and we only quote the result:

$$\left\{\beta mc^2+\frac{\beta p^2}{2m}+\sum_{n=0}^{\infty}\left[\left\{\epsilon_n+\frac{\hbar}{2mc}\mu_{n-1}+\frac{1}{2}\left(\frac{\hbar}{2mc}\right)^2\epsilon_{n-1}\right.\right.\right.$$
$$\left.+\cdots\right\}\Box^n\varphi-\left\{\mu_n+\frac{\hbar}{2mc}\epsilon_n+\frac{1}{2}\left(\frac{\hbar}{2mc}\right)^2\mu_{n-1}\right.$$
$$\left.\left.\left.+\cdots\right\}\Box^n\beta\boldsymbol{\sigma}\cdot\mathbf{H}\right]\right\}\psi=i\hbar\frac{\partial\psi}{\partial t}. \quad (8)$$

In writing down this equation we have again indicated explicitly only those terms which are of no higher order than $(\hbar/mc)^2$ relative to the rest energy term. Also, in view of the fact that we have omitted terms nonlinear in the electromagnetic field and interaction terms which vanish for vanishing momentum of the particle in Eq. (4), we have likewise omitted such terms in Eq. (8). This explains the absence of the point-current term and the spin-orbit coupling term (for example) in this last equation.

We can now analyze the physical significance of the various interaction terms in Eq. (8). It will be noted that they fall into two general classes—electric interactions and magnetic interactions. In particular, we may note:

(a) The term $\epsilon_0\varphi$ represents the usual point charge interaction of the particle with the scalar potential which allows us immediately to identify it with the electric charge of the particle.

(b) The term $\{\mu_0+(\hbar/2mc)\epsilon_0\}\beta\boldsymbol{\sigma}\cdot\mathbf{H}$ represents the interaction of a magnetic moment of magnitude $\mu_0+(\hbar/2mc)\epsilon_0$ with the magnetic field. Since $(\hbar/2mc)\epsilon_0$ represents just the normal moment for the particle, μ_0 can immediately be identified with the anomalous or "intrinsic" magnetic moment of the particle.

(c) The term $\{\epsilon_1+(\hbar/2mc)\mu_0+\frac{1}{2}(\hbar/2mc)^2\epsilon_0\}\Box\varphi$ has just the form of a "Darwin" term ($\Box\varphi=-\text{div}\mathbf{E}=-4\pi\rho$) and so represents a direct interaction of the particle with the charge density of the sources of the electromagnetic field. It consists of three contributions, the part depending on $\frac{1}{2}(\hbar/2mc)^2\epsilon_0$, which is just the ordinary Darwin term, a contribution depending on $(\hbar/2mc)\mu_0$ and therefore arising from the anomalous magnetic moment, and an "intrinsic" part depending on ϵ_1. To have a name for this last quantity we shall call it the "intrinsic" Darwin coefficient for the particle. In the case of the neutron, it determines the "intrinsic" electron-neutron interaction, that is, the portion of this interaction not accounted for by the anomalous moment of the neutron.

(d) Further terms in the series have a character similar to the higher order terms described briefly in our earlier example. It will be noted that every coefficient ϵ_n or μ_n in the Dirac representation of the equation appears not only in the coefficient of the corresponding term in the Foldy-Wouthuysen representation but in the coefficients of all succeeding terms.

It is thus apparent that the same electromagnetic interaction which is described by the set of coefficients $\epsilon_0, \mu_0, \epsilon_1, \cdots$ in the Dirac representation is described by the alternate set of coefficients ϵ_0, $\mu_0+(\hbar/2mc)\epsilon_1$, $\epsilon_1+(\hbar/2mc)\mu_0+\frac{1}{2}(\hbar/2mc)^2\epsilon_0$, $\cdots$ in the Foldy-Wouthuysen representation. Although the latter coefficients have the more direct physical interpretation, it is presumed that the coefficients in the Dirac representation should be regarded as having the more fundamental significance. The important point, however, is that it is necessary to specify the representation of the Dirac equation to which one is referring in order to describe unambiguously the electromagnetic properties of a Dirac particle.

DISCUSSION

The development presented above may be considered to be a phenomenological description of certain electromagnetic properties of Dirac particles. In this sense it represents a framework into which may be fitted either empirical or theoretical values of the characterizing coefficients. Of course there is no binding reason why values of the coefficients determined empirically cannot be considered to be intrinsic properties of the particle which cannot be determined by any more fundamental theory, but this would represent a very unsatisfying conclusion. It is the general hope that the values are actually determined through the interactions of the particle with quantized fields; that the latter is very probably the true state of affairs is strongly suggested by the recent developments in the quantum electrodynamics of the electron. In spite of the fact that the rather unsatisfactory device of infinite renormalizations must be employed in this theory, one cannot ignore the fact that all observed electromagnetic properties of the electron find a correct quantitative prediction in terms of only two fundamental parameters, the observed charge and mass of this particle.

PAPER 15

The Electron-Neutron Interaction*

L. L. Foldy
Case Institute of Technology, Cleveland, Ohio
(Received April 30, 1952)

The known electromagnetic properties of nucleons, assuming that the electron-neutron interaction is fundamentally of electromagnetic origin, are fitted into the phenomenological framework developed in the preceding paper and the results compared with predictions of weak coupling meson theories. The detailed comparison shows that the intrinsic electron-neutron interaction is somewhat smaller than predicted and it is suggested that even in the more favorable cases, the rough agreement as to order of magnitude may be largely due to a fortuitious cancellation of different contributions, which may easily be upset when higher order effects are included in the theory. Even apart from the detailed calculations, it is indicated that the observed intrinsic electron-neutron interaction is considerably smaller than order-of-magnitude expectations from general meson-theoretical principles. The results emphasize the importance of more accurate experimental determinations of the electron-neutron interaction, since a smaller value of the intrinsic interaction will either pose a very stringent test for any meson theory or require a critical re-evaluation of our present ideas regarding nucleonic structure. Some phenomena related to the electron-neutron interaction and the possibility that the intrinsic interaction may be nonelectromagnetic in origin are briefly discussed.

RECENT measurements of the magnitude of the electron-neutron interaction by Hughes[1] and by Hamermesh, Ringo, and Wattenberg,[2] when combined with previous measurements by Fermi and Marshall,[3] and by Havens, Rabi, and Rainwater,[4] now yield an experimental value for this quantity with an accuracy of the order of ten percent. While there appear prospects for a considerably more accurate determination of this interaction in the near future, it appears appropriate, nevertheless, to examine the available results in the

* This work was supported by the AEC. Some of the results contained herein were presented at the Columbus, Ohio, meeting of the American Physical Society, March 20–22, 1952. [Phys. Rev. **86**, 646 (1952)].

[1] D. J. Hughes, New York meeting of the American Physical Society [Phys. Rev. **86**, 606 (1952)].

[2] Hamermesh, Ringo, and Wattenberg, Phys. Rev. **85**, 483 (1952).

[3] E. Fermi and L. Marshall, Phys. Rev. **72**, 1139 (1947).

[4] Havens, Rainwater, and Rabi, Phys. Rev. **82**, 345 (1951).

light of current notions concerning the origin of this interaction at the present time. Such an examination as given in this paper indicates the possibility of a rather severe conflict between these experimental results and current ideas which ascribe the electron-neutron interaction to the charge cloud of virtual mesons surrounding the neutron. The importance of further and more accurate measurements of the electron-neutron interaction is thus emphasized.

We begin with a summary of experimental results concerning the electromagnetic properties of nucleons and their characterization in the phenomenological scheme developed in the preceding paper. The results are then compared with expectations from meson theory and some of the difficulties discussed. Finally the possibility of a nonelectromagnetic origin of the electron-neutron interaction is considered and some other phenomena which bear on this question are briefly discussed.

At the present time we have experimental knowledge concerning four purely electromagnetic properties of nucleons, namely, (1) the charge on the proton $=|e|$ where e is the electronic charge, (2) the magnetic moment of the proton $=2.7896$ nuclear magnetons, (3) the magnetic moment of the neutron $=-1.9135$ nuclear magnetons, and (4) the electron-neutron interaction. The last quantity is a short range interaction between a neutron and an electron which is given (perhaps prematurely) an electromagnetic interpretation by considering it to be a direct interaction of the neutron with the charge density responsible for an electromagnetic field. The experimental determinations of this interaction have been executed only in the case where this charge density is that associated with electrons in atoms, hence the ascription of the name electron-neutron interaction. Its magnitude is usually specified by the convention of giving the magnitude of the potential which must extend over a spherical volume of radius equal to the classical electron radius e^2/mc^2 which will give the same scattering matrix element at low energies as does the actual interaction.[5] The experimental determinations of this potential V_0 are given in Table I together with their weighted mean. At present we have no information concerning the corresponding interaction for the proton.

TABLE I. Experimental determinations of the electron-neutron interaction V_0.

Investigators	V_0, ev
Fermi and Marshall	-300 ± 5000
Havens, Rabi, and Rainwater	-5300 ± 1000
Hughes	-4200 ± 700
Hammermesh, Ringo, and Wattenberg	-4100 ± 1000
Weighted mean	-4400 ± 400
Contribution of magnetic moment	-4080
Residual (intrinsic interaction)	-320 ± 400

[5] The use of the classical electron radius is very arbitrary and somewhat inappropriate, since this radius presumably has nothing to do with the actual range of the interaction. In fact, as will be clearer later, the Compton wavelength of the neutron would be a considerably more appropriate radius to employ.

We may note first by a comparison of these results with the phenomenological framework developed in the preceding paper[6] for characterizing electromagnetic properties of Dirac particles, that this framework is adequate for the description of experimental results. Thus for the proton we may immediately identify ϵ with the charge of the proton and μ_0 with the anomalous magnetic moment of the proton:

$$\epsilon_0{}^p=|e|,\quad \mu_0{}^p=1.7896|e|\hbar/2Mc.$$

We have no information concerning the values of the succeeding coefficients $\epsilon_1{}^p$, $\mu_1{}^p$, etc.

Correspondingly, we have for the neutron the identifications:

$$\epsilon_0{}^n=0;\quad \mu_0{}^n=-1.9135|e|\hbar/2Mc.$$

The electron-neutron interaction, however, allows us to obtain a rough value for the next coefficient $\epsilon_1{}^n$. To obtain this we note that the volume integral of the term in $\mathrm{div}\mathbf{E}=-\Box\varphi$ in Eq. (8) of the preceding paper, where $\mathbf{E}$ is the electric field due to an electron, may be immediately identified with V_0 multiplied by the volume over which it is assumed to exist:

$$\frac{4\pi}{3}\left(\frac{e^2}{mc^2}\right)^3 V_0=|e|\left\{\epsilon_1{}^n+\frac{\hbar}{2Mc}\mu_0{}^n+\frac{1}{2}\left(\frac{\hbar}{2Mc}\right)^2\epsilon_0{}^n\right\}.$$

The last term in the brackets on the right vanishes for the neutron, and the second term in the brackets, as shown in a previous publication,[7] accounts for -4080 ev of the observed potential V_0. The remainder -320 ± 400 ev then yields for $\epsilon_1{}^n$ the value

$$\epsilon_1{}^n=-(0.08\pm0.10)|e|(\hbar/Mc)^2.$$

Before discussing these results further we compare them with the predictions obtained from meson theory in the limit of weak coupling.[8] A direct comparison is made somewhat difficult by the fact that the meson theory results depend on the value of the coupling constant assumed. To circumvent this difficulty we have tabulated in Table II the values of the ratios $\epsilon_1{}^n/(\mu_0{}^n\hbar/2Mc)$ and $\mu_0{}^p/\mu_0{}^n$ which, in weak coupling theory, are independent of the choice of coupling constant. However, it must be remembered that this

[6] L. L. Foldy, Phys. Rev. **87**, 688 (1952) (preceding paper).

[7] L. L. Foldy, Phys. Rev. **83**, 688 (1951). The difference between the present value quoted for the contribution of the neutron's magnetic moment and that quoted in this reference (-3900 ev) is due simply to the use of very rough values for fundamental constants in the previous calculation. The present value should be correct to approximately 1 ev. See also G. Breit, Proc. Nat. Acad. Sci. U. S. **37**, 837 (1951).

[8] J. M. Luttinger, Phys. Rev. **74**, 893 (1948); M. Slotnick and W. Heitler, Phys. Rev. **75**, 1645 (1949); Helv. Phys. Acta **21**, 1645 (1949); K. M. Case, Phys. Rev. **76**, 1 (1949); S. M. Dancoff and S. D. Drell, Phys. Rev. **76**, 205 (1949); S. Borowitz and W. Kohn, Phys. Rev. **76**, 818 (1949); B. D. Fried (to be published).

will no longer be the case if higher order terms in the meson theory were retained. Calculations have been made for the neutral, charged, and symmetrical scalar and pseudoscalar theories. The calculations for the neutral theory have been omitted from Table II since they lead to zero neutron magnetic moment and zero electron-neutron interaction.

An examination of the table shows immediately that it is not possible to fit simultaneously the nucleon magnetic moments and the electron-neutron interaction to the observed results by any choice of the coupling constant in any of these theories. The best fit is provided by the charged pseudoscalar theory but this can hardly be taken as evidence for its validity. Of particular interest, however, is the sensitivity of the electron-neutron interaction to the type of meson theory. There is a difference of a factor of thirty between the results in the scalar and the pseudoscalar theories. The pseudoscalar result is somewhat smaller than one would expect on rough dimensional grounds and this suggests that its smallness is at least partly the result of an accidental cancellation. This conjecture appears to be substantiated by some calculations of the author of the value of the ratio $\epsilon_1^n/(\mu_0^n\hbar/2Mc)$ as a function of the ratio of meson to nucleon mass. These calculations indicate this quantity is positive for small mass ratio but becomes negative for larger mass ratios, and the result passes through zero not far from the experimental ratio of pi-meson to nucleon mass. This is an important point, since if we do have an accidental near cancellation in the pseudoscalar theory, it is likely to be upset when other effects (higher order corrections, for example) are included and the discrepancy with the experimental value thereby increased. The smallness of the observed intrinsic electron-neutron interaction would then be a very stringent test for any meson theory. In this connection, the discrepancy by a factor of one hundred (even apart from the discrepancy in sign) between the experimental value of $\epsilon_1^n/(\mu_0^n\hbar/2Mc)$ and that predicted by the scalar meson theory would seem to be a strong argument against this theory, since it indicates that either the meson charge cloud in this theory is far too extended or the region over which the currents that give rise to the anomalous moment are distributed is far too compact.[9]

The discrepancies between the experimental results and meson theory calculations is not too surprising in view of the other well-known deficiencies of meson theory. However, there is nevertheless a rather striking anomaly in the experimental results which can be stated in a manner which is independent of any direct reference to meson theory. We may see this by remembering that at the present time we know of only two electromagnetic interactions of the neutron (remembering that the neutron has no electric charge) which are

[9] This is due, of course, to the fact that in the scalar theory, the charge cloud is produced principally by the mesons, but the mesons do not contribute to the magnetic moment.

TABLE II. Comparison of experimental results on electromagnetic properties of nucleons with predictions of weak coupling meson theories.[a]

Theory	$\epsilon_1^n/(\mu_0^n\hbar/2Mc)$	μ_0^p/μ_0^n
Symmetrical pseudoscalar	0.318	−0.128
Charged psuedoscalar	0.318	−0.422
Symmetrical scalar	−9.05	0.627
Charged scalar	−9.05	0.088
Experimental	0.08±0.10	−0.935

[a] The theoretical values in this table have been compiled from the publications listed in reference 8.

measured by the two fundamental parameters: μ_0^n the magnetic moment of the neutron, and ϵ_1^n the intrinsic Darwin coefficient which measures the intrinsic electron-neutron interaction. The ratio of these two parameters ϵ_1^n/μ_0^n is a quantity of the dimensions of a length and represents the only "electromagnetic radius" of the neutron of which we have present knowledge. The experimental ratio is $\epsilon_1^n/\mu_0^n=(0.04\pm0.05)\hbar/Mc$ and is, therefore, twenty-five times smaller than the "mechanical radius" of the neutron given by the neutron's Compton wavelength. This is certainly much smaller than would be expected from any *a priori* notions. This odd disparity can be demonstrated in another way: if we assume that q represents the effective distributed electric charge of the neutron and that the charge and current of the neutron are both spread over a spherical volume whose radius is of the order a, then we would expect

$$\epsilon_1^n\sim qa^2, \quad \mu_0^n\sim qa.$$

Solving these for q and a we find

$$a\sim\epsilon_1^n/\mu_0^n\sim 0.04\hbar/Mc, \quad q\sim(\mu_0^n)^2/\epsilon_1^n\sim -25|e|,$$

which is a result quite out of line with current notions. If we assume that the effective distributed charge of the neutron is actually of the order of $-|e|$, then we must assume that the charge density of the neutron is spread over a region whose radius is of the order of 1/25 of the radius of the region over which the current density of the neutron is distributed.

The situation is not quite so dark as painted above, however, when we note that in the pseudoscalar meson theory we find also a small theoretical value for the ratio ϵ_1^n/μ_0^n, namely, $0.16\hbar/Mc$. An explanation for the smallness of this result may be formulated as follows: In the pseudoscalar theory, the emission of a negative meson by a neutron (which simultaneously is converted into a proton) is accompanied by a relatively large recoil of the proton. Hence, not only is the negative meson charge spread out over a finite volume, but so also is the positive proton charge. If the spatial spread of the two is nearly the same, the intrinsic electron-neutron interaction will be considerably reduced over its value when the recoil of the proton is neglected. Hence the smallness of the interaction in the pseudoscalar theory probably results from a cancellation between the negative meson charge distribution and the positive proton charge distribution. This conjecture is substantiated by the fact that the intrinsic electron-neutron interaction changes sign when the meson mass becomes comparable with the nucleon mass, indicating that in this case because of the larger proton recoil, the proton charge is actually spread over a larger volume than the meson charge. Also in line with this explanation is the fact that in the scalar theory where the proton recoil is relatively smaller, the computed electron-neutron interaction is considerably larger than in the pseudoscalar theory. However, it should also be mentioned that the failure of the pseudoscalar meson theory to give approximately equal but opposite anomalous magnetic moments to the proton and neutron, as observed experimentally, seems also to be due to the large nucleon recoil effects;[10] this would suggest a difficulty in formulating a meson theory which simultaneously yields a small intrinsic electron-neutron interaction and approximately equal and opposite anomalous magnetic moments for the proton and neutron.

Our discussion above has been based on the assumption that the intrinsic electron-neutron interaction is essentially an electromagnetic interaction between the neutron and the charge density producing an external electromagnetic field. If this is a valid assumption, then the short range interaction of the neutron with an electron is not specific to the electron but would be present in the interaction of the neutron with any charged particle to the same magnitude but with a sign corresponding to an attraction between the neutron and negatively charged particles and repulsion between the neutron and positively charged particles. It is, in principle, possible to detect this interaction in the case of the neutron-proton interaction, but the presence of the large specifically nuclear interaction whose exact nature is not known makes this unfeasable at the present time.[11] The possibility of detecting a neutron-positron interaction or the interaction of a neutron and mu-mesons also appears very remote at the present time in view of the experimental difficulties. The interaction of the neutron and charged pi-mesons is also obscured, in this case by a strong meso-nucleonic interaction of nonelectromagnetic origin about which we also know very little. Hence, it is not likely that we may verify the assumption that the observed intrinsic electron-neutron interaction is fundamentally electromagnetic in nature in the near future. The detection of an intrinsic short range electron-proton interaction arising from a nonzero intrinsic Darwin coefficient for the proton is also possible, in principle, from its contribution to the Lamb shift in hydrogen, but some refinement of both the theory and the experimental determination of the Lamb shift is necessary before a quantitative result would be available. In this connection, we may also note that the electron-neutron interaction would be expected to contribute to a very slight difference in the Lamb shift in hydrogen and deuterium.

Before closing, it is of interest to consider the possibility of nonelectromagnetic contributions to the intrinsic electron-neutron interaction. Since this interaction can be formulated as a direct interaction between two incoming and two outgoing Dirac particles, one can express it in a manner analogous to beta-decay interactions—that is, as a Fermi-type coupling. It might even be expected that, in view of other evidence for the existence of a universal Fermi interaction between all fermions, such a Fermi interaction between neutrons and electrons should exist. If the entire intrinsic electron-neutron interaction were represented by a Fermi interaction, the corresponding coupling constant G_{e-n}, which has the dimensions erg-cm^3, can be directly identified with the observed volume integral of the electron-neutron interaction and, expressed in absolute units, would have the value

$$G_{e-n} = (5\pm 6)\times 10^{-47} \text{ erg-cm}^3.$$

Comparing this with the Fermi constant for beta-decay $G_\beta = 2.5\times 10^{-49}$ erg-cm^3 we see that the observed intrinsic electron-neutron interaction is, at most, two orders of magnitude greater than beta-decay interactions, and, in fact, the large error in the experimental results does not yet preclude the possibility of them being identical. If the last possibility were actually the case, then the intrinsic electron-neutron interaction would have a magnitude of only 1.6 ev.

We summarize with the observation that the intrinsic electron-neutron interaction is somewhat smaller than would be expected on the basis of semiquantitative conclusions obtained from meson theory. Its experimental determination is not yet sufficiently precise to indicate how much of a hurdle this fact represents for meson theory, and the need for more precise measurements is clearly indicated. Should the interaction turn out to be appreciably smaller than -300 ev, a real challenge will be presented to currently popular forms of meson theory, since it appears that only a rather unlikely accidental cancellation of contributions to the interaction would lead to a predicted interaction as small as this. In such an eventuality, a complete and critical re-evaluation of our current ideas concerning the structure of nucleons would be necessitated.

[10] K. M. Case, Phys. Rev. **76**, 1 (1949).
[11] See, however, J. Schwinger, Phys. Rev. **78**, 135 (1950).

PAPER 16

The Neutron-Electron Interaction*

D. J. HUGHES, J. A. HARVEY, M. D. GOLDBERG, AND MARILYN J. STAFNE
Brookhaven National Laboratory, Upton, New York
(Received March 10, 1953)

AFTER it was pointed out by Foldy[1] that approximately 4000 ev (well depth for e^2/mc^2 range) of the neutron-electron interaction could be attributed to the neutron moment, it was clear that more accurate measurements were necessary in order to isolate the electrostatic dissociation effect arising from the meson charge distribution. At this time an experiment was already under way at Brookhaven designed to increase the experimental accuracy by means of mirror reflection of neutrons. Previous measurements had utilized the variation of scattering cross section with angle[2] or with wavelength[3] to detect the form factor behavior of the electron scattering. The observed effects in each case were small and of the same order of magnitude as various corrections. Since the form factor is exactly unity for mirror reflection, however, the neutron-electron scattering is observed at its maximum value. Fortunately, the use of a balancing technique makes the critical angle for total reflection a sensitive measure of the neutron-electron interaction.

The experimental arrangement used was one in which the critical angle is measured for total reflection of long wavelength neutrons at the interface of bismuth and liquid oxygen. As the nuclear scattering (per unit volume) of oxygen and bismuth differ by only two percent while the electron scattering is much stronger in bismuth, the index of oxygen relative to bismuth is to a large extent determined by the electron scattering amplitude. A highly collimated neutron beam, Fig. 1, filtered through graphite, was incident on the interface at an adjustable angle of the order of a few minutes of arc. The critical angle was measured by techniques developed for other mirror experiments.[4] The measurement consists essentially of an observation of the incident angle at which the reflected intensity drops suddenly, this angle being the critical angle for the cut-off wavelength (6.7A) of the incident filtered neutrons. In order to determine the critical angle accurately, the experimental points (Fig. 1) are compared to a calculated curve that takes into account the finite reflectivity beyond the critical angle and the resolution of the incident neutron beam (about 0.25 minutes of arc). The final value, based on several measurements similar to that illustrated in Fig. 1, is 3.64±0.04 minutes.

The equation relating the critical angle to the coherent bound scattering amplitude a is

$$\frac{\pi}{\lambda^2}\theta_c^2 = N_{\mathrm{Bi}}a_{\mathrm{Bi}}\left\{\frac{N_{\mathrm{O}}a_{\mathrm{O}}}{N_{\mathrm{Bi}}a_{\mathrm{Bi}}}-1\right\}+\{N_{\mathrm{Bi}}Z_{\mathrm{Bi}}-N_{\mathrm{O}}Z_{\mathrm{O}}\}a_e, \qquad (1)$$

where N is the number of nuclei per cm^3, λ the neutron wavelength, and the subscripts O, Bi, and e refer to oxygen, bismuth, and the electron. This equation consists of three parts: the first involving the measured critical angle, the second the coherent amplitudes, and the last the neutron-electron interaction. Since the nuclear amplitudes of oxygen and bismuth are nearly equal, the two terms on the right-hand side of the equation are of the same order of magnitude. In order to reach reasonable accuracy in the electron amplitude, the coherent nuclear amplitudes must be measured with much higher accuracy. These amplitudes are obtained from the free atom cross sections by application of the reduced mass factor and subtraction of incoherent scattering.

It is not necessary to measure the absolute values of the free atom cross sections of oxygen and bismuth, for it is only the ratio that enters into the result in a sensitive way. This ratio was

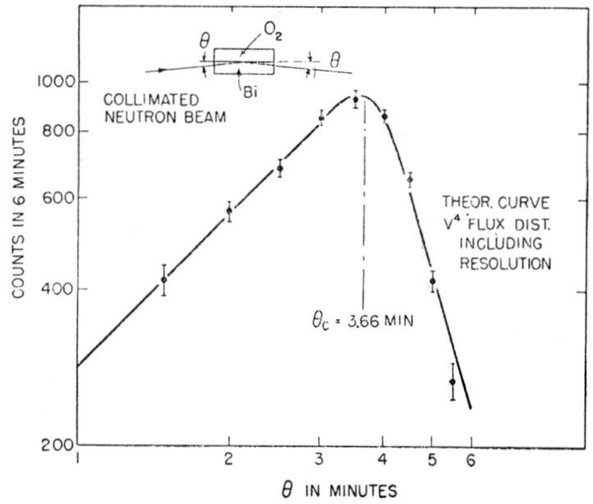

FIG. 1. Intensity of neutrons reflected from oxygen-bismuth interface as a function of incident angle.

measured by transmission for neutrons of average energy 8 ev: these neutrons being produced by a boron difference measurement for a pile neutron beam. Two nearly identical beams were used, and the intensity was measured after passage through samples of oxygen and bismuth, one in each beam. The intensities were again measured after the samples were alternated. In this method the cross-section ratio was corrected for several tenth-percent effects still present at an energy of 8 ev: the crystal interference, paramagnetic scattering, residual neutron-electron scattering, and Doppler effects. A small correction was also made for the incoherent scattering of bismuth, measured by transmission for long wavelength neutrons.[5]

The numerical results, $\theta_c = 3.64\pm0.04$ minutes and $N_{\mathrm{O}}a_{\mathrm{O}}/N_{\mathrm{Bi}}a_{\mathrm{Bi}} = 1.0204\pm0.0008$, when substituted into Eq. (1), give $a_e = 1.40\times10^{-16}$ cm, corresponding to a well depth of 3860±370 ev. The errors include statistics as well as uncertainty in the various constants in Eq. (1). Assuming the legitimacy of the Foldy effect, we conclude that the electrostatic meson dissociation effect can be no more than a few hundred volts. There have been several recent discussions[6] of possible explanations for the magnitude of the observed effect, but none of these seems able to account satisfactorily for the measured result. We wish to express thanks to G. W. Johnson, H. R. Muether, and R. C. Garth, who have been of great assistance at various stages of the work.

* Work carried out under contract with the U. S. Atomic Energy Commission.

1 L. L. Foldy, Phys. Rev. 83, 688 (1951); references to previous theoretical work may be found in this paper; further discussion of the magnetic moment contribution has been given by G. Breit, Proc. Natl. Acad. Sci. 37, 837 (1951); B. D. Fried, Phys. Rev. 86, 434 (1952); 88, 1142 (1952); S. Borowitz, Phys. Rev. 86, 567 (1952); L. L. Foldy, Phys. Rev. 87, 693 (1952).

2 E. Fermi and L. Marshall, Phys. Rev. 72, 1139 (1947); Hamermesh, Ringo, and Wattenberg, Phys. Rev. 85, 483 (1952).

3 Havens, Rainwater, and Rabi, Phys. Rev. 82, 345 (1951).

4 D. J. Hughes and M. T. Burgy, Phys. Rev. 81, 498 (1951); Ringo, Hughes, and Burgy, Phys. Rev. 84, 1160 (1951).

5 Palevsky, Hughes, and Eggler, Phys. Rev. 83, 234 (1951).

6 L. L. Foldy, Phys. Rev. 87, 675 (1952); R. G. Sachs, Phys. Rev. 87, 1100 (1952); G. F. Chew, private communication.

PAPER 17

Scattering of High-Energy Electrons and the Method of Nuclear Recoil*†

R. HOFSTADTER, H. R. FECHTER, AND J. A. MCINTYRE
Department of Physics and Microwave Laboratory, Stanford University, Stanford, California
(Received April 29, 1953)

IN an effort to exhibit the finite dimensions and charge distribution within atomic nuclei, an electron scattering program has been initiated. The external electron beam of the Stanford linear electron accelerator is resolved in energy to about 1 percent, deflected, cleared of gamma-rays, and focused in vacuum at the center of a 20-inch diameter scattering chamber. Scattering targets are placed within the chamber and their position is remotely controlled. Scattered electrons emerge from the target foil, pass through the 0.006-inch aluminum window of the chamber and through a 0.003-inch aluminum foil into the vacuum chamber of a double-focusing magnetic spectrometer. The spectrometer is similar to that of Snyder *et al.*,[1] has a radius of 16 inches, and bends electrons of 135 Mev (maximum) through 180°. Scattered electrons are detected by a 4-inch long Čerenkov counter buried in a large lead shield. The main beam is monitored by a helium-filled ionization counter.

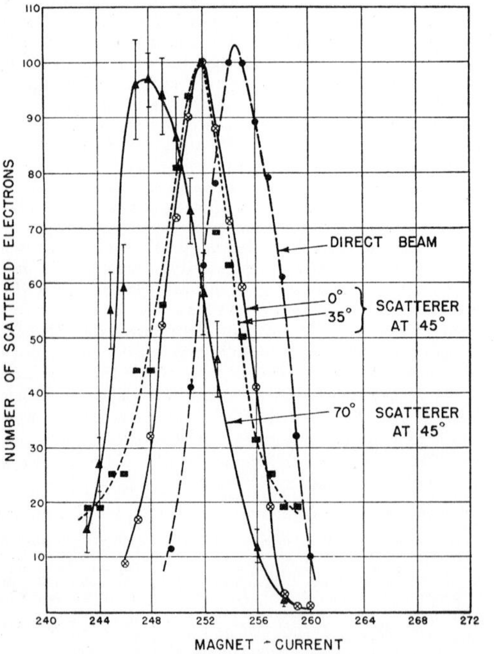

FIG. 1. Elastic scattering curves in beryllium (0.100 inch). The abscissa is proportional to the electron energy. The energy of the direct beam is 116 Mev and has about a 1 percent spread. The curve at 70° shows the effect of the nuclear recoil.

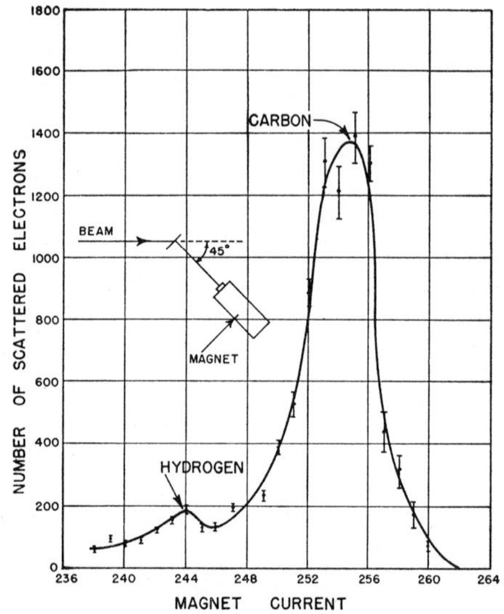

FIG. 2. Elastic scattering curves at 116 Mev for carbon and hydrogen in a polyethylene target.

Elastic scattering profiles have been taken at various angles for incident electrons of 116 Mev and a 0.002-inch gold foil. The curves are quite similar at all angles. The energy loss in the gold foil may be observed as a shift towards lower energy between the direct beam and the scattered beams. The width at half-maximum of the elastic curves is about 2.8 percent and is largely due to the wide slit at the spectrometer exit.

Figure 1 shows elastic scattering profiles in beryllium. The elastic curves are shifted to lower energies due, as expected, to energy loss in the target. The elastic curve at 70°, however, is shifted considerably farther toward lower energies. This additional shift is a function of angle and is due to the recoil of the beryllium nucleus.

Figure 2 substantiates this interpretation and shows the two elastic curves observed with a polyethylene (CH_2) target. The magnitude of the energy shift of the hydrogen peak has been studied at various angles and agrees with the recoil hypothesis.

Thus a new method is available for studying "elastic" scattering of electrons in compounds or with unseparated isotopes. Each isotope should present its own elastic peak. The recoil shift is a quadratic function of the incident energy and therefore improved separation of isotope peaks will occur at higher incident energies. This new method clearly permits a study of the scattering from hydrogen and deuterium using solid targets.

A preliminary angular distribution (Fig. 3) has been obtained for gold by using the peak intensity of the elastic curves as a measure of the scattering cross section. The width of the accepted energy range is approximately 1.3 percent and centers on the peak. While systematic errors have not been investigated, it appears probable from the results of many runs that the shape of the curve in Fig. 3 will not change appreciably. Thus the prominent diffraction peaks predicted by Parzen[2] and others (e.g., at 75°) for a uniform distribution of charge in heavy nuclei are not observed. Possible interpretations of the curve are: (a) the nuclear boundary in gold is not sharp and the charge distribution tapers off gradually, (b) inelastic effects may "fill up" the minima of the diffraction curves. Because of the very large fall-off in intensity as a function of angle of scattering (approximately 10^4 between 35° and 100°) the explanation (b) would not appear to be complete.

The angular distribution observed experimentally in beryllium at 116 Mev appears to fit (though not perfectly) a point charge distribution much more closely than in gold. This fact suggests that no large systematic error is present in the experiments.

One of the authors (R.H.) wishes to thank Professor D. L. Webster for a fruitful discussion.

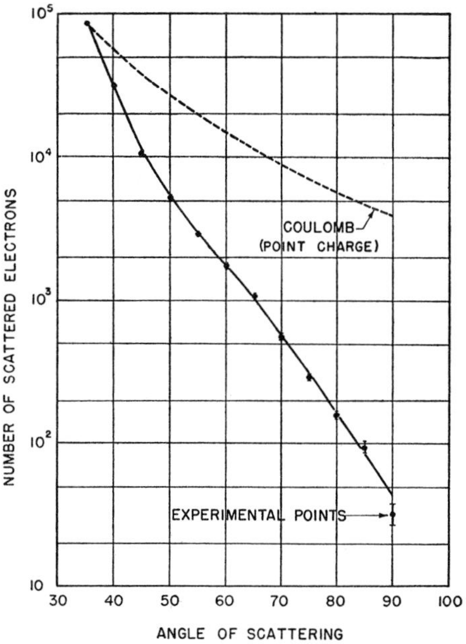

FIG. 3. Typical angular distribution obtained at 116 Mev with a 0.002-inch gold foil. The gold foil was oriented at 45° with respect to the incident beam for all angular settings of the spectrometer magnet.

* This work was initiated and aided at all stages by a grant from the Research Corporation.

† Assisted by the joint program of the U. S. Office of Naval Research and the U. S. Atomic Energy Commission.

1 Snyder, Rubin, Fowler, and Lauritsen, Rev. Sci. Instr. 21, 852 (1950).

2 G. Parzen, Phys. Rev. 80, 335 (1950).

PAPER 18

High-Energy Electron Scattering by Nuclei*

R. W. PIDD, C. L. HAMMER, and E. C. RAKA
Randall Laboratory of Physics, University of Michigan, Ann Arbor, Michigan
(Received June 19, 1953)

The Michigan race-track synchrotron has been used as a source of electrons for the study of elastic scattering of 30- to 45-Mev electrons by nuclei of $Z=46-52$ and $Z=74$. The experimental results for tungsten can be interpreted to give a value of the nuclear radius equal to $(1.0\pm0.1)\times10^{-13}A^{\frac{1}{3}}$ cm if a constant proton density is assumed for the nucleus. The radius of the tin nucleus is $(1.1\pm0.1)\times10^{-13}A^{\frac{1}{3}}$ cm. Any discontinuity in r_0 *versus* A at the closing of the $g_{9/2}$ shell is about 1 percent or less; a step increase of 2 percent at $Z=48$ gives a best fit to the lower Z data.

INTRODUCTION

THE angular dependence of the differential cross section for the scattering of electrons by nuclei depends on the nuclear charge distribution when the electron de Broglie wavelength is comparable with the nuclear size. Several measurements of the cross section have been made at incident electron energies between 30 and 45 Mev. The results for a tungsten target are in agreement with a nuclear radius given by $R=r_0A^{\frac{1}{3}}$, $r_0=(1.0\pm0.1)\times10^{-13}$ cm, for an assumed uniform spherical model of the nucleus. A somewhat larger value of r_0 is found for tin and neighboring elements. A comparison of these radii with the values obtained by other means shows the inadequacy of the simple uniform model and to some extent how it should be modified.

APPARATUS

The source of electrons is the internal beam of the Michigan synchrotron. A target is located in one of the field-free straight sections at a position just inside the equilibrium beam orbit. The beam is scattered by contracting the orbit to the target radius. Figure 1 shows the equilibrium orbit, target location, and the detecting systems.[1] Scattered electrons emerge from the vacuum chamber through 5-mil aluminum windows into the detecting systems on either side of the chamber. One detector fixed at 90° is used as an intensity monitor, while the other can be set at angles between 60° and 120° with respect to the incident beam direction. The detecting systems include a collimator, magnetic analyzer, and a pair of shielded Geiger counters, all shown approximately to scale in the figure. The scattered beam is deflected through an angle of 15° in the anlayzer magnetic field and then is detected as a coincidence in the pair of counters. Background coincidences are recorded in either of two ways, by plugging the collimator hole or by increasing the analyzer field so that electrons elastically scattered from the target cannot reach the counters. Both methods give the same result. A typical spectrum of the scattered electrons shows a symmetrical peak centered at the incident beam energy, an energy half-width of ±20 percent, and a height about 10 times the background level. The counting rate is adjusted to about $\frac{1}{8}$ count per synchrotron pulse. All data are corrected for systematic counting errors.

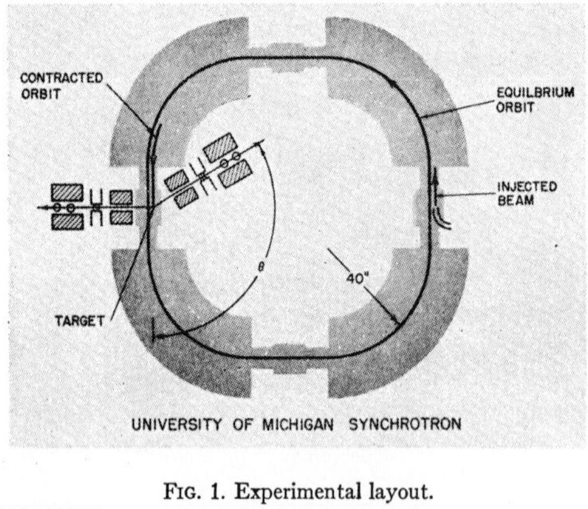

FIG. 1. Experimental layout.

EXPERIMENTAL RESULTS

In Fig. 2 are plotted the cross sections for a tungsten target at 33 Mev. For comparison, theoretical curves for 30-Mev electrons are drawn for a point nucleus[2] and a uniform speherical model,[3] $r_0=1.45\times10^{-13}$ cm. Both data and curves are normalized at 90°. It can be seen that the experimental points deviate from the uniform model toward the point nucleus. A choice of $r_0=1.0\times10^{-13}$ cm, about 30 percent smaller than the assumed value, leads to the best agreement between data and calculation. In this range of energies, the cross section is a function of the product of electron energy and nuclear radius. Therefore the uniform sphere prediction for $E=30$ Mev, $r_0=1.45\times10^{-13}$ cm, applies equally well for the combination, $E=43$ Mev, $r_0=1.0\times10^{-13}$ cm. The data obtained at 43 Mev, plotted in the same graph, are in much better agreement with this predicted angular distribution than the 33-Mev points.

The systematic errors in the experimental cross

* This research was supported by the U. S. Atomic Energy Commission.
[1] Raka, Hammer, and Pidd, Phys. Rev. **90**, 341 (1953).
[2] H. Feshbach, Phys. Rev. **88**, 295 (1952).
[3] L. K. Acheson, Jr., Phys. Rev. **82**, 488 (1951).

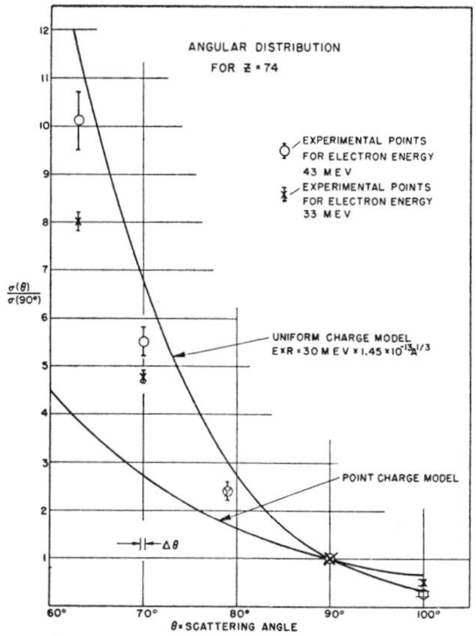

FIG. 2. Differential cross sections for tungsten.

sections are considerably less than the standard deviations which are shown. The tungsten target is 0.007 inch thick and is oriented at 45° with respect to the incident beam direction. The variable-angle detector is on the transmitting side of the target. Relative corrections depending on the target thickness at angles between 60° and 100° are less than 2 percent. The errors include corrections for multiple and plural scattering, and straggling in the target. At angles larger than 100° these errors become much larger especially due to plural scattering and the data are not considered reliable. Thus the conclusions reached in the preceding paragraph refer to the more reliable forward angles. The error calculations are confirmed experimentally by a repeat run with the target thickness reduced by one-half, in which no detectable change in the cross sections could be observed. The Schwinger correction, while important to the absolute cross section, would lead to a negligible differential correction within the angular range in the experiment.

Similar data have been obtained for a series of target elements from $Z=46$ to $Z=52$ at an energy of 34 Mev. In an effort to find any systematic differences from element to element, the targets were alternated inside the vacuum system in a series of runs so that any experimental bias could be minimized. A total of 12 500 counts was accumulated for each element at two angles, 60° and 90°. The ratios, $\sigma(60°)/\sigma(90°)$ are plotted in Fig. 3. The ratio predicted for a point nucleus[2] is 5.2 and for a uniform sphere,[3] $r_0=1.45\times10^{-13}$ cm, about 11 for all the elements. The value $r_0=(1.1\pm0.1)\times10^{-13}$ cm is consistent with the data, 10 percent larger than in the case of tungsten. Individual variations among the target elements are less than the standard deviation except for the break between $Z=48$ and $Z=49$.

CONCLUSIONS

Coefficients of the nuclear radius less than 1.45×10^{-13} cm have been found in other experimental work. In particular, electron scattering at 15.7 Mev,[4] and μ-meson absorption by nuclei[5] agree with a value of 1.2×10^{-13} cm. It appears from this that observations which depend only on the electric charge distribution in the nucleus may give a consistently smaller value for the nuclear size than the value obtained from reactions which depend on nuclear interaction. The data on beta decay of mirror nuclei, on the other hand, are consistent with the larger value of the radius, if the uniform model is used. Since these data extend only up to $Z=20$ they cannot be readily compared with electron scattering results now available.

Methods of measuring the nuclear size which are available at present fail to determine a nuclear model. In each case they measure an effective radius for an interaction and not a nuclear density distribution. It

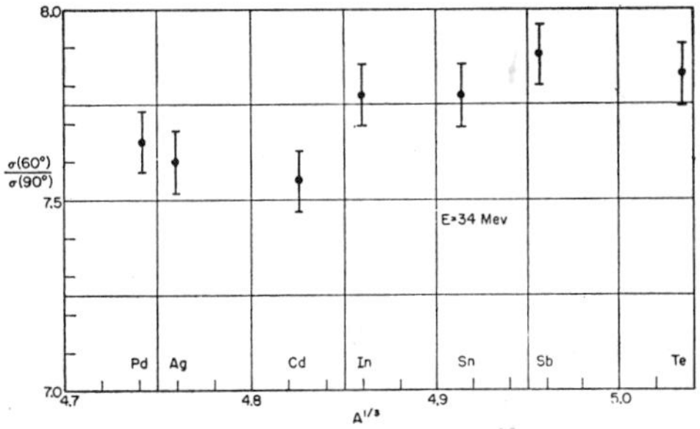

FIG. 3. Ratios of differential cross sections at 60° and 90° for elements from $Z=46$ to $Z=52$.

is not surprising then that different observations and different interactions should give conflicting results when interpreted on the basis of a uniform model with a sharp boundary. Nevertheless, saturation in nuclear structure is a common point of agreement among all measurements and any new model must retain this property. In view of this, the nuclear model suggested by Wilson,[6] a saturated core surrounded by an exponentially decreasing distribution, may lead to the best agreement among all data on the nuclear size. Some scattering models such as this have been used and they show that the angular dependence of the cross section for electron scattering depends mostly on the core size. It is possible that the radius measured by neutron scattering, for example, would extend toward the edge of the distribution. Electron scattering at much higher energies is model-dependent and should yield more detailed information about the shape of the proton distribution in the nucleus.

[4] Lyman, Hanson, and Scott, Phys. Rev. **84**, 626 (1951).
[5] L. N. Cooper and E. M. Henley, Bull. Am. Phys. Soc. **28**, No. 3, 56 (1953).
[6] R. R. Wilson, Phys. Rev. **88**, 350 (1952).

PAPER 19

Studies of X-Rays from Mu-Mesonic Atoms*

Val L. Fitch and James Rainwater
Department of Physics, Columbia University, New York, New York
(Received July 23, 1953)

A new technique of x-ray spectroscopy of μ-mesonic atoms has been developed. The x-rays are produced when a μ^-meson undergoes transitions between Bohr orbits about nuclei of various Z. The mesons are produced by the Columbia University 164-in. Nevis cyclotron. The x-rays are detected, and their energies are measured to better than 1 percent accuracy (for $Z \geq 22$) using a NaI crystal scintillation spectrometer. The $2p \rightarrow 1s$ transition energies were measured to be 0.35, 0.41, 0.955, 1.55, 1.60, 3.50, 5.80, 6.02, and 6.02 Mev for $Z=13$, 14, 22, 29, 30, 51, 80, 82, and 83. Special attention was paid to the Pb spectrum, and it is believed that an 0.2-Mev fine structure splitting has been observed. This is the expected splitting if the μ^- meson is a spin $\frac{1}{2}$ Dirac "heavy electron" of 210 electron masses, having the expected Dirac magnetic moment and having no strong nonelectromagnetic interaction with nuclear matter.

Since the μ^-meson Bohr orbits are 210 times closer to the nucleus than the equivalent electron orbits, the x-ray energies are quite sensitive to nuclear size for medium and large Z. In the case of Pb, a 1 percent change in nuclear radius gives a 1 percent change in the calculated x-ray energy. Assuming constant proton density inside a spherical nucleus of radius $R_0 = r_0 A^{\frac{1}{3}}$ and the above properties for the μ meson, we obtain $r_0 = 1.17$, 1.21, 1.22, and 1.17×10^{-13} cm for $Z=22$, 29, 51, and 82. The significance of these results in relation to other nuclear size measurements is discussed.

INTRODUCTION

When a μ^- meson is slowed to rest in condensed matter through loss of its kinetic energy to electrons, it is captured in Bohr type orbits about a nucleus. Then, by a series of radiative and nonradiative (Auger) transitions, the meson proceeds to its K shell in an elapsed time of roughly 10^{-13} to 10^{-14} sec.[1] Thereafter, two competing mechanisms, natural beta decay and nuclear capture, account for the disappearance of the meson from the K shell. The characteristic decay time has been measured to be 2.1 μ sec. The mean time for nuclear capture has been investigated over a wide range of atomic numbers and has been found[2] to vary as Z^{-4} for low Z materials and saturate near 7×10^{-8} sec for $Z=82$. This is a manifestation of the extremely weak interaction (nonelectromagnetic) of μ mesons with nuclear matter. In comparison, the π^- meson will seldom reach the K shell except in the case of nuclei with low atomic number. Experimental studies of π-mesonic x-rays in light elements have been made[3] for low Z elements to investigate this strong absorption. Previously reported results[4] for μ^- mesons have been of a more qualitative nature than the present work and will not be discussed in detail since they are in rough agreement with the present more definite determinations of the transition energies.

When a μ^- meson is "stopped" in a target material and is captured in a Bohr orbit about a particular nucleus, the initial states are characterized by large quantum numbers n and l in view of the large statistical weight associated with these states. The decrease in n soon reaches the point where $n=l+1$, and subsequent transitions have $\Delta n = \Delta l = -1$. Thus the lower states in the cascade usually possess the largest l value consistent with the given total quantum number n (circular orbits).

* This research was supported by the joint program of the U. S. Office of Naval Research and the U. S. Atomic Energy Commission.

[1] E. Fermi and E. Teller, Phys. Rev. **72**, 399 (1947); see also R. E. Marshak, *Meson Physics* (McGraw-Hill Book Company, Inc., New York, 1952), Chaps. 5 and 6 for a general discussion of matters related to the present papers, and for further references.

[2] Keuffel, Harrison, Godfrey, and Reynolds, Phys. Rev. **87**, 942 (1952); see also J. M. Kennedy, Phys. Rev. **87**, 953 (1952).

[3] Camac, McGuire, Platt, and Schulte, Phys. Rev. **88**, 134 (1952).

[4] W. Y. Chang, Revs. Modern Phys. **21**, 166 (1949); E. P. Hinks, Phys. Rev. **81**, 313 (1951); G. G. Harris and T. J. B. Shanley, Phys. Rev. **89**, 983 (1953); F. D. S. Butement, Phil. Mag. **44**, 208 (1953); see G. R. Burbidge and A. H. de Borde, Phys. Rev. **89**, 189 (1953) for other references.

It has been shown[5] that the transitions involving states of high quantum number will be primarily nonradiative (Auger processes), while these in the region of low quantum number will be radiative. These x-rays have a small natural line width compared to the transitional energies between the lowest states. For example, in the case of lead the transition rate $2p\rightarrow 1s$ is approximately 10^{18} sec^{-1}, while the capture rate is approximately 10^{7} sec^{-1}. The resulting natural line width is approximately 1 kev for a total x-ray energy of 6 Mev.

Considering the nucleus as a point charge, the radius of a Bohr orbit is 2.82×10^{-13} $(m_e 137^2/\mu Z)n^2$ cm, where m_e and μ represent the electron and μ^--meson masses. Thus the μ-mesonic orbit will be smaller than the corresponding electron orbit by the mass factor 210. In the case of lead this gives $r=3.07\times 10^{-13}$ cm for $n=1$, which is well inside the nucleus, and $r=1.23\times 10^{-12}$ cm for $n=2$, which is just outside the nuclear surface. Again in the case of Pb, the predicted $2p_{\frac{3}{2}}\rightarrow 1s$ transition energy for a point nucleus is 16.41 Mev, whereas we have measured the energy of this transition as 6.02 Mev. Thus the finite nuclear size results in almost a factor of three decrease in the transition energy. Assuming a nuclear model of constant density inside a sphere of radius R_0, with a sharp edge and zero density outside, we find that a 1 percent change in R_0 gives a 1 percent calculated change in the transition energy. Since the x-ray energy is measured to better than 1 percent accuracy, a corresponding accuracy is obtained for the best fitting value of R_0. This great sensitivity of the μ^- meson as a "probe" of the nucleus was first pointed out by Wheeler[5] and served as a stimulus for the research reported in this paper. This sensitivity to nuclear size decreases rapidly with decreasing Z and amounts to only a 2 percent total effect for aluminum. The transition energy is mainly sensitive to the meson mass rather than nuclear size for low Z, and mainly sensitive to nuclear size for high Z materials. By exploiting this fact we have obtained an independent evaluation of the μ-meson mass in agreement with the results of other techniques.

The fine structure splitting of the $2p$ level depends on the spin and magnetic moment of the μ meson which is usually assumed to be a Dirac particle of spin $\frac{1}{2}$. Thus the anomalous g factor of 2 is expected. Other spin $\frac{1}{2}$ particles believed to obey the Dirac theory include the electron, proton, neutron, and neutrino. The electron moment in the hydrogen atom is now known to be slightly different from one electron magneton, and this has recently been explained in terms of higher-order effects in quantum electrodynamics. The neutron and proton moments deviate considerably from the expected Dirac values of 0 and 1 nuclear magnetons, presumably because of their strong coupling to meson fields. The μ meson, unlike the nucleons, has no known strong (non-electromagnetic) coupling to other particles, and it is reasonable to expect, therefore, that its magnetic moment would be close to one μ-mesonic magneton if it is a spin $\frac{1}{2}$ Dirac type particle. (The $\pi^-\rightarrow\mu^-+\nu$ and $\mu^-\rightarrow e^-+2\nu$ processes and the nature of the stars produced following nuclear capture seem to require that the μ meson have Fermi-Dirac statistics, and thus odd half-integral spin.) Results of the investigation of cosmic-ray bursts seem to rule out spin $\frac{3}{2}$ or higher.

For spin $\frac{1}{2}$, the $2p$ level will split into $2p_{\frac{3}{2}}$ and $2p_{\frac{1}{2}}$ with relative statistical weighting factors of 2 and 1. (This weighting is found theoretically to apply even for the situation where the $2p$ level is reached by successive transitions having $\Delta n=\Delta l=-1$.) In the case of a point Pb nucleus, the expected fine structure splitting is 0.55 Mev. This is reduced to about 0.2 Mev for the actual size, and we believe that we have probably observed this fine structure splitting in the Pb spectrum. If the μ meson has spin 0, there would be no fine structure splitting. If its spin is 1 or more, there will be three lines in the fine structure. Thus a study of the fine structure can determine both the spin and magnetic moment of the μ meson.

This paper reports experimental studies of the x-rays from the $2p\rightarrow 1s$ transition in μ-mesonic atoms for $Z=13$, 14, 22, 29, 30, 51, 80, 82, and 83. The Columbia University Nevis Cyclotron produces an external meson flux which is collimated in the main shielding wall to produce meson beams of relatively well-defined momenta. The beams consist of both π and μ mesons, the mu's originating from decay of pi's close to the cyclotron target. The μ mesons with the same momenta as the π mesons have a greater range, thus the π mesons can be removed from the beam by using absorbers. The x-rays associated with the μ mesons stopping in various materials were studied using a NaI crystal spectrometer with an accuracy of about 1 percent or better in the energy determination, depending on the Z of the target material.

THEORY

Wheeler[5] has calculated the $1s$, $2p_{\frac{1}{2}}$, $2p_{\frac{3}{2}}$, and $2s_{\frac{1}{2}}$ levels for a μ^- meson of $200m_e$ in atoms of various Z. Since the results quoted were not found to be sufficiently accurate for a precise comparison with our experiments, we have recalculated these levels using more exact methods using $\mu=210m_e$ and a model of the nucleus having constant charge density to $R_0=1.30A^{\frac{1}{3}}\times 10^{-13}$ cm, with zero density for $r>R_0$. The μ meson was assumed to obey the Dirac equation and only the electrostatic potential was considered. In this case the Dirac equation becomes[6]

$$[E-V+c\boldsymbol{\alpha}\cdot\mathbf{p}+\beta\mu c^2]\psi=0, \qquad (1)$$

[5] J. A. Wheeler, Revs. Modern Phys. **21**, 133 (1949); R. E. Marshak, reference 1, Chap. 5. See also G. R. Burbidge and A. H. de Borde, Phys. Rev. **89**, 189 (1953).

[6] See L. I. Schiff, *Quantum Mechanics* (McGraw-Hill Book Company, Inc., New York, 1949), Chap. 12 for derivations of the following equations, or of approximations to them. The notation follows that of Schiff for the most part.

where $E=\mu c^2+E'$ = total meson energy, and E' = binding energy, V is the potential energy, and $\mathbf{p}$ is the meson momentum. $\boldsymbol{\alpha}$ and β are 4×4 Dirac operators. $\psi=\begin{pmatrix}\varphi_a\\ \varphi_b\end{pmatrix}$ is the 4-component wave function, where φ_a and φ_b, representing the (1, 2) and the (3, 4) terms of ψ respectively, are two-component functions. This is easily transformed to the form

$$\{(E-V)^2-c^2p^2-\mu^2c^4\}\psi-\left\{i\hbar c\left(\frac{1}{r}\frac{\partial V}{\partial r}\right)(\boldsymbol{\alpha}\cdot\mathbf{r})\right\}\psi=0, \quad (2)$$

where the first bracket corresponds to the Klein-Gordon equation appropriate for a spin zero particle, and the last term is the characteristic Dirac term. Expressed in terms of φ_a and φ_b, Eq. (2) becomes

$$\{(E-V)^2-c^2p^2-\mu^2c^4\}\varphi_a-\left\{i\hbar c\left(\frac{1}{r}\frac{\partial V}{\partial r}\right)(\boldsymbol{\sigma}\cdot\mathbf{r})\right\}\varphi_b=0, \quad (3a)$$

$$\{(E-V)^2-c^2p^2-\mu^2c^4\}\varphi_b-\left\{i\hbar c\left(\frac{1}{r}\frac{\partial V}{\partial r}\right)(\boldsymbol{\sigma}\cdot\mathbf{r})\right\}\varphi_a=0, \quad (3b)$$

where $\boldsymbol{\sigma}$ is the usual 2×2 Pauli spin operator ($\mathbf{S}=\hbar\boldsymbol{\sigma}/2$ = meson spin operator). Similar expansion of Eq. (1) gives two coupled equations for φ_a and φ_b in a form that shows that φ_b is the "larger" component for $E>0$ and yields the relation

$$\varphi_a=-c[E'+2\mu c^2-V]^{-1}(\boldsymbol{\sigma}\cdot\mathbf{p})\varphi_b. \quad (4)$$

On insertion of Eq. (4) in (3b), using $(\boldsymbol{\sigma}\cdot\mathbf{r})(\boldsymbol{\sigma}\cdot\mathbf{p})=\mathbf{r}\cdot\mathbf{p}+i\boldsymbol{\sigma}\cdot\mathbf{L}$, where $\mathbf{L}=\mathbf{r}\times\mathbf{p}$ = orbital angular momentum, this gives the exact relation

$$\{(E-V)^2-c^2p^2-\mu^2c^4\}\varphi_b+\frac{\hbar}{2}\left[1+\frac{(E'-V)}{2\mu c^2}\right]^{-1}\frac{\partial V}{\partial r}\left[\hbar\frac{\partial}{\partial r}-(\boldsymbol{\sigma}\cdot\mathbf{L})\right]\varphi_b=0. \quad (5)$$

The first bracket again contains the Klein-Gordon term and the last contains the characteristic Dirac terms. In the last bracket, the second term gives the usual spin-orbit interaction. Since $\boldsymbol{\sigma}\cdot\mathbf{L}$ and L^2 are not constants of the motion, it is perferable to use the variable $\hbar k=\beta(\boldsymbol{\sigma}'\cdot\mathbf{L}+\hbar)$ which is a constant of the motion. Here $|k|=(j+\frac{1}{2})$, and $k=-1$, $+1$, and -2 for the $1s_{\frac{1}{2}}$, $2p_{\frac{1}{2}}$, and $2p_{\frac{3}{2}}$ states, respectively. The Dirac equation reduces to a purely radial equation for a two component wave function with components $[F(r)/r]$ and $[G(r)/r]$ respectively, where G is the "large" component function in the coupled equations:

$$(E'+2\mu c^2-V)F-\hbar c\left(\frac{d}{dr}+\frac{k}{r}\right)G=0, \quad (6a)$$

$$(E'-V)G+\hbar c\left(\frac{d}{dr}-\frac{k}{r}\right)F=0. \quad (6b)$$

Solving Eq. (6a) for F and substituting in (6b) gives

$$\left\{(2\mu c^2+E'-V)^2-\mu^2c^4+\hbar^2c^2\left[\frac{d^2}{dr^2}-\frac{k(k+1)}{r^2}\right]\right\}G$$
$$+\left\{\frac{\hbar^2}{2}\left[1+\frac{(E'-V)}{2\mu c^2}\right]^{-1}\frac{dV}{dr}\left[\frac{d}{dr}+\frac{k}{r}\right]\right\}G=0, \quad (7)$$

which is similar to Eq. (5). Since the second bracket Dirac terms are small compared to the first bracket main Klein-Gordon term, there is very little error made by replacing $[1+(E'-V)/2\mu c^2]^{-1}$ in the second bracket by unity. This is usually done.

In the case of a point nucleus Eqs. (6a, b) may be solved exactly to give

$$E'=\mu c^2\left\{\left[1+\frac{(Z/137)^2}{\{n-|k|+[k^2-(Z/137)^2]^{\frac{1}{2}}\}^2}\right]^{-\frac{1}{2}}-1\right\}, \quad (8)$$

where the fine structure constant is taken approximately as 1/137.

The energies given by Eq. (8) are listed in Table I for selected values of Z along with the modified values using $R_0=1.3A^{\frac{1}{3}}\times10^{-13}$ cm and a nucleus of uniform charge distribution. Several methods of varying precision were used to obtain the values listed for finite nuclear radius. Particular attention was paid to the case of Pb($Z=82$) since the various corrections to approximate calculations are most serious for high Z, and since Pb is a particularly interesting material to

TABLE I. Calculated energies of μ-meson orbits for $\mu=210m_e$. All energies are in Mev.

	Dirac energies $R_0=0$			Dirac energies $R_0=1.3A^{\frac{1}{3}}\times10^{-13}$ cm			Klein-Gordon energies $R_0=1.3A^{\frac{1}{3}}\times10^{-13}$ cm	
Z	$E(1s)$	$2p_{\frac{3}{2}}\to1s$	$2p_{\frac{1}{2}}\to1s$	$E(1s)$	$2p_{\frac{3}{2}}\to1s$	$2p_{\frac{1}{2}}\to1s$	$E(1s)$	$2p\to1s$
13	0.4849	0.3631	0.3628					
14	0.5614	0.4213	0.4209					
22	1.3917	1.0455	1.0432	1.282	0.935	0.933		
29	2.4300	1.8277	1.8208	2.12	1.52	1.51		
30	2.6026	1.9579	1.9500					
51	7.7071	5.8332	5.7627	5.22	3.41	3.37		
80	20.181	15.508	15.011					
82	21.328	16.414	15.857	10.11	5.48	5.30	10.24	5.52
83	21.919	16.880	16.291					

TABLE II. Comparison of the calculated μ-meson orbit energies for Pb using the various computational methods discussed in the text.

	Dirac energies	Klein-Gordon energies	Klein-Gordon correction terms $\frac{1}{r}\left(\frac{dV}{dr}\right)\mathbf{L}\cdot\mathbf{S}$	Klein-Gordon correction terms $\frac{dv}{dr}\frac{d\psi}{dr}$	Klein-Gordon energies plus correction terms
$E(1s)$	−10.11	−10.24		+0.157	−10.08
$E(2p_{\frac{1}{2}})$	−4.807	−4.72	−0.125	+0.032	−4.81
$E(2p_{\frac{3}{2}})$	−4.63	−4.72	+0.062	+0.032	−4.63

use to investigate the fine structure splitting. We include a discussion of the more approximate methods to illustrate the order of magnitude of the different terms and the errors introduced by various approximate methods. The first method used the Klein-Gordon

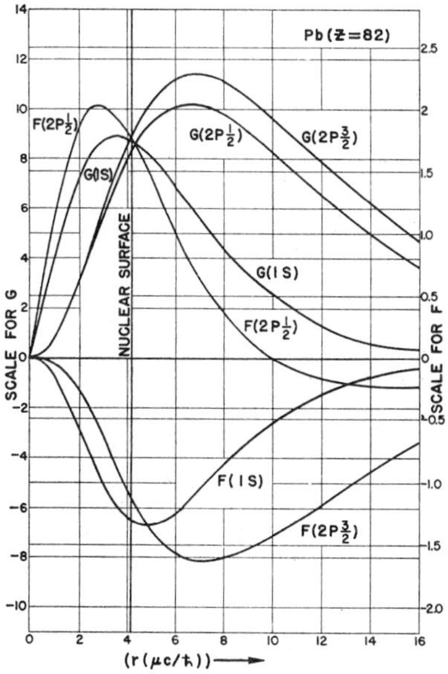

FIG. 1. The $1s$, $2p_{\frac{1}{2}}$, and $2p_{\frac{3}{2}}$ unnormalized meson radial wave functions G and F [of Eq. (6a, b)] in the field of a Pb nucleus. A uniform nuclear model is used with $r_0=1.3\times10^{-13}$ cm. Radii are expressed in units of $h/\mu c=1.84\times10^{-13}$ cm, with the position of the nuclear surface (4.18 units) indicated.

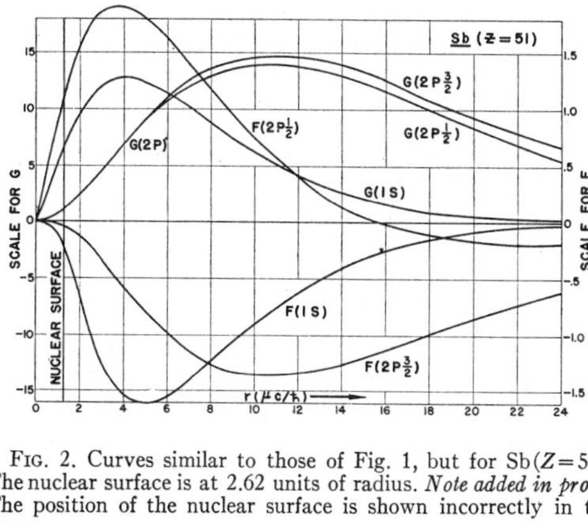

FIG. 2. Curves similar to those of Fig. 1, but for Sb($Z=51$). The nuclear surface is at 2.62 units of radius. *Note added in proof:* The position of the nuclear surface is shown incorrectly in the figure.

equation and the $V(r)$ for finite nuclear size. A point by point method of numerical integration was employed, trying various grid lengths, starting at $r=0$ and continuing until it was clear that E' had been chosen too large or too small. This method was poor for the L shell due to the $2/r^2$ angular momentum term, and a (semiconvergent) series method was tried and found to be much easier to use. In the case of $r<R_0$ a series in positive powers of r was used. For $r>R_0$ a solution of the form $e^{-br}r^m\sum a_n r^{-n}$ was used. The values of (G'/G) for the two functions at $r=R_0$ were compared as a function of E', with the correct value usually determined by interpolation after the first two trials. The $(dV/dr)(dG/dr)$ and the $(k/r)(dV/dr)G$ terms in Eq. (7) were then treated as perturbations and evaluated by first-order perturbation theory with the results shown in Table II. Similarly, the effect of changing the value of the nuclear radius R_0 was evaluated in the Klein-Gordon term by treating the *difference* in V for the two choices of R_0 as a perturbation. It was found that an attempt to calculate the effect of finite nuclear radius by using $R_0=0$ functions to calculate the entire effect as a first-order perturbation gave quite poor results. However, the result of a change of ±10 percent in R_0 about the chosen radius is given with good accuracy.

It was later found to be feasible to carry out the (semiconvergent) series expansions of the inside and outside functions, using the complete coupled equations (6a, b) directly, and this has been carried through for a number of cases with results in close agreement with the previous method. For a given l and j, the G function starts as r^{l+1} and the F function as r^l when $j=l-\frac{1}{2}$, and as r^{l+2} when $j=l+\frac{1}{2}$. A plot of these unnormalized functions for Pb and Sb ($Z=82$ and 51) are shown in Figs. 1 and 2, where the F and G functions are shown with the proper relative amplitudes indicated by the two ordinate scales.

Additional effects of interest include (a) the effect of the polarization of the nucleus by the μ meson, (b) the hyperfine splitting due to the nuclear magnetic moment for odd-A nuclei (Pb has mainly spin-zero isotopes), (c) the effect of a nuclear electrical quadrupole moment, (d) the effect of nonuniform charge distribution as a function of r within the nucleus, including the effect of an expected gradual dropping off of the nuclear charge density beyond the nuclear "surface," (e) the effect of other forces not considered, or of a different spin for the μ meson.

Cooper and Henley[7] have studied some of these effects. They estimate that nuclear polarizability may effect the Pb transition energies by about 0.06 Mev or less (a 1 percent effect or less) and set 0.15 Mev as an upper limit for this effect. Wheeler[4] has calculated the hyperfine splitting for Al($Z=13$) as 9.7 ev. For higher Z the splitting should vary more slowly than Z^3, so the splitting would probably be less than 1 kev in all cases.

The effect of the quadrupole splitting has been investigated by Wheeler.[8] It should be negligible for the materials reported in this paper. The possibility of spin $\frac{1}{2}$ will affect the number of fine structure lines and

[7] L. Cooper and E. Henley (following article), Phys. Rev. **92**, 801 (1953).
[8] J. A. Wheeler (Paper III of this series), Phys. Rev. **92**, 812 (1953).

would be observed experimentally. The existence of any other important attractive interaction between the μ meson and nuclei seems very unlikely but cannot be completely excluded. It would shift the energies in a manner similar to that of a decrease in nuclear radius.

EXPERIMENTAL METHOD

The two main facilities required for this experiment are (1) a source of reasonably monoenergetic μ^- mesons which can be made to stop in a relatively thin target material of selected atomic number under conditions such that the background radiation effects are not too severe, and (2) a photon detector of high sensitivity and good energy selection for the region of 50 kev to 10 Mev.

The μ^- mesons were obtained as follows. Referring to the floor plan, Fig. 3, the 385-Mev protons rotating clockwise inside the cyclotron chamber strike a thin Be target and produce various reaction products including fast neutrons, π^+, π^-, and π^0 mesons, which are emitted in all directions. Near the target the π^0 mesons decay to photons and eventually some electron-positron pairs are formed. These contribute some

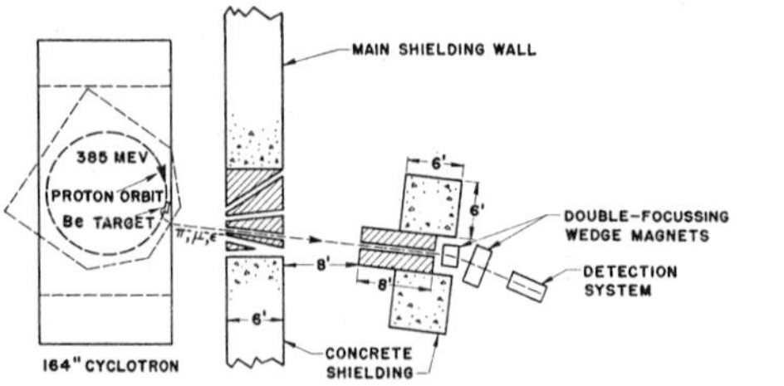

FIG. 3. Floor plan showing location of cyclotron shielding, focusing magnets, and detection system. A typical meson path is shown.

electrons to the final beam. The π^- mesons of approximately 100-Mev kinetic energy have a mean path of approximately 10 meters for $\pi^- \rightarrow \mu^- + \nu$ decay and a certain fraction decay near the target, where the π^- density is highest. The fringing magnetic field of the cyclotron provides a horizontal focusing action for negative particles of any definite energy group emitted in the horizontal plane at angles inward from the forward proton direction. Ports through the shielding wall then serve to select definite momentum beams of negative particles. A beam analysis indicates that approximately 10 percent of the beam particles are μ^- mesons of the same momentum as the π^- mesons. Most of the μ^- mesons originating from decay of the pi's in the beam are projected out of the beam and lost. A typical useful path is indicated in Fig. 3.

The general level of background radiation in the region just outside the shielding was found to be too large for successful performance of this experiment, mainly as a result of the secondary effects of fast neutrons. The method finally employed to reduce background in the photon detector to a reasonable level

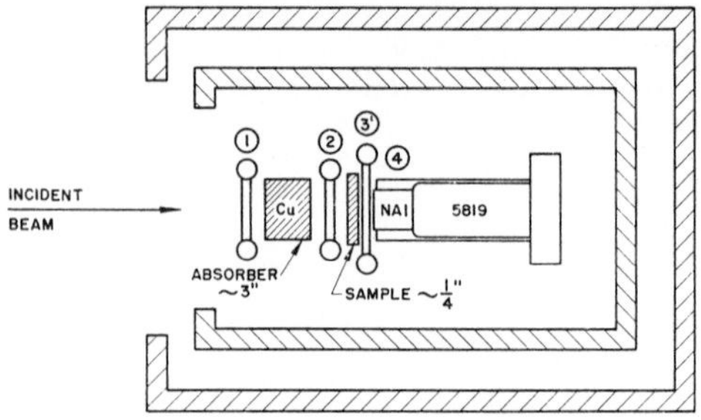

FIG. 4. Diagram of detection system. Stilbene scintillation counters 1, 2, and 3′ select particles stopping in the sample material. NaI scintillation counter 4 serves as the photon detector. The copper absorber between counters 1 and 2 removes the π mesons from the beam. Magnetic shielding is provided by a double walled box of $\frac{1}{2}$-in. iron plate.

is shown in Fig. 3. A secondary barricade of concrete blocks was used starting 8 feet from the main shielding wall. The beam traversed a 6-in. diameter hole in an 8-ft long shielding block and was then double-focused using two magnets having triangular "wedge" pole faces. The magnets served to deflect the beam from the direct line of the collimator and to concentrate it at the detection system.

The detection system is illustrated in Fig. 4. Counters 1, 2, and 3 consist of stilbene scintillation crystals viewed by 1P21 phototubes. Counter 4 functions as the photon detector. It consists of a NaI(Tl) crystal viewed by a 5819 phototube. All pertinent counter dimensions are listed in Table III. For the purpose of shielding the phototubes from stray magnetic fields the whole detection system is surrounded by a double-walled steel box made of $\frac{1}{2}$-in. material except in the region where the meson beam enters. This assembly was then mounted on an adjustable rolling cart.

The beam was analyzed as follows. One inch of carbon

TABLE III. Approximate values of counting parameters.

1. (1, 2) rate, no absorber: 450/sec.
2. (1, 2) rate, full absorber: 50/sec.
3. Approximate beam composition:
   115-Mev $\pi^- \approx 90\%$
   130-Mev $\mu^- \approx 10\%$
   214-Mev $e^- < 3\%$
4. Detector dimensions:

Counter	Diameter, in.	Thickness, in.
1	2	$\frac{1}{8}$
2	2	$\frac{1}{8}$
3	3	$\frac{1}{4}$
4	$1\frac{1}{2}$	1

5. Approximate interval counting rate of the x-ray. Analyzer near the peak of the spectrum.

Element	Interval width	Interval counts/min
Pb (5 Mev)	100 kv	1
Cu (1.53 Mev)	50 kv	2
Al (0.35 Mev)	20 kv	6

was placed in the sample position directly in front of counter 3, and a count of 123′ (123′ denotes coincidence between counters 1 and 2 and anticoincidence with counter 3) was taken as a function of copper thickness yielding a differential range curve of the meson beam. The beam was monitored by a second counter telescope positioned in one of the other beams. A sample curve is shown in Fig. 5. Two groups of particles with the same momentum are present. If the short range group is identified as π mesons then from range consideration the particles in the second group must have a mass of approximately 210 electron masses, and these are identified as μ mesons. For a further check on this identification, the decay of the μ meson to an energetic electron was utilized. An organic crystal of 1 square inch replaced the NaI crystal as counter 4. A delayed coincidence between counters 3 and 4 was tabulated in 8

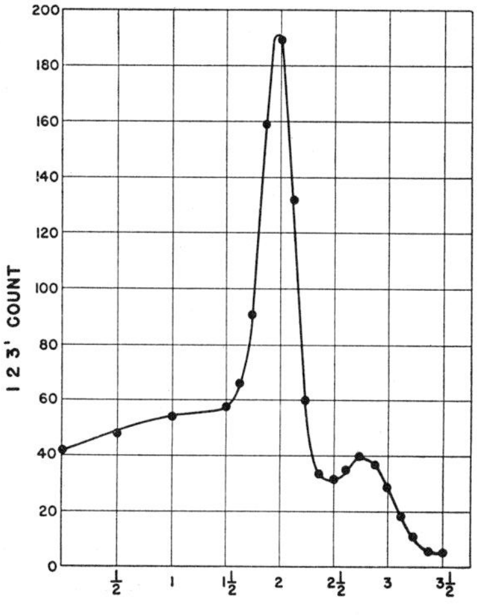

FIG. 5. Differential range curve of the meson beam. The peaks at 2 in. and $2\frac{3}{4}$ in. correspond to π and μ mesons respectively.

consecutive time intervals each approximately one microsecond in duration. The timing chain was triggered by 123′. Subtraction of the sum of the counts received in the final four channels from the sum of those in the initial four channels gives a measure of the short-lived activity associated with particles stopping in the carbon sample. This measurement was made as a function of copper absorber thickness between counters 1 and 2. The results are plotted in Fig. 6. It is observed that the delayed activity is a maximum for that thickness of copper which corresponds to the range of the second group of particles in Fig. 5. This delayed activity we associate with the decay of the μ^- mesons in the carbon. That the thickness of copper determined in this way was the optimum value was confirmed later by examining the μ-mesonic x-ray spectra as a function of copper thickness.

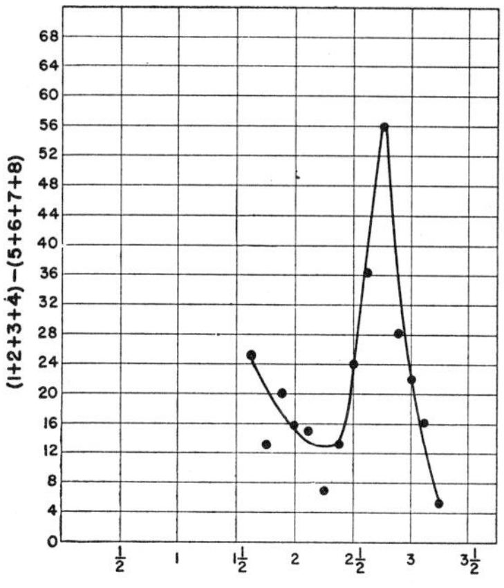

FIG. 6. Delayed activity [channels (1+2+3+4)−(5+6+7+8)] associated with particles stopping in carbon sample as a function of copper thickness between counters 1 and 2.

When the NaI detector pulses were also analyzed for pulse height to measure the photon energy, a fast 1, 2, 3′, 4 coincidence, using the collector anode of the 5819 tube, was used to trigger the pulse height analyzer which then measured the slower pulse from the 8th dynode of the 5819 tube. Provisions were also made to render the circuit insensitive for approximately 8 microseconds after each NaI pulse to assure complete recovery of the pulse level to the reference value. A thermostatic temperature control for the detector box was found to improve stability.

In addition to the NaI photon detector, the scintillation spectrometer consisted of a 10-channel differential pulse-hieght analyzer and associated amplifiers, scaling circuits, and registers. For the measurements reported here, the pulse-height analyzer was adjusted to separate the pulse spectrum into sixty intervals, which could be explored ten at a time. Thus, over a 6-Mev energy spectrum, the minimum channel width was 100 kev. All amplifier circuits were designed for optimum stability consistent with reasonable speed and insensitivity to extreme overload both in pulse rate and amplitude. The over-all spectrometer system was stable to better than $\frac{1}{2}$ percent over operating periods of three days.

Interpretation of the NaI pulse-height distribution is somewhat complicated by the fact that the primary processes by which the photon loses energy to the NaI crystal above 1 Mev are the Compton scattering and pair production. Figure 7 shows the probability per cm *vs* photon energy, of a primary interaction corresponding to photoelectric absorption, Compton scattering, or pair production. The photoelectric effect becomes negligible above approximately 1 Mev but is important at lower energies, particularly for the absorption of lower-energy Compton scattered photons.

The energy transfer in the Compton scattering of a photon of energy E_0 shows a continuous distribution from zero to about $(E_0-0.25)$ Mev (the energy transfer for backscattering). The distribution rises to a sharp peak at the high-energy end,[9] and this peak is evident when a thinner NaI crystal is used. However, the scattered photons here have approximately 0.25 Mev and are strongly absorbed in a thick detector. Thus the upper end of the Compton distribution is depleted and contributes somewhat to a full energy peak. This is again complicated, in principle, by the fact that the range of the knock-on electrons, for approximately 5-Mev photons, is not small compared to a radiation length in NaI and brehmsstrahlung processes should occur frequently. Fortunately this mainly involves the emission of low-energy x-rays which are readily absorbed.

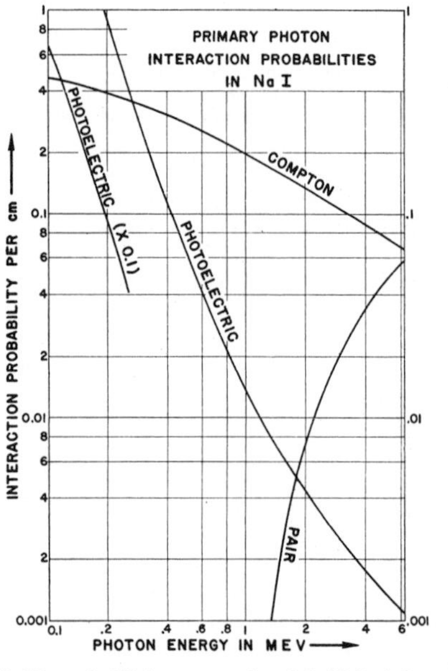

FIG. 7. The probabilities per cm of path in NaI of photoelectric absorption, Compton scattering, or pair production primary interactions as a function of photon energy.

The pair production process becomes increasingly important as the energy is increased above approximately 2 Mev. However, the direct pair process gives a pulse 1.02 Mev lower than the full energy with two 0.511-Mev annihilation gamma rays emitted when the positron stops. Again, one or both of these secondary photons may be wholly or partially absorbed to contribute to a peak at $(E_0-0.51$ Mev), or at E_0.

The curves of Fig. 7 thus are useful in showing the efficiency of various primary processes as a function of primary photon energy, but they do not tell the full story because of the complications of secondary processes. The spectrum shape $f(E_0, E)$ obtained from a photon of energy E_0 is thus a complicated function of E_0 and E which, we believe, cannot readily (or reliably) be computed by multiple application of the laws for primary interactions. It is thus necessary to obtain $f(E_0, E)$ experimentally by using known energy calibration sources. This problem is separate from the calibration of the pulse height scale in energy units. We have detected no observable deviation from linearity in the calibration of pulse height *vs* energy based on the comparison of pulse-height distribution curves using photons of the following energies: annihilation photons (0.511 Mev); Cs^{137} photons (0.662 Mev), Na^{24} photons (1.38, 2.76 Mev), C^{12*} photons (4.43 Mev), and Co^{60} (1.17, 1.33 Mev) photons, for the full energy and the different reduced energy peaks.

The spectrometer energy calibration was performed occasionally during cyclotron runs by measuring the pulse spectrum of the gamma rays from Na^{24}. The extrapolation to higher energies was accomplished by the use of carefully calibrated attenuators in the amplifier circuits. Confidence in the method was established by comparing the measured energies of known gamma rays using the same attenuation settings. Possible rate dependence of the measured pulse amplitude was explored by subjecting the spectrometer to background radiation from natural sources which

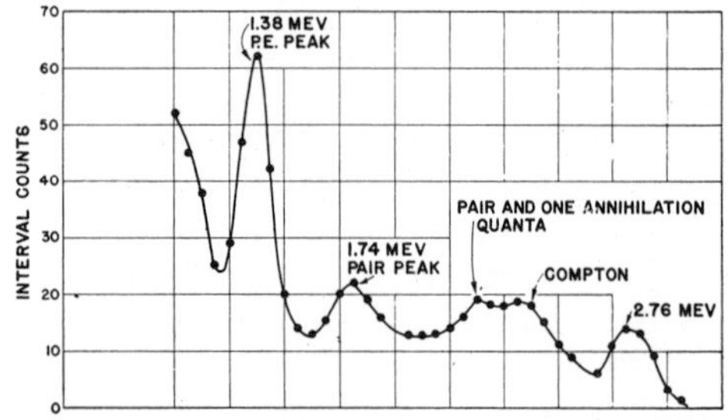

FIG. 8. Typical energy calibration curve using Na^{24}. The two γ rays at 2.76 and 1.38 Mev occur in equal number. The relative heights of the various peaks gives information about the relative efficiencies of the several interaction processes in NaI.

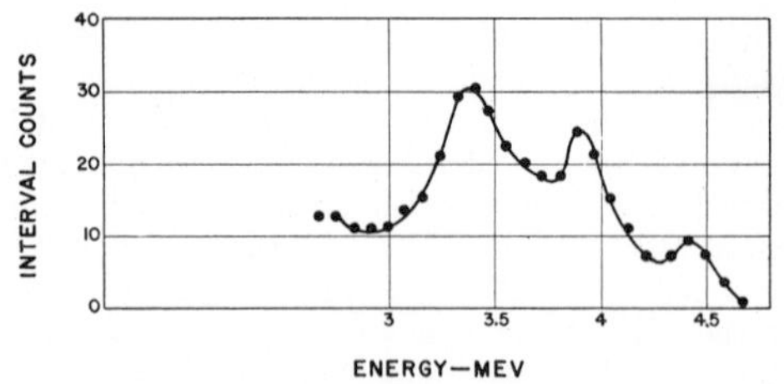

FIG. 9. Pulse-height distribution for the 4.43-Mev γ rays from C^* produced in the reaction $\alpha+Be^9\rightarrow C^{12*}+n$, using Po as a source of α particles. The peaks show a Doppler broadening of ~ 2 percent due to the motion of the C^{12*} nuclei.

[9] C. M. Davisson and R. D. Evans, Revs. Modern Phys. 24, 79, (1952). See Fig. 49 for several such plots. (The curves in Fig. 8 were calculated from Table XIV of this reference.)

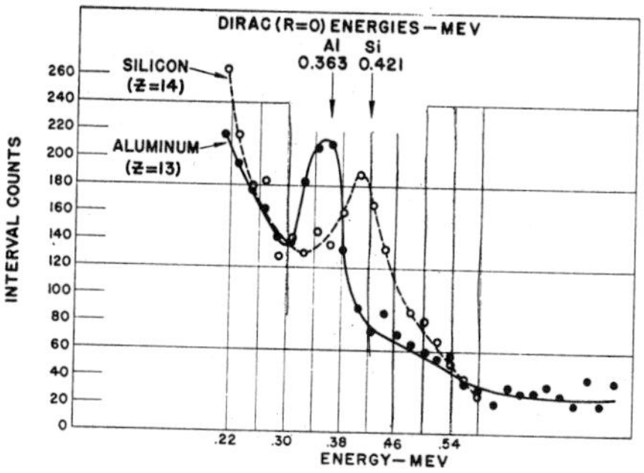

FIG. 10. Pulse-height distribution using Al and Si as the target materials ($Z=13$, 14). The peaks represent the full energies of the x-rays emitted in the $2p\rightarrow 1s$ transition. The expected energies for a point nucleus using $\mu=210m_e$ are included for reference. The shift in energy due to the finite extension of the nucleus is ~ 2 percent. In the case of Al in the region below 0.39 Mev the points are based on double the indicated number of counts. The interval width is approximately 50 kev.

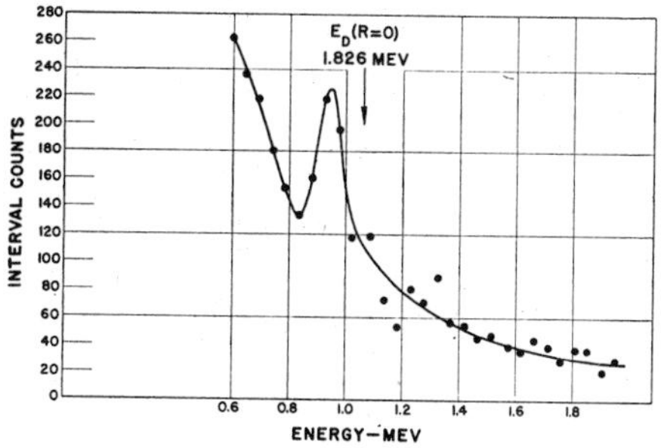

FIG. 11. Pulse-height distribution for Ti($Z=22$). The energy shift of 5 percent of the measured value due to finite nuclear extension is apparent. (In the figure 1.826 mev should read 1.045 mev.)

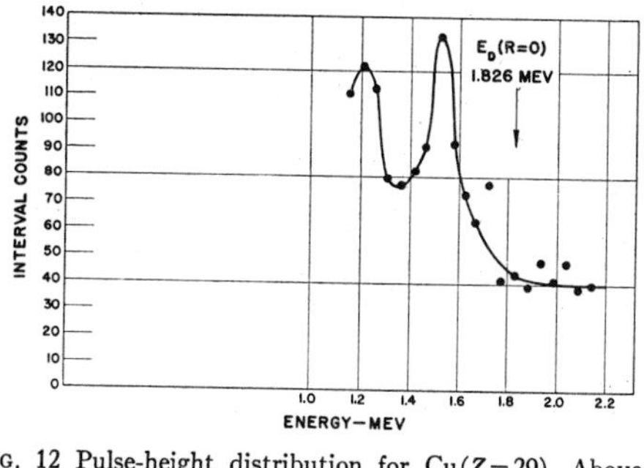

FIG. 12 Pulse-height distribution for Cu($Z=29$). Above 1.7 Mev the points are based on 0.6 the indicated number of counts. The energy shift due to finite nuclear extension is 18 percent of the measured value.

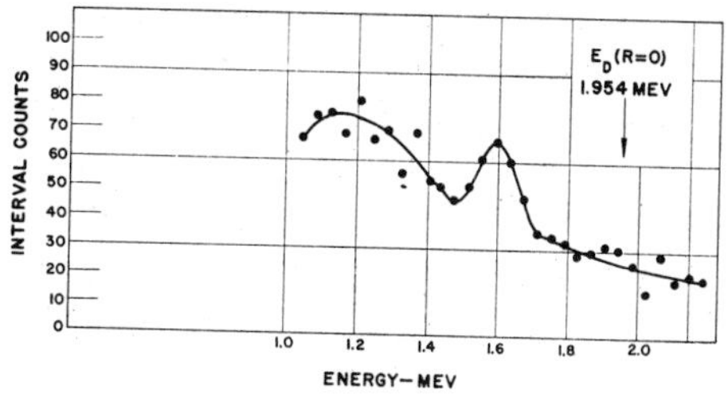

FIG. 13. Pulse-height distribution of Zn($Z=30$). In the region of the peak the points are based on 3 times the indicated number of counts. The energy shift due to finite nuclear extension is 22 percent of the measured value.

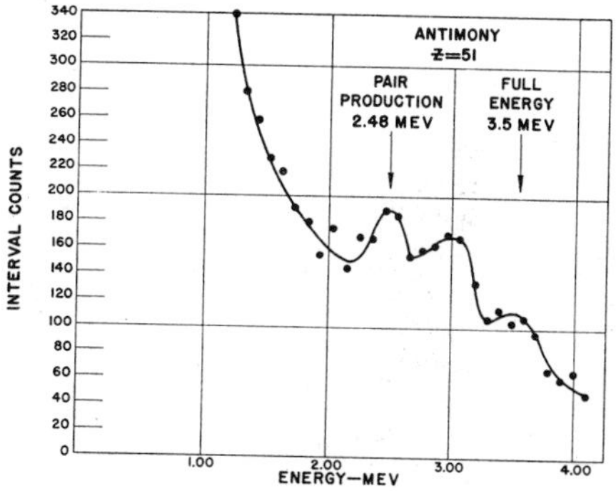

FIG. 14. Pulse-height distribution for Sb($Z=51$). The three peaks expected for a single photon of this energy are observed. The energy shift due to finite nuclear extension is 66 percent of the measured value.

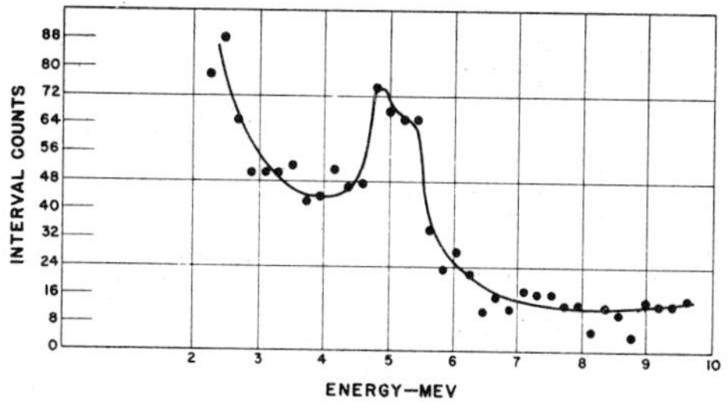

FIG. 15. Pulse-height distribution for Pb($Z=82$) taken with relatively coarse resolution (212 kev) and poor statistics over a wide energy range. The distinctive peak around 5 Mev defines the region of interest which was then investigated with higher resolution as is shown in the next figure.

contributed a pulse rate that was considerably higher than the instantaneous rates encountered when using the cyclotron. No shift in pulse amplitude was observed until the rate was about four times the instantaneous rate experienced with the cyclotron. Also large variations in the cyclotron intensity did not cause noticeable shifts in the positions of the peaks.

Interpretation of the observed pulse height distribution curves is facilitated by examination of the Na^{24} and C^{12*} calibration curves of Figs. 8 and 9. In Fig. 9 the full energy peak of the 2.76-Mev photon is due mainly to the backward Compton scattering followed by the absorption of the secondary photon. The full energy peak for the 1.38-Mev photon is much larger. The 2.76-Mev photon also contributes peaks corresponding to pair production, and pair plus one annihilation photon. The effect of the Compton scattering, modified by some secondary absorption is also evident for the

2.76-Mev photon. It is important to remember that the 2.76- and 1.38-Mev photons are in cascade and are thus emitted in equal number. The relative peak heights thus give direct evidence concerning the relative efficiencies of various processes for these two energy photons.

Figure 9 shows the pulse spectrum resulting from the radiation from the Po-Be neutron source. The 4.43-Mev gamma rays result from a transition from the first excited level[10] of O^{12} to the ground state following the neutron-producing reaction. The source is uot monochromatic but shows a 2 percent Doppler broadening due to the momentum of the C^{12*} nucleus in the reaction. This Doppler broadening affects the shape of the pulse-height curve since the peaks would be expected to be significantly higher and narrower for a monochromatic source.

The coincidence resolution was somewhat better than 10^{-7} sec. This is sufficient to remove from the spectrum approximately half of the gamma rays originating from nuclear capture of the μ^- meson in the high-Z materials, and essentially all of them for lower-Z materials where nuclear absorption is slower.

EXPERIMENTAL RESULTS

The pulse-height distribution curves of Figs. 10 to 18 show the experimental results for studies of the x-rays resulting when μ^- mesons are stopped in Al, Si, Ti, Cu, Zn, Sb, Pb, Hg, and Bi ($Z=13$, 14, 22, 29, 30, 51, 82, 80, and 83). In the first few curves the predicted full energy position of the $2p\rightarrow 1s$ transition for a point nucleus is shown for reference (using $\mu=210m_e$). The x-ray energies vary from about 0.35 Mev for Al to 6.0 Mev for Pb and Bi. In the cases of Al, Si, Ti, Cu, and Zn, the main x-ray peak occurs at the full energy and general background and Compton scattering pulses contribute other pulse heights to the spectrum. For Sb the full energy occurs at about 3.5 Mev and three peaks, like those of Fig. 9, are obtained for E_0, $E_0-0.51$ Mev and $E_0-1.02$ Mev superimposed on a general background level.

Figure 15 shows the results for Pb over a region from about 2 Mev to 10 Mev using an interval width of about 210 kev. The x-ray peak stands out strongly near 5 Mev. The region from 4.2 to 6.0 Mev was then investigated using approximately 100-kv resolution width, with the typical results given in Fig. 16. This curve should be compared with Fig. 9 for interpretation. We have adopted, as most likely, the interpretation that the 5.0-Mev peak is the $2p_{3/2}\rightarrow 1s$ pair peak corresponding to 6.0 Mev for the x-ray energy. The $2p_{1/2}\rightarrow 1s$ peak should be 0.2 Mev lower in energy with half the intensity of the other. The peak near 5.3 Mev and the effects near 4.8 Mev and 5.6 Mev are not consistent with the pattern of Fig. 9 of three nearly symmetric peaks 0.5 Mev apart. In using Fig. 9 for reference, it should be noted that theoretical considerations, and the experimental results of other investigators (using similar sized NaI crystals), show that the pair peak should be relatively much larger compared to the intermediate and full energy peaks at 6 Mev than for 4.5-Mev photons.

Our tentative interpretation of Fig. 16 is thus that there are present $2p_{3/2}\rightarrow 1s$ and $2p_{1/2}\rightarrow 1s$ x-rays of 6.0 and 5.8 Mev respectively. The main peak at 5.0 Mev and the shoulder at 5.5 Mev followed by a sharp drop at

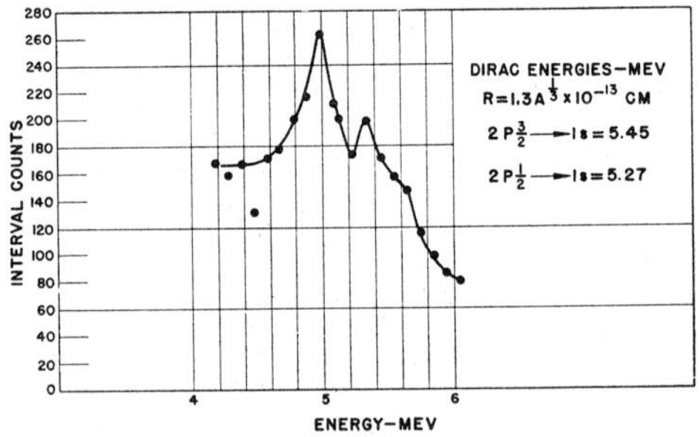

FIG. 16 Pulse-height distribution for Pb with ~100-kev interval width. The main peak at 5.00 Mev is interpreted as the pair production peak due to the x-rays from the $2p_{3/2}\rightarrow 1s$ transition. Further discussion of this curve is in the text. The energy shift due to finite extension is 172 percent of the measured value.

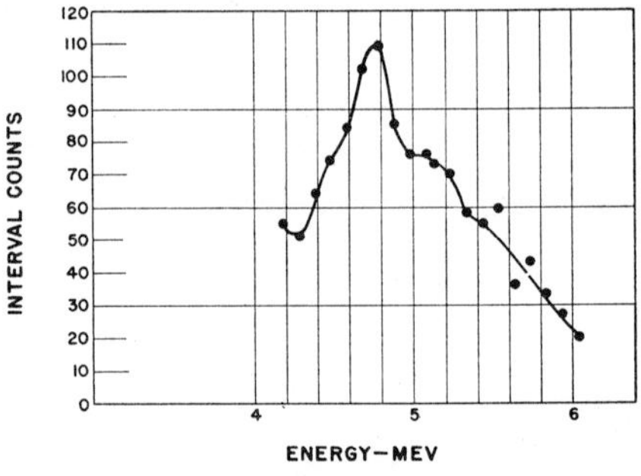

FIG. 17. Pulse-height distribution for Hg($Z=80$). The peak at 4.8 Mev obviously corresponds to the one at 5.0 Mev for Pb.

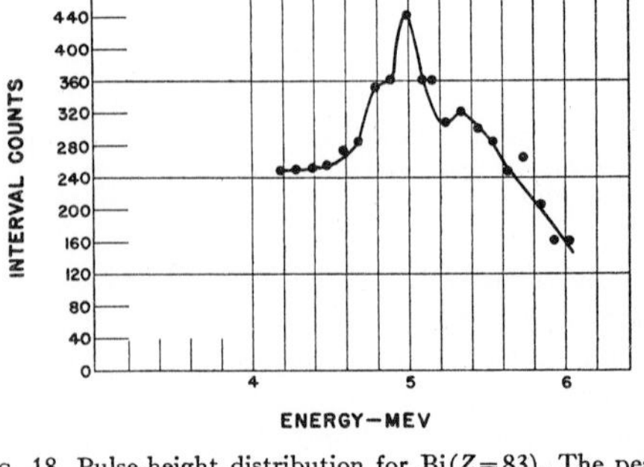

FIG. 18 Pulse-height distribution for Bi($Z=83$). The peak at 5.0 Mev obviously corresponds to the similar peak at the same energy for Pb.

[10] F. Ajzenberg and T. Lauritsen, Revs. Modern Phys. 24, 354–359 (1952).

higher energies are thus the pair and pair plus one annihilation photon peaks for the 6.0-Mev photon. The effects at 4.8 and 5.3 Mev then correspond to the similar peaks for the 5.8-Mev photon. The assymetry and other features would seem to preclude a single photon. The peaks at 5.0 and 5.3 Mev would be hard to reconcile with the expected 0.51-Mev spacing expected for a single photon. Thus we believe that we see the expected fine structure splitting for Pb. The total counts for each point are indicated on the ordinate. The statistics suggest considerable uncertainty in the proper drawing of a curve. However, many separate runs of this type were taken and the essential features of this curve repeated in most of the runs. Thus we believe that the effects are much more likely to be real than the statistics of Fig. 16 alone would suggest. The absence of a large pair peak at 4.0 to 4.7 Mev in Figs. 15 and 16 seems to exclude an interpretation having the x-ray energy near 5.0 or 5.5 Mev. We intend to continue these measurements using a smaller interval width and faster resolving time to eliminate most of the nuclear gamma rays following the absorption of the μ meson.

The similar curves for Hg and Bi are shown in Figs. 17 and 18 and show similar structure. The main peak which came at 5.0 Mev for Pb is at 4.8 Mev for Hg and at 5.0 Mev also for Bi. Rembembering that the x-ray energy increases as the nuclear size decreases, the relatively high energy of the Pb peak compared with that for Bi (i.e., the same x-ray energy for $Z=82$ as for $Z=83$) may be associated with the closed proton shell at $Z=82$, giving a particularly "tight" configuration.

In the analysis of the experimental curves various assumptions are possible about what is assumed "known" or "unknown." Such parameters include (a) the meson mass, (b) the nuclear radius (for a uniform model of the nucleus), (c) the meson spin and magnetic moment. Since the meson mass is known[11] to be close to $210m_e$, we can first consider (b) and (c) using this mass value. As mentioned above, we believe that our results for Pb can best be explained in terms of the expected fine structure splitting for spin $\frac{1}{2}$ and the expected Dirac magnetic moment. Wheeler[8] discusses the expected effect of an anomolous moment.

TABLE IV. Assuming $\mu=210m_e$ and using a uniform nuclear model with $R_0=r_0A^{\frac{1}{3}}$, values of r_0 shown in column 3 give the best fit to the experimental measured $2p_{\frac{3}{2}}\rightarrow 1s$ transition energies given in column 2 as a function of Z.

Z	$E(2p_{\frac{3}{2}}\rightarrow 1S)$ (experimental, Mev)	r_0 (10^{-13} cm)
22	0.955	1.17
29	1.55	1.21
51	3.50	1.22
82	6.02	1.17

[11] See R. E. Marshak, reference 1, Chap. 6, for a discussion and listing of further reference.

Using $\mu=210m_e$, the nuclear radii which provide the best fit to the data for various elements are given in Table IV. The values all lie near $R_0=1.2\times10^{-13}A^{\frac{1}{3}}$ cm which is much smaller than the radius indicated by other nuclear "size sensitive" experiments. This matter is discussed in more detail below.

For a low-Z element the probability density of the K shell meson near $r=0$ varies as Z^3 and the probability of finding it in the nucleus as $Z^3R_0^3$. The mean change, ΔV, in the potential energy inside the nucleus, because of its nonzero size, is proportional to Z/R_0. Thus the energy shift ΔE due to finite nuclear size should be proportional to $Z^4R_0^2$ for light nuclei. Since the binding energy is proportional to Z^2, the *fractional* energy shift should be proportional to $Z^2R_0^2$. The x-ray energy is relatively insensitive to R_0 for elements of low Z. In the case of Al the total nuclear size effect is only approximately 2 percent. Thus, in principle, the most precise determination of the meson mass could be made using a material of very low Z. However, the limited number of photons producing photoelectrons at the 5819 cathode causes the fractional resolving power of the NaI-5819 detection system to be proportional to $E^{\frac{1}{2}}$ for small E (photon energy). The greatest accuracy in the determination of μ with the present detection system was obtained using $Z=22$, where the energy resolution is not too poor and the nuclear size effect is still small.

The curve for Ti is shown in Fig. 11. Because of the prominent nature of x-ray peak for this element, it was often measured when an over-all check of the operation of the complete system was desired. Since independent calibration runs were made at regular intervals during all runs, a large number of independent evaluations of the x-ray energy for Ti were obtained, all values falling within 1 percent of the mean energy 0.955 Mev. Figure 19 gives a plot of the predicted x-ray energy as abscissa *vs* the μ-meson mass as ordinate. The four lines are for four possible choices of nuclear radius parameter $r_0=R_0A^{-\frac{1}{3}}$ in units of 10^{-13} cm. The experimental results all came within the cross-hatched region about 0.955 Mev. For $\mu=210m_e$, this gives $r_0=1.17\times10^{-13}$ cm in essential agreement with the results for higher Z. The choice $r_0=1.4\times10^{-13}$ cm gives $\mu=217m_e$ which is outside the range allowed by other experimental determinations.

The calculated nuclear radii of a number of elements for $Z=22$ to $Z=83$ (Table IV) are in close agreement and require $r_0\approx1.2\times10^{-13}$ cm, with $r_0=1.17\times10^{-13}$ cm for Pb (in terms of the uniform model). Since many other nuclear-size-sensitive experiments seemed to agree on a choice $r_0=1.4$ to 1.5×10^{-13} cm, and since the precision of the present results for high-Z materials is better than 1 percent for r_0, it is important to examine the present results in more detail. This is done by Cooper and Henley in a following paper.[7] The alternative choices seem to be (a) the present results need large corrections due to effects not considered in the present analysis, or (b) a modification of the "uniform model" of the nucleus is necessary to account simultaneously for the results of the present experiment and also those of other methods.

Under possibility (a) above we consider the nuclear polarizability in the field of the meson. This would increase the interaction energy and thus the x-ray energy. As mentioned above, estimates[7] of this effect indicate that it is probably less than 0.06 Mev for Pb. The similar results for $Z=80$, 82, and 83 seem to rule out the possibility of any strong "resonance" effect in the polarizability of Pb due to accidental features of the position of its low-lying nuclear energy levels. The second possibility is that there is some additional, at present unknown, specific interaction of μ mesons with nuclear matter. This would have to be an attractive interaction of 3-Mev depth to shift r_0 for Pb from 1.17 to 1.4×10^{-13} cm. Although this possibility cannot be completely dismissed, it seems the least likely of the alternative choices. Thus we believe that neither of these effects are present in significant amount in our measurements.

The alternate choice is to accept the results of the present experiment as stated and also accept the 15 to 20 percent larger results for r_0 of other methods and try to arrive at a nuclear model which will "explain" all of the results simultaneously. To do this we note that total cross sections from scattering experiments, and α-decay lifetimes, are mainly sensitive to conditions at the "edge" of the nucleus. The present experiment is mainly sensitive to the proton density in the inner region of the nucleus and requires an interior charge density $(1.4/1.17)^3=1.7$ times larger (on the uniform model) than do other experiments. This would suggest a nuclear model with a central density two or more times the usually accepted value. The density should then fall off relatively gradually in an extended "edge" region to give the effectively larger radius found by "edge-sensitive" experiments.

It is easily seen that the nuclear "surface" *cannot* be sharp. Even if we consider a nuclear model where the nucleons move in an effective potential with a sharp edge, the nucleon wave functions still have an exponential attenuation in the classically forbidden region. Furthermore, since the effective potential is due to the presence of other nucleons in forming a "self-consistent nuclear box", and in view of the $1\text{–}3\times10^{-13}$ cm range of the basic nuclear forces, the effective potential and nucleon density must require a dropping-off region significantly larger than the range of the nuclear forces.

In α-decay theory, the effective value of R_0 is where the nuclear density is large enough to essentially overcome the Coulomb barrier effects. This is further complicated by the question of the position of the α particle's effective "surface," which must be some distance from its center. The usual addition[12] of 1.2 $\times10^{-13}$ cm for these effects could certainly be much too small.

Similarly, fast neutron scattering experiments are somewhat difficult of exact interpretation for a nucleus with a gradual falling off of nuclear density at the "surface." For neutrons of a few Mev energy particularly, there is probably strong interaction with the outer regions of the nucleus.[13] Similar remarks apply for meson scattering experiments.

The evaluation of nuclear radii for low-Z elements from the Coulomb energy difference of mirror nuclei leads to values of r_0 from 1.39 to 1.47×10^{-13} cm when a uniform model is employed. Since the Coulomb energies for mirror nuclei would seem to have about the same dependence on the nuclear density distribution as does the K-shell μ-meson binding, this would seem to constitute a serious disagreement with the results of the present experiment. However, further study of this matter has been made by Cooper and Henley[7] who find that various corrections should be applied to the mirror

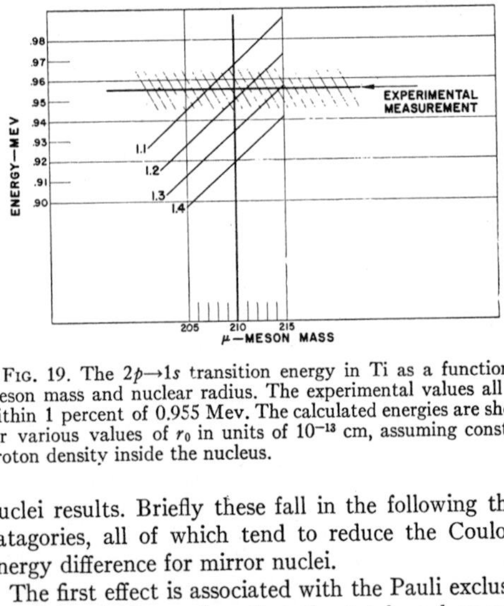

FIG. 19. The $2p\to1s$ transition energy in Ti as a function of meson mass and nuclear radius. The experimental values all fall within 1 percent of 0.955 Mev. The calculated energies are shown for various values of r_0 in units of 10^{-13} cm, assuming constant proton density inside the nucleus.

nuclei results. Briefly these fall in the following three catagories, all of which tend to reduce the Coulomb energy difference for mirror nuclei.

The first effect is associated with the Pauli exclusion principle which requires that the total nuclear wave function be antisymmetric in all of the protons. This leads to an excess of space-antisymmetric pairings of protons which means that they have a tendency to correlate their motions in such a way as to *increase* their average spacing. Furthermore, it is not the *average* Coulomb energy per proton that is measured, but the *change* in Coulomb energy when the last nucleon changes from a neutron to a proton. Thus the Coulomb energy difference involves the total increase in the number of antisymmetric pairings when $Z\to Z+1$. The second effect comes from a study of the predictions of the shell model[14] of Mayer and Haxel, Jensen, and Suess which

[12] See J. M. Blatt and V. W. Weisskopf, *Theoretical Nuclear Physics* (John Wiley and Sons, Inc., New York, 1952), Chap. 11, Eq. (2.19).

[13] R. Jastrow and J. Roberts, Phys. Rev. 85, 757 (1952).

[14] See P. F. A. Klinkenberg, Revs. Modern Phys. 24, 63 (1952).

identifies the transforming nucleon as being in a single-particle d state for the important region $Z=9$ to perhaps 20. The radial probability density for a d state gives an effective radius which is appreciably greater than the average over all of the protons, even for a square well potential. If a harmonic oscillator potential is used, the radius at which $E=V$ increases with increasing individual particle energy. Since the transforming nucleon is considered to occupy the highest filled individual-particle state, its wave packet tends to fill a larger volume than the other individual particle wave packets. This third effect is true even for the one-dimensional problem and is thus not directly related to the angular momentum of the state. Considering all of these three effects together, it seems that the mirror nuclei results can probably be brought into agreement with the results of the present experiment. It may be noted that Wilson[15] has reanalyzed the results for mirror nuclei using a gradual falling off of nuclear density at the surface, but without considering the special effects mentioned above.

If a gradual dropping off of nuclear density at the "surface" of the nucleus is assumed, it is still of interest to consider the variation $\rho(r)$ of the proton density inside this boundary region. Feenberg[16] particularly has emphasized the Coulomb repulsion effect and favored a nuclear model where the proton density is larger near the surface than at the center. This leads also to a quite different explanation[16] of the "magic" numbers and is in disagreement with the model more generally favored at present,[14] which essentially assumes a potential closer to that of the oscillator model. In conclusion we note that results for high-energy electron scattering by nuclei were presented by R. Hofstadter *et al.* at the 1953 Washington Meeting of the American Physical Society. Preliminary analysis of their results seemed to favor a model where $\rho(r)$ is a maximum at $r=0$ and drops off steadily at larger r. It seems likely that the most precise determination of the correct $\rho(r)$ *vs* r will come from combining the results of such electron scattering experiments, which suggest the shape of $\rho(r)$ *vs* r, with the μ-meson x-ray results, which give a precision evaluation of the scale factor r_0 for any assumed shape $\rho(r/r_0)$.

It is also possible to obtain information concerning nuclear size by using the results of ordinary (electron) x-ray spectroscopy, as has been pointed out by Schawlow and Townes.[17] The $2p_{\frac{3}{2}}$, $2p_{\frac{1}{2}}$ fine structure splitting for high-Z elements is affected by nuclear size to a very small, but measurable extent. The analysis[17] of available x-ray data gives $r_0 \approx 1.5\times 10^{-13}$ cm, with much lower precision than the results of the μ-mesonic x-ray measurements. With improvements in the experimental accuracy of the (ordinary) x-ray measurements, and re-examination of the theoretical analysis to see that no significant higher-order effects (of quantum electrodynamics) have been neglected, the x-ray fine structure splitting should be capable of providing independent, precise information concerning nuclear size.

We wish to thank the many members of the Columbia Physics Department with whom we have discussed various aspects of the problem. Particular thanks are due Dr. Henley and Mr. Cooper, and Professor Wheeler for communication of the results of their calculation prior to publication. Mr. Samuel Koslov has given considerable valuable assistance in the later phases of the experimental measurements and in the calculations.

[15] R. R. Wilson, Phys. Rev. **88**, 350 (1952).

[16] E. Feenberg and K. C. Hammack, Phys. Rev. **75**, 1877 (1949). See also other papers by L. W. Nordheim and M. G. Mayer in the same issue (pp. 1968, 1969, and 1894).

[17] A. L. Schawlow and C. H. Townes, Science **115**, 284 (1952).

PAPER 20

High-Energy Electron Scattering and Nuclear Structure Determinations*,†,‡

R. Hofstadter, H. R. Fechter, and J. A. McIntyre
Department of Physics and W. W. Hansen Laboratories, Stanford University, Stanford, California
(Received June 26, 1953)

Electrons of energies 125 and 150 Mev are deflected from the Stanford linear accelerator and brought to a focused spot of dimensions 3 mm×15 mm at a distance of 9 feet from a double magnet deflecting system. The focus is placed at the center of a brass-scattering chamber of diameter 20 inches. Thin foils are inserted in the chamber and elastically-scattered electrons from these foils pass through thin aluminum windows into the vacuum chamber of a double focusing analyzing magnet of the inhomogeneous field type. The energy resolution of the magnet has been about 1.5 percent in these experiments. This resolution is enough to separate clearly hydrogen or deuterium elastic peaks from carbon peaks in the same scattering target. The energy loss in the foils is readily measurable. In the case of light nuclei, e.g., H, D, Be, C, the shift of the peak of the elastic curve as a function of scattering angle indicates the recoil of the struck nucleus. Relative angular distributions are measured for Be, Ta, Au, and Pb. It is possible to interpret these data in terms of a variable charge density within the nucleus.

I. INTRODUCTION

In a recent publication[1] it was suggested that the gold nucleus does not have a sharp boundary. In this paper it is proposed to amplify this statement and to present data on other nuclei which tend to bear out this conclusion.

Guth[2] first pointed out that the finite size of the nucleus should produce large deviations from the expected scattering resulting from a point charge whenever the electron wavelength is of the order of nuclear dimensions. In principle, such deviations might be wholly or partially ascribed to departures from the Coulomb law of electric interaction at very small distances. In the following discussions it will be assumed that the Coulombian interaction holds at small distances and that the departures, if any, from point charge scattering are assignable to the finite dimensions of the nuclear charge distribution.

Other authors have subsequently considered the problem of the finite size of nuclei in relation to scattering experiments.[3–8] Parzen, Smith, and Schiff have dealt with energies of the order of 100 Mev and higher, while the other authors have been concerned mainly with lower energies. Parzen has made an exact calculation at a high energy (100 Mev). Unfortunately, a numerical error crept into Parzen's work and his published scattering curve cannot be considered reliable.[9] For nuclei having a uniform or spherical shell distribution of charge all Born approximation calculations predict maxima and minima in the angular distribution. These features are essentially diffraction phenomena and are similar to the observations in electron diffraction studies of atoms. The first Born approximation[2,4,7] for these models produces the first of a set of zeros in the angular intensity pattern at those angles where

$$qa \cong 3.5, \tag{1}$$

$$q = (4\pi/\lambda)\sin(\theta/2), \tag{2}$$

in which λ is the wavelength of the incident electrons and "a" is the rms value of the nuclear radius, calculated with the charge as the weighting factor. Yennie *et al.*[10] have shown that for a uniform model the exact calculation provides a result in which the first diffraction minimum is practically washed out and the second and third less pronounced than in the Born approximation but approximately in the same angular positions. Experimental indications of a deviation from point charge scattering have been found by Lyman, Hanson, and Scott[11] at an electron energy of 15.7 Mev. $\lambda\!\!\!^{-} = \lambda/2\pi$ is, in this case, of the order of 1.25×10^{-12} cm and, if one uses a conventional radius for gold ($R=8.1\times10^{-13}$ cm, $a=6.3\times10^{-13}$ cm), qa is found to be close to or less than unity. Thus, no maxima or minima are to be expected in the experiment of Lyman *et al.*, although marked deviations in the angular distribution were expected and, in fact, found. The experimental data proved to be consistent with a uniformly charged model of the nucleus in which

$$R = r_0 A^{\frac{1}{3}}, \tag{3}$$

where r_0 was 1.45×10^{-13} cm. In gold a twenty percent smaller radius gave a very slightly improved fit of the

* This work was initiated and aided at all stages by a grant from the Research Corporation. It was supported by the joint program of the U. S. Office of Naval Research and the U. S. Atomic Energy Commission. In the latter stages of the work, support has been received from the Office of Scientific Research, Air Research, and Development Command.

† This material was presented in part at the April 29, 30–May 1, 1953 Meeting of the American Physical Society in Washington, D. C.

‡ Portions of the theoretical interpretation were revised in proof.

1 Hofstadter, Fechter, and McIntyre, Phys. Rev. **91**, 422 (1953).

2 E. Guth, Wiener Anzeiger Akad. Wissenschaften No. 24, 299 (1934).

3 G. Parzen, Phys. Rev. **80**, 261 (1950); **80**, 355 (1950).

4 L. R. B. Elton, Proc. Phys. Soc. (London) **A63**, 1115 (1950); **65**, 481 (1952); Phys. Rev. **79**, 412 (1950).

5 H. Feshbach, Phys. Rev. **84**, 1206 (1951); **88**, 295 (1952).

6 L. K. Acheson, Phys. Rev. **82**, 488 (1951).

7 J. H. Smith, Ph.D. thesis, Cornell University, 1951 (unpublished).

8 L. I. Schiff, following paper, Phys. Rev. **93**, 988 (1953).

9 G. Parzen (private communication). The error was first found by Elizabeth Baranger (private communication).

10 Yennie, Wilson, and Ravenhall have recently recalculated the exact scattering at high energies (private communication).

11 Lyman, Hanson, and Scott, Phys. Rev. **84**, 626 (1951).

data. Lyman *et al.* have noted that the smaller radius in gold might indicate a more dense packing of protons in the interior of the nucleus. A suggestion of this type had been made previously by Born and Yang.[12]

The experiments to be described below were intended to search for possible clear-cut signs of nuclear finite dimensions and by this means to find nuclear radii and charge distributions.

II. APPARATUS

Only the main features of the experimental equipment will be described at this time. Figure 1 shows the principal experimental arrangement. A monoenergetic group of electrons is deflected by a system of two magnets from the main beam of the Stanford linear accelerator.[13] The first magnet bends and disperses the beam and the second magnet bends in a reverse direction and refocuses the spread-out beam. A slit at position S determines the width of the accepted energy band, in this case about 3 percent. The initial width of the beam entering the first magnet is determined by the collimator C, in this case a $\frac{1}{4}$-inch cylindrical hole in a uranium block 1.0-inch long. A well focused beam emerges from the second magnet and closes to a small spot 9 feet from the second magnet. The position of the spot is accurately given by simple first-order calculation of trajectories. The size of the spot is approximately 1-mm high and 3-mm wide for a $\frac{1}{16}$-inch collimator and 3 mm$\times$15 mm for a $\frac{1}{4}$-inch collimator. The beam has extremely little divergence because of the 9.0-foot focal distance and small slit S used (0.75). As many as 2×10^8 electrons per pulse have been measured in the focused beam, sixty pulses occurring per second, each lasting about 0.5 microsecond. The beam is quite free of any gamma rays produced at the collimator and slit because of the double deflection. The beam stopper B prevents gamma rays produced at C from traveling down the accelerator tube and producing unwanted background in the experimental area.

The focused beam is directed towards a scattering target, usually a thin foil of any one of various materials. The scattering target is placed at the center of a brass scattering chamber of diameter twenty inches and twelve inches high. The scattering chamber is built in the form of a large bell-jar which can be detached readily from the main base plate. The whole deflection system and scattering chamber are evacuated to high vacuum. The base of the scattering chamber contains electrical lead-in connections and provisions for mounting and internally moving one or more scintillation counters on a large ring gear whose position is controllable remotely. A thin aluminum window (0.006 in.) stretches around the chamber from about $-150°$ to $150°$ over a vertical distance of three inches. Scattered electrons from the target emerge from the chamber

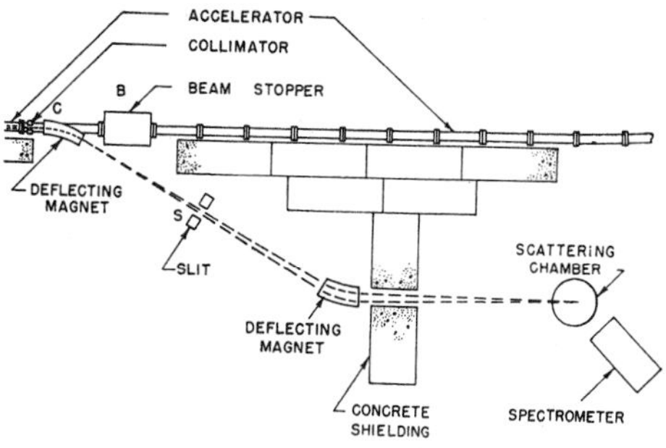

FIG. 1. The experimental arrangement of the electron-scattering system.

through the aluminum window and pass through about one inch of air before reaching the entrance port of the vacuum chamber of the analyzing magnet M. The C-shaped vacuum chamber lies between the shaped pole pieces of the inhomogeneous field magnet. The entrance and exit ports of the vacuum chamber are fitted with 3-mil aluminum windows. The magnet M is similar to the design of Snyder *et al.*,[14] weighs about two and a half tons and has a mean radius of curvature of 16 inches. It is located on the movable platform of a modified twin 40-mm anti-aircraft gun mount kindly lent us by the U. S. Navy, with the cooperation of the U. S. Office of Naval Research.[15] The magnet is of the double focusing variety and employs an inhomogeneous field of index $n=\frac{1}{2}$. Fields up to 12 or 13 kilogauss have been obtained and maintained over long periods of time without excessive heating. The field is usually maintained constant by manual regulation of the current.

A rotatable foil-holder that can be remotely controlled is now being installed in the scattering chamber. The experiments to be described were carried out with a substitute foil-holder which could be rotated and raised or lowered. The raising or lowering operation was remote, but the rotation was not. The holder could accommodate two foils at a time.

After the scattered electrons are analyzed in the magnet they leave the vacuum chamber and are collimated by a $\frac{1}{2}$-in. cylindrical hole in a lead block $2\frac{1}{2}$ inches long. Behind this collimator a conical Čerenkov counter, four inches long, detects the electrons admitted by the collimator. The Čerenkov counter is made of highly polished lucite and is one inch at the narrow input end and 1.5 in. at the output end where the lucite is coupled via heavy silicone oil to a 6292 Dumont

[12] M. Born and L. M. Yang, Nature **166**, 399 (1950).

[13] Among those mainly responsible for this system are Dr. J. A. McIntyre and Dr. W. K. H. Panofsky.

[14] Snyder, Rubin, Fowler, and Lauritsen, Rev. Sci. Instr. **21**, 852 (1950); C. W. Li, Ph.D. thesis, California Institute of Technology, 1951 (unpublished).

[15] The gun mount was modified and machined most capably by the machine shop of the Mare Island Shipyard of the U. S. Navy. We are very grateful to the officers and civilians of the yard for the excellent job done. The U. S. Office of Naval Research very kindly helped us make the necessary arrangements with the shipyard.

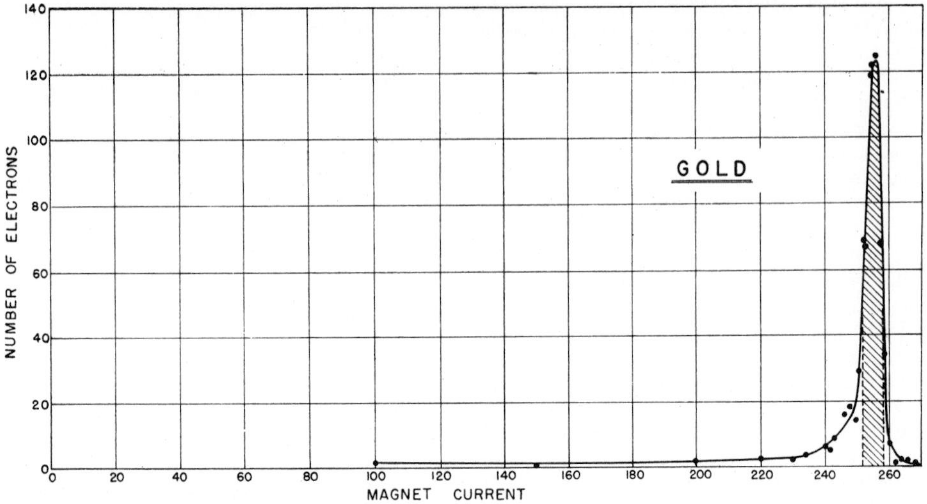

FIG. 2. An elastic-scattering curve in gold taken at 125 Mev, at a scattering angle of 35°, and with a 2-mil foil set at 45° with respect to the beam. The shaded portion of the peak shows the fraction of electrons counted in an individual peak setting. The abscissa is proportional to electron energy.

Photomultiplier. The pulses from the photomultiplier are amplified in an Elmore model 501 amplifier and fed to a gated scaler (gate 12 microseconds long) and also to an oscilloscope viewed by a monitor photomultiplier which has been made to act as a counter.[16] Both counters are gated by the main trigger signal of the linear accelerator. The biases against which both counters operate are adjusted so that the two agree on number of counts. Good plateaus in counting rates are thus obtained. An effort is made to count not more than one count a second so that pileup and loss of counts may be avoided. A large lead shield surrounds the Čerenkov counter and photomultiplier and has greatly helped in avoiding background troubles.

The main beam passing through the scattering target is monitored by a helium-filled ionization chamber designed by W. C. Barber of this laboratory. Dr. Barber has kindly calibrated and tested the chamber with 25-Mev electrons and has verified that it does not saturate under beam intensities up to 2×10^8 electrons per pulse, where a pulse lasts about 0.3 microsecond, and where the beam is about 2 cm^2 or larger on entering the chamber. Under the conditions of the experiments here reported the ion chamber does not saturate. The output of the chamber is brought to a charge integrator of a conventional type.

The deflecting magnets are presently stabilized by an electronic regulator to better than one part in a thousand. The analyzing magnet is manually controlled by an operator who reads the voltage across a shunt in series with the current. A Rubicon potentiometer is used to read the shunt voltage. With careful control the analyzing magnet current may be maintained constant between limits of ±0.1 percent during a run of 10 minutes duration.

The magnet has been calibrated by using the known energy of the Am^{241} α particles and by measurement of the magnetic field at the center of the magnet.

The angular position of the magnet on the gun mount stand is controlled remotely and measured by a combination of high and low speed selsyn indicators. The error in determining position is less than 0.1°.

III. EXPERIMENTAL PROCEDURE

Because of the temporary nature of the target holder the scattering foils were not rotated during the angular runs. This procedure has the advantage that one always uses the same region of the scattering foil provided that the beam spot does not shift during a run. When setting the analyzing magnet from one side of zero to the other, it is of course necessary to rotate the target foil and this was done. Also when points beyond 90° were examined, the foil was rotated to a new fixed position. A typical setting of the foil for a run between 35° and 90° was with foil plane at 45° with respect to the beam. The lineup of the beam was carefully carried out at the beginning of each run by a photographic method.

At a given angular position of the analyzing magnet an "elastic curve" can be obtained by measuring the total number of counts per unit integrated beam for various settings of the magnetic field. The magnetic field settings are assumed to be proportional to the magnet currents and the former are also proportional to the electronic momenta. For these high energies, the currents are therefore also proportional to the electronic energies. Typical elastic curves so obtained are shown in

[16] R. Hofstadter and J. A. McIntyre, Rev. Sci. Instr. 21, 52 (1950)

Figs. 2, 3, 4, and 5. The abscissa on these curves is proportional to the magnet current, and in all cases except Fig. 2 the zero of abscissa is far off to the left of the ordinate axis. The curve of magnetic field against magnet current shows little saturation in the region here investigated[14] (about 100 amperes).

The elastic curves show typical bremsstrahlung tails on the low-energy side and sharper cutoffs on the high-energy side, as expected. Figure 2 shows the appearance of an elastic curve for gold and indicates also the fraction of electrons collected in individual peak settings. Figure 3 shows a typical displacement between the peak of the main beam and that of the transmitted beam at zero degrees, the difference being the result of the energy loss in the gold foil (2-mils thick). Figures 3 and 4 show that the elastic curves have the same appearance at angular settings of 0°, 35°, and 70° and presumably, therefore, at other angles. Figure 5 and Figs. 1 and 2 of our earlier communication[1] show that the elastic curves of hydrogen and deuterium in polyethylene as well as beryllium shift with the angular position. This shift has been explained[1] by the recoil of the struck nucleus (H, D, Be, C). With improved resolution this recoil shift will permit scattering measurements to be made on unseparated isotopes in the same foil and also with the elements of compounds. In the case of Ta, Au, and Pb the recoil shift is too small to be observed at the present time. In those cases in which the elastic curves have the same appearance at all angles, it is sufficient to measure the total elastic yield at a given angle by an average of two measurements taken at positions on

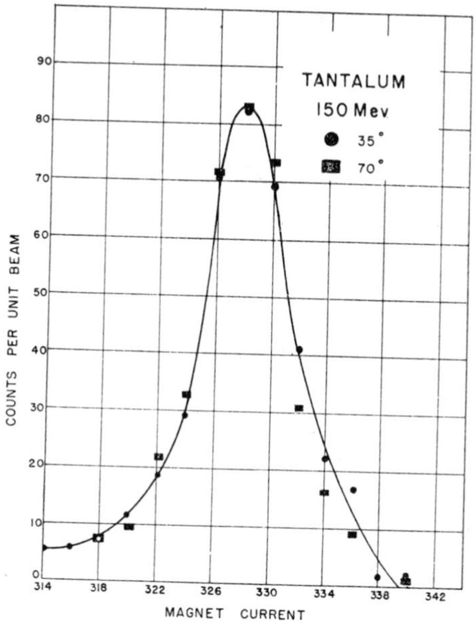

FIG. 4. Elastic-scattering curves in tantalum at 150 Mev. The data at 35° and 70° are essentially identical when normalized to the same peak value. The foil was 2.6 mils thick and was placed at 30° with respect to the direction of the beam.

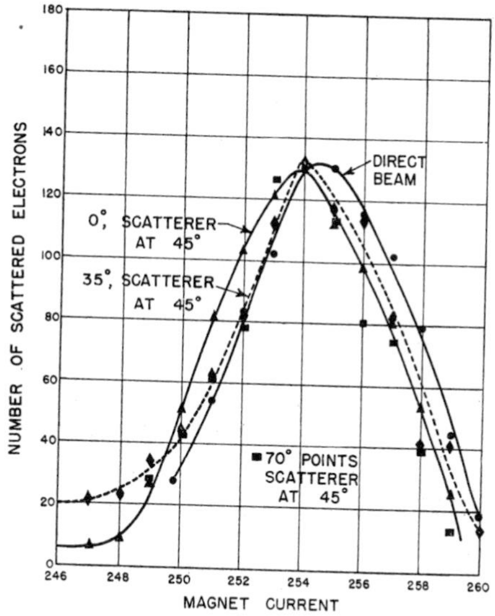

FIG. 3. Elastic-scattering curves for a 2-mil gold foil at 125 Mev. The foil was placed at 45° with respect to the beam. The abscissa is proportional to electron energy. Some of the curves were observed with a CsBr(Tl) detector by a dc method and have higher residual backgrounds (directly and indirectly the result of neutrons) than the normal Čerenkov detector curves.

either side of the peak, for example, at abscissas 326 and 330 in Fig. 4 for tantalum. All angular distributions have been measured in this way. Measurements in light elements, for example, Be or C, must be taken at the positions of the shifted peaks. Figure 6 shows how the Be elastic curves shift with angular position. In fact, in Be the elastic curve changes in appearance as well as shifts with change in angular position. The peculiar curve in Be at 90° requires further investigation. It is possible that inelastic scattering may be observed in such light elements at large angles.

The shift of the peak in Be is the result not only of the recoil energy but also of the energy loss of the incoming and outgoing electrons in the target foil. At a scattering angle of 45°, and a target setting of 45° with respect to the beam, the average energy loss in the 50-mil beryllium target is 0.49 Mev, and the recoil shift is 0.46 Mev. At 70° the corresponding figures are 0.51 Mev and 1.04 Mev, and at 90° they are 0.58 Mev and 1.58 Mev. The expected shifts relative to 35° are therefore 0.60 Mev for 70° and 1.21 Mev for 90°. The observed relative shifts are 0.60±0.20 Mev and 1.20 ±0.20 Mev and are in good agreement with the calculations. Similarly, good agreement has been obtained for the hydrogen and deuterium shifts. In fact the H, D shifts relative to carbon or some other standard may be used to measure the energy of the incident beam. With the present resolution and the accompanying experimental error in measuring the shifts, the calculated beam energy is of the order of 140±20 Mev while the

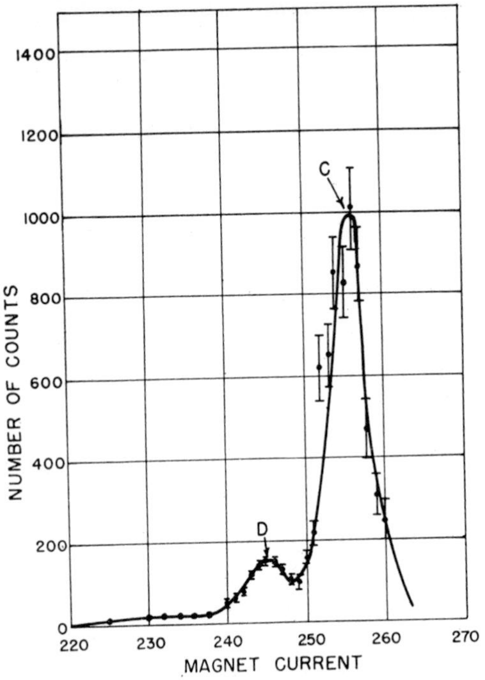

FIG. 5. An elastic curve at 125 Mev, showing the deuterium and carbon peaks observed in deuterated polyethylene at a scattering angle of 65°.

value obtained by calibration with alpha particles gives a value of 125±5 Mev. Obviously, the method can be refined.

A further check on the internal consistency of the scattering data is obtained by comparison of the ratio of the areas under the carbon and hydrogen or deuterium peaks in Fig. 1 of this paper and also in Fig. 2 of reference 1. The ratio in Fig. 5 is $\sigma_C/\sigma_D = 14 \pm 5$ and

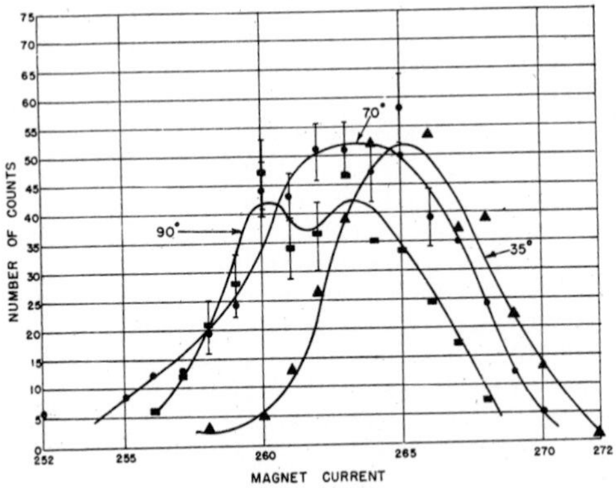

FIG. 6. Elastic curves in Be at 125 Mev at 35°, 70°, and 90°, observed with a 50-mil scattering target. The elastic peak shifts to lower energies at larger angles of scattering and also broadens as it shifts.

for Fig. 2 of reference 1 the ratio $\sigma_C/\sigma_H = 20 \pm 5$, where σ_C, σ_H, σ_D, are the respective cross sections. The accuracy of these measurements is not high because of the carbon bremsstrahlung background which must be subtracted from the H or D peaks. An average of the two results gives 17 which is close to the ratio, $Z_C^2/2(Z_{H,D})^2 = 18$, of the scattering from carbon and hydrogen or deuterium in polyethylene. Again, with better resolution this measurement of relative areas can be greatly improved, and, in fact, this method suggests itself for measuring the hydrogen and deuterium scattering cross sections relative to carbon as a standard.

To check the over-all behavior of the scattering measurements, two tests have been made: (1) the scattering

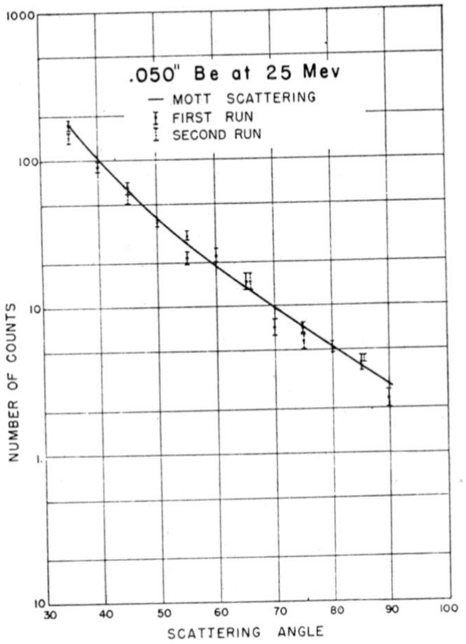

FIG. 7. The angular distribution of electrons scattered from a Be target, 50 mils thick, at 25 Mev. The target plane was at 45° with respect to the beam. The Mott curve for a point charge is shown. Arbitrary normalization is made at 35°.

of Be has been examined in the angular range 35°–90° at 25±2 Mev, and (2) the scattering from a gold foil of $\frac{1}{4}$-mil thickness has been studied in the same angular range at 25 Mev. In case (1), because of the relatively low energy, the Be nucleus may be approximated by a point charge and the exact calculations of Feshbach[5] and Parzen[3] for a point charge may be compared with the experimental data. In case (2) the observed angular distribution may be compared with the data of Lyman *et al.* at 15.7 Mev.

Figure 7 shows the Be data at 25 Mev using a 50-mil foil. The data are in excellent agreement with the accurate calculations and also with the Mott formula, which for low Z's is very close to the accurate formulas.

Figure 8 shows the data for gold found at 25 Mev

with a $\frac{1}{4}$-mil foil. The observed curve is seen to lie above the Mott curve, just as in the work of Lyman *et al.*[11] Our data show slightly less rise relative to the Mott curve as compared with the data of Lyman *et al.*, but this is to be expected, to some extent, because of the higher energy and therefore the shorter wavelength relative to nuclear size. On the whole, the agreement is better than might have been anticipated, since our windows were not designed for energies as low as 25 Mev. It is gratifying that the results for Be and Au at 25 Mev are so well in accord with expectation.

To check whether some systematic error might be prejudicing results on one side of zero preferentially the data for tantalum at 150 Mev have been observed on both sides of zero. Figure 9 shows the data and shows there is nothing special on either side. The data agree very well, and, in fact, the only point seriously off is at 80° on the left side where there was a steel supporting post blocking out part of the solid angle seen by the magnet chamber.

It is also pleasing that the background counting rate has been virtually absent. Without the target in place we have never observed a background count at angles between 35° and 120°. If some of the concrete shields and lead around the Čerenkov counter are removed it is easily possible however to obtain background counts. These are usually small pulses in the photomultiplier and it is anticipated that with further study even these can be removed by applying a higher bias.

IV. CORRECTIONS TO DATA

The corrections usually applied to the raw scattering data have been excellently summarized by Lyman *et al.*[11] Many of these corrections are not needed in the present work, because the data to be presented are entirely of a relative kind. A precise absolute calibration of the scattering data has not been attempted up to the present time, although work is now under way to obtain absolute cross sections in gold.

Since we shall be concerned only with relative data, there is probably no need to take into account such small corrections as the radiative type of Schwinger[17] which were calculated with Born approximation and depend very little on angle.

In order to avoid a variable loss of counts due to pileup, we have made an attempt to count approximately at the same rate at all angles so that a dead-time correction, if present, will be the same for all positions. Actually the dead time correction is negligible.

The largest corrections for multiple scattering are encountered in the case of the gold foils. For most measurements a foil 2 mils thick was used. In one run, to get more intensity at angles larger than 120° a four-mil foil was used. For the 2-mil foil the multiple scattering correction amounts to −0.3 percent at 35°, to −0.1 percent at 90°, and to −0.1 percent at 140°.

[17] J. Schwinger, Phys. Rev. 75, 898 (1949).

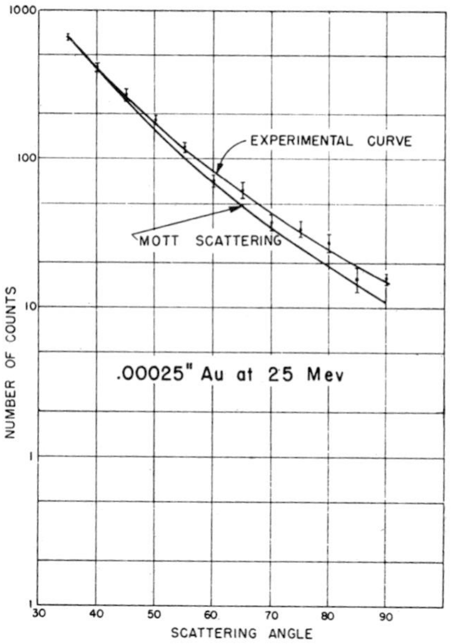

Fig. 8. The angular distribution of scattered electrons from a gold foil, $\frac{1}{4}$-mil thick, at 25 Mev. The foil plane was at 45° with respect to the beam. The Mott curve for a point charge is shown. Arbitrary normalization is made at 35°.

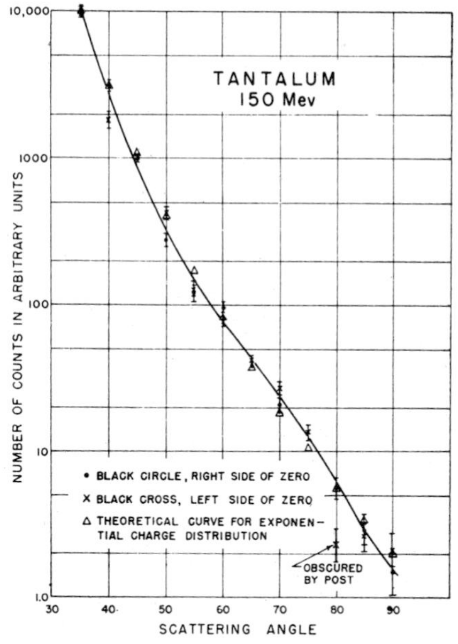

Fig. 9. The angular distribution of scattered electrons from a tantalum foil, 2.6-mil thick, at 150 Mev. The foil plane was at 30° relative to the beam direction. Curves on the left and right of zero are shown. A theoretical curve based on an exponential charge distribution is shown as well as the Feshbach point charge curve. All curves are normalized arbitrarily at 35°.

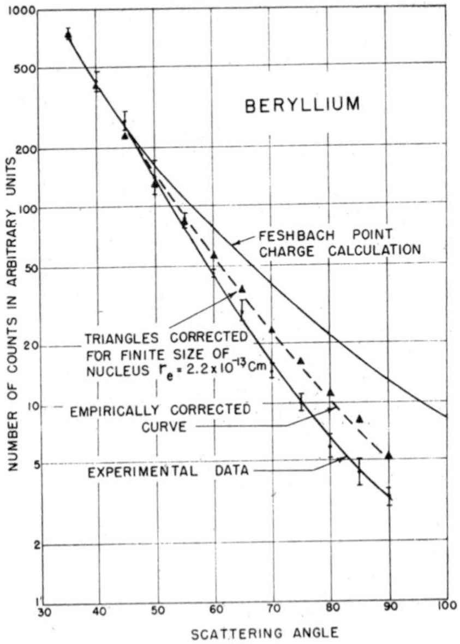

FIG. 10. The angular distribution of scattered electrons from a beryllium foil, 50-mils thick, at 125 Mev. The experimental curve has been corrected empirically for the broadening observed in the elastic curves at larger scattering angles. (See Fig. 6.) The dashed curve is the corrected curve. A theoretical curve based on the first Born approximation for an exponential charge distribution is shown. Also shown is the point charge calculation of Feshbach. Arbitrary normalization of all curves is made at 35°.

Thus, multiple scattering corrections in the target foil are unnecessary for the accuracy involved in this work. The multiple scattering in the aluminum windows is of the order of 0.4° and can be neglected since it is 4 times as small as the rms scattering angle in the gold foil. The beryllium 50-mil foil has an rms scattering angle of 0.6° which is negligible also.

The errors resulting from double (large-angle) scattering are estimated to be 0.15 percent at 90° for two mils of gold at 125 Mev and 0.01 percent at 150° under the same conditions. For 50 mils of Be at 125 Mev the errors are 1.5 percent at 150° and 0.04 percent at 90°. Hence, all double scattering corrections are ignored since they are very small effects.

The geometrical corrections for the aperture can be estimated from the effective aperture which is approximately 0.8 square inch at twelve inches. A calculation similar to that of Lyman *et al.* leads to corrections of a few tenths of a percent, which are thus negligible for our purposes.

The angular resolution of our scattering results depends on the size of the beam spot on the target foil and on the effective aperture of the entrance port of the analyzing magnet. Each of these contributions is about the same at the present time and each contributes about 2°, fairly independently of angles between 35° and 140°, for a target foil setting of 45°. Hence, our angular acceptance width is about ±4°, or a total of 8°. Structure in the scattering curves within such small angular ranges would not be resolved in our experiments. On the other hand, such fine structure is not expected.

Radiative straggling and electron-electron straggling affect the shape of the elastic-scattering peaks. Since in all the cases we have studied, with the exception of Be, the elastic profile is the same at all angles, no relative corrections for these effects need to be made. As a matter of fact, the same argument applies to the Schwinger correction.

With the exception of Be, all corrections are extremely small and will be ignored. In the case of Be (Fig. 6) the elastic profile changes as a function of angle, because of the combination of the recoil effect and the energy loss straggling in the target. Both effects are appreciable for Be. The correction has been taken into account empirically by measuring the areas under the elastic curves taken at various angles. At 90° the area is approximately 1.5 times the area at 35° when both curves are normalized to the same peak values. Hence, a correction of 50 percent is applied to the counting rate at 90°. At 35° the correction is zero, and a smooth curve has been drawn in Fig. 10 (the dashed line) to represent the corrected data at intermediate angles. Since the cross section varies rather violently with angle, the largest correction of 50 percent produces only a mild effect.

V. RESULTS

The relative angular distributions have been measured in Be, Au, and Pb at 125 Mev and in Ta at 150 Mev. In addition, as mentioned previously, check runs

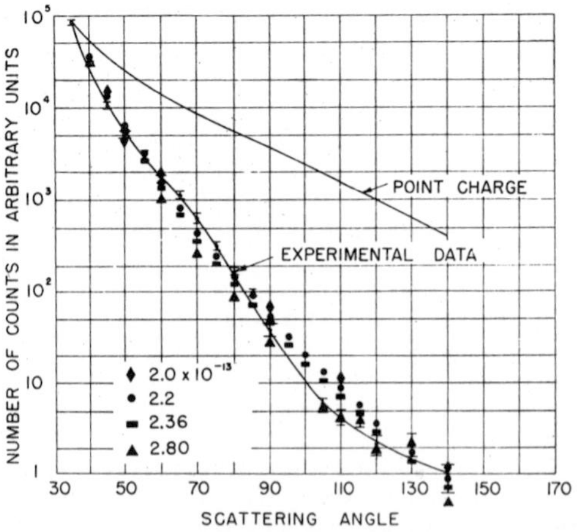

FIG. 11. The angular distribution of electrons scattered from a 2-mil gold foil at 125 Mev. The point charge calculation of Feshbach is indicated. Theoretical points based on the first Born approximation for exponential charge distributions are shown. Values of $\alpha = 2.0$, 2.2, 2.36, 2.8×10^{-13} cm are chosen to demonstrate the sensitivity of the angular distribution to change of radius. All curves are normalized arbitrarily at 35°.

were made on Be and Au at 25 Mev. The experimental curves are shown in Figs. 9, 10, 11, 12. The limits of errors indicated in the figures are entirely of statistical origin. In all cases except gold, the background counting rates were zero so that the present data represent the actual numbers taken in a run. In only one case, namely Au beyond 120°, was a small background observed in one of the counters. The other counter showed no background. The small background makes the data beyond 120° slightly less reliable than the other data.

Near 100° on the right side of zero it has not been possible to obtain data because of the presence of a steel post which is used as a support for the upper half of the scattering chamber. There is a similar post near 80° on the left-hand side of zero. In future experiments it will be possible to move the posts to other positions while taking data near these two angles.

In occasional runs we have noticed that after long periods of time the data do not check exactly. For example, after a couple of hours of running a point at 70° may change by 30 percent or so. Invariably the neighboring points will be down by the same factor. Thus, a slow drift in some part of the counting system or magnetic field appears at irregular times. The explanation of this effect is being sought. However, we do not feel that this effect is significant because the relative counting rates agree with those first obtained to better than 30 percent.

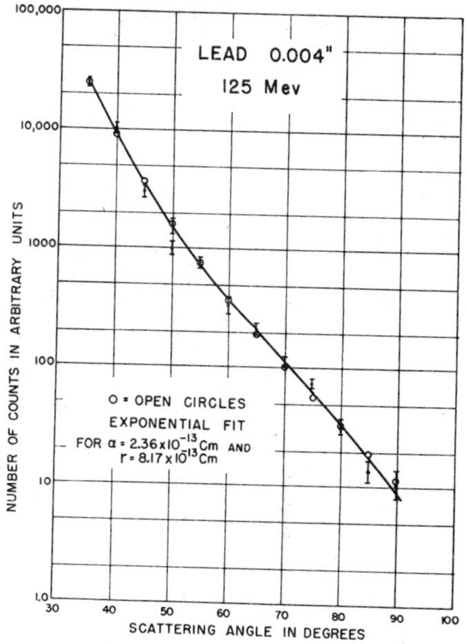

FIG. 12. The angular distribution of electrons scattered from a 4-mil lead foil at 125 Mev. A theoretical curve based on the first Born approximation for an exponential charge distribution is shown. Arbitrary normalization is made at 35°.

VI. ANALYSIS OF THE DATA

The experimental distributions lie far below the point charge calculations of Feshbach[5] which are shown typically in Fig. 11. Within the resolution of the experimental data (points were taken every 5 degrees apart) there is no pronounced evidence of diffraction minima or maxima. These curves are in striking contrast to the beautiful curves of Cohen and Neidigh[18] which show diffraction peaks in the scattering of 22-Mev protons.

The absence of pronounced diffraction peaks suggests that, from the viewpoint of the Born approximation, heavy nuclei do not have sharp boundaries. The accurate calculations of Yennie *et al.*[10] confirm this suggestion in a qualitative way but not quantitatively. We shall sketch briefly some qualitative considerations provided by the Born approximation, merely in order to obtain a feeling for the meaning of the experimental results. In the discussion below we have used the exact calculations of Feshbach for the point charge and have multiplied the point charge curve by the appropriate form factors obtained from the first Born approximation[2,4] for various assumed charge-density distributions.

Among the types of charge-density (ρ) distributions tried[19] were the following:

(A) exponential

$$\rho=\rho_0 e^{-r/\alpha}; \tag{4}$$

(B) "half-uniform and half-Gaussian"

$$\rho=\rho_1,\quad 0\leqslant r\leqslant c;\quad \rho=\rho_1 \exp[-\tfrac{1}{2}(r-c)^2/d^2],\quad r\geqslant c; \tag{5}$$

(C) gaussian

$$\rho=\rho_2 \exp(-\tfrac{1}{2}r^2/r_0^2); \tag{6}$$

(D) uniform

$$\rho=\rho_3,\quad 0\leqslant r\leqslant c;\quad \rho=0,\quad r\geqslant c. \tag{7}$$

The ρ_0, ρ_1, ρ_2, and ρ_3 are all constants with the dimensions of charge density. For these charge distributions the root-mean-square radii, calculated with the charge as the weighting factor are, respectively:

$$\text{(A)}\quad r_e=3.46\alpha, \tag{8}$$

$$\text{(B)}\quad r_{ug}=2.31c \quad \text{for} \quad d=c,. \tag{9}$$

$$\text{(C)}\quad r_g=1.732r_0, \tag{10}$$

$$\text{(D)}\quad r_u=0.775c. \tag{11}$$

In the following, we discuss the data obtained for the various elements.

[18] B. L. Cohen and R. V. Neidigh, Phys. Rev. (to be published). We wish to thank Dr. A. M. Weinberg and Dr. B. L. Cohen for informing us of these results. See also J. W. Burkig and B. T. Wright, Phys. Rev. 82, 451 (1951).

[19] See also L. I. Schiff (reference 8) for other charge distributions and relevant remarks. A slightly different approach from ours has been used in Schiff's paper.

Gold

The "best fit" with the experimental data was obtained for the exponential charge distribution with $\alpha=2.3\pm0.3\times10^{-13}$ cm and $r_e=7.95\times10^{-13}$ cm. The experimental data and the exponential fit are shown in Fig. 11. The half-uniform and half-Gaussian model provides a "best fit" which is somewhat inferior to the exponential fit and requires $c=2.46\times10^{-13}$ cm and $r_{ug}=5.7\times10^{-13}$ cm. This angular distribution is a poor fit at angles greater than 110° where it drops off too rapidly. The pure Gaussian model (C) is also not as good as the exponential but gives a best fit for $r_0=2.48\times10^{-13}$ cm with $r_g=4.3\times10^{-13}$ cm. As in the last case the pure Gaussian drops off too rapidly beyond 115°. These rms radii are to be compared with the usual rms value of about 6.3×10^{-13} cm for gold and are of the correct order of magnitude.

The Born approximation is clearly quite poor for a uniform distribution of charge because of its true zeros. Therefore, no attempt will be made to use the Born approximation for this model. On the other hand, the exact calculations of Yennie *et al.*,[10] carried out both for a uniform charge distribution and an exponential charge distribution, show that the exponential fits better because of the absence of diffraction structure, which does occur for the uniform distribution. In either event, the most important conclusion is that the exact theoretical curves reflect the very steep falloff of cross section with angle shown by the experiments. The large departures from a point charge are, therefore, satisfactorily demonstrated in theory, as well as experiment. The rather extreme exponential model, when treated exactly, appears to fit the experimental data (35°–120°) quite well, but it is by no means ruled out that other less violent models with, e.g. Gaussian tails, might not do equally well. To see the qualitative effect of a small rounding off of the edge of a uniform charge distribution, a uniform model and Gaussian tail with parameter $d=0.2c$ in Eq. (5) has been tried in Born approximation but does not remove the zeros. This model simply moves the zeros out a little towards larger angles. A uniform model with a small exponential tail has a similar behavior, as shown by Smith.[7]

Lead

The lead foil used in the experiments was an isotopic mixture in the natural proportions and was 4-mils thick. The experimental curve for 125 Mev is given in Fig. 12. It may be seen that the points are fitted quite well by a theoretical Born curve based on an exponential model. The theoretical curve is hardly distinguishable from the experimental curve. The radius obtained from the best exponential fit is $r_e=8.17\times10^{-13}$ cm or $\alpha=2.36\times10^{-13}$ cm. This value is slightly larger than the radius for gold in the ratio 1.03.

Tantalum

The experimental curve for 2.6 mils of tantalum at 150 Mev is given in Fig. 9. By fitting with an exponential charge distribution corresponding to $\alpha=2.80\pm0.3\times10^{-13}$ cm or $r_e=9.7\times10^{-13}$ cm, an excellent reproduction of the data is obtained. Again, as in lead, the theoretical Born points are scarcely distinguishable from the experimental ones. While the tantalum should have a radius slightly smaller than lead or gold according to the rule expressed by Eq. (3), the scattering data indicate a larger radius. Relative to lead the rms radius is 1.18 times as large. This result may possibly have some connection with the extremely large quadrupole moment of Ta.

Beryllium

Beryllium has been studied at 125 Mev. The results obtained with a 50-mil scattering target are shown in Fig. 10. The curve which has been empirically corrected for the change in elastic profile as a function of angle is shown as a dashed line in the figure. The point charge curve of Feshbach is shown in open circles. In the case of beryllium the Born approximation should be quite valid. The triangles represent the point charge curve as modified by the "best fit" form factor corresponding to an exponential charge distribution with $r_e=2.2\times10^{-13}$ cm or $\alpha=6.36\times10^{-14}$ cm. This radius is quite a bit smaller than the radii measured for heavy nuclei and is in good agreement with what might be expected from Eq. (3). In the case of such a small nucleus as Be, the form factor can be chosen quite arbitrarily to correspond either to the exponential, Gaussian, or uniform model, since all give essentially the same behavior. For example, the best fit for a uniformly charged model gives $r_u=1.90\times10^{-13}$ cm and for a Gaussian model $r_g=1.96\times10^{-13}$ cm.

VII. CONCLUSIONS

With the angular resolution attained in these experiments, the absence of diffraction maxima and minima in the observed scattering of 125- and 150-Mev electrons from Ta, Au, and Pb suggests tentatively the concept that these nuclei have charge distributions tapering off gradually from near the center to the outside. This conclusion is not definite at this time because both theory and experiment are in preliminary stages.

The differences between the nuclear diffraction patterns observed in the scattering of 22-Mev protons[18] and the electron scattering results reported here may perhaps reflect the facts that nuclei interact with protons through short-range forces (also to a lesser extent through Coulomb forces) and are not transparent to protons of 22-Mev energy, while nuclei interact with electrons through long-range Coulomb forces and are transparent to electrons. Hence, the elastically-scattered protons interact effectively only with the outer edges of the nucleus giving the impression of a sharp boundary. Electrons interact with the entire nuclear volume.

It might be wondered whether the peaked charge distribution suggested here could influence arguments concerning saturation of nuclear forces. A simple electrostatic calculation was carried out for the exponential charge distribution with $\alpha=2.3\times10^{-13}$ cm for gold. The result obtained indicates that the Coulomb energy is changed by not more than a factor of two relative to that of the uniform distribution. Hence, on this score there will be no serious change regarding nuclear saturation.

It is recognized that the charge distribution in heavy nuclei tentatively suggested by this work differs rather seriously from the uniform model generally proposed. For this reason we are attempting to improve the accuracy of the experiments by increasing the angular resolution, energy resolution and stability of all parts of the apparatus.

ACKNOWLEDGMENTS

We wish to thank Mrs. P. Hanson, Mr. G. Masek, and assistant crew members for their kind and efficient help in running the accelerator. Miss E. Wiener and Mr. J. Fregeau have kindly assisted in taking some of the data. V. Prosper, E. Wright, B. Chambers, B. Stuart, F. Renga, and P. Abreu deserve our special thanks for the skill they have shown in building and designing various parts of our scattering apparatus. Mr. R. H. Helm was of great assistance in designing the magnet support and in constructing the spectrometer. We appreciate the help of Drs. W. A. Fowler and W. Whaling of California Institute of Technology, who provided us with the drawings and advice needed in constructing the analyzing magnet, and Dr. I. Perlman of the University of California Radiation Laboratory, for lending us an alpha-particle calibration source. We are grateful to the Office of Naval Research which gave us early support in this project and particularly to Dr. Urner Liddel, Mr. F. Niemann, and Lt. M. S. Jones who helped us obtain the gun mount for this work. We wish to thank Dr. L. I. Schiff and Dr. W. E. Lamb, Jr., who have given us valuable advice in theoretical matters. Dr. E. Guth has read our work critically and has our special thanks for his comments. Drs. D. R. Yennie and D. G. Ravenhall and Mr. R. N. Wilson are to be thanked most cordially for their kindness in permitting us to use their results before publication. We acknowledge with thanks the recent support of the Office of Scientific Research of the Air Research and Development Command. Finally we are grateful for a grant received from the Research Corporation which enabled this project to obtain its start.

PAPER 21

Phase-Shift Calculation of High-Energy Electron Scattering by Nuclei*

D. R. YENNIE, R. N. WILSON, AND D. G. RAVENHALL
Stanford University, Stanford, California
(Received October 14, 1953)

EXPERIMENTS on the elastic scattering of high-energy electrons ($E\sim 125$ Mev) by several elements have been carried out by Hofstadter, Fechter, and McIntyre.[1] The results have been analyzed by them[1] and by Schiff[2] using the Born approximation to estimate the effects of the finite nuclear size. On the basis of such an analysis, the results can be fitted well by assuming an exponential distribution of the nuclear charge. Other charge distributions, such as the uniform distribution, are discriminated against because in Born approximation they predict diffraction maxima and minima in the angular distribution. In view of the fact that the Born approximation is not accurate for the heavier elements considered, we have carried out a numerical phase-shift calculation of the process. Our object in the present note is to examine the accuracy of the Born approximation, rather than to attempt to fit the experimental results. Our results are in disagreement with those of Parzen.[3]

The details of the calculation will be published later. Generally the calculation follows the methods given by Parzen[3] and Acheson,[4] with minor modifications. The phase shift relative to the Coulomb phase shift is calculated for the first nine partial waves; the last phase shift used is less than 0.003° in all cases. All the phase shifts are negative and tend monotonically to zero, in disagreement with Elton's assertion[5] that the phase shifts should tend to zero from positive values. We have found it necessary to increase the accuracy of the point scattering amplitudes given by Feshbach,[6] since at large angles this amplitude is largely canceled out by the nuclear size modifications. We estimate that the calculated cross sections given below are accurate to about 5 percent out to 110°; the major errors are contained in the first two phase shifts, which are known to only 0.01°.

The following charge distributions have been used for gold ($Z=79$):

(a) Uniform; $\rho(r)=\rho_0,\quad r<R,$
$\qquad\qquad\qquad\; =0,\quad r>R;\quad kR=5.4;$

(b) Exponential; $\rho(r)=\rho_0 e^{-r/a};\quad ka=0.91.$

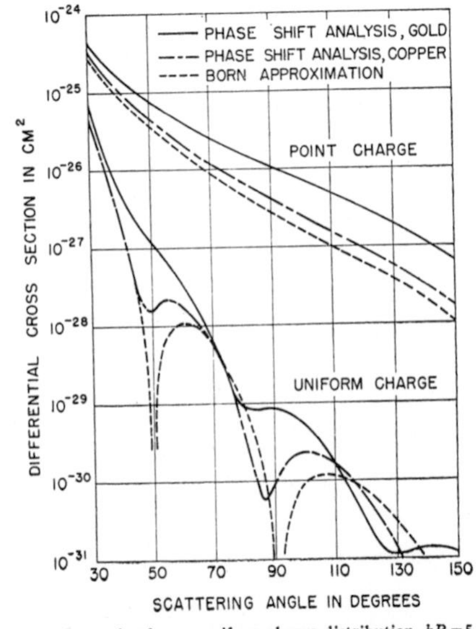

FIG. 1. Scattering from a uniform charge distribution, $kR=5.4$.

The cross sections given by (a) and (b) are found to decrease in approximately the same ratio between 30° and 90°, and this ratio is roughly that given by Hofstadter's experiment.

For purposes of comparison, we carried through the calculation for copper ($Z=29$) for the uniform charge distribution, with

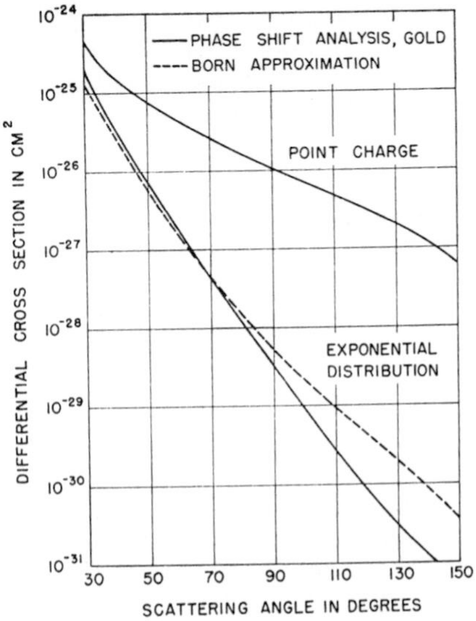

FIG. 2. Scattering from an exponential charge distribution, $ka=0.91$.

$kR=5.4$. The Born approximation to this cross section is the same, apart from a constant factor $(Z_{\text{copper}}k_{\text{gold}}/Z_{\text{gold}}k_{\text{copper}})^2$, as the Born approximation to (a).

In Fig. 1 are shown the cross sections given by the two uniform charge distributions. If we assume a nuclear radius $r_0A^{\frac{1}{3}}$, with $r_0=1.22\times10^{-13}$ cm, the curves as shown there correspond to electron energies of 150 and 224 Mev for gold and copper, respectively. (The choice of r_0, and consequently of k, affects the cross sections by a constant factor only. For instance, if $r_0=1.45\times10^{-13}$ cm, the energies are 126 and 188 Mev, respectively.) As is expected, the cross section for copper agrees more closely with the Born approximation than does the cross section for gold. The first minimum predicted by the Born approximation appears in gold as a point of inflection only. The shift of the maxima and minima to smaller angles can be understood qualitatively as due to an increase in wave number as the electron enters the attractive potential of the nucleus. This also makes plausible the increase in slope of the cross section for the exponential distribution compared with the Born approximation, as shown in Fig. 2, and permits the experimental data to be fitted with a smaller a than is required in Born approximation.[1,2]

Further calculations are in progress with charge distributions of intermediate shape.

We wish to thank Professor L. I. Schiff for his advice and suggestions, and Professor W. E. Lamb, Jr. for interesting conversations. Discussions with Professor R. Hofstadter concerning the experiments and his analysis of them have been very stimulating.

* Supported by the Office of Scientific Research, Air Research and Development Command.
[1] Hofstadter, Fechter, and McIntyre, Phys. Rev. **92**, 978 (1953).
[2] L. I. Schiff, Phys. Rev. **92**, 988 (1953).
[3] G. Parzen, Phys. Rev. **80**, 355 (1953). Parzen (private communication to R. Hofstadter) has found an error in his work and is recomputing his results.
[4] L. K. Acheson, Jr., Phys. Rev. **82**, 488 (1951).
[5] L. R. B. Elton, Proc. Phys. Soc. (London) **A63**, 1115 (1950).
[6] H. Feshbach, Phys. Rev. **88**, 295 (1952).

PAPER 22

Inelastic Scattering of 190-Mev Electrons in Beryllium*†‡

J. A. McIntyre, B. Hahn,§ and R. Hofstadter
Department of Physics and W. W. Hansen Laboratories, Stanford University, Stanford, California
(Received March 19, 1954)

In investigating the elastic scattering of high-energy electrons from various nuclei[1] we reported preliminary evidence of structure in the "elastic" profiles observed at 70° and 90° in beryllium at 125 Mev. We have re-examined this problem with a newly rewound analyzing magnet which permits studies up to 200 Mev. With incident electrons of 190 Mev in a band 1.0-Mev wide we have confirmed this structure and the details have now been more clearly revealed. Figure 1 shows the elastically scattered peak *A* and two additional inelastically scattered peaks *B* and *C* at 70° for a 100-mil beryllium target set at 45° with respect to the incident beam. The abscissa is given in terms of the settings of the potentiometer reading the current through the analyzing magnetic spectrometer. Figure 2 shows similar data at 90°. We have also observed inelastic scattering at 60° and have observed the peaks *A* and *B*, but unfortunately did not carry the observations below *B* to look for peak *C*. Table I shows the positions of the peaks at 90°, 70°, and 60° and also shows the differences $A-B$, $A-C$. These differences may be converted into the excitation energies of the levels excited in beryllium by 190-Mev electrons when the energy calibration of the abscissa is known. An initial calibration in terms of magnetic field measured at the center of the spectrometer trajectories gave the instantaneous slope of the curve of energy *versus* potentiometer setting as 0.20 Mev per division of potentiometer reading. Averaging the intervals $A-B$ and $A-C$ provides $A-B=12.7$ divisions or 2.54 Mev and $A-C=34.8$ divisions or 6.96 Mev. These values are in good agreement with those excitation levels reported by Britten,[2] and the single low-lying level of Davis and Hafner[3] and Rhoderick.[4] Britten's values are 2.5±0.2 Mev and 6.8±0.3 Mev. Britten's third level at 11.6 Mev was not sought.

Table I. Summary of data on elastic and inelastic peaks.

Angle \ Peak	A	B	C	$A-B$	$A-C$
60°	418.0	404.0	—	14.0	—
70°	413.6	400.0	378.4	13.6	35.2
90°	404.5	394.0	370.0	10.5	34.5
			Average	12.7±1.5	34.8±1.5

The beryllium levels previously observed have been found by inelastic scattering of protons whereas these levels have now been excited by fast electrons. Presumably a specifically nuclear interaction is not involved, which suggests that there may be similarities between electron excitation of levels and Coulomb excitation by heavy particles.

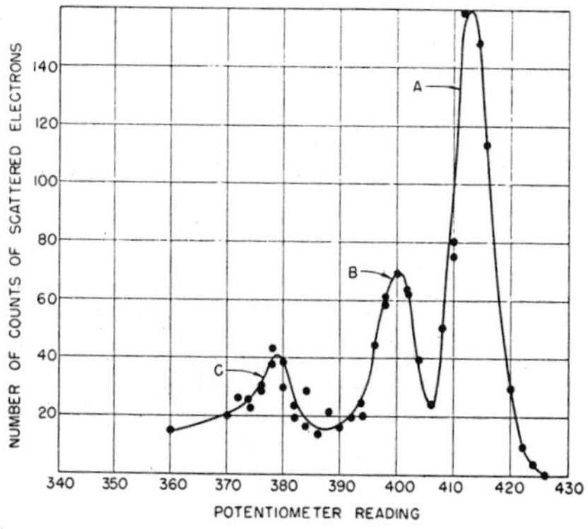

Fig. 1. Elastic peak (*A*) and first and second inelastic peaks (*B* and *C*) in beryllium at 70°.

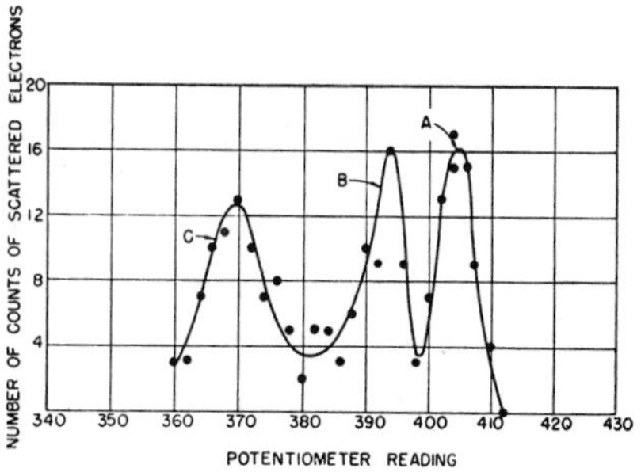

Fig. 2. Elastic peak (*A*) and first and second inelastic peaks (*B* and *C*) in beryllium at 90°.

Figures 1 and 2 and the data at 60° permit a rough, limited measurement of the angular distribution of the cross section for the inelastic scattered electrons. These data are plotted in Fig. 3 along with the elastic cross section. The flatter angular distributions of the inelastic electrons appear to be in agreement with a preliminary theory.[5]

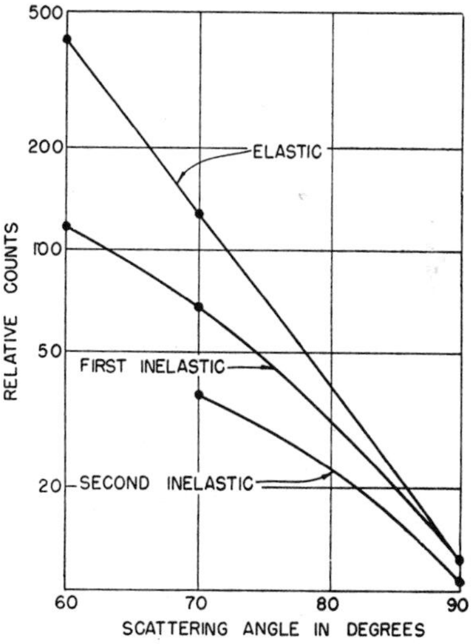

Fig. 3. Elastic and inelastic cross sections on a relative scale as a function of scattering angle.

Inelastic processes have also been observed in copper.

We wish to thank A. W. Knudsen, B. Chambers, and V. Prosper for help in setting up the apparatus for these experiments.

* Supported by the joint program of the U. S. Office of Naval Research and the U. S. Atomic Energy Commission.
† This research was supported by the United States Air Force, through the Office of Scientific Research of the Air Research and Development Command.
‡ Aided by a grant from the Research Corporation.
§ Visiting Research Fellow of the *Schweizerische Arbeitsgemeinschaft in Mathematik und Physik*, Switzerland.

[1] Hofstadter, Fechter, and McIntyre, Phys. Rev. **92**, 978 (1953).
[2] R. Britten, Phys. Rev. **88**, 283 (1952).
[3] K. E. Davis and E. M. Hafner, Phys. Rev. **73**, 1473 (1948).
[4] E. H. Rhoderick, Proc. Roy. Soc. (London) **A201**, 348 (1950).
[5] L. I. Schiff (private communication).

PAPER 23

Phase-Shift Calculation of High-Energy Electron Scattering*

D. R. Yennie, D. G. Ravenhall, and R. N. Wilson
Department of Physics, Stanford University, Stanford, California
(Received March 22, 1954)

The details of a phase-shift calculation of high-energy electron scattering by nuclei are given, together with some preliminary results. A new method for summing the Legendre series for the Coulomb scattering amplitude is described. The results indicate that the first Born approximation does not give cross sections accurate enough for a reliable interpretation of the experiments. From a comparison of the few theoretical cross sections already obtained with the experiments in gold at 125 Mev, very tentative conclusions about the nuclear charge distribution are drawn. It is pointed out that an analysis of results at two or more energies will be a much more sensitive test of possible charge distributions.

I. INTRODUCTION

EXPERIMENTS on the elastic scattering of high-energy electrons by nuclei carried out by Hofstadter, Fechter, and McIntyre,[1] and by Pidd, Hammer, and Raka[2] exhibit clearly the finite extension of the nuclear charge distributions. Analyses of the results of Hofstadter's group by Hofstadter *et al.*[1] and by Schiff,[3] using the first Born approximation, led to the tentative conclusion that the charge distribution was peaked at the center of the nucleus, tapering gradually towards the edge. In view of the fact that the Born approximation is not accurate for heavy elements, we have carried out a phase-shift analysis of the process. A brief report of preliminary results has already been made.[4] We wish in this paper to give an account of our methods and of the trend of our results. Our calculations have been of an exploratory nature, with a view to fitting the experimental data at 125 Mev,[1] and we can as yet draw no definite conclusions about nuclear charge distributions. To do so will require a thorough examination of the new and more accurate results of Hofstadter's group at several energies, and we hope to report on this in the near future.

The literature on electron scattering by nuclei is very extensive, and we shall not survey all of it here. That relating to estimates of the effect of the finite nuclear size using the first Born approximation has been summarized in Schiff's paper.[3] Phase-shift analyses of this process for the energy region where only one Coulomb phase shift is modified by the finite nuclear size have been made in papers by Elton,[5] Acheson,[6] and Feshbach.[7] Bitter and Feshbach[8] showed that experiments in this region can measure only one parameter of the nuclear charge distribution, namely its root-mean-square radius. Until very recently the only calculation for an energy high enough to require the modification of several Coulomb phases, thus yielding a cross section characteristic of the particular shape of the nuclear charge distribution, has been that of Parzen,[9] but unfortunately his results are not correct.[10] Other calculations in this energy range have now been made by E. Baranger,[11] and Brenner, Brown, and Elton.[12]

The model we use is the Dirac equation for an electron in the electrostatic potential of a static, spherically symmetric charge distribution. The cross section is obtained by a numerical calculation of the phase shift of each partial wave. It is unfortunate that the complexity of the calculation tends to obscure the relationship between the details of the charge distributions and of the corresponding cross sections. A method which avoided the decomposition into partial waves might give more insight into the process. We do not take into account the interaction of the electron with nuclear magnetic or electric quadrupole moments, or the effect of nuclear excitation. Calculations by Schiff[13] using the first Born approximation suggest that the first is not important at the energies under consideration, and that the other two are small except with particular elements at large angles. We also ignore quantum electrodynamic radiative corrections. Schwinger's analysis[14] predicts a very small change in the angular dependence of the differential cross section (of the order of one or two percent), but this also is on the basis of the first Born approximation.

In Part II we give an account of scattering theory for the Dirac equation, neglecting the mass term, as is justified at high energies. As an excuse for presenting such a well-studied topic again, we claim that our version, in which the omission of the mass term is made before the reduction to partial waves, is simpler and more transparent than the usual treatment. The only

* Supported in part by the U. S. Office of Scientific Research, Air Research and Development Command.
[1] Hofstadter, Fechter, and McIntyre, Phys. Rev. **91**, 422 (1953); **92**, 978 (1953).
[2] Pidd, Hammer, and Raka, Phys. Rev. **92**, 436 (1953).
[3] L. I. Schiff, Phys. Rev. **92**, 988 (1953).
[4] Yennie, Wilson, and Ravenhall, Phys. Rev. **92**, 1325 (1953).
[5] L. R. B. Elton, Phys. Rev. **79**, 412 (1950); Proc. Phys. Soc. (London) **A63**, 1115 (1950); **A65**, 481 (1952); **A66**, 806 (1953).
[6] L. K. Acheson, Phys. Rev. **82**, 488 (1951).
[7] H. Feshbach, Phys. Rev. **84**, 1206 (1951).
[8] F. Bitter and H. Feshbach, Phys. Rev. **92**, 837 (1953).
[9] G. Parzen, Phys. Rev. **80**, 355 (1950).
[10] An error was discovered by E. Baranger (see reference 11).
[11] E. Baranger, Phys. Rev. **93**, 1127 (1954). We wish to thank Mrs. Baranger for an interesting discussion of her work and ours.
[12] Brenner, Brown, and Elton (to be published). We thank Dr. Brown for communicating these results to us prior to their publication.
[13] Reference 3, and L. I. Schiff (private communication).
[14] J. Schwinger, Phys. Rev. **75**, 898 (1949).

new feature is our summing of the series for the Coulomb scattering amplitude. It is with reluctance that we introduce a new notation for the quantum number characterizing the partial wave. We think it clearer and more consistent to use j than the k, n, and l of previous authors, since j^2, the familiar total angular momentum operator, is actually diagonal in the representation used.

The results are presented in Part III, together with a brief comparison with the work of other authors, and the qualitative conclusions that we feel able to draw at present.

II. THEORY

1. Dirac Equation at High Energies

We shall be concerned with the scattering of electrons at very high energies ($E>50\ mc^2$). We then expect that it should be possible to neglect the rest energy of the electron in comparison with its total energy. It is physically obvious that such an approximation should not introduce any qualitative changes into the scattering properties of the electron, and in fact the only quantitative changes introduced are of relative order (m^2c^4/E^2).[6,12]

In the Dirac equation,

$$(\boldsymbol{\alpha}\cdot\mathbf{p}c+\beta mc^2+V)\psi=E\psi, \tag{1}$$

we choose a representation for the Dirac matrices which will facilitate neglecting the mass term:

$$\alpha_i=\rho_3\sigma_i,\quad \beta=\rho_1.^{15} \tag{2}$$

If we write ϕ and χ for two two-component wave functions, the Dirac equation can then be written

$$\begin{aligned}(\boldsymbol{\sigma}\cdot\mathbf{p}c+V-E)\phi&=-mc^2\chi,\\(-\boldsymbol{\sigma}\cdot\mathbf{p}c+V-E)\chi&=-mc^2\phi.\end{aligned} \tag{3}$$

Neglecting the mass, we obtain two sets of uncoupled equations:

$$(\boldsymbol{\sigma}\cdot\mathbf{p}c+V-E)\phi=0, \tag{4a}$$

$$(-\boldsymbol{\sigma}\cdot\mathbf{p}c+V-E)\chi=0. \tag{4b}$$

That such two-component equations should exist can be seen directly from the original Dirac equation (1) by noting that when the term involving β is neglected, the remaining three hypercomplex quantities α_i can be represented by two component σ matrices. Solutions of both (4a) and (4b) are needed, however, in order to have a complete set of states for Eq. (1).[16]

Consider plane wave solutions of Eqs. (4a) and (4b) in the absence of a potential:

$$\begin{aligned}\phi&=u\exp(i\mathbf{k}\cdot\mathbf{x}),\\\chi&=v\exp(i\mathbf{k}\cdot\mathbf{x}),\end{aligned} \tag{5}$$

[15] P. A. M. Dirac, *The Principles of Quantum Mechanics* (Oxford University Press, Oxford, 1947), third edition, p. 256.

[16] A discussion of the relation between our analysis and that of previous authors is given in the Appendix.

where

$$\begin{aligned}\boldsymbol{\sigma}\cdot(\hbar c\mathbf{k})u&=Eu,\\\boldsymbol{\sigma}\cdot(\hbar c\mathbf{k})v&=-Ev.\end{aligned} \tag{6}$$

For a given $E(>0)$ and $\mathbf{k}$, these two solutions correspond to the two different spin states of the electron. Loosely speaking, for the first solution the spin is parallel to the momentum while for the second it is antiparallel. The normalized solutions of (6) are

$$u=\begin{pmatrix}\cos\frac{1}{2}\theta\\ \sin\frac{1}{2}\theta\exp(i\varphi)\end{pmatrix},\qquad v=\begin{pmatrix}-\sin\frac{1}{2}\theta\exp(-i\varphi)\\ \cos\frac{1}{2}\theta\end{pmatrix}, \tag{7}$$

where θ and φ are the polar angles specifying the direction of $\mathbf{k}$.

If we reintroduce the potential (which for the moment we assume has a finite extent), scattering states will have the asymptotic form[17]

$$\begin{aligned}\phi&\sim\begin{pmatrix}1\\0\end{pmatrix}e^{ikz}+r^{-1}f_1(\theta,\varphi)\begin{pmatrix}1\\ \tan\frac{1}{2}\theta\exp(i\varphi)\end{pmatrix}e^{ikr},\\\chi&\sim\begin{pmatrix}0\\1\end{pmatrix}e^{ikz}+r^{-1}f_2(\theta,\varphi)\begin{pmatrix}-\tan\frac{1}{2}\theta\exp(-i\varphi)\\1\end{pmatrix}e^{ikr}.\end{aligned} \tag{8}$$

It is easily seen that for a spherically symmetric potential the scattering in a given direction will be the same for both spin orientations.[18] In the following, we will therefore restrict our attention to Eq. (4a).

2. Scattering Theory of the Dirac Equation at High Energies

Any solution of Eq. (4a) can be decomposed into partial waves characterized by the total angular momentum and its z component:

$$\phi=\sum a_{jm}\phi_{jm}, \tag{9}$$

with

$$J^2\phi_{jm}=j(j+1)\hbar^2\phi_{jm}, \tag{10}$$

[17] Acheson (see reference 6) has already shown that the two components of the scattered wave differ by only a factor $\tan\frac{1}{2}\theta\exp(i\varphi)$. His proof is based on relationships between spherical harmonics occurring in the expansions of the components. Our derivation gives the underlying reason for this.

[18] This may be seen as follows: If $\phi(\mathbf{x})$ is a solution of (4a), then $\chi(\mathbf{x})=\phi(-\mathbf{x})$ is a solution of (4b). If the incident wave part of $\phi(\mathbf{x})$ is traveling in the positive z direction, the incident wave part of $\chi(\mathbf{x})$ is traveling in the minus z direction. If now we rotate the second solution through 180° about the x axis, we have both incident waves traveling in the positive z direction and the intensity of the scattered waves in a given direction is the same for both solutions. Further analysis along this line shows that when we consider the scattering of electrons from randomly oriented nonsymmetric nuclei there can be no polarization of the scattered electrons; this refers only to static moments, of course. At lower energies where the mass cannot be neglected, polarization in scattering by a spherically symmetric potential is possible.

and

$$J_z\phi_{jm}=m\hbar\phi_{jm}, \tag{11}$$

where

$$\mathbf{J}=\mathbf{r}\times\mathbf{p}+\tfrac{1}{2}\boldsymbol{\sigma}\hbar.$$

For a plane-wave incident in the z direction

$$J_z\begin{pmatrix}1\\0\end{pmatrix}e^{ikz}=\tfrac{1}{2}\hbar\begin{pmatrix}1\\0\end{pmatrix}e^{ikz}, \tag{12}$$

so that we need be concerned only with the states $\phi_{j,\frac{1}{2}}$. The spin-angular parts of these states have the forms

$$\chi_j^1=\begin{pmatrix}(j+\frac{1}{2})P_{j-\frac{1}{2}}(\cos\theta)\\ -P_{j-\frac{1}{2}}{}^1(\cos\theta)\exp(i\varphi)\end{pmatrix},$$
$$\chi_j^2=\begin{pmatrix}(j+\frac{1}{2})P_{j+\frac{1}{2}}(\cos\theta)\\ P_{j+\frac{1}{2}}{}^1(\cos\theta)\exp(i\varphi)\end{pmatrix}. \tag{13}$$

The partial wave solutions of (4a) then take the form

$$\phi_{j,\frac{1}{2}}=r^{-1}[G_j(r)\chi_j^1+iF_j(r)\chi_j^2]. \tag{14}$$

In deriving the equations satisfied by F_j and G_j, the following identities are useful:

$$\boldsymbol{\sigma}\cdot\mathbf{L}\chi_j^1=\hbar(j-\tfrac{1}{2})\chi_j^1,$$
$$\boldsymbol{\sigma}\cdot\mathbf{L}\chi_j^2=-\hbar(j+\tfrac{3}{2})\chi_j^2, \tag{15}$$

$$\boldsymbol{\sigma}\cdot\mathbf{r}\chi_j^1=r\chi_j^2,$$
$$\boldsymbol{\sigma}\cdot\mathbf{r}\chi_j^2=r\chi_j^1, \tag{16}$$

$$\boldsymbol{\sigma}\cdot\mathbf{p}=r^{-2}(\boldsymbol{\sigma}\cdot\mathbf{r})(\mathbf{r}\cdot\mathbf{p})+ir^{-2}(\boldsymbol{\sigma}\cdot\mathbf{r})(\boldsymbol{\sigma}\cdot\mathbf{L}). \tag{17}$$

It is then easily found that[16]

$$\frac{dG_j}{dr}-\frac{(j+\frac{1}{2})}{r}G_j+\frac{(E-V)}{\hbar c}F_j=0,$$
$$\frac{dF_j}{dr}+\frac{(j+\frac{1}{2})}{r}F_j-\frac{(E-V)}{\hbar c}G_j=0. \tag{18}$$

It is convenient to handle these equations in dimensionless form. We therefore set

$$x=kr \tag{19}$$

and

$$v=V/E, \tag{20}$$

where

$$k=E/\hbar c.$$

Then

$$\frac{dG_j}{dx}-\frac{(j+\frac{1}{2})}{x}G_j+(1-v)F_j=0,$$
$$\frac{dF_j}{dx}+\frac{(j+\frac{1}{2})}{x}F_j-(1-v)G_j=0. \tag{21}$$

For use in the scattering calculation, we need those solutions of Eq. (21) which are regular at the origin.

We shall next review briefly the standard scattering theory for the non-Coulomb case, and finally modify the results thus obtained to take into account the peculiar nature of the Coulomb field. At large distances we expect to find an asymptotic solution of the form

$$\phi\sim\begin{pmatrix}1\\0\end{pmatrix}e^{ix\cos\theta}+x^{-1}kf(\theta)\begin{pmatrix}1\\ \tan\frac{1}{2}\theta\exp(i\varphi)\end{pmatrix}e^{ix}$$
$$=\phi_{\text{inc}}+\phi_{\text{scatt}}. \tag{22}$$

The differential cross section is then given by

$$d\sigma/d\Omega=|f|^2(1+\tan^2\tfrac{1}{2}\theta)=\sec^2\tfrac{1}{2}\theta|f|^2. \tag{23}$$

Using the well-known expansion of plane waves,[19] we may express the incident wave as a sum of partial waves of the form (14):

$$\phi_{\text{inc}}=\sum_{j-\frac{1}{2}=0}^{\infty}\left(\frac{\pi}{2x}\right)^{\frac{1}{2}}i^{j-\frac{1}{2}}[J_j\chi_j^1+iJ_{j+1}\chi_j^2]. \tag{24}$$

The total wave, determined by the condition that its incoming wave part is the same as that of (24), is

$$\phi=\sum_{j-\frac{1}{2}=0}^{\infty}x^{-1}i^{j-\frac{1}{2}}e^{i\eta_j}[G_j\chi_j^1+iF_j\chi_j^2]. \tag{25}$$

The phase shifts η_j are determined by comparing the asymptotic radial functions in (25) with those in (24):

$$(\pi x/2)^{\frac{1}{2}}J_j(x)\sim\sin[x-\tfrac{1}{2}(j-\tfrac{1}{2})\pi],$$
$$G_j\sim\sin[x-\tfrac{1}{2}(j-\tfrac{1}{2})\pi+\eta_j]. \tag{26}$$

Combining Eqs. (25), (24), and (22) we find that the scattered wave is given by

$$f(\theta)=\frac{1}{2ik}\sum(e^{2i\eta_j}-1)(j+\tfrac{1}{2})(P_{j-\frac{1}{2}}+P_{j+\frac{1}{2}})$$
$$=\frac{1}{2ik}\sum e^{2i\eta_j}(j+\tfrac{1}{2})(P_{j-\frac{1}{2}}+P_{j+\frac{1}{2}}). \tag{27}$$

In going from the first form of Eq. (27) to the second, the terms dropped sum to zero, except in the forward direction ($\theta=0$).[20]

In the case of a Coulomb potential produced by an extended nucleus, the potential outside the nucleus takes the form

$$v=-\gamma/x,$$

where

$$\gamma=Ze^2/\hbar c. \tag{28}$$

The potential inside the charge distribution may be

[19] G. N. Watson, *Theory of Bessel Functions* (MacMillan Company, New York, 1946), revised edition, p. 128.
[20] This is best seen by putting $a_l^{(0)}=2l+1$ in Eq. (46) below. This gives $a_l^{(1)}=0$.

calculated by using the expression

$$-v(x)=4\pi\gamma x^{-1}\int_0^x \rho(x')x'^2dx'+4\pi\gamma\int_x^\infty \rho(x')x'dx', \quad (29)$$

where the dimensionless charge density ρ has the normalization

$$4\pi\int_0^\infty \rho x^2 dx=1. \quad (30)$$

The results of the scattering theory must be modified slightly because of the long-range nature of the Coulomb potential. The proper asymptotic form of the scattered wave is

$$\phi_{\text{scatt}}=x^{-1}kf(\theta)\begin{pmatrix}1\\ \tan\frac{1}{2}\theta\exp(i\varphi)\end{pmatrix}e^{i(x+\gamma\ln 2x)}, \quad (31)$$

while the individual partial waves have the form

$$G_j(x)\sim\sin[x+\gamma\ln 2x-\tfrac{1}{2}(j-\tfrac{1}{2})\pi+\eta_j]. \quad (32)$$

The scattering amplitude $f(\theta)$ is still given by (27).

A complication of the Coulomb potential is that the phase shifts do not approach a limit as j increases. In fact, the magnitude of the phase shift increases roughly like ($\gamma\ln j$) with increasing j. Nevertheless it is possible to sum the series (27).[21,22] An improved method for carrying out this summation is given in Sec. 4.

3. Method of Calculation

The computational problem is, of course, to integrate Eqs. (21) to determine the phase shifts, and from these to calculate the differential cross section. In this section we shall outline the method, and leave the computational details to Sec. 4 and the Appendix.

Unless we wish to use simple special expressions for the potential v, it is not easy to obtain the solutions of (21) in a closed form, or even as a power series expansion. Except for the pure Coulomb case (point charge), we therefore rely on numerical methods to integrate (21). These methods are presented in detail in the Appendix. It suffices to say here that in each step of the integration all the derivatives of F_j and G_j through the fourth are treated correctly. In future calculations we plan to include all derivatives through the sixth.

Starting with a regular solution obtained by a power series expansion about the origin, the differential equations (21) are integrated from $x=0.1$ to a point x_0 (the "fitting-on radius") which lies outside the nuclear charge distribution. At x_0 the pair of functions $G_j(x_0)$, $F_j(x_0)$ is fitted to two pairs of linearly independent Coulomb functions

$$\begin{aligned}G_j(x_0)&=C_jG_{j,R}(x_0)+D_jG_{j,I}(x_0),\\ F_j(x_0)&=C_jF_{j,R}(x_0)+D_jF_{j,I}(x_0).\end{aligned} \quad (33)$$

[21] N. F. Mott, Proc. Roy. Soc. (London) A135, 429 (1932).
[22] H. Feshbach, Phys. Rev. 88, 295 (1953).

Here the subscript R (I) denotes a Coulomb function which is regular (irregular) at the origin. Both the regular and irregular Coulomb functions used here are given by power series expansions about the origin. The series used are given in the Appendix.

The asymptotic forms of the Coulomb functions are well known:

$$\begin{aligned}G_{j,R}&\sim\sin[x+\gamma\ln 2x-\tfrac{1}{2}(j-\tfrac{1}{2})\pi+\eta_j^c],\\ G_{j,I}&\sim\sin[x+\gamma\ln 2x-\tfrac{1}{2}(j-\tfrac{1}{2})\pi+\eta_j'^c],\end{aligned} \quad (34)$$

the Coulomb phase shifts being given by[23]

$$\exp 2i\eta_j^c=\frac{\rho_j-i\gamma}{j+\frac{1}{2}}\frac{\Gamma(\rho_j-i\gamma)}{\Gamma(\rho_j+i\gamma)}e^{\pi i(j+\frac{1}{2}-\rho_j)} \quad (35)$$

$$\exp i(\eta_j'^c-\eta_j^c)=\frac{1-i\tan\pi(j+\frac{1}{2}-\rho_j)\coth\pi\gamma}{|1-i\tan\pi(j+\frac{1}{2}-\rho_j)\coth\pi\gamma|}e^{-\pi i(j+\frac{1}{2}-\rho_j)}, \quad (36)$$

where

$$\rho_j=[(j+\tfrac{1}{2})^2-\gamma^2]^{\frac{1}{2}}.$$

The phase shift of the function G_j is given by

$$\tan(\eta_j-\eta_j^c)=\frac{\sin(\eta_j'^c-\eta_j^c)}{(C_j/D_j)+\cos(\eta_j'^c-\eta_j^c)}. \quad (37)$$

Tables of Coulomb phase shifts and functions are being prepared and will be published in a separate paper. Some sample phase shifts are presented in Table I.

We now estimate the precision required in the calculation of the phase shifts. According to Eq. (27), an error of $\Delta\eta_j$ in η_j introduces the following error into the scattering amplitude:

$$\Delta_j f=k^{-1}\Delta\eta_j e^{2i\eta_j}(j+\tfrac{1}{2})(P_{j-\frac{1}{2}}+P_{j+\frac{1}{2}}). \quad (38)$$

In any particular case it is possible to use this relation

TABLE I. Values of phase shifts for gold. The phase shift of the regular Coulomb functions η_j^c are defined in Eq. (35), and the difference in phase between the irregular and regular Coulomb functions $\eta_j'^c-\eta_j^c$ in Eq. (36). δ_j^1 and δ_j^2 are the additional phase shifts caused by the finite nuclear charge distributions uniform, $kR=4.0$ and Gaussian, $b=2.12$, respectively. $\delta_j=\eta_j-\eta_j^c$ is defined by Eq. (37).

j	η_j^c	$\eta_j'^c-\eta_j^c$	δ_j^1	δ_j^2
1/2	0.40736	−1.17386	−0.85820	−0.71689
3/2	−0.23797	−0.54728	−0.27143	−0.18795
5/2	−0.53303	−0.36074	−0.07633	−0.04846
7/2	−0.72659	−0.26951	−0.01494	−0.01064
9/2	−0.87098	−0.21523	−0.00199	−0.00199
11/2	−0.98623	−0.17918	−0.00017	−0.00030
13/2	−1.08218	−0.15350	−0.00001	−0.00004
15/2	−1.16438	−0.13426	−0.00000	−0.00000
17/2	−1.23628	−0.11931	−0.00000	−0.00000

[23] N. F. Mott and H. S. W. Massey, *The Theory of Atomic Collisions* (Oxford University Press, Oxford, 1952), second edition, p. 79.

to get a fairly accurate estimate of the error in the differential cross section. For simplicity, however, we shall make some crude approximations in estimating the errors. For the charge distributions considered in the present calculations the greatest errors occur in the first few phase shifts. We therefore estimate the total error in $|f|$ to be given by a small multiple m of the error arising from $\Delta\eta_{\frac{1}{2}}$:

$$\Delta|f| = mk^{-1}|\Delta\eta_{\frac{1}{2}}|E(\theta), \tag{39}$$

where m is of the order 2 or 3, and $E(\theta)$ is a factor of order 1 which decreases to zero at $\theta=\pi$. Analysis of the quantity $(P_{j-\frac{1}{2}}+P_{j+\frac{1}{2}})$ exactly for small j and asymptotically for large j shows that a suitable form for $E(\theta)$ is $\cos\frac{1}{2}\theta$. This gives for the error in the differential cross section

$$\frac{\Delta(d\sigma/d\Omega)}{d\sigma/d\Omega} = \frac{2m|\Delta\eta_{\frac{1}{2}}|}{k(d\sigma/d\Omega)^{\frac{1}{2}}}. \tag{40}$$

It is seen that the fractional error tends to be greatest where the cross section is least.

For the purpose of comparison with the present experiments it is generally sufficient to require that the relative error in the calculated cross section be less than 10 percent at the largest angle compared. Since the differential cross section decreases rapidly with increasing angle, the relative error at smaller scattering angles will then be quite negligible. We therefore require

$$|\Delta\eta_{\frac{1}{2}}| < 0.02k(d\sigma/d\Omega)_{\min}{}^{\frac{1}{2}}. \tag{41}$$

Equation (41) has two interpretations: given the cross section approximately, it tells us how accurately the phase shifts must be calculated; or when (as in practice) we know $|\Delta\eta_{\frac{1}{2}}|$, it tells us roughly the limit of the reliability of our calculations. In the present calculations we have estimated $|\Delta\eta_{\frac{1}{2}}|$ to be smaller than 0.0002 radian, based on the operations involved in obtaining $\eta_{\frac{1}{2}}$; accordingly our calculations should be sufficiently accurate whenever $k(d\sigma/d\Omega)^{\frac{1}{2}}>0.01$.

There is some empirical evidence that this estimate of the error may be too pessimistic. This is provided by the calculations for exponential and Gaussian charge distributions which yield nearly straight lines for $\log(d\sigma/d\Omega)$ *vs* θ plots. These curves continue to be linear in a region where, according to Eq. (40) and the estimate $|\Delta\eta_{\frac{1}{2}}|=0.0002$ radian, the error should be comparable in magnitude to the cross section itself! If the error were actually as large as predicted by Eq. (40), the curves should have a tendency to level off at large angles.

There are two main sources of error in the present calculation. The first is the lack of accuracy of the Coulomb functions at the fitting-on radius, due to their calculation by means of a series expansion about the origin. Cancellations which occur in the summing of the series make the final sum have a greater relative error than any of the individual terms. This error can be reduced only by computing the terms more accurately; such calculations are now in progress. The second source of error is the wave function integration. This error can be reduced by using a smaller interval or by improving the accuracy of each integration step. These two sources of error contribute about equally to the phase shift errors $\Delta\eta_j$.

4. Scattering Amplitude Series

In this section we present a new method for summing the scattering amplitude series. In previous calculations, it has been the practice to calculate first the Coulomb scattering amplitude, Eq. (27) with phase shifts given by Eq. (35), and then the corrections to it due to the finite nuclear size:

$$f=f_c+(f-f_c), \tag{42}$$

where

$$f-f_c=\frac{1}{2ik}\sum(\exp 2i\eta_j-\exp 2i\eta_j{}^c)(j+\tfrac{1}{2})(P_{j-\frac{1}{2}}+P_{j+\frac{1}{2}}). \tag{43}$$

Since $(\eta_j-\eta_j{}^c)$ approaches zero with increasing j, the series (43) converges quite rapidly even though η_j and $\eta_j{}^c$ do not individually approach zero. One sees from the Born approximation[3] that at high energies and large angles the scattering amplitude f is much smaller in magnitude than the Coulomb scattering amplitude f_c. This implies that there is almost complete cancellation between the two terms of Eq. (42), and that they must both, therefore, be known to high precision. We were unable to use the published tables of Feshbach,[22] where kf_c is given to only three decimal places and at large angular intervals.

We can discover the reason for the poor convergence of the series (27) for the case of a Coulomb potential by looking at the corresponding problem in the nonrelativistic case, where the Coulomb scattering amplitude is known analytically:

$$f_{\text{N.R.}}(\theta)=\frac{\alpha}{2k\sin^2\frac{1}{2}\theta}\exp[2i\alpha\ln\sin\tfrac{1}{2}\theta+2i\bar{\eta}_0] \tag{44}$$

$$=\frac{1}{2ik}\sum_{l=0}^{\infty}(2l+1)[\exp(2i\bar{\eta}_l)-1]P_l(\cos\theta), \tag{45}$$

where

$$\bar{\eta}_l=\arg\Gamma(l+1-i\alpha), \tag{46}$$

and

$$\alpha=Ze^2/\hbar v.$$

The series (45) with the phase shifts (46) can be rearranged in form so that it closely resembles the series (27) with the phase shifts (35).[21] For our present purposes, however, it is not necessary to do this. From Eq. (44) we see that $f_{\text{N.R.}}(\theta)$ has a singularity in both magnitude and argument at $\theta=0$. This accounts for the poor convergence of the series (45). Since for large j values the relativistic phase shifts are nearly the same as the nonrelativistic ones for $l=j-\frac{1}{2}$, the relativistic series probably has a similar type of singularity. We accordingly transform $f(\theta)$ to make it less singular for small values of θ. This is accomplished by multiplying $f(\theta)$ by a function which vanishes at $\theta=0$ and then expanding the new function in a series of Legendre polynomials.

Let us represent $f(\theta)$ by

$$2ikf=\sum a_l P_l(\cos\theta). \tag{47}$$

Then the mth "reduced" series is defined by:

$$(1-\cos\theta)^m 2ikf=\sum a_l^{(m)} P_l(\cos\theta). \tag{48}$$

Using the recurrence relations for Legendre polynomials, we find that

$$a_l^{(i+1)}=a_l^{(i)}-\frac{l+1}{2l+3}a_{l+1}^{(i)}-\frac{l}{2l-1}a_{l-1}^{(i)}. \tag{49}$$

For large l, it turns out that

$$|a_l^{(i+1)}|=O(|a_l^{(i)}|/l^2), \tag{50}$$

so that after a few reductions the series converges quite rapidly. We have found three reductions ($m=3$) to be optimum for our present calculations. For gold, the results are illustrated in Table II, where the coefficients of the series in Eq. (47) are compared with those of the third reduction.

TABLE II. Coefficients of the Legendre series for the Coulomb scattering amplitude. a_l are those for the original series in Eq. (47), and $a_l^{(3)}$ are the third reduced coefficients defined by Eq. (49).

l	Re a_l	Im a_l	Re $a_l^{(3)}$	Im $a_l^{(3)}$
0	0.68608	0.72753	−0.40271	0.64187
1	2.46374	−0.18893	0.46429	−0.39809
2	3.22837	−3.54238	0.28802	−0.66577
3	1.92010	−6.59828	−0.48598	0.40511
4	−0.38223	−8.89930	0.10826	0.02838
5	−3.19735	−10.44940	0.01935	−0.00448
6	−6.26093	−11.32514	0.00547	−0.00298
7	−9.41473	−11.61261	0.00194	−0.00162
8	−12.55937	−11.39191	0.00078	−0.00091
9	−15.63076	−10.73364	0.00034	−0.00053
10	−18.58706	−9.69883	0.00016	−0.00032
11	−21.40100	−8.33997	0.00007	−0.00020
12	−24.05511	−6.70216		
13	−26.53869	−4.82425		
14	−28.84572	−2.73981		

III. DISCUSSION OF THE RESULTS

To obtain the cross section for a given charge distribution at an energy $k\hbar c$ we must use in Eq. (29) the corresponding dimensionless function $\rho(x)$, x being the radial coordinate measured in units of $k^{-1}=\lambda\!\!\!^{-}$. Equations (21) and (22), together with Eq. (29), then present the scattering problem in dimensionless form, with $kf(\theta)$ as a dimensionless scattering amplitude. The energy $k\hbar c$ thus enters the calculation in two ways: first, in the determination of the radial scale of $\rho(x)$; second, in the absolute magnitude of the cross section. For another energy $k'\hbar c$, this particular $\rho(x)$ corresponds to a physical charge distribution whose dimensions are altered by a factor k/k', and whose cross section is altered by a factor $(k/k')^2$. In the following discussion the term "shape" refers to the various analytic forms used for $\rho(x)$, and "size" refers to the value of the radial parameter involved.

We have considered the following shapes:

exponential, $\rho(x)=\rho_0 e^{-x/a}$;
Gaussian, $\rho(x)=\rho_0\exp[-(x/b)^2]$;
uniform, $\rho(x)=\rho_0,\ x<kR$,
$=0,\ x>kR$;
smoothed uniform, $\rho=\rho_0[1+e^{K(x-c)}]^{-1}$;
wine-bottle, $\rho=\rho_0(1+(x/d)^4)[1+e^{K(x-c)}]^{-1}$.

Most of the calculations reported here are for gold ($Z=79$, $\gamma=Ze^2/\hbar c=0.5765$). A few are for copper ($Z=29$, $\gamma=0.2116$) and for aluminum ($Z=13$, $\gamma=0.09486$).

5. Comparison with the First Born Approximation

The differential cross section predicted by the first Born approximation is

$$\frac{d\sigma}{d\Omega}=\left(\frac{\gamma}{2k}\right)^2\frac{\cos^2\frac{1}{2}\theta}{\sin^4\frac{1}{2}\theta}\left|\int\rho(x)e^{i\mathbf{q}\cdot\mathbf{x}}d^3x\right|^2,$$

where $|\mathbf{q}|=2\sin\frac{1}{2}\theta$, and ρ, as in Eq. (30), has unit volume integral.[3] The scattering amplitude is real. For simpler shapes the "form factor" $F=\int\rho(x)\exp(i\mathbf{q}\cdot\mathbf{x})d^3x$ has the following forms:

exponential, $F=(1+q^2a^2)^{-2}$;
Gaussian, $F=\exp(-q^2b^2/4)$;
uniform, $F=3(\sin qkR-qkR\cos qkR)/(qkR)^3$.

The cross sections for the first two shapes are, on a semilog plot, smooth functions of θ; for the uniform shape, on the other hand, F has zeros (where $qkR=\tan qkR$) and the cross section is a wildly varying function of θ. In Figs. 1, 2, and 3 the dashed curves are the Born approximation cross sections for a uniform shape $kR=5.4$, exponentials $a=0.91$ and $a=1.06$, and Gaussians $b=2.12$ and $b=3.4$, respectively.

The cross sections obtained from the phase-shift analysis are, for gold, usually considerably different from the first Born approximation cross sections.[4] For the uniform shape, the first zero of the Born cross section appears only as a slight undulation, and the second zero barely as a minimum, which is shifted to a slightly smaller angle. In Fig. 1 is shown the cross section for the uniform shape $kR=5.4$, together with the cross section for the same shape in copper, suitably normalized to have the same Born cross section. For copper the agreement with the Born approximation is much better than for gold, as is to be expected.

The results of the phase-shift analysis for the ex-

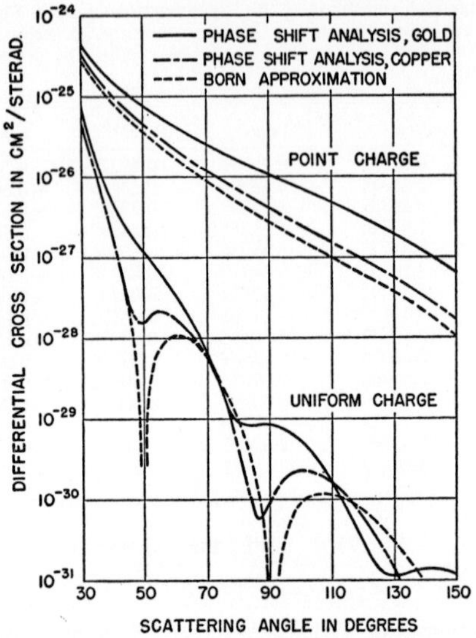

FIG. 1. Differential cross sections at 150 Mev for scattering by a point charge and by the uniform charge distribution $kR=5.4$, for gold and copper. The cross sections for copper have been multiplied by a factor that makes their first Born approximations the same as those for gold.

ponential shape are shown in Fig. 2. The cross section is a smooth function of θ, but has a considerably greater over-all slope than the Born cross section. Thus fitting experimental results with the phase-shift analysis predicts a smaller nucleus than fitting with the Born approximation.

For the Gaussian shape with $b=2.12$, the phase-shift analysis cross section, shown in Fig. 3, is almost identical with the Born cross section, whereas for $b=3.4$ it slopes less steeply. The phase-shift analysis results for the exponential and uniform shapes could be understood, as suggested previously,[4] in terms of the increase in wave number as the electron entered the attractive field of the nucleus. The results for Gaussian shapes, however, lie if anything in the opposite direction, so that such a simple interpretation is ruled out.

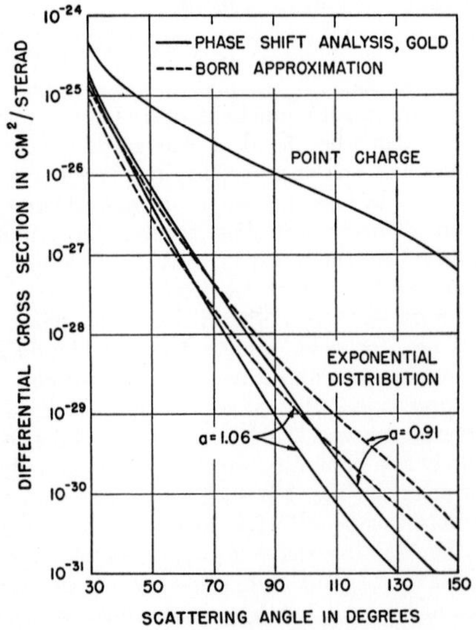

FIG. 2. Cross sections at 150 Mev for scattering by the exponential shapes $a=0.91$ and $a=1.06$, for gold.

The difference between the phase-shift analysis and the first Born approximation is even more pronounced in the scattering amplitude, which in the phase-shift analysis is, of course, complex. In Figs. 4 and 5 we exhibit this complex behavior by making polar plots of $\log_{10}|f(\theta)|$ *versus* argument $(f(\theta))$. The values $\theta=30°$, $50°$, $70°$, $\cdots$ are indicated on each curve. In Fig. 4 are

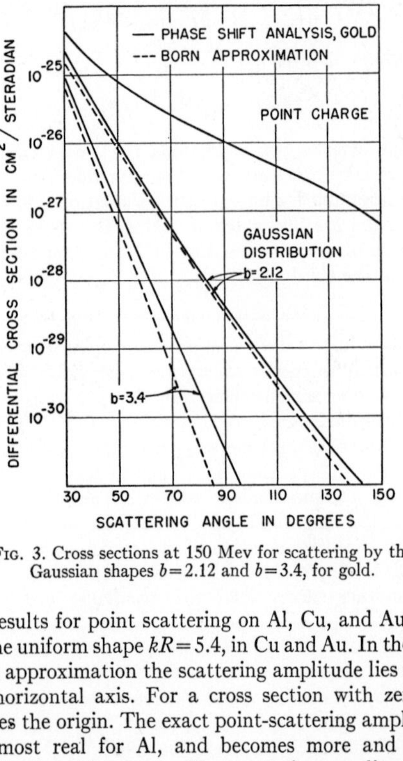

FIG. 3. Cross sections at 150 Mev for scattering by the Gaussian shapes $b=2.12$ and $b=3.4$, for gold.

the results for point scattering on Al, Cu, and Au, and for the uniform shape $kR=5.4$, in Cu and Au. In the first Born approximation the scattering amplitude lies along the horizontal axis. For a cross section with zeros it crosses the origin. The exact point-scattering amplitude is almost real for Al, and becomes more and more complex as Z increases. The scattering amplitude for the uniform shape $kR=5.4$ is for Cu a flattened spiral whose major axis is at about 30° to the horizontal axis and the Born approximation amplitude, while for Au it is an unflattened spiral. The filling in of the zeros in the Born approximation cross section and the fact that the exact scattering amplitude is complex are thus the same phenomenon. In Fig. 5 are scattering amplitudes for a number of charge shapes in gold. We find that for a given shape the polar plot is remarkably independent of size. For the Gaussian shape, for instance, the curves for $b=3.4$ and $b=2.12$ are almost the same. The difference in the corresponding cross sections occurs because values of θ on the $b=3.4$ curve are shifted relative to the corresponding values of θ on the $b=2.12$ curve. Another peculiar fact is that the exponential shape $ka=0.91$ and the Gaussian shape $kb=2.12$ have very different scattering amplitudes but almost identical cross sections.

The first Born approximation cross sections are thus of little value in suggesting the correct sizes to use when fitting the data. The fact that the phase-shift analysis yields cross sections which are always smoother functions of θ means that a much wider range of shapes gives a tolerable fit with experiment than was suggested by the use of the Born approximation.

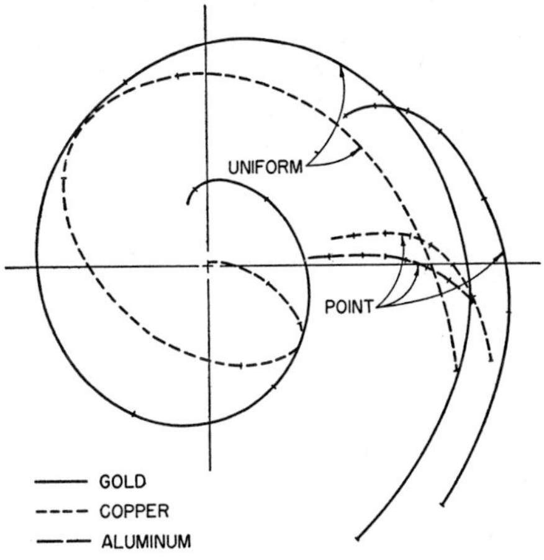

FIG. 4. Plots of $\log_{10}|f(\theta)|$ *versus* $\arg f(\theta)$, in polar coordinates, for point scattering in gold, copper, and aluminum, and for the uniform shape $kR=5.4$ in gold and copper. The values $\theta=30°$, $50°$, $70°$, $\cdots$ are indicated on each curve.

6. Interpolation

It is useful to be able to estimate the effect on the cross section of changing the size slightly, without doing a large number of trial calculations. For the smooth cross sections yielded by the Gaussian shapes, it is possible to interpolate by fitting cross sections at a particular value of θ to a polynomial in the size parameter. Since we usually need only relative cross sections, our procedure is to fit the ratio of the values of $\log_{10}[d\sigma(\theta)/d\Omega]-\log_{10}[d\sigma(\theta')/d\Omega]$ given respectively by the phase-shift analysis and the first Born approximation to a polynomial in the size parameter b. Extrapolating in this way from cross sections for $b=3.4$ and $b=2.69$ gives a cross section for $b=2.12$ which by later comparison with the phase-shift analysis we have found to be accurate to about 2 percent. The cross section for the Gaussian shape $b=3.05$ shown in Fig. 10 was obtained by this method.

Such a method is clearly unsuitable for cross sections given by uniform shapes. For these we make use of the fact that the "form factor" $\mathfrak{F}(\theta,kR)$ defined in terms of the phase-shift analysis cross sections by

$$\{\mathfrak{F}(\theta,kR)\}^2=\{d\sigma(\theta)/d\Omega\}/\{d\sigma(\theta)/d\Omega\}_{\text{point}}$$

has properties very similar to those of the form factor $F(\theta,kR)$ of the first Born approximation.[24] There, F is a function of $2kR\sin\frac{1}{2}\theta$ whose analytic form is the same for all kR (see the beginning of Sec. 5), so that $F(\theta,kR)$ and $F(\theta',kR')$ for two sizes have equal values when $kR'\sin\frac{1}{2}\theta'=kR\sin\frac{1}{2}\theta$. Hence in the first Born approximation the cross sections for all sizes can be obtained from a knowledge of the point cross section and the form factor F for one size. In the case of the phase-shift analysis we find that the two angles defined by

$$\mathfrak{F}(\theta,5.4)=\mathfrak{F}(\theta',4.0)$$

are connected by the relation $\sin\frac{1}{2}\theta/\sin\frac{1}{2}\theta'=\text{constant}\pm 4$ percent over the angular range 30° to 150°. The "constant" is roughly $(4.0/5.4)^{0.8}$. Hence to within 4 percent $\mathfrak{F}$ can be written $\mathfrak{F}(g(kR)\sin\frac{1}{2}\theta)$, and, as with the first Born approximation, is (approximately) a universal function independent of size. When obtained by the phase-shift analysis for a particular size it can be used for other slightly different sizes. Of the family of uniform shapes shown in Fig. 6, the $kR=4.0$ curve was obtained by the phase-shift analysis, and the rest by this interpolation method, as was also the uniform $kR=5.8$ curve of Fig. 10.

[24] This was suggested to us by Dr. McIntyre.

7. Comparison with Other Calculations

Calculations of other authors seem to confirm our results fairly well. Numerical errors have been discovered in the published work of Parzen.[9,10] In any case it seems physically rather unlikely that the phase-shift

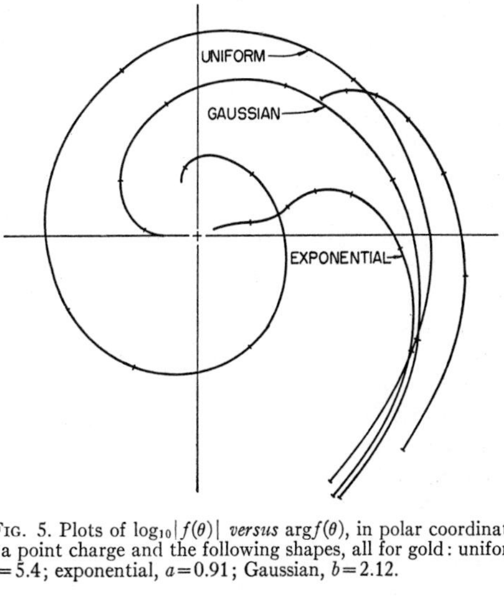

FIG. 5. Plots of $\log_{10}|f(\theta)|$ *versus* $\arg f(\theta)$, in polar coordinates, for a point charge and the following shapes, all for gold: uniform, $kR=5.4$; exponential, $a=0.91$; Gaussian, $b=2.12$.

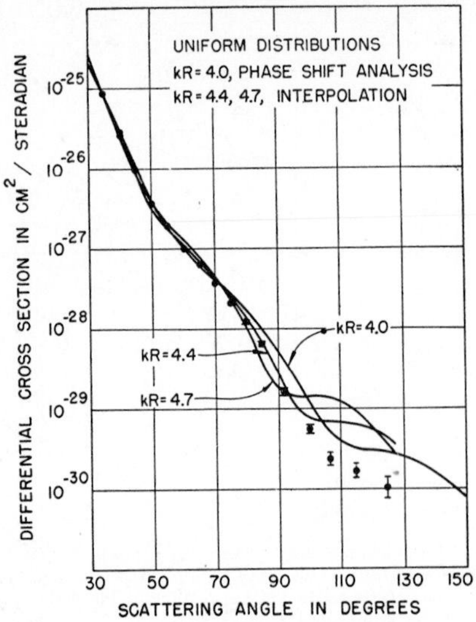

FIG. 6. Cross sections at 125 Mev for scattering by three uniform shapes, $kR=4.0$, 4.4, 4.7, for gold, together with the experimental data. All have been normalized to the same value at 35°. The ordinate scale refers to the $kR=4.0$ curve. This was obtained by the phase-shift analysis, the other two by interpolation. The nuclear radii corresponding to these shapes have r_0 values of 1.09×10^{-13} cm, 1.19×10^{-13} cm, 1.27×10^{-13} cm, where $R=r_0A^{\frac{1}{3}}$. From Eq. (40) the estimated error in the $kR=4.0$ curve is 10 percent when $d\sigma(\theta)/d\Omega\cong3\times10^{-30}$ cm² per steradian, i.e., when $\theta\cong120°$. For θ larger than 120° the error is larger.

analysis cross sections should be many times the first Born cross sections. A phase-shift analysis in which the phase shifts were obtained by the W.K.B. approximation has been made by Baranger.[11] The cross section she obtains for the uniform shape $kR=5.0$, in mercury, $Z=80$, resembles closely our cross section for the uniform shape $kR=5.4$ in gold, although its plateau (corresponding to the Born approximation second zero) is a little higher than that of our curve. Brenner, Brown, and Elton[12] have obtained phase shifts by numerical integration. Their cross section for the uniform shape $kR=4.4$ in mercury seems to agree very closely with our uniform $kR=4.4$ shape in gold. For the uniform $kR=5.28$ shape, however, their cross section tends to be rather larger than ours (obtained by interpolation from $kR=5.4$) at large angles. Their results for a smoothed uniform shape, with a slightly different analytic function from that we have used, check very closely our conclusions on this shape in Sec. 8. Both Baranger, and Brenner, Brown, and Elton, however, have used Feshbach's values of the Coulomb scattering amplitude[22] for mercury, $Z=80$. Results for $Z=80$ should not differ appreciably from results for $Z=79$, but, as we point out in Sec. 4, Feshbach's values are probably not accurate enough to yield reliable cross sections at large angles.

8. Cross Sections for Gold at 125 Mev

Experimental results for gold at 125 Mev are included in Figs. 6, 7, and 8. They are part of the new data obtained recently by Hofstadter's group.[25] They indicate a cross section which decreases steadily with θ (on this semilog plot) out to about 120°, with a slight dip at about 60°. We have found a wide variety of charge shapes all of which give cross sections having roughly this character, although these cross sections do not all fit the experimental results equally well. Since it appears that a comparison with experiment at several

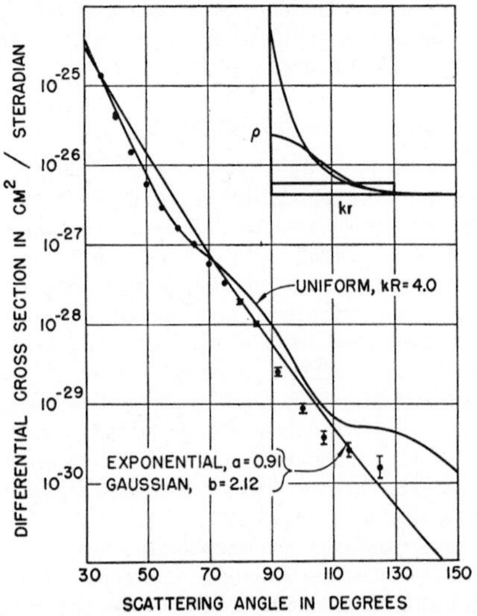

FIG. 7. Cross sections at 125 Mev for scattering by the uniform shape $kR=4.0$, the exponential $a=0.91$, and the Gaussian $b=2.12$, for gold, together with the experimental data. When all are normalized to the same value at 35° the cross sections for the Gaussian and exponential shapes coincide. The ordinate scale refers to the Gaussian shape. The rms radii of the three shapes are, respectively, 3.10ƛ, 3.16ƛ, and 2.60ƛ Inset are scale drawings of ρ.

energies is required to obtain the charge distribution accurately, we want in this paper only to give the trend that our present calculations suggest.

In Fig. 6 the cross sections of a family of uniform charge distributions are plotted together with the experimental results. That for $kR=4.0$ is obtained from our phase-shift analysis, the others by the interpolation method given in Sec. 6. Since the measured cross section is only relative, the scale of the interpolated curves has been altered so that they have the same value at 35° as the cross section for $kR=4.0$, and the

[25] The data with which we compared our calculations as they were made were means of the earlier published cross sections (see reference 1) and later unpublished ones, all obtained before improvements in the experimental apparatus enabled Hofstadter's group to obtain their new and more accurate data. These means of the old data agreed very well with the new data, although their probable error was of course much larger. We are grateful for Professor Hofstadter's permission to quote the new results before their publication.

experimental 35° point has been plotted here also. It seems from Fig. 6 that it will be difficult to fit both the general slope in the range 35°–80°, and the fact that there is no plateau, with a uniform charge distribution.

Figure 7 contains the cross sections for the exponential $a=0.91$, Gaussian $b=2.12$, and uniform $kR=4.0$ charge distributions, normalized at 35°, together with the experimental results. It is remarkable that over the whole range of θ used, the cross sections for the first two shapes are so closely proportional that in this figure we are unable to distinguish between them. Indeed, for angles less than 90° the cross sections of all three shapes are not very different. As regards comparison with experiment, it is seen that the cross sections of the exponential and Gaussian do decrease steadily with angle, but they have no dip at 60°. A shape having some of the features of each of those of Fig. 7 seems to be indicated. The root-mean-square radius may be taken as a measure of the relative size

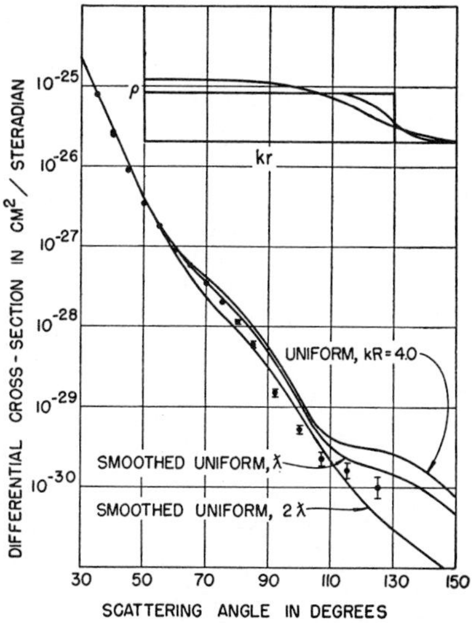

FIG. 8. Cross sections at 125 Mev for scattering by the uniform shape $kR=4.0$ and two smoothed uniform shapes: $K=4.40$, $c=3.86$; and $K=2.20$, $c=3.51$, for gold, together with the experimental data. The "smoothing distances" of the second and third shapes are $\lambda\!\!\!^-$ and $2\lambda\!\!\!^-$ at this energy. The rms radii of the three shapes are all $3.10\lambda\!\!\!^-$. Inset are scale drawings of ρ.

of these charge distributions. In units of k^{-1} it is respectively 3.16, 2.60, and 3.10 for these three shapes.

The smoothed uniform shape represents a charge distribution intermediate between uniform and exponential. The two cross sections in Fig. 8 are for smoothed uniform shapes having the same rms radius as the uniform $kR=4.0$ distribution. They have smoothing distances of 1 and 2, in units of k^{-1}. (We define smoothing distances as the distance over which ρ decreases from 0.9 $\rho(0)$ to 0.1 $\rho(0)$.) The shape with a smoothing distance of 1, that is $\lambda\!\!\!^-$, has a cross section almost the same as that of the uniform shape, whereas the shape with a smoothing distance of 2 (i.e., $2\lambda\!\!\!^-$) has a cross section which approaches that of an exponential. It thus appears that at this energy only smoothed uniform shapes with smoothing distances between $\lambda\!\!\!^-$ and $2\lambda\!\!\!^-$ have cross sections distinctly different from those of uniform or exponential. It seems likely that by appropriately choosing c and K a cross section can be obtained which will have the features shown by the experimental one. Such a shape would have about the same rms radius as those of Fig. 8.[25a]

As a shape in which charge is dispersed towards the edge of the nucleus we have considered the "wine-bottle."[26] As Fig. 9 shows, such a shape, with $d=c$, having the same rms radius as the uniform $kR=4.0$, and a maximum charge density 1.46 times its central density, has a cross section almost identical with the uniform $kR=4.0$ shape.

The experimental data at 125 Mev can probably be fitted with quite a range of charge distributions. The situation is much more definite, however, if a fit is made at two energies. For example, Fig. 10 shows the cross sections at 180 Mev given by the Gaussian and uniform nuclear charge distributions whose cross sections at 125 Mev are shown in Fig. 7. These were obtained by the interpolation methods described in Sec. 6. Experimental results at 180 Mev should be able to discriminate between them.

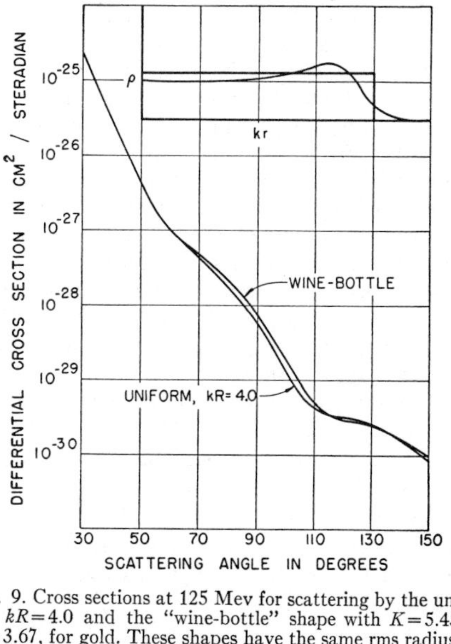

FIG. 9. Cross sections at 125 Mev for scattering by the uniform shape $kR=4.0$ and the "wine-bottle" shape with $K=5.45$ and $c=d=3.67$, for gold. These shapes have the same rms radius, and the second has a maximum charge density 1.46 times the central density. Inset are scale drawings of ρ.

[25a] *Footnote added in proof.*—Later calculations indicate that the rms radius will be a little larger (about 5 or 10 percent) than those of the charge distributions of Fig. 8.

[26] Such a charge distribution has been suggested by E. Feenberg, Phys. Rev. **59**, 593 (1941).

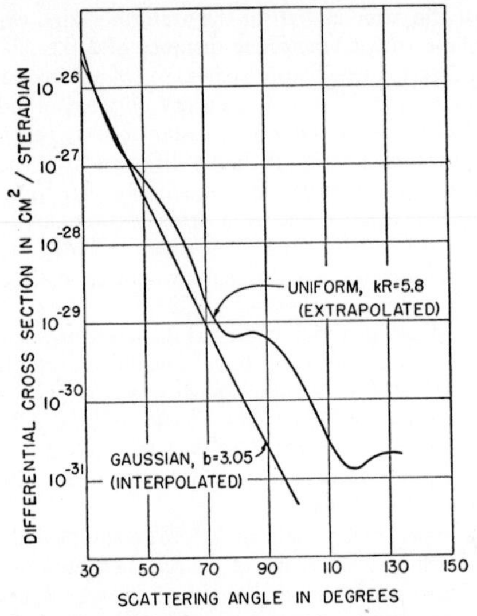

FIG. 10. Cross sections at 180 Mev for scattering by the Gaussian and uniform nuclear charge distributions whose cross sections at 125 Mev are shown in Fig. 7. At 180 Mev they correspond to the uniform $kR=5.8$ and Gaussian $b=3.05$ shapes. The cross sections were obtained by the interpolation methods of Sec. 6.

9. Conclusions

It seems likely that the experimental results in gold at 125 Mev, or at any one energy, can be fitted by quite a range of charge distributions, and that comparisons between theory and experiment at several energies will be needed to obtain a unique result. From the few calculations we have already made it appears that a smoothed uniform charge distribution with smoothing distance a little greater than $\lambda\!\!\!^{-}$ (for terminology, see Sec. 8) could fit the 125 Mev data. It would have a root-mean-square radius about equal to that of a uniform distribution with radius $R=1.1\times10^{-13}A^{\frac{1}{3}}$ cm.[25a] But we have tried only a small sample of all conceivable charge distributions, and it may well be possible to find another one quite different from this which also fits the data at 125 Mev.

We wish to thank Professor L. I. Schiff for his advice on all phases of the work, and Professor R. Hofstadter and Dr. J. A. McIntyre for many stimulating and fruitful conversations. Advice on programming for the Stanford I.B.M. Card-Programmed Calculator by Professor J. G. Herriot and Mr. J. Carter, and instruction in its operation by Mrs. H. Van Heusen, are much appreciated.

APPENDIX

1. Comparison of the Present Treatment of the Dirac Equation with Those of Other Authors

Most previous treatments of the electron-scattering problem are based on the separation of the Dirac equation given by Darwin.[27] It seems worth while to show here the connection between Darwin's treatment and ours.

In place of (1), Darwin uses

$$(-\boldsymbol{\alpha}'\cdot\mathbf{p}c-\beta' mc^2+V)\psi'=E\psi', \tag{A1}$$

where[15]

$$\alpha'_i=\rho_1\sigma_i,\quad \beta'=\rho_3. \tag{A2}$$

The two representations are connected by

$$-\alpha_i'=U^{-1}\alpha_iU,\quad -\beta'=U^{-1}\beta U, \tag{A3}$$

where

$$U=U^{-1}=(1/\sqrt{2})(\rho_1-\rho_3). \tag{A4}$$

The partial wave solutions of (A1) take the form

$$\psi_n'=r^{-1}\begin{pmatrix}-i\mathfrak{F}_n(r)\chi_{n+\frac{1}{2}}^2\\ \mathcal{G}_n(r)\chi_{n+\frac{1}{2}}^1\end{pmatrix}(n=0,1,2,\cdots), \tag{A5}$$

$$\psi_{-n-1}'=r^{-1}\begin{pmatrix}-i\mathfrak{F}_{-n-1}(r)\chi_{n-\frac{1}{2}}^1\\ \mathcal{G}_{-n-1}(r)\chi_{n-\frac{1}{2}}^2\end{pmatrix}(n=1,2,3,\cdots), \tag{A6}$$

where the two-component functions χ^1 and χ^2 are given by Eq. (13). The radial functions $\mathfrak{F}_n$ and $\mathcal{G}_n$ satisfy

$$\begin{aligned}\frac{d\mathcal{G}_n}{dr}-\frac{(n+1)}{r}\mathcal{G}_n+\frac{(E-V+mc^2)}{\hbar c}\mathfrak{F}_n&=0,\\ \frac{d\mathfrak{F}_n}{dr}+\frac{(n+1)}{r}\mathfrak{F}_n-\frac{(E-V-mc^2)}{\hbar c}\mathcal{G}_n&=0.\end{aligned} \tag{A7}$$

$\mathfrak{F}_{-n-1}$, $\mathcal{G}_{-n-1}$ satisfy the same equations with n replaced by $-n-1$. Comparing Eq. (A7) with Eq. (18), we find that in the limit $m\to0$

$$\begin{aligned}\mathcal{G}_n&=\mathfrak{F}_{-n-2}=G_{n+\frac{1}{2}},\\ \mathfrak{F}_n&=-\mathcal{G}_{-n-2}=F_{n+\frac{1}{2}}.\end{aligned} \tag{A8}$$

Transforming Eqs. (A5) and (A6) to the representation used in the present paper, we obtain

$$\begin{pmatrix}\phi_{j,\frac{1}{2}}\\ 0\end{pmatrix}=\frac{1}{\sqrt{2}}(\psi_n-i\psi_{-n-2}), \tag{A9}$$

$$\begin{pmatrix}0\\ \chi_{j,\frac{1}{2}}\end{pmatrix}=\frac{1}{\sqrt{2}}(\psi_n+i\psi_{-n-2}). \tag{A10}$$

The states (A5) and (A6) have definite parity while (A9) and (A10) do not.

The index n in Eqs. (A5) and (A6) seems to have been selected because it is the order of the spherical harmonics in the third and fourth components of ψ_n' and ψ_{-n-1}' and not because of its connection with any particular quantum number. An alternative is to use the quantum number $k(=\pm(j+\frac{1}{2}))$, defined by the operator

$$\hbar k=\beta'(\boldsymbol{\sigma}'\cdot\mathbf{L}+\hbar). \tag{A11}$$

[27] C. G. Darwin, Proc. Roy. Soc. (London) **A118**, 654 (1928).

This notation has been used by Acheson.[6] His radial functions $f_{\pm\kappa}$ and $g_{\pm\kappa}$ are related to those of Darwin as follows:

$$f_\kappa = \mathfrak{F}_{\kappa-1}, \quad g_\kappa = \mathcal{G}_{\kappa-1}(\kappa = k = j+\tfrac{1}{2}), \tag{A12}$$

$$f_{-\kappa} = \mathfrak{F}_{-\kappa-1}, \quad g_{-\kappa} = \mathcal{G}_{-\kappa-1}(\kappa = -k = j+\tfrac{1}{2}). \tag{A13}$$

With this notation the radial equations become

$$\frac{dg_{\pm\kappa}}{dr} \mp \frac{\kappa}{r} g_{\pm\kappa} + \frac{(E-V+mc^2)}{\hbar c} f_{\pm\kappa} = 0,$$
$$\frac{df_{\pm\kappa}}{dr} \pm \frac{\kappa}{r} f_{\pm\kappa} + \frac{(E-V-mc^2)}{\hbar c} g_{\pm\kappa} = 0. \tag{A14}$$

We have not used this notation because the partial waves (A9) and (A10) are not eigenfunctions of k.

2. Calculation of Coulomb Functions

Mott and Massey have given the Coulomb functions in terms of confluent hypergeometric functions.[23] We use instead the more rapidly convergent series solution given by Elton:[28]

$$G_j = x^{s_j} N_j \sum_{m=0}^{\infty} a_m^{(j)} x^m,$$
$$F_j = x^{s_j} N_j \sum_{m=0}^{\infty} b_m^{(j)} x^m, \tag{A15}$$

where

$$s_j = \pm\rho_j = \pm[(j+\tfrac{1}{2})^2 - \gamma^2]^{\frac{1}{2}}.$$

The positive sign gives the regular solution, and the negative sign the irregular solution. The coefficients of the series are given by

$$a_0 = 1, \quad b_0 = \gamma/(s_j+j+\tfrac{1}{2}), \tag{A16}$$

together with the recurrence relations:

$$m(m+2s_j)a_m^{(j)} = -\gamma a_{m-1}^{(j)} - (s_j+m+j+\tfrac{1}{2})b_{m-1}^{(j)},$$
$$m(m+2s_j)b_m^{(j)} = -\gamma b_{m-1}^{(j)} + (s_j+m-j-\tfrac{1}{2})a_{m-1}^{(j)}. \tag{A17}$$

The normalization, obtained by comparison with Mott and Massey's solutions, is

$$N_j = \frac{s_j}{|s_j|} \frac{2^{s_j}|\Gamma(s_j+i\gamma)|}{\Gamma(2s_j+1)} \left[\frac{(j+\frac{1}{2})(j+\frac{1}{2}+s_j)}{2}\right]^{\frac{1}{2}} e^{\frac{1}{2}\pi\gamma}. \tag{A18}$$

3. Numerical Integration of the Radial Dirac Equations

We use a step-by-step procedure based on derivatives rather than differences. Let $y_n, y_n', y_n'', \cdots$ be a function and its derivatives at $x=x_n$. Alternative approximate formulas, given by Milne,[29] for y_{n+1} at $x_{n+1}=x_n+h$ are

$$y_{n+1} = y_n + \tfrac{1}{2}h(y_n' + y_{n+1}'), \tag{A19}$$

$$y_{n+1} = y_n + \tfrac{1}{2}h(y_n' + y_{n+1}') + (1/12)h^2(y_n'' - y_{n+1}''), \tag{A20}$$

$$y_{n+1} = y_n + \tfrac{1}{2}h(y_n' + y_{n+1}') + (1/10)h^2(y_n'' - y_{n+1}'') + (1/120)h^3(y_n''' + y_{n+1}'''). \tag{A21}$$

The respective errors are of order $h^3y'''/12$, $h^5y^{(5)}/720$, $h^7y^{(7)}/100\,800$. The method can easily be extended to take more derivatives into account. We use Eq. (A20) to obtain the results of Part III.

Since Eqs. (21) are linear,[30] we may solve Eqs. (A19–A21) exactly for y_{n+1} in terms of y_n. Let y_n be a column matrix composed of $F_{j,n}$ and $G_{j,n}$

$$y_n = \begin{pmatrix} F_j \\ G_j \end{pmatrix}_n. \tag{A22}$$

Then from Eqs. (21), the derivatives of y_n can be represented by matrices acting on y_n:

$$y_n' = A_n y_n, \quad y_n'' = B_n y_n, \quad y_n''' = C_n y_n. \tag{A23}$$

For example,

$$A_n = \begin{pmatrix} -(j+\frac{1}{2})/x_n & (1-v_n) \\ -(1-v_n) & (j+\frac{1}{2})/x_n \end{pmatrix}. \tag{A24}$$

The solutions of Eqs. (A19–A21) are given by

$$y_{n+1} = \left(1 - \frac{h}{2}A_{n+1}\right)^{-1}\left(1 + \frac{h}{2}A_n\right)y_n, \tag{A25}$$

$$y_{n+1} = \left(1 - \frac{h}{2}A_{n+1} + \frac{h^2}{12}B_{n+1}\right)^{-1} \times \left(1 + \frac{h}{2}A_n + \frac{h^2}{12}B_n\right)y_n, \tag{A26}$$

$$y_{n+1} = \left[1 - \frac{h}{2}A_{n+1} + \frac{h^2}{10}B_{n+1} - \frac{h^3}{120}C_{n+1}\right]^{-1} \times \left[1 + \frac{h}{2}A_n + \frac{h^2}{10}B_n + \frac{h^3}{120}C_n\right]y_n. \tag{A27}$$

[28] L. R. B. Elton, Proc. Phys. Soc. (London) **A66**, 806 (1953). There is a sign error in Elton's Eq. (3.14).

[29] W. E. Milne, *Numerical Solution of Differential Equations* (John Wiley and Sons, Inc., New York, 1953), pp. 76–78.

[30] When this method is applied to nonlinear differential equations y_{n+1} is obtained from y_n by an iteration procedure.

We can make some estimates of the errors involved in using this method. Inside the turning point (which is at $x \cong j$), any small errors made in an integration step will bring in a small amount of irregular function. However, in this region the regular function increases rapidly with increasing x, while the irregular function decreases rapidly. Thus, in this region, the effect of a small error tends to be damped quickly. Of course the normalization near the origin may differ from that outside the turning point because of these errors, but that does not affect the present calculations since we need only the ratio (F_j/G_j) at the fitting-on radius.

Outside the turning point the error in the phase can be estimated by replacing the Eqs. (21) by the equations

$$g' = -f, \quad f' = +g, \qquad \text{(A28)}$$

which have the solutions

$$g = \cos x, \quad f = \sin x.$$

Equations (A19–A21) have the solution[31]

$$g = \cos\lambda x, \quad f = \sin\lambda x,$$

where

$$\lambda = 1 - h^2/12,$$

$$\lambda = 1 - h^4/720,$$

$$\lambda = 1 - h^6/100\,800,$$

respectively. The total phase error in a distance L is therefore

$$\delta\phi = h^2 L/12,$$

$$\delta\phi = h^4 L/720,$$

$$\delta\phi = h^6 L/100\,800,$$

for the three approximations.

If we require $\delta\phi < 10^{-4}$, for $L = 8$ we find in the respective cases:

$$h < 10^{-2}, \quad h < 0.3, \quad h < 1.$$

The interval that would be required using Eq. (A19) is prohibitively small. With Eq. (A20) there is more computing work at each step of the integration, but the interval is reasonable. One could not use such a large interval with Eq. (A21) as estimated here because of the variation of A_n with x. With a smaller interval Eq. (A21) may be useful in obtaining greater accuracy.

[31] This was pointed out to us by Professor L. I. Schiff.

PAPER 24

High-Energy Electron Scattering and Nuclear Structure Determinations. II*†‡

R. Hofstadter, B. Hahn,§ A. W. Knudsen, and J. A. McIntyre
Department of Physics and W. W. Hansen Laboratories of Physics, Stanford University, Stanford, California
(Received April 1, 1954)

Elastic scattering measurements have been carried out with electrons in Au^{197} at energies of 84, 126, 154, and 183 Mev and in Pb^{208} at 84, 153, and 186 Mev. Diffraction effects are observed which appear to vary with momentum and angular position as if a fundamental parameter $p\sin(\theta/2)$ were equal to a constant for a given diffraction feature. Such a behavior would be predicted by the Born approximation. A comparison of the scattering in Au^{197} and Pb^{208} suggests that inelastic scattering does not materially influence the scattering curves presented. The appearance of diffraction effects indicates a model more nearly uniform in charge density than early tentative conclusions based on Born approximation calculations.

I. INTRODUCTION

In the first paper of this series with the above title[1] experimental electron scattering curves were presented for several materials at 125 Mev. Elastic profiles were shown, the apparatus was described, various checks on the experimental information were discussed, and other relevant information was given. A preliminary attempt to explain the at-that-time unexpected absence of prominent diffraction peaks was made in terms of a first-order Born approximation calculation for various nuclear charge distributions.[1,2] These approximate calculations led to a tentative interpretation which indicated a smooth decrease of charge density from the center to the outer regions of heavy nuclei such as gold and lead. It must be borne in mind that the conventional values of nuclear radius (for example, root-mean-square values) were retained in this interpretation.

It has recently been shown by Yennie, Wilson, and Ravenhall[3] that an accurate phase shift calculation for

* The research reported in this document was supported jointly by the U. S. Office of Naval Research and the U. S. Atomic Energy Commission, and by the U. S. Air Force through the Office of Scientific Research of the Air Research and Development Command.

† Aided by a grant from the Research Corporation.

‡ This material was presented in part at the New York Meeting of the American Physical Society in January, 1954 [Phys. Rev. 94, 773 (1954)].

§ Visiting Post Doctoral Research Fellow of the Schweizerische Arbeitsgemeinschaft in Mathematik und Physik, Switzerland.

[1] Hofstadter, Fechter, McIntyre, Phys. Rev. **92**, 978 (1953). We shall refer to this paper as I.

[2] L. I. Schiff, Phys. Rev. **92**, 988 (1953).

[3] Yennie, Wilson, and Ravenhall, Phys. Rev. **92**, 1325 (1953).

a more conventional nuclear model with uniform charge density and a sharp edge provides elastic scattering curves with washed-out minima and maxima for nuclei with $Z \cong 80$. For copper ($Z=29$) the minima and maxima are pronounced and the Born approximation is more pertinent although not completely reliable even in this case. The calculations of Yennie *et al.*, and also those of Baranger,[4] carried out by a less accurate method, therefore implied that perhaps the experimental data can be fitted by a uniform, or nearly uniform, model. In any case, it became apparent immediately that more experimental and theoretical information would be required before definite conclusions on the type of charge distribution could be made. The tentative interpretation which led to a strong taper at the center has to be abandoned although the early suggestion of a taper at the edge is confirmed (see below).

It has been a major goal of our program to carry out elastic scattering at different energies in order to provide more than one "fix" on a given nucleus. For this reason we have presently continued the earlier studies and in this paper we give the experimental curves for Au^{197} and Pb^{208} at several energies.[5]

Since the first energy level in the Pb^{208} nucleus is at 2.6 Mev it is possible with the energy resolution of our spectrometer magnet to select only elastically scattered electrons.[6] In contrast, in the Au^{197} nucleus there is an energy level below 100 kev, and electrons exciting this level could not be rejected as inelastically scattered electrons by our apparatus. If one then assumed that inelastic scattering events significantly modified the gold angular distribution, it would be very unlikely that the gold and lead angular distributions would be similar. Experimental evidence of such a similarity would thus be evidence for a negligible contribution of inelastic scattering from gold.

II. APPARATUS

The main features of the experimental apparatus have been described in I (pp. 979 and 980). Some recent additions and improvements in the apparatus are noted below. A remotely controlled uranium slit at the exit of the analyzing magnet has been added. A beam "sniffer" which indicates small horizontal shifts in the position of the beam emerging from the second deflecting (refocusing) magnet has also been added. This is an ionization chamber split vertically in two with the readings of each half balanced against the other, and the slit being located on the beam line. The sniffer is used to control the beam manually from time to time as the occasion demands. The analyzing magnet current

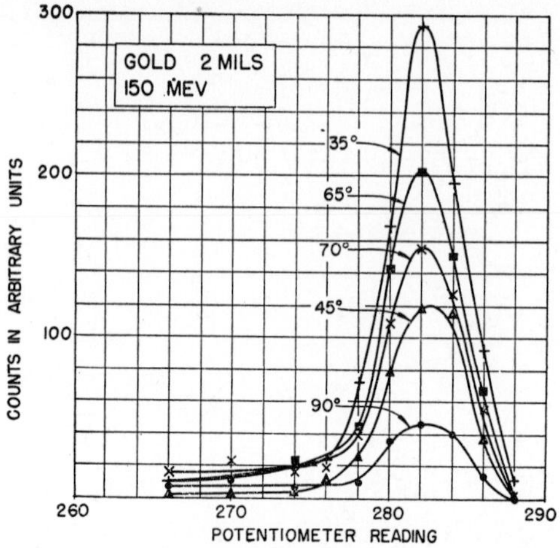

FIG. 1. Representative elastic scattering curves at 150 Mev in gold. The ordinates of the individual curves are unrelated.

is now regulated to better than 0.1 percent by means of electronic control of the generator field winding.

The analyzing magnet has also been rewound with hollow conductor square copper rod so that its upper bending limit is now 195 Mev, whereas it was previously about 150 Mev. The focusing properties at the highest energies have not been studied carefully although they are presumably not bad judging by the quality of the elastic curves. However, the magnet shows increasing saturation at the high energies so that the current scale is no longer proportional to energy. In order to deter-

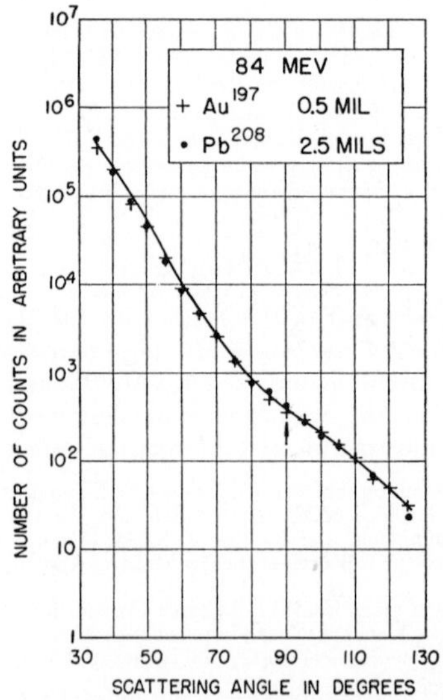

FIG. 2. Elastic scattering in Au^{197} and Pb^{208} at 84 Mev. The arrow marks an estimate of the angular position of a diffraction washed-out minimum. Curves normalized arbitrarily.

[4] E. Baranger, Phys. Rev. 93, 1127 (1954). We wish to thank Mrs. Baranger for early communication of her results.

[5] The 96-percent pure Pb^{208} sample was obtained from the Isotopes Division, U. S. Atomic Energy Commission, Oak Ridge, Tennessee.

[6] We have recently observed inelastic electron scattering peaks in beryllium and other materials at 190 Mev.

TABLE I. Summary of data on minima in gold.

Energy (Mev)	θ_I (degrees)	θ_{II} (degrees)	$E \sin(\theta_I/2)$	$E \sin(\theta_{II}/2)$
84	90	...	59	...
126	51	109	55	103
154	45	90	58	109
183	...	70	...	105

mine the energy scale, a calibration curve was prepared by measuring the magnetic field (at the half-way point of the electron trajectories) against the current through the magnet windings.

III. PROCEDURE

The angular distributions have been obtained from elastic profiles taken at the various angular positions. In most cases "complete" elastic curves have been taken at all angular settings and the area under each elastic curve has been plotted as an individual point in the angular distribution. As an example, a few members in a set of elastic curves are shown in Fig. 1. In this case the energy spread in the incident 150-Mev beam was 0.5 percent, the thickness of the gold foil was 2 mils. The exit slit of the spectrometer was set at a width corresponding to 0.5 percent in energy and the entrance slit was $\frac{3}{4}$ in. wide and $\frac{3}{4}$ in. high at a distance of 11 in. from the center of the scattering foil. In the case of Pb^{208} the measurements have usually been made with five points straddling the center of the peak instead of a complete elastic curve. The best energy resolution realized to date with the analyzing magnet is 0.28 percent at 125 Mev.

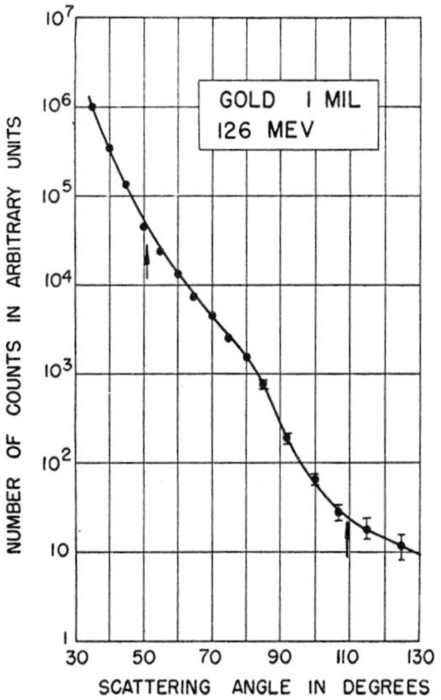

FIG. 3. Elastic scattering in Au^{197} at 126 Mev. The arrows mark an estimate of the angular position of diffraction washed-out minima.

IV. RESULTS

Experiments were carried out at 84, 126, 154, and 183 Mev in Au^{197} and at 84, 153, and 186 Mev in Pb^{208}. The angular distributions so obtained are shown in Figs. 2, 3, 4, and 5. In Figs. 2, 4, and 5 both the lead and gold data are plotted, while in Fig. 3 only the gold data appear. The statistical errors are also shown in Fig. 3 and are typical of those obtained at the other energies. It is clear from these curves that the angular distributions for lead and gold are identical within the accuracy of the experiments, and it may therefore be presumed that inelastic processes contribute a negligible amount to the angular distributions. The newer data are also more consistent internally than the data in paper I and the study in gold at 126 Mev has therefore been repeated. The agreement is quite good and the slight differences observed are within the old experimental errors.

The data for gold and lead show clearly the signs of washed-out diffraction structure. The 84-Mev data for

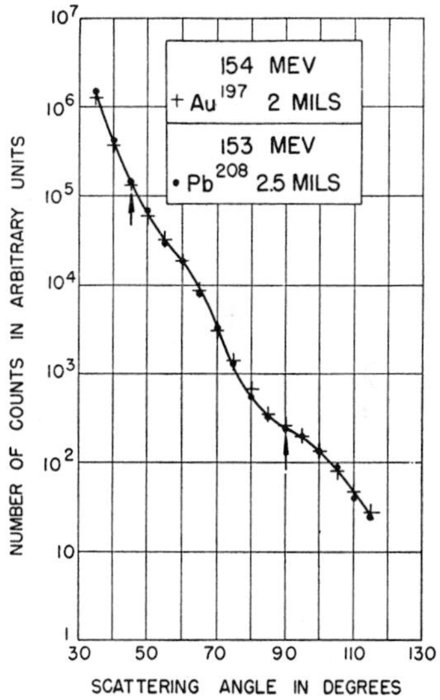

FIG. 4. Elastic scattering in Au^{197} and Pb^{208} at 154 and 153 Mev, respectively. The arrows mark estimates of the angular positions of diffraction washed-out minima. Curves normalized arbitrarily.

gold and lead show a washed-out minimum near 90°. At 126 Mev in gold there is a similar point at 51° and a second washed-out minimum at 109°. At 154 Mev the first "minimum" appears near 45° and a second more pronounced one at 90°. The second "minimum" at 154 Mev falls at 90° where we found the first "minimum" at 84 Mev, an energy close to one-half of 154 Mev. At 183 Mev the first "minimum" has moved near 35° and is not clearly visible. The second one has now moved to about 70°. Hence it is now possible to trace the diffraction structure through many scattering curves at different energies. The diffraction peaks and valleys are not prominent but nevertheless are definite, as shown by a "form factor" plot of Fig. 6 in which the point charge calculations have been divided into the experimental curves at the various energies. It is to be noted that a uniform charge distribution with square edge[3] gives an appearance somewhat like the experimental data but with more pronounced diffraction features.

Table I shows a summary of the data on "minima" in gold. From these it may be seen that the product

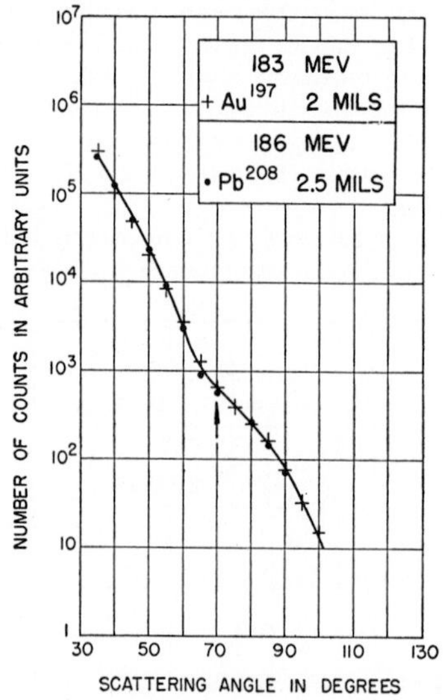

FIG. 5. Elastic scattering in Au^{197} and Pb^{208} at 183 and 186 Mev, respectively. The arrow marks an estimate of the angular position of a diffraction washed-out minimum. Curves normalized arbitrarily.

$E\sin\theta/2\cong 57$, where E is the energy in Mev ($E=pc$ at these energies), for the first "minimum" in all the gold and lead curves. The product $E\sin\theta/2\cong 106$ for the second "minimum." These figures imply a nuclear radius for a uniformly charged model, $R=r_0A^{\frac{1}{3}}$, where $r_0=(1.1\pm0.1)\times10^{-13}$ cm for both Au^{197} and Pb^{208} where we have used the curves of Yennie *et al.*[3] Therefore the charge density is considerably higher than that given by previous models where $r_0=1.45\times10^{-13}$ cm. A rounded-off model gives a better fit than the uniform, but as yet not an exact fit of the experimental data.[7,8] Similar

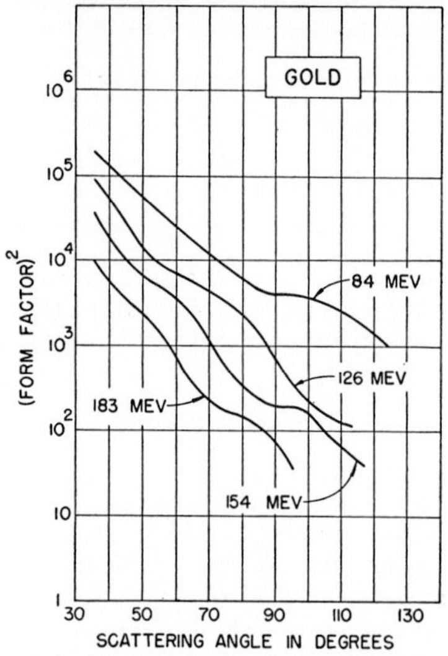

FIG. 6. The squares of form factors plotted against angle for gold at 84, 126, 154, and 183 Mev. The ordinate is obtained by plotting the quotient of the observed scattering by the point charge scattering curve. The ordinates of individual curves are unrelated.

conclusions concerning a smaller nuclear size have been drawn recently from the measurements of Fitch and Rainwater[9] and Pidd, Hammer, and Raka.[10]

A model such as a Gaussian or exponential will not explain simultaneously the scattering data at 126 and 183 Mev because the theoretical curves for such peaked distributions fall off too rapidly toward large angles at the higher energies. Furthermore, the observed diffraction structure implies a type of finite boundary rather than the smooth taper which predicts an entirely smooth scattering curve.[3,7]

ACKNOWLEDGMENT

We are grateful to Professor L. I. Schiff for many interesting and fruitful conversations. We wish to thank Dr. D. R. Yennie, Dr. D. G. Ravenhall, and Mr. R. N. Wilson for many stimulating discussions concerning their theoretical calculations. We should also like to express our great appreciation to Mr. B. Chambers, Mr. V. Prosper, and Mr. J. Fregeau for their help in building parts of our experimental apparatus.

[7] Yennie, Ravenhall, and Wilson, preceding paper [Phys. Rev. **95**, 500 (1954)].

[8] Brenner, Brown, and Elton (to be published). We wish to thank Prof. R. E. Peierls for early communication of these results.

[9] V. L. Fitch and J. Rainwater, Phys. Rev. **92**, 789 (1953).

[10] Pidd, Hammer, and Raka, Phys. Rev. **92**, 436 (1953).

PAPER 25

Results of a Phase Shift Calculation of High-Energy Electron Scattering*

D. G. Ravenhall and D. R. Yennie
Stanford University, Stanford, California
(Received August 6, 1954)

USING the phase shift analysis described previously,[1] an attempt has been made to fit the experimental data of Hofstadter *et al.*[2] on the elastic scattering of electrons on gold at energies of 84, 126, 154, and 183 Mev. Only scattering from a static spherically symmetric charge distribution is considered; all other interactions are neglected. The one-parameter charge distributions such as uniform, Gaussian, and exponential considered earlier[1] are clearly ruled out by the experimental data because of both the shape of the individual cross sections and their energy dependence. The present results are for "smoothed uniform" distributions, characterized by a central region of almost constant density and a surface region in which the density drops to zero. Of the two parameters required to identify a distribution of this type (a radius and a surface thickness), it turns out that the surface thickness is small enough compared with the electron's de Broglie wavelength λ that the detailed surface structure is unimportant; this is not true at higher energies, of course.

We define[3] a radius c by

$$c=\int_0^\infty \rho(r)dr/\rho(0), \tag{1}$$

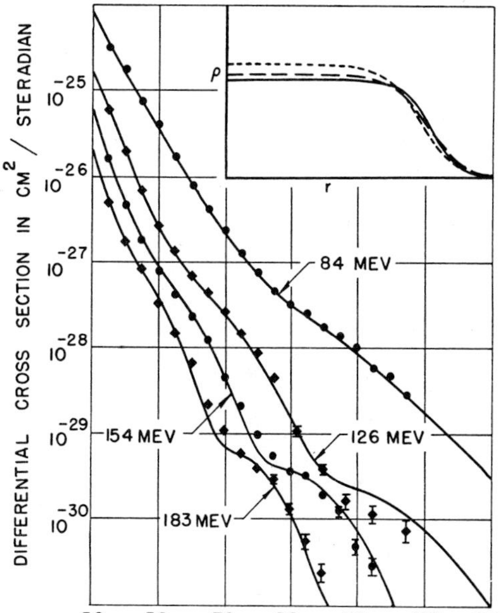

FIG. 1. Cross sections at 84, 126, 154, and 183 Mev for the elastic scattering of electrons by gold, using the charge distribution (4) with the parameters $K=2.20$, $c=6.63$ ($r_0=1.20$, $s=1.65$). (Distances are in units of 10^{-13} cm.) Inset is the charge distribution (full line), together with that for Fig. 2 (dashed line) and Fig. 3 (dotted line). The experimental values are of Hofstadter *et al.* (reference 2).

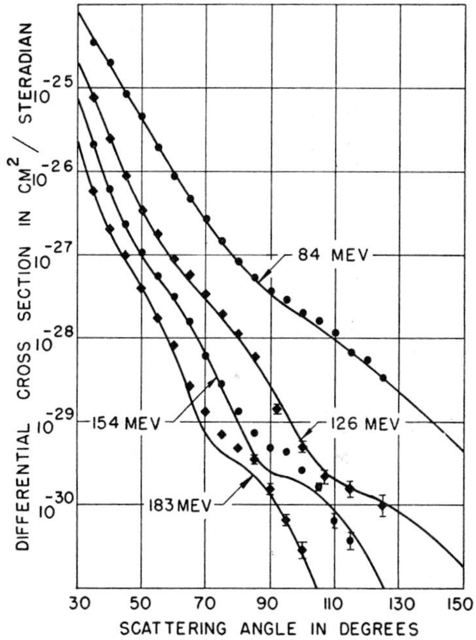

FIG. 2. Cross sections for the parameters $K=1.85$, $c=6.51$ ($r_0=1.20$, $s=1.96$).

and a surface thickness s by

$$s^2=-4\int_0^\infty (r-c)^2(d\rho/dr)dr/\rho(0). \quad (2)$$

To relative order $(s/c)^4$, the root-mean-square radius is then given by

$$\langle r^2\rangle^{\frac{1}{2}}=\left(\frac{3}{5}\right)^{\frac{1}{2}} c\left(\frac{1+(5/2)(s/c)^2}{1+(3/4)(s/c)^2}\right)^{\frac{1}{2}}$$
$$=(3/5)^{\frac{1}{2}} r_0 A^{\frac{1}{3}}\times 10^{-13}\text{ cm.}$$

In the results presented here, we have used for the charge density the form

$$\rho=\rho_0[1+e^{K(r-c)}]^{-1}. \quad (4)$$

For $e^{Kc}\gg 1$ the c of Eq. (4) is the same as that defined by Eq. (1). The surface thickness s is $2\pi/\sqrt{3}K(=3.63/K)$, which is slightly smaller than the previously defined "smoothing distance"[1] $(=4.40/K)$. To confirm theoretical arguments that the cross section depends only on c and s, and is independent of the surface shape,[3] calculations at 183 Mev have been carried out for several shapes having the same value of s and c as those of Fig. 1. The most extreme of these has a surface which varies linearly with r. For angles less than 105° the cross section for all of these shapes agreed to within 10 percent; by a slight alteration of parameters to allow for the terms in $(s/c)^4$ this agreement could be improved still further.

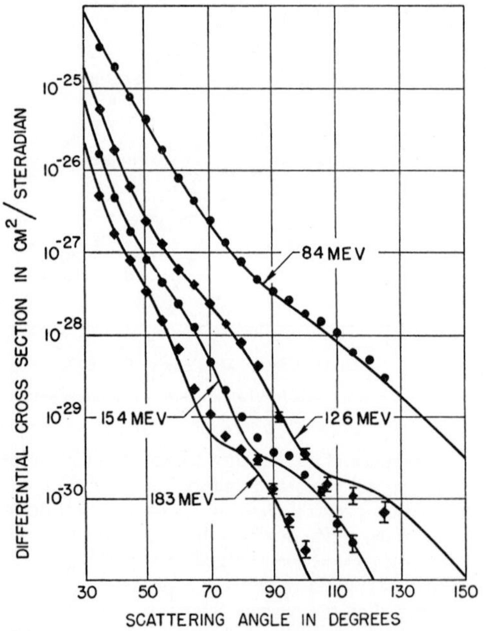

FIG. 3. Cross sections for the parameters $K=1.85$, $c=6.19$ $(r_0=1.16,\ s=1.96)$.

In Figs. 1–3 we compare the results of the phase shift calculations with the experimental data, which have been arbitrarily normalized for each energy to give the best agreement with the theory. Perhaps the best fit is that of Fig. 1, where $s=1.65\times 10^{-13}$ cm, $r_0=1.20$ $(c=6.63\times 10^{-13}$ cm).[4] The charge distributions of Figs. 2 and 3, which are for slightly different values of s and r_0, show that the cross section depends rather sensitively on these parameters.

The slight differences between the experiments and the results of Fig. 1, if significant, can be due to a number of different effects. Perhaps a more complicated charge distribution is required; preliminary calculations indicate that a decrease in the central charge density alters the cross sections in such a way as to improve the fit with the 183-Mev data.[5] There may also be appreciable contributions from the static quadrupole moment, nuclear excitations, and radiative corrections. L. I. Schiff and B. Downs[6] have considered the first of these, together with quadrupole excitations to low-lying levels, on the basis of a modified Born approximation.[3] They find that in gold these effects add at most three percent to the elastic cross section. The other effects have not yet been estimated.

For values of s and r_0 quoted above, the cross sections in Pb^{208} also agree very well with the data of Hofstadter *et al.*[2]

These calculations were made on the computer Univac at the University of California Radiation Laboratory at Livermore. We thank the authorities of this Laboratory, particularly Dr. S. Fernbach, for permission to use Univac, and Mr. H. Hanerfeld for instruction and advice in coding. We wish to thank Professor R. Hofstadter, Dr. B. Hahn, and Dr. J. A. McIntyre for discussions about their work and ours, and Professor L. I. Schiff and Professor G. C. Wick for helpful conversations. We also thank Dr. G. E. Brown for communicating his results and those of Drs. S. Brenner and L. R. B. Elton prior to their publication.

* Supported in part by the Office of Scientific Research, Air Research and Development Command.

[1] Yennie, Ravenhall, and Wilson, Phys. Rev. **95**, 500 (1954).
[2] Hofstadter, Hahn, Knudsen, and McIntyre, Phys. Rev. **95**, 512 (1954).
[3] An elaboration of the following results will be presented later, together with some applications.
[4] This is slightly larger than the tentative value of r_0 $(r_0=1.1\pm 0.1)$ obtained in reference 2.
[5] Dr. G. E. Brown informs us that he and Drs. S. Brenner and L. R. B. Elton have come to a similar conclusion.
[6] L. I. Schiff, Phys. Rev. (to be published) and private communications.

PAPER 26

Nuclear Multipole Transitions in Inelastic Electron Scattering*

L. I. Schiff
Stanford University, Stanford, California
(Received July 26, 1954)

Expressions are obtained for the differential cross sections for inelastic scattering of fast electrons with excitation of various nuclear multipole transitions. The most probable transitions are those that involve collective motion of many nucleons, and in this case the term arising from the transition charge density dominates those that come from the current and magnetization densities. There is then a close relation between the probability for inelastic electron scattering and the probability for the corresponding radiative electric multipole transition, although an assumption must be made as to the shape of the transition charge density. This is illustrated with a detailed discussion of the collective electric quadrupole transitions, using the model of Bohr and Mottelson. When the transition is produced by one or a small number of nucleons, or when it is of magnetic multipole type, there is likely to be little relation between inelastic scattering and radiation probabilities. The electric monopole transition (0+→0+) is also discussed. It is shown how the elastic scattering can be corrected for unresolved inelastic scattering as well as elastic quadrupole scattering before an analysis is made in terms of the spherically symmetric part of the static nuclear charge density, and also how the strength as well as the shape of the transition charge density can be determined experimentally when only relative measurements of inelastic scattering are available.

I. INTRODUCTION

RECENT experimental work of Hofstadter and collaborators[1,2] has demonstrated the possibility of obtaining precise distributions in energy and angle for electrons of very high initial energy scattered by nuclei, and has yielded specific results in a number of cases. Analysis of the angle distributions of such elastically scattered electrons[3] has already provided information on the radial dependence of the static charge density in various nuclei. There are two main reasons why a similar analysis must be made for the inelastically scattered electrons. First, with imperfect energy resolution, some inelastically scattered electrons corresponding to excitation of low-lying nuclear states will be included in the measurement of elastic scattering, and may affect the charge density inferred from these measurements. Second, when inelastically scattered electrons can be resolved in energy, it is anticipated that their distribution in angle can often be used to determine the strength and multipole character of the corresponding nuclear transition.

The information concerning nuclear transitions that can be obtained from inelastic electron scattering is very similar to that which can be obtained from Coulomb excitation by heavy charged particles that are slow enough so that they do not penetrate the nuclear Coulomb barrier appreciably.[4] In both cases, the interaction between incident particle and nucleus is essentially all electromagnetic and is calculable. Thus far, Coulomb excitation experiments have yielded total excitation probabilities as a function of the charge, mass, and velocity of the incident particle, which can be used to determine the strength and multipolarity of nuclear electric multiple transitions. Accurate measurements of the angle dependence of inelastically scattered electrons can determine these quantities independently and can, in addition, give the radial dependence of the transition charge density. In principle, such experiments can also provide similar information concerning magnetic multipole transitions; it will be shown, however, that such transitions are likely to be less probable than electric multipole transitions, and that they are more difficult to interpret.

In the present paper, the nucleus is described by charge, current, and magnetization densities ρ, $\mathbf{j}$, and $\mathbf{M}$, which are treated as classical quantities. Actually, they should be regarded as quantum-mechanical operators of the type discussed by Foldy,[5] in which case appropriate matrix elements between initial and final nuclear states must ultimately be calculated. However, for all except the very simplest nuclei, the nuclear wave functions are not known well enough to warrant such detailed calculations.. We shall, therefore, be satisfied with a semiclassical treatment, according to which ρ, $\mathbf{j}$, and $\mathbf{M}$ are c numbers which represent the static densities (expectation values for the nuclear ground state) in the case of elastic scattering, and the transition densities (matrix elements between nuclear ground and excited states) in the case of inelastic scattering. It is then expected that the resulting formulas can be used phenomenologically, perhaps with a hydrodynamical model for the combined contributions of nucleons and mesons to these densities (see Sec. VIII).

It is inherent in the present work that the dynamic interaction between electron and nucleus is treated by

* Supported in part by the Office of Scientific Research, Air Research and Development Command.

[1] Hofstadter, Fechter, and McIntyre, Phys. Rev. **92**, 978 (1953); Hofstadter, Hahn, Knudsen, and McIntyre, Phys. Rev. **95**, 512 (1954).

[2] McIntyre, Hahn, and Hofstadter, Phys. Rev. **94**, 1084 (1954).

[3] Yennie, Ravenhall, and Wilson, Phys. Rev. **95**, 500 (1954), and private communication.

[4] T. Huus and Č. Zupančič, Kgl. Danske Videnskab. Selskab, Mat.-fys. Medd. **28**, 1 (1953); C. L. McClelland and C. Goodman, Phys. Rev. **91**, 760 (1953); N. P. Heydenburg and G. M. Temmer, Phys. Rev. **93**, 906 (1954); K. Alder and A. Winther, Phys. Rev. **91**, 1578 (1953).

[5] L. L. Foldy, Phys. Rev. **92**, 178 (1953).

first-order perturbation theory, and this seems to be a reasonable approximation.[6] In addition to this, we shall assume that the static interaction is also small, and use plane wave functions for the incident and scattered electrons; this is justified only for light elements, and is equivalent to the use of the Møller potentials and fields.[7] This latter approximation can be improved by using Coulomb wave functions for the electron like those calculated numerically in connection with elastic scattering,[3] and such calculations are now under way.

The work reported here differs from other recent calculations of radiative transitions[8,9] and of inelastic electron scattering[10] in one or both of two respects: the reduced wavelength $1/q$ associated with the change of momentum $\hbar\mathbf{q}$ of the electron is not necessarily large in comparison with nuclear dimensions, and this wavelength is usually much smaller than $\hbar c$ divided by the energy loss of the electron.[11] The first point means that there may be retardation within the nucleus, so that the radial dependences of the transition densities may be significant. Also, the transition probabilities do not necessarily decrease as the multipole order increases; the expansion in multipoles is nevertheless useful since nuclear selection rules often limit possible transitions to one or two multipole types. The second point means that the probability for inelastic electron scattering is fundamentally different from that for radiation, since in the latter case the reduced wavelength of the photon is equal to $\hbar c$ divided by the energy of the photon. It turns out that there is a close relation between the leading terms in the probabilities for the two processes in the case of electric, but not in the case of magnetic multipole transitions.

II. GENERAL FORMULATION AND MAGNETIC MULTIPOLE CALCULATION

We start from the interaction energy H' between the nuclear densities ρ, $\mathbf{j}$, $\mathbf{M}$, and an arbitrary external electromagnetic field that is described by the potentials φ, $\mathbf{A}$ or the field strengths $\mathfrak{E}$, $\mathfrak{H}$:

$$H' = \int (\rho\varphi - c^{-1}\mathbf{j}\cdot\mathbf{A} - \mathbf{M}\cdot\mathfrak{H})d\tau. \quad (1)$$

In order that H' result in a transition that conserves the energy, the time variations of the nuclear and field quantities must cancel, so we assume that the nuclear quantities vary like $e^{i\omega t}$ and the field quantities like $e^{-i\omega t}$, where $\hbar\omega$ is the energy of the transition. The electric field strength may be expressed in terms of the potentials in either of the forms

$$\mathfrak{E} = -\partial\mathbf{A}/\partial ct - \mathbf{grad}\,\varphi = (i\omega/c)\mathbf{A} - \mathbf{grad}\,\varphi,$$

and the equation of continuity is

$$\mathrm{div}\mathbf{j} = -\partial\rho/\partial t = -i\omega\rho.$$

Substitution into Eq. (1) and integration by parts leads to

$$H' = \int [(i/\omega)\mathbf{j}\cdot\mathfrak{E} - \mathbf{M}\cdot\mathfrak{H}]d\tau; \quad (2)$$

the partial integration assumes that the nuclear densities have a finite extension in space, so that boundary terms at infinity vanish.

We wish to decompose H' into parts that correspond to electric and magnetic multipole transitions of all possible orders. Since the treatment of the magnetic transitions is the same whether the external field is a free radiation field (emission or absorption of photons) or arises from external sources (inelastic electron excitation), we start with this case. For magnetic multipole radiation of order l, the electric field is transverse and has the parity $(-1)^l$. We therefore substitute for $\mathfrak{H}$ in Eq. (2) from one of Maxwell's equations which is valid whether or not there is an external charge and current density,

$$\mathbf{curl}\,\mathfrak{E} = -\partial\mathfrak{H}/\partial ct = (i\omega/c)\mathfrak{H}, \quad (3)$$

to obtain

$$H' = \int [(i/\omega)\mathbf{j}\cdot\mathfrak{E} + (ic/\omega)\mathbf{M}\cdot\mathbf{curl}\,\mathfrak{E}]d\tau$$
$$= (i/\omega)\int (\mathbf{j} + c\,\mathbf{curl}\,\mathbf{M})\cdot\mathfrak{E}d\tau. \quad (4)$$

Now as discussed by Blatt and Weisskopf,[8] any vector function of the polar angles θ, ϕ can be expanded in terms of three kinds of vector spherical harmonics. The first kind, of total angular momentum l, is

$$\mathbf{X}_{lm}(\theta,\phi) = -i[l(l+1)]^{-\frac{1}{2}}(\mathbf{r}\times\nabla)Y_{lm}(\theta,\phi), \quad (5)$$

where Y_{lm} is the ordinary scalar spherical harmonic. $\mathbf{X}_{lm}$ is transverse and has the parity $(-1)^l$; the other two kinds of the same total angular momentum have the parity $(-1)^{l+1}$. The three kinds together, for all l, constitute a complete orthonormal set of vector functions with respect to integration of θ and ϕ over the sphere. We can therefore write for the part of H' that

[6] An order of magnitude estimate of the second-order dynamic interaction (nuclear dispersion) indicates that it is relatively small.

[7] C. Møller, Z. Physik **70**, 786 (1931).

[8] J. M. Blatt and V. F. Weisskopf, *Theoretical Nuclear Physics* (John Wiley and Sons, Inc., New York, 1952), Appendix B.

[9] W. Franz, Z. Physik **127**, 363 (1950); P. R. Wallace, Can. J. Phys. **29**, 393 (1951).

[10] Amaldi, Fidecaro, and Mariani, Nuovo cimento **7**, 553, 757 (1950); Thie, Mullin, and Guth, Phys. Rev. **87**, 962 (1952); R. Gatto, Nuovo cimento **10**, 1559 (1953); J. H. Smith, Phys. Rev. **95**, 271 (1954).

[11] The importance of the difference between the short wavelength associated with the electron momentum transfer and the long wavelength associated with the nuclear excitation energy, in the case of high-energy electrons, was pointed out by J. S. Blair in a letter to Richard Wilson, July 1952.

gives rise to magnetic l-pole transitions:

$$H'_{lm}{}^{(M)}=(i/\omega)\int(\mathbf{j}+c\,\mathbf{curl}\,\mathbf{M})\cdot\mathbf{X}_{lm}{}^*(\theta,\phi)\times\left[\int\mathbf{X}_{lm}(\theta',\phi')\cdot\mathfrak{E}(r,\theta',\phi')d\Omega'\right]d\tau. \quad (6)$$

Summation of Eq. (6) over l and m, with inclusion of the corresponding terms that come from the other two kinds of vector spherical harmonics will, because of the completeness of these functions, yield Eq. (4). These other two classes of terms give rise to electric multipole transitions, and are more conveniently expressed in terms of an integral that involves $\mathbf{X}_{lm}$ and a different combination of nuclear densities (see Sec. III).

We now evaluate the square-bracketed integral in Eq. (6), assuming that the electric field has the form

$$\mathfrak{E}=\mathbf{e}e^{i\mathbf{q}\cdot\mathbf{r}}=\mathbf{e}\sum_l[4\pi(2l+1)]^{\frac{1}{2}}i^l j_l(qr)Y_{l0}(\theta',\phi'). \quad (7)$$

The vector $\hbar\mathbf{q}$ is the photon momentum in the radiation case, or the momentum change of the electron in the electron scattering case; the way in which Eq. (7) is written assumes that the direction of $\mathbf{q}$ is the polar or z axis with respect to which the spherical harmonics are defined. Substitution of Eqs. (5) and (7) into the square-bracketed integral of Eq. (6) yields, after a partial integration,

$$\int\mathbf{X}_{lm}(\theta',\phi')\cdot\mathfrak{E}(r,\theta',\phi')d\Omega'=[\pi(2l+1)]^{\frac{1}{2}}i^l(e_x\pm ie_y)j_l(qr),$$

if $m=\pm1$, and zero otherwise. Equation (6) now becomes, after use of Eq. (5) and integration by parts,

$$H'_{l,\pm1}{}^{(M)}=(i^l/\omega)[\pi(2l+1)/l(l+1)]^{\frac{1}{2}}(e_x\pm ie_y)\times\int j_l(qr)Y_{l,\pm1}{}^*\mathbf{r}\cdot\mathbf{curl}(\mathbf{j}+c\,\mathbf{curl}\,\mathbf{M})d\tau. \quad (8)$$

III. ELECTRIC MULTIPOLE TRANSITIONS

For electric multipole radiation of order l, the magnetic field is transverse and has the parity $(-1)^l$. We therefore substitute for $\mathfrak{E}$ in Eq. (2) from another of Maxwell's equations,

$$\mathbf{curl}\,\mathfrak{H}=\partial\mathfrak{E}/\partial ct+4\pi\mathbf{j}_e/c=(-i\omega/c)\mathfrak{E}+4\pi\mathbf{j}_e/c,$$

to obtain

$$H'=-\int[(c/\omega^2)\,\mathbf{curl}\,\mathbf{j}+\mathbf{M}]\cdot\mathfrak{H}d\tau+(4\pi/\omega^2)\int\mathbf{j}\cdot\mathbf{j}_e d\tau. \quad (9)$$

Here, $\mathbf{j}_e$ is the transition current density that arises from the change in state of the electron; it is zero for a radiative transition and is given by

$$\mathbf{j}_e=ec\mathbf{a}e^{i\mathbf{q}\cdot\mathbf{r}} \quad (10)$$

in the case of electron scattering, where $\mathbf{a}$ is the matrix element of the Dirac $\boldsymbol{\alpha}$ operator between initial and final electron plane wave states of momenta $\mathbf{p}_0$ and $\mathbf{p}$, and $\hbar\mathbf{q}=\mathbf{p}_0-\mathbf{p}$.

The first integral in Eq. (9) can be reduced in precisely the same way as Eq. (4). We put $\mathfrak{H}=\mathbf{h}e^{i\mathbf{q}\cdot\mathbf{r}}$, and obtain for the electric l-pole part of this integral, which is the entire interaction energy for a radiative transition:[12]

$$H''_{l,\pm1}{}^{(E)}=i^{l+1}[\pi(2l+1)/l(l+1)]^{\frac{1}{2}}(h_x\pm ih_y)\times\int j_l(qr)Y_{l,\pm1}{}^*\,\mathbf{r}\cdot\mathbf{curl}[\mathbf{M}+(c/\omega^2)\,\mathbf{curl}\,\mathbf{j}]d\tau \quad (11a)$$

$$=-i^{l+1}[\pi(2l+1)/l(l+1)]^{\frac{1}{2}}(h_x\pm ih_y)\times\left\{\int j_lY_{l,\pm1}{}^*\,\mathrm{div}(\mathbf{r}\times\mathbf{M})d\tau-(ic/\omega)\int(j_l+rdj_l/dr)Y_{l,\pm1}{}^*\rho d\tau-(cq^2/\omega^2)\int j_lY_{l,\pm1}{}^*(\mathbf{r}\cdot\mathbf{j})d\tau\right\}. \quad (11b)$$

In the latter form, use has been made of the equation of continuity to replace $\mathrm{div}\mathbf{j}$ by $-i\omega\rho$.

In the electron excitation case, we must also decompose the second integral of Eq. (9) into electric multipole contributions. We cannot now use the symmetry of the magnetic field as a guide, and must rely on the symmetry of the nuclear charge-current density instead. Inspection of the first integral of Eq. (9) and the second integral of Eq. (11b) shows that the $\mathbf{X}_{lm}$ part of $\mathbf{curl}\,\mathbf{j}$ and the Y_{lm} part of ρ give rise to electric l-pole transitions. We therefore transform the second integral of Eq. (9) so that only these combinations of nuclear densities appear. The electron current density can be written as the sum of the gradient of a scalar (irrotational part) and the curl of a divergenceless vector (solenoidal part):

$$\mathbf{j}_e=\mathbf{grad}\,\chi+\mathbf{curl}\,\boldsymbol{\psi},\quad \mathrm{div}\boldsymbol{\psi}=0.$$

From this

$$\mathrm{div}\mathbf{j}_e=\nabla^2\chi,\quad \mathbf{curl}\,\mathbf{j}_e=-\nabla^2\boldsymbol{\psi}.$$

With the form (10) for $\mathbf{j}_e$, we find that

$$\chi=-(i/q^2)(\mathbf{q}\cdot\mathbf{j}_e),\quad \boldsymbol{\psi}=(i/q^2)(\mathbf{q}\times\mathbf{j}_e).$$

[12] Some relations given in reference 8 are useful in deriving Eq. (11b) from (11a).

Thus with the help of some partial integrations and the equation of continuity, we obtain

$$\int \mathbf{j}\cdot\mathbf{j}_e d\tau = (\omega/q^2)\int \rho(\mathbf{q}\cdot\mathbf{j}_e)d\tau + (i/q^2)\int \mathbf{curl\,j}\cdot(\mathbf{q}\times\mathbf{j}_e)d\tau. \quad (12)$$

Equation (12) can now be broken down into multipole parts in analogy with the decomposition of Eq. (4) into terms of the type (6). The result for the contribution of the second integral of (9) to the electric l-pole transition is

$$H'''_{l,m}{}^{(E)} = (4\pi/\omega q^2)\int \rho Y_{lm}^*(\theta,\phi) \times\left[\int Y_{lm}(\theta'\phi')(\mathbf{q}\cdot\mathbf{j}_e)d\Omega'\right]d\tau + (4\pi i/\omega^2 q^2)\int \mathbf{curl\,j}\cdot\mathbf{X}_{lm}^*(\theta,\phi) \times\left[\int \mathbf{X}_{lm}(\theta',\phi')(\mathbf{q}\times\mathbf{j}_e)d\Omega'\right]d\tau.$$

Since the z axis is along $\mathbf{q}$, the first square-bracketed integral vanishes unless $m=0$, and the second square-bracketed integral vanishes unless $m=\pm1$. Use of the form (10) for $\mathbf{j}_e$ leads to the following results:

$$H'''_{l,0}{}^{(E)} = (8\pi i^l eca_z/\omega q)[\pi(2l+1)]^{\frac{1}{2}} \times\int j_l(qr)Y_{l,0}\rho d\tau, \quad (13)$$

$$H'''_{l,\pm1}{}^{(E)} = -(4\pi i^{l+1}ec/\omega^2 q)(a_y\mp ia_x)[\pi(2l+1)]^{\frac{1}{2}} \times\int j_l\mathbf{X}_{l,\pm1}^*\cdot(\mathbf{curl\,j})d\tau. \quad (14)$$

The external fields $\mathfrak{E}$ and $\mathfrak{H}$ may be found from solution of Maxwell's equations with the electron current (10). The results are the Møller fields,[7] which have the forms used above, with

$$\mathbf{e} = 4\pi ie(k\mathbf{a}+\mathbf{q}a_0)/(q^2-k^2),$$

$$e_x\pm ie_y = 4\pi iek(a_x\pm ia_y)/(q^2-k^2),$$

$$\mathbf{h} = 4\pi ie(\mathbf{q}\times\mathbf{a})/(q^2-k^2),$$

$$h_x\pm ih_y = -4\pi ieq(a_y\mp ia_x)/(q^2-k^2),$$

where $k=\omega/c$ and a_0 is the matrix element of the Dirac unit operator between initial and final electron states. It can now be shown without difficulty that Eq. (14) is just equal to $-(q^2-k^2)/q^2$ times the lm part of the **curl j** term in the first integral of Eq. (9). Thus when Eqs. (11) and (14) are added together, the result is to leave the **M** integral in (11a) or (11b) unchanged, and multiply the other integrals by a factor k^2/q^2.

We give here the interaction energies for electric and magnetic l-pole transitions in the electron excitation case. Equation (13) has been changed slightly by making use of the Dirac equation to write $\mathbf{q}\cdot\mathbf{a}+(\omega a_0/c)=0$, or $a_z=-(ka_0/q)$, and a substitution has been made for $e_x\pm ie_y$ in Eq. (8).

$$H'_{l,0}{}^{(E)} = -(4\pi i^l ea_0/q^2)[4\pi(2l+1)]^{\frac{1}{2}} \times\int j_l(qr)Y_{l,0}\rho d\tau; \quad (15)$$

$$H'_{l,\pm1}{}^{(E)} = [4\pi i^l eq(a_y\mp ia_x)/(q^2-k^2)] \times[\pi(2l+1)/l(l+1)]^{\frac{1}{2}}\int j_l(qr)Y_{l,\pm1}^* \mathbf{r}\cdot\mathbf{curl}[\mathbf{M}+(cq^2)^{-1}\mathbf{curl\,j}]d\tau; \quad (16)$$

$$H'_{l,\pm1}{}^{(M)} = [4\pi i^{l+1}e(a_x\pm ia_y)/c(q^2-k^2)] \times[\pi(2l+1)/l(l+1)]^{\frac{1}{2}}\int j_l(qr)Y_{l,\pm1}^* \mathbf{r}\cdot\mathbf{curl}[\mathbf{j}+c\,\mathbf{curl\,M}]d\tau. \quad (17)$$

Equations (16) and (17) can of course be further transformed in analogy with the change from Eq. (11a) to (11b).

IV. ORDERS OF MAGNITUDE

We now estimate the relative orders of magnitude of the various terms in the above three equations. For this purpose, we note that a_0, a_x and a_y are of order unity and that $k\ll q$ for situations of current interest, and assume that all integrals over nuclear densities can be represented by a common form factor F. Then Eq. (15) is of order eFQ/q^2, where Q is the total charge involved in the transition.

The first (magnetization) term in Eq. (16) involves a derivative operator which, by partial integration, is seen to introduce a factor of order q. The vector $\mathbf{r}$ introduces a factor R, which is an average radial distance from the center of the nucleus for the main contributions to the integral; for large q, R is expected to be somewhat larger than $1/q$ and somewhat smaller than the nuclear radius. Then the order of magnitude of this term is $(eF/q)(qR)(Q'\hbar/Mc)$, where $Q'\hbar/Mc$ is the total magnetization involved in the transition, and M is the nucleonic mass. In the second (current) term of Eq. (16), the two derivative operators introduce a factor q^2, and there is again a factor R. Thus its order of magnitude is $(eF/q)(R/c)Q''v$, where $Q''v$ is the total current involved in the transition, and v is the nuclear convection velocity associated with motion of the charge Q''.

In similar fashion, we find that the current and magnetization terms in Eq. (17) have the orders of magnitude $(eF/cq^2)qRQ''v$ and $(eF/cq^2)(cq^2R)(Q'\hbar/Mc)$, respectively.

If now we call the order of magnitude of Eq. (15) unity, then the relative orders of magnitude of the magnetization and current terms in Eq. (16) are, respectively,

$$(qR)(q\hbar/Mc)(Q'/Q), \quad (qR)(v/c)(Q''/Q),$$

and the orders of magnitude of the current and magnetization terms in Eq. (17) are, respectively,

$$(qR)(v/c)(Q''/Q), \quad (qR)(q\hbar/Mc)(Q'/Q).$$

For large-angle scattering of electrons with about 200-Mev energy, $q\hbar/Mc\sim\frac{1}{3}$ and $qR\sim 3$. For single-particle excitation of a nucleus, Q, Q', and Q'' are all expected to be of order unity, and $v/c\sim\frac{1}{5}$. For a collective mode of excitation, Q' should still be of order unity, Q and Q'' should have the same order of magnitude and be much larger than unity, and v/c should be much less than $\frac{1}{5}$.

We conclude, therefore, that for single-particle excitation in this energy range, all terms of Eqs. (15), (16), and (17) can be of the same order of magnitude. For excitation of collective modes, on the other hand, it is likely that Eq. (15) is not only the leading term for the electric multipole transitions, but is significantly larger than either of the magnetic multipole terms, which are comparable with each other. Further, if we assume that the current density associated with a collective mode is irrotational,[13] then **curl j**$=0$ and the current terms in Eqs. (16) and (17) are zero.

It may be noted at this point that summation of Eq. (15) over l yields, with the help of Eq. (7),

$$\sum_l H'_{l,0}{}^{(E)} = -(4\pi e a_0/q^2)\int e^{i\mathbf{q}\cdot\mathbf{r}}\rho d\tau. \qquad (18)$$

This is just what would have been obtained if only the first factor in Eq. (1) had been retained, and the static, nonretarded, Coulomb interaction had been used in calculating φ. Thus the present paper provides a justification for the use of this term by itself, at least so far as excitation of collective nuclear oscillations is concerned.[14]

V. DIFFERENTIAL SCATTERING CROSS SECTION

Each of the interaction energies (15) through (18) is of the form AV, where A is one of the quantities a_0, $a_x\pm ia_y$, $a_y\mp ia_x$, which involves only the electron spin functions, and V involves only integrals over nuclear quantities. In order to obtain a differential scattering cross section, it is necessary to sum $|AV|^2$ over final electron spin states, average over initial spin states, multiply by $2\pi/\hbar$ times the energy density of final electron states, and divide by the incident electron flux.

In the extreme relativistic region, the spin sum operation on $|A|^2$ yields $\cos^2\frac{1}{2}\theta$ when $A=a_0$, where θ is the angle between $\mathbf{p}_0$ and $\mathbf{p}$. When $A=a_x\pm ia_y$ or $A=a_y\mp ia_x$, the spin sum leads to

$$[(p_0+p)^2(1-\cos\theta)-p_0p\sin^2\theta]/\hbar^2q^2$$
$$=[1+\sin^2(\tfrac{1}{2}\theta)]\left[1+\frac{\hbar^2k^2}{2p_0p[1+\sin^2(\frac{1}{2}\theta)]}\right]\times\left[1+\frac{\hbar^2k^2}{4p_0p\sin^2(\frac{1}{2}\theta)}\right]^{-1};$$

except for very small scattering angles, this is very nearly equal to $[1+\sin^2(\frac{1}{2}\theta)]$ when the nuclear excitation is moderate. The last group of multiplicative factors involving the incident flux and the density of final states is, in the extreme relativistic region, $(p/2\pi\hbar^2c)^2$. Thus the differential scattering cross section per unit solid angle is equal to $[p\cos(\frac{1}{2}\theta)/2\pi\hbar^2c]^2|V|^2$ when either (15) or (18) is used for V, and is approximately equal to $(p/2\pi\hbar^2c)^2[1+\sin^2(\frac{1}{2}\theta)]|V|^2$ when either (16) or (17) is used for V.

VI. COMPARISON WITH RADIATIVE TRANSITIONS

It may be desirable in some cases to relate the inelastic electron scattering cross section to the radiation probability for the same nuclear transition. We therefore examine the expressions for the electric and magnetic l-pole moments, which are respectively[8]

$$\int r^lY_{lm}^*\rho d\tau - ik(l+1)^{-1}\int r^lY_{lm}^*\operatorname{div}(\mathbf{r}\times\mathbf{M})d\tau, \qquad (19)$$

$$-[c(l+1)]^{-1}\int r^lY_{lm}^*\operatorname{div}(\mathbf{r}\times\mathbf{j})d\tau - \int r^lY_{lm}^*\operatorname{div}\mathbf{M}d\tau. \qquad (20)$$

Estimates like those of Sec. IV show that the relative orders of magnltude of the two terms of (19) and the two terms of (20) are

$$1, \quad (k\hbar/Mc)(Q'/Q);$$
$$(v/c)(Q''/Q), \quad (\hbar/McR)(Q'/Q).$$

Here, R is the nuclear radius. Since $k\hbar/Mc\ll 1$, the first term of Eq. (19) dominates the electric l-pole moment, whether the nucleus undergoes a single-particle or collective transition. Likewise, the first term of Eq. (20) is the larger in the single-particle case, while the two terms are more nearly comparable for a collective transition.

It follows that there is a close relation between the leading terms for electric multipole transitions in the radiative case [first term of Eq. (19)] and in the electron excitation case [Eq. (15)]. The same quantity ρ appears in both terms, and indeed the former is simply

[13] A. Bohr, *Rotational States of Atomic Nuclei* (Ejnar Munksgaards Forlag, Copenhagen, 1954), Appendix.

[14] Equation (18) has been used in much of the earlier work on inelastic electron scattering (see reference 10).

the first term in the expansion of the latter in powers of q. A similar relation obtains between the first (current) terms of Eqs. (17) and (20) in the magnetic multipole case, since $\mathbf{r}\cdot\mathbf{curl}\,\mathbf{j}=-\operatorname{div}(\mathbf{r}\times\mathbf{j})$. However, the second (magnetization) terms are much less closely related to each other, and this term is more important in the electron excitation than in the radiative case. Thus it is much easier to connect the probabilities for the two types of transitions in the electric than in the magnetic multipole case; an assumption must of course be made concerning the radial dependence of ρ (see for example Sec. VIII).

VII. ELECTRIC MONOPOLE TRANSITIONS

The electric monopole interaction energy $H'_{0,0}{}^{(E)}$ is responsible for the elastic scattering from a static spherically symmetric charge density, which is the expectation value for the nuclear ground state. In this case, either Eq. (15) or Eq. (18) can be used.

The transition between nuclear states with total angular momentum $I=0$ and the same parity (which is even in all known cases), is of considerable interest. It is essential to realize here that the orthogonality of the initial and final nuclear states makes $\int\rho d\tau$ vanish. Thus for small q, the apparently leading terms in Eqs. (15) and (18) are actually zero. As a reminder that this occurs, one should replace the spherical Bessel function in Eq. (15) by $j_0(qr)-1$, and the exponential in Eq. (18) by $\exp(i\mathbf{q}\cdot\mathbf{r})-1$. Thus for small q, the electric monopole and electric quadrupole transitions have the same q dependence.

The difference in behavior between the elastic and inelastic monopole transitions corresponds to the fact that a static spherically symmetric charge density has a field that extends to large distances, whereas a radially oscillating charge density has no time-dependent field external to itself. Therefore interaction with the spherically symmetric part of the electron potential can occur only through its variation over the nucleus, and the leading term, which is independent of r, results in no interaction.

VIII. COLLECTIVE ELECTRIC QUADRUPOLE TRANSITIONS

There is a close relation between the contribution of the static nuclear electric quadrupole moment to the elastic scattering[15] and the contribution of the transition quadrupole moment to the inelastic scattering. This is because the collective model relates both the static and the transition moments to an intrinsic quadrupole moment.[13,16] The relation is worth exploring, since with imperfect energy resolution the two effects may be experimentally indistinguishable.

In both cases we use Eq. (15), and neglect the difference between the two values of q for the same incident electron energy and angle of scattering. We consider first the case of a uniformly charged nucleus of radius R, for which the quadrupole parts of the static and transition charge densities both have the approximate form $\delta(r-R)$.[15,16] Then the integral in Eq. (15) in the static case is equal to that in the transition case for all values of q, except for a multiplicative constant. For small q, the integral is proportional to the static quadrupole moment Q in the elastic case, and to the transition quadrupole moment in the inelastic case, both of which can be expressed in terms of the intrinsic quadrupole moment Q_0. The two integrals can then be expressed in terms of Q_0 for small q, and hence also for all q.

It seems plausible to assume that the situation is similar when the nucleus is not a uniformly charged sphere;[3] this situation is now under study. We assume that the static and transition quadrupole charge densities have the same radial dependence, so that the elastic and inelastic form factors are constant multiples of each other for all q. They can then be related to Q_0 for small q, and hence found for all q if some radial dependence is assumed.

From Eq. (15) and Sec. V, the differential cross section for elastic scattering is given by [compare with Eqs. (2) and (14) of reference 15]

$$\sigma_e(\theta)=[e^2\cos^2(\tfrac{1}{2}\theta)/4E^2\sin^4(\tfrac{1}{2}\theta)]|F_e|^2,$$

$$|F_e|^2=(2I+1)^{-1}\sum_{m_i}\sum_{m_f}\left|(4\pi)^{\frac{1}{2}}\int[j_0(qr)Y_{00}-5^{\frac{1}{2}}j_2(qr)Y_{20}]\rho_e(m_i,m_f)d\tau\right|^2, \tag{21}$$

where $\rho_e(m_i,m_f)$ is the matrix element of the static charge density between initial and final magnetic substates of the nuclear ground state of total angular momentum I.[17] We choose the axis with respect to which the magnetic substates are defined as $\mathbf{q}$, which is the axis of Y_{l0}, in which case the integrals fail to vanish only if $m_f=m_i$. We call this common value m, and note that the Y_{00} part of the integral is independent of m, while the Y_{20} part of the integral depends on m through the factor[18]

$$f_m=[3m^2-I(I+1)]/I(2I-1)$$

[15] L. I. Schiff, Phys. Rev. **92**, 988 (1953).

[16] A. Bohr and B. R. Mottelson, Kgl. Danske Videnskab. Selskab, Mat.-fys. Medd. **27**, 16 (1953).

[17] Alternatively, $\rho_e(\mathbf{r})$ may be regarded as an operator (see reference 5), and the matrix element taken after the integration is performed over $\mathbf{r}$; all results are the same.

[18] Reference 8, p. 28. The numerator of f_m is the quantum-mechanical transcription of $P_2(\cos\theta)$, and the denominator merely normalizes it so that $f_I=1$. Thus the fact that f_m is indeterminate when $I=0$ or $\frac{1}{2}$ is not significant; in these cases f_m should be regarded as zero since the numerator vanishes. Equation (24) is consistent with this interpretation.

in the following way:

$$|F_e|^2=[4\pi/(2I+1)]\sum_m\left\{\left|\int j_0Y_{00}\rho_e(I,I)d\tau\right|^2 - (20)^{\frac{1}{2}}f_m Re\int j_0Y_{00}\rho_e(I,I)d\tau\int j_2Y_{20}\rho_e(I,I)d\tau + 5f_m^2\left|\int j_2Y_{20}\rho_e(I,I)d\tau\right|^2\right\}.$$

Now $\sum_m f_m=0$, so that the interference term vanishes. Also,

$$\sum_m f_m^2=(2I+1)/5A_I^2 = (I+1)(2I+1)(2I+3)/5I(2I-1),$$

where A_I is the quantity defined in reference 15. We thus obtain

$$|F_e|^2=4\pi\left\{\left|\int j_0Y_{00}\rho_e(I,I)d\tau\right|^2 + [(I+1)(2I+3)/I(2I-1)] \times\left|\int j_2Y_{20}\rho_e(I,I)d\tau\right|^2\right\}. \quad (22)$$

The first term of Eq. (22) gives the scattering from the spherically symmetric part of the nuclear charge density, and the second term we call the quadrupole part of the elastic scattering.

In order to relate the second term of Eq. (22) to the intrinsic quadrupole moment Q_0, we note that for small q,

$$\int j_2Y_{20}\rho_e(I,I)d\tau\rightarrow(q^2/15) \times\int r^2Y_{20}\rho_e(I,I)d\tau=(q^2/15)(5/16\pi)^{\frac{1}{2}}eQ,$$

where the observed quadrupole moment Q is given in terms of Q_0 by Eq. (V.6) of reference 16:

$$Q=[I(2I-1)/(I+1)(2I+3)]Q_0.$$

Q_0 is calculated in the same way as Q, except that the axis of Y_{20} is the nuclear symmetry axis rather than **I**. Thus if we fix the magnitude of ρ_e by the equation

$$eQ_0=(16\pi/5)^{\frac{1}{2}}\int r^2Y_{20}\rho_e d\tau, \quad (23)$$

and infer its shape in some other way, then the quadrupole part of $|F_e|^2$ is

$$|F_{eq}|^2=4\pi[I(2I-1)/(I+1)(2I+3)] \times\left|\int j_2(qr)Y_{20}\rho_e d\tau\right|^2. \quad (24)$$

It must be remembered that in Eqs. (23) and (24), the axis of Y_{20} is the symmetry axis of the nuclear charge distribution ρ_e.[19] Note that there is no elastic quadrupole scattering if $I=0$ or $\frac{1}{2}$, just as there is no observed quadrupole moment; the charge distribution as viewed by the incident electron is spherically symmetric in this case, even though Q_0 may not be zero.

The differential cross section for inelastic scattering is given by the first of Eqs. (21), with F_e replaced by the quantity F_i:

$$|F_i|^2=(2I_i+1)^{-1}\sum_{m_i}\sum_{m_f}|F_i(m_i,m_f,0)|^2, \quad (25)$$

where

$$F_i(m_i,m_f,m)=-(20\pi)^{\frac{1}{2}}\int j_2(qr)Y_{2m}\rho_i(m_i,m_f)d\tau,$$

and $\rho_i(m_i,m_f)$ is the transition charge density between the initial state I_i, m_i and the final state I_f, m_f. Since the summations in Eq. (25) are carried over all m_i and m_f, the result is independent of the axis chosen for Y_{20}, and hence has the same value if $F_i(m_i,m_f,0)$ is replaced by $F_i(m_i,m_f,m)$ where m is not necessarily equal to zero. Then

$$|F_i|^2=[5(2I_i+1)]^{-1}\sum_m\sum_{m_i}\sum_{m_f}|F_i(m_i,m_f,m)|^2 =(1/5)\sum_m\sum_{m_f}|F_i(m_i,m_f,m)|^2;$$

the second equality holds because the summations over all m and m_f make the result independent of the value of m_i.

For small q,

$$F_i(m_i,m_f,m)\rightarrow-(20\pi)^{\frac{1}{2}}(q^2/15)\int r^2Y_{2m}\rho_i(m_i,m_f)d\tau.$$

The reduced radiative transition probability is defined in Eq. (VII.2) of reference 16 as

$$B(E2)=\sum_m\sum_{m_f}\left|\int r^2Y_{2m}\rho_i(m_i,m_f)d\tau\right|^2,$$

so that for small q,

$$|F_i|^2\rightarrow4\pi(q^2/15)^2B(E2).$$

There are in general two possible quadrupole transitions from the ground state I: to the first excited state $I+1$, and to the second excited state $I+2$.[20] From Eqs. (33) and (36) of reference 13, the reduced transition proba-

[19] The averaging over nuclear orientations was not performed correctly in reference 15; the charge density defined by Eq. (17) of that reference is the same as the quantity ρ_e of the present paper except for a normalization factor Ze, but in Eqs. (20) and (21), ρ_2 should be replaced by $A_I\rho_2$. This does not affect the estimate of the quadrupole scattering below Eq. (22), since only the ratio of (21) to (20) enters there.

[20] If the ground state I is zero, the first excited state has $I=2$, and if the ground state I is $\frac{1}{2}$, the results below may be altered (see references 13 and 16).

bility in the first case is

$$B_1(E2) = (15/16\pi)(eQ_0)^2[I/(I+1)(I+2)],$$

and from Eqs. (34) and (36) of reference 13, this quantity in the second case is

$$B_2(E2) = (15/16\pi)(eQ_0)^2[2/(I+2)(2I+3)].$$

We thus find for the transition $I \to I+1$ and small q

$$|F_{i1}|^2 \to (5/4)(eQ_0)^2(q^2/15)^2[3I/(I+1)(I+2)], \quad (26)$$

and for the transition $I \to I+2$

$$|F_{i2}|^2 \to (5/4)(eQ_0)^2(q^2/15)^2[6/(I+2)(2I+3)]. \quad (27)$$

We now assume that the extrapolation from small to large q can be made as in Eq. (24). We then find that the inelastic scattering is also described by Eq. (24), except that the square bracket there must be replaced by the square bracket in Eq. (26) or (27). Some numerical values are given in Table I. It must be remembered that these results may not apply when the ground state I is equal to $\frac{1}{2}$, and that Eq. (27) represents the transition to the first (not the second) excited state when $I=0$.[20]

It is interesting to note that there is a kind of sum rule for the three kinds of quadrupole scattering, which are the only possible kinds

$$[I(2I-1)/(I+1)(2I+3)]+[3I/(I+1)(I+2)] + [6/(I+2)(2I+3)] = 1.$$

TABLE I. Values of the square bracket factors in Eqs. (24), (26), and (27), for a few values of I.

I	Elastic $I \to I$, Eq. (24)	Inelastic $I \to I+1$, Eq. (26)	$I \to I+2$, Eq. (27)
0	0	0	1
3/2	1/5	18/35	2/7
5/2	5/14	10/21	1/6
7/2	7/15	14/33	6/55

IX. CONCLUSIONS

Excitation of nuclear multipole transitions by inelastic electron scattering occurs along with the elastic scattering of high-energy electrons. If sufficiently accurate measurements of the distribution of the scattered electrons in energy and angle can be made, the elastically scattered electrons give information concerning the static nuclear charge distribution, and the inelastically scattered electrons give information concerning both the strength and shape of the transition charge density. The static quadrupole scattering must be allowed for when interpreting the angle distribution of the elastically scattered electrons in terms of a radial distribution of nuclear charge. If the energy resolution is not good enough to separate the inelastic from the elastic scattering, then it must also be allowed for before the elastic scattering is analyzed.

It is important to note that absolute measurements of the inelastic scattering are not necessary in order to determine the strength of the transition charge density. Analysis of the relative elastic scattering, even if no absolute cross sections are available, yields a shape for the static charge density. The magnitude of the nuclear charge is of course known, so that an absolute elastic cross section can be computed. Then comparison of the relative magnitudes of inelastic and elastic scattering at each angle gives absolute values for the former, from which the strength as well as the shape of the transition charge density can be determined.

The order of magnitude estimates given in Sec. IV are of course not completely reliable, and simply indicate that Eq. (15) or Eq. (18) is likely to be the dominant term, especially for collective transitions, which appear to be much the strongest in any event. For single-particle transitions, where detailed nuclear wave functions are more likely to be available, it would be worth while to make more careful estimates of the relative importance of Eqs. (16) and (17).

PAPER 27

Electron Scattering from the Proton*†‡

Robert Hofstadter and Robert W. McAllister
Department of Physics and High-Energy Physics Laboratory, Stanford University, Stanford, California
(Received January 24, 1955)

With apparatus previously described,[1,2] we have studied the elastic scattering of electrons of energies 100, 188, and 236 Mev from protons initially at rest. At 100 Mev and 188 Mev, the angular distributions of scattered electrons have been examined in the ranges 60°–138° and 35°–138°, respectively, in the laboratory frame. At 236 Mev, because of an inability of the analyzing magnet to bend electrons of energies larger than 192 Mev, we have studied the angular distribution between 90° and 138° in the laboratory frame. In all cases a gaseous hydrogen target was used.

We have found that deviations in excess of Mott scattering are readily apparent at large scattering angles. The early results (reported at the Seattle meeting, July, 1954) at smaller angles showed the expected agreement with the Mott formula within experimental error. Deviations from the Mott formula such as we have found may be anticipated at large angles because of additional scattering from the magnetic moment of the proton.[3] We have observed this additional scattering but in an amount smaller than predicted by theory.

The experimental curve at 188 Mev is given in Fig. 1. It may be observed that the experimental points do not fit either the Mott curve or the theoretical curve of Rosenbluth,[3] computed for a point charge and point (anomalous) magnetic moment of the proton. Furthermore, the experimental curve does not fit a Rosenbluth curve with the Dirac magnetic moment and a point charge. The latter curve would lie close to the Mott curve and slightly above it. Similar behavior is observed at 236 Mev.

The correct interpretation of these results will require a more elaborate explanation (probably involving a good meson theory) than can be given at the moment, although Rosenbluth already has made weak-coupling calculations in meson theory which predict an effect of the kind we have observed.[4]

Nevertheless, if we make the naive assumption that the proton charge cloud and its magnetic moment are both spread out in the same proportions we can calculate simple form factors for various values of the proton "size." When these calculations are carried out we find that the experimental curves can be represented very well by the following choices of size. At 188 Mev, the

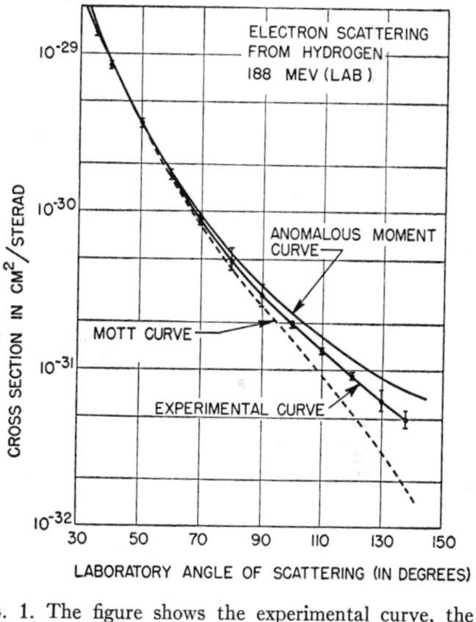

Fig. 1. The figure shows the experimental curve, the Mott curve, and the point-charge, point-magnetic-moment curve. The experimental curve passes through the points with the attached margins of error. The margins of error are not statistical; statistical errors would be much smaller than the errors shown. The limits of error are, rather, the largest deviations observed in the many complete and partial runs taken over a period of several months. Absolute cross sections given in the ordinate scale were not measured experimentally but were taken from theory. The radiative corrections of Schwinger have been ignored since they affect the angular distribution hardly at all. The radiative corrections do influence the absolute cross sections. Experimental points in the figure refer to areas under the elastic peaks taken over an energy interval of ±1.5 Mev centering about the peak. The data at the various points are unchanged in relation to each other when the energy interval is increased to ±2.5 Mev about the peak; the latter widths include essentially all the area under the peak.

data are fitted accurately by an rms radius of $(7.0\pm 2.4)\times 10^{-14}$ cm. At 236 Mev, the data are well fitted by an rms radius of $(7.8\pm 2.4)\times 10^{-14}$ cm. At 100 Mev the data are relatively insensitive to the radius but the experimental results are fitted by both choices given above. The 100-Mev data serve therefore as a valuable check of the apparatus. A compromise value fitting all the experimental results is $(7.4\pm 2.4)\times 10^{-14}$ cm. If the proton were a spherical ball of charge, this rms radius would indicate a true radius of 9.5×10^{-14} cm, or in round numbers 1.0×10^{-13} cm. It is to be noted that if our interpretation is correct the Coulomb law of force has not been violated at distances as small as 7×10^{-14} cm.

These results will be reported in more detail in a paper now in preparation.

We wish to thank Dr. D. R. Yennie for his generous aid in discussions of the theory. We wish to thank Mr. E. E. Chambers for assistance with several phases of the work. In the early phases of this research, the late Miss Eva Wiener made important contributions.

* The research reported in this document was supported jointly by the U. S. Navy (Office of Naval Research) and the U. S. Atomic Energy Commission, and the U. S. Air Force through the Office of Scientific Research of the Air Research and Development Command.

† Aided by a grant from the Research Corporation.

‡ Early results were reported at the Seattle Meeting of the American Physical Society [Phys. Rev. **96**, 854(A) (1954)]. More recent results were presented at the Berkeley meeting of the American Physical Society [Bull. Am. Phys. Soc. **29**, No. 8, 29 (1954)].

[1] Hofstadter, Fechter, and McIntyre, Phys. Rev. **92**, 978 (1953).

[2] Hofstadter, Hahn, Knudsen, and McIntyre, Phys. Rev. **95**, 512 (1954).

[3] M. N. Rosenbluth, Phys. Rev. **79**, 615 (1950).

[4] See also the classical calculation of L. I. Schiff reported in Rosenbluth's paper.

High-Energy Electron Scattering and Nuclear Structure Determinations. III. Carbon-12 Nucleus*†

JEROME H. FREGEAU‡ AND ROBERT HOFSTADTER

Department of Physics and W. W. Hansen Laboratories of Physics, Stanford University, Stanford, California

(Received May 10, 1955)

The elastic scattering peak in carbon-12 is accompanied by a number of additional peaks corresponding to inelastic scattering of electrons from the various excited levels of the carbon nucleus. Three levels have been investigated by this method and correspond to the three known states at 4.43 Mev, 7.68 Mev, and 9.61 Mev. Angular distributions of the inelastically-scattered electrons have been obtained as well as the angular distribution of the elastically-scattered electrons. The angular distributions of the inelastic peaks fall off less steeply with angle than the elastic peak. By comparing the scattering from carbon with scattering from the proton, and using the theoretical value of the cross section of electrons scattered from the proton, it is possible to obtain "absolute" values for the elastic and inelastic scattering cross sections. From the elastic-scattering curve, information about the size and charge distribution in the carbon-12 nucleus may be derived. The charge distribution lies halfway between a Gaussian and a uniform model. The root mean square radius of the resultant charge distribution is $(2.40\pm0.25)\times10^{-13}$ cm.

I. INTRODUCTION

THE study of electron scattering at high energies (100–200 Mev) has led to certain conclusions about the electromagnetic size of nuclei and to interesting information about the variation of charge density near the surface of the nucleus.[1–4] Recently it has been shown[5] that electrons may be scattered from nuclei inelastically as well as elastically and that sharp peaks corresponding to nuclear levels accompany the elastic peak. We have thought it worthwhile to make a more intensive study of such inelastic and elastic structure at various angles of scattering in a light, well-known nucleus. In this way phenomenological information about the behavior of the inelastic scattering might be obtained and could assist possible theoretical interpretations of the experimental data.[6,7] Carbon-12 seemed an ideal nucleus in view of the large amount of information available in the literature on its excited levels. Furthermore, there is considerable interest in the nature of the second level at 7.68 Mev both in regard to the type of transition (probably 0^+-0^+) and to its influence in the production of stellar energy.

II. APPARATUS

The apparatus used in these studies has been described in two previous publications.[1,2] Several improvements have been made, as follows:

(1) The slits at the entrance and exit of the magne are now remotely controlled.

(2) The lining up of the beam has been greatly facilitated by the use of a luminescent crystal placed on the axis of the scattering system and viewed by a system of mirror (or mirrors) and telescope. The latter is placed in the laboratory room where the counting is carried on. Thallium-activated cesium bromide has proved very successful in this application and exhibits a bright green glow which can be seen even at fifty feet without the telescope. The crystal darkens surprisingly little under intense electron bombardment. Thallium-activated potassium iodide has also been used but is not as useful as the cesium bromide. The viewing system was suggested and perfected by A. W. Knudsen.

(3) A device has been installed to calibrate the photomultiplier-Čerenkov counter system. The Čerenkov counter is used as the detector of the analyzed electrons. A radioactive source (actually the uranium slit-jaw at the exit of the spectrometer) provides gamma rays which impinge on an anthracene crystal. The anthracene crystal is situated on a movable plate which slides the crystal either in front of the entrance to the Čerenkov counter or removes it and substitutes a thin aluminum window through which the scattered electrons pass into the Čerenkov counter after emerging from the magnetic analyzer. Thus, when it is desired to calibrate the counter system, the anthracene crystal is moved in front of the Čerenkov counter (now acting as a light pipe) and the number of counts is recorded for a given interval of time. After checking, the anthracene is moved out of the way by remote control and the system is ready to receive electrons through the thin window. Under the optical conditions prevailing, the anthracene pulses are quite similar in size to the Čerenkov pulses from the high-energy electrons. The details of this calibration scheme were worked out by E. E. Chambers and B. Chambers.

(4) A secondary emitter has been installed for beam

---

* The research reported in this document was supported jointly by the Office of Naval Research and the U. S. Atomic Energy Commission, and by the U. S. Air Force through the Office of Scientific Research of the Air Research and Development Command.

† Aided by a grant from the Research Corporation.

‡ International Business Machines Fellow for the year 1954–55.

[1] Hofstadter, Fechter, and McIntyre, Phys. Rev. **91**, 422 (1953); **92**, 978 (1953).

[2] Hofstadter, Hahn, Knudsen, and McIntyre, Phys. Rev. **95**, 512 (1954).

[3] D. G. Ravenhall and D. R. Yennie, Phys. Rev. **96**, 239 (1954).

[4] D. L. Hill and K. Ford (private communication).

[5] McIntyre, Hahn, and Hofstadter, Phys. Rev. **94**, 1084 (1954).

[6] L. I. Schiff, Phys. Rev. **96**, 765 (1954); Phys. Rev. **98**, 1281 (1955).

[7] C. J. Mullin and E. Guth, Phys. Rev. **98**, 277(A) (1955).

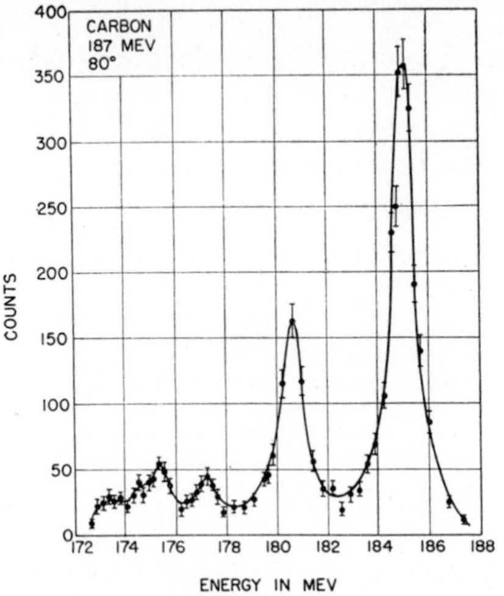

FIG. 1. The elastic and inelastic peaks at 187 Mev in carbon at a scattering angle of 80°.

monitoring purposes. Such a beam monitor has been described recently.[8]

III. PROCEDURE

Our general procedure has been to make a run at a given angular setting of the magnet during which the number of scattered electrons is measured as a function of the current in the magnet. Since the calibration curve of magnetic field *vs* magnetizing current is known, the number of scattered electrons may then be plotted as a function of their energy. At any angle the elastic and inelastic features are thus measured during the same run. At some later time the elastic peaks are related to each other by measuring in a single run all the elastic peaks alone at the various angles previously studied. Since the ratio of inelastic to elastic peaks is known from the previous runs, all the inelastic peaks can be related to each other.

In the course of taking the elastic runs in carbon, the elastic peaks of hydrogen (or sometimes a single peak) are also observed and measured. The protons in polyethylene (CH_2)[9] are used for this purpose. By carrying out the comparison runs of the proton peaks *vs* the carbon elastic peaks, the carbon peaks may be normalized. If the theoretical values of the proton cross section are used, the ratio of the areas of the carbon peaks to the proton peaks times the theoretical cross section for the proton gives the "absolute" cross section of the elastic scattering from carbon. Similarly the inelastic cross section may be derived absolutely by reference to electron scattering from the proton.

In Figs. 1 and 2 we show two typical runs of the elastic and inelastic peaks at a given angle and at a given energy (187 Mev). In Fig. 3 we give a set of elastic peaks at a given incident energy at the various angles studied. Also given in Fig. 3 is a comparison proton peak which has been used for normalization of the carbon data. It will be noticed that the carbon peaks shift slightly in energy as the angle of scattering is changed. This effect has been noticed previously[1] and is due to a combination of recoil of the carbon nucleus and energy loss in the scattering layer. In these experiments the target plane was rotated so that the normal to the target always bisected the angle of scattering. The thickness of the target in the beam was therefore variable and appropriate correction was made in reduction of the data. The large shift in energy of the proton peak may also be noted. This shift has álso been observed previously.[1] In all the runs the angular width accepted by the spectrometer was $\pm 1.3°$.

In these experiments the exit slit was maintained at constant width during all the runs. Thus the slit selected a fixed percentage of the particular energy at which the spectrometer was set. Consequently, the absolute energy interval accepted by the exit slit varies since the peaks appear at slightly different energies at the various angles. Curves taken with a wide (energy) slit give proportionately more counts in the peak than those curves taken with a narrow (energy) slit. Therefore a correction has to be applied to the raw data. In the case of the carbon peaks the correction is less than one percent over the range of angles studied. In the case of hydrogen, however, the largest correction amounts to approximately seven percent.

The inelastic peaks appear to "ride" on the bremsstrahlung tail of the elastic peak. This tail falls off approximately as the reciprocal of the energy interval between a given energy and that of the elastic peak. A subtraction of the background in the tail is required in order to obtain the ordinate of the inelastic peak. In most cases it has not proved more accurate to use the

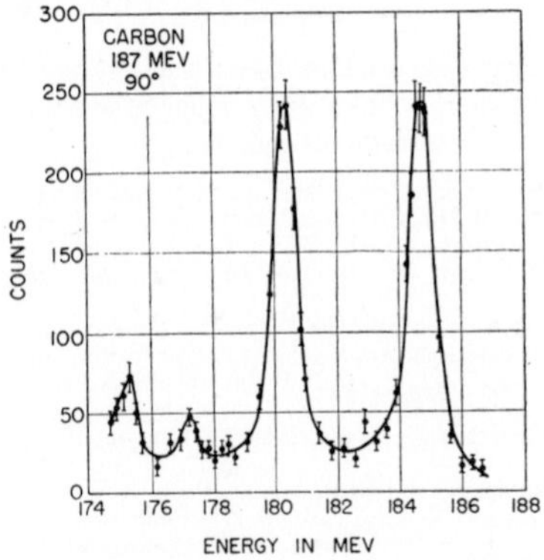

FIG. 2. The elastic and inelastic peaks at 187 Mev in carbon at a scattering angle of 90°.

[8] G. W. Tautfest and H. R. Fechter, Phys. Rev. **96**, 35 (1954); Rev. Sci. Instr. **26**, 229 (1955).

[9] The number of protons is assumed to be exactly twice the number of carbon nuclei. This figure is probably accurate to a few tenths of a percent or better.

$1/E$ dependence in estimating the bremsstrahlung tail, than sketching in the background by inspection of the regions higher and lower in energy than the inelastic peak and continuing this background under the peak. The latter procedure has been used in estimating the inelastic scattering.

IV. RESULTS

A. Inelastic Data

Data have been taken at three energies: 187 Mev, 150 Mev, and 80 Mev. The data at 187 Mev are the most extensive. At 80 Mev very few data have been obtained because of the difficulty in seeing the inelastic peaks over the bremsstrahlung tails of the elastic peaks.

The 187-Mev data are summarized in Fig. 4. This figure shows the angular distributions of the elastic scattering (Curve A) and the distributions of the inelastic scatterings corresponding to the three inelastic levels (Curve B, 4.43 Mev; Curve C, 7.68 Mev; and Curve D, 9.61 Mev). Table I also gives a summary of the data shown in Fig. 4. The cross sections are given in absolute units because of the normalization made in terms of the theoretical cross section of electron scattering from the proton.

A word of explanation is necessary here. In using the theoretical cross section for hydrogen, the formula of Rosenbluth[10] has been used. We have employed his point-charge and point-magnetic moment (anomalous value) approximation, except as modified slightly by results obtained recently in this laboratory.[11] Finally the radiative correction of Schwinger[12] has been applied to the hydrogen data. The latter correction amounts to a decrease of approximately 15 percent at 187 Mev for the 3-Mev band width of the hydrogen peak used in our normalization. For example, the hydrogen cross

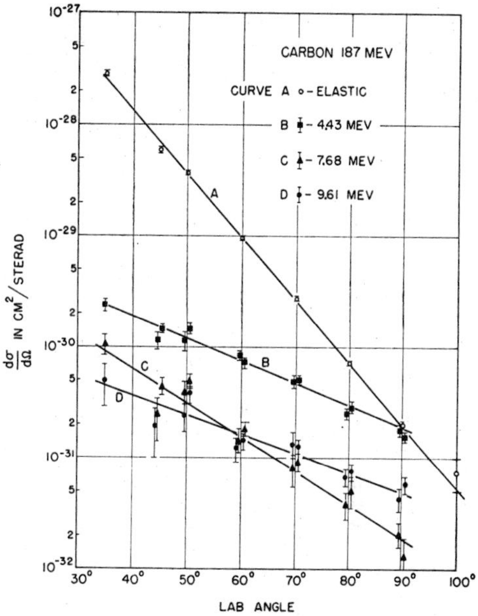

FIG. 4. The angular distributions of the elastic and inelastic peaks at 187 Mev in carbon. The absolute cross sections have been obtained by the proton-normalization method discussed in the text.

TABLE I. Cross section of elastic and inelastic scattering peaks in microbarns per steradian for various angles at an incident energy of 187 Mev. The radiative correction is included.

Lab angle	Elastic	4.43 Mev	7.68 Mev	9.61 Mev
35°	283±14	2.35±0.28	1.05±0.22	0.49±0.20
45°	68.7±3.5	1.13±0.19	0.24±0.10	0.19±0.09
		1.41±0.11	0.44±0.08	
50°	36.3±1.1	1.12±0.22	0.39±0.09	0.24±0.07
		1.46±0.16	0.49±0.07	0.39±0.08
60°	9.42±0.38	0.828±0.083	0.144±0.035	0.121±0.030
		0.715±0.086	0.180±0.027	0.141±0.024
70°	2.72±0.11	0.484±0.063	0.080±0.025	0.133±0.035
		0.500±0.050	0.092±0.017	0.127±0.019
80°	0.714±0.028	0.251±0.025	0.038±0.010	0.068±0.012
		0.286±0.034	0.051±0.016	0.075±0.013
90°	0.199±0.014	0.179±0.021	0.021±0.005	0.043±0.010
		0.157±0.017	0.013±0.006	0.058±0.010

section at 50° is 3.6×10^{-30} cm²/sterad and with the radiative correction it becomes 3.0×10^{-30} cm²/sterad. This means that the carbon cross sections computed from these figures *include* a radiative correction.

Data similar to those in Fig. 4 are presented in Fig. 5 for the case of 150 Mev. Table II gives the corresponding summary of data. Figure 6 shows a typical run taken at 90° at this energy. One notes the strong contrast of these data with those shown in Fig. 2 which are also taken at 90° but at the higher energy (187 Mev). One observes the clear effect of the diminution in the elastic peak at the higher energy which makes the inelastic peak appear more prominent at the higher

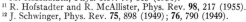

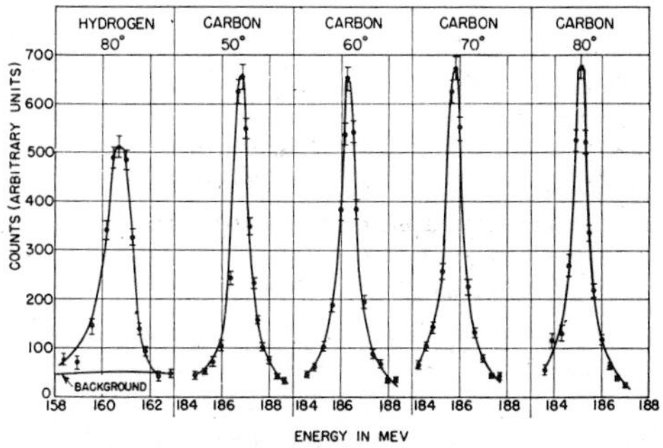

FIG. 3. The elastic peaks in carbon at an incident energy of 187 Mev and at various angles of scattering. The elastic scattering curve for the protons in polyethylene is also shown at a scattering angle of 80°. The greater half-width of the proton peak is due principally to recoil effects. The background under the hydrogen peak is taken from another run.

[10] M. Rosenbluth, Phys. Rev. **79**, 615 (1950).
[11] R. Hofstadter and R. McAllister, Phys. Rev. **98**, 217 (1955).
[12] J. Schwinger, Phys. Rev. **75**, 898 (1949); **76**, 790 (1949).

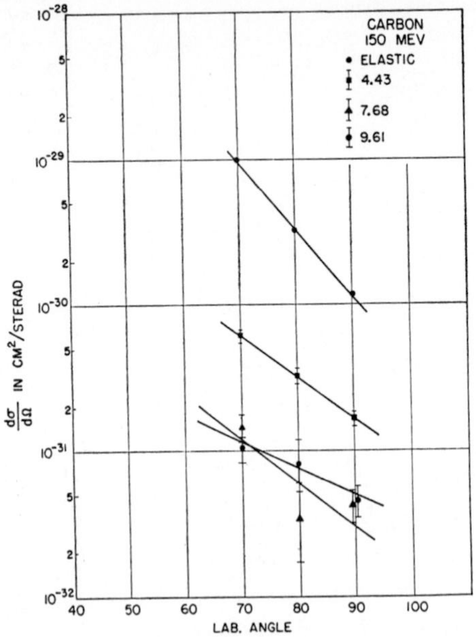

FIG. 5. The angular distributions in carbon at 150 Mev of the elastic and inelastic peaks. The absolute cross sections have been obtained by the proton-normalization method discussed in the text.

energy. In fact, it is only because of the large reduction in elastic scattering[1] due to the finite nuclear size that the inelastic peaks have become evident.[5] The bremsstrahlung tail goes down in proportion to the elastic scattering and the inelastic peaks may thus be seen more easily on the lower backgrounds at higher energies. The data at 187 Mev and at 150 Mev show that the

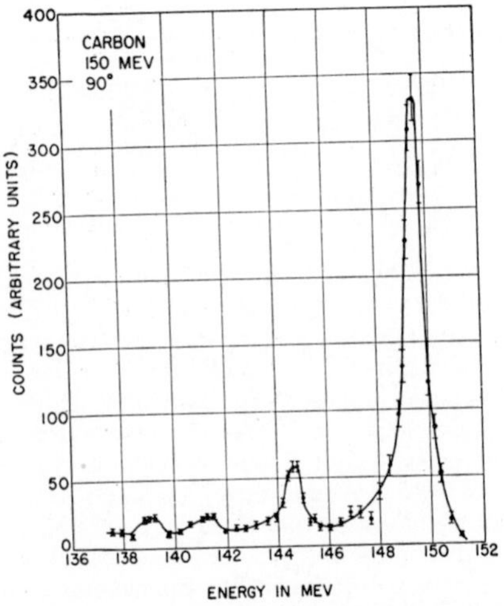

FIG. 6. The elastic and inelastic peaks at 150 Mev in carbon at a scattering angle of 90°. This figure should be compared with Fig. 2.

angular distribution of the inelastic scattering is less steep than the corresponding data for the elastic scattering. This appears to be a general conclusion for all the levels thus far studied in carbon. One also notices that the angular distributions of the 4.43-Mev and 9.61-Mev peaks appear to be similar to each other and both are different from that of the 7.68-Mev peak. The two subsidiary peaks 10.80 Mev and 11.75 Mev (combined with 11.1 Mev) in the various figures seem to vary in roughly, but not exactly, the same way as the 9.61-Mev peak, but the resolution of these peaks and the small number of counts recorded for them do not permit any strict conclusions to be drawn.

In view of the assignment 2^+ for the 4.43-Mev state and the similarity of angular distributions of the 4.43- and 9.61-Mev peaks, we are tempted to make the assignment of 2^+ to the 9.61-Mev state. The interpretation of the 7.68-Mev transition as 0^+-0^+ is not inconsistent with the differences observed between the angular distributions of the 7.68- and 4.43-Mev peaks.

The strong dependence on energy of the "visibility" of the inelastic peaks above the bremsstrahlung tail has prompted us to examine the inelastic and elastic

TABLE II. Cross section of elastic and inelastic scattering peaks in microbarns per steradian for various angles at an incident energy of 150 Mev. The radiative correction is included.

Lab. angle	Elastic	4.43 Mev	7.68 Mev	9.61 Mev
70°	9.90±0.40	0.618±0.068	0.150±0.026	0.104±0.021
80°	3.23±0.13	0.323±0.042	0.034±0.017	0.081±0.021
90°	1.17±0.04	0.166±0.018	0.042±0.011	0.046±0.011

scattering at 80 Mev. Figure 7 shows the corresponding data at 90° at this energy. From the data taken at the three energies one may obtain the absolute cross section for the 4.43-Mev peak at 90° as a function of the incident energy. See also Fig. 10. It may be observed that the absolute cross section at 90° is essentially constant as the energy is varied. Unfortunately for the observation of these peaks, the elastic cross section increases in a very rapid fashion because of the increasing de Broglie wavelength relative to the finite size of the carbon-12 nucleus.

The difficulty in observing the inelastic peaks above the bremsstrahlung at low values of the incident energy is matched by the difficulty in observing these peaks at small angles even at a high energy. Figure 8 shows the weak inelastic peaks at 187 Mev at small angles relative to both the elastic peak and its bremsstrahlung tail. Figures 2, 6, 7, and 8 suggest that perhaps for light nuclei the cross section for the inelastic peaks may be essentially a point charge cross section σ_p multiplied into the square of a form factor just as the elastic cross section can be represented in this way when the Born approximation is valid (light nuclei).[1,13–16] Here σ_p is given by

$$\sigma_p = \left(\frac{Ze^2}{2E}\right)^2 \frac{\cos^2(\theta/2)}{\sin^4(\theta/2)}. \tag{1}$$

The form factor for the inelastic cross section might be expected to be a function of the momentum transfer q, where

$$q = (4\pi/\lambda)\sin(\theta/2), \tag{2}$$

or more appropriately qa, where a is a parameter having to do with the nuclear radius or size and having the dimensions of a length; qa is thus dimensionless; λ is the de Broglie wavelength of the incident electrons; and θ is the angle of scattering. [See reference 1, formulas (1) and (2) and accompanying discussion.]

To bring out such facts more clearly, the cross section

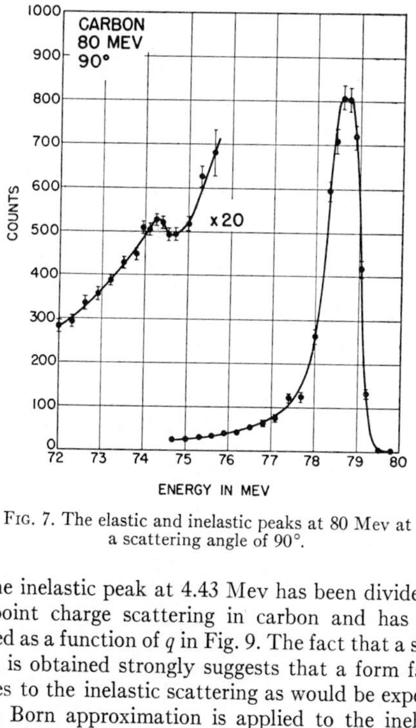

FIG. 7. The elastic and inelastic peaks at 80 Mev at a scattering angle of 90°.

for the inelastic peak at 4.43 Mev has been divided by the point charge scattering in carbon and has been plotted as a function of q in Fig. 9. The fact that a single curve is obtained strongly suggests that a form factor applies to the inelastic scattering as would be expected if the Born approximation is applied to the inelastic scattering. Ravenhall[17] has employed the Born approximation and has found the type of form factor appropriate to the inelastic scattering.

It is also interesting to attempt to learn something of the origin of the inelastic peaks, i.e., to find out if the excitation of a level corresponds to a single particle excitation or to some more complicated type of nuclear

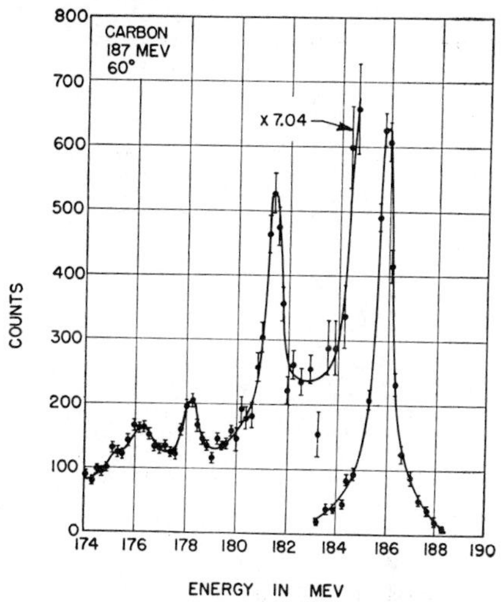

FIG. 8. The elastic and inelastic peaks at 187 Mev in carbon at a scattering angle of 60°.

excitation. In this connection it may be of potential value to compare the inelastic cross section for excitation of a particular level with the elastic cross section for electron scattering from a single proton. This ratio can be obtained from the data of Fig. 9 by multiplying the ordinate by Z^2. A tabulation of values is given in Table III.

Finally we show in Fig. 10 the behavior of the

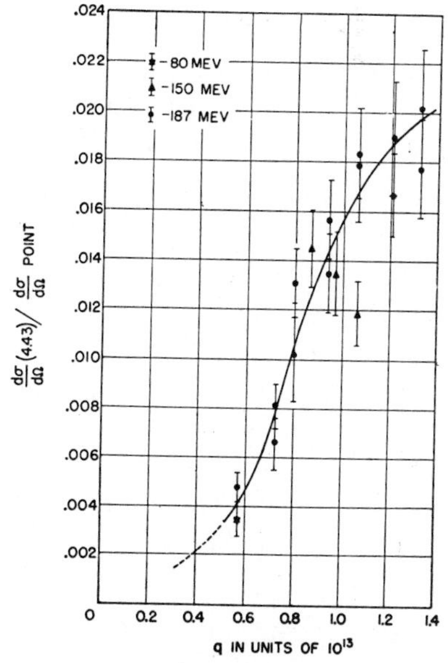

FIG. 9. The ratio of the cross section for the inelastic peak at 4.43 Mev to the point charge cross section for carbon as a function of the momentum transfer q. The black circles refer to 187 Mev, the triangles to 150 Mev and the star to 80 Mev.

[13] E. Guth, Wien. Anzeiger Akad. Wiss. No. 24, 229 (1934).
[14] M. E. Rose, Phys. Rev. 73, 282 (1948).
[15] J. H. Smith, Phys. Rev. 95, 271 (1954).
[16] L. I. Schiff, Phys. Rev. 92, 988 (1953).
[17] D. G. Ravenhall (to be published).

TABLE III. Ratio of cross section for excitation of 4.43-Mev level to point-nucleus scattering cross section for carbon.

Energy (Mev)	Lab angle	Ratio
80	90°	0.0035±0.0008
150	90°	0.0119±0.0013
150	80°	0.0135±0.0017
150	70°	0.0145±0.0016
187	90°	0.0202±0.0024
		0.0178±0.0020
187	80°	0.0167±0.0017
		0.0190±0.0023
187	70°	0.0179±0.0023
		0.0184±0.0019
187	60°	0.0157±0.0016
		0.0135±0.0016
187	50°	0.0103±0.0020
		0.0131±0.0014
187	45°	0.0066±0.0011
		0.0081±0.0010
187	35°	0.0048±0.0006

inelastic peaks at 90° as a function of energy for the three levels studied. These data indicate what may be expected in going to the lower energies available in the conventional betatron.

B. Elastic Data

Calculations made with the Born approximation are expected to be accurate to better than 5% for carbon ($Z=6$). Therefore one may attempt to fit the experimental elastic curves in carbon at 187 Mev and 150 Mev by a product of a point charge curve and the square of a form factor. The form factor may be chosen from among those appropriate to several different nuclear charge distributions. The particular charge distribution giving the best agreement with experiment will then be assumed to provide the best model for the carbon nucleus. At 187 Mev the best fit appears to lie between a Gaussian charge distribution with an rms radius of 2.47×10^{-13} cm and a uniform charge distribution with an rms radius of 2.20×10^{-13} cm. A uniform charge distribution does not appear to fit unless modified by adding a taper at the edge. A half-uniform half-Gaussian model[1] would undoubtedly provide an excellent fit to

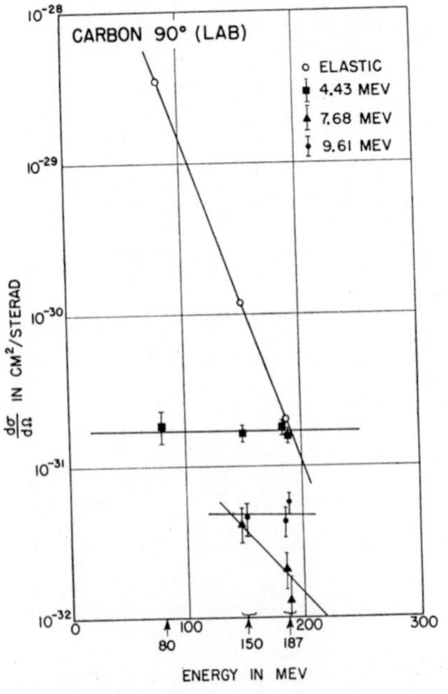

FIG. 10. The cross sections for the elastic and inelastic peaks at 90° as a function of energy.

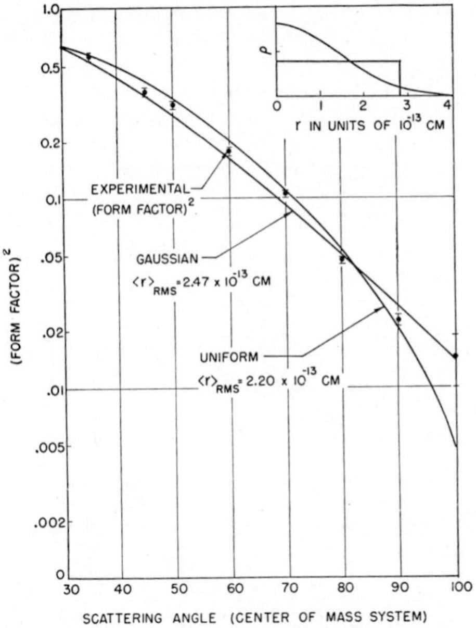

FIG. 11. This figure shows the square of the form factor plotted against scattering angle in degrees in the center-of-mass system. The square of the form factor represents the ratio of the experimental carbon cross section to the point charge cross section. The experimental points are shown in black circles, while the theoretical curves for a uniform charge distribution with rms radius of 2.20×10^{-13} cm and for a Gaussian charge distribution with rms radius of 2.47×10^{-13} cm, are given as solid lines. Neither curve fits exactly and the points lie in between the curves. This suggests a half-uniform half-Gaussian model with rms radius of approximately 2.40×10^{-13} cm. The appropriate charge distributions are shown in the upper right hand corner of the figure. The ordinate is the charge density on a linear scale.

the data and the rms radius would be close to 2.40×10^{-13} cm. However the calculations of Ravenhall[17] on a model very close to the half-uniform and half-Gaussian make computations for this compromise model unnecessary. The shell model calculations of this author favor an rms radius of 2.41×10^{-13} cm and a charge distribution lying close to a half-uniform and half-Gaussian model, in excellent agreement with the calculations reported in this paper. It is to be noted that the experimental shape as well as the absolute values of cross section are in agreement with the theoretical calculations of this paper and also with those of Ravenhall. The agreement with our calculations is shown in Fig. 11.

We have also carried out calculations at 150 Mev. In this case the Gaussian model again fits excellently with an rms radius of 2.47×10^{-13} cm. The uniform model provides a good fit with an rms radius of 2.31×10^{-13} cm. The data at 150 Mev do not permit as extensive a check as those at 187 Mev and hence are less discriminatory with respect to the uniform charge distribution than the data at the higher energy.

Finally the single point observed at 80 Mev and 90° does not distinguish the type of charge distribution but provides an rms radius of 2.02×10^{-13} cm accompanied by a large experimental error of plus or minus 0.4×10^{-13} cm. Thus the data observed at all energies and angles are consistent with a model lying between a Gaussian charge distribution and a uniform model. An exponential charge distribution is not possible. The best determination of an rms radius provides a value near $(2.40\pm0.25)\times10^{-13}$ cm. Any error in this figure due to the use of the Born approximation instead of the exact phase shift calculations of Ravenhall and Yennie would amount to less than 1 percent and would make the radius smaller by this amount. It is interesting to examine the equivalent value of r_0 given by this determination, where

$$R=r_0A^{\frac{1}{3}}\times10^{-13}\text{ cm},\qquad(3)$$

and R is the usual "radius" (not rms) of the uniformly charged model of the nucleus. r_0 is thus determined to be 1.36 and is larger than the value appropriate to heavier nuclei.[2,3]

V. ACKNOWLEDGMENTS

We are indebted to Dr. D. G. Ravenhall for many fruitful discussions and also for the communication before publication of the results of his calculations. We also appreciate the assistance of Dr. B. Hahn and Dr. J. A. McIntyre in taking the elastic data at 100°.

PAPER 29

High-Energy Electron Scattering and the Charge Distributions of Selected Nuclei*†

BEAT HAHN,‡ D. G. RAVENHALL, AND ROBERT HOFSTADTER
Department of Physics and W. W. Hansen Laboratories of Physics, Stanford University, Stanford, California
(Received October 19, 1955)

Experimental results are presented of electron scattering by Ca, V, Co, In, Sb, Hf, Ta, W, Au, Bi, Th, and U, at 183 Mev and (for some of the elements) at 153 Mev. For those nuclei for which asphericity and inelastic scattering are absent or unimportant, i.e., Ca, V, Co, In, Sb, Au, and Bi, a partial wave analysis of the Dirac equation has been performed in which the nuclei are represented by static, spherically symmetric charge distributions. Smoothed uniform charge distributions have been assumed; these are characterized by a constant charge density in the central region of the nucleus, with a smoothed-out surface. Essentially two parameters can be determined, related to the radius and to the surface thickness. An examination of the Au experiments shows that the functional forms of the surface are not important, and that the charge density in the central regions is probably fairly flat, although it cannot be determined very accurately. An analysis of the experiments on the nuclei Ca, V, Co, In, Sb, Au, and Bi, assuming for convenience the Fermi smoothed uniform shape (1), then leads to the following results: the radial parameter c (the distance to the midpoint of the surface) scales as $A^{\frac{1}{3}}$ for the nuclei we have examined and is $(1.07\pm0.02)A^{\frac{1}{3}}\times10^{-13}$ cm; the surface thickness t (the $0.9\rho_0$ to $0.1\rho_0$ distance) is constant for all of these nuclei, to within the estimated error, and is $(2.4\pm0.3)\times10^{-13}$ cm.

I. INTRODUCTION

In the last two years several investigations[1–4] have been carried out at Stanford University in an attempt to discover the size and shape of the charge distribution in various atomic nuclei. These investigations have been of an experimental and theoretical nature. The experiments have obtained the angular distributions of high-energy electrons scattered elastically from the atomic nuclei and have employed the narrow momentum selection permitted by the use of a magnetic spectrometer in order to ensure elastic scattering. The theoretical analysis of the experimental observations rests on a phase shift calculation applied to the Dirac equation for a model of the nucleus having a static spherically symmetric charge distribution.[3] Comparisons between the experiments and the theoretical angular distributions for various specialized models of the nuclei have permitted conclusions to be drawn about the size of nuclei, the nuclear charge distribution, and the validity of the assumptions made in the theoretical interpretation. The size obtained from this work, and from the investigations of others,[5–11] has come to be called the "electromagnetic size" in contrast to a "nuclear" size determined from pure nucleon-nuclear interactions. The method of electron scattering is fortunately quite direct in its approach, since its only fundamental untested assumption is that there is no specifically nonelectromagnetic interaction between the scattered electron and the nucleus. Thus far there is no definite evidence of any appreciable deviation of the electron-nucleon interaction from the strict electromagnetic type, so that the foundation on which the theoretical analysis operates seems to be quite secure.

Until the present time the more detailed published data have concerned the heavy nuclei Au^{197} and Pb^{208}. These elements were studied[2] at several different energies in order to test the validity of the theoretical method as applied to a specific nuclear charge-density model. The analysis[4] indicated that two main parameters of the charge distribution could be determined in the present status of the experimental studies extending up to electron energies of 190 Mev. These two parameters may be said to be a mean radius and a surface thickness.

It is the purpose of the present paper to investigate how these two parameters vary over the range of new nuclei studied: Ca, V, Co, In, Sb, Au, and Bi. Another aim of this investigation is to examine, for a specific nucleus, Au, the range of values of the two parameters permitted by a fit of theory to experiment within the experimental errors. Our results for Au and Pb are in agreement with analyses of our earlier experiments by Ravenhall and Yennie,[4] by Brown and Elton,[7] and by Hill *et al.*[8] Furthermore, new experimental data are presented without analysis for nuclei which are probably not intrinsically spherically symmetric in their ground states and which require a more extensive analysis involving their quadrupole moments. Such nuclei as we have studied included Hf, Ta, W, Th, and U.

---

* The research reported in this document was supported jointly by the Office of Naval Research and the U. S. Atomic Energy Commission, and by the U. S. Air Force through the Office of Scientific Research.

† Aided by a grant from the Research Corporation.

‡ Visiting Research Fellow of the Schweizerische Arbeitsgemeinschaft in Mathematik und Physik.

[1] Hofstadter, Fechter, and McIntyre, Phys. Rev. **92**, 978 (1953).

[2] Hofstadter, Hahn, Knudsen, and McIntyre, Phys. Rev. **95**, 512 (1954).

[3] Yennie, Ravenhall, and Wilson, Phys. Rev. **95**, 500 (1954).

[4] D. G. Ravenhall and D. R. Yennie, Phys. Rev. **96**, 239 (1954).

[5] R. W. Pidd and C. L. Hammer, Phys. Rev. **99** 1396 (1955).

[6] Lyman, Hanson, and Scott, Phys. Rev. **84**, 626 (1951).

[7] G. E. Brown and L. R. B. Elton, Phil. Mag. **46** 164 (1955).

[8] Hill, Freeman, and Ford, Phys. Rev. **99**, 649 (1955)(A).

[9] V. L. Fitch and J. Rainwater, Phys. Rev. **92** 789 (1953).

[10] L. N. Cooper and E. M. Henley, Phys. Rev. **92** 801 (1953).

[11] D. L. Hill and K. W. Ford, Phys. Rev. **94**, 1617 (1954).

II. APPARATUS AND PROCEDURE

The scattering apparatus used in these experiments has been described in earlier papers.[1,2] The following improvements in the apparatus may be mentioned:

(a) The electron beam can now be centered on the target, by observing the visual luminescence produced by the electron beam in a thin CsBr(Tl) crystal, which can be brought into the target position. A bright beam spot can be seen from the control room through a telescope and two mirrors. This fluorescing crystal method (due to Mr. A. W. Knudsen) became possible when the aluminum window of the scattering chamber was replaced by a 6-mil "Mylar" window, the transparency of which permits observation of the inside of the scattering chamber. During a 12-hour run no drifts in the beam-spot position larger than 1/16 in. occur.

(b) A secondary emission beam monitor of the type described by Tautfest and Fechter[12] has been installed inside the scattering chamber just beyond the scattering target. The secondary emission monitor has been found to have a linear response up to full electron-beam intensity and now replaces the helium ion-chamber monitor, which in previous use was found to be slightly nonlinear.

The Čerenkov counter which we use for detecting the scattered electrons is carefully shielded with lead and paraffin. On the average only one background pulse in two minutes has been registered under conditions of full electron beam, target in place, closed analyzing magnet slits, and magnet at 90°. With open slits, typical counting rates of 50 to 100 counts in the same time period are obtained.

In most of the experiments described here an energy spread of 0.5 percent of the energy in the primary electron beam was chosen. The beam spot at the target was approximately $\frac{3}{8}$ in. wide and $\frac{1}{8}$ in. high. In all experiments the target was held at an angle of 45° with respect to the direction of the primary beam.

The collision energy loss of the electrons in the target was a maximum in the case of Ca, where it was approximately one Mev. The loss of energy due to recoil of the target nucleus, at 183 Mev and at a scattering angle of 90°, amounts in Ca to 0.9 Mev, and in Au to 0.18 Mev.

The angular resolution of the scattering experiment depends mainly on the multiple scattering of the primary electrons in the target, on the finite acceptance angle of the analyzing magnet, and on the finite size of the beam spot. Multiple scattering is the main effect limiting the target thickness. The multiple scattering angle was kept smaller than $\pm 1.5°$. For Au a maximum target thickness of 5 mils at 183 Mev (target angle 45°) was used. The acceptance angle (in the scattering plane) of the analyzing magnet was adjusted to $\pm 1.5°$. In the preparation of the theoretical scattering curves the finite experimental angular resolution has been taken into account (see Sec. III).

A major problem in these experiments was to separate elastic scattering events from inelastic scattering events. By an inelastic scattering event we understand here an event in which the bombarding electron gives up some of its energy to the target nucleus, which is thereby left in an excited state. Inelastic scattering in high-energy scattering experiments has been observed in Be,[13] C,[14] Mg,[15] Si,[15] S,[15] and Sr,[15] and in other nuclei.

In all of our experiments the number of counts per unit integrated beam is measured for various magnet current settings. Thus an elastic peak is obtained and in some cases one or more inelastic peaks, depending on the target nucleus and on the scattering angle, are found. In Fig. 1 a typical elastic peak is shown for Ca together with a small inelastic peak superimposed on the bremsstrahlung tail of the elastic peak. The number of counts is plotted *vs* energy of the scattered electron. In this particular case the inelastic peak is small and well separated from the elastic peak.

The best energy resolution of the scattering apparatus obtained in these studies corresponds to a peak width energywise of 0.4 percent (full width at half-maximum). It is therefore possible to recognize inelastic contributions arising from excitation of nuclear levels with energy down to approximately 300 kev. For the nuclei

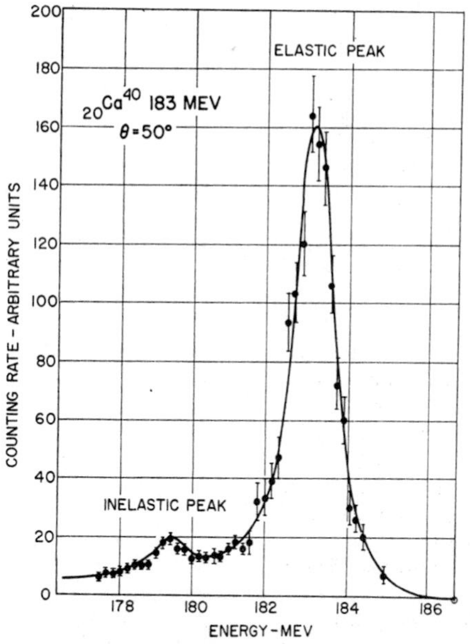

FIG. 1. A typical curve of counting rate *vs* electron energy for calcium at 183 Mev and $\theta = 50°$.

[12] G. W. Tautfest and H. R. Fechter, Phys. Rev. **96**, 35 (1954); Rev. Sci. Instr. **26**, 229 (1955).

[13] McIntyre, Hahn, and Hofstadter, Phys. Rev. **94**, 1084 (1954).
[14] J. Fregeau and R. Hofstadter, Phys. Rev. **99**, 1503 (1955).
[15] R. H. Helm and R. Hofstadter (to be published).

Ca, V, Co, In, Sb, Au, and Bi inelastic scattering was either clearly resolved from the elastic events or else no evidence from line shape studies for an appreciable inelastic scattering contribution down to 300 kev was found.

As a measure of the differential elastic cross section, a sum of the counting rates at 6 points defining an elastic peak was usually taken. No absolute cross sections have been measured so far. Results with any given target material are however subjected to a kind of standardization by associating the measurement at each angle with a corresponding measurement using a standard Au target. After correcting for the target thicknesses, cross section ratios with respect to Au become available. In Sec. IV these ratios will be compared to the theoretical ratios (see Table II). The individual Au runs agree with one another at each angle almost to within the counting statistics. At angles smaller than 90° the statistical error amounts to ±5–7 percent.

The over-all accuracy of the relative cross sections obtained in these experiments is of the order of ±10 percent. At least half of this error is due to counting statistics. The remainder has to be ascribed to drifts in various parts of the experimental equipment. No corrections were found to be important enough to be applied to the direct experimental data and no background effects need to be subtracted. A discussion of possible sources of corrections has been given in earlier papers.[1,2,6]

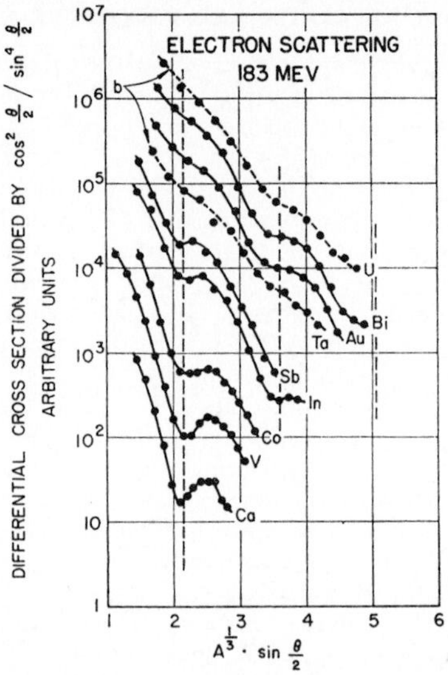

FIG. 2. Experimental results for several nuclei. The differential cross sections, divided by $\cos^2(\theta/2)/\sin^4(\theta/2)$ to display diffraction structure, are plotted *vs* $A^{\frac{1}{3}}\sin(\theta/2)$. The solid lines are smooth curves drawn through the experimental points. They have been shifted arbitrarily in the y-direction. The dashed vertical lines indicate approximately the location of the first, second and third diffraction dips.

III. THEORY

A. Introduction

The experimental results for Ca, V, Co, In, Sb, Ta, Au, Bi, and U are represented in Fig. 2. In order to display diffraction structure, the experimental cross sections have been divided by the angular factor $\cos^2(\theta/2)/\sin^4(\theta/2)$. (This factor is proportional to the theoretical cross section for point scattering obtained using the first Born approximation.) From Fig. 2 and Fig. 13, we see that while for the nuclei Ca, V, Co, In, Sb, Au, and Bi the cross sections show pronounced diffraction structure, this structure is much less marked for the nuclei Hf, Ta, W, Th, and U. The experiments thus separate the nuclei we have examined into these two groups, which we shall call (a) and (b), respectively. In this paper we shall analyze the results of only group (a) nuclei.

The nuclei of group (a) are believed to have little or no "intrinsic deformation" in the Bohr-Mottelson sense,[16] and the electron scattering is elastic. The nucleus can therefore be represented by a static, spherically symmetric charge distribution. The electrostatic potential due to an assumed nuclear charge distribution is obtained numerically. The differential cross section for electron scattering is then calculated by means of a partial wave analysis of the Dirac equation for an electron moving in this potential.[17] This analysis, which is also performed numerically,[18] is very complicated; for gold at 183 Mev, for example, the first ten phase shifts are modified appreciably by the finite nuclear size. The relation between charge distributions and differential cross sections is therefore known to us only empirically, as it were, from experience with many such calculations. One relationship, namely that between the observed diffraction structure and the relatively abrupt nuclear surface, shows up very clearly. This might also be inferred from the first Born approximation, which predicts smooth cross sections for smooth charge distributions such as the Gaussian shape $\rho=\rho_0\exp(-r^2/a^2)$, but undulating cross sections with diffraction zeros for the uniform and "smoothed uniform" shapes.[19,20] As can be seen from Fig. 2, the experimentally observed diffraction structure becomes more pronounced for the lighter elements, where the Born approximation is more reliable. This approximation also predicts that the diffraction structure is a function of $[2E_0R\sin(\theta/2)]/\hbar c$, where E_0 is the electron

[16] A. Bohr and B. R. Mottelson, Kgl. Danske Videnskab. Selskab, Mat.-fys. Medd **27**, No. 16 (1953).

[17] A detailed description of this calculation was given in reference (3).

[18] These calculations were performed on the computer Univac at the University of California Radiation Laboratory at Livermore (unpublished).

[19] J. H. Smith, Ph.D. thesis, Cornell University, 1951 (unpublished); Phys. Rev. **95**, 271 (1954).

[20] L. I. Schiff, Phys. Rev. **92**, 988 (1953).

energy, and R the nuclear radius. Hence the fact that diffraction dips of the same order occur at approximately the same value of $A^{\frac{1}{3}}\sin(\theta/2)$, which is displayed in Fig. 2 by using $A^{\frac{1}{3}}\sin(\theta/2)$ as the scale for the abscissa, indicates that some parameter describing the radius varies roughly as $A^{\frac{1}{3}}$ from element to element. This prediction is confirmed by the detailed analysis presented in the next section.

The nuclei of group (b) all have properties indicative of collective motion of their outer nucleons.[16] (Evidence for this from other experiments is cited at the end of Sec. IV.) Hence we expect contributions to the electron scattering arising from the asymmetry of their charge distributions, and from transitions to their "rotational" levels, which are so low in energy as to be unresolvable in these experiments. It can be shown that for suitably chosen nuclear parameters these contributions fill in the diffraction dips to yield smooth cross sections, like those observed experimentally. The analysis of this process will be given in another report.[21] Some of the nuclei of group (a) show properties characteristic of a little collective nuclear motion, also, but to a negligible extent as regards the electron scattering.

B. Charge Distributions

As is to be expected, for a given experimental error the amount of detail that can be observed in the charge distribution is limited by the electron's reduced de Broglie wavelength, which at 183 Mev is 1.08×10^{-13} cm. Let us first consider "smoothed uniform" charge distributions, for which the charge density is roughly uniform in the central regions, with a smoothed-out surface. We have used the following functional forms:

Fermi:

$$\rho(r)=\rho_1/\{\exp[(r-c)/z_1]+1\};\qquad(1)$$

Modified Gaussian[22]:

$$\rho(r)=\rho_2/\{\exp[(r^2-c^2)/z_2^2]+1\};\qquad(2)$$

Trapezoidal:

$$\begin{aligned}\rho(r)&=\rho_3,\quad 0<r<c-z_3,\\ &=\rho_3(c+z_3-r)/2z_3,\quad c-z_3<r<c+z_3,\\ &=0,\quad r>c+z_3.\end{aligned}\qquad(3)$$

Experience has shown us that at energies up to 183-Mev differential cross sections depend essentially on only two parameters, a mean radius and a surface thickness, and are almost independent of the particular analytic form used for ρ. Roughly speaking, the radius determines the angular position of the diffraction dips, and the surface thickness their depth. Of course, for each of the above shapes the parameter c adjusts the radius, while the surface thickness is related to z_1, z_2, and z_3 in (1), (2), and (3), respectively. But the exact relationship among the parameters of equivalent shapes [i.e., particular examples of (1), (2), and (3) which yield almost identical differential cross sections] is known to us only numerically. Approximate relationships can be obtained by using the fact that the electron wave functions in the neighborhood of the nucleus are approximately plane waves with modified amplitude and argument.[21] A simple analysis on the lines of the Born approximation then shows that the scattering depends, to lowest order in $(s/c')^2$, on the quantities c' and s defined by the relations

$$c'=\int_0^\infty \rho(r)dr/\rho(0),\qquad(4)$$

$$s^2=-4\int_0^\infty (r-c')^2\rho'(r)dr/\rho(0).\qquad(5)$$

c' is the distance at which ρ has dropped to half of its value at the center, and s is proportional to the rms thickness of the surface. (The last two statements are true strictly for only (1) and (3), where ρ obeys the additional condition that $\rho(c'+\delta)=\rho(0)-\rho(c'-\delta)$.) Since the value of s is found to vary appreciably with the functional form of ρ, we quote in our results also t, the distance over which ρ drops from 0.9 to 0.1 of its central value. It turns out that t is less dependent on the form of ρ than s. Since the rms radius has been used extensively in the literature as a measure of nuclear radius, we quote also R, which is proportional to it:

$$R=(5\langle r^2\rangle/3)^{\frac{1}{2}}.\qquad(6)$$

We shall also use $r_0=A^{-\frac{1}{3}}R$ and $r_1=A^{-\frac{1}{3}}c$. The quantities c, s, and R are connected by the approximate relation

$$R^2\simeq c^2[1+(5s^2/2c^2)]/[1+(3s^2/4c^2)].$$

The surface parameters s and t are related to the quantities occurring in (1), (2), and (3) as follows: (1), the Fermi shape, $s=2\pi z_1/\sqrt{3}=3.63z_1$, $t=(4\log_e 3)z_1=4.40z_1$; (2), the modified Gaussian shape, $t=(c^2+2z_2^2\log_e 3)^{\frac{1}{2}}-(c^2-2z_2^2\log_e 3)^{\frac{1}{2}}\simeq2.20z_2^2/c$ (the expression for s is only known to us numerically for special cases); (3), the trapezoidal shape, $s=2z_3/\sqrt{3}=1.15z_3$, $t=1.60z_3$. In terms of these quantities the central charge density is given by

$$\rho(0)=3Ze/\{4\pi c^3[1+(3s^2/4c^2)]\}.\qquad(7)$$

The effect of a variation in the central charge density has been examined in gold by using the functional form

$$\rho(r)=\rho_8[1+(wr^2/c^2)]/\{\exp[(r-c)/z_8]+1\}.\qquad(8)$$

Since this variation turns out to have little influence on the cross sections, we have used only two-parameter charge distributions in our examination of the other nuclei. Such an effect, if present, will probably show up more clearly when experiments at higher energies include several of the diffraction dips.

---

[21] Downs, Ravenhall, and Yennie (to be published).

[22] Note that this shape is roughly uniform with a Gaussian surface. It is *not* the Gaussian shape $\rho=\rho_0\exp(-r^2/a^2)$ used previously.

C. Analysis of the Experiments

The present procedure for finding the nuclear charge distributions predicted by the experimental cross sections is necessarily one of successive trials. For any assumed charge distribution the cross section obtained by means of the phase-shift analysis is folded over a small angular range to allow for the finite experimental resolution. We assumed a Gaussian distribution,

$$\bar{\sigma}(\theta)=(\pi^{\frac{1}{2}}\Delta)^{-1}\int_{-\infty}^{\infty}\sigma(\theta')\exp[(\theta-\theta')^2/\Delta^2]d\theta', \quad (9)$$

and for Δ have used the fixed value of 2°. This is intended to represent approximately a spread in incident beam energy, multiple scattering in the target and finite beam size, besides the acceptance angles of the spectrometer (usually ±1.5°).

Comparison with experiment is made by least squares. The probability that theory and experiment are in agreement is

$$P=\prod_i \exp\{-[(\sigma_i/\lambda\epsilon_i)-1]^2N_i/2\}, \quad (10)$$

where σ_i is the theoretical cross section at θ_i, and ϵ_i and N_i are, respectively, the experimental value and the number of counts. The parameter λ is required because the experimental cross section is not known absolutely, and we therefore maximize P with respect to λ. The maximum occurs when $\lambda=M_2/M_1$, where $M_n=\sum_i(\sigma_i/\epsilon_i)^nN_i$; for this value of λ the logarithm of the probability is given by

$$-\log P=\tfrac{1}{2}(M_0M_2-M_1^2)/M_2. \quad (11)$$

Thus, for each theoretical cross section we calculate (11) and then look for the values of r_0 and s which make it a minimum. This is then the best fit for that particular shape. We can thus compare the relative merits of various shapes, and also have an idea of the error in our results due to statistics. A comparison of results for various experimental runs in gold shows us the error due to any slight lack of repeatability in the experiments. We discuss this more fully in the next section.

D. Other Effects

For simplicity we ignore radiative corrections to scattering in the above analysis. Suura[23] has shown that, independently of Z, the relative correction to the cross section is to a good approximation the same as was calculated by Schwinger[24] using the Born approximation. For typical experimental conditions ($E=183$ Mev, $\Delta E/E=0.5$ percent) Schwinger's analysis predicts a relative change in the theoretical cross sections between 35° and 120° of 4.3 percent. Since the radiative correction varies smoothly with angle, however, its

[23] H. Suura, Phys. Rev. **99**, 1020 (1955).
[24] J. Schwinger, Phys. Rev. **76**, 780 (1949).

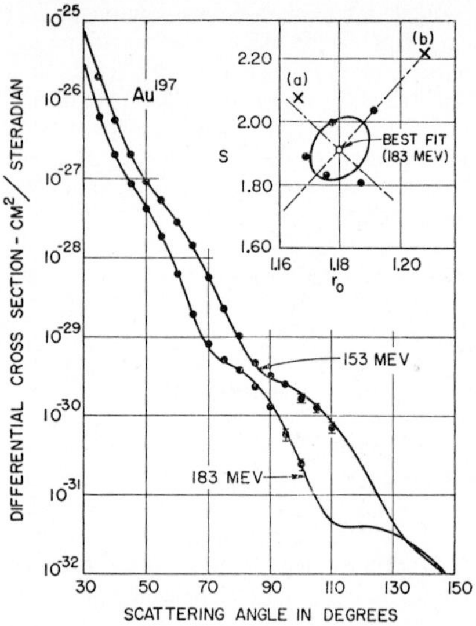

Fig. 3. Angular distributions for gold. The experimental points at 183 Mev are the average of five runs. The solid curve at 183 Mev is the theoretical best fit obtained by using the Fermi smoothed uniform charge distribution (1). It corresponds to the open circle in the inset figure of s *vs* r_0. Its coordinates are the weighted average of those corresponding to the best fits for the individual runs, represented by the points. The ellipse in the inset figure corresponds to charge distributions for which the probability of agreement with experiment is half of its maximum value, attained for the best fit. The crosses (a) and (b) correspond to charge distributions whose parameters differ from those of the best fit by about two probable errors. Their cross sections are shown in Fig. 4. The solid curve at 153 Mev is for the same parameters as the best fit at 183 Mev. Numerical values of the parameters for all of the nuclei are given in Table III.

inclusion would make the theoretical cross section a little steeper while not altering its detailed shape. This would decrease the surface thickness of the predicted charge distribution a little (~0.4 percent), and would not alter the radius appreciably. In view of possible uncertainties in the theoretical analysis, and of their small and easily predicted effect, it seemed better to omit radiative corrections altogether.

For those nuclei of group (a) having nonzero spin values and magnetic moments, there should be a magnetic dipole contribution to the elastic scattering. Since the magnetic moment (μ) arises in the surface region of the nucleus, this contribution can be expected to show about the same dependence on the finite nuclear size as the charge scattering. The ratio of these two contributions will thus vary approximately as $(\mu/Z)^2$, so that although the magnetic effect is appreciable for hydrogen,[25,26] it is negligible at this energy for the nuclei examined here.

The analysis of the elastic scattering in terms of static charge distributions is quite general, but the

[25] R. Hofstadter and R. W. McAllister, Phys. Rev. **98**, 217 (1955).
[26] M. N. Rosenbluth, Phys. Rev. **79**, 615 (1950).

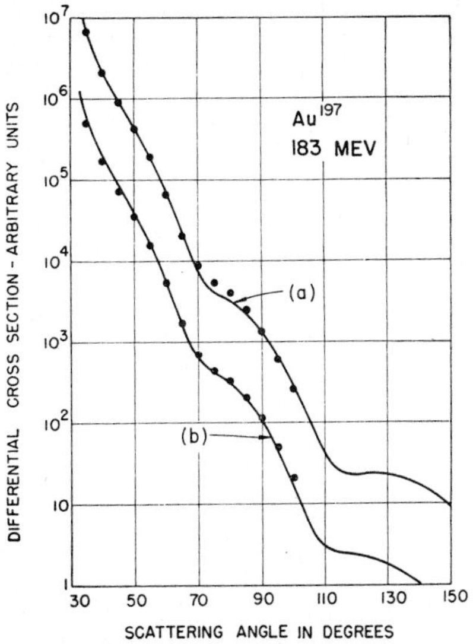

FIG. 4. Comparison with experiment at 183 Mev of cross sections for charge distributions whose parameters differ by about two probable errors from those of the best fit. They correspond to the crosses (a) and (b) in the inset in Fig. 3. In vertical scale one of the cross sections has been shifted by a factor 10 for clarity.

connection between this charge distribution and the nuclear wave function may not be so direct. Although the major part of $\rho(r)$ comes from $|\Psi_{\text{ground}}(r)|^2$, there will also occur, in higher orders of the perturbing interaction between the electron and the nucleus, contributions involving nuclear excited states arising from virtual excitation. For light nuclei Schiff,[27] using the Born approximation, has estimated that this "dispersion scattering" is only about 1/137 of the scattering from the ground state alone. In our analysis this effect would show up as a contribution to the charge distribution which might be energy-dependent, because of the energy denominators in the perturbation theory. In Sec. IV we have analyzed the scattering from Bi at both 153 and 183 Mev, but the results at the two energies are probably not significantly different.

Our calculations assume the Coulomb law of force between the electron and each element of the nuclear charge. Any alteration in the law of force at small distances would modify the relationship between the charge distributions and the potentials used in the Dirac equation. Correction of our results to allow for this effect would not involve much recalculation. From the *potentials* corresponding to our quoted best fits the altered relationship between potential and force law would immediately give us the modified charge distributions. There is at present no strong evidence for such an altered force law.

[27] L. I. Schiff, Phys. Rev. **98**, 756 (1955).

IV. RESULTS

Gold.—In gold-197 there are five experimental runs at 183 Mev. The average of these runs is shown in Fig. 3 together with the theoretical best fit using shape (1), which has been folded to allow for finite experimental resolution. Inset in that figure are points indicating the values of r_0 and s for the best fits to the individual runs at 183 Mev. Corresponding to each of these points, for which P, the probability of agreement between theory and experiment, is a maximum, there is a curve describing charge distributions for which P is a half of its maximum value. Since we are close to the best fit, this curve is of only second degree in r_0 and s, i.e., it is an ellipse. It tells us the error due to statistics. The scatter of these points about their mean (measured by using as weighting factor $\sum N_i$, the total number of counts in the run) arises both from statistics and from a slight lack of repeatability of the runs. Our analysis indicates that the latter is only about half as important as the former. The ellipse shown in the inset figure combines both sources of error. In Fig. 4 we compare with experiment the cross sections of two shapes whose parameters differ from those of the best fit by about two probable errors. (They correspond to the crosses in the inset to Fig. 3.) We feel that these are a significantly poorer fit to experiment than the shape chosen in Fig. 3; this shows that the estimates of error given by the least squares analysis are in rough agreement with intuitive ideas obtained from inspection.

A feature of our results which is not too marked for gold, but which is very noticeable for the lighter elements, is that the major axis of the ellipse corresponds to shapes with the same value of the radial parameter c. This means that c is the parameter that can be specified most accurately, a result which agrees with our experience that the angular position of the diffraction dips, the most prominent feature of the cross section, is determined mainly by c. The eccentricity of the ellipses increases for the lighter elements, implying that for these elements the accuracy of s decreases relative to the accuracy of c. This is linked with the fact that in the diffraction dips, the angular region where the surface thickness is most evident, the agreement between theoretical and experimental cross sections is poorer for the light elements than for the heavy elements. The

TABLE I. Results of the analysis of the gold experiments at 183 Mev. The first three shapes are two-parameter shapes of the smoothed uniform type, while the fourth contains an additional parameter which allows alteration of ρ in the central region. All lengths are in units of 10^{-13} cm, and the charge density in units of 10^{19} coulomb/cm^3. The accuracy of the radial parameters c, c', and R is about ± 1 percent; for the surface thickness parameter t it is about ± 5 percent.

Shape	c	z_i	w	c'	R	s	t	ρ_0
(1) Fermi	6.38	0.535	···	6.38	6.88	1.94	2.35	1.09
(2) Modified Gaussian	6.36	2.72	···	6.17	6.85	2.04	2.61	1.13
(3) Trapezoidal	6.28	1.49	···	6.28	6.66	1.72	2.39	1.15
(8) 3-parameter	6.07	0.613	0.64	···	6.92	···	···	0.85

errors in the results on the other elements are in any case somewhat larger than those for gold, since the results are less numerous (usually only two runs for each element). For all of the above reasons, the errors quoted at the beginning of Sec. V should be regarded as orders of magnitude rather than precisely known quantities.

To examine the experiments on gold for dependence on surface shape, the same procedure as that just described for shape (1) was followed for shapes (2) and (3). The maximum values of P for the three cases were found all to lie within a factor 1.3 of each other, i.e., the agreement with experiment is not significantly different for the three shapes. The values of the parameters for the best fits are presented in Table I. The variation in the radial parameters quoted is very small: in c [the parameter occurring in the definitions (1), (2), and (3)] it is 1.6 percent, while in c' [defined by the integral relation (4)] and in R [proportional to the rms radius, as defined by (6)] it is 3.3 percent. There is a much larger variation in the parameters describing the surface thickness, as is to be expected, although t, the distance over which ρ drops from 0.9 to 0.1 of its central value, varies less (10 percent) than s, defined by the integral relation (5) (17 percent). It should be possible to define a radial and a surface parameter so that their values are independent of shape, but as these results show, we have been able to do this only in an approximate way. The charge distributions corresponding to the best fits for shapes (1), (2), and (3) are shown in Fig. 5. It is remarkable how closely they agree over the surface region, especially at the two outermost points of intersection. Needless to say, the cross sections corresponding to these charge distributions differ so little that Fig. 3 can be taken to represent also shapes (2) and (3), with a slight shift in the vertical scale.

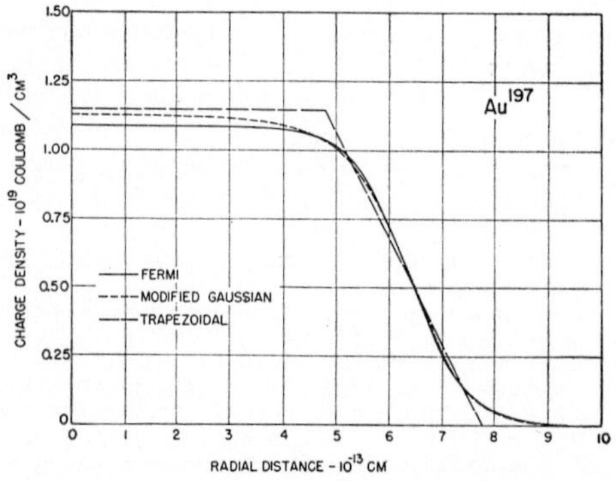

FIG. 5. Three charge distributions in gold, the best fits to the experimental results at 183 Mev for the Fermi, modified Gaussian, and trapezoidal shapes (1), (2), and (3); the charge distribution parameters are listed in Table I. The cross section for the Fermi best fit is shown in Fig. 3; those for the other two shapes differ from it only slightly.

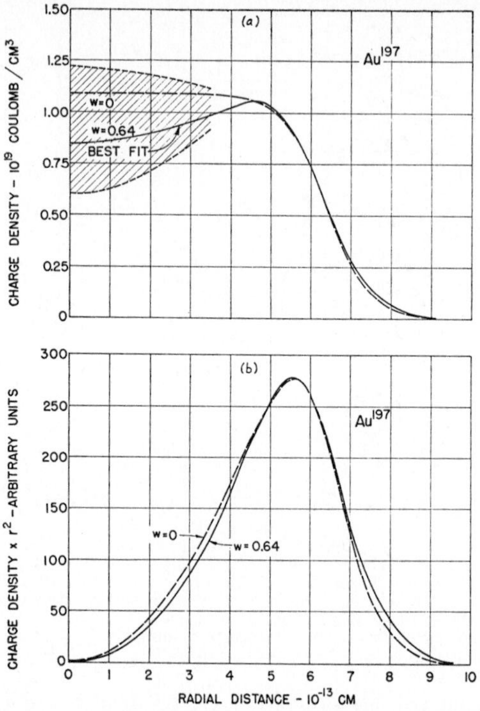

FIG. 6. (a) Charge distributions in gold obtained using shape (8), which allows variations in the charge density near the center. The full curve is the best fit to the experimental data at 183 Mev, and the two dotted curves give cross sections for which the probability of agreement between theory and experiment (10) is a half of its value for the best fit. The dashed curve, drawn for comparison, is the best fit using shape (1). (b) The charge distributions represented by the full and dashed curves in (a) have been multiplied by r^2, to show the distribution of the actual amount of charge with radius.

We have used shape (8) to detect any dependence of the cross section on the central charge density. The procedure is closely similar to the preceding ones: for chosen values of w, the parameter fixing the variation in central charge density, the best fit for varying z_8 and c is obtained. We then minimize (11) with respect to w. The "best" value of w corresponds to a ratio $\rho(0)/\rho_{max}$ of 0.80; the value of P is 1.5 times its value for the Fermi smoothed uniform shape (1), a difference which lies within the probable error. The charge distribution is shown in Fig. 6, and the cross section is almost indistinguishable from that shown in Fig. 3. It turns out that the cross sections are rather insensitive to w so that the limits that can be put on w are rather wide. The reason for this weak dependence on w is clear from Fig. 6, in the plot of $r^2\rho(r)$, the amount of charge at a distance r from the center, vs r. We see that what looks from the plot $\rho(r)$ vs r to be an important alteration in shape actually involves the shifting of only a small amount of charge. This is, of course, why our analysis predicts most accurately the

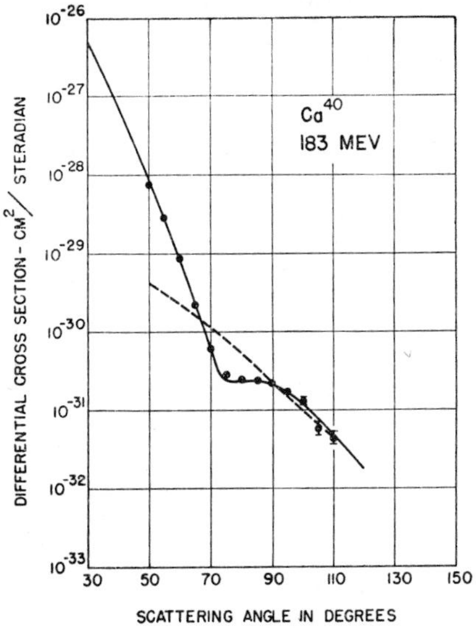

FIG. 7. Experimental and theoretical cross sections for the scattering of 183-Mev electrons by calcium. The full line in this figure, and in Figs. 8–12, is the theoretical best fit at 183 Mev obtained by using shape (1). The dashed line in this figure is the experimental cross section for the inelastic scattering corresponding to excitation of nuclear levels at about 3.7 Mev.

position of the nuclear surface—that is, the place where most of the charge resides.

To summarize, the analysis of gold-197 yields the results that first, there is no discernible dependence on the details of the shape of the surface of the charge distribution, although the relation between parameters of equivalent charge distributions is known only numerically; secondly, there is only a weak dependence on the variation in the central density, and the best fit has charge density almost uniform in the center. Hence, in our analysis of the other elements, which we do in order of increasing Z, we have used only shape (1). With the assumption that the relations between parameters of equivalent shapes is the same for the other elements as those found in gold (Table I), the numerical results, presented in Table III, can be reinterpreted in terms of shapes (2) and (3), respectively, by scaling the parameters therein as follows: c, by factors 1.00 and 0.98; R, by factors 0.99 and 0.97; and t, by factors 1.11 and 1.02.

The experimental angular distributions for the nuclei Ca, V, Co, In, Sb, and Bi together with their best theoretical fits (using Fermi smoothed uniform charge distributions) are shown in Figs. 7–12. The errors quoted in these figures are only due only to counting statistics. For small angles, where no error is indicated, this error is smaller than 10 percent. All nuclei in this group, except Sb, have an isotopic purity greater than 95 percent. The target thicknesses, measured in mils, were 120 (Ca), 26 (V), 42 (Co), 10 (In), 15 (Sb), and 10 (Bi). The results for the individual nuclei will now be discussed briefly.

Ca.—(Fig. 7.) A natural Ca target containing 96.9 percent of doubly magic Ca^{40} was used. Besides the elastic scattering peak a strong inelastic peak has also been found, which is probably due to excitation of the known levels in Ca at 3.73 and 3.90 Mev. There seems to be no evidence for the lowest known level in Ca at 3.35 Mev (0^+) from this experiment. The angular distribution of the inelastic scattering is indicated by the dashed line in Fig. 7. As can be seen from Fig. 1, the inelastic scattering in Ca was easily separated from elastic scattering. Between 70° and 80° there appears, approximately 1 Mev down from the elastic peak, an additional small inelastic peak, the origin of which is unknown to us.

V.—(Fig. 8.) 99.75 percent of natural V is V^{51}. This nucleus has a level at 320 kev, which, if excited in our experiment, should show up as a broadening of the elastic peak. No evidence for such an effect was seen, and there is probably no more than 10 percent inelastic contribution to the measured cross section at any angle. Such an inelastic contribution would not alter the values of the charge distribution parameters by more than the quoted errors.

Co.—(Fig. 9.) Co^{59} (natural Co) is known to have excited states at approximately 1.1 and 1.3 Mev. Some evidence has been found in this experiment for excitation of several levels above 1 Mev, the relative cross section with respect to the elastic cross section being largest at about 65° and amounting to approximately 20 percent. This elastic scattering has been resolved experimentally.

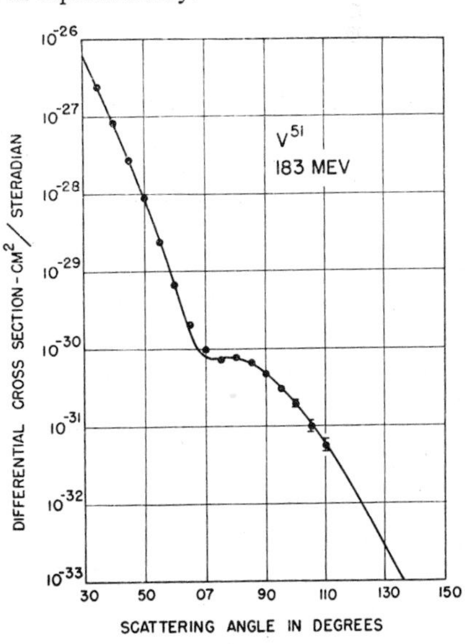

FIG. 8. Experimental and theoretical cross sections for the scattering of 183-Mev electrons by vanadium. (In the abscissa, 07 should be 70.)

In.—(Fig. 10.) Natural In contains 95.8 percent In^{115} and 4.2 percent In^{113}. In a high-resolution run, 0.8 Mev full width at half-maximum of the elastic peak, no inelastic peaks have been found. The charge distribution parameters obtained from a least square fit to the 813-Mev data have been used to calculate the theoretical angular distribution at 153 Mev, yielding a curve which is in good agreement with the experimental data.

Sb.—(Fig. 11.) Natural Sb contains approximately half and half Sb^{121} and Sb^{123}. Sb^{123} has a known level at 0.15 Mev. This level, if excited in our experiment, could not be resolved from elastic scattering. The measured cross section therefore may include some inelastic contribution. We know however from our inelastic scattering work that the relative inelastic scattering contribution becomes in general smaller by going to large nuclei, with the possible exception of nuclei with large distortions from spherical symmetry (like Hf, Ta, W, etc.).

Au.—(Fig. 3.) The low-lying levels in Au at 77 and 268 kev, which have been excited in Coulomb excitation experiments, are believed to give no appreciable contribution to the measured cross sections. According to calculations by Downs *et al.*,[21] such a contribution becomes important only at very large scattering angles, amounting to about 10 percent at the third diffraction dip at 115°. A line-shape study of the Au peaks did not reveal any broadening of the peaks by going to large angles. The theoretical Au curve at 153 Mev is obtained by using the same charge distribution parameters as gave the best fit at 183 Mev.

Bi.—(Fig. 12.) The lowest known levels in Bi^{209} (natural Bi) lie at 0.91 and 1.63 Mev. No experimental evidence has been found for the excitation of these levels by 183-Mev electrons. The angular distributions at 183 and 153 Mev have each been analyzed theoretically and the best fits are plotted in Fig. 12. The values of the parameters are $r_0=1.201$, $s=2.25$, and $r_0=1.214$, $s=2.03$, respectively. These values agree to within the errors quoted in Sec. V.

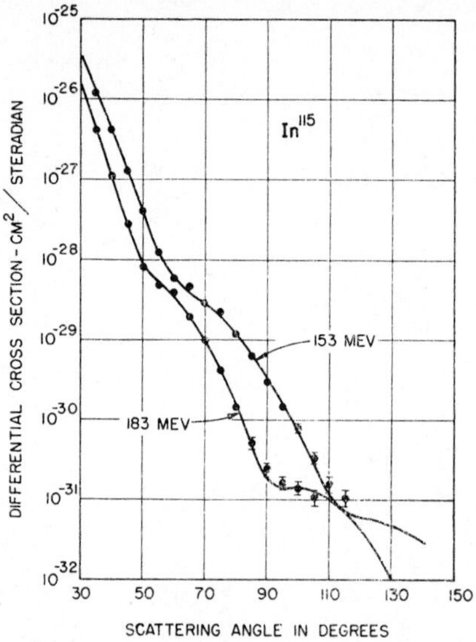

FIG. 10. Experimental and theoretical cross sections for the scattering of 183- and 153-Mev electrons by indium. The theoretical cross section at 153 Mev is calculated for the same parameters as the 183-Mev result.

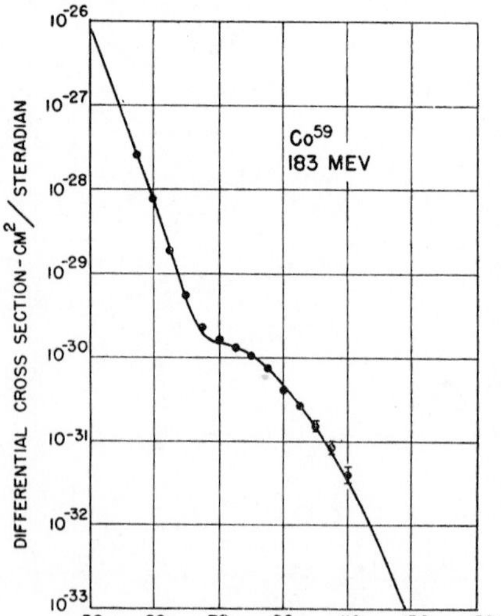

FIG. 9. Experimental and theoretical cross sections for the scattering of 183-Mev electrons by cobalt.

A valuable check on the consistency of the theoretical results has been obtained by comparing the experimental cross section ratios (with respect to Au) with the corresponding theoretical ratios. An average cross-section ratio over the five smallest angles measured has been chosen. The experimental ratios divided by the theoretical ratios are listed in Table II. In view of the fact that cross sections vary by large factors with changes in angle and from element to element, these ratios are remarkably close to unity.

In Fig. 13 angular distributions at 183 Mev for the nuclei Hf, Ta, W, Th, and U are plotted. The fact that these curves show almost no diffraction structure is believed to be connected with distortion of nuclear matter from spherical symmetry. All of these nuclei have low-lying nuclear levels which are strongly excited by Coulomb excitation, indicating high intrinsic quadrupole moments. The averages for natural Hf, Ta, and W of the intrinsic quadrupole moments deduced from measurements of the γ-ray yield in Coulomb excitation are approximately 10, 4, and 7 barns, respectively.[28] The quadrupole moments of Th and U are

[28] McClelland, Mark, and Goodman, Phys. Rev. **97**, 1191 (1955).

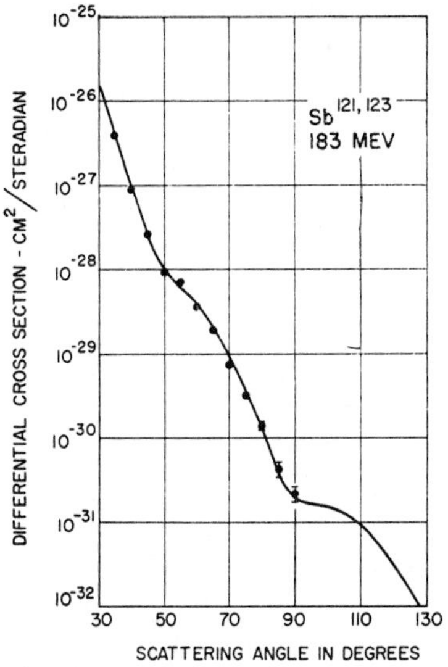

FIG. 11. Experimental and theoretical cross sections for the scattering of 183-Mev electrons by antimony.

not known to us. There are, however, levels at 50 and 44 kev for U, found by Coulomb excitation, suggesting large nuclear distortion. An analysis of electron scattering from such nuclei will, as mentioned in Sec. III, be presented in another report.[21]

V. DISCUSSION

Results of the analysis of gold, the nucleus studied most intensively in this investigation, are presented in Table I and Fig. 3, and have been commented on fully in Sec. IV. Briefly, the following information has been obtained about the charge distribution: while not too much can be said about the central region, except that ρ is probably fairly flat, the surface region is now known with the following precision: the radius c (the distance to the half-point) is 6.4×10^{-13} cm, accurate to about $\pm$ one percent, and the surface thickness t (the 0.9 to 0.1 distance) is 2.4×10^{-13} cm, accurate to about ±5 percent, although the precise values depend slightly on the particular shape chosen. These values are in agreement with the preliminary prediction of Ravenhall and Yennie,[4] and with analyses of our earlier data by Brown and Elton[7] and by Hill *et al.*[8]

The charge distributions for all of the nuclei examined are plotted in Fig. 14, and the values of the various parameters are given in Table III. The choice of the Fermi smoothed uniform shape has no special significance, and the formulae for converting the results to apply to the other two-parameter shapes, assumed to be the same as for gold, are given in Sec. IV. As regards the accuracy of the entries in Table III, we feel that as an order of magnitude the errors can be said to be about twice those quoted for gold, i.e., ±2 percent for radial parameters, and ±10 percent for the surface thicknesses. These errors are, however, difficult to estimate and, as mentioned in Sec. IV, the error in s for the lighter elements may be a little larger. Not included is a possible error due to uncertainty in the energy of the primary electron beam, estimated to be smaller than 1 percent. This uncertainty would affect all data by the same amount, and in the same direction.

To examine the dependence of the radial parameters c and R [defined by (4) and (6)] on A and Z, the quantities $r_0=R/A^{\frac{1}{3}}$, $r_1=c/A^{\frac{1}{3}}$, and $r_2=R/(2Z)^{\frac{1}{3}}$ are also given in Table III. r_0 varies appreciably with A, but both r_1 and r_2 are remarkably constant from element to element, the total variations being only 4 percent and 5 percent, respectively. Our result that r_1 is constant means that for the nuclei we have investigated the midpoint of the surface of the charge distribution varies as $A^{\frac{1}{3}}$ to within ±2 percent. These results are to be compared with those of Fitch and Rainwater,[9] who measured level splitting in the mu-mesonic atoms of Ti, Cu, Sb, and Pb. The analysis of the experiments by these authors and by Cooper and Henley[10] assumes a uniform charge distribution (zero surface thickness), but it appears that at least for the light nuclei the

TABLE II. Experimental cross-section ratios with respect to Au divided by theoretical cross-section ratios with respect to Au for group (a) nuclei. An average cross-section ratio over the five smallest angles measured has been chosen.

Element	Ca	V	Co	In	Sb	Bi
$\dfrac{(\sigma_X/\sigma_{Au})_{exp}}{(\sigma_X/\sigma_{Au})_{theor}}$	1.06	1.03	0.85	0.95	1.01	1.09

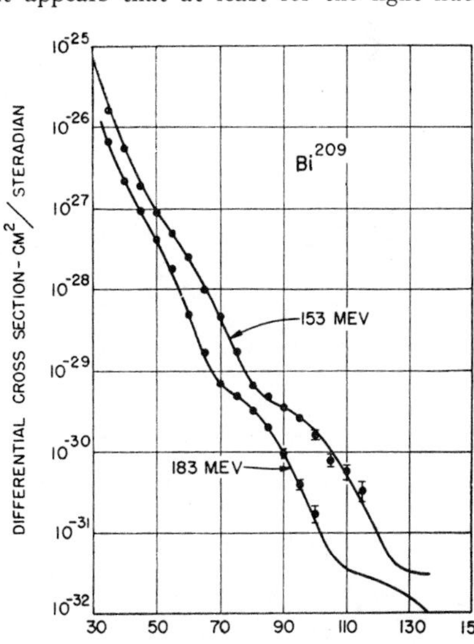

FIG. 12. Experimental and theoretical cross sections for the scattering of 183- and 153-Mev electrons by bismuth. The experiments at the two energies were analyzed separately.

only parameter that can be determined is the rms radius, i.e., R. They find that the radius of the uniform distribution is given roughly by $1.10A^{1/3}\times10^{-13}$ cm for Ti and Cu (assuming a mu-meson mass of 207 electron masses). A more elaborate analysis of their experiments in Pb by Hill and Ford,[11] using charge distributions with finite surface thicknesses, yields the value for r_0 of 1.18×10^{-13} cm, in good agreement with our results. There remains, however, a discrepancy between the values of r_0 obtained from the mu-mesonic atom experiments and from our electron scattering experiments for the lighter nuclei, especially Cu and Ti; we should expect results for these elements to agree with our results on Co, V, and Ca. The origin of this discrepancy is not known to us.§

As regards the other quantities listed in Table III, we note first that the surface thickness t is approximately constant, to within the quoted errors, and equal

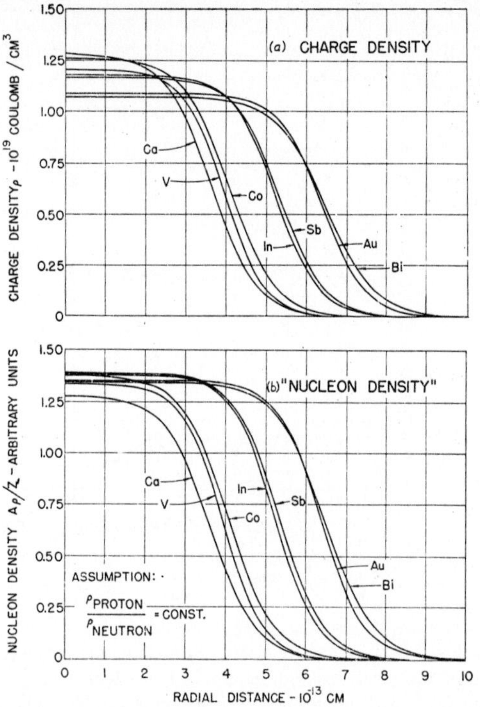

FIG. 14. (a) Charge distributions $\rho(r)$ for Ca, V, Co, In, Sb, Au, and Bi. They are Fermi smoothed uniform shapes, with the parameters given in Table III, and yield the cross sections shown in Figs. 3 and 8–12. (b) A plot of $(A/2Z)\rho(r)$ for the above nuclei. On the assumption that the distribution of matter in the nucleus is the same as the distribution of charge, this represents the "nucleon density."

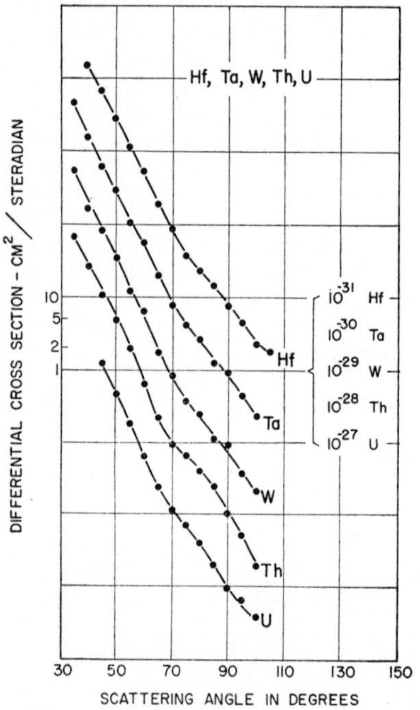

FIG. 13. Experimental cross sections at 183 Mev for the nuclei Hf, Ta, W, Th, and U. Absolute cross sections have been obtained from the counting rate ratio with respect to gold, and from the absolute cross section for gold given in Fig. 3. The dashed lines are smooth curves connecting the experimental points, and are *not theoretical*. The curves have been shifted vertically by factors of ten as indicated.

to about 2.4×10^{-13} cm. Expressed in terms of s [defined by the integral relation (5)], this is 2.0×10^{-13} cm. The central charge density $\rho(0)$, calculated from c and s by means of Eq. (7), is given in units of 10^{19} coulomb per cm^3. For gold, for example, it corresponds to 0.068 proton per $(10^{-13}\text{ cm})^3$. It shows a significant decrease

TABLE III. Results of the analysis of the group (a) nuclei in terms of charge distribution (1), the Fermi smoothed uniform shape. All lengths are in units of 10^{-13} cm, charge densities in 10^{19} coulombs/cm^3, and energies in Mev. The accuracy of these results (except for gold, for which the accuracy is given in the caption of Table I) is estimated as follows: radial parameters, ±2 percent; surface thickness parameter, ±10 percent, although the last figure may be perhaps a little larger for the lighter nuclei. The quantity ρ_0 is the normalization parameter occurring in the definition (1), and physically is probably an average value of ρ for the central regions. It is *not* the actual central density, which cannot be determined accurately from these experiments.

	c	R	$c/A^{1/3}=r_1$	$R/A^{1/3}=r_0$	$R/(2Z)^{1/3}=r_2$	t	ρ_0	E_c
$_{20}Ca^{40}$	3.64	4.54	1.06	1.32	1.33	2.5	1.28	78
$_{23}V^{51}$	3.98	4.63	1.07	1.25	1.29	2.2	1.21	100
$_{27}Co^{59}$	4.09	4.94	1.05	1.27	1.30	2.5	1.26	130
$_{49}In^{115}$	5.24	5.80	1.08	1.19	1.26	2.3	1.18	360
$_{51}Sb^{122}$	5.32	5.97	1.07	1.20	1.28	2.5	1.17	380
$_{79}Au^{197}$	6.38	6.87	1.096	1.180	1.270	2.32	1.09	790
$_{83}Bi^{209}$	6.47	7.13	1.09	1.20	1.30	2.7	1.07	840

§ *Note added in proof*.—Professor E. P. Wigner has kindly pointed out to us that, following his suggestion, B. G. Jancouici (Phys. Rev. **95**, 389 (1954)) made a detailed calculation on the Coulomb energy in the pairs (N^{15}, O^{15}) and (F^{17}, O^{17}) and showed that nuclear radii determined from mirror nuclei data were larger than those obtained by using the results of Fitch and Rainwater for light elements ($r_0=1.2\times10^{-3}$ cm). Thus this discrepancy had been noted earlier.

for the heavy elements. It seems worth noting that if, on the assumption that the distribution of matter in the nucleus is the same as the distribution of charge, we calculate $(A/Z)\rho(r)$, as in Fig. 14(b), the central value of this "nucleon density" remains roughly constant from element to element. In the last column of Table III we give the electrostatic Coulomb energy of the nuclear charge distributions $(E_c=\frac{1}{2}\int\rho(r)V(r)d^3r)$. This turns out to be approximately the same as the Coulomb energy of a uniformly charged sphere of radius R.

These results may be summarized as follows: for seven elements between calcium-40 and bismuth-209 the nuclear charge distribution is found to have a radius c (to the midpoint of the surface) of $(1.07\pm.02)A^{\frac{1}{3}}\times10^{-13}$ cm, and a surface thickness t (0.9 to 0.1 distance) of $(2.4\pm0.3)\times10^{-13}$ cm.

ACKNOWLEDGMENTS

The work described in this paper was materially aided by many people, to whom we would like to express our appreciation. On the experimental side we wish to thank Phyllis Hansen, T. O. McKinney, K. H. Sherwin, R. E. Steele, R. M. Friedman, R. H. Helm, R. W. McAllister, and G. W. Tautfest for operation of the accelerator; Dr. H. Mark and Professor C. Goodman for the loan of some hafnium metal; B. R. Chambers and B. G. Stuart for the machining of some of the target foils, and Mr. A. W. Knudsen, Dr. J. A. McIntyre, and Professor J. F. Streib, Jr., for useful discussions. On the theoretical side we would like to thank the authorities of the University of California Radiation Laboratory at Livermore, particularly Dr. S. Fernbach, for the use of the computer Univac, and Dr. G. J. Lasher for assistance in its operation; the staff of the Stanford Computation Center for advice and assistance in the use of the Card-Programmed Calculator; Dr. D. L. Hill for an account of his calculations on electron scattering before their publication; and Dr. D. R. Yennie and Professor L. I. Schiff for helpful discussions. One of us (B.H.) acknowledges with thanks financial help from the Schweizerische Arbeitsgemeinschaft in Mathematik und Physik.

PAPER 30

Elastic Scattering of 188-Mev Electrons from the Proton and the Alpha Particle*†‡§||¶

R. W. McAllister and R. Hofstadter
Department of Physics and High-Energy Physics Laboratory, Stanford University, Stanford, California

(Received January 25, 1956)

The elastic scattering of 188-Mev electrons from gaseous targets of hydrogen and helium has been studied. Elastic profiles have been obtained at laboratory angles between 35° and 138°. The areas under such curves, within energy limits of ± 1.5 Mev of the peak, have been measured and the results plotted against angle. In the case of hydrogen, a comparison has been made with the theoretical predictions of the Mott formula for elastic scattering and also with a modified Mott formula (due to Rosenbluth) taking into account both the anomalous magnetic moment of the proton and a finite size effect. The comparison shows that a finite size of the proton will account for the results and the present experiment fixes this size. The root-mean-square radii of charge and magnetic moment are each $(0.74\pm 0.24)\times 10^{-13}$ cm. In obtaining these results it is assumed that the usual laws of electromagnetic interaction and the Coulomb law are valid at distances less than 10^{-13} cm and that the charge and moment radii are equal. In helium, large effects of the finite size of the alpha-particle are observed and the rms radius of the alpha particle is found to be $(1.6\pm 0.1)\times 10^{-13}$ cm.

I. INTRODUCTION

In principle, it is possible to discover the finite size and structure of nuclei by methods of elastic electron scattering at high energies.[1–3] It is even possible to determine the structure of the proton by these methods.[4] For the light nuclei the Born approximation is adequate to analyze the experimental data, while for heavier nuclei such as gold or even copper[5] Yennie *et al.* have shown that a more accurate phase shift analysis is required.

The proton, deuteron, and alpha particle are most interesting to study because they are among the simplest nuclear structures. Furthermore, nuclei are built up out of protons and neutrons and it is fascinating to think of what the proton itself is built. In this paper we shall examine the structure of the proton and alpha particle. In an earlier paper[6] the scattering from the deuteron was reported.

* The research reported in this document was supported jointly by the U. S. Navy (Office of Naval Research) and the U. S. Atomic Energy Commission, and by the U. S. Air Force through the Air Force Office of Scientific Research, Air Research and Development Command.

† Aided by a grant from the Research Corporation.

‡ These results were briefly reported at the Seattle Meeting of the American Physical Society, in July, 1954, but a comparison was not made at that time with the Rosenbluth results.

§ Miss Eva Wiener assisted in the early phases of this research. She was the victim of a fatal automobile accident in 1953.

|| Some of the material now reported was published earlier in brief form, *viz.*, R. Hofstadter and R. W. McAllister, Phys. Rev. **98**, 217 (1955).

¶ *Note added in proof.*—Results more recent than those reported in this paper and extending to 550 Mev, were presented at the New York meeting of the American Physical Society [Bull. Am. Phys. Soc. Ser. II, **1** (1956)] by Hofstadter, Chambers, and Blankenbeder. The newer experiments confirm in greater detail the results presented in this paper. The newer results are being submitted for publication in *The Physical Review.*

[1] Hofstadter, Fechter, and McIntyre, Phys. Rev. **91**, 422 (1953).

[2] Hofstadter, Fechter, and McIntyre, Phys. Rev. **92**, 978 (1953).

[3] Hofstadter, Hahn, Knudsen, and McIntyre, Phys. Rev. **95**, 512 (1954).

[4] R. Hofstadter and R. W. McAllister, Phys. Rev. **98**, 217 (1955).

[5] Yennie, Wilson, and Ravenhall, Phys. Rev. **92**, 1325 (1953).

[6] J. A. McIntyre and R. Hofstadter, Phys. Rev. **98**, 158 (1954).

II. EXPERIMENTAL METHODS

Many of the experimental procedures have been reported in earlier papers.[2,3] The only important new variation over earlier methods has been the substitution of a gaseous target for the previously used metallic foils. The gaseous target will now be described.

In Fig. 1, the basic design of the target assembly is given. The cylinder is made of 410 stainless steel and has been heat-treated to increase its strength. The end plates are made of 0.010-inch stainless steel and are deformed by the high-pressure gases into the approximate shape shown in the figure. The target cylinder is $3\frac{1}{8}$ inches long and $\frac{3}{4}$ inch in diameter. The end plates are sealed by means of 0-rings shown in the figure. Pressures as high as 2000 pounds per square inch have been used successfully in this chamber over long periods of time.

The geometry of the scattering experiment using the gaseous target chamber is shown in Fig. 2. Because of the double-focusing characteristic of the magnetic spectrometer and because of the defining slits at the entrance and exit of the spectrometer, the effective target viewed by the spectrometer has the appearance indicated schematically in Fig. 2. It is evident that to a very good approximation the scattering yield at any given angle will be proportional to the cosecant of the angle of observation in the laboratory system since the

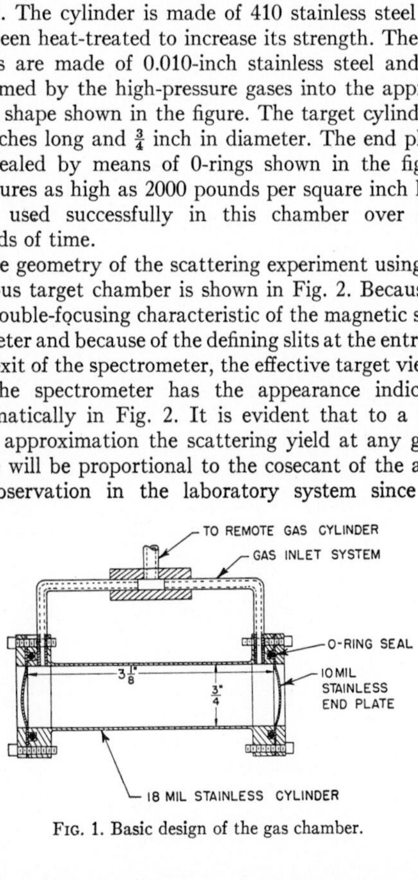

Fig. 1. Basic design of the gas chamber.

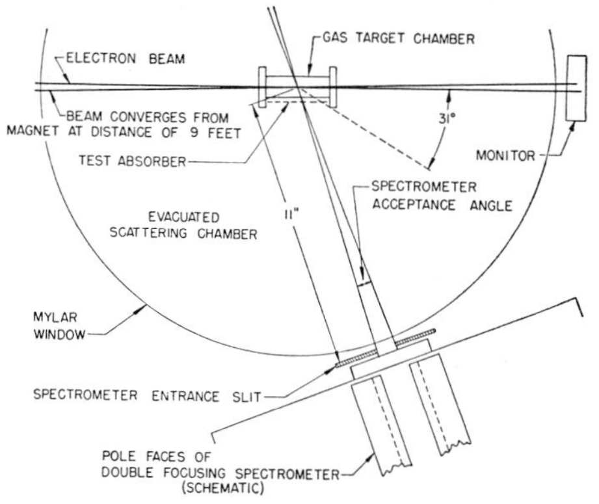

FIG. 2. Arrangement of parts in experiments on electron scattering from a gas target.

target thickness viewed by the spectrometer is proportional to this trigonometric function. Thus, to normalize the data to the same target thickness, the yield at any angle must be divided by the cosecant of the angle. In these experiments the effective target width viewed by the spectrometer is approximately $\frac{1}{2}$ inch at the gas chamber and this dimension is given by the vertical exit slit width (0.5 inch) imaged at the source.

The slit defining the acceptance angle in the plane common to the beam, scattering target, and entrance to the spectrometer, was $\frac{3}{4}$ inch wide and is indicated in Fig. 2. The exit collimator at the top of the magnet had a horizontal slit $\frac{5}{8}$ inch wide defining the energy band accepted by the Čerenkov detector, and a vertical slit $\frac{1}{2}$ inch wide. The vertical slit, together with the $\frac{3}{4}$ inch entrance slit, served to define the effective width of the target. In all the experiments herewith reported the incident beam was monochromatic within ± 1.0 Mev in 187 Mev.

At small angles, that is, angles less than 30°, it is possible for the spectrometer to view the end walls of the chamber and thus accept spurious electrons scattered by the target end plates. At 35° and 40°, a small residual effect of this type is present and is always subtracted from the yield furnished by the gas plus the target chamber. In other words, the scattering intensity is measured first with the gas in the chamber and then again with the gas removed from the target. The latter measurement gives the "background" due to the end wall effects. At all other angles, this effect is negligible.

Multiple scattering and radiation straggling from the 0.018-inch cylinder walls introduce only minor errors at the angles studied. This has been determined empirically by inserting a 0.010-inch stainless steel test absorber in the position so marked in Fig. 2. The test absorber was placed in the path of electrons scattered at angles 50°, 90°, and 130°. Elastic profiles were measured with the test absorber in and out of the path. The peak of the elastic scattering profile was reduced 1 percent per mil of stainless steel in the direction of the scattered electrons, but the half-width of the curve was also increased by an amount such that the area under the elastic curve was the same, within 5 percent, whether the test absorber was in or out. This behavior may be understood as follows: The double focusing action of the spectrometer assures collection of all the electrons directed into the effective solid angle of the spectrometer, whether multiply-scattered or not and brings them to a focus beyond the energy slit (and from there into the Čerenkov detector). The only effects of multiple-scattering in the chamber walls are (a) to fuzz out the source of the scattered electrons in the gas, i.e., to increase or decrease the depth from which the scattered electrons appear to emerge from the target, (b) to reduce the angular resolution, and (c) to mix electrons scattered originally at different angles. Effect (a) may easily be seen to be of negligible importance. Effect (b) amounts to approximately $(\Delta\theta)_{\text{rms}} = \pm 1°$. Since the angular opening of the lower spectrometer slit is $\pm 2°$ and the multiple scattering is essentially Gaussian, the uncertainty in measuring the scattering angle is not appreciably increased by the effect of the side walls. The incoming end plate also contributes an uncertainty of $(\Delta\theta)_{\text{rms}} = \pm 0.7°$. The resulting uncertainty, combining all causes, is approximately $(\Delta\theta)_{\text{rms}} = \pm 2.4°$. The effect of multiple scattering in the hydrogen or helium gas volumes is of the order of 0.1° and hence negligible. In case (c), the error so introduced is of the order of tenths of a percent and is here neglected. In fact, plural scatterings are eliminated because of the energy selection of the spectrometer.

Radiation straggling of the electrons coming out through the walls of the chamber may be shown theoretically to contribute not more than a 5 percent relative correction between 50° and 90° and an equal figure between 90° and 130°, i.e., both the 50° yield and the 130° yield would each be lowered by something less than 5 percent with respect to the 90° yield. Our experiments with the test absorber have not demonstrated a consistent loss greater than 5 percent which could be attributed to straggling in the chamber walls. The statistical accuracy and drifts of the apparatus could have concealed an error of the order of 5 percent. Hence, we have not made a correction for straggling.

The lining-up procedure used a CsBr(Tl) crystal which could be moved remotely into or out of the beam. The crystal was placed along the beam axis just outside the scattering chamber. When it was desired to know the position of the beam, the crystal was moved into the beam and observed with a telescope. When the beam was lined up, say within $\pm\frac{1}{16}$ inch at the target, the crystal was withdrawn. Periodic checks showed whether or not the beam had moved. Very little beam motion was observed after an initial alignment.

An ion chamber was used in the early runs as a monitor of the incident beam, and a secondary electron emitter[7] in the later runs. The ion chamber showed a small amount of saturation at large beams and its runs were corrected by the empirically determined calibration of ion chamber *versus* secondary electron emitter. No correction so obtained was larger than 10 percent. If the correction had not been included, the proton size (see below) would have been a trifle larger.

The theoretical Schwinger radiation correction has not been applied since its angular dependence is very weak and well within the statistics of our experimental observations.

III. RESULTS

A. Hydrogen

Typical elastic profiles observed in a run with hydrogen at an incident energy of 185 Mev are shown in Fig. 3. Because of recoil of the struck proton the energy of the elastically deflected electron is a decreasing function of the angle of scattering. This may be observed by noting the variable position of the peaks in Fig. 3. Figure 4 shows the theoretical behavior of the energy of the scattered electron plotted against laboratory scattering angle for an incident energy of 187 Mev. The solid points show the positions of the peaks of the elastic scattering curves taken at the various angular positions during an experimental run at 187 Mev. The agreement is excellent except at extreme angles where small deviations are observed. The deviations are actually expected because of an increasing energy loss in the wall as the angle of entry becomes more and more oblique. The observed reduction in energy of the scattered electrons below the theoretical curve is in good agreement with the energy loss in the wall.

Because of the variation in energy of the scattered electrons we have been concerned that the solid angle effective in collecting electrons could have been smaller at small angles (high energies), where magnet saturation is important, than at large angles (smaller energies), where saturation is less important. To test this possibility we have measured the number of scattered electrons as a function of the entrance slit width at both high (188 Mev) and low (139 Mev) energies. We have found that in both cases the number of scattered electrons for the $\frac{3}{4}$-inch entrance slit width is 15 percent below the number expected from the initial slope of the curve of number of scattered electrons *versus* slit width. The 15 percent reduction is due to the widest trajectories striking the magnet chamber walls. In the radial direction in the magnet no electrons are lost because of the small extent of the beam in this direction. In other words, the effective solid angle is the same at both low and high energies provided that the entrance slit width is not larger than $\frac{3}{4}$ inch. Hence correction for magnet saturation is not required.

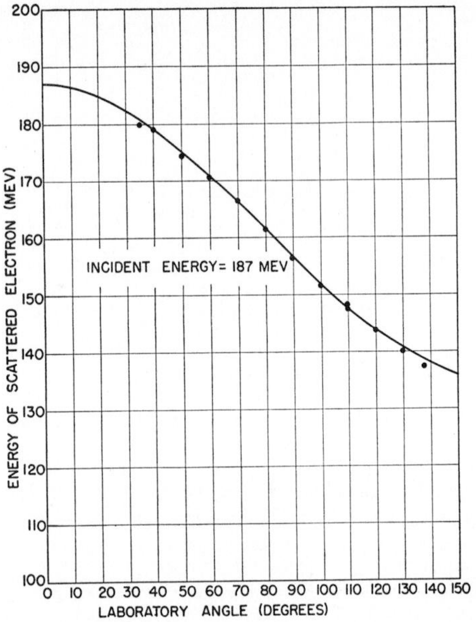

FIG. 4. The solid line gives the theoretical energy of the scattered electrons for an incident energy of 187 Mev. Relativistic kinematics are used to obtain the theoretical curve. The experimental points correspond to peak values of the elastic profiles and refer to experimental observations.

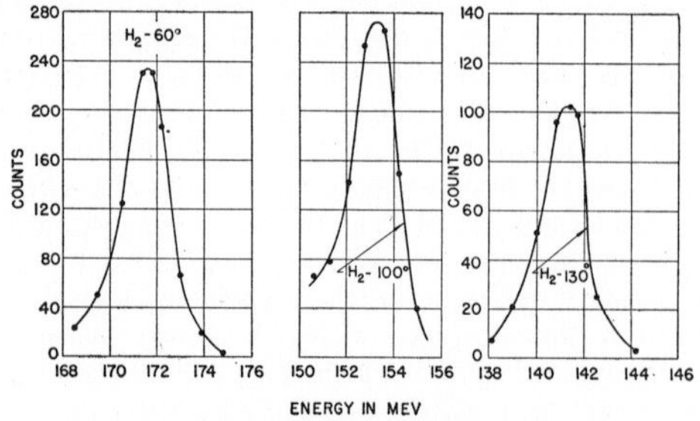

FIG. 3. Typical elastic profiles obtained with hydrogen gas at 185 Mev.

Areas under the elastic peaks, such as those of Fig. 3, have been measured by numerical integration over a width of ± 1.5 Mev about the peak. Such values have been plotted against laboratory angle as in Fig. 5. Areas over ± 2 and ± 2.5 Mev widths have also been obtained by numerical integration, but the relative results are essentially the same. Only the ± 1.5 Mev results will be presented below.

Figure 5 presents a summary of all the data obtained over a period of several months. It may be noticed that the experimental spread of points is somewhat larger than the statistical errors might lead one to expect. The causes of the spread are probably connected with small, unnoticed horizontal shifts of beam, hysteresis in the spectrometer magnet, small changes in the bias of the Čerenkov counter detection equipment, variations

[7] G. W. Tautfest and H. R. Fechter, Phys. Rev. **96**, 35 (1954); Rev. Sci. Instr. **26**, 229 (1955).

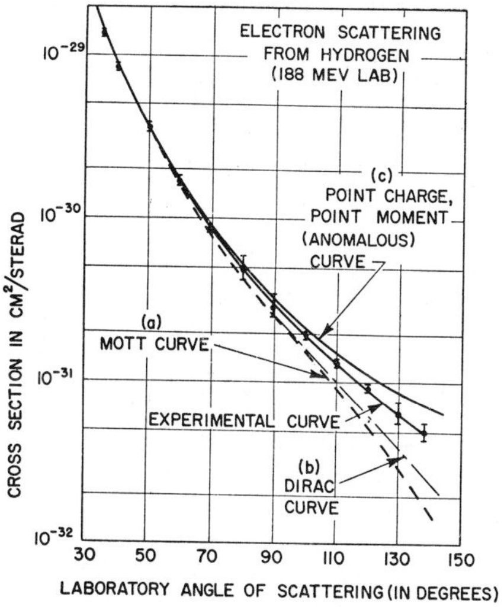

FIG. 5. Curve (a) shows the theoretical Mott curve for a spinless point proton. Curve (b) shows the theoretical curve for a point proton with the Dirac magnetic moment, curve (c) the theoretical curve for a point proton having the anomalous contribution in addition to the Dirac value of magnetic moment. The theoretical curves (b) and (c) are due to Rosenbluth.[8] The experimental curve falls between curves (b) and (c). This deviation from the theoretical curves represents the effect of a form factor for the proton and indicates structure within the proton, or alternatively, a breakdown of the Coulomb law. The best fit indicates a size of 0.70×10^{-13} cm.

in saturation of the ion chamber monitor response and in the integrating voltmeter, and perhaps other unknown items. In Fig. 5 we have drawn a curve, labeled "experimental curve," which is our best estimate of the accumulated data at 188 Mev. The limits of error represent the greatest variations we have observed in any runs. However all runs, not being absolute, are normalized to each other by "best fitting." The experimental curve is also normalized to the theoretical curve at small angles. Also plotted in Fig. 5 are (a) the theoretical Mott curve for a spinless point proton, (b) the theoretical curve for a point proton with the Dirac value of magnetic moment (gyromagnetic ratio 2.00), (c) the theoretical curve for a point proton with the anomalous value of the proton moment in addition to the Dirac moment (gyromagnetic ratio=5.58). The theoretical curves (b), (c) are obtained from calculations of Rosenbluth.[8] The experimental curve deviates from curves (a), (b), and (c) at the larger angles and is lower than the curve for a point proton with anomalous moment, but higher than the curve for a point proton with Dirac moment. This reduction at large angles below the curve for point charge represents the effect of a "structure factor" or a "form factor" for the proton and hence indicates the finite size of the proton. Since the usual electromagnetic relations and the Coulomb interaction have been used in Rosenbluth's calculation, we are here assuming the validity of these interactions at small distances ($<10^{-13}$ cm). Subject to this assumption, the experiment indicates the proton is not a point.

In order to carry out the form factor calculations, we have made use of Rosenbluth's formalism.[8] However we have given the charge and magnetic moment phenomenological interpretations in place of the meson theoretic interpretations originally presented by Rosenbluth.[9] We may write Rosenbluth's formulas as follows: for a point charge we have

$$\sigma=\sigma_{NS}\left\{1+\frac{q^2}{4M^2}\left[2(1+\mu)^2\tan^2(\theta/2)+\mu^2\right]\right\},\qquad(1)$$

where

$$\sigma_{NS}=\frac{e^4}{4E^2}\left(\frac{\cos^2(\theta/2)}{\sin^4(\theta/2)}\right)\frac{1}{1+(2E/M)\sin^2(\theta/2)},\qquad(2)$$

and where

$$q=\frac{(2/\lambda\!\!\!^{-})\sin(\theta/2)}{\left[1+(2E/M)\sin^2(\theta/2)\right]^{\frac{1}{2}}}.\qquad(3)$$

Here natural units, $\hbar=c=1$, are used and the equations are written in terms of the laboratory coordinates; q is the invariant momentum transfer in the center-of-mass frame expressed in laboratory coordinates; E is the energy of the incident electrons; M the mass of the proton, and μ is the anomalous part of the proton's magnetic moment ($\mu=1.79$). $\lambda\!\!\!^{-}$ is the reduced de Broglie wavelength of the electron in the laboratory system.

For a diffuse proton we may write:

$$\sigma=\sigma_{NS}\left\{F_1^2+\frac{q^2}{4M^2}\left[2(F_1+\mu F_2)^2\tan^2(\theta/2)+\mu^2F_2^2\right]\right\},\qquad(4)$$

where F_1 is the charge form factor (which also influences the intrinsic "Dirac" magnetic moment) and F_2 the anomalous magnetic moment form factor. In principle F_1 does not have to be the same as F_2. F_1 and F_2 may be written as functions of $(q\langle r\rangle)$, where $\langle r\rangle$ is the root-mean-square radius of the appropriate charge, or moment distribution. F_1 and F_2 may also be identified with e'/e and $k'e'/k_0e$ in Rosenbluth's article.

We have not made detailed analyses for different F_1 and F_2. Rather, as may be seen below, we have assumed $F_1=F_2$. However, the data at all energies are quite consistent with this choice.

At the energies used in these experiments, the form factor (F_1 or F_2) is not appreciably shape dependent, i.e., one cannot distinguish between uniform, exponential, or Gaussian charge (or magnetic moment) distributions. All that can be determined is a mean square radius. Therefore we have tried to fit the experi-

[8] M. N. Rosenbluth, Phys. Rev. 79, 615 (1950).

[9] We are indebted to Dr. D. R. Yennie for formulation of Eqs. (1)–(4).

mental data with a phenomenological form factor corresponding to various values of the mean square radii up to values of $q\langle r\rangle \cong 1.0$. q is again the momentum transfer and $\langle r\rangle$ the root-mean-square radius of the charge or magnetic moment distributions. For simplicity, as stated above, we have assumed that $\langle r\rangle_{\text{charge}} = \langle r\rangle_{\text{anomalous magnetic moment}}$, although in principle this is not a necessary restriction. Hence we can expect only to obtain a first approximation to the structure and size of the proton.

When such form factors are applied to the point charge-point moment curve, the behavior of the experimental curve can be reproduced very well. In fact for $\langle r\rangle_{\text{charge}} = \langle r\rangle_{\text{magnetic moment}} = 0.70\times10^{-13}$ the theoretical curve cannot be distinguished from the experimental curve within the limits of error. A separate theoretical curve for 0.70×10^{-13} cm therefore has not been included in Fig. 5. The limits of error in the radius are conservatively estimated at $\pm0.24\times10^{-13}$ cm.

A similar fitting procedure can be employed with data obtained with electrons at 236 Mev in the incident beam. In this case our measurements could be made only at angles larger than or equal to 90° since our magnetic spectrometer cannot bend electrons of energy higher than those scattered at 90° (or smaller angles): For an incident energy of 236 Mev the scattered electron at 90° has an energy of 189 Mev, the approximate limit of our apparatus.

Figure 6 shows the experimental points obtained in several runs at 236 Mev. The shape of the point charge-point moment curve is shown as well as the experimental points. No absolute values are known for the experimental points so that the best that can be done is to try to fit the shape of the experimental curve with Eq. (4) for various values of F_1 and F_2. Again the assumption $F_1=F_2$ is made. Such attempts are shown in Fig. 6 and are labeled rms 6.2, 7.8, and 9.3×10^{-14} cm. The dotted curves corresponding to 6.2×10^{-14} cm and 9.3×10^{-14} cm may be shifted down or up respectively to try to fit the experimental points, but neither curve will do so within the limits of error. Hence the data at 236 Mev support a "best" value of rms radius of $(0.78\pm0.20)\times10^{-13}$ cm, conservatively speaking. This value is in good agreement with the best value $(0.70 \pm0.24)\times10^{-13}$ cm obtained above at 188 Mev.

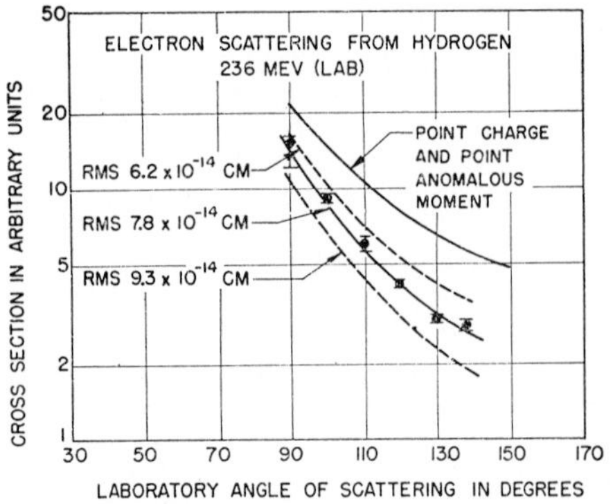

FIG. 6. This figure shows the experimental points at 236 Mev and the attempts to fit the shape of the experimental curve. The best fit lies near 0.78×10^{-13} cm.

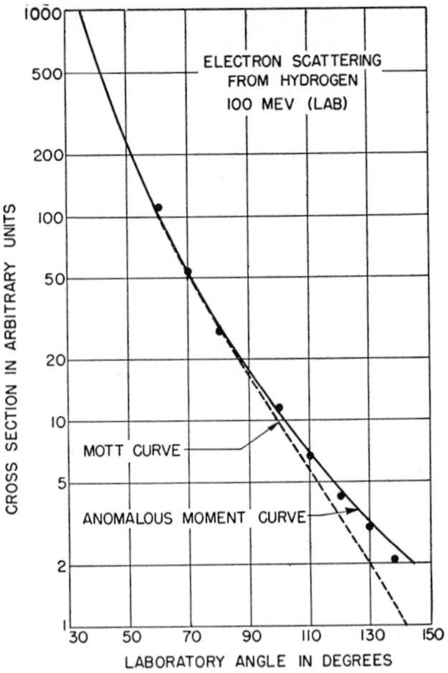

FIG. 7. Theoretical curves are shown for electrons of 100 Mev, along with the experimental observations at that energy.

In order to test some features of the apparatus, we have carried out a scattering experiment at an incident energy of 100 Mev. In this case, if our model of the proton is correct, the observed scattering should be quite close to the curve for a point charge and point moment because the $q\langle r\rangle$ value is small and $F^2=1.0$. Figure 7 shows that the agreement observed is highly satisfactory. At 100 Mev, the magnetic spectrometer is never saturated at any angle. Hence the "saturation" aspect and possible defocusing effects are not tested by this experiment. However, the 236-Mev and 188-Mev runs do test such possible effects since different energies correspond to different angular positions. The good agreement obtained between these latter two sets of data and the satisfactory behavior at 100 Mev is essentially what we have published earlier.[4]

These results may be summarized in the following way: If the proton can be assumed to (a) have distributions of charge and magnetic moment equal, or at least similar, in size and (b) if the Coulomb law and the usual electromagnetic laws are obeyed at distances of the order of 0.7×10^{-13} cm, then these experiments show that the proton has an rms radius of $(0.74\pm0.24) \times10^{-13}$ cm. Of course, if the Coulomb law and the usual interactions are not valid, these findings could also be

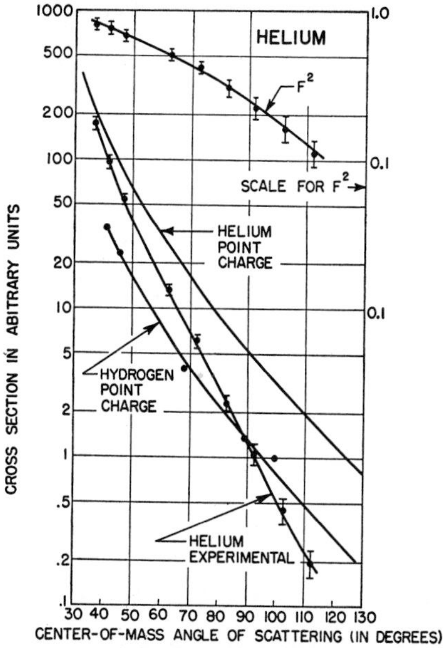

FIG. 8. The experimental curve for helium in the center-of-mass system, hydrogen normalizing points, and the helium point charge construction are shown. This figure also exhibits the square of the form factor as a function of angle. The best fit of theory to experiment corresponds to an rms radius of 1.60×10^{-13} cm.

interpreted in terms of a point charge and point moment. We suspect that the breakdown of the Coulomb law would have exhibited other consequences, possibly already recognized in the literature. Phenomenologically we cannot distinguish, at the present time with these experiments alone, between a finite size of the proton and a breakdown of the Coulomb law. Nevertheless, any meson theory would predict a finite size of the proton's magnetic moment and this is what we may have found in the proton.

B. Helium

The elastic peaks observed in helium are similar to those found in hydrogen, except that the recoil shifts are approximately four times smaller. To measure the form factor of the alpha particle with respect to electron scattering, we have made essentially simultaneous measurements of the scattering from helium and hydrogen and compared the results. The procedure involved carrying out the helium measurements, emptying the target chamber, and finally substitution of hydrogen for the helium. A series of measurements in hydrogen is thus made almost at the same time as the helium measurements. From a few representative hydrogen points, we can construct a point-charge *Mott curve* for hydrogen, say, between 35° and 90°. If we multiply this curve by four ($Z_{He}^2=2^2=4$) we obtain a theoretical point-charge curve for helium. Note that we use a Mott curve (spinless particle) since the alpha particle has no spin or magnetic moment. The ratio of the actually observed experimental curve in helium to the point charge curve for helium gives the square of the form factor. Thus the form factor can be compared with theoretical form factors for various size charge distributions.

Figure 8 shows the helium experimental curve in the center-of-mass system, the hydrogen normalizing points, and the helium point-charge construction. The incident energy was 188 Mev for these experiments. Corrections for the different energies in the center-of-mass system and for the different effective solid angles have been made. A glance at the figure shows that the elastic scattering from the alpha particle is considerably smaller at large angles (a factor of 10 at 110°) than that from a point charge.

Figure 8 also shows the ratio of the alpha-particle scattering to that of a point charge with $Z=2$. This curve represents the square of the "form factor." The scale is given in the upper right hand corner of Fig. 8. This curve is indistinguishable from a (form factor)^2 curve for an rms radius of $(1.60\pm0.10)\times10^{-13}$ cm. For such a small nucleus and an energy 188 Mev, our analysis will not give more than an rms radius from these measurements. It is curious that the rms radius of the alpha particle is approximately twice that of the proton as determined from these scattering measurements. Allowing for the rms radius of each of the two protons in the alpha particle, as determined above, the rms radius of the alpha particle would be smaller. By subtracting mean squares, the rms radius to the charge centroid would be 1.41×10^{-13} cm. This approximate calculation probably overemphasizes the effect of the finite protonic size.

ACKNOWLEDGMENTS

We wish to acknowledge the valuable cooperation of Mr. E. E. Chambers in helping with some of the measurements. We wish to thank Dr. R. H. Dalitz, Dr. D. G. Ravenhall, Dr. L. I. Schiff, and Dr. D. R. Yennie for many interesting conversations. We acknowledge with much appreciation the valued help of the late Miss Eva Wiener.

PAPER 31

Coherent Neutron Scattering Amplitudes of Krypton and Xenon, and the Electron-Neutron Interaction*

M. F. CROUCH,† V. E. KROHN, AND G. R. RINGO
Argonne National Laboratory, Lemont, Illinois
(Received February 23, 1956)

The coherent scattering amplitudes of krypton and xenon for thermal neutrons have been measured by a comparison method involving reflection of a neutron beam from liquid mirrors. The results were $(7.68\pm0.19)\times10^{-13}$ cm for krypton and $(5.10\pm0.17)\times10^{-13}$ cm for xenon. When these results are used with the scattering measurements of Hamermesh, Ringo, and Wattenberg, one obtains (3900 ± 800) ev for the electron-neutron interaction.

INTRODUCTION

THE electron-neutron interaction[1] is of obvious interest as a test of any complete theory of elementary particles and it has received considerable theoretical[2] and experimental[3–5] attention. At present there is particular interest in the question of whether the interaction shows any structure-dependent effects in addition to a relativistic effect pointed out by Foldy.[6] What is probably the most accurate experimental result[5] is that the interaction is equivalent to a square well of 3860 ± 370 ev depth when the radius, by convention, is taken as $e^2/(mc^2)$. The relativistic effect is approximately 4000 ev, so quite accurate measurements are needed to decide if there is any interaction beyond this. The electron-neutron interaction is so much smaller than the interaction of the neutron with the nucleus or the magnetic dipole interaction that it is very hard to be sure in any measurement that some obscure residual effect of these large interactions is not affecting the experiment. For this reason it seems very desirable to have the measurement made by several methods that are as independent as possible.

The method used by Hamermesh, Ringo, and Wattenberg[4] is considerably different from that of Hughes *et al.* It was devised by Fermi and Marshall[7] and consists of a measurement of the anisotropy of the scattering of a beam of thermal neutrons by gaseous krypton and xenon. The electron-neutron interaction affects this anisotropy through the electronic form factors (more properly, the atomic scattering factors) of the gases. Most of the anisotropy is due to the center-of-mass

* Work supported by the U. S. Atomic Energy Commission.

† On summer leave from Case Institute of Technology, Cleveland, Ohio.

1 In this article we mean by electron-neutron interaction the interaction additional to the large one between the magnetic moments of the electron and neutron. This last interaction is given by the ordinary magnetic dipole interaction expression and accounts for the magnetic scattering of neutrons.

2 G. Salzman, Phys. Rev. **99**, 973 (1955) and references therein.

3 Melkonian, Rustad, and Havens, Bull. Am. Phys. Soc. Ser. II, **1**, 62 (1956).

4 Hamermesh, Ringo, and Wattenberg, Phys. Rev. **85**, 483 (1952).

5 Hughes, Harvey, Goldberg, and Stafne, Phys. Rev. **90**, 497 (1953).

6 L. L. Foldy, Phys. Rev. **83**, 688 (1951).

7 E. Fermi and L. Marshall, Phys. Rev. **72**, 1139 (1947).

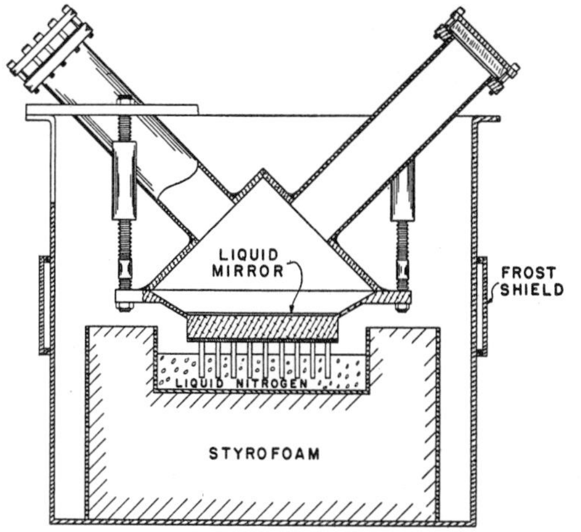

FIG. 1. Section of the mirror tray and accessories. Most of the assembly was made of aluminum.

motion of the scattering system which can be calculated. The remainder is ascribed, not to the electron-neutron interaction alone, but to an interference between the electronic and the nuclear scattering which are coherent in any single atom. Thus, the anisotropy is proportional to a term of the form

$$aa_e f/\sigma_s,$$

where a is the coherent neutron scattering amplitude of the nucleus, a_e is the scattering amplitude ascribable to the electron-neutron interaction, f is the atomic scattering factor of the gas involved, and σ_s is the total neutron scattering cross section.

The use of krypton and xenon is dictated by the necessity of having monatomic gases (to avoid diffraction effects) of zero electronic magnetic moment (to avoid the magnetic dipole interaction) and high atomic number (to maximize the electron-neutron interaction effects and minimize the center-of-mass motion effects). It has the awkward consequence that it is necessary to know the coherent scattering amplitudes of krypton and xenon which have never been measured. Hamermesh, Ringo, and Wattenberg made the assumption that the coherent scattering amplitudes of these gases were given by

$$a=0.9(\sigma_s/4\pi)^{\frac{1}{2}}.$$

This was based on the observation that the equation was accurate within $\pm 10\%$ for almost all elements (whose coherent scattering amplitudes had been measured) with more than two isotopes of appreciable abundance. In their measurement they found quite different results for the electron-neutron interaction strength from the measurements on krypton (5000 ev) and xenon (2900 ev). It was thought that some of this discrepancy was probably due to errors in the estimates of the coherent scattering amplitudes. In any event, any great improvement in the accuracy of the result would clearly require a much more exact knowledge of these amplitudes. Accordingly, we decided to measure them directly.

EXPERIMENTAL METHOD

Coherent scattering amplitudes are usually measured by powder diffraction of a compound containing the element of unknown a and an element of known a. This method is not practical with the noble gases. Powder diffraction methods can be used to give a without a comparison standard in the same crystal, but this involves several rather difficult corrections and was therefore rejected in favor of a method using liquid mirror reflection. The method depended upon a comparison of the reflected intensities from a thermal neutron beam incident on liquid mirrors of krypton and xenon with the reflected intensities from mixtures of ordinary and heavy water which approximately matched the indicies of refraction of the liquified rare gases. It was assumed that the only thing which could affect the quality of the surface of a liquid as far as neutron reflection was concerned was a macroscopic lack of smoothness which would show up in a widening of the reflected beam and permit the elimination of reflections from defective surfaces. It follows that two liquids giving the same reflected intensity in the same geometry must have the same critical wavelength, and hence, the same index of refraction.

Total reflection from a liquid mirror occurs for wavelengths greater than the critical wavelength,

$$\lambda_c=\theta(\pi/\sum N_i a_i)^{\frac{1}{2}}, \tag{1}$$

where θ is the angle of incidence measured from the surface of the mirror, N_i is the density of the ith nuclear species in nuclei per unit volume, and a_i is the coherent scattering amplitude of the ith species. The sum over a

TABLE I. Data concerning water mixtures.

Run	Mixture	D_2O content (grams)	H_2O content (grams)	Σa_iN_i calculated (cm^{-2})	Ratio (reflected beam ×100 / direct beam)	Ratio minus back-ground	Mirror length correction factor	Corrected intensity ratio
1	*A*	28.66	74.43	11.79×10^9	8.05	7.25	1.019	7.39
2	*B*	19.25	82.68	6.01×10^9	2.60	1.80	1.000	1.80
5	*B*	19.25	82.68	6.01×10^9	2.59	1.79	1.000	1.79
6	*A*	28.84	74.68	11.84×10^9	7.88	7.08	1.000	7.08

TABLE II. Xenon and krypton data.

Run	Liquid	Pressure (lb gauge)	Liquid density minus vapor density (g/cm³)	Ratio (reflected beam ×100 / direct beam)	Ratio minus back-ground	Mirror length correction factor	Absorption correction factor	Density correction factor[a]	Corrected intensity ratio
3	Xe	27	2.79	2.55	1.75	1.045	1.240	1.045	2.36
		16.5	2.83	2.655	1.855	1.040	1.179	1.013	2.32
		15.3		2.58	1.78				2.18
		14.3	2.85	2.74	1.94	1.038	1.167	1.000	2.35
		13.8		2.58	1.78				2.14
		12.3	2.86	2.745	1.945	1.035	1.154	0.996	2.31
		6.8	2.89	2.74	1.94	1.026	1.126	0.974	2.18
									Mean = 2.26
4	Kr	55	2.197	6.81	6.01	1.035	1.274	1.068	8.47
		45.5	2.225	7.11	6.31	1.024	1.236	1.040	8.31
		38	2.249	7.55	6.75	1.019	1.208	1.020	8.45
		29	2.274	7.63	6.83	1.007	1.172	0.997	8.08
		23	2.295	8.26	7.46	1.000	1.149	0.980	8.39
		17	2.320	8.30	7.50	0.994	1.126	0.958	8.03
		15.5	2.328	8.44	7.64	0.991	1.120	0.950	8.06
									Mean = 8.25

[a] To arbitrary densities of 2.85 g/cm³ for xenon and 2.27 g/cm³ for krypton.

natural mixture of the isotopes of a single element,

$$\sum N_i A_i = a \sum N_i,$$

where a is the coherent scattering amplitude of the element. The critical wavelengths in the present experiment (approximately 5.4 A for Kr and 7.2 A for Xe) corresponded to velocities well below the peak of the thermal distribution, and the detector was black to the reflected neutrons. Hence, the observed intensities were inversely proportional to the fourth power of the critical wavelengths so that [from Eq. (1)] they (the reflected intensities) varied as the square of the scattering amplitudes.

For the water mixtures the sum which occurs in Eq. (1) was calculated from the known scattering amplitudes of hydrogen, deuterium, and oxygen.[8]

APPARATUS

A sketch of the mirror tray is shown in Fig. 1. The liquified gases could be observed visually through the two tubes which protrude from the top of the assembly. During low temperature operation the top ends of these tubes were held near room temperature by electrical heating tapes. This eliminated condensation of moisture on the plate glass windows and protected the O-ring seals. The tray assembly was constructed of aluminum and was joined to a vacuum system by an O-ring seal at the end of a 20-inch aluminum pipe welded to the side of the tray. The ends of the tray made an angle of 30° with the horizontal plane and, in addition, it was necessary to apply a thin coat of silicone grease to the ends in order to assure that the meniscuses of the water mixtures would be convex.

The temperature of the mirror was controlled by setting the level of the liquid nitrogen using an automatic level control.[9] The brass pins beneath the tray were added to permit finer temperature control. The direct neutron beam came from the Argonne Research Reactor, CP-5. It was defined by two cadmium slits (Fig. 2) which established a beam angle 12 minutes below horizontal. A third slit was mounted on the detector assembly and was the entrance to the detector. The latter consisted of a group of BF_3 counters protected from stray neutrons by a shield of cadmium and paraffin. The height of the mirror and the height of the detector assembly were variable.

MEASUREMENTS

The major difficulty encountered during the preliminary phases of the experiment was the tendency of the liquified krypton surfaces to exhibit local boiling and turbulence. This was overcome by arranging to work at pressures above an atmosphere and by taking data when the temperature of the liquid mirror was falling. Xenon did not give so much trouble in this respect. All of the final data were obtained with mirror surfaces which appeared to be perfectly smooth.

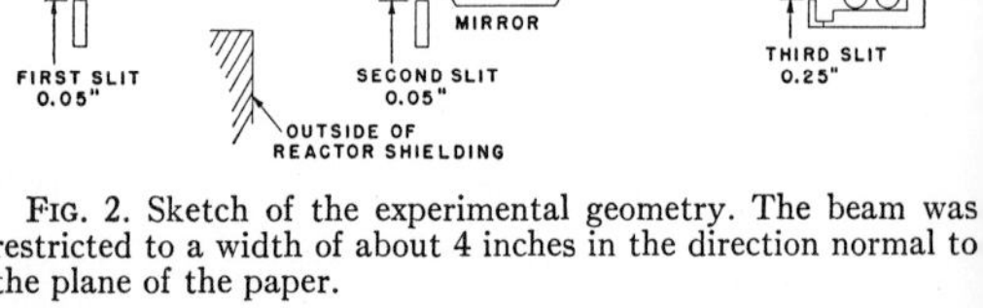

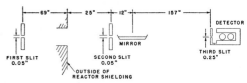

FIG. 2. Sketch of the experimental geometry. The beam was restricted to a width of about 4 inches in the direction normal to the plane of the paper.

[8] The values used were: for H, $(3.78\pm0.02)\times10^{-13}$ cm; for D, $(6.56\pm0.09)\times10^{-13}$ cm; and for O, $(5.78\pm0.02)\times10^{-13}$ cm. [Based on values given by D. J. Hughes and J. A. Harvey, *Neutron Cross Sections*, Brookhaven National Laboratory Report BNL-325, (Superintendent of Documents, U. S. Government Printing Office, Washington, D. C., 1955).]

[9] M. S. Fred and E. G. Rauh, Rev. Sci. Instr. **21**, 258 (1950).

TABLE III. Uncertainties in percent.

Source of uncertainty	Krypton	Xenon
Coherent amplitudes of materials in the standards	1.6	2.6
Absorption correction	1.3	1.0
Background variations[a]	0.5	1.5
Statistics in measurement of standards[a]	1.2	0.2
Statistics in measurement of liquified gases[a]	0.5	0.8
Mirror length correction	0.1	0.4
$(\Sigma\,\delta^2)^{\frac{1}{2}}$	2.5	3.3

[a] From the scatter of the data.

The runs proceeded as follows: The intensity of the reflected beam was measured with the third slit fixed at the maximum and with the height of the mirror tray variable. This intensity was constant over a region of heights for which the entire mirror surface was in the direct beam. Then, with the tray set near the middle of this region, the third slit was varied over the reflected beam. As the third slit was wider (actually higher) than the reflected beam, this intensity was also constant near the maximum. The position of the direct beam was checked during some of the runs. All counts with the detector in the direct beam were taken with about 95% of the beam absorbed by a cadmium mask which was introduced at a standard position in front of the third slit. Also, all direct beam observations were made at a tray position which kept the mirror surfaces well below the beam. After the above information was obtained, a series of observations were made with the third slit, the cadmium mask, and the tray all adjusted alternately for the maxima of the reflected and the direct beams, and for an extra point which was sensitive to changes in the shape of the reflected beam. The direct beam readings served to monitor the measurements and to eliminate errors which might have resulted from drifts in the detector sensitivity. The data were discarded if the extra point failed to show that the mirror surface was good. Also, for the liquified gases, the positions of the tray which gave maximum reflection varied with pressure, so it was necessary to locate the position of the maximum at two or more pressures. In some instances data were discarded because the tray was not set at a height which was definitely in the region of maximum reflection. The average ratios (reflected beam maximum to direct beam maximum) obtained in each of these series of measurements were used in the final calculations.

There is a correction for the variatio[n] ... the mirror. This was determined by the de... liquid as indicated by the positions of the tray wh... gave maximum reflection. Also, since neutron absorption is proportional to wavelength, the reflected beam is attenuated more than the direct beam, and there is a correction for absorption in the gas above the liquid. Finally, the density of the liquified gases varies with temperature[10] so that the results at different pressures must be corrected to some arbitrary density. All of these corrections vary with the pressure, so they must be made before data obtained at different pressures can be compared.

The results and corrections have been collected in Tables I and II, and Table III gives a summary of the known uncertainties. The results for the coherent scattering amplitudes are $(7.68\pm0.19)\times10^{-13}$ cm for krypton and $(5.10\pm0.17)\times10^{-13}$ cm for xenon.

DISCUSSION

From the coherent scattering amplitudes and the total scattering cross sections[11] one can calculate that the incoherent scattering cross section is $(0_{-0}^{+12})\%$ of the total scattering cross section for krypton and $(32\pm12)\%$ of the total in the case of xenon.

When the results of Hamermesh, Ringo, and Wattenberg[4] are revised by substituting the present results in place of the values they assumed for the coherent scattering amplitudes, one obtains 4500 ev and 3000 ev, respectively, from their krypton and xenon measurements, and their final value for the electron-neutron interaction becomes (3900 ± 800) ev, where the uncertainty includes an estimate of the systematic errors in their measurement. It should be practical to reduce this error appreciably by repeating the scattering measurements[4] with better statistics, better geometry, and a more accurate correction for the center-of-mass motion. The objection of Halpern and Hsu[12] regarding the way in which this correction has been made in the past[4,7] can be met by obtaining sufficient information about the neutron spectrum and the response of the detectors.

[10] Patterson, Cripps, and Whytlaw-Gray, Proc. Roy. Soc. (London) **86**, 579 (1912) (xenon); Crommelin, Mathias, and Meihuizen, Comp. rend. **204**, 630 (1937) (krypton). In the case of xenon the 1912 data were used for the variation of density with pressure, but these data did not include the pressures used in the present work, so the liquid xenon density was measured at a pressure of 14 psi gauge and found to be 2.87 g/cm³.
[11] S. P. Harris, Phys. Rev. **80**, 20 (1950).
[12] O. Halpern and C. P. Hsu, Phys. Rev. **87**, 519 (1952).

PAPER 32*

Calculation of Electron-Deuteron Scattering Cross Sections*†

V. Z. Jankus‡
Stanford University, Stanford, California
(Received March 5, 1956)

Elastic and inelastic cross sections for electron-deuteron scattering with large momentum transfer have been investigated. The calculation has been performed in the first Born approximation. The neutron-proton interaction has been described by a phenomenological potential, and the nucleons have been represented by point charges and point magnetic moments. Finite size of nucleons causes major correction to these results.

I. INTRODUCTION

The scattering of electrons with large momentum transfer has yielded some new and quite definite information about the charge distribution in a number of heavy nuclei. Experimental accuracy is improving to such an extent that this method holds promise of yielding new information even when applied to a relatively simple and well-understood nucleus, such as the deuteron. Some measurements[1] have already been made, in which the deuteron has been bombarded by high-energy electrons and the energies of the electrons scattered at large angles have been measured. A narrow elastic peak has been obtained, and a wide inelastic peak, corresponding to the breakup of the deuteron, has also been observed.

A few calculations[2] intended mainly for small momentum transfers have already been made. These calculations of elastic cross sections still give quite accurate results even at large momentum transfers. On the other hand, in the calculations of inelastic cross sections only the lowest electric and magnetic multipole moments have been considered. These results cannot be applied to the scattering with large momentum transfer when the contribution of higher multipole moments is quite important. Thus, it is necessary to perform a calculation that accounts for all multipoles.

Since the interaction between electron and nucleus is of electromagnetic nature, the matrix elements involved are similar to those used in calculating the photodisintegration of the deuteron. Calculations[3] and experimental data are plentiful in this case. The results cannot, however, be easily applied to our case, since in the photoprocess we have only real (transverse) photons, while in the electrodisintegration the main contribution comes from the longitudinal part of the

* This research was supported by the U. S. Air Force through the Air Force Office of Scientific Research, Air Research and Development Command.

† Based on a dissertation submitted to Stanford University in partial fulfillment of the requirements for the Ph. D. degree in Physics.

‡ Now at Argonne National Laboratory, Lemont, Illinois.

[1] J. A. McIntyre and R. Hofstadter, Phys. Rev. **98**, 158 (1955); J. A. McIntyre (private communication).

[2] H. A. Bethe and R. Peierls, Proc. Roy. Soc. (London) **A148**, 146 (1935); B. Peters and C. Richman, Phys. Rev. **59**, 804 (1941); M. E. Rose, Phys. Rev. **73**, 282 (1948); J. H. Smith, Ph. D. dissertation, Cornell University, 1951 (unpublished); Phys. Rev. **95**, 271 (1954); Thie, Mullin, and Guth, Phys. Rev. **87**, 962 (1952); L. I. Schiff, Phys. Rev. **92**, 988 (1953).

[3] Y. Yamaguchi and Y. Yamaguchi, Phys. Rev. **95**, 1635 (1954); J. M. Berger, Phys. Rev. **94**, 1698 (1954); L. Hulthén and B. C. H. Nagel, Phys. Rev. **90**, 62 (1953); H. Feshbach and J. Schwinger Phys. Rev. **84**, 194 (1951); L. I. Schiff, Phys. Rev. **78**, 733 (1950); J. F. Marshall and E. Guth, Phys. Rev. **78**, 738 (1950).

* *See page 683 of this volume for corrections and addenda.*

electromagnetic field. Moreover, the lowest order process in photodisintegration is the absorption of the photon, and a large momentum transfer is necessarily accompanied by a large energy transfer. In electrodisintegration, such a large momentum transfer usually causes a much smaller transfer of energy.

In our calculation, therefore, we have treated the deuteron nonrelativistically, while the electron may be considered extremely relativistic. Also, since the charge of the deuteron is small, we have treated the problem in the first Born approximation. Thus the wave functions for incident and scattered electrons have been represented by plane waves and the deflection of the electrons has generated Møller potentials[4] ϕ and $\mathbf{A}$ to act upon the charge and current distributions in the deuteron:

$$\phi(r) = -4\pi e a_0 (q^2 - \Delta E^2)^{-1} \exp(i\mathbf{q}\cdot\mathbf{r}),$$
$$\mathbf{A}(r) = 4\pi e \mathbf{a} (q^2 - \Delta E^2)^{-1} \exp(i\mathbf{q}\cdot\mathbf{r}),$$

where $\mathbf{q}$ and ΔE are the momentum and energy losses of the electron; $\mathbf{a}$ and a_0 are the matrix elements of the Dirac $\boldsymbol{\alpha}$ and unit operators between initial and final electron states. Also, we have chosen the system of units where $\hbar = c = M = 1$ (M is the mass of the nucleon). Assuming, in addition, that exchange currents can be neglected and the nucleons can be represented by point charges and point magnetic moments, the perturbation upon the deuteron becomes equal to

$$\sum_{k=1,2} \{q_k\phi(\mathbf{r}_k) + \tfrac{1}{2}iq_k[\mathbf{A}(\mathbf{r}_k)\cdot\nabla_k + \nabla_k\cdot\mathbf{A}(\mathbf{r}_k)] - \tfrac{1}{2}ie\mu_k\boldsymbol{\sigma}_k\cdot[\nabla_k\times\mathbf{A}(\mathbf{r}_k)]\}, \quad (1)$$

where $\mathbf{r}_k$ is the position of the kth nucleon, q_k is its charge and μ_k its magnetic moment in multiples of a nuclear magneton. Thus, with the preceding assumptions the calculation of cross sections is reduced to the calculation of the matrix element of (1) between initial and final states of the deuteron.

II. ELASTIC CROSS SECTION

Our calculation has been performed in the laboratory system, so that the deuteron is at rest initially. Taking (1) as a perturbation and eliminating the coordinate of the mass center of the deuteron, we obtain the elastic cross section:

$$d\sigma_e = \tfrac{1}{4}e^4[p_0^2 \sin^4(\tfrac{1}{2}\theta)]^{-1}[1+p_0\sin^2(\tfrac{1}{2}\theta)]^{-1}d\Omega_p \times |\langle f|[a_0 - \tfrac{1}{2}\nabla\cdot\mathbf{a} + \tfrac{1}{2}i\mu_p\boldsymbol{\sigma}_p\cdot(\mathbf{q}\times\mathbf{a})]e^{\frac{1}{2}i\mathbf{q}\cdot\mathbf{r}} + \tfrac{1}{2}i\mu_n\boldsymbol{\sigma}_n\cdot(\mathbf{q}\times\mathbf{a})e^{-\frac{1}{2}i\mathbf{q}\cdot\mathbf{r}}|0\rangle|^2, \quad (2)$$

where $\frac{1}{2}\mathbf{r}$ is the position of the proton with respect to the mass center; $\mathbf{p}_0$ is the momentum of the incident electron; $\mathbf{p}$ is the momentum of the scattered electrons; $d\Omega_p$ is the element of solid angle into which the electron has been scattered; θ is the scattering angle, $\cos\theta = \mathbf{p}_0\cdot\mathbf{p}/p_0 p$. For the elastic scattering, the initial state $|0\rangle$ and final state $|f\rangle$ of the deuteron are ground states. The wave functions for the ground state in the presence of tensor forces can be written in the form

$$\phi_m = (4\pi)^{-\frac{1}{2}}r^{-1}[u(r) + 8^{-\frac{1}{2}}S_{np}w(r)]\chi_m, \quad m = 0, \pm 1,$$

where χ_m is a triplet spin function and S_{np} is the conventional tensor operator:

$$S_{np} = 3r^{-2}(\boldsymbol{\sigma}_n\cdot\mathbf{r})(\boldsymbol{\sigma}_p\cdot\mathbf{r}) - (\boldsymbol{\sigma}_n\cdot\boldsymbol{\sigma}_p).$$

Substituting this wave function into the matrix element of (2), averaging over initial directions of spin of the deuteron and the electron of positive energy, and summing over final directions (since the spins are not determined experimentally), we obtain the following for the elastic cross section:

$$d\sigma_e = \tfrac{1}{4}e^4\cos^2(\tfrac{1}{2}\theta)[p_0^2\sin^4(\tfrac{1}{2}\theta)]^{-1} \times [1+p_0\sin^2(\tfrac{1}{2}\theta)]^{-1}d\Omega_p\cdot F^2, \quad (3)$$

where

$$F^2 = \left[\int (u^2+w^2)j_0(\tfrac{1}{2}qr)dr\right]^2 + \left[\int 2w(u - 8^{-\frac{1}{2}}w)j_2(\tfrac{1}{2}qr)dr\right]^2 + \tfrac{2}{3}(\tfrac{1}{2}q)^2[(2/\cos^2(\tfrac{1}{2}\theta)) - 1] \times \left[\int \{[(\mu_p+\mu_n)(u^2+w^2) - \tfrac{3}{2}(\mu_p+\mu_n-\tfrac{1}{2})w^2]j_0(\tfrac{1}{2}qr) + 2^{-\frac{1}{2}}w[(\mu_p+\mu_n)(u+2^{-\frac{1}{2}}w) + 3\times 8^{-\frac{1}{2}}w]j_2(\tfrac{1}{2}qr)\}dr\right]^2. \quad (4)$$

The first term here comes from the spherically symmetric part of the charge distribution in the deuteron, the second is a "quadrupole term," and the last is a "magnetic moment term." The first two terms in this expression have been given previously by Schiff.[2]

We can estimate the quadrupole term rather easily since we know the values of the functions u and w outside the range of nuclear forces. u is determined quite accurately by the experimental value of triplet effective range, and w is known roughly from the quadrupole moment of the deuteron.[5] In this way it can be shown that the quadrupole term is approximately equal to $(8/9)(\frac{1}{2}q)^4Q^2$ (where $Q = 0.274\times 10^{-26}$ cm^2 is the quadrupole moment of the deuteron) for small recoil momenta; it rapidly reaches a maximum value ≈ 0.002 and remains of this order of magnitude for moderate recoil momenta ($q < 3\times 10^{13}$ cm^{-1}). Thus,

[4] C. Møller, Z. Physik **70**, 786 (1931); W. Heitler, *The Quantum Theory of Radiation* (Oxford University Press, Oxford, 1954), third edition, p. 231.

[5] J. M. Blatt and V. F. Weisskopf, *Theoretical Nuclear Physics* (John Wiley and Sons, Inc., New York, 1952), p. 106.

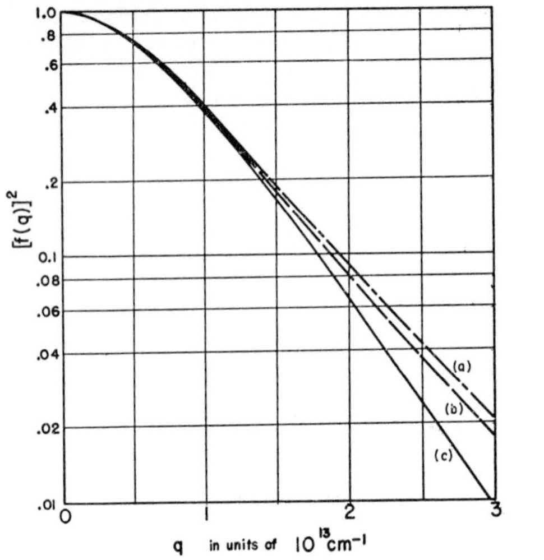

FIG. 1. The square of the Fourier transform of the charge distribution in the deuteron f^2 if neutron-proton interaction is described by (a) a Hulthén potential corresponding to triplet effective range $r_t = 1.7\times10^{-13}$ cm; (b) a Hulthén potential corresponding to $r_t = 1.8\times10^{-13}$ cm; (c) a Hulthén potential outside the hard core of radius 0.65×10^{-13} cm, $r_t = 1.7\times10^{-13}$ cm.

neglecting this and other small terms, we have

$$F^2 \approx \{1+\tfrac{2}{3}(\tfrac{1}{2}q)^2(\mu_p+\mu_n)^2[(2/\cos^2(\tfrac{1}{2}\theta))-1]\}f^2, \quad (5)$$

where

$$f=\int (u^2+w^2)j_0(\tfrac{1}{2}qr)dr$$

is the Fourier transform of the charge distribution in the deuteron. Since w^2 accounts only for about 4% of the charge distribution and its Fourier transform is not likely to become negative, we can disregard the ^3D part in the charge distribution without incurring an error larger than 4%. The tail of u^2 is determined by the effective range and binding energy and we are uncertain about the behavior of the charge distribution u^2 only within the range of nuclear forces. Since $j_0(\frac{1}{2}qr)$ is a decreasing function within the range of nuclear forces, we decrease the form factor f^2 by pushing the charge distribution outward. Thus the experimental form factor can be expected to fall between the extremes that correspond to a smooth charge distribution such as is caused by the Hulthén potential, and to a pushed-out charge distribution caused by a potential with a large hard core of radius $\approx 0.7\times10^{-13}$ cm. Such form factors have been illustrated in Fig. 1.

III. DEUTERON BREAKUP

Since the deuteron is a weakly bound structure, the impact of a high-energy electron is likely to break it up. The energy distribution of electrons scattered at large angles shows not only an elastic peak, but also a considerable inelastic peak. In analogy with (2), the expression for the inelastic cross section is

$$d\sigma_{\text{in}}=(4\pi)^{-3}e^4[p_0^2\sin^4(\tfrac{1}{2}\theta)]^{-1}kdpd\Omega_p d\Omega_k \times|\langle f|[a_0-i\nabla\cdot\mathbf{a}+\tfrac{1}{2}i\mu_p\boldsymbol{\sigma}_p\cdot(\mathbf{q}\times\mathbf{a})]e^{\frac{1}{2}i\mathbf{q}\cdot\mathbf{r}} +\tfrac{1}{2}i\mu_n\boldsymbol{\sigma}_n\cdot(\mathbf{q}\times\mathbf{a})e^{-\frac{1}{2}i\mathbf{q}\cdot\mathbf{r}}|0\rangle|^2, \quad (6)$$

where, in addition to previous notation, $\mathbf{k}$ represents the final momentum of the proton with respect to the mass center of the recoiling deuteron, so that the wave function for the final state is $e^{i\mathbf{k}\cdot\mathbf{r}}+$ the incoming wave.

Using this expression later on, we shall compute the energy spectrum of the electrons scattered at a given angle. We shall find that the inelastic peak is fairly narrow. Therefore, over the energy range from which the bulk of the contribution to the cross section comes, the recoil momentum q does not vary much. Considering $\mathbf{q}$ constant, the interaction in (6) does not depend explicitly upon the disintegration energy k^2, and we can quickly estimate the total cross section to be expected, using the closure property for the final wave functions of the deuteron. The total (elastic plus all inelastic) cross section is found to be nearly independent of the wave function of the deuteron in the ground state. Subtracting the value of the elastic cross section [(3) and (5)] from the value of the total cross section computed in this way, we obtain the total inelastic cross section, which is approximately

$$d\sigma_{\text{in}}\approx\tfrac{1}{4}e^4\cos^2(\tfrac{1}{2}\theta)[p_0^2\sin^4(\tfrac{1}{2}\theta)]^{-1}[1+p_0\sin^2(\tfrac{1}{2}\theta)]^{-1}d\Omega_p \times\{(1-f^2)+(\tfrac{1}{2}q)^2[(2/\cos^2(\tfrac{1}{2}\theta))-1](\mu_p^2+\mu_n^2)\} \quad (7)$$

for large values of the recoil momentum. For small values of recoil momentum ($q<\alpha\approx\frac{1}{4}\times10^{13}$ cm^{-1}, where α^{-1} is the "size" of the deuteron), the terms retained in (7) become about as small as the terms neglected. Comparison of our expressions for the elastic and inelastic cross sections shows that as the recoil momentum increases, the inelastic cross section increases at the expense of the elastic, and the magnetic spin terms assume more importance in the inelastic cross section than in the elastic. Using the approximation that leads to Eq. (7), we can also estimate the portion of the inelastic cross section that is caused by transitions from the ground state (considered spherically symmetric) to all final states of given angular momentum and spin. The result is independent of the particular complete set of radial wave functions chosen and depends only upon the wave function of the ground state and the magnitude of q. The calculation shows that states of high angular momentum contribute appreciably to the total cross section.

Thus, in calculating the energy spectrum for the inelastically scattered electrons, we start by taking a plane wave for the final nucleon wave function (neglecting incoming waves), and later correct for the neutron-proton interaction in the sates of successively increasing angular momentum. To simplify the calculation, we assume that the ground state has the Hulthén form:

$$\phi_m=(4\pi)^{-\frac{1}{2}}r^{-1}(2\alpha)^{\frac{1}{2}}(1-\alpha r_t)^{-\frac{1}{2}}u_g\chi_m, \qquad (8)$$

where $u_g=e^{-\alpha r}-e^{-\gamma r}$, and γ is determined by the triplet effective range r_t. Taking plane waves for the final state makes the calculation of the inelastic cross section (6) straightforward. We perform the integrals involved, do the spin sums, and then integrate over the directions of disintegration ($d\Omega_k$) to obtain

$$d\sigma_{\text{in}}=(4\pi)^{-1}e^4\cos^2(\tfrac{1}{2}\theta)[p_0^2\sin^4(\tfrac{1}{2}\theta)]^{-1}2\alpha(1-\alpha r_t)^{-1} \times q^{-2}k^{-1}dp\,d\Omega_p O^2, \qquad (9)$$

where

$$\begin{aligned}O^2=&\left\{\frac{1}{z^2-1}+\frac{1}{z_1^2-1}-\frac{2}{z_1-z}[Q_0(z)-Q_0(z_1)]\right\}\\ &\times\{1+[k^2+2(\tfrac{1}{2}q)^2(\mu_p^2+\mu_n^2)]\\ &\times\tfrac{1}{2}[(2/\cos^2(\tfrac{1}{2}\theta))-1-z^2k^2]\}\\ &-\left\{\frac{z}{z^2-1}+\frac{z_1}{z_1^2-1}-\frac{z_1+z}{z_1-z}[Q_0(z)-Q_0(z_1)]\right\}2zk^2\\ &-\left\{2+\frac{1}{z^2-1}+\frac{1}{z_1^2-1}-\frac{2zz_1}{z_1-z}[Q_0(z)-Q_0(z_1)]\right\}\\ &\times k^2\{\tfrac{1}{2}[(2/\cos^2(\tfrac{1}{2}\theta))-1-z^2k^2]-z^2k^2\}\\ &-\frac{(z_1-z)^2}{z_1z(z_1+z)}[Q_0(z)+Q_0(z_1)]\\ &\times(-\tfrac{1}{3}\mu_p\mu_n)(\tfrac{1}{2}q)^2[(2/\cos^2(\tfrac{1}{2}\theta))-1-z^2k^2], \qquad (10)\end{aligned}$$

where $Q_0(z)=\coth^{-1}z$ is a Legendre function of the second kind, and z and z_1 are the abbreviations for

$$\begin{aligned}z&=[\alpha^2+(\tfrac{1}{2}q)^2+k^2]/qk,\\ z_1&=[\gamma^2+(\tfrac{1}{2}q)^2+k^2]/qk.\end{aligned} \qquad (11)$$

Examination of this expression shows that the terms coming entirely from the convection current ($\mathbf{a}\cdot\nabla$) are fairly small for moderate values of the disintegration energy k^2. The cross term between the convection current and the electric charge (a_0) becomes small because of the averaging over the directions of the nucleons, since $\mathbf{a}\cdot\mathbf{q}=-\Delta E a_0$.

However, in calculating O^2 in (10) with unperturbed final nucleon wave functions we have committed a large error. Since the neutron-proton interaction is felt very strongly in the final S states, we have to replace the erroneously calculated S contributions to O^2 in (10) by the contributions obtained using the correct final S wave functions. Neglecting the convection current ($\mathbf{a}\cdot\nabla$), the ^3S contribution towards O^2 is

$$\{1+\tfrac{2}{3}(\tfrac{1}{2}q)^2(\mu_p+\mu_n)^2[(2/\cos^2(\tfrac{1}{2}\theta))-1-z^2k^2]\}A_{gt}^2,$$

and the ^1S part is

$$\tfrac{1}{3}(\tfrac{1}{2}q)^2(\mu_p-\mu_n)^2[(2/\cos^2(\tfrac{1}{2}\theta))-1-z^2k^2]A_{gs}^2,$$

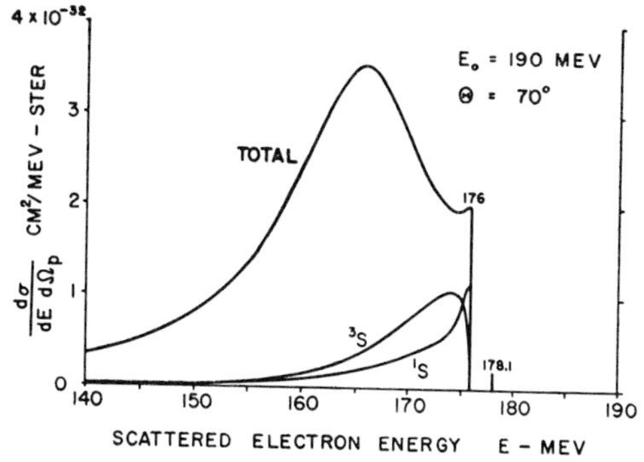

FIG. 2. Energy spectrum of 190-Mev electrons scattered inelastically at 70°. The total inelastic cross section is plotted, and the contributions to this cross section from the transitions to final S states are also indicated. The size of the elastic cross section ($=29.7\times10^{-32}$ cm²/steradian for the Hulthén potential) at 178.1 Mev is not indicated.

where

$$A_{gt(s)}=q\int u_{t(s)}{}^*j_0(\tfrac{1}{2}qr)u_g dr.$$

In previous calculation of these parts we have effectively used the unperturbed S wave function $\sin(kr)$ instead of the correct $u_{t(s)}$. The "correct" wave functions have been obtained assuming that the neutron-proton potential is an Eckart potential of the type[6]

$$V(r)=-\frac{2\lambda^2}{\cosh^2(\lambda r-\theta')}. \qquad (12)$$

Then the wave functions in the S states are

$$\begin{aligned}u(r)=&(k^2+\lambda^2\tanh^2\theta')^{-\frac{1}{2}}(k^2+\lambda^2)^{-\frac{1}{2}}\\ &\times\{[(k^2-\lambda^2\tanh\theta')\sin(kr)+(1+\tanh\theta')k\lambda\cos(kr)]\\ &-\lambda[1-\tanh(\lambda r-\theta')][-\lambda\tanh\theta'\sin(kr)+k\cos(kr)]\},\end{aligned}$$

and the phase shifts satisfy the "shape-independent approximation" formula[7] exactly for all energy values. The wave function for the bound state is ($\theta_t'>0$)

$$u_g=\exp(-\lambda\tanh\theta_t' r)\{1-(1+\tanh\theta_t')^{-1} \times[1-\tanh(\lambda_t r-\theta_t')]\}.$$

The parameters λ, θ' have been adjusted to yield the experimental scattering lengths and effective ranges for triplet and singlet scattering, and the integrals A_{gt} and A_{gs} have been performed with the help of an additional approximation,

$$1-\tanh(\lambda r-\theta')\approx(1+\tanh\theta')[1+(1+\tanh\theta')\lambda r]e^{-2\lambda r}.$$

The corresponding contributions (^3S and ^1S) towards the inelastic cross section are illustrated in Figs. 2 and 3 for two combinations of incident electron energy E_0

[6] V. Bargmann, Revs. Modern Phys. **21**, 488 (1949); C. Eckart, Phys. Rev. **34**, 1303 (1930).
[7] J. M. Blatt and V. F. Weisskopf, reference 5, p. 62.

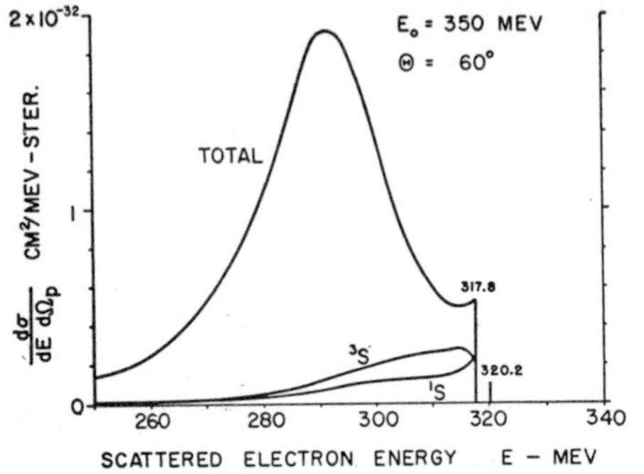

FIG. 3. Energy spectrum of 350-Mev electrons scattered inelastically at 60°. The total inelastic cross section is plotted, and the contributions to this cross section from the transitions to the final S states are also indicated. The size of the elastic cross section ($=6.77\times10^{-32}$ cm²/steradian for the Hulthén potential) at 320.2 Mev is not indicated.

and scattering angle θ. The total cross section indicated in each of these figures is the cross section calculated by (9) and (10) after the correction for the interaction in S states has been made.

The Eckart potential (12) is, of course, only a special case of a potential consistent with the information derived from neutron-proton scattering at low energies. For this reason the electric monopole part (^3S) has been checked by recalculating it for a potential with a hard core. Also, the effect of tensor forces has been investigated by computing the matrix element for the transition to final 1α states[8] and comparing it with the matrix element for the transitions to the ^3S states calculated previously. In both cases the change in the electric monopole cross section is small for small disintegration energy, since the wave functions then are adequately described by the shape-independent approximation. The change increases percentagewise for larger disintegration energies, but is still unimportant in computing the total cross section since the S part itself then becomes negligible.

The effect of neutron-proton interaction in the final states of higher angular momentum ($l>0$) is considerably smaller than in the S states, since the interaction is shielded by the centrifugal potential $l(l+1)r^{-2}$. Thus we have estimated it using the Born approximation to obtain the final wave functions and representing the neutron-proton interaction by a Yukawa potential,

$$V(r)=-cr^{-1}\exp(-\beta r), \tag{13}$$

of such strength and range[9] that it would yield the experimental scattering length and effective range if acting in the ^3S states. The calculation has been performed in momentum space so that to the wave function for the ground state,

$$\phi_g(\mathbf{r})=r^{-1}(e^{-\alpha r}-e^{-\gamma r}),$$

corresponds

$$\psi_g(\boldsymbol{\kappa})=(2\pi)^{-\frac{3}{2}}4\pi\left(\frac{1}{\alpha^2+\kappa^2}-\frac{1}{\gamma^2+\kappa^2}\right)$$

in momentum space. The wave function for the final state in the Born approximation is

$$\psi(\boldsymbol{\kappa})=(2\pi)^{\frac{3}{2}}\left[\delta(\boldsymbol{\kappa}-\mathbf{k})+\frac{c}{2\pi^2}\frac{1}{\kappa^2-k^2+i\epsilon}\frac{1}{\beta^2+|\boldsymbol{\kappa}-\mathbf{k}|^2}\right].$$

Then the matrix element

$$M=qk\int\phi^*(\mathbf{r})e^{\frac{1}{2}i\mathbf{q}\cdot\mathbf{r}}\phi_g(\mathbf{r})d\mathbf{r}/4\pi$$

$$=qk\int\psi^*(\boldsymbol{\kappa})\psi_g(\boldsymbol{\kappa}-\tfrac{1}{2}\mathbf{q})d\boldsymbol{\kappa}/4\pi,$$

can be expanded in spherical harmonics, corresponding to transitions into the states of appropriate angular momentum. Using the relation[10]

$$1/(z-\cos\vartheta)=\textstyle\sum_l(2l+1)P_l(\cos\vartheta)Q_l(z),$$

we see that

$$M=\sum_l(2l+1)P_l(\cos\vartheta)\times\Big\{[Q_l(z)-Q_l(z_1)]$$

$$+\frac{c}{2\pi}\int_{-\infty}^{+\infty}\frac{d\kappa}{\kappa^2-k^2-i\epsilon}Q_l(z_2')[Q_l(z')-Q_l(z_1')]\Big\}, \tag{14}$$

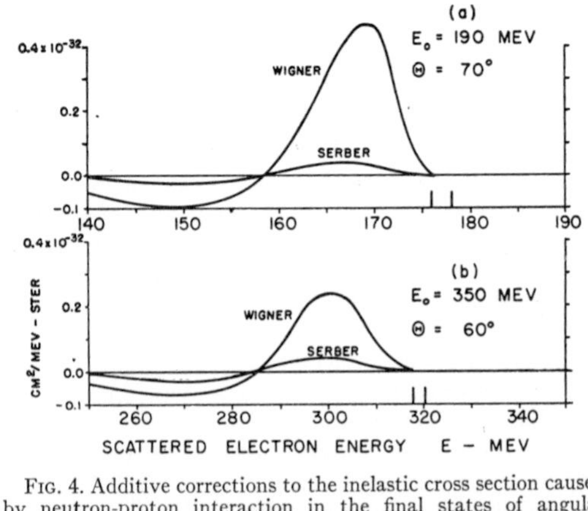

FIG. 4. Additive corrections to the inelastic cross section caused by neutron-proton interaction in the final states of angular momenta $l\geq1$, when the same potential is effective in states of all angular momenta (Wigner), and when the potential acts only in states of even angular momenta (Serber). (a) Correction to the total cross section of Fig. 1; (b) Correction to the total cross section of Fig. 2.

[8] For notation see J. M. Blatt and L. C. Biedenharn, Phys. Rev. **86**, 399 (1954).
[9] J. M. Blatt and J. D. Jackson, Phys. Rev. **76**, 18 (1949).
[10] E. W. Hobson, *The Theory of Spherical and Ellipsoidal Harmonics* (Cambridge University Press, Cambridge, 1931), p. 58.

where $\cos\vartheta = \mathbf{k}\cdot\mathbf{q}/kq$, z and z_1 are abbreviations (11), and

$$z' = [\alpha^2 + (\tfrac{1}{2}q)^2 + \kappa^2]/q\kappa,$$
$$z_1' = [\gamma^2 + (\tfrac{1}{2}q)^2 + \kappa^2]/q\kappa,$$
$$z_2' = [\beta^2 + k^2 + \kappa^2]/2k\kappa.$$

The integral in (14) has been transformed into a proper integral over a finite range by introducing a new variable of integration:

$$x \begin{cases} = \kappa/k & \text{for } |\kappa| < k, \\ = k/\kappa & \text{for } |\kappa| > k. \end{cases}$$

The quadratures were then performed numerically. The resulting corrections to the inelastic cross section decrease very rapidly with increasing angular momentum, so that the calculation has been performed only for $l=1, 2, 3$; the magnitude of the correction to be expected from neutron-proton interaction in these final states is indicated in Fig. 4. Two possibilities have been considered: when the same potential (13) acts in states of all angular momenta $l=1, 2, 3$ (Wigner force); when it acts only in the state of even angular momentum $l=2$ (Serber force). The results obtained here are only approximate, since the Born approximation has been used and only the Yukawa-type interaction has been considered.

IV. DISCUSSION

In the preceding calculation we have shown that the elastic cross section is somewhat sensitive to the presence or absence of the hard core in the interaction and that the inelastic cross section is somewhat sensitive to the presence or absence of the neutron-proton interaction in the final ^3P state. However, the calculation has been made using bare nucleons to represent the proton and the neutron. Actually, since the wavelength associated with our recoil momentum is of the order of the meson Compton wavelength, the finite size of the nucleons should be felt. Since the deuteron is a weakly bound structure, the proton and neutron spend most of the time outside the range of nuclear forces, and we can roughly describe the charge and current distributions around each nucleon as if they were free. In this approximation previous expressions for the matrix elements remain unchanged except that the nominal values for the charges and magnetic moments have to be replaced by effective charges and effective magnetic moments that depend upon the recoil momentum q. Then numerical values for the cross sections can easily be obtained if the form factors for the proton and neutron are known separately. Assuming, as an example, that the effective charge of the neutron vanishes and the charge of the proton has an rms radius 0.7×10^{-13} cm, as favored by present experimental evidence,[11] and that the form factors for the magnetic moments are the same as the form factor for the proton charge, we find that both elastic and inelastic cross sections are to be multiplied by the factor $[1-\frac{1}{6}(q\times0.7\times10^{-13}\text{ cm})^2+\cdots]^2$. This factor lowers the elastic cross section more than does the introduction of a hard core.

However, spreading out the charges and magnetic moments of the nucleons accounts only for one-particle terms in Foldy's phenomenological theory.[12] The charge and current distribution terms that depend on the coordinates of both particles are significant only within the range of the nuclear forces, and some idea about the contribution of these terms can be obtained by expanding the exponential $\exp(i\mathbf{q}\cdot\mathbf{r}')$ in power series of q and taking only the lowest nonvanishing terms. Of these, the exchange moment operators, which contribute to the magnetic moments of nuclei, have been investigated in more detail.[13] They are not important for the elastic cross section, since their contribution to the magnetic moment of the deuteron is very small.[14] The contribution of exchange moments to the inelastic cross section has been evaluated following Berger,[3] and has been found to be small for the moderate disintegration energy considered.

V. ACKNOWLEDGMENTS

I wish to acknowledge my indebtedness to Professor L. I. Schiff under whose patient guidance this work has been performed. I am grateful to Dr. John A. McIntyre and to Professor R. Hofstadter whose experiments have motivated this calculation and whose willingness to apprise me of the progress of their experiments has been most helpful and stimulating. I wish also to thank Professor Willis E. Lamb, Jr., Professor Donald R. Yennie, Professor Richard H. Dalitz, Dr. D. Geoffrey Ravenhall, and Dr. Kent G. Dedrick for their interest in the problem and for numerous enlightening discussions.

[11] Hughes, Harvey, Goldberg and Stafne, Phys. Rev. **90**, 497 (1953); R. Hofstadter and R. W. McAllister, Phys. Rev. **98**, 217 (1955).

[12] L. L. Foldy, Phys. Rev. **92**, 178 (1953).

[13] J. M. Berger and L. L. Foldy, Case Institute of Technology Technical Report No. 18 (unpublished).

[14] M. Sugawara, Phys. Rev. **99**, 1601 (1955) and to be published.

PAPER 33[*]

Electron Scattering and Nuclear Structure[*]

ROBERT HOFSTADTER

Department of Physics, Stanford University, Stanford, California

TABLE OF CONTENTS

	Page
I. Introduction	214
II. Scattering Theory	
(a) Scattering from Point Charges	215
(b) Scattering from Nuclei of Finite Size	216
(c) Phase-Shift Analysis of Electron Scattering	219
III. Various Scattering Phenomena	
(a) Nuclear Recoil	221
(b) Inelastic Scattering	222
(1) Excitation of Nuclear Levels	222
(2) Electrodisintegration—The Momentum Distribution of Nucleons in a Nucleus	223
(3) Breakup of the Nucleus	224
(4) Mesonic Processes	224
(5) Radiation	224
(c) Magnetic Scattering	225
(d) Angular Shapes of Nuclei	227
IV. Experimental Matters	
(a) The 190-Mev Apparatus	227
(b) The 550-Mev Spectrometer	231
(c) Behavior of Čerenkov Detectors	232
V. Results	
(a) The Proton	233
(b) The Deuteron	236
(c) The Alpha Particle	237
(d) Lithium and Beryllium	238
(e) Carbon	239
(f) Mg, Si, S, A, Sr	241
(g) The Medium-Heavy and Heavy Elements	242
VI. The Neutron	246
VII. The Validity of Electrodynamics	247
VIII. Comparisons with Other Measurements of Nuclear Sizes	248
IX. Summary	252
X. Conclusions	253
XI. Acknowledgments	254

I. INTRODUCTION

UNTIL a few years ago the principal information concerning geometric details of nuclear structure was derived from experiments on comparative energy releases in mirror nuclei, on fast neutron capture (and total) cross sections, on binding energies as they related to the Weiszacker semiempirical formula, and, in the case of the heaviest elements, on the energies and half-lives of alpha activities. All approaches led to the same general range of values of the nuclear radii for a uniformly charged sphere, which was taken universally as the appropriate model of the nucleus. The results can be summarized in a well-known formula for the radius of a uniform sphere

$$R=r_0A^{\frac{1}{3}}\times 10^{-13}\text{ cm.} \tag{1}$$

Henceforth, we shall measure all distances in terms of 10^{-13} cm as a unit and shall call this unit the fermi. For example, this formula puts the edge of the nuclear sphere of gold at a distance of 8.45 fermis from the center of the nucleus, if the constant r_0 is given a good compromise value of somewhere near 1.45 fermis. This model gives a uniform mass density to all nuclei, i.e.,

$$\rho_M=\frac{A}{(4/3)\pi R^3}\frac{\text{nucleons}}{(\text{fermi})^3}=\frac{1}{(4/3)\pi r_0^3}\frac{\text{nucleons}}{(\text{fermi})^3}=0.080\frac{\text{nucleons}}{(\text{fermi})^3}, \tag{2}$$

and a variable charge density to the nuclei,

$$\rho_C=\frac{Ze}{(4/3)\pi R^3}=e\frac{Z}{A}\frac{1}{(4/3)\pi r_0^3}=\frac{Z}{A}\times 0.080\frac{\text{proton charges}}{(\text{fermi})^3}. \tag{3}$$

These formulas are represented in Figs. 1(a) and 1(b) and show the relative size and shapes of a few representative nuclei.

In the last few years the work of Lyman *et al.*[1] Hofstadter *et al.*,[2–4] Pidd *et al.*,[5] and Fitch and Rainwater[6] on electron scattering and μ-mesonic atoms showed that the radii determined by these methods were approximately 20% smaller for the heavier elements than those given by Eq. (1) with $r_0=1.45$ fermi. The μ-mesonic results also indicated that the lighter elements possessed smaller radii reduced according to

* The research reported here was supported jointly by the Office of Naval Research and the U. S. Atomic Energy Commission, and by the U. S. Air Force, through the Office of Scientific Research of the Air Research and Development Command.

[1] Lyman, Hansen, and Scott, Phys. Rev. 84, 626 (1951).
[2] Hofstadter, Fechter, and McIntyre, Phys. Rev. 91, 422 (1953).
[3] Hofstadter, Fechter, and McIntyre, Phys. Rev. 92, 978 (1953). (The theoretical interpretation of the data was carried out by Yennie *et al.* See Secs. IIc and Vg.)
[4] Hofstadter, Hahn, Knudsen, and McIntyre, Phys. Rev. 95, 512 (1954).
[5] Pidd, Hammer, and Raka, Phys. Rev. 92, 436 (1953).
[6] V. L. Fitch and J. Rainwater, Phys. Rev. 92, 789 (1953).

* *See page 683 of this volume for corrections and addenda.*

the same formula: $r_0=1.20$ fermi. At the same time Cooper and Henley[7] suggested that the data on mirror nuclei, relating, of course, to light nuclei, could be explained in terms of the smaller radii. Subsequently, some doubt has been expressed about this conclusion.[8] In any case, the smaller radii obtained by these methods have come to be called "electromagnetic" radii. For want of a better word, the radii given by Eq. (1) for $r_0=1.45$ fermis may be called "nucleonic" radii, since the larger values arise from experiments in which nucleons interact with nuclei.

A considerable amount of work has been carried out on electron scattering at Stanford University in the period 1953–1956. This work has provided information on the charge densities of nuclei ranging from the proton to uranium. It appeared that something like a status report covering this material would be timely. Such a report could have the effect of gathering together various bits of existing information so that workers in the more general field of nuclear radii might have "electron scattering" radii and charge densities for comparison with their own data. It is the purpose of this review to present such an organization of the data, including some as yet unpublished work. This report should not be looked upon as a final word on the nuclear sizes and shapes determined by electron-scattering methods. Indeed, the future electron scattering program at high energies will undoubtedly yield some conclusions differing from the present ones and perhaps some surprises. However, it does not seem probable that major differences will arise and, therefore, a report at this time may be appropriate.

Although neither a historical nor a comprehensive report on the work of other laboratories engaged in electron scattering work is here intended, it is sincerely hoped that the present review will act as a stimulus to encourage workers in this and other fields to assemble their data on nuclear radii and even perhaps to encourage new experiments. A review on nuclear charge distributions by Ford and Hill[9] has recently appeared and is one step in this direction.

II. SCATTERING THEORY

(a) Scattering from Point Charges

At the root of all elastic scattering processes involving charged particles lies Rutherford's famous formula. This formula,

$$\sigma(\theta)=\frac{z^2Z^2e^4}{16E^2}\frac{1}{\sin^4\frac{1}{2}\theta}, \tag{4}$$

expresses the differential cross section $\sigma(\theta)$ for scattering incident charged point particles (charge ze) of *kinetic* energy E against immovable charged point centers,

[7] L. N. Cooper and E. M. Henley, Phys. Rev. **92**, 801 (1953).
[8] B. G. Jancovici, Phys. Rev. **95**, 389 (1954).
[9] K. W. Ford and D. L. Hill, "The Distribution of Charge in the Nucleus," Ann. Revs. Nuclear Sci. **A**, 25–72 (1956).

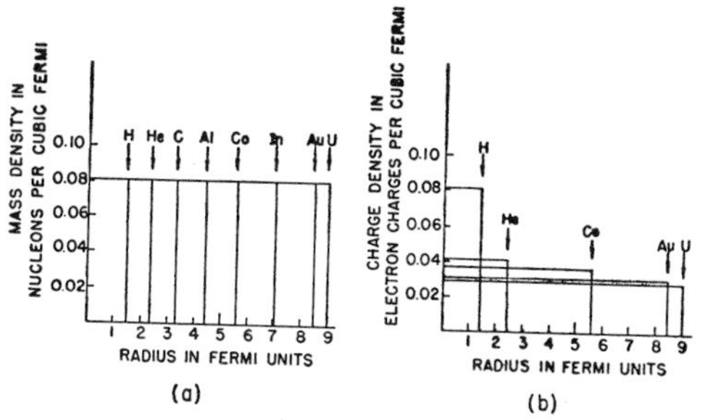

FIG. 1. (a) Mass density of nuclei for the uniform sphere [Eq. (2)]. (b) Charge density of nuclei for the uniform spherical model [Eq. (3)].

such as heavy nuclei (charge Ze), conceived as intense sources of an electric force field; θ is the polar angle of scattering. Rutherford scattering, [Eq. (4)], has been shown to be valid in quantum mechanics as well as in classical mechanics.[10]

While the Rutherford scattering law applies to alpha particles and protons of medium energies, it is not a relativistic formula and takes no account of the possible spins of the scattering partners nor of their possible identity.

Relativistic scattering of Dirac particles, such as electrons, against point nuclei, has been considered by Mott in a well-known paper.[11] In this case the incident particle, the electron, is assumed to have a spin (and a Dirac magnetic moment), although the scattering center (the nucleus) is assumed to have neither a spin nor a magnetic moment. Mott developed a series expression for the elastic scattering cross section and also gave an approximate formula, derived for elements that satisfy the inequality

$$\frac{Z}{137}=Z\frac{e^2}{\hbar c}\ll 1. \tag{5}$$

The approximation of Mott has been called Mott scattering and is given below in Eq. (6):

$$\sigma_M(\theta)=\left(\frac{Ze^2}{2mc^2}\right)^2\left(\frac{1-\beta^2}{\beta^4}\right)\frac{1}{\sin^4\frac{1}{2}\theta}(1-\beta^2\sin^2\tfrac{1}{2}\theta), \tag{6}$$

where

$$\beta=v/c,\quad z=1; \tag{7}$$

v and c are velocity of the incident particle and the velocity of light, respectively. m is the rest mass of the electron. Equation (6) is written in terms of center-of-mass coordinates. Under conditions such as will be described in this review, β is always very close to unity and, consequently, in Eq. (6), β^4 will be put equal to

[10] N. F. Mott and H. S. W. Massey, *The Theory of Atomic Collisions* (Clarendon Press, Oxford, 1949).
[11] N. F. Mott, Proc. Roy. Soc. (London) **A124**, 426 (1929); **A135**, 429 (1932).

unity, so that

$$1-\beta^2\sin^2\tfrac{1}{2}\theta\approx\cos^2\tfrac{1}{2}\theta \tag{8}$$

to a high degree of accuracy. Furthermore, the total energy of an electron is

$$E=\frac{mc^2}{(1-\beta^2)^{\frac{1}{2}}} \tag{9}$$

so that

$$1-\beta^2=(mc^2/E)^2. \tag{10}$$

Making these changes in Eq. (6) results in the relativistic formula of Mott[12] for the elastic scattering of electrons

$$\sigma_M(\theta)=\left(\frac{Ze^2}{2E}\right)^2\frac{\cos^2\frac{1}{2}\theta}{\sin^4\frac{1}{2}\theta} \tag{11}$$

with spin against spinless point nuclei of charge Ze. This formula is a very simple expression, indeed.

Equation (11) is quite accurate when condition (5) is satisfied. However, for more massive nuclei, where Z is large, Eq. (11) has been shown to be in error, as expected. Improvement of Eq. (11) has been attempted by many investigators and a description of these calculations will not be given here. McKinley and Feshbach[13] and Feshbach[14] have summarized the various investigations and have themselves put forward the proper corrections of Eq. (11) for nuclei of larger Z values. Their work has been confirmed by Dalitz,[15] who used Born's second approximation.

When $Z/137$ is not large, a better approximation to Eq. (11) has been given by the above authors[13,15]:

$$\sigma_F(\theta)=\left(\frac{Ze^2}{2E}\right)^2\frac{\cos^2\frac{1}{2}\theta}{\sin^4\frac{1}{2}\theta}\left[1+\frac{\pi Z}{137}\frac{(\sin\frac{1}{2}\theta)(1-\sin\frac{1}{2}\theta)}{\cos^2\frac{1}{2}\theta}\right] \tag{12}$$

under the same conditions applying to Eq. (11), except that condition (5) has been relaxed. At small angles, Eqs. (11) and (12) are equivalent to each other. Even at larger angles, the errors are rather small. The relative error in using (12) instead of (11) amounts to 3% and 7% for Si and Zn at $\theta=90°$, respectively, and to 17% and 35% for Si and Zn at 135°. Equation (12) may not be used for the heaviest nuclei. A closed formula, similar to (12) cannot be given for all values of Z, but numerical evaluation of the scattering for high Z is given in the paper of Feshbach.[14] This author also gives the corresponding scattering results for positrons. Bartlett and Watson[16] have made exact numerical calculations for the heavy nucleus mercury ($Z=80$). It may be noticed that the angular distributions given in Eqs. (11) and (12) are independent of incident energy. However, it must be remembered that these equations apply to scattering from an infinitely heavy nucleus and will, therefore, be strictly applicable only in the center-of-mass system of coordinates. For more realistic nuclei of conventional mass values, the center of mass will move forward at a considerable speed when the incident electrons have energies above 100 Mev and there will be a forward peaking of the angular distributions due to this effect at higher energies. This subject will be mentioned again later (see Sec. III-c).

Exact calculations for point-charge elastic scattering in copper and gold have been carried out at high electron energies by Yennie, Ravenhall, and Wilson[17,18] by phase-shift methods and have been compared with the corresponding expressions in the first Born approximation (Fig. 1 of reference 17).

(b) Scattering from Nuclei of Finite Size

The first consideration of the effects of finite nuclear size on electron scattering appears to have been made by Guth.[19] Later, and independently, similar ideas were developed by Rose.[20]

Using more exact methods, Elton,[21] Feshbach,[22] and Acheson[23] have considered the finite size problem in relation to electron-scattering experiments at lower energies (up to 20 Mev), while Parzen[24] has dealt with an energy of 100 Mev for Pb. Still later, Smith[25] made a detailed study of this problem at high electron energies using the first Born approximation and subsequently presented the principal results in abbreviated form.[26]

The results of Smith can be applied with accuracy only to light nuclei (Z small), but some of his results refer to both elastic and inelastic scattering. Schiff[27] has carried out similar first Born approximation calculations at high energies and has calculated other matters of interest in his paper.

Because the first Born approximation can be applied safely to light elements, and also, because the qualitative effects of finite nuclear size may be appreciated easily with this approximation, we shall devote the next few paragraphs to this topic.

(1) *The First Born Approximation*

Rose,[20] Smith,[25] and others have shown that, corresponding to Eq. (11) for a point charge, a scattering

[12] See Eq. (36) for modifications required for the laboratory system of coordinates.
[13] W. A. McKinley, Jr., and H. Feshbach, Phys. Rev. **74**, 1759 (1948). [These authors point out that Eq. (12) (above) was derived also by J. Schwinger.]
[14] H. Feshbach, Phys. Rev. **88**, 295 (1952).
[15] R. H. Dalitz, Proc. Roy. Soc. (London) **A206**, 509 (1951). [See also G. Parzen and T. Wainright, Phys. Rev. **96**, 188 (1954).]
[16] J. H. Bartlett and R. E. Watson, Proc. Am. Acad. Arts Sci. **74**, 53 (1940).
[17] Yennie, Ravenhall, and Wilson, Phys. Rev. **92**, 1325 (1953).
[18] Yennie, Ravenhall, and Wilson, Phys. Rev. **95**, 500 (1954).
[19] E. Guth, Wiener Anz. Akad. Wiss. No. 24, 299 (1934).
[20] M. E. Rose, Phys. Rev. **73**, 279 (1948).
[21] L. R. B. Elton, Proc. Phys. Soc. (London) **A63**, 1115 (1950); **65**, 481 (1952); Phys. Rev. **79**, 412 (1950).
[22] H. Feshbach, Phys. Rev. **84**, 1206 (1951).
[23] L. K. Acheson, Phys. Rev. **82**, 488 (1951).
[24] G. Parzen, Phys. Rev. **80**, 261 (1950); **80**, 355 (1950). [A numerical slip exists in the latter reference and the scattering curve (Fig. 1 of that paper) is not correct.]
[25] J. H. Smith, Ph.D., thesis, Cornell University, February, 1951 (unpublished).
[26] J. H. Smith, Phys. Rev. **95**, 271 (1954).
[27] L. I. Schiff, Phys. Rev. **92**, 988 (1953).

formula for elastic scattering, which replaces Eq. (11) when the nucleus is finite, must have the form

$$\sigma_s(\theta)=\left(\frac{Ze^2}{2E}\right)^2\frac{\cos^2\frac{1}{2}\theta}{\sin^4\frac{1}{2}\theta}\left|\int_{\substack{\text{nuclear}\\ \text{volume}}}\rho(r)e^{i\mathbf{q}\cdot\mathbf{r}}d\tau\right|^2 \tag{13}$$

where $\rho(\mathbf{r})$ is the charge density within a nucleus as a function of radius vector from the center of the nucleus and $\hbar\mathbf{q}$ is the momentum transfer vector. The numerical magnitude of q for elastic scattering is, thus, given by

$$q=\frac{2E}{\hbar c}\sin\tfrac{1}{2}\theta=\frac{2}{\bar{\lambda}}\sin\tfrac{1}{2}\theta \tag{14}$$

as shown in Fig. 2 where $|p_1|=|p_0|$. $\mathbf{p}_0$ and $\mathbf{p}_1$ are the incident and scattered momenta, respectively. $\bar{\lambda}$ in Eq. (14) is the reduced de Broglie wavelength of the high-energy incident electron:

$$\bar{\lambda}=\hbar/p_0; \tag{15}$$

qr in Eq. (13) is, thus, a dimensionless phase factor.

The assumption is made once more that the nucleus does not recoil, or equivalently, that Fig. 2 is imagined to be in the center-of-mass frame.

It can be shown[25] that the integral in Eq. (13) can be reduced, so that

$$\sigma_s(\theta)=\left(\frac{Ze^2}{2E}\right)^2\frac{\cos^2\frac{1}{2}\theta}{\sin^4\frac{1}{2}\theta}\left[\int_0^\infty\rho(r)\frac{\sin qr}{qr}4\pi r^2dr\right]^2. \tag{16}$$

Since the quantity in square brackets multiplies the point charge cross section given by Eq. (11), it is customary to follow the precedent established in the electron diffraction and x-ray diffraction analogs of this equation and call this quantity

$$F=\frac{4\pi}{q}\int_0^\infty\rho(r)\sin(qr)rdr \tag{17}$$

the "form factor" or "structure factor" corresponding to a finite nuclear charge distribution. Indeed, the analogy is very close[28] and it is merely necessary to replace the electron cloud of an atom by the proton cloud of a nucleus. If the charge density in Eq. (16) is normalized to unity, the form factor F is a dimensionless quantity.

In dealing with the first Born approximation, the central idea is as follows: To obtain the actual scattering from a finite nucleus, it is necessary merely to multiply

FIG. 2. The momentum transfer $\mathbf{q}$ in electron scattering. For elastic scattering in the center-of-mass frame $|p_1|=|p_0|$.

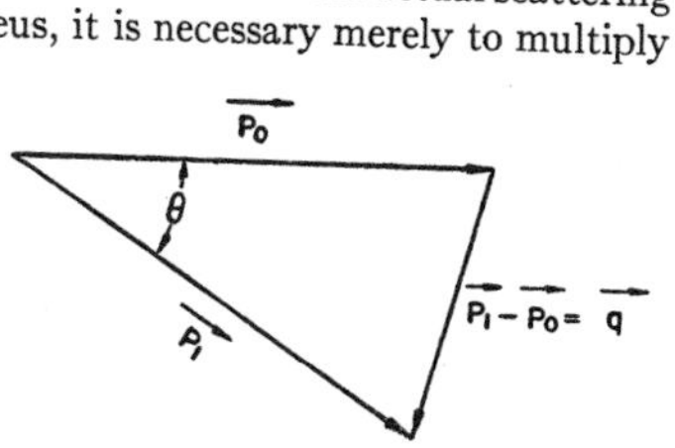

[28] See, for example, Z. G. Pinsker *Electron Diffraction* (Butterworth Scientific Publications, London, 1953), p. 148, Eq. (7,25).

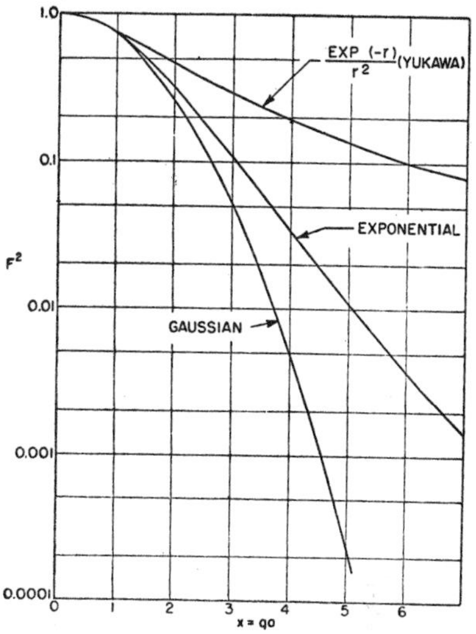

FIG. 3. The square of the form factor for typical charge distributions.

the point charge scattering cross section by the square of a form factor appropriate to the particular model of a nucleus under consideration. This procedure makes the calculations quite direct and usually quite s mple, since it is only necessary to evaluate a single quadirature [Eq. (17)]. For light nuclei this is satisfactory. Unfortunately, for medium and heavy nuclei, this procedure fails. As is well known, the first Born approximation is equivalent to considering both the incident and diffracted waves as plane waves. Actually, the waves are distorted by the intense nuclear electromagnetic field, so that they can no longer be considered plane waves. Perhaps an equivalent way of saying this is that the first Born approximation amounts to a single scattering in the force field, while the exact scattering depends on a plurality of scatterings in the same force field.

In any event, the application of the Born formalism to elastic scattering provides a most valuable tool for analyzing electron scattering by light nuclei and is of qualitative value in discussing heavier nuclei. We shall make further remarks about the accuracy of the first Born approximation at a later time.

Making use of Eq. (17), we shall now give the results for a number of useful nuclear models. In order to present the calculations in the most succinct way, we have prepared in Table I[29] a series of form factors for several nuclear charge density distributions. In the table "a" represents the root-mean-square radius, weighted according to charge, and defined as

$$a=\int_0^\infty r^2 4\pi r^2\rho dr=4\pi\int_0^\infty \rho r^4 dr, \tag{18}$$

[29] This convenient form of the table is due to E. E. Chambers.

TABLE I. In this table $\rho(r)$ is the charge density function; "a" is the root-mean-square radius of the charge distribution; $F(qa)$ is the form factor; $x=qa$.

Model number	Name of model	Expression for charge density $4\pi a^3\rho(r)$; $y=r/a$	$F(qa)$; $x=qa$
I	Point	δ function	1
II	Uniform	$\begin{cases} \frac{9}{5}\left(\frac{3}{5}\right)^{\frac{1}{2}} \text{ for } y\leqslant\left(\frac{5}{3}\right)^{\frac{1}{2}} \\ 0 \text{ for } y\geqslant\left(\frac{5}{3}\right)^{\frac{1}{2}} \end{cases}$	$5\left(\frac{5}{3}\right)^{\frac{1}{2}}x^{-3}\left[\sin\left(\frac{5}{3}\right)^{\frac{1}{2}}x-\left(\frac{5}{3}\right)^{\frac{1}{2}}x\cos\left(\frac{5}{3}\right)^{\frac{1}{2}}x\right]$
III	Gaussian	$3\left(\frac{6}{\pi}\right)^{\frac{1}{2}}\exp\left(-\frac{3}{2}y^2\right)$	$\exp(-x^2/6)$
IV	Exponential	$12\sqrt{3}\exp(-(12)^{\frac{1}{2}}y)$	$\left(1+\frac{x^2}{12}\right)^{-2}$
V	Shell	$\delta(y-1)$	$x^{-1}\sin x$
VI	Hollow exponential	$\frac{200}{3}y\exp(-(20)^{\frac{1}{2}}y)$	$\left(1-\frac{x^2}{60}\right)\left(1+\frac{x^2}{20}\right)^{-3}$
VII	...	$\frac{75}{2}(30)^{\frac{1}{2}}y^2\exp(-(30)^{\frac{1}{2}}y)$	$\left(1-\frac{x^2}{30}\right)\left(1+\frac{x^2}{30}\right)^{-4}$
VIII	Yukawa I	$\sqrt{2}y^{-2}\exp(-\sqrt{2}y)$	$\sqrt{2}x^{-1}\tan^{-1}(x/\sqrt{2})$
IX	Yukawa II	$6y^{-1}\exp(-\sqrt{6}\,y)$	$\left(1+\frac{x^2}{6}\right)^{-1}$
X	Hollow Gaussian	$\frac{50}{3}\left(\frac{5}{2\pi}\right)^{\frac{1}{2}}y^2\exp\left(-\frac{5}{2}y^2\right)$	$\left(1-\frac{x^2}{15}\right)\exp\left(-\frac{x^2}{10}\right)$
XI	Generalized shell model	$\begin{cases} \frac{8}{\sqrt{\pi}}\frac{k^3}{(2+3\alpha)}(1+\alpha k^2y^2)\exp(-k^2y^2) \\ \text{where } k=\left[\frac{3(2+5\alpha)}{2(2+3\alpha)}\right]^{\frac{1}{2}} \end{cases}$	$\left[1-\frac{\alpha x^2}{2k^2(2+3\alpha)}\right]\exp\left(-\frac{x^2}{4k^2}\right)$
XII	Modified exponential	$\frac{27}{\sqrt{2}}[1+(18)^{\frac{1}{2}}y]\exp[-(18)^{\frac{1}{2}}y]$	$\left(1+\frac{x^2}{18}\right)^{-3}$

where $\int_0^\infty 4\pi r^2\rho dr$ is normalized to unity. The ratio $r/a=y$ and is a measure of radial distance in terms of the rms radius. In Table I, x is defined as qa.

If qa is small, where a is the root-mean-square radius, all form factors reduce to the simple expansion

$$F=1-(q^2a^2/6)+\cdots. \tag{19}$$

At high energies this approximation is not useful because higher terms are needed.

Almost all useful nuclear shapes are included or approached more or less closely by one or another of the models listed in Table I. It is possible that repulsive core models are not sufficiently well approximated by any item of Table I. Several (form factors)^2 are shown in Figs. 3 and 4.

The usual procedure employed by the present author when using the Born method has been to try to fit experimental data in light nuclei with a few of the simple models. The search for a proper model is soon narrowed to one or possibly two of those given in Table I. The best fits of the parameter (or parameters) are then made.

It is also possible to invert the procedure and calculate the charge distribution from the experimental form factor. This has been done by Ravenhall[30] in analyzing accurate data on C^{12} and will be a useful procedure when the experimental data become very precise. In the author's opinion, present-day accuracy does not warrant this approach in most cases, although

[30] D. G. Ravenhall (unpublished).

it should not be very long before this procedure will become valuable. In inverting Eq. (17) one obtains

$$\rho(r)=\frac{1}{2\pi^2 r}\int_0^\infty F(q)\sin(qr)qdq. \quad (20)$$

A useful fitting procedure has also been given by Schiff[27] for comparing the form factor F with a certain experimental quantity he finds which should agree with F if the correct model has been chosen.

(c) Phase-Shift Analysis of Electron Scattering

The work of Yennie, Ravenhall, and Wilson,[17,18] Brenner, Brown, and Elton,[31] and Elizabeth Baranger,[32] showed conclusively that, for most nuclear models of medium and heavy elements, the exact elastic scattering cross sections departed markedly from those furnished by the first Born approximation. There appear to be two principal types of discrepancies, both apparent in Fig. 5, which is taken from the paper of Yennie *et al.*[17] This figure refers to a uniform charge distribution in gold corresponding to an energy of about 150 Mev, and a similar charge distribution in copper corresponding to an energy of about 225 Mev. First, the Born approximation puts true zeroes into the form factors, while the accurate calculations show minima rather than true zeroes and in some cases only points of inflection corresponding to the zeroes of the first Born approximation. In the second place, radii determined from the Born approximation are, in general, larger than the exact calculations show. This may be made plausible by noticing the fact that the de Broglie wave of the incident electron appears to be shorter inside the nuclear electric force field than it is when free. This follows from the simple consideration that the effective kinetic energy appears to be greater within the field than outside the field because of the

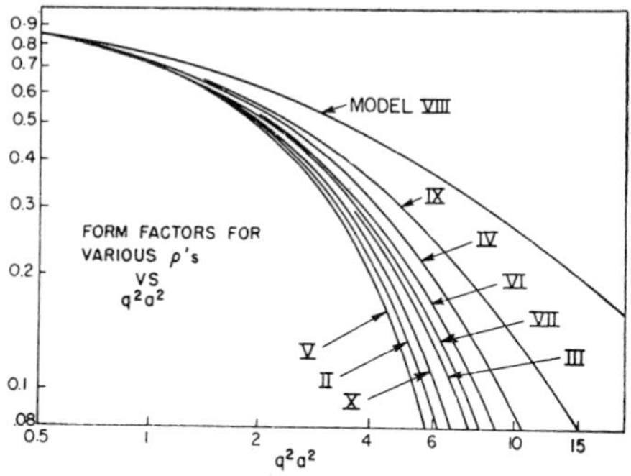

FIG. 4. The square of the form factor for several useful charge distributions at small values of qa. The model numbers refer to the charge densities of Table I. The graph was prepared by E. E. Chambers.

[31] Brenner, Brown, and Elton, Phil. Mag. (7) **45**, 524 (1954).
[32] Elizabeth Baranger, Phys. Rev. **93**, 1127 (1954).

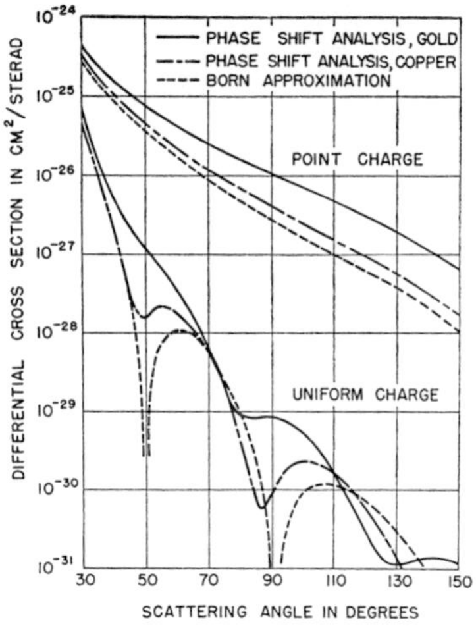

FIG. 5. Phase shift analyses by Yennie *et al.*[17,18] for uniform spherical models of gold and copper. The point charge curves are shown as well as Born approximation results for all cases. The data refer to gold at approximately 150 Mev and copper at 225 Mev.

potential trough. The Born approximation does not take this fact into account. Since all lengths are measured by the electrons in units of $\lambdabar$, the nucleus appears larger in the Born approximation, where $\lambdabar$ is not affected by the nuclear field, than in the exact case. Another way of saying this is that the diffraction features are associated with a given value of qR, where R is a typical radius parameter. Since $qR\propto R/\lambdabar$, a given diffraction feature will yield a smaller value of R, if $\lambdabar$ is smaller than in free space. An argument of this type was given by Yennie *et al.*,[17] but later it appeared that the Gaussian and exponential charge distribution did not conform exactly to the expected behavior. Perhaps the latter fact arises because the Gaussian and exponential charge distributions give monotonic angular distributions and, therefore, exhibit no diffraction features, a point upon which the plausibility argument rests. This matter is of some interest in understanding the physical features of the scattering phenomenon and it is to be hoped that an explanation may be forthcoming.

In any case, it is established that the first Born approximation may not be used for the heavy elements. In the case of copper, Fig. 5 shows that the Born approximation is much better than in gold, though by no means adequate. It is particularly bad in the neighborhood of the diffraction minima, which correspond to the true zeroes of the Born approximation. For nuclei with Z less than 10, the Born approximation will be satisfactory except right near the zeroes.

One reason why the first Born approximation is not good has been pointed out by Yennie *et al.*[18] These authors find that the scattering amplitude, a complex

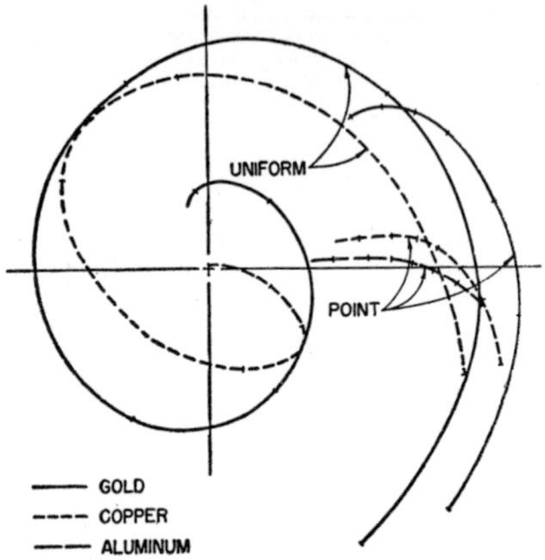

FIG. 6. Log_{10} of the modulus of the scattering amplitude plotted against θ (polar plot) for uniform models of gold, copper, and aluminum. Aluminum gives a result closest to a real number, indicating the validity of the Born approximation for light nuclei.

number in general, is widely different in the case of gold, from the scattering amplitude of the Born approximation. In the Born approximation the scattering amplitude is a real number and may be positive or negative and zero at a diffraction minimum. Figure 6 taken from their paper, shows the typical appearance of the $\log_{10}$ of the modulus of the scattering amplitude plotted against the angle θ in a polar plot for a model of Type II (Table I).

Since the Born approximation cannot be used for the medium and heavy elements, and since no other simple method of approximation has yet been developed, the exact phase shift methods must be employed at present. There appears to be no other method available, at least, up to now, of fitting the experimental data other than by choosing a model and calculating the angular distribution. If differences from experiment are observed, the model is changed and a new calculation made. Successive attempts converge on a model, or series of related models. This procedure has been described in the paper of Yennie *et al.*[18] where the Fermi smoothed uniform model was introduced. This particular model has the form of a Fermi type function[33] [Eq. (21)] and a typical shape is shown in Fig. 7. As may be seen later this model seems to be fairly close to the actual shape of the medium-heavy and heaviest nuclei.

$$\rho(r)=\frac{\rho_1}{\exp[(r-c)/z_1]+1}. \tag{21}$$

Experience with results of the type illustrated in Fig. 8 is helpful in deciding on the best model to fit the experimental data. Figure 8 shows three charge distributions in the inset and the three corresponding theoretical angular distributions for gold at about 125 Mev obtained by the phase shift method. The uniformly charged sphere (square edge) shows the most prominent diffraction features. The most smoothed curve shows, as expected, the smoothest angular distribution. Brown and Elton[34] have carried out calculations with related models and have come to similar conclusions. Hill, Freeman, and Ford[35] have carried out a similar analysis using slightly different models and have also obtained the same kind of results. Simpler models have been treated by Glassgold.[36]

Some brief remarks may be appropriate regarding the calculations of Yennie *et al.*[18] and those of Brenner *et al.*[31] These authors use the Dirac equation applied to a spherically symmetric static charge distribution. Quadrupole distortions are specifically avoided[37] and other dynamic effects are not taken into account such as possible dispersion corrections or correlations. The dispersion corrections have been considered by Schiff[38] who indicates that they should be small. The assumptions implicit in the theory, *viz.*, that the Dirac equation can be applied to the scattering, that the charge distribution can be treated as static, that electron-nucleon nonelectromagnetic forces do not exist, that the Coulomb law is valid at small distances, etc. can only be tested by the consistency of the theory and the scattering experiments at several energies and by the consistency of these conclusions with those found in other branches of nuclear physics. Thus far, there appear to be no reasons to doubt that the simple hypotheses made are not suitable, except possibly in the case of the proton (see Sec. VII).

Correlations between protons in the nucleus have

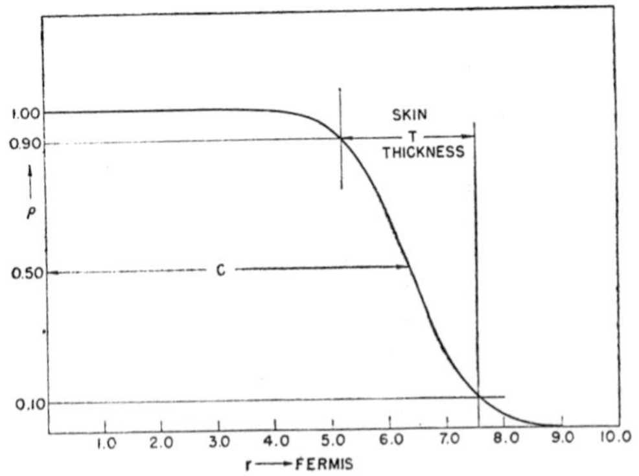

FIG. 7. The Fermi model. c is the distance to the half-density point and t is the skin thickness (90%–10% distance).

[33] Hahn, Ravenhall, and Hofstadter, Phys. Rev. **101**, 1131 (1956). (The terminology of this paper is used for the Fermi model.)

[34] G. E. Brown and L. R. B. Elton, Phil. Mag. **46**, 164 (1955).

[35] Hill, Freeman, and Ford (private communication). (See also item 28 in reference 9.)

[36] A. E. Glassgold, Phys. Rev. **98**, 1360 (1955).

[37] These will be discussed in Sec. Vg.

[38] L. I. Schiff, Phys. Rev. **98**, 756 (1955).

been considered recently by Lewis[39] who has studied nonpotential scattering and who also gives some details about the second Born approximation.[40]

III. VARIOUS SCATTERING PHENOMENA

Scattering phenomena can be broadly divided into elastic and inelastic types. In elastic scattering the kinetic energy of the two colliding particles remains constant in the center-of-mass frame. Alternatively, one may say that neither of the colliding bodies is raised to an excited state nor is a new particle produced. In our case, where one of the bodies is the electron, it suffices to observe that the nucleus remains in the ground state before and after the collision even though the nucleus may acquire a kinetic energy in the laboratory system. In inelastic scattering several types of behavior are observed, and they will be enumerated and described later.

In reality, because of the radiation by the electron of large numbers of soft quanta in the electric field surrounding the nucleus, it can truly be said that no scattering is precisely elastic. For example, if a 300-Mev electron is scattered by a heavy nucleus and emits three successive quanta of energies 0.1 ev, 1.0 ev, and 3.0 ev, the energy of the scattered electron is so minutely different from that of the incident energy that the collision may be termed elastic. In other words, if the detecting equipment cannot distinguish a 300-Mev electron from one with energy one part in 10^8 different from that energy, then the collision is elastic in any practical sense. We shall understand the term elastic collision in this sense. A correction for the radiation can be made when needed in comparing the experimental results with theoretical expectations of elastic scattering.

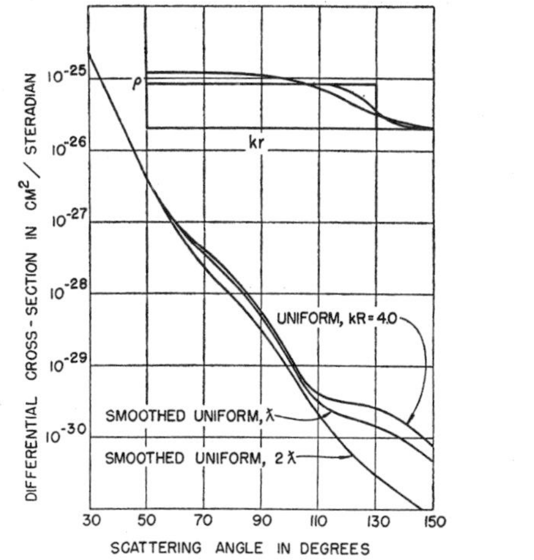

FIG. 8. Angular distributions for the three nuclear models shown in the inset. The uniform model shows the most prominent diffraction features.

[39] R. R. Lewis, Jr., Phys. Rev. **102**, 544 (1956).
[40] R. R. Lewis, Jr., Phys. Rev. **102**, 537 (1956).

(a) Nuclear Recoil

Before discussing the various types of inelastic scatterings, let us consider that kind which appears to be inelastic scattering in the laboratory frame, but which really is elastic scattering as seen in the center-of-mass frame. We mean to point simply to the change in energy suffered by a scattered electron arising from the transfer of kinetic energy and momentum to the struck nucleus. For example, an electron of incident energy 400 Mev will fly off with an energy of 326 Mev at 60° after scattering from a proton initially at rest. The remainder of the energy, 74 Mev, goes into the kinetic energy of the struck proton, which recoils at the appropriate angle demanded by the conservation theorems of energy and linear momentum. The collision is, of course, highly relativistic.

The relativistic kinematics of the collision are similar to those in the Compton effect, since at the high energies used in the scattering experiments ($E\gg mc^2$) the energy of the electron,

$$E=(c^2p^2+m^2c^4)^{\frac{1}{2}}, \tag{22}$$

may be approximated with high accuracy by

$$E=cp, \tag{23}$$

and this is identical with the relation for x-rays. In place of the struck electron in the Compton effect, we now put the mass of the struck nucleus, and we are led to the result

$$E_n=\frac{E^2}{Mc^2}\frac{1-\cos\theta}{1+(E/Mc^2)(1-\cos\theta)}, \tag{24}$$

where E_n is the kinetic energy of the struck nucleus and M its rest mass. This equation provides a simple and accurate means of calculating the energy of the scattered electron which is simply

$$E'=E-E_n. \tag{25}$$

At high energies it is entirely safe to use this expression, the error being less than 1% for 20 Mev and less than 0.1% for 200 Mev. When it is desired to calculate the exact energy loss, the kinematic collision equations can be obtained from many sources, e.g., Jánossy's book.[41]

An interesting observation from Eq. (24) results when θ is placed equal to π. In this case one obtains the usual result of the Compton effect

$$E_n=E\frac{2\alpha}{1+2\alpha}, \tag{26}$$

where

$$\alpha=E/Mc^2 \tag{27}$$

[41] L. Jánossy, *Cosmic Rays* (Clarendon Press, Oxford, 1950), pp. 82–83.

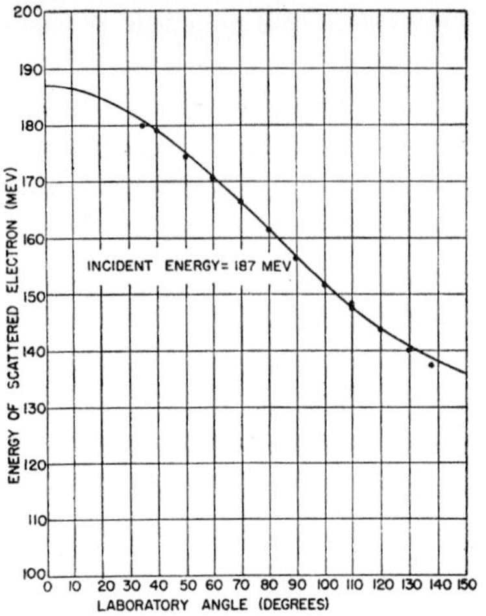

FIG. 9. Energy of electrons scattered from protons as a function of laboratory angle. The incident energy was approximately 187 Mev. The solid line is calculated from Eq. (24).

and

$$E' = E\frac{1}{1+2\alpha}. \tag{28}$$

When $2\alpha \gg 1$, thus, when the energy of the incident electron is large compared with Mc^2,

$$E' \to (Mc^2/2) \tag{29}$$

and the energy of the electron scattered near 180° saturates at one half of the rest energy of the struck nucleus. For a collision of an electron with a proton, the limiting energy of an electron scattered backward is 469 Mev. Therefore, valuable scattering experiments, using relatively small detecting devices, should be possible in the backward hemisphere even at very high electron energies, say, at 10 Bev, and possibly at higher energies if the cross sections are not too small.

To illustrate the application of Eq. (24) to an actual scattering problem,[42] Fig. 9 shows the experimentally determined kinetic energy of the electrons scattered at various angles from a beam of 187-Mev electrons incident on a gaseous target of hydrogen. The solid line is the theoretical curve computed from Eq. (24). The points are experimental. The small deviations at small and large angles are due to energy loss of the electrons as they go obliquely through the gas chamber walls. The energies were measured from several sets of data obtained with a magnetic spectrometer from elastic scattering peaks such as those in Fig. 10. The incident energy for the several runs averaged together in Fig. 9 varied by about 1%.

The recoil energies in Eq. (24) vary inversely as the mass number of the target nucleus and, hence, it is possible to separate the elastic scattering peaks from two elements in a compound target or even from two isotopes of the same element. In studying the scattering of electrons from protons, polyethylene proves to be a valuable target material, since the proton elastic scattering peak is situated far from the elastic carbon peak and the background subtraction problem is greatly simplified. The method has advantages, but to use it one must be sure that inelastic scattering from the heavier target does not fall at the same energy as the elastic peak of the element or isotope studied.

[42] R. W. McAllister and R. Hofstadter, Phys. Rev. **102**, 851 (1956).

(b) Inelastic Scattering

In elastic scattering the nucleus is observed in its ground state before and after the scattering event. In scattering of an inelastic variety, the nucleus is left in a different condition after the scattering event has taken place: the passing electron has produced a transition from the nuclear ground state to some excited state or to a level in the continuum. We describe the following possibilities.

(1) *Excitation of Nuclear Levels*

The nucleus may be raised to a discrete excited state by the incident electron. The electron then flies off with its energy reduced by just the amount by which the nucleus has been excited. Figure 11 shows an example[43] of this phenomenon observed in carbon at an incident energy of 187 Mev and at a scattering angle of 80°. The elastic peak is seen near 185.1 Mev, shifted slightly downward because of the recoil of the carbon nucleus (and straightforward collision energy loss in the target). To its left, near 180.7 Mev, is an inelastic scattering peak somewhat less than half as large as the elastic peak. This scattering arises from excitation of the 4.43-Mev level of C^{12}. Also apparent in Fig. 11 are the smaller peaks due to scattering from the levels at 7.65 Mev, 9.61 Mev, and other higher levels. This behavior is characteristic of the inelastic scattering observed in many elements arising from the excitation

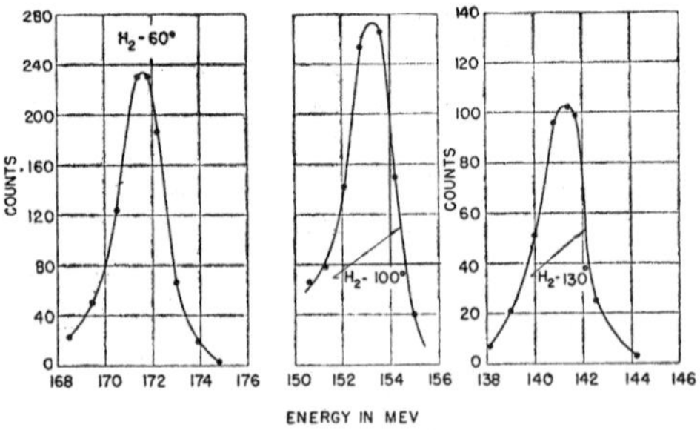

FIG. 10. Elastic peaks showing 187-Mev incident electrons scattered from protons at 60°, 100°, 130°. Note the shifts arising from recoil of the proton.

[43] J. H. Fregeau and R. Hofstadter, Phys. Rev. **99**, 1503 (1955).

of nuclear levels. This effect was first found in the case of beryllium[3,44] and has since been observed in lithium,[45] magnesium, silicon, sulfur, calcium, strontium,[46] etc.

Inelastic scattering of this type has great intrinsic interest, because it permits the nucleus to be examined while it makes transitions to higher levels and, in fact, to higher levels than reached by most other methods. The values of transition matrix elements and the nuclear angular momenta and parities of states may also be found.[47] In qualitative language one sees, in this type of inelastic scattering, the dynamic character of the nucleus, while in the elastic scattering the static character of the nucleus in its ground state is revealed. Experimentally speaking, however, inelastic scattering of this type poses some problems when one is attempting to disentangle the elastic scattering peaks from others nearby. More will be said later about inelastic scattering and its interpetation.

(2) *Electrodisintegration—(The Momentum Distribution of Nucleons in a Nucleus)*

A second type of inelastic scattering occurs when a proton or neutron is ejected by the passing electron. This process may be called "electrodisintegration" and was observed in the case of deuterium[48] and has subsequently been seen also in helium[49] and in other elements. Figure 12 demonstrates the inelastic continuum due to this process in helium at *BCDE* where *A* shows the elastic peak in the scattering of 400-Mev (more exactly, 395-Mev) electrons from the alpha particle as

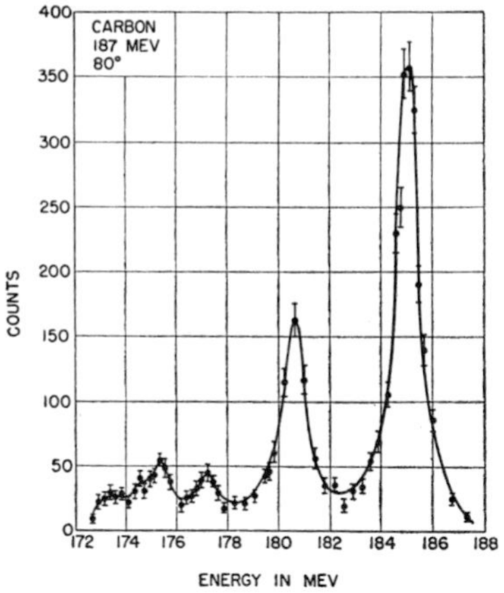

FIG. 11. The elastic scattering peak from carbon near 185 Mev and the inelastic scattering peaks from excited states of carbon. The peak near 180.7 Mev is associated with the 4.43-Mev level.

[44] McIntyre, Hahn, and Hofstadter, Phys. Rev. **94**, 1084 (1954).
[45] W. Hutchsinson and J. F. Streib (unpublished).
[46] R. H. Helm, Ph.D. thesis, Stanford University, February, 1956.
[47] L. I. Schiff, Phys. Rev. **96**, 765 (1954).
[48] J. A. McIntyre and R. Hofstadter, Phys. Rev. **98**, 158 (1955).
[49] R. Blankenbecler and R. Hofstadter, Bull. Am. Phys. Soc. Ser. II, **1**, 10 (1956).

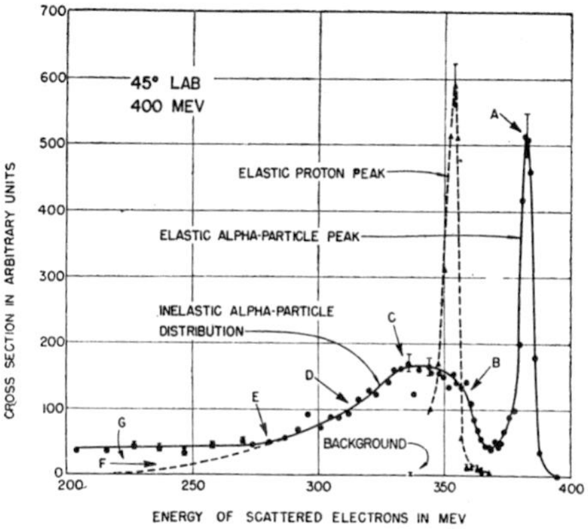

FIG. 12. Electrodisintegration of the alpha particle at 400 Mev and 45°. The elastic peak is shown at *A*. The inelastic continuum *BCDE* is related to the momentum distribution of nucleons within the alpha particle. *G* points to negative pion production. (See Sec. IVc in text.)

observed at a scattering angle of 45°. The figure also shows a comparison electron scattering peak from free protons in hydrogen. The different recoil energies of the proton and alpha particle may be noted. In scattering accompanied by the ejection of a nucleon, the scattered electron's energy must be reduced by at least the binding energy of that particular nucleon in the nucleus. In the case of the alpha particle, the ejection of one neutron or proton takes approximately 20 Mev and Fig. 12 shows that the high-energy slope of the inelastic continuum will plunge into the axis at approximately this interval from the elastic alpha peak

The low-energy side of the continuum results from the fact that a proton or neutron may be ejected with a higher energy than that given to a free proton, e.g., as given by the position of the free-proton peak in Fig. 12. The ejected proton or neutron may likewise receive *less* energy than a free proton recoil if that nucleon was moving with a velocity component, prior to ejection, in a direction opposite to that of the incident electron. If the nucleon was moving with a component parallel to the incident electron's path, the recoiling energy will be larger and the scattered electron will, therefore, have less energy. If, finally, the nucleon is moving essentially perpendicular to the path of the incident electron, the scattered electron will have an energy, coinciding in first approximation, with the energy of electrons scattered from the free proton, except for the correction mentioned above, *viz.*, the energy required to remove the nucleon from the nucleus, i.e., its binding energy. This makes plausible the appearance of the peak of the elastic continuum at an energy approximately 20 Mev below the free-proton peak in Fig. 12. Similar features are seen in Fig. 13 where the scattering angle is 60° and the elastic alpha

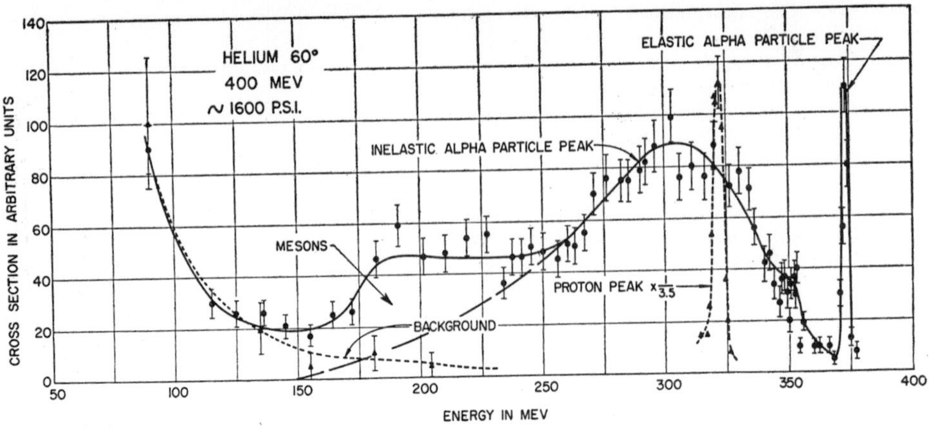

FIG. 13. The elastic and inelastic scattering of electrons from the alpha particle at 400 Mev and 60°. The area labeled "mesons" refers to negative pions produced in the target and emerging with the same momentum as the corresponding scattered electrons. The free proton peak is shown for comparison.

peak has become much smaller relative to the inelastic continuum. The same phenomena are observed in the case of inelastic scattering from the deuteron[48] where the binding energy is only 2.23 Mev. The study of such inelastic continua will, therefore, furnish valuable information about the momentum distribution of nucleons in a nucleus.

(3) *Breakup of the Nucleus*

A process similar to (2) may occur, except that more than one particle may be ejected simultaneously. It could be expected that fragments such as deuterons or alpha particles could be emitted. Possibly even fission may occur in some of the heavier nuclei. Such nuclear breakup undoubtedly occurs and contributes to the continua such as shown in Fig. 12. It will be difficult to separate single- and multi-nucleon breakup processes experimentally unless coincidence experiments or separate experiments searching specifically for nucleonic fragments can be performed.

(4) *Mesonic Processes*

A passing electron may cause charged or neutral mesons of various types to be emitted from the nucleus or from a nucleon. The materialization energy of such a particle must, of course, be provided and this is in the neighborhood of at least 140 Mev. Hence, scattered electrons engaging in this process will lie at low energies in the inelastic continua. Pi mesons made by this process have been detected in the very same apparatus in which the electrons were detected.[49,50] In fact, part of the low energy tail of Fig. 13, indicated by the label, is due to pi mesons having the same momenta as electrons received by the spectrometer at this setting. The electrons themselves, the meson producers, so to speak, have not yet been separated from the others scattered into the inelastic continuum by moving nucleons, but there is no doubt that they are present.

(5) *Radiation*

Accompanying both elastic and inelasting scattering of electrons is a radiation of photons. When the radiation goes mainly forward, this radiation is the familiar bremsstrahlung x-ray beam observed in betatrons and synchrotrons. Bremsstrahlung may be observed at any angle and may result from an electron scattered at almost any angle. Thus, the low-energy side of any elastic or inelastic peak will show a tail which decreases in the manner typical of radiative phenomena, i.e., as the reciprocal of the energy of the emitted radiation. At large energy losses of the incident electron (>10 Mev), a single x-ray will be emitted. At small energy losses, say less than 1 ev, a Poisson distribution in the number of emitted photons will represent the distribution of prevailing radiation. Of ccurse, a large single loss may also be accompanied by a shower of very low-energy photons. The radiative loss is probably well explained by the Bethe-Heitler theory, although it would be interesting to study the $1/(E-E_0)$ spectrum in some detail at large angles. This has not yet been done. A Born approximation theory has been formulated by Biel and Burhop for the process involving a finite nucleus.[51]

The foregoing remarks refer to the emission of real quanta. It is well known that virtual emission and absorption of radiation also occur during the act of scattering. The calculations including this process as well as real radiation were performed by Schwinger[52] and

[50] Blankenbecler, Hofstadter, and Yearian (unpublished).

[51] S. J. Biel and E. H. S. Burhop, Proc. Phys. Soc. (London) **A68**, 165 (1955).

[52] J. Schwinger, Phys. Rev. **75**, 898 (1949).

later by Suura.[53] Suura has given more general validity to the Schwinger calculation. For most practical purposes a correction must be added to the experimental scattering to compensate for the real and virtual radiative processes for photon energies less than or equal to ΔE. This correction is given by Schwinger as

$$I=I_0e^{-\delta_r}, \tag{30}$$

where I is the measured scattering intensity and I_0 the value to be compared with a theory assuming elastic scattering alone. δ_r is the Schwinger radiative correction which is given sufficiently well by

$$\delta_r=\frac{4\alpha}{\pi}\left\{K\left[\log\left(\frac{2E}{Mc^2}\sin\frac{1}{2}\theta\right)-\frac{1}{2}\right]+\frac{17}{12}\right\}, \tag{31}$$

where

$$K=\log\frac{E}{\Delta E}-\frac{13}{12}, \tag{32}$$

and in which E is the energy of the scattered electron, α the fine structure constant, and m the rest mass of the electron. In practice, ΔE amounts to the smallest energy considered to be resolvable from the main elastic peak. This is usually something like the half-width of the elastic peak. The Schwinger correction is not very sensitive to practical values of ΔE and besides has a very small angular dependence. For this reason, it may usually be omitted in discussing angular distributions, although, in cases where accuracy is important, it must be taken into account. In studies where absolute cross sections are important, it is essential to include it. No detailed experimental test of the Schwinger correction has been made. A typical Schwinger correction may vary from 14% at 40° to 17% at 135°, where $E/\Delta E$ is in the neighborhood of 100.

The emission of real radiation, i.e., bremsstrahlung, by electrons emerging from a target of finite thickness, must also be corrected for. This results in a correction such that

$$I_1=Ie^{\delta_B} \tag{33}$$

where δ_B is given by[54]

$$\delta_B=\frac{t}{\log 2}\log\frac{E}{\Delta E}, \tag{34}$$

and where "t" is the average target thickness through which the electrons pass (along the directions of the incident beam and scattered beam) and ΔE is the full width of an elastic peak at half-maximum. I_1 is the corrected intensity.

(c) Magnetic Scattering

For most nuclei, the elastic scattering is due entirely to the electric charge of the nucleus, i.e., to the electric field of force surrounding it. However, owing to finite size effects, we have seen that the elastic scattering at large angles and high energies can be reduced by many orders of magnitude below the scattering expected from a point charge and the Coulomb interaction. We shall ask the question: Does *any* elastic scattering remain at all after the charge scattering has dropped below experimental recognition? Another related question is: Does a neutron scatter electrons at high energy and do neutrons in a nucleus scatter electrons? The answers are affirmative in all cases and magnetic scattering has actually been observed in experiments at Stanford.[42,55]

The proton.—Elastic scattering of high-energy electrons by the magnetic moment of the proton had actually been predicted by Rosenbluth[56] in 1950. Rosenbluth showed that there is a contribution to the elastic scattering from both the Dirac and the Pauli components of the proton's magnetic moment. The Pauli moment is usually referred to as the "anomalous" part of the proton's magnetic moment. Rosenbluth's results may be presented as follow: For a protonic point charge and point magnetic moment, the differential cross section σ_p is[56a]:

$$\sigma_p(\theta)=\sigma_{\mathrm{NS}}\left\{1+\frac{q^2}{4M^2}\left[2(1+\mu)^2\tan^2\tfrac{1}{2}\theta+\mu^2\right]\right\}, \tag{35}$$

where

$$\sigma_{\mathrm{NS}}=\frac{e^4}{4E^2}\frac{\cos^2\frac{1}{2}\theta}{\sin^4\frac{1}{2}\theta}\frac{1}{1+(2E/M)\sin^2\frac{1}{2}\theta} \tag{36}$$

and

$$q=\frac{2}{\lambda}\frac{\sin\frac{1}{2}\theta}{\left[1+(2E/M)\sin^2\frac{1}{2}\theta\right]^{\frac{1}{2}}}. \tag{37}$$

Equation (36) is simply Eq. (11), when $Z=1$ (proton) and when proper modifications are made in going from the center-of-mass frame to the laboratory frame of reference. The subscripts NS refer to the fact that Eq. (36) is the proper scattering formula for a proton without magnetic moment or spin (NS=no spin). Corresponding to the "q" of Eq. (14), the new q ($\hbar=1$) in Eq. (37), is the momentum transfer in the laboratory frame and has a suitable modifying factor required in this frame of reference. [Note that Eq. (37) follows simply from Eq. (24) by placing $1-\cos\theta=2\sin^2\frac{1}{2}\theta$ and putting $\hbar q=p_n$ where $E_n=p_n^2/2M$. Equation (37) is not restricted, however, to these approximations.]

Finally, Eq. (35) shows that a point proton scatters as a Mott proton would except that the scattering

[53] H. Suura, Phys. Rev. **99**, 1020 (1955).

[54] H. A. Bethe and J. Asjkin, *Experimental Nuclear Physics*, edited by E. Segré (John Wiley and Sons, Inc., New York, 1953), Vol. I, Part II, p. 272. This result is derived from the original Bethe-Heitler theory.

[55] R. Hofstadter and R. W. McAllister, Phys. Rev. **98**, 217 (1955).

[56] M. N. Rosenbluth, Phys. Rev. **79**, 615 (1950). See also the reference to L. I. Schiff in this paper.

[56a] Because of common practice we write Rosenbluth's formula in units such that $\hbar=c=1$. $e\hbar/Mc=e/M$, in these units and is the nuclear magneton. Thus, μ represents 1.79 nuclear magnetons (Pauli moment) and 1.00 represents the Dirac moment. 1.00+1.79 =2.79 is the entire proton moment in nuclear magnetons.

formula is modified by a factor S_p, which takes magnetic scattering into account:

$$S_p=1+S=1+\frac{q^2}{4M^2}[2(1+\mu)^2\tan^2\tfrac{1}{2}\theta+\mu^2]. \quad (38)$$

S_p is an energy-dependent term, since q depends on energy $[\lambda\propto(1/E)]$. S_p also depends on the scattering angle θ. The factor S_p becomes much larger than unity at high energies (q large) and large angles ($\tan\frac{1}{2}\theta$ large). Under these conditions S_p is dominant in the scattering phenomenon, and the principal part of the scattering is now due to the quantity S which contains a $\tan^2\frac{1}{2}\theta$ term. When associated with Eq. (36), the factor S_p produces a flattening-off of the cross section at large angles and as a result the magnetic moment scattering by a point is much more isotropic than Mott scattering from a pure charge.

Now if the proton should happen to be neither a point charge nor a point magnetic moment (as meson theory might lead us to expect), this would require the existence of form factors, whose presence would lead to a reduction of the effective values of the charge and magnetic moment. In fact, Rosenbluth[56] carried out such a calculation using a weak coupling meson theory. However, since a satisfactory meson theory is not known to exist nowadays, it is preferable to use phenomenological form factors to allow for the finite size effects in the proton. The "size" of the proton and its "shape" are assigned to the virtual cloud of mesons, both charged and neutral, which the proton may emit and reabsorb. Phenomenological form factors, F_1 and F_2, have been introduced by Yennie, Lévy, and Ravenhall[57,42] in accordance with the Rosenbluth scheme and a formalism due to Foldy.[58] F_1 is introduced to take care of a spread-out charge and a spread-out Dirac magnetic moment. F_2 is an independent quantity and takes care of a spread-out Pauli moment. Equation (39) shows how S_p is modified by the introduction of F_1 and F_2:

$$\sigma(\theta)=\sigma_{\mathrm{NS}}\left\{F_1^2+\frac{q^2}{4M^2}[2(F_1+\mu F_2)^2\tan^2\tfrac{1}{2}\theta+\mu^2F_2^2]\right\}. \quad (39)$$

F_1 and F_2 are each independent functions of the momentum transfer q.

The neutron.—In the case of the neutron, because its charge is zero, a naive approach would be to place $F_1=0$. This is actually correct in the static limit $q\rightarrow 0$. However, as the energy of the incident electrons increases and the wavelength, therefore, decreases, an electron which passes through a neutron cloud becomes sensitive to the positive and negative charge (or effective charge) clouds it sees and can suffer a deflection due to these charges. The effect would be expected to be small if the dimensions of the neutron's positive and negative meson clouds are small. Thus, F_1 for a neutron really approaches a term $-\frac{1}{6}q^2r_{1n}^2$ as indicated by Eq. (19), with the leading static term there placed equal to zero.[57] The quantity F_2 for a neutron will be more conventional since the neutron does have a *static* magnetic moment equal to -1.91 nuclear magnetons. Hence,

$$F_{2n}=1-\frac{q^2r_{2n}^2}{6}+\cdots \quad (40)$$

as long as qr_{2n} is small.

A critical review of the concepts discussed above is given by Yennie *et al.* in reference 57. We shall merely note here the further thought that a breakdown of electrodynamics, say, a failure of the Coulomb law at small distances, will have exactly the same effect as a finite size. We shall return to this point later (Sec. VII).

The deuteron.—In the case of magnetic scattering from the deuteron, the expected cross section should be smaller than the proton's, because the deuteron's static magnetic moment is $\mu_D=0.858$ nuclear magneton, whereas the moment of the proton is 2.79 nuclear magnetons. Since the cross section is expected to vary as the square of the magnetic moment, the deuteron's magnetic scattering will only amount to approximately $\frac{1}{9}$ that of the proton. Hence, in the scattering of electrons from the deuteron, we shall expect to see almost pure charge scattering. This crude expectation is borne out by the result of Jankus[59] who has shown that the actual elastic scattering from the deuteron, neglecting very small quadrupole terms, is

$$\sigma_D(\theta)=\sigma_{\mathrm{NS}}\left\{1+\frac{2}{3}\frac{q^2}{4M^2}[2\mu_D^2\tan^2\tfrac{1}{2}\theta+\mu_D^2]\right\}F_D^2, \quad (41)$$

where σ_{NS} is given, as before, by Eq. (36), (with, of course, the deuteron mass M_D in place of the proton mass M in Eqs. (36) and (37)), μ_D is the static deuteron magnetic moment, and F_D is the form factor obtainable from the deuteron's charge density, as determined from the wave function of the deuteron in its ground state. The second term in the bracket is the magnetic term and its form confirms the remark made above about the small magnetic scattering. The spin of the deuteron is 1 and this accounts for the difference in the coefficient of the q^2 term between Eq. (35) and Eq. (41).

Naturally, if the magnetic moment μ_D is a sum of spreadout moments of the neutron and proton, a form factor will arise and will multiply μ_D. However, just how this modification needs to be made poses a difficult problem. This question has been considered briefly by Jankus[59] and in more detail by Yennie *et al.*[57] In any case, it is clear that the magnetic moment effects in the coherent (elastic) scattering from the deuteron will be smaller ($\sim\frac{1}{9}$) than the corresponding scattering from the proton. Further details will be discussed in Secs. Vb and VI.

[57] Yennie, Lévy, and Ravenhall (to be published).
[58] L. L. Foldy, Phys. Rev. 87, 688 (1952); 87, 693 (1952).
[59] V. Z. Jankus, Phys. Rev., to be published.

In the case of breakup of the deuteron, involving inelastic scattering, Jankus also shows that for large momentum transfers

$$\sigma_D^{\text{in}}(\theta)=\sigma_{\text{NS}}\left\{1-F_D^2+\frac{q^2}{4M^2}[2(\mu_p^2+\mu_n^2-3F_D^2)\tan^2\tfrac{1}{2}\theta+\mu_p^2+\mu_n^2-3F_D^2]\right\} \quad (42)$$

or, when F_D is small,

$$\sigma_D^{\text{in}}(\theta)=\sigma_{\text{NS}}\left\{1+\frac{q^2}{4M^2}[2(\mu_p^2+\mu_n^2)\tan^2\tfrac{1}{2}\theta+\mu_p^2+\mu_n^2]\right\}. \quad (43)$$

In these equations, $\sigma_D^{\text{in}}(\theta)$ is the inelastic cross section. μ_p and μ_n are the proton and neutron magnetic moments, respectively, and F_D is the deuteron elastic form factor. When the momentum transfer is large, $F_D \cong 0$. We shall return to Eq. (43) in Sec. VI when we consider actual experiments on the proton and neutron.

It is clear that other spin-bearing nuclei will also show elastic magnetic scattering under the proper conditions. However, it may be expected that magnetic scattering will only be important for light elements with nonzero spins, for example, Li^7. For a medium or heavy element, the magnetic moment and spin are due to only a few unpaired particles among the many particles which otherwise bear a charge. The magnetic effects reside in the surface and will be associated with a form factor decreasing perhaps even faster than that of charge scattering.

(d) Angular Shapes of Nuclei

Up to now we have discussed only radial variations of charge density in allowing for the effects of finite nuclear size. Actually the spectroscopic literature on quadrupole moments of nuclei and other evidence suggest that those nuclei lying between shell closures (magic number nuclei) should be distorted and not spherical. Nuclei lying close to magic numbers are quite probably very close to a spherical shape. Data obtained in the last few years in experiments on Coulomb excitation by alpha particles and protons give further reason to believe that many nuclei are ellipsoidal in their ground state. The Bohr-Mottelson[60] model explains this shape in terms of a collective motion of nucleons associating together to produce a traveling bulge moving about the nuclear surface. Such motions correspond to low-lying energy levels called "rotational levels" because of the analogy to rotational states in molecules. Whatever the actual shape of such nuclei, e.g., the rare earths, Ta, W, U, etc., there is little doubt that there is something special about them. The peculiarities of these nuclei are exhibited also in electron scattering studies. In these studies, the diffraction features seem more washed-out and smoothed than in the case of spherical nuclei such as Pb^{208} and Au^{197}.

In interpreting the experimental curves, it is necessary to include the effect of an ellipsoidal shape and to average it appropriately in all the aspects seen by approaching electrons. The averaging has the effect of rounding-off the nuclear surface and making the apparent surface thicker than it actually is. However, the rounding-off does not produce a large change in the scattering mainly because the surface is thick already. In any case, it is not enough to explain the smooth character of the scattering. The fact that low-lying levels exist means that the effects of scattering to these states must also be included: Transitions up to these levels are involved in electron scattering. The one-way transitions from the ground state to the excited rotational levels give rise to inelastic scattering. However, because of the small energy interval between the ground state and the rotational state, such inelastic scattering would be concealed, considering the presently attained resolution in the experiments on scattering. A resolving power of 1 part in 2000 would be required to separate the rotational scattering from the static scattering.

A theoretical treatment of the quadrupole effects on scattering has been given by Schiff[47] and also by Downs, Ravenhall, and Yennie,[61] for nuclei in the region of tantalum. Further discussion of this work will be postponed until the experimental results are discussed.

IV. EXPERIMENTAL MATTERS

Two independent spectrometer installations have been used in the experiments at Stanford. They will be described separately below:

(a) 190-Mev Apparatus ("Halfway" Station)

Starting at approximately the halfway point along the length of the linear accelerator[62] and continuing a length of some forty feet paralleling the accelerator, a shielded vault encloses the medium energy (up to 190 Mev) spectrometer and its associated equipment. Figure 14 shows the general layout of the main parts of the equipment. After passing through a brass collimator, a group of accelerated electrons of nearly uniform energy, selected by the uranium or brass slit S, is deflected and dispersed by "Deflecting Magnet C" in Fig. 14.[3,63] This operation secures a relatively monoenergetic band of electrons which continues on its way into the field of a refocussing magnet "R." The magnet R straightens the beam again to its original direction and refocuses it to a point approximately 9 feet from the end of the magnet R. The principal idea of the

[60] A. Bohr and B. R. Mottelson, Kgl. Danske Videnskab. Selskab. Mat.-fys. Medd. 27, No. 16 (1953).

[61] Downs, Ravenhall, and Yennie (to be published).

[62] Chodorow, Ginzton, Hansen, Kyhl, Neal, Panofsky, and Staff, Rev. Sci. Instr. 26, 134 (1955).

[63] W. K. H. Panofsky and J. A. McIntyre, Rev. Sci. Instr. 25, 287 (1954).

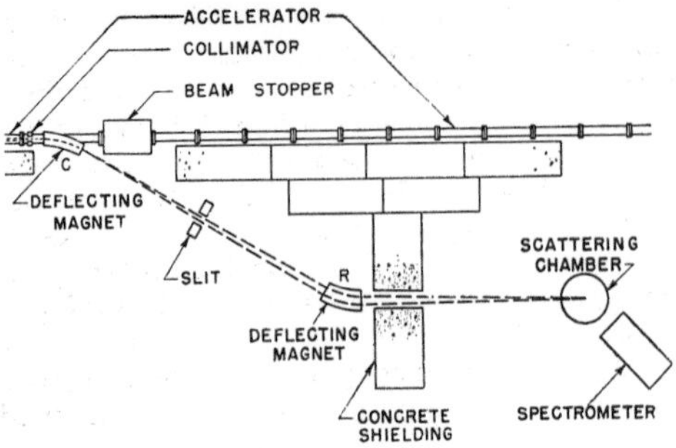

FIG. 14. The general layout of the equipment at the halfway point and the accelerator. Experiments, limited by the spectrometer to 190 Mev, are carried out in this area.

double deflection shown in Fig. 14 is to obtain a gamma-free beam of electrons. The second magnet bends the desired electrons away from the direction in which the large bremsstrahlung beam, produced at slit *S*, travels towards the concrete shield.

The arrangement of Fig. 14 produces vertical focusing at the target. A wedge at the exit face of magnet *R* is used to vary the focus and, thus, to position the spot exactly as desired. A slight curvature of the wedge face also helps to reduce the horizontal spot size. The path of electrons, from the gun of the accelerator all the way to the scattering target, lies in high vacuum. The size of the target spot depends on the size of the collimator opening and is approximately 1 mm high and 3 mm wide with a $\frac{1}{16}$-inch diameter collimator and 3 mm$\times$15 mm for a $\frac{1}{4}$-inch diameter collimator. Rectangular collimators have been used frequently to make the spot approximately circular and to obtain the maximum intensity for a given spot diameter. The largest spot size used has been $\frac{1}{8}$ inch high and $\frac{3}{8}$ inch wide.

The spot can be observed through a telescope and mirror arrangement focusing on a CsBr(Tl) fluorescent crystal plate one inch square and one millimeter thick. The luminescence produced by the beam appears very clearly on this plate and can be observed at 80 feet even at quite low beam intensities—on the order of 10^6 electrons per pulse (60 pulses per second). CsBr(Tl) is remarkably resistant to the electron radiation, perhaps due to the fact that a large fraction of the impinging energy leaves the crystal in the form of light, instead of remaining as heat or energy causing structural damage.

The beam at the halfway station, focused at the target, has contained as many as two to three times 10^9 electrons per pulse in a band of energy about 2 Mev wide at 188 Mev. Since the accelerator produces pulses at a rate of 60 times a second, this is equivalent to an average current of a few hundredths of a microampere of useful resolved beam. [In the end station (see later) more intense beams are obtained.] This is a powerful beam and permits the measurement of small scattering cross sections.

Unfortunately, the pulsed short-duty-cycle characteristic of this beam is not entirely favorable for the beam lasts only 0.6 microsecond per pulse. Consequently, all the counting must be carried on in this brief period and conventional coincidence techniques become virtually useless. At the same time, there is a huge background of gamma rays and fast neutrons, which make it extremely difficult to operate a scintillation counter [anthracene, NaI(Tl)] without pileup and other unwanted pulses. Nevertheless, there is a good way out of this situation which is solved as follows: (1) a Čerenkov counter is used as the detector, (2) magnetic bending and focusing of the scattered electrons are accomplished so that the detector may be positioned at a point where shielding can be erected about it, (3) through magnetic analysis, portions of the radiation spectrum coming from the target which would interfere with the wanted events are eliminated. These characteristics can be secured by using a magnetic momentum analyzing spectrometer which selects only the scattering events of the desired type, for example, purely elastic events. Other events are separated, and, thus, the counting of electrons of any energy with low background can be achieved. With the experimental arrangement described, a maximum beam, magnet in position of maximum background, closed spectrometer entrance slit, and target in place, the greatest background counting rate is about one pulse in two minutes.

FIG. 15. The semicircular 190-Mev spectrometer, to the left, is shown on the gun mount. The upper platform carries the lead and paraffin shielding that encloses the Čerenkov counter. The brass scattring chamber is shown below with the thin window encircling it. Ion chamber monitors appear in the foreground.

The low background has been achieved with the spectrometer, detector, and shield now to be described. A photograph of the apparatus is given in Fig. 15. It may be seen that while the scattering plane is horizontal, the magnetic spectrometer is vertical. Scattered electrons emerge from the scattering chamber (Fig. 14) in all directions. Some fall within the angular aperture of the entrance slit of the magnetic spectrometer. The entrance slit is made of lead and can be opened to approximately one inch in the horizontal scattering plane or closed to zero. In typical cases it is used at a width of one-half inch. The vertical-slit dimension can be varied and is usually about one inch. The entrance slit is remotely controlled and is attached to the input face of the vacuum chamber of the spectrometer. Electrons enter the thin window (3–6 mils of aluminum) of the magnet chamber situated just behind the slit, and then fall into the magnetic field of the spectrometer where they are analyzed.

The spectrometer is of the double-focusing variety invented by Siegbahn and Svartholm[64] and modified by Snyder *et al.*[65] The pertinent details of this particular spectrometer are as follows: The field is inhomogeneous and falls off as $r^{-\frac{1}{2}}$ where r is the radius vector to the orbit trajectory. The mean radius of curvature is 16 inches and the pole faces are six inches wide, thus, stretching from radius 13 to 19 inches. The pole faces extend through a 180° arc and the electrons are bent, therefore, through this angle. A small fringing field extends beyond the input (and exit) slit but the deflection produced here is quite small. The width of the pole gap is 2 inches on the central trajectory and the slope of the pole faces is such that

$$dy/y=dr/2r \tag{44}$$

in order to obtain the required dependence of magnetic field on radius. "y" is the pole gap at any radius. Thus, the pole faces have a linear taper. A lip is machined on the inner and outer edge of the pole in order to prevent the field from falling too quickly to zero.

The magnet itself weights $2\frac{1}{2}$ tons and is supported by four jacks on an obsolete 40-mm twin antiaircraft gun mount obtained some time ago on loan from the U. S. Navy through the cooperation of the Office of Naval Research. As shown in Fig. 15, a platform has been erected on the magnet to support the heavy shield surrounding the Čerenkov detector. The shield material consists mostly of lead and paraffin and weighs over 2 tons. Buried within the shield is a small Lucite Čerenkov counter built in the form of a truncated cone.

After the 180° deflection and momentum analysis of the electrons in the magnet, they leave the vacuum chamber through a thin window (0.006-inch aluminum) and pass through the horizontal opening in the jaws

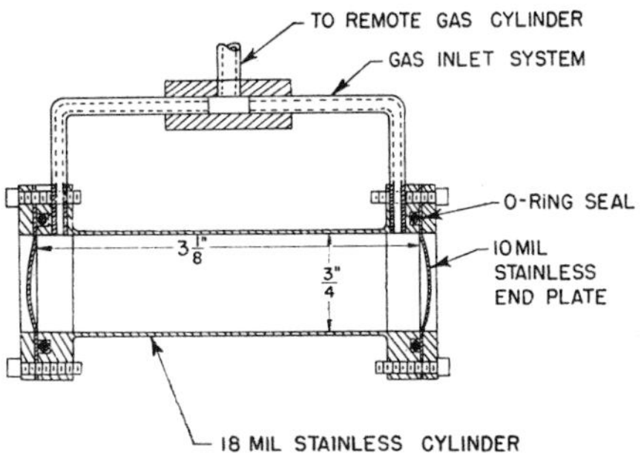

FIG. 16. A typical gas target chamber useful up to pressures of 2000 lb/sq in.

of a uranium slit one inch thick. The jaws of the vertical slit are made of lead and are usually fixed at a width of $\frac{1}{2}$ inch. The horizontal opening of the slit jaws determines the energy limits passed by the spectrometer into the Čerenkov counter and the vertical jaws define the effective width of the target. The dispersion of the instrument is 1.6% per inch at the horizontal slit opening.

The Čerenkov counter is made of highly polished Lucite, four inches long, one inch in diameter at the smaller input end, and 1.5 inch in diameter at the output end. The output end is coupled to a DuMont 6292 photomultiplier. A conical shape of the counter helps the internally reflected light to reach the photosurface. The Čerenkov counter itself is enclosed in a lead jacket. The combination is placed in a brass tube which is fastened to the photomultiplier cathode follower head and is, thus, a complete optical-electronic unit. The counter is kept in a fixed position behind the exit slit and the shield, platform, and magnet rotate rigidly together on the gun mount. The angular position of the gun mount is controlled remotely and is measured by a combination of high- and low-speed selsyn indicators. No trouble has been experienced in obtaining positional errors smaller than 0.1 degree.

The target is maintained in vacuum in the scattering chamber shown in Figs. 14 and 15. A six-position target frame, built in the form of a vertical ladder, holds the desired scattering foils in place and, since it is remotely controlled, allows changing of the target at will during a run. The angular positions of the target can also be varied remotely.

When it is desired to work with a gas such as hydrogen or helium, a gas target chamber, shown in Fig. 16, is placed inside the bell jar. The bell jar is described in the next paragraph.

As stated previously, the scattering foils or gas target are held in the 20-inch diameter evacuated brass-scattering chamber. A schematic diagram of the scattering geometry is shown in Fig. 17. To keep the scattered electron's path as free of unwanted scattering material as possible, the wall of the scattering chamber is made

[64] K. Siegbahn and N. Svartholm, Arkiv Mat. Astron. Fysik **33A**, No. 21 (1946); N. Svartholm **33A**, No. 24 (1946).

[65] Snyder, Rubin, Fowler, and Lauritsen, Rev. Sci. Instr. **21**, 852 (1950).

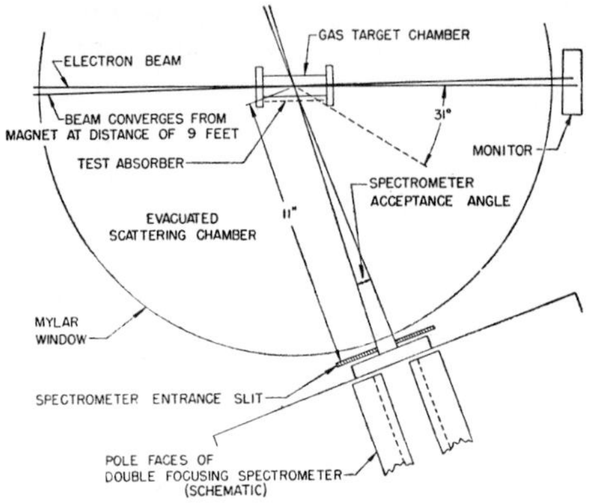

FIG. 17. Schematic diagram of scattering geometry employed with the gas target chamber.

of only 0.006-inch Mylar. This is achieved by holding the Mylar to the thick chamber walls by rubber gaskets. The Mylar window is allowed to stretch into the chamber, as it is pushed there by the force due to atmospheric pressure. The Mylar window extends from $-150°$ to $-15°$ and $+15°$ to $+150°$. The window extends 1.5 inches above and below the scattering plane, corresponding to a total of 3 inches in unobstructed height. In between $-15°$ and $+15°$ there are two brass posts to help hold the top and bottom of the chamber apart against the force of the atmospheric pressure. A 0.006-inch aluminum window occupies the forward region between $\sim -14°$ to $+14°$. Mylar windows were employed in this region also, but usually weakened and collapsed after a few hundred hours of full beam. Aluminum windows appear to hold indefinitely. The scattering chamber, containing the windows referred to, is built in the form of a bell jar and can be detached readily from the base plate. It contains a top port through which foils may be changed without removing the bell jar from the base plates. The base of the scattering chamber contains many well-insulated electrical lead-in connections. There are also provisions for moving monitoring or counting apparatus, inside the bell jar and in vacuum, by means of a large ring gear controlled remotely. At the present time, a secondary electron monitor[66] is mounted on the ring gear and can be moved into position either behind the scattering target or in front of it. The usual position has been behind the target. The plates of the monitor are large enough ($1\frac{3}{4}$ inches diameter) to contain safely all the beam after it is broadened by multiple scattering in the target. A conventional electronic accumulating charge type of integrator is employed to measure the total number of electrons passing through the foil and monitor. The advantage of the secondary monitor is that it is linear and does not saturate. Unfortunately, it is useful in a practical sense only for beams larger than about 10^6 electrons per pulse. For smaller beams an ion chamber monitor is used outside the chamber and in the forward multiply-scattered beam. The outside monitor is sketched in Fig. 17.

The counting equipment is simple and consists of a model-501 Elmore amplifier whose pulses are fed to a gated scaler constructed according to a design of J. Narud. The gate can be varied and is usually about 10 or 12 microseconds long. The pulse size, plotted against the discriminator voltage of the gated scaler, shows a good plateau and is obtained before each run. A twenty-channel pulse-height discriminator has been very useful in obtaining the plateau curves. In the energy range over which the Čerenkov counter has been operated, 84–190 Mev, no dependence of pulse height on energy has been observed, and the efficiency is, thus, a constant over this range.

The magnet current is controlled to better than 0.1% by a feedback amplifier, where the input is a voltage taken from a shunt placed in series with the magnet windings. The magnet windings are constructed of hollow-conductor square copper rod $\frac{1}{2}$ inch on a side and water-cooled. Eight hundred amperes can be put through the coils and a maximum magnetic field on the central trajectory of 16 500 gauss has been attained. This field corresponds to approximately 192 Mev. The focusing at this highest energy is not as good as at lower energies (150 Mev) but is still usable. The energy calibration of the magnet has been carried out by (a) knowing the incident energy and placing the magnet in the forward direction, (b) knowing the incident energy and calibrating with hydrogen recoil energies given by Eq. (24), (c) using the known energies of the inelastic scattering from the carbon excited levels, (d) employing a rotating coil fluxmeter halfway along the trajectories, and finally by (e) using magnetic-induction proton-resonance devices. Small differences exist between the various methods, but thus far no experiment has warranted knowing the calibration better than the present differences among them ($\sim$1%). Magnetic induction devices are now being installed permanently.

In practice, the method employed in taking data at a given angle consists in (1) setting the magnet current, (2) counting electrons in the Čerenkov counter for a given charge accumulated on the calibrated monitor-condenser, and (3) taking the ratio of these two values. Points such as these are plotted for various values of the magnet current, as measured by the potentiometer reading of the voltage across the magnet shunt. Figure 11 shows typical data obtained in this way. From the elastic peak one may see that the full width at half-maximum is about 0.8 Mev or about 0.4%. Occasionally, with considerable loss of counting rate, 0.2% full width has been observed.

Absolute counting can be carried out approximately

[66] G. W. Tautfest and H. R. Fechter, Phys. Rev. 96, 35 (1954).

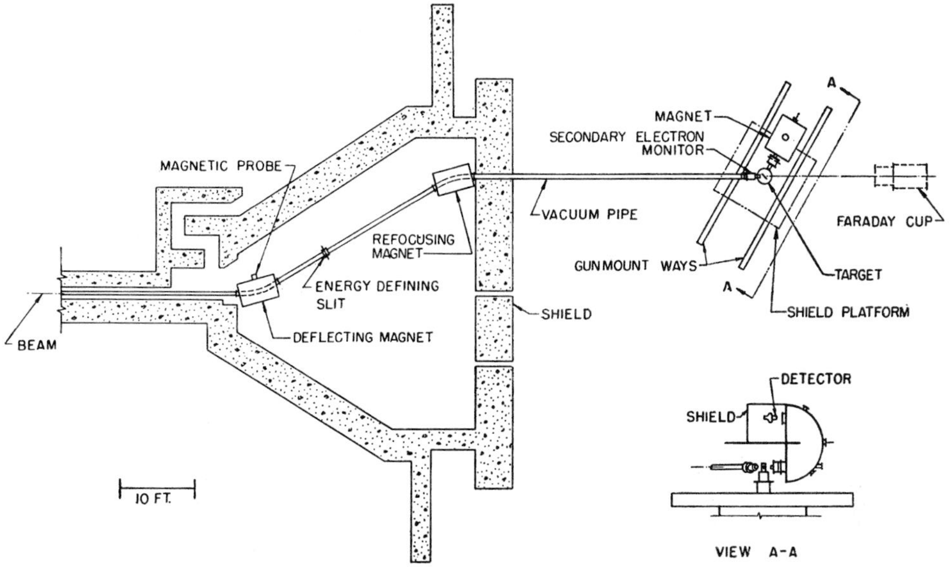

FIG. 18. The experimental installation of the 550-Mev spectrometer.

by using the absolute calibration of the secondary monitor[66] and the effective solid-angle calculations by Judd.[67] Accurate absolute counting has not been attempted up to the present time, but semiabsolute standardization has been carried out by measuring the unknown scattering and comparing the results simultaneously with the intensity of electrons scattered from protons. The cross section for scattering from protons may be taken from theory, as corrected by the results of McAllister and Hofstadter.[42] Provisions are now being made, however, to obtain directly measured absolute cross sections.

(b) 550-Mev Spectrometer ("End Station")

The larger spectrometer (550 Mev) has dimensions scaled up considerably over that of the 190-Mev installation. Otherwise, many of the features of the larger installation are similar to those discussed in Sec. IV(a). It will only be necessary here to give the details where differences are important or where new devices are used such as, e.g., the spectrometer itself.

Figure 18[68] shows the experimental area where electron scattering studies are carried on. For other details of the end station and accelerator, reference 62 may be consulted. Schematic details of the spectrometer, platform target, monitor, detector, etc. are shown in Fig. 18. A photograph is shown in Fig. 19.

Some details of the larger magnet may be pertinent here. A scale drawing of the magnet and vacuum chamber is shown in Fig. 20. This spectrometer is, like the smaller spectrometer, a double-focusing 180° modified Siegbahn-Svartholm design. This instrument weighs approximately 30 tones. It is not a scaled-up version of the 16-inch spectrometer. The maximum useful aperture is approximately 0.001 of the entire solid angle. The radius of curvature on the central orbit is 36 inches, and the pole gap at this orbit is 3.0 inches. The pole faces have a linear taper as given by Eq. (44) and a lip is machined on each pole edge. The width of the pole face is 15 inches. The dispersion of

FIG. 19. Photograph of the 550-Mev spectrometer, the gun mount, and shield. The electron beam is brought to the target, shown under the platform, through the vacuum pipe in the foreground.

[67] D. L. Judd, Rev. Sci. Instr. **21**, 213 (1950).
[68] E. E. Chambers and R. Hofstadter (to be published).

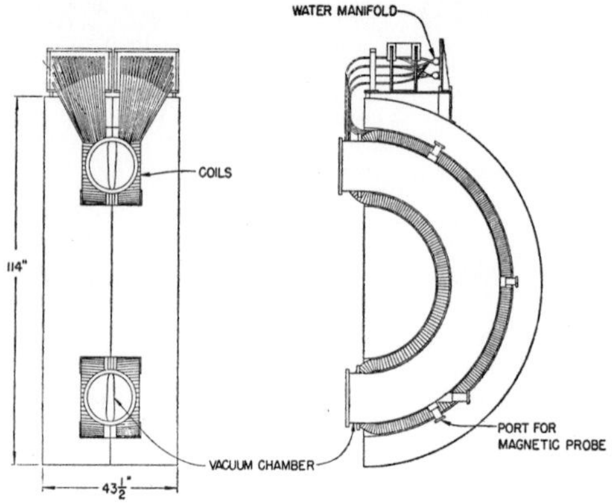

FIG. 20. Scale drawing of the 550-Mev, 36-inch spectrometer, and vacuum chamber.

this spectrometer is 0.75% per inch. On the central trajectory a maximum field of 20 000 gauss has been obtained, although the magnet is not often used at this high value because of saturation at the pole edges and other places in the gap. Although the cross-sectional area between the poles is 15 inches ×3 inches, the full area has not been used, because of the presence of a thick-walled bronze vacuum chamber. The internal free dimensions have been reduced to 14 inches×2 inches by this chamber.

Passing through the outer yoke, as shown in Fig. 20, are three radial holes, each 4 inches in diameter. There are similar but smaller connecting holes in the vacuum chamber. These are used to allow the insertion of radial probes for magnetic measurements. At the 30° and 120° ports, the field has been observed to be 2% smaller than in the 90° hole at the center of the magnet. A magnetization curve for the spectrometer is given in Fig. 21 and shows that the field is proportional to the current up to 14 000 gauss (or up to 400 Mev). The region in which the field falls off as the square root of r lies between radii 33.5 and 38.5 inches and at higher fields it contracts so that it is only two inches wide at 550 Mev. At high fields the vertical aperture is, therefore, stopped down at the entrance slit to prevent electrons from entering the saturated region of the gap. The fringing field has been measured and is virtually negligible for all energies. A fourth hole, shown in Fig. 20, permits a bremsstrahlung beam to pass through the vacuum chamber and through a thin window from the target while all electrons and positrons are cleared out of the way by the magnetic field. Further constructional details are given in reference 68.

The poor duty cycle makes it necessary to use a massive ten-ton shield to protect the Čerenkov counter from background radiation. This shield is supported high above floor level on a platform on the magnet itself. The magnet, platform, and shield can be moved radially on the two ways shown in Fig. 18. The magnet is supported on a modified double five-inch antiaircraft gun mount kindly provided on loan by the U. S. Navy. Remote control of the gun mount to 0.05 degree has been obtained with the standard selsyn indicators provided in the mount.

The Čerenkov detector is much like the smaller one described previously, but its dimensions are increased. Its input diameter is 2.75 inches, output diameter 3.75 inches, and the length is 5.0 inches. The truncated cone of Lucite couples to a DuMont five-inch photomultiplier. The slit system used with this detector resembles that of the smaller spectrometer.

The beam spot at the target position is usually about $\frac{3}{8}$ inch wide and $\frac{1}{8}$ inch to $\frac{1}{4}$ inch high. Under certain conditions it can be made considerably smaller. Gas target chambers of the kind shown in Fig. 16 have been used in this installation. The length of the gas target is increased so that small-angle studies can be made with less interference from the end windows than the small chambers allow. A ten-place target ladder is used with the larger spectrometer for foils and solid laminas. A snout-like extension of the vacuum chamber extends from the spectrometer near to the target so that only a few inches of air lie between the scatterer and the thin-windowed input port of the spectrometer. Figure 22 shows some of the details. Nevertheless, electrons scattered from this air layer have been detected and in a short time all experiments in the end station will be carried out in vacuum with a bell jar, as in the halfway station.

Finally Fig. 18 shows a large Faraday cup, which is now being installed and which will be used to make absolute measurements of cross section.

(c) Behavior of Čerenkov Detectors

While carrying on studies of the neutron,[50] (see later, Sec. VI) for which scattering targets of CH_2 and CD_2

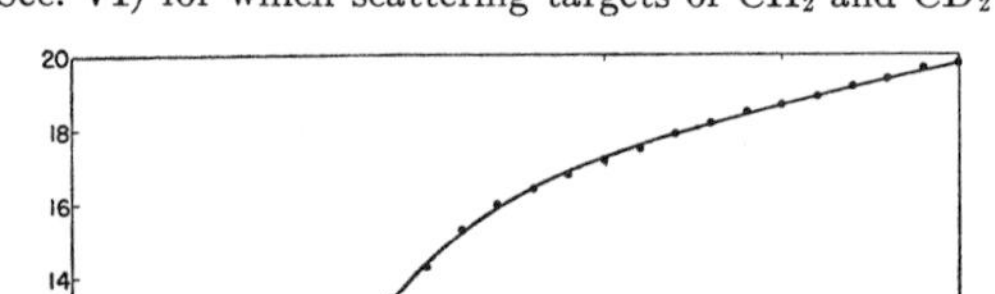

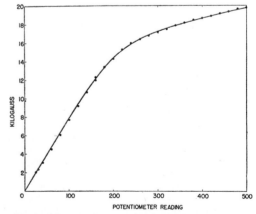

FIG. 21. Magnetization curve for the 550-Mev spectrometer. The potentiometer reading is proportional to the current in the magnet coils.

are used, a peculiar behavior was noted at high energies and large angles. Figure 23 shows the observed pattern at 120° and 550 Mev and is typical of the findings. Note the customary sharp free proton peak at a potentiometer setting of 127. In addition to this peak, very large peaks are observed in the energy spectra of CH_2 and CD_2, centering at a reading of 90 on the potentiometer. There is a slight bulge in CD_2 near the position of the free proton peak. The bulge (Sec. VI) was the object under study, but it was completely masked by the large peaks noted above. An investigation, which will not be reported here, showed that the large peaks were due to negative pions produced in the target and carrying the same momenta as scattered electrons under investigation. Under careful investigation, the left side of the peaks turned out to be exceedingly sharp and corresponded exactly to the threshold velocity of pions required to first register a pulse in a Lucite (index of refraction $n=1.50$) Čerenkov detector. When the Lucite was replaced by the liquid $C_8F_{16}O$ (index 1.276), the pion peaks disappeared almost completely and the deuteron bulge could be seen clearly. It is, thus, quite advantageous to use a material with the smallest possible index of refraction when it is desired to isolate electrons. Of course, the index must be larger than unity or no light will be observed. A gaseous Čerenkov detector could have important uses in this instance.

In Fig. 13 the step near 175 Mev represents a pion background even for the smaller incident energy of 400 Mev.

V. RESULTS

The results obtained in investigating atomic nuclei with the two instruments described in this paper will be discussed below in the order of increasing atomic number. *Note*: Often the rms radius of an "equivalent uniform model" is mentioned in the text. This refers to a radius found from r_0 defined by Eq. (52).

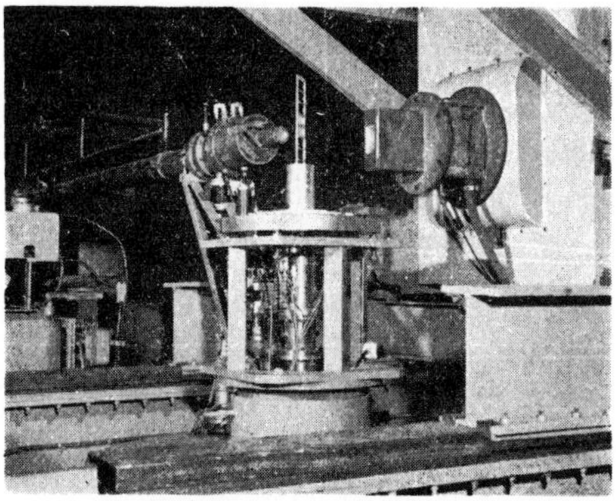

FIG. 22. Details of the monitor, target ladder, and magnet input port.

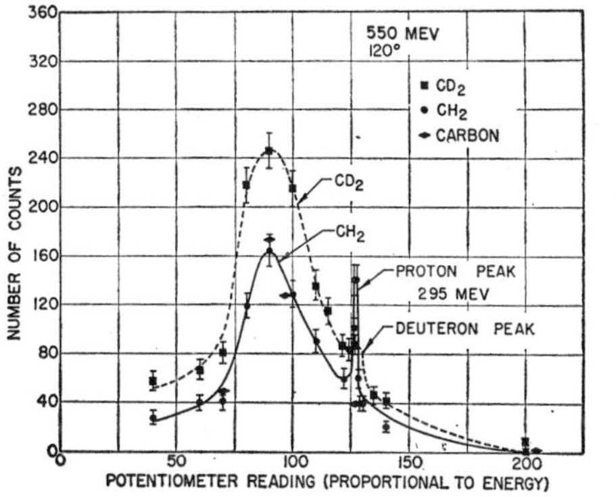

FIG. 23. The free proton peak, the deuteron incoherent peak, and the negative pion peaks. The first two peaks are associated with scattered electrons, the remaining three (CH_2, CD_2, C) are caused by negative pions having the same momenta as electrons scattered inelastically in this momentum range. See also Sec. VI.

(a) The Proton

Electron scattering from the proton has been investigated at energies extending from 100 Mev up to an energy of 550 Mev. Hydrogen gas at high pressure (2000 psi) has been used at energies of 100, 188, 210, 236 Mev by McAllister and Hofstadter.[42] The earliest experimental results showed departures from the point-charge-point magnetic-moment calculations of Rosenbluth,[56] Eq. (35). The data are shown at 188 Mev in Fig. 24. The topmost curve (c) is the Rosenbluth curve for a point charge and point magnetic moment, where the magnetic moment has the full anomalous value, $1+\mu=2.79$ nuclear magnetons. The lowest curve (a) corresponds to no magnetic moment at all and is, therefore, the Mott curve, Eq. (36), in the laboratory system's coordinates. The large interval between curves (c) and (a) demonstrates the theoretical contribution of the magnetic scattering of a point. Curve (b) is Rosenbluth's cross section if the magnetic moment of the proton had a pure Dirac moment, i.e., the 1 of the $1+\mu$ nuclear magnetons. The experimental points shown in the figure lie in between the Dirac curve and the point charge point moment curve and, therefore suggest that the proton's magnetic moment is not a point and that form factors must be assigned to the proton.

Without further information, there is no way of deciding *a priori*, whether F_1 or F_2, the Dirac or Pauli form factors of Eq. (39), respectively, are separately responsible for the smaller amount of backward scattering in Fig. 24, or whether both together share in the responsibility. However, Eq. (39) shows that F_1 and F_2 produce different angular distributions. For example, it can be shown that a point charge ($F_1=1$) and a spread-out Pauli moment ($F_2<1$) will result in a form factor that is nearly unity at small momentum transfers ($q<1$) and will begin to fall off more rapidly at larger momentum transfers. On the other hand, a spread-out

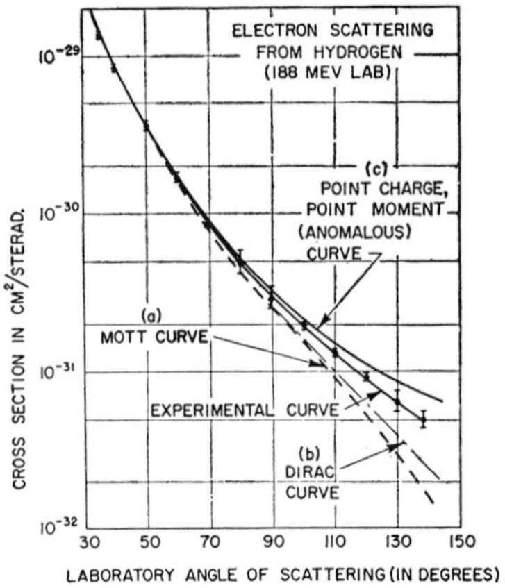

FIG. 24. Electron scattering from the proton at an incident energy of 188 Mev. The experimental points lie below the point-charge point-moment curve of Rosenbluth, indicating finite size effects.

charge ($F_1<1$) and a point Pauli moment ($F_2=1$) will show weaker scattering at small values of q and will show almost the entire amount of Rosenbluth point scattering at large momentum transfers. This is another way of saying qualitatively that the charge is responsible for small-angle low-energy scattering and the Pauli-magnetic moment is responsible for most of the large-angle high-energy scattering. It must be remembered that even if F_2 is zero there is a contribution to magnetic scattering from F_1, namely, from the Dirac moment. However, the effect from F_2 is larger. A spread-out charge ($F_1<1$) *and* a spread-out moment ($F_2<1$) will produce a weakening of the scattering at *both* small and large values of q. Hence, in principle, by studying the scattering over a large range of energies and angles, it should be possible to disentangle the separate contributions of F_1 and F_2.

The proton results were, therefore, analyzed at the energies 100, 188, 210, 236 Mev with choices of (1) point-charge ($F_1=1$) spread-out moment ($F<1$), (2) point-moment ($F_2=1$) spread-out charge ($F_2<1$), and (3) both spread-out ($F_1<1$, $F_2<1$).

It should be noticed that at the lower energies (q small), only the mean square radii can influence the form factor, as shown by Eq. (19). Hence, the determination of F_1 and F_2 at energies less than 200 Mev will determine a radius r_e for the Dirac cloud and a radius r_m for the Pauli meson cloud, and not the shape of either of these distributions as a function of radius. The analysis showed further that $r_e=r_m=0.74\pm0.24$ fermi where r_e and r_m are the radii associated with the Dirac and Pauli parts of the proton's charge and magnetic moment density distributions. These values of r_e and r_m fitted the data excellently at all energies. The solid line in Fig. 24 shows the theoretical curve for $r_e=r_m=0.70$ fermi, i.e., the foregoing choice (3), and is one particular example of the fit to the experimental data. The accuracy of the experimental points was not great enough to decide definitely that the other possible choices (1) and (2) could be eliminated.

The same type of experiment was, therefore, continued by Chambers and Hofstadter[68] between energies of 200 Mev and 550 Mev in the laboratory frame. Data were obtained in these cases with polyethylene (CH_2). Brief check data with hydrogen gas were also obtained at the single energy of 400 Mev. An elastic peak, showing electrons scattered against protons in polyethylene at 400 Mev and 60°, is plotted in Fig. 25. Because of the recoil of the proton, the electron carries off only an energy of 326 Mev at 60°. The area under the proton peak is the quantity measured in this experiment and is proportional to the differential cross section[69] for scattering at this laboratory angle. In obtaining this area, the carbon background is subtracted and the low energy side of the peak is extended as indicated by the dashed line AC in Fig. 25. When the proton peak areas are normalized by the monitor reading to unit incident electron, the cross sections at various angles may be compared. A typical curve is shown in Fig. 26; the experimental points at 400 Mev are indicated with their corresponding limits of error. Plotted as a solid line above the experimental curve is the Rosenbluth theoretical curve [Eq. (35)] for a point charge and point magnetic moment. This is indicated by the symbols $r_e=0$ and $r_m=0$ standing, respectively, for rms charge radius (Dirac) and moment radius (Pauli).

At the high energies used in these experiments (200, 300, 400, 500, 550 Mev) quantities higher than the second power of qa enter Eq. (19) and the shapes of the charge and moment distributions become important.

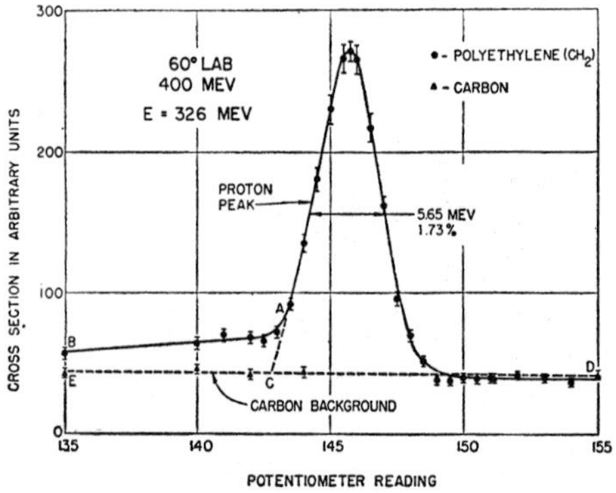

FIG. 25. Elastic scattering of 400-Mev electrons from protons in polyethylene at a laboratory angle of 60°.

[69] Since a constant slit width was used in all the experiments, there is a well-known correction in beta spectroscopy that must be applied to the areas because of the dispersion of the instrument (constant dp/p). This correction has been made in a standard manner to all cross sections.

Furthermore, the same distribution must fit the data at all energies if the particular model and the interpretation given by Eq. (39) are correct. Without going into details at this point the fit of one particular model is shown in Fig. 26. In this case, the model is the exponential distribution for both charge density and magnetic moment density. The rms radius of each distribution is taken as 0.80 fermi. From Eq. (39) and the F_1 and F_2 obtained from row IV in Table I, a theoretical curve can be prepared for this particular model. This theoretical curve is indicated by the solid line passing through the experimental points in Fig. 26. The experimenta points can be moved upwards or downwards to make the best fit. No other adjustment is made. This procedure is necessary since absolute values are not known. The ratio of the experimental values (now normalized in an absolute way by the fit at smaller angles) to the point-charge point-moment values are the desired F^2 (form factor)^2 values. Independent fits of the experimental data were made at all the energies between 200 and 550 Mev and then assembled together in Fig. 27. The ordinate in this figure is F^2 as just described. The abscissa is the square of the momentum transfer $\times 10^{-26}$ cm^2. The fit of this particular model is good and it is consistent at all energies and angles.

The consistency of the fit under these diverse conditions lends confidence to the use of Eq. (39) and the phenomenological introduction of the F_1 and F_2 form factors. The good fit to the experimental data is not

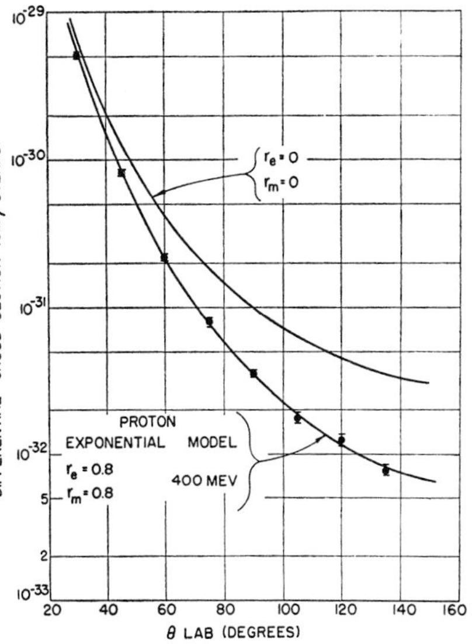

FIG. 26. Typical angular distribution for elastic scattering of 400-Mev electrons against protons. The solid line is a theoretical curve for a proton of finite extent. The model providing the theoretical curve is an exponential with rms radii $=0.80\times 10^{-13}$ cm.

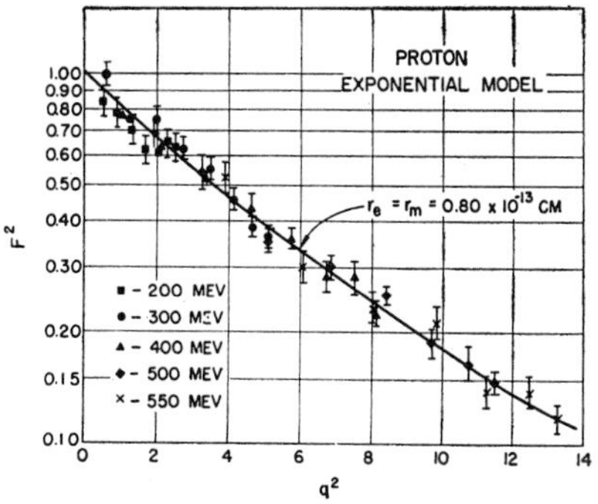

FIG. 27. The square of the form factor plotted against q^2. q^2 is given in units of 10^{-26} cm^2. The solid line is calculated for the exponential model with rms radii $=0.80\times 10^{-13}$ cm.

unique, however. A Gaussian model with $r_e=r_m=0.72$ fermi provides a similar fit and equally good consistency at all energies. Many other models have been studied in this way. Among those examined are II through X, inclusive, in Table I. With all these models the choice $r_e=r_m$ was made and the shapes were assumed to be the same for the charge (Dirac) cloud and the magnetic moment (Pauli) cloud. The best choices are shown in Table II. All other models do not fit well enough at all energies to be considered seriously.

Several of the models are shown in Fig. 28. In this figure $4\pi r^2\rho$ is plotted. This is a quantity proportional to the amount of charge in a shell at radius r. Either one among the Gaussian, exponential, or "hollow" exponential models fits equally well. Any model, lying within a band in Fig. 28 including all the three models, represents a "best" present approximation to the charge distribution within the proton. The magnetic moment density distribution has the same appearance. The Yukawa model, also shown in the figure, will not fit the data. Neither will a uniform model.

All models considered above have involved the assumption of similar shapes and equal radii for the Dirac and Pauli charge and moment clouds. If differences among these shapes are assumed and F_1 is not to be the same as F_2, the field of possible models is enlarged enormously. Considerable effort has been expended in attempts to find pairs of different radii and different shapes which could match the experimental data. Many

TABLE II. This table represents a summary of the proton models and the appropriate values of their root-mean-square radii which give the best fits to the data. Equal radii for Dirac and Pauli clouds are assumed.

Model number	Shape	rms radius for best fit ($r_e=r_m$) in fermi units
III	$\exp(-r^2)$	0.72±0.05
IV	e^{-r}	0.80±0.05
VI	re^{-r}	0.78±0.05
VII	r^2e^{-r}	0.75±0.05
Mean (best fit)	...	0.77±0.10

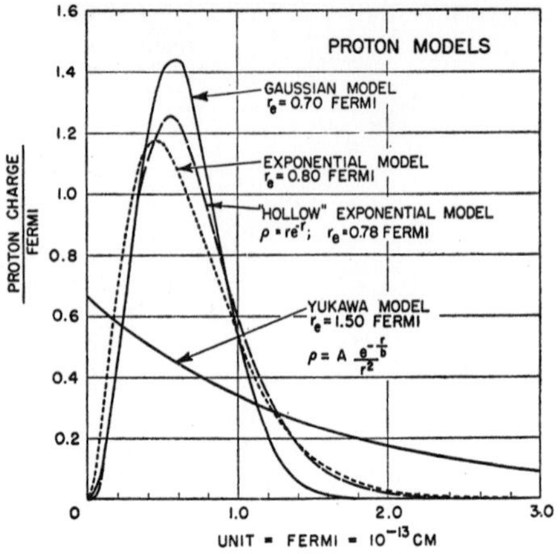

FIG. 28. The Gaussian, exponential, and "hollow" exponential models fit the proton data equally well. The Yukawa model will not fit. The ordinate is $4\pi r^2\rho$.

possibilities have been eliminated. A single example is shown in Fig. 29 and shows a typical behavior observed for a choice of a magnetic cloud of small dimensions. It is not possible to make a realistic F_2 correspond to a small radius.

Without going into details it is possible to summarize the model testing by saying that if different radii are chosen for the Dirac and Pauli clouds, the limits on each *independently* lie approximately at 0.6 and 1.5 fermi units. Higher accuracy of the experiments can reduce these limits and can also decide between the models shown in Fig. 28. The experiments have the least accuracy in determining the region near zero radius and perhaps as far as 0.3 fermi. Among all the models tested the "hollow" exponential model with $r_e = r_m = 0.78$ fermi gives the best fit. This does not mean that $\rho = 0$ at $r = 0$ since, as has just been remarked, there is only a small accuracy at $r = 0$.

The interpretation of these experiments on the proton is also considered in Secs. VII and VIII. It is interesting, however, that the proton's "Dirac size" (r_e) seems to be just as large as the "Pauli size" (r_m), and is very large, indeed, being about three times the nucleon Compton wavelength. We call attention once more to the fact that the apparent finite size effects can be explained equivalently with point particles and a breakdown of electrodynamics.

(b) The Deuteron

Elastic scattering from the deuteron was investigated at high energies (192 Mev) by McIntyre and Hofstadter,[70] and recently in considerably greater detail at 188 Mev and 400 Mev by McIntyre.[71] The interest in the deuteron is manifest since it is the only two-nucleon system which is known to be stable and, in some respects, its position as a tool in resolving the problem of nuclear forces resembles that of the hydrogen atom in atomic physics. Because of this simplicity, the deuteron wave function in the ground state can be calculated for many possible nuclear potentials acting between the neutron and the proton. Among these are the square well, Hulthén, Blatt-Kalos, Gartenhaus, and the repulsive core potentials. It is well known that all give virtually the same behavior if adjusted for the proper binding energy of the deuteron, $\epsilon = -2.226$ Mev and the triplet scattering length. All that can be determined from the nuclear experiments is the effective range, a quantity essentially independent of the shape of the deuteron potential at the scattering energies investigated. In studying the deuteron it was hoped that electron scattering might cast a new and independent light on the neutron-proton potential.

From the deuteron wave function $\psi(r_{12})$ and the accepted value of the effective range 1.70 ± 0.03 fermi, the charge density in the deuteron can be computed from $\rho = e|\psi|^2$, where r_{12} is the internucleon distance. For a given potential, and, therefore, a given charge density ρ, the form factor for the deuteron F_D [see Eq. (41)] can be computed. Now, the electron scattering method also furnishes an independent value of the experimental form factor. Hence, the prediction of nuclear theory can be compared with the experimental electron scattering result. Such a comparison is given in Fig. 30 for three different potentials.

Experimentally, the data can be taken with deu-

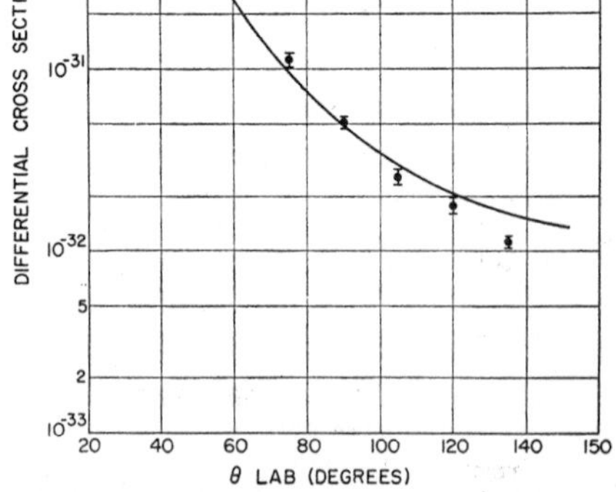

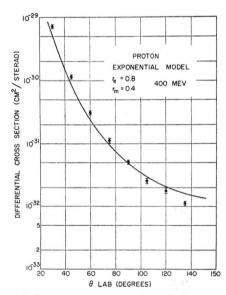

FIG. 29. Example of a model that will not fit the experiments. This model has a magnetic moment distribution which is too small.

[70] J. A. McIntyre and R. Hofstadter, Phys. Rev. 98, 158 (1955).
[71] J. A. McIntyre (to be published).

terium and hydrogen alternately in the gas target chamber and, thus, the deuterium data can be normalized to hydrogen. This is an important point since a vital calibration datum is furnished by the result of the proton experiment.

From the figure, it is evident that the actual scattering lies outside the limits of any of the theoretical curves and it is apparent that an additional form factor is needed to obtain agreement. When it is realized that the deuteron's charge density $e|\psi|^2$ has been computed as if the neutron and proton were points, it may not seem so surprising that agreement with experiment is unattainable in Fig. 30. As we have remarked in IIIc, the question of how to introduce this form factor requires great care and involves considerations that concern both the meson clouds surrounding the neutron and proton and also the Dirac "cores" in these particles.

Agreement in Fig. 30 can, of course, be achieved by increasing the effective range. This requires an increase from 1.70 to at least 2.2 fermis and appears to be outside the limit of permissible errors (± 0.03 fermi) in the effective range. On the other hand, McIntyre obtains excellent agreement with experiment by empirically using a finite Gaussian proton of rms radius $r_e = 0.80$ fermi with the repulsive core potential of Jankus.[59] Figure 31 shows the agreement for three proton radii. The consistency of this analysis with that of the proton[68] is remarkable. Similar agreement with slightly larger radii (0.85 fermi) are obtained with other potentials such as the Hulthén type.

We have noted before that the introduction of nucleon form factors due to finite size effects in the neutron and proton, must be considered carefully from a meson theoretic point of view. Naively we should expect that a finite proton's form factor would multiply F_D directly where F_D is the deuteron form factor. Actually, the finite size of the neutron also should contribute. Since the specific electron-neutron interaction

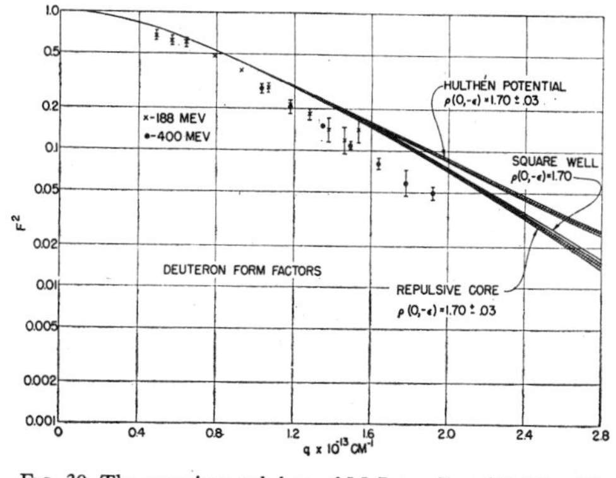

FIG. 30. The experimental data of McIntyre[71] at 400 Mev. The ordinate is the square of the form factor. Conventional form factors, derived from well-known nuclear potentials, do not fit the experimental data.

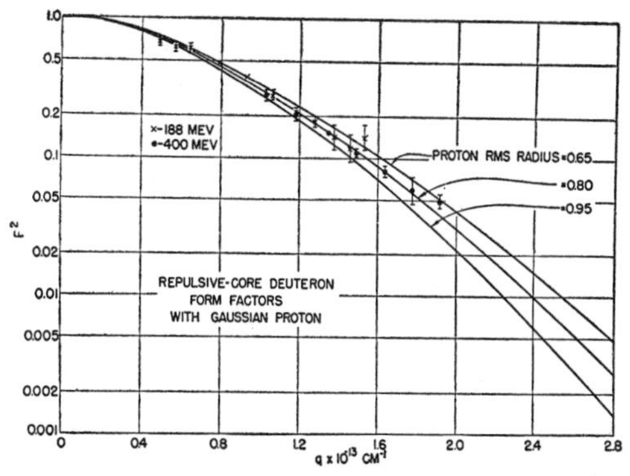

FIG. 31. Introduction of a finite proton core allows the experimental data to be fitted with conventional form factors (McIntyre).

has been shown to be very small, the neutron's apparent size can be assumed to be very small. (See Sec. VI and reference 90.) In this event only the proton's finite size would be important. However, the situation is more complicated and is the subject of an investigation by Yennie *et al.*[57] These authors show that, for the deuteron, a finite negative meson cloud in the neutron should cancel the proton's positive meson cloud, leaving as residue only the effect of the cores of the proton and neutron. While, it might be expected that the cores would be very small, it seems necessary to introduce an appreciable nucleon size to interpret the deuteron experiment. This is an indication that the nucleon core size is quite large (0.7 fermi).

Inelastic scattering from the deuteron has been discussed in Sec. IIIc and will be taken up again in the consideration of the size of the neutron (Sec. VI).

(c) The Alpha Particle

Scattering from the alpha particle in helium gas has been carried out by McAllister and Hofstadter[42] at 188 Mev and by Blankenbecler and Hofstadter[49] at 400 Mev. Both experiments agree quite well with each other and show that there are very large effects due to the finite size of the alpha particle. Since the spin and magnetic moment of the alpha particle are both zero, the elastic scattering is due entirely to the charge alone. However, the large angle *inelastic* scattering will depend significantly on the magnetic moments of the nucleons.

Figure 32 shows the experimental data in helium gas at approximately 1500 psi. The gas target chamber was alternate y filled with helium and hydrogen at certain angular settings. The scattered intensities were measured under the same experimental conditions. Hence, the helium data can be normalized to proton scattering and a Mott curve Eq. (36) can be constructed for helium. The solid line in Fig. 32, labeled "Theoretical Mott Curve," has been prepared in this way. Figure 33 shows that beyond 70° the elastic scattering is smaller by a factor of over a hundred from that expected from a point alpha particle. This figure exhibits the square of the form factor as a function of laboratory angle obtained from the data in Fig. 32. The points carrying limits of error are the experimental points and the three solid curves represent three theoretical form factor curves for possible models of the alpha particle of the indicated rms radii. It is clear that the Gaussian with rms radius 1.61 fermi is the best fit of the three. This radius is in close agreement with one previously obtained.[42] No attempt is made here to introduce the finite sizes of the nucleons although, when the data are compared ultimately with a form factor calculated from a nuclear theory of the alpha particle, the finite size effects must be taken into account.

One brief study, needing repetition, was attempted by Blankenbecler and Hofstadter[49] to examine the inelastic continuum in helium at a large q value: 400 Mev, 60°. The results are shown in Fig. 13 and have been commented on briefly in Secs. IIIb2 and IIIb4. The incoherent scattering from the protons and neutrons in the alpha particle add up to a considerably greater cross section than the coherent scattering, represented by the elastic peak at 373 Mev. As far as is known to the author, there is no explicit theory giving the momentum distribution of the nucleons in the alpha particle for comparison with the inelastic continuum of Fig. 13.

The size of the alpha particle *can* be compared with the radius, 1.61 fermi, given by the phenomenological

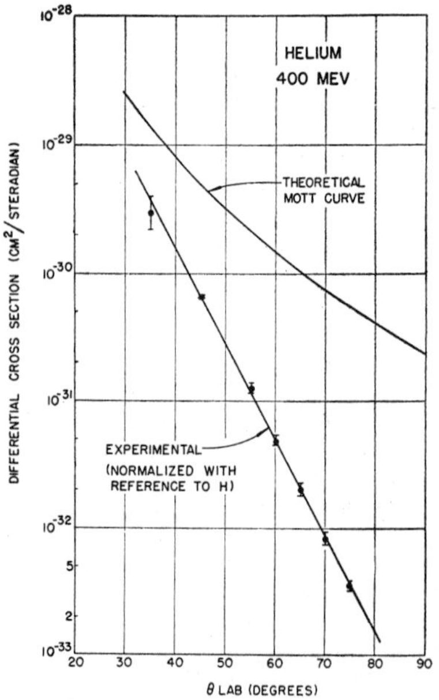

FIG. 32. Experimental angular distribution of 400-Mev electrons scattered from helium gas. The point charge curve is shown here.

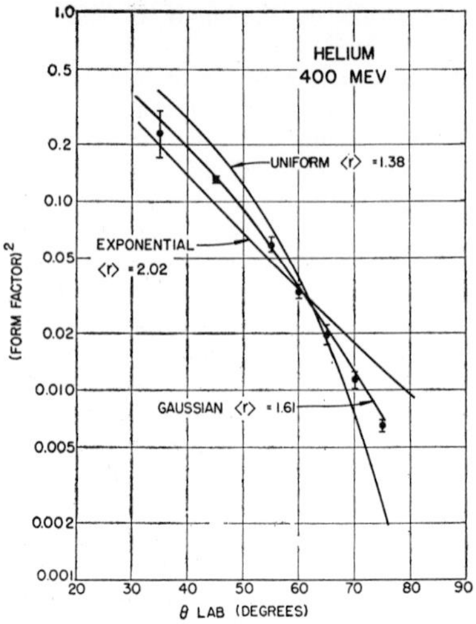

FIG. 33. The square of the form factor of the alpha particle for three possible models. The experimental points indicate that a Gaussian model with rms radius$=1.61\times10^{-13}$ cm provides the best fit.

analysis of Fig. 33 for the best-fitting Gaussian model. To make this comparison Dalitz and Ravenhall[72] computed an rms radius from the wave functions of Clark[73] who used a variational method to fit the binding energy of the alpha particle. The resulting radius was only about $\frac{2}{3}$ of the required size. Perhaps this discrepancy is due to the use of only two D states in Clark's calculations.

It may be noticed that there is an apparent peak in Fig. 13 at 352 Mev and perhaps other structure in the immediate neighborhood of the high-energy side of the inelastic continuum. Whether this points to an excited state of the alpha particle is difficult to say with the meager evidence at hand. This work needs early repetition to decide whether such structure is real or not.

(d) Lithium and Beryllium

The separate isotopes Li^6 and Li^7 have been studied by J. F. Streib[74] who finds that both nuclei appear to have the same rms radius to within a few percent. Both isotopes possess charge densities resembling closely model XII of Table I. The best type of fit to the elastic scattering was found by Streib[75] to be model XII with rms radii "a" $(Li^6)=2.78$ fermi and "a" $(Li^7)=2.71$ fermi with an accuracy of $\pm2\%$. The ratio $(a\,Li^6/a(Li^7))$ could be measured quite carefully and more accurately than either size, and gave the value 1.026 ± 0.008. The effects of the magnetic moment of Li^7 were calculated

72 R. H. Dalitz and D. G. Ravenhall (private communication).
73 A. C. Clark, Proc. Phys. Soc. (London) **A67**, 323 (1954).
74 J. F. Streib, Phys. Rev. **100**, 1797(A) (1955).
75 J. F. Streib (private communication). These are results more recent than those given in reference 74. The sizes were based on a comparison with scattering from the proton.

with a Rosenbluth-like formula [Eq. (35)] and were removed in arriving at the above values of nuclear radii. It is interesting that Li^7 appears to have a smaller size than Li^6. This may be because the Li^6 nucleus behaves in some respects as if it had a deuteron outside its closed shell. For Li^6, the value of r_0 is 1.98 fermis and for Li^7, 1.83 fermis, for the equivalent uniform model [Eq. (1)].

In the case of Be^9, an early study[44] showed that inelastic scattering to nuclear levels was quite prominent. The inelastic and elastic scattering have been studied again more intensively by Streib[75] who finds good agreement with the older results. Streib has analyzed the beryllium results, using model XII of Table I, which is a modified exponential charge distribution and finds an rms radius of 3.04 ± 0.07 fermis. This corresponds to an r_0 of 1.89 fermis, for an equivalent uniform model.

Shell model calculations of p-shell nuclei have been carried out by Ferrell and Visscher[76] who find that the nucleus Li^6 should have an rms radius of 2.8 fermis. This is in good agreement with Streib's value of 2.78 fermis. The experimental value of Li^7 (2.71 fermis) is higher than the theoretical value 2.3 ± 0.2 fermis, and the experimental radius of Be^9 (3.04 fermis) is likewise larger than the theoretical value of 2.3 ± 0.2 fermis.

(e) Carbon

C^{12} is a relatively simple nucleus and it is important that it should be investigated thoroughly. This nucleus has been examined by Fregeau and Hofstadter[43] and subsequently by Fregeau[77] in considerably greater detail. In Sec. IIIb1 we have illustrated the type of

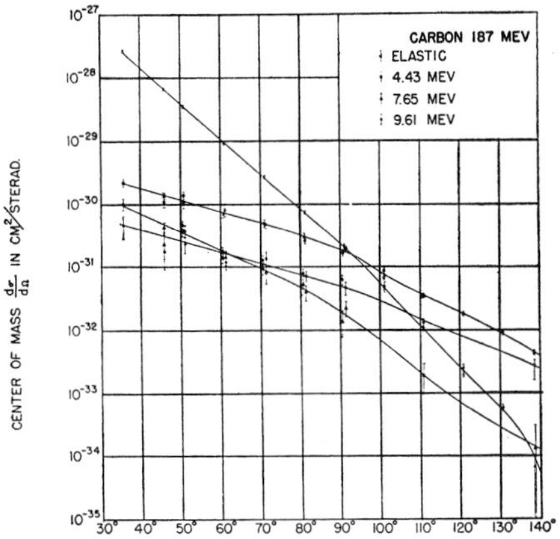

FIG. 34. Fregeau's data on the elastic and inelastic scattering of 187-Mev electrons as a function of center-of-mass angle.

[76] R. A. Ferrell and W. M. Visscher, Bull. Am. Phys. Soc. Ser. II, 1, 17 (1956).

[77] J. H. Fregeau, Ph.D. thesis, Stanford University, June, 1956. A shorter account is to be published.

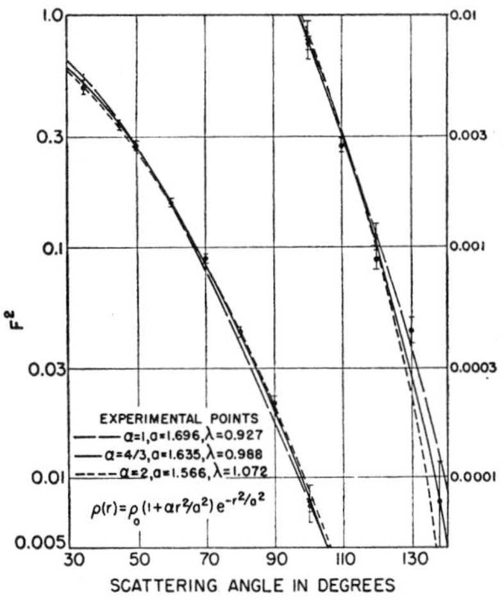

FIG. 35. The square of the form factor for C^{12}. Theoretical curves for Model XI of Table I, corresponding to Eq. (45), are shown in the figure. The parameter λ is a normalizing factor which should be unity if the theory and experiment fit exactly. The value $\lambda = 0.988$ for $\alpha = 4/3$ is very satisfactory.

data taken at a given scattering angle with this nucleus and have seen there not only the elastic peak, but the scattering due to the various levels of C^{12}. A summary of the data obtained at 187 Mev up to the present time is shown in Fig. 34. The graph includes the behavior of the elastic peak which shows a variation with scattering angle of about a factor 2×10^6 from 35° to 138°. The figure also shows the angular behavior of the scattering cross sections associated with the excited states of C^{12} at 4.43, 7.65, and 9.61 Mev. At the largest angles the elastic scattering is exceeded by the scattering from each of the nuclear levels. Angular distributions of the 4.43- and 9.61-Mev scattering cross sections appear to be similar to each other and less steep than the behavior of the elastic or 7.65-Mev peaks. Since the 4.43-Mev transition is a $0^+ - 2^+$ transition and the 7.65 Mev is believed to be a $0^+ - 0^+$ transition, the difference in angular behavior may be correlated with the radial oscillations of the $0-0$ transition. On the basis of an angular behavior similar to that of the 4.43 transition, the 9.61-Mev transition might be thought to be $0^+ - 2^+$.

The elastic scattering leads to a determination of the radial charge density in the ground state of C^{12}. It is possible to compare the carbon scattering, directly in the experiment, with scattering from the proton and, hence, to obtain an "absolute" determination of the experimental form factor. In the early work[43] a comparison of an "absolute" form factor with those obtained from three trial models, i.e., the Gaussian, uniform, and exponential, led to a best fit lying between a Gaussian with rms radius 2.47 fermis and a uniform model with rms radius 2.20 fermis. This suggested a "best" value of 2.40 fermis for the rms radius. A con-

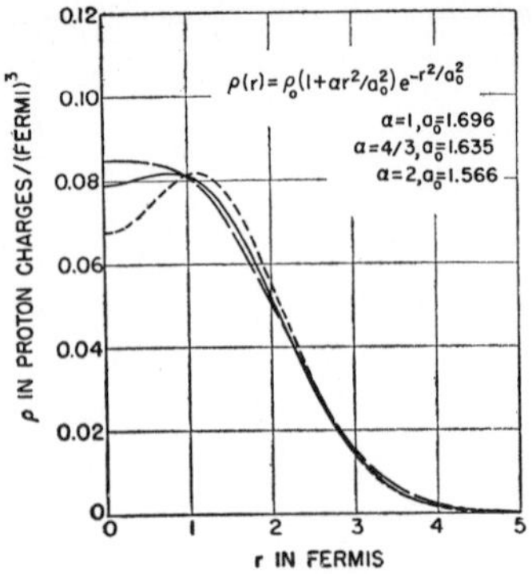

FIG. 36. The charge distribution for Model XI for three values of α. All three charge distributions fit the experimental data equivalently. $\alpha=4/3$ has some theoretical justification.

siderably better determination has been made recently by Fregeau[77] who finds excellent agreement with this conclusion

Fregeau's results are shown in Fig. 35 which gives F^2 as a function of angle for three models of a type suggested by Ravenhall,[78] and more recently by Morpurgo,[79] based on the oscillator shell model. (See also Model XI and Table I.) On this model the charge density ρ has the same behavior for JJ and LS coupling and has the appearance

$$\rho=\rho_0\left(1+\alpha\frac{r^2}{a_0^2}\right)\exp[-(r^2/a_0^2)], \tag{45}$$

where

$$\alpha=4/3 \tag{46}$$

for the shell model and "a_0" is a parameter proportional to the rms value of the radius. α may be varied to find a best fit, as indicated in Fig. 35. It appears that $\alpha=4/3$ is as good a fit as can be obtained. Figures 36 and 37 show the charge distribution ρ, given by Eq. (45), for three values of α, and also $4\pi r^2\rho$, for these same values. The solid line shows the case $\alpha=4/3$. With present accuracy it has not been possible to determine the exact behavior of ρ near $r=0$, but the charge density at larger values of radius is rather well determined. Other models have been investigated by Fregeau, but all successful models give $4\pi r^2\rho$ curves similar to Fig. 37. For the best-fitting model, the rms radius has the value 2.40±0.05 fermis. The value of r_0 for an equivalent uniform model [Eq. (1)] is 1.36 fermis.

The behavior of the inelastic scattering curves has been examined by Ravenhall and by Morpurgo. In the case of the 4.43-Mev level, both Ravenhall and Morpurgo find that LS coupling gives better agreement with experiment than the JJ coupling scheme. Morpurgo is also able to explain the behavior of the ratio of the inelastic cross section relative to the elastic cross section as a function of energy. He also gives a satisfactory explanation of the constancy of the inelastic cross section (4.43 Mev) at 90° between the energies 80–187 Mev. Neither the LS nor the JJ coupling scheme gives exact quantitative agreement with the ratio of the inelastic (4.43 Mev) to elastic cross sections at all the energies studied. The experimental values are larger on the average by a factor of two, as found earlier by Ravenhall. Considering the crudity of the harmonic well model, this disagreement is not considered serious. The angular distribution of the (4.43-Mev) inelastic scattering seems to be given adequately by theory.

Of course, it should be noted that the Born approximation commits an error in dealing with the elastic and inelastic scattering. We have commented on this previously (Secs. IIb and IIc). However, in the case of elastic scattering, the reduction factor (γ) in rms radius between the exact value and the Born approximation value has been estimated by Ravenhall[80]

$$\gamma=\frac{r_{\text{exact}}}{r_{\text{Born}}}=\frac{1}{1+(3Z\alpha/2kR)} \tag{47}$$

for an equivalent uniform charge distribution of radius R, where α is the fine structure constant and k is the wave number of the incident electrons. In the case of carbon the exact rms radius should, therefore, be 2.37±0.05 fermis instead of 2.40±0.05 fermis. The corrected r_0 of Eq. (1) will then become 1.34 fermis for C^{12}.

On the theoretical side, a fair amount of work has been carried out on the carbon nucleus. The rms radius estimate of Ferrell and Visscher[76] for the ground state of C^{12} ($a=2.3\pm0.2$ fermis) is in good agreement with the experimental value 2.37 fermis. Besides the calculations on the scattering from the 4.43 level,[78,79] other calculations on the 7.65-[81] and 9.61-[82] Mev levels have

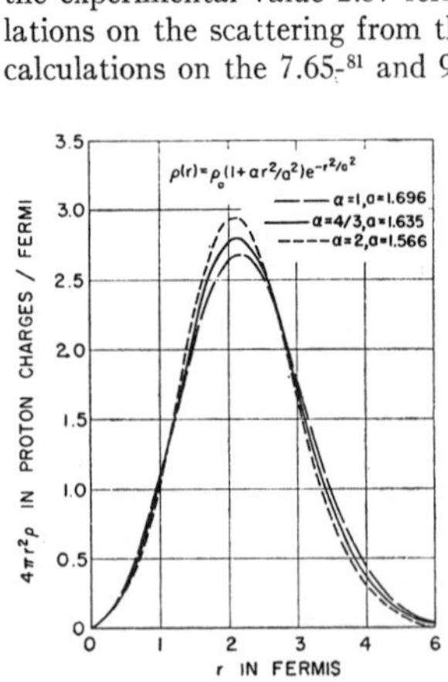

FIG. 37. The same charge distributions appearing in Fig. 36 when multiplied by $4\pi r^2$. Note the similarity of the resulting distributions.

[78] D. G. Ravenhall (to be published).
[79] G. Morpurgo, Nuovo cimento **III**, No. 2, 430 (1956).

[80] D. G. Ravenhall (private communication).
[81] L. I. Schiff, Phys. Rev. **98**, 1281 (1955).
[82] D. G. Ravenhall, Phys. Rev. **100**, 1797 (1955).

been made. Schiff[81] has found that an alpha-particle model of C^{12} and an elastic fluid model both yield too-large values of the transition matrix element from the 7.65-Mev level to the ground state. He has also used the independent particle model and a JJ coupling scheme to investigate a two-nucleon transition between the $p_{3/2}$ and $p_{1/2}$ shells. In this case the transition matrix element turned out to be too small by about a factor of six. Schiff concludes that an intermediate type of model is required, i.e., one more collective in character than the independent particle model (with only pair interactions) and less collective than the alpha-particle model or elastic fluid model. Glassgold and Galonsky[83] have shown than an alpha-particle model of the C^{12} nucleus is consistent with the radius of the charge distribution in the ground state. However, this model, though successful for O^{16}, predicts a state at 5.54 Mev in C^{12} which has not been observed.

(f) Magnesium, Silicon, Sulfur, Argon, and Strontium

R. H. Helm[46] has made an electron-scattering survey of the even-even nuclei: ${}_{12}Mg^{24}$, ${}_{14}Si^{28}$, ${}_{16}S^{32}$, ${}_{18}A^{40}$, and ${}_{38}Sr^{88}$, in order to study the $0-2$ transitions between the ground and first excited states, in addition to the elastic scattering. The first excited levels are sufficiently far removed from the ground state so that inelastic scattering can be resolved from the elastic scattering.

Helm's experimental results for the elastic scattering are shown in Fig. 38 and include Fregeau and Hofstadter's curve for C^{12}. Typical diffraction features are exhibited by the ordinate, which is the square of the form factor. The inelastic data of Helm are summarized

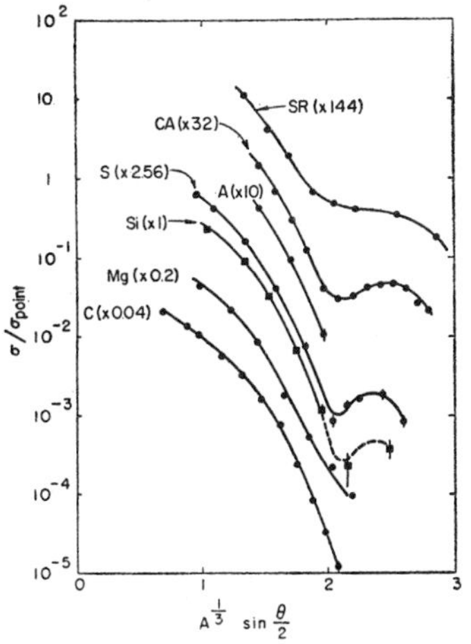

FIG. 38. The square of the form factor for elastic scattering of 187-Mev electrons from even-even nuclei. The diffraction dips occur at essentially the same value of the abscissa. This suggests that a radial parameter varies as $A^{\frac{1}{3}}$. This figure is due to Helm.[46]

[83] A. E. Glassgold and A. Galonsky (to be published).

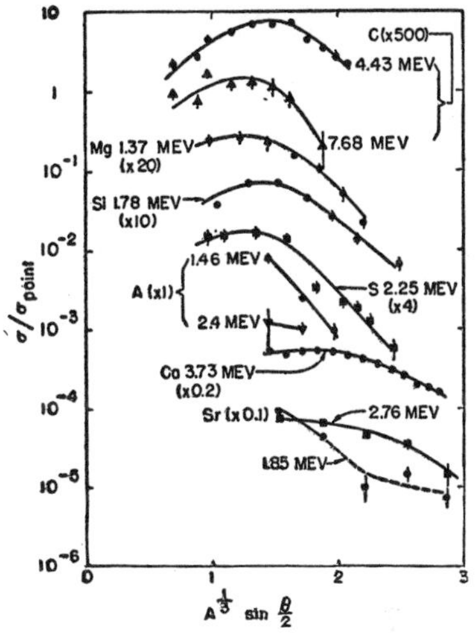

FIG. 39. Inelastic data for even-even nuclei. The ordinate is the square of a form factor for the inelastic processes.

in Fig. 39 as well as some of the carbon results. Here again the actual cross section is divided by the point charge cross section to obtain an effective (form factor)^2 for inelastic scattering.

Helm has developed a new and interesting "folded" charge distribution given, for example, by

$$\rho(r)=\int \rho_0(r')\rho_1(r-r')d^3r', \tag{48}$$

where $\rho_0(r)$ is a uniform charge distribution out to a distance $r=R$, i.e.,

$$\rho_0(r)=\begin{cases} 3/4\pi R^3 & r\leqslant R \\ 0 & r>R \end{cases} \tag{49}$$

and where

$$\rho_1(r)=\frac{1}{(2\pi g^2)^{\frac{3}{2}}}\exp[-(r^2/2g^2)]. \tag{50}$$

Helm calls this particular model the "Gaussian uniform" or gU distribution. This formulation has the advantage that the resultant form factor is the product of the two individual form factors

$$F(q)=F_0(q)F_1(q), \tag{51}$$

where the F_0 and F_1 are defined as usual by Eq. (17). Helm uses uU, or uniform-uniform folds, also. The folding procedure is satisfactory only as long as the Born approximation is valid.

The results obtained by applying the gU model to the data give the values in Table III. The radial estimates are corrected for the error made in using the Born approximation, *viz.*, Eq. (47). To compare the results with other experiments, the rms radius can be calculated from the gU distribution and can be equated

TABLE III. gU distribution. This table gives Helm's results for the radii of even-even nuclei and includes the C^{12} data of Fregeau and Hofstadter. The accuracy in the table is about 2–3%. Lengths are in units of 10^{-13} cm.

Element	r_0	$r_1 = cA^{-\frac{1}{3}}$	t
C^{12}	1.35	0.95	2.2
Mg^{24}	1.33	0.99	2.6
Si^{28}	1.29	0.97	2.8
S^{32}	1.30	1.03	2.6
Ca^{40}	1.28	1.08	2.4
Sr^{88}	1.20	1.08	2.3

to the rms radius for an "equivalent" uniform distribution of charge given by Eq. (1). An equivalent r_0 in Eq. (1) can, therefore, be deduced. This is the quantity given under the r_0 column of Table III. Such a procedure results in the expression for r_0.

$$r_0 = (5/3)^{\frac{1}{2}} aA^{-\frac{1}{3}}, \qquad (52)$$

where a is the root-mean-square radius of any charge distribution. The columns r_1 and t are related to the parameters defined by Hahn *et al.*[33] and refer to the "half-density" distance (c) and the skin thickness (t) of the charge distributions defined in that paper (see also Sec. Vg). The quantity r_1 is defined as

$$r_1 = cA^{-\frac{1}{3}}, \qquad (53)$$

and t is the 90%–10% distance in the skin. The values obtained by Helm are reproduced in Table III and will be commented on later in the resumé on nuclear radii. Helm's uU results are similar to the gU results.

The most interesting result on inelastic scattering is shown in Fig. 40. This figure shows that, if the experimental cross sections are divided by the point-charge cross sections and arbitrarily normalized together at the maximum values of the form factors, several "universal" curves are obtained. The suggestion is made, therefore, that each electric multipole transition

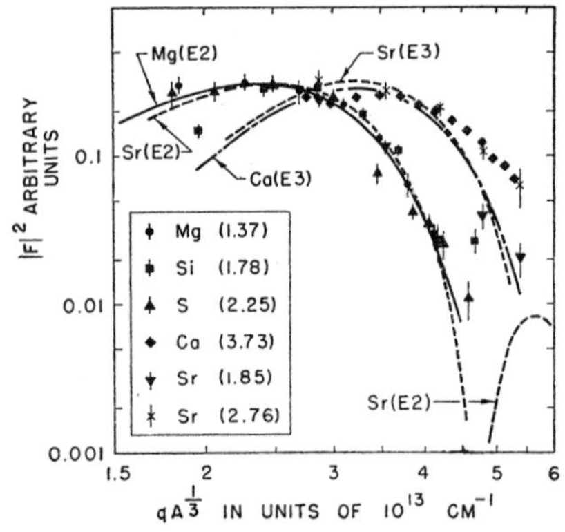

FIG. 40. The square of a form factor for inelastic scattering is plotted against a variable proportional to $A^{\frac{1}{3}} \sin\theta/2$. When the maxima are normalized together, Helm[46] obtains "universal" curves for various multipole transitions.

corresponds to its own universal curve for each value of $l=0$, 2, 3, etc. This, of course, may not be a general rule, but it seems to apply to these cases. As a result the assignment $J=2^+$ for S^{32} (2.25 Mev) and $J=3^-$ for Ca^{40} (3.73 Mev) can be made.[84] Helm[46] has also interpreted the relative intensities of the inelastic transitions in terms of a theory of Ravenhall[85] based on the Schiff treatment[47] which yields values for the partial level widths due to radiation.

(g) Medium-Heavy and Heavy Elements

The elements Ca, V, Co, In, Sb, Hf, Ta, W, Au, Bi, Th, and U were investigated by Hahn, Ravenhall, and Hofstadter[33] at an energy of 183 Mev and In, Au, and Bi at 153 Mev. Special attention was given to gold because of the previous information already available on this element. The early results on Au^{197} and Pb^{208} [4,86]

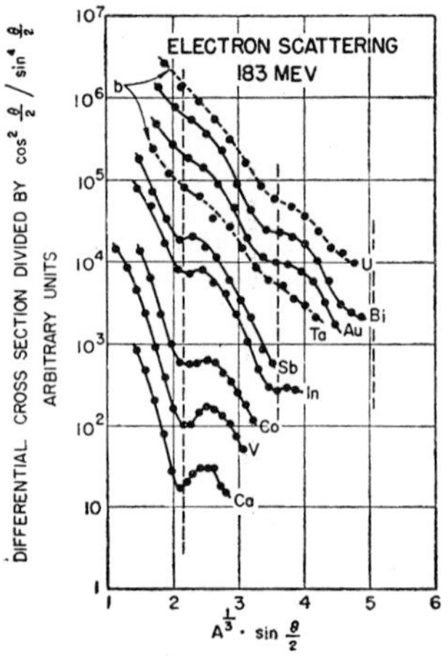

FIG. 41. Experimental results of Hahn *et al.*[33] which show that a radial parameter of the various charge distributions follows an $A^{\frac{1}{3}}$ law. The diffraction features are clearly evident and are emphasized at lower atomic numbers.

showed that two principal parameters governing the charge distribution were determinable from the experiments at these energies. These two parameters are called c and t and have been referred to previously. They are shown for a special model (Fig. 7), herein called the Fermi model. In general, these quantities refer to a radius parameter and to a surface thickness. The purpose of the investigation of Hahn *et al.* was to study how the two parameters varied over the range of nuclei from Ca to Bi. Only spherical nuclei were investigated in this connection. It was also desired to know how widely the two parameters might be adjusted so that they could still produce a good fit with experiment for the selected model. Other nonspherical nuclei (Hf, Ta, W, Th, and U) were investigated experimentally but no detailed interpretation of the results was given.

[84] D. G. Ravenhall and B. Hahn have also pointed out that these assignments appeared reasonable (unpublished).
[85] D. G. Ravenhall (to be published).
[86] D. G. Ravenhall and D. R. Yennie, Phys. Rev. 96, 239 (1954).

The main experimental results are shown in Fig. 41, in which the Mott cross section has been arbitrarily divided out to better exhibit the diffraction effects. The phase shift method was employed in the manner of Yennie *et al.*[17,18] since the Born approximation would be very poor for many of the elements investigated. Nevertheless, the angular positions of the diffraction dips in Fig. 41 occur at nearly the same value of $A^{\frac{1}{3}}\sin\theta/2$. According to the Born approximation, this fact suggests that some parameter, related to a radius, varies approximately as $A^{\frac{1}{3}}$. The parameter c, as we shall see later, is such a quantity. Some of the nuclei were chosen for study because they are near magic numbers such as Ca, In, Sb, Au, Bi, and presumably are spherical. Some were selected because they consist essentially of no more than a single isotope (Ca, V, Co, In, Ta, Au, Bi). The principal findings are given below.

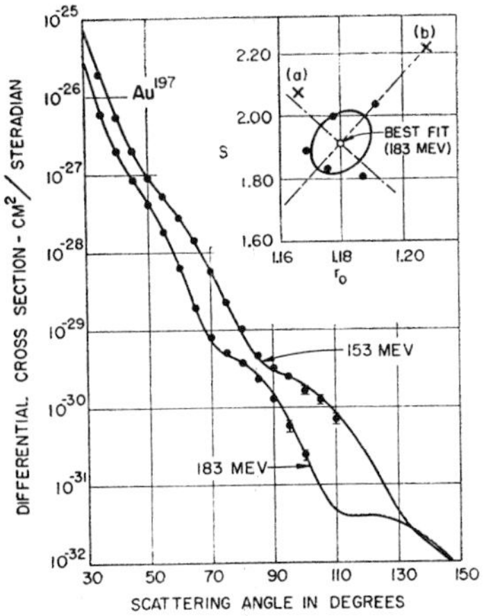

FIG. 42. Experimental points in gold at 153 and 183 Mev are compared with theoretical curves of Hahn *et al.*[33] obtained by phase shift methods. Sketch in inset is concerned with finding best statistical fit.

(*1*)

Au was studied in some detail. The experimental results are shown in Fig. 42 at two energies, 153 and 183 Mev. The diffraction dips are visible particularly if the curves are viewed along their lengths. These curves are not divided by a Mott factor, as in Fig. 41. The sketch in the insert refers to parameters used in Hahn *et al.* to find the best fit. The parameters s and r_0 are related to t and c. r_0 is the coefficient in Eq. (1) for the equivalent uniform sphere.

To fit the experimental curves, three test models were chosen.[87] Their forms are

$$\text{Fermi}: \rho(r)=\rho_1/\{\exp[(r-c)/z_1]+1\};\ (54)$$

$$\text{Modified Gaussian}: \rho(r)=p_2/\{\exp[(r^2-c^2)/z^2{}_2]+1\};\quad (55)$$

$$\begin{aligned}\text{Trapezoidal}: \rho(r)&=\rho_3,\quad 0<r<c-z_3\\ &=\rho_3(c+z_3-r)/2z_3,\\ &\qquad c-z_3<r<c+z_3,\\ &=0,\quad r>c+z_3.\end{aligned}\quad (56)$$

[87] The terminology of Hahn *et al.*[33] is used here.

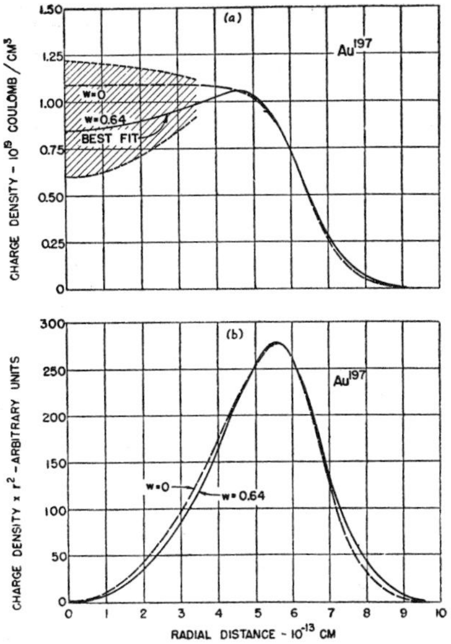

FIG. 43. Various gold charge density models which yield theoretical scattering curves very close to the best fitting ones of Fig. 42. The "best fit" in Fig. 43 (a) appears to have a small central depression; but the difference between the central depression ($w=0.64$) and the Fermi model ($w=0.0$) lies within the probable error of the determination. Figure 43 (b) shows why this is so. The curves represent $4\pi r^2\rho$ or the amount of charge in a unit shell. Very little charge resides near the origin, and the amount of charge in a shell is very similar for models $w=0.64$ and $w=0.0$.

The parameters are defined by the equations themselves. For the various shapes it is useful to define the parameter c.

$$c=\frac{1}{\rho(0)}\int_0^\infty \rho(r)dr. \qquad (57)$$

For shapes with a symmetrical skin, c is the distance from the center of the nucleus to the radius where the

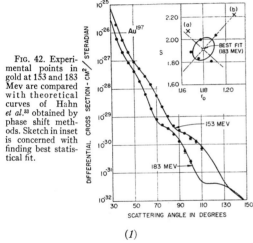

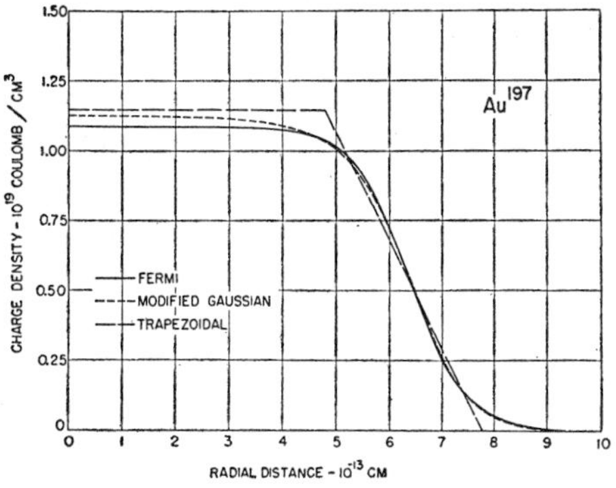

FIG. 44. Three models which fit the data in gold equally well.

charge density ρ has dropped to half its value at the center. For the Fermi shape, the skin parameter "t," which gives the distance between the 90% and 10% values of ρ, is given by 4.40 z_1. For the modified Gaussian, $t=2.20\ z_2^2/c$ and for the trapezoidal model, $t=1.60\ z_3$.

The central charge density in Au was varied by using the model

$$\rho(r)=\rho_8[1+(wr^2/c^2)]/\{\exp[(r-c)/z_8]+1\} \quad (58)$$

to see the effects of low and high central densities. In all cases a least square analysis was used to find the models with minimum errors. Figures 43(a) and 43(b) show the attempts made to fit the experimental Au points of Fig. 42. The best fit is indicated for $w=0.64$. However, Fig. 43(b) shows that the Fermi model ($w=0$) is so little different from the best fit, when expressed as $4\pi r^2\rho$, that the added complication of carrying a third parameter w appears to be unnecessary with the present experimental accuracy.

Furthermore, Fig. 44 shows the three models which give "best fits" in their classes. The experiments are unable to distinguish between these three possibilities within the present limits of accuracy. It is to be noted that the three charge densities cross each other almost in the same positions on the downward slope of the skin. Such results show that only two parameters can be determined at present, namely, c and t, or something close to these two. These two parameters represent the common features of all models that fit the data.

The same model (Fermi shape), with the same numerical values of the parameter, fits the Au points at both 153 and 183 Mev as shown by the solid lines of Fig. 42. On the other hand, Fig. 45 shows definite discernible discrepancies. The two theoretical curves (a) and (b) which show discrepancies are based on the Fermi model with parameters differing slightly from those of the best fit. Both (a) and (b) refer to 183 Mev.

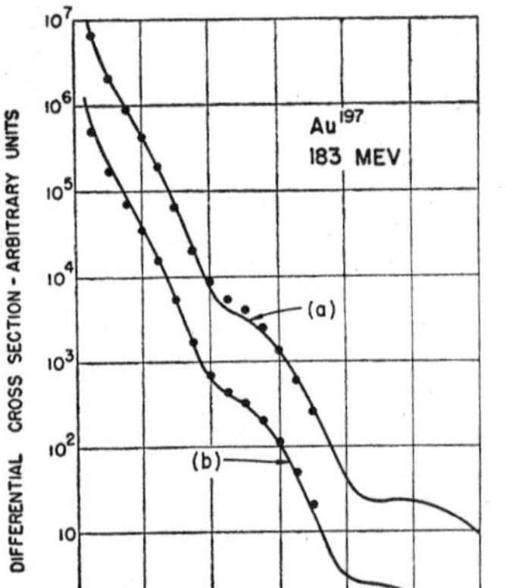

FIG. 45. Theoretical curves which are believed *not* to fit the experimental points. such curves lead to the limits of error assigned to the gold radius and thickness parameters.

The differences between models (a) and (b) are about the same as those between the models of Fig. 44.

(2)

Other elements were examined with only the Fermi model as the theoretical vehicle. The accuracy of these experimental runs is not as great as that in gold and different models are not at present justified. Figure 46 shows the experimental points for In as well as the solid theoretical lines. The fit is quite good.

Experience with the Fermi model shows that the parameter c mainly determines the angular position of the diffraction dips while the parameter t is concerned with the depth of the dips. Thus, the behavior exhibited in Fig. 41 must be correlated with a variation of c as the one-third power of A. This conclusion is verified below (see paragraph 3).

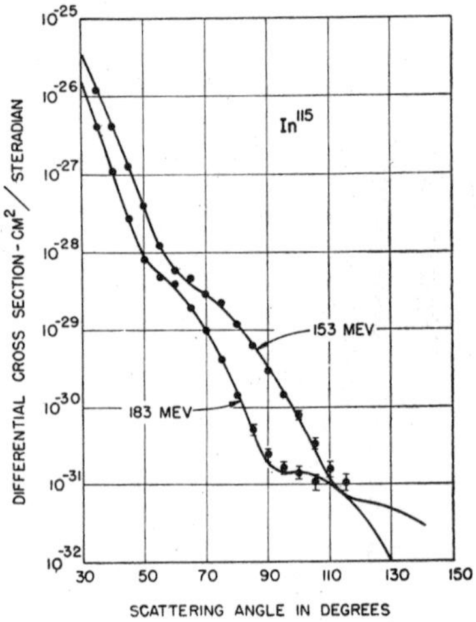

FIG. 46. Theoretical and experimental curves for In^{115} at two energies.

(3)

The results for the various nuclei are summarized in Fig. 47. These results are all based on the Fermi model. Table IV presents the relevant numerical data. Several interesting facts are revealed by Fig. 47 and Table IV: (a) The nuclear skin thickness seems to be a constant $\cong$2.4 fermis for all the nuclei investigated; (b) The radius parameter c varies as 1.08 $A^{\frac{1}{3}}$ as suggested by Fig. 41. Thus, the flat portion shrinks towards the center as the nuclei become lighter. In the very light nuclei ($Z\leq 6$) it disappears. The behavior of r_0 of Eq. (1) is now seen to vary from low values, $\sim$1.19, for heavy elements to 1.32 for Ca. This trend continues towards lighter elements as we may see by examining Table III (1.33 for Mg^{24} and 1.35 for C^{12}). The differences between Helm's value 1.28 for Ca^{40} (Table III) and Hahn *et al.*'s value are due to the use of different models.

For the lighter nuclei, where the central flatter area shrinks towards nothing, and where, e.g., in carbon, a modified Gaussian is a better fit (Fregeau), the significance of t can be expected to decline. In still lighter elements the whole nucleus is not even as large as the skin -2.4 fermis.

Thus, a comparison of these results with the assumed constancy of r_0 in Eq. (1) is not favorable. These models do not give a constant r_0. The trend appears to be: small r_0 at large A, larger r_0 at small A. However, further data on other nuclei are required before this conclusion may be accepted for all nuclei. It is probable that local variations of r_0 may show exceptions to the rule.

$$(4)$$

For the nonspherical nuclei, Hahn *et al.* give the results shown in Fig. 48. These nuclei show smoother,

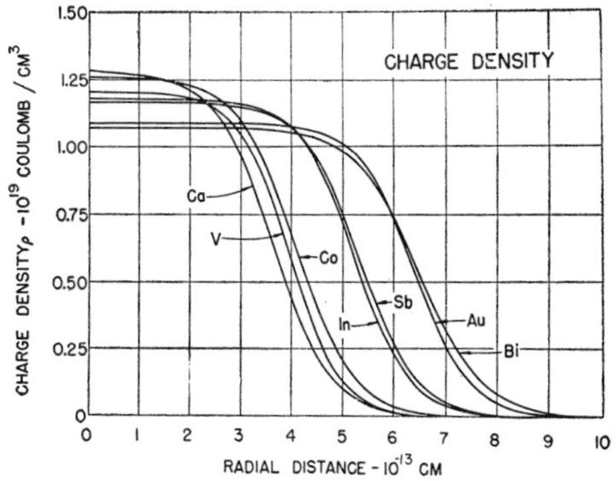

Fig. 47. Fermi models for various nuclei. Note the increase in average central charge density as Z decreases.

less well-defined diffraction features than, e.g., gold in Fig. 42. This has been interpreted qualitatively as evidence for quadrupole (ellipsoidal) distortions of such nuclei.

It is well known from other experiments that the nuclei of Fig. 48 have low-lying levels appearing strongly in Coulomb excitation and indicating large intrinsic-quadrupole moments. This is suggestive of large distortions from spherical symmetry which are associated with the collective motion of the outer nucleons.[60]

A detailed calculation has been carried out by Downs and Downs *et al.*,[88] etc. who have used a modified-Born approximation approach to estimate the effect of quadrupole scattering in "filling up" the diffraction dips observed in the scattering from spherical nuclei.

[88] B. W. Downs, Ph.D. thesis, Stanford University, October, 1955; Downs, Ravenhall, and Yennie, Phys. Rev. **98**, 277(A) (1955); Yennie, Ravenhall, and Downs, Phys. Rev. **98**, 277(A) (1955).

TABLE IV. Results of the analysis of nuclei in terms of the Fermi smoothed uniform charge distribution. All lengths are in Fermi units, charge densities in 10^{19} coulombs/cm³. The accuracy of these results is thought to be: radial parameters, $\pm2\%$; surface thickness parameter, $\pm10\%$. For lighter elements, the errors are probably larger. The accuracy for gold is higher. R is the radius of uniform charge distribution having the same rms radius as the Fermi distribution.

Nucleus	c	t	R	$c/A^{\frac{1}{3}}=r_1$	$R/A^{\frac{1}{3}}=r_0$
$_{20}Ca^{40}$	3.64	2.5	4.54	1.06	1.32
$_{23}V^{51}$	3.98	2.2	4.63	1.07	1.25
$_{27}Co^{59}$	4.09	2.5	4.94	1.05	1.27
$_{49}In^{115}$	5.24	2.3	5.80	1.08	1.19
$_{51}Sb^{122}$	5.32	2.5	5.97	1.07	1.20
$_{79}Au^{197}$	6.38	2.32	6.87	1.096	1.180
$_{83}Bi^{209}$	6.47	2.7	7.13	1.09	1.20

There are three contributions which arise from quadrupole effects; (1) The ellipsoidal distortions must be averaged over all orientations and lead to a nuclear density ρ_s having an effective surface thicker than one appropriate to a nucleus without the distortions. The elastic scattering from this type of quadrupole smoothing is shown as σ_s in Fig. 49, due to Downs. (2) A second type of elastic scattering corresponds to changing the orientation of the nuclear spin axis, that is, "spin flip." Since the nucleus is aspherical, this type of transition can occur. This scattering, when averaged over all orientations of the nuclei, adds independently to the elastic scattering (1) above. For oriented nuclei interference effects might be observed. (3) An inelastic scattering, representing the transitions from the ground

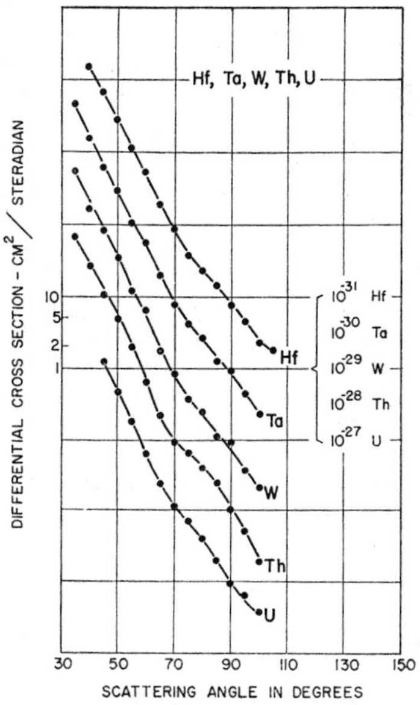

Fig. 48. The experimental data for nuclei believed to be appreciably nonspherical. The diffraction features appear to be smoothed out relative to gold.

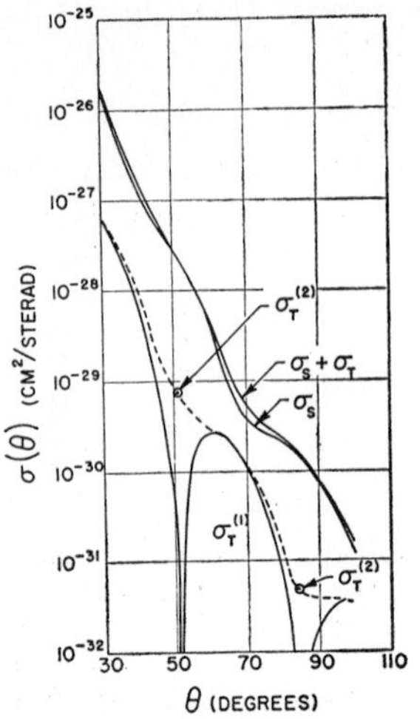

FIG. 49. Theoretical curves of Downs *et al.*[88] for the tantalum nucleus calculated with assumptions described in the text concerning quadrupole scattering.

state to the low-lying excited states, though actually inelastic, makes a contribution to the scattering usually called elastic. This contribution lies so close to the elastic scattering ($\sim$1 part in 2000) that it may be considered at present to be elastic, from a practical point of view.

As a result of (2) and (3), the contribution in Fig. 49, labeled $\sigma_T(2)$ adds to the elastic scattering σ_S to give the total scattering $\sigma_S+\sigma_T$. The latter should be compared with experiment. The curve σ_T, thus, represents the quadrupole scattering. Curve $\sigma_T(2)$ is an approximation and was estimated from the Born approximation $\sigma_T(1)$ for a pure quadrupole and a higher order approximation which does not vanish at the zeroes of the Born-quadrupole scattering. Curve $\sigma_T(2)$ is sketched as shown and is not calculated, except for the two points indicated by circles.

Figure 50 shows the same kind of computation for tantalum, using three values of the intrinsic quadrupole moment Q_0, which represent three increasing states of nuclear distortion. The experimental points of Hahn and Hofstadter[89] are shown in the figure. It is clear that an intermediate value of Q_0 between 7 and 14 barns will fit the data. However, the calculations are not considered reliable enough by Downs to extract an actual value of the quadrupole moment. The probable reason for the smoothness of the curves in Fig. 48 is, with little doubt, due to such quadrupole contributions to the scattering.

VI. THE NEUTRON

It would be of great interest to determine the internal structure of the neutron, or at least to determine as much as is now known about the structure of the proton. The neutron-electron interaction has been investigated by Fermi, Rabi, Hughes, and their collaborators[90] and shows a surprisingly small effective charge distribution. These experiments, however, throw no light on the size or shape of the neutron's magnetic moment. It is precisely here that the electron scattering method can contribute significant information.

As a method of seeking this information, the following thought occurred to the present author: When large momentum transfers occur in the inelastic scattering of electrons from the deuteron (or Be^9 where there is a well-known loose neutron on the outside of the nucleus), the neutron and proton can be considered essentially as free particles since the binding in the deuteron is weak. Furthermore, at large angles and high energies, the electron scattering is almost entirely governed by the magnetic moment of the nucleon (Rosenbluth). Consequently, since the magnetic moment of the neutron is -1.91 nuclear magnetons and that of the proton is 2.79 nuclear magnetons, the scattering of electrons from protons should be only $[(2.79/1.91)^2 \cong 2]$ or about twice as large as from the neutron. This assumes that the particles are points or that their magnetic moment clouds have equal sizes. However, if the neutron should have smaller dimensions than the proton, its magnetic scattering should approach and perhaps exceed that of the proton. If the sizes are similar the neutron should scatter about half as much as the proton. By scattering electrons inelastically from deuterium[70] and comparing such scattering with that from free protons in hydrogen, the deuterium-hydrogen difference should yield the neutron scattering cross section and, hence, its size.

This argument is borne out by the detailed theory of Jankus.[59] In fact, whenever F_D is small, Eq. (43) can be

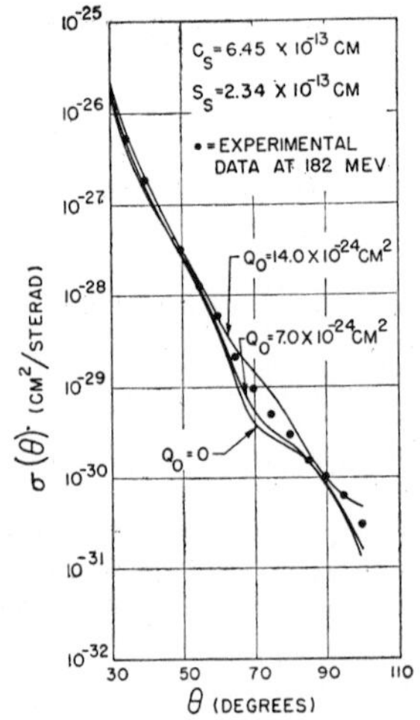

FIG. 50 Comparison of the calculation of Downs *et al.*[88] with the experiment of Hahn and Hofstadter[89] on tantalum.

[89] B. Hahn and R. Hofstadter, Phys. Rev. **98**, 278(A) (1955).

[90] For a summary, see B. T. Feld, *Experimental Nuclear Physics*, edited by E. Segré (John Wiley and Sons, Inc., New York, 1953), Vol. II, p. 208.

written as follows:

$$\sigma_D^{\text{in}}(\theta)=\sigma_{\text{NS}}\{1+(q^2/4M^2)[2\mu_p^2\tan^2\tfrac{1}{2}\theta+\mu_p^2]\}$$
$$+\sigma_{\text{NS}}\{(q^2/4M^2)[2\mu_n^2\tan^2\tfrac{1}{2}\theta+\mu_n^2]\}. \quad (59)$$
$$\sigma_D^{\text{in}}(\theta)=\sigma_p+\sigma_n. \quad (60)$$

Equation (60) is equivalent to the qualitative statement given above, but the latter is now expressed in exact form. Consequently, by a deuterium-hydrogen difference method, the value of σ_n may be found. From σ_n a form factor calculation, in association with σ_p, will yield the dimensions of the neutron.

The actual experiment is difficult to perform because of the spreading-out of the inelastic continuum due to the motion of the neutron and proton inside the deuteron. Figure 51 shows the approximate shape of this distribution obtained by Blankenbecler, Hofstadter, and Yearian[50] in recent preliminary experiments and shows the momentum distribution in the deuteron. The proton comparison peak is, however, a sharp one with a bremsstrahlung tail on the low-energy side. The elementary scattering from the deuteron's moving neutron and proton will show the same bremsstrahlung tails, but this radiative cross section will itself lie in the inelastic continuum. Proper appreciation of this correction is necessary in carrying out the subtraction.

Only preliminary data are available. The first indications suggest that the neutron's magnetic scattering is perhaps less than, but comparable with, the proton scattering at 135° and 500 Mev,[42,68] but the accuracy is poor. If this result should continue to be true as the experiments improve, the neutron would have about the same dimensions of its magnetic moment cloud as the proton or perhaps a bit smaller. The present experiments appear to indicate more definitely that the neutron's magnetic cloud is not as small as found in the static experiments.[90]

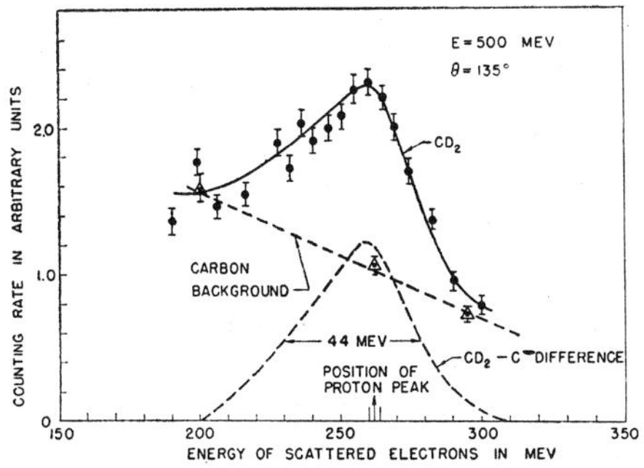

FIG. 51. Inelastic electron scattering in the deuteron for 500-Mev incident electrons deflected through 135°.[50] The upper curve shows the data in deuterated polyethylene (CD_2) and the triangular points show the corresponding contribution from pure carbon. The difference between the CD_2 and C data furnishes the dotted curve indicated in the lower position. The data are corrected for the dispersion of the spectrometer. The dotted curve is a preliminary indication of the momentum distribution in the deuteron and represents $\sigma_D^{\text{in}}(135°)=\sigma_p+\sigma_n$ as expressed in Eq. (59). After subtraction of the area under the sharp free proton peak σ_p, the remainder represents σ_n.

Other preliminary data on Be^9 have recently been obtained by Chambers and Hofstadter[91] which show that the method is feasible with beryllium and perhaps with many other nuclei, including isotopes differing by one neutron.

VII. VALIDITY OF ELECTRODYNAMICS

It was pointed out[3] that the deviations observed in electron scattering experiments between actual scattering cross sections and those expected from a point charge could be wholly or partially ascribed to departures, at small distance, from the Coulomb law of electric interaction. In other words, the deviations which have been explained as finite size effects would be attributed to a failure of electrodynamics and the bodies themselves could be considered to be points. There are now too many independent pieces of evidence to the contrary to suppose that this view could be maintained for nuclei. It could, however, still be thought that the "differences" between electromagnetic sizes and nucleonic sizes could be due to such a failure, but this also appears to be unlikely, since, as the experiments and the interpretations are improved, the differences become smaller and smaller.

In the case of the proton and the neutron, we are confronted with a different situation, for it has not proved possible experimentally to fix any size on these particles prior to the recent experiments in electron scattering. It is true that meson theories predict that the meson clouds around the fundamental nucleons have dimensions lying somewhere between the Compton wavelengths of the nucleon and the pion, 0.2 fermi and 1.4 fermis, respectively, and probably closer to the smaller dimensions. Although the methods of meson theory have been fruitful qualitatively, they have not been spectacularly successful quantitatively, and at the present time it is difficult to have confidence in the predictions of any meson theory. Consequently, it would be quite consistent with known facts to attribute the radial dimensions, measured by McAllister, Chambers, and Hofstadter, of 0.77 fermi for the proton to a failure of electrodynamics, and to assume that the meson clouds are really quite small compared to 0.77 fermi. As far as concerns the electron-scattering experiments on the proton, either explanation is tenable[57] and, in fact, both finite size effects and a failure of electrodynamics may occur together. The final explanation of the scattering results would be identical in either of the two. There may even be some doubt that finite size effects and a breakdown of electrodynamics are not two aspects of the same phenomenon.

A simple illustration of how similar the two possibilities appear is the following: To explain the experi-

[91] E. E. Chambers and R. Hofstadter (unpublished).

ments, a finite size and a given model, say, a Gaussian, are ascribed to the proton charge cloud. The Coulomb-potential function, in consequence, is rounded off so that it becomes finite at zero radius, whereas, if the proton is considered to be a point, the potential goes to minus infinity at zero radius. The algebraic difference between these two potential functions can be considered to be the law of deviation from the Coulomb interaction at small distances. A new potential, incorporating this deviation, will represent the "revised Coulomb law." We shall then have a specific model showing how the electrodynamic laws break down at small distances: i.e., a new law of force valid at all ordinary distances but with a new behavior at very small distances. A parallel situation would occur in the case of the magnetic charge density of the proton. The same breakdown would cover both cases simultaneously.

There may be several possible ways of distinguishing between a finite size and a failure of electrodynamics: One way would be to scatter electrons against electrons at high enough energies ($\sim$20 Bev) so that the center-of-mass de Broglie wavelength becomes comparable with the small dimensions inside which the Coulomb law may be conceived of as breaking down. Another way, more amenable to present experimental technique, would be to determine the neutron's dimensions, as discussed in Sec. VI. If the neutron's size turns out to be identical with that of the proton, it would appear that electrodynamics breaks down at certain small dimensions, and all objects smaller than these dimensions, including the neutron and the proton, appear to have the same size. On the other hand, if the neutron's size (or shape) appears to be different from the proton's, then it would seem reasonable to say that the sizes represent, at least in part, real structural effects and that the laws of electrodynamics are probably still valid even at small distances. A third way would be to see whether the radii of very light nuclei measured by, say, mirror nuclei methods, are the same as those measured by electron scattering methods. If consistancy is obtained between these sets of measurements, this would be evidence for the validity of the Coulomb law. Unfortunately, the accuracy of the two sets of determinations is perhaps one order of magnitude smaller than needed to make an accurate assay of the situation. Other methods, making only light demands on nuclear theory, might also be acceptable for such a test. It is also possible that experiments on bremsstrahlung or pair production at large angles, perhaps in hydrogen or other nuclei, could help to settle this unresolved question. Perhaps mesonic atoms will help here, too.

It is entirely pertinent, at this stage, to ask about the size of the electron. It is conceivable that many of the facts pertaining to nucleon sizes could be attributed to a radius of the electron. The question cannot be answered in a very satisfactory way because, if finite electrons are permitted to enter the picture, the Dirac theory, the backbone of the calculations with electrons, cannot be used without trepidation. In other words, the point electron and the Dirac theory go together at the present stage of knowledge. Of course, due to the electron's recoil during the ever-present virtual emission and absorption of photons to and from the radiation field, the electron *does* have a size and is not, strictly speaking, a point. But this size is equivalent in essence to the effects of the Schwinger radiative correction. These effects are not large and are one order of magnitude smaller than the proton's radius. Thus, at the moment, the question of electron size must be left unanswered. Consistency tests between electron scattering measurements and other types of measurements will help to provide a clear-cut answer to the question of electron size.

VIII. COMPARISONS WITH OTHER MEASUREMENTS OF NUCLEAR SIZES

There are many ways in which nuclear sizes and charge distributions may be measured. The recent review article by Ford and Hill[9] presents a good summary of the available methods. Besides electron scattering, some of the various possible methods are the following:

I. Charge sensitive methods
- a. Coulomb effects in mirror nuclei.
- b. μ-mesonic atoms and μ-meson scattering.
- c. Fine structure in x-ray spectra.
- d. Isotope shifts.
- e. Hyperfine structure in hydrogen.

II. Range of nuclear force methods
- f. Medium-energy (14 Mev–25 Mev) neutron-scattering experiments.
- g. Higher energy (90-Mev) neutron-scattering measurements.
- h. Ultra-high energy (1.4-Bev) neutron-scattertering measurements.
- i. Proton-scattering experiments (20 Mev–340 Mev).
- j. Alpha-particle-scattering experiments (13–42 Mev).

Combination of I and II
- k. Weiszacker semiempirical formula for binding energies.
- l. Alpha-particle radioactivities.

There are probably many other methods in which nuclear sizes are important and, consequently, through which they may be measured.[92]

It is not the purpose of this report to enter into a detailed discussion of the results of the various methods listed above. This has been well done in the article by Ford and Hill. It is probably useful, however, to point out that the present circumstances do not favor making

[92] An example is given by Millburn, Birnbaum, Crandall, and Schecter, Phys. Rev. **95**, 1268 (1954).

accurate comparisons among the different methods, primarily because of a paucity of experimental data and the reliable interpretations of these data. This is an understandable situation in view of our present ignorance of the nuclear law of force. Nevertheless, it may still be worthwhile to compare briefly a few examples where the data and interpretation appear to be satisfactory. We shall do this below.

a. On the basis of the shell model, including exchange effects for mirror nuclei pairs, Jancovici[8] calculates a quantity he defines as a ratio of a Coulombic to a mesonic radius of O^{17} and N^{15}. These ratios are 1.18 for O^{17} and 1.07 for N^{15}. Experimentally, one finds 1.27 and 1.17 for these same ratios assuming that the mesonic radii for light nuclei follow Eq. (1) with $r_0=1.20$ fermis. This seems to imply a discrepancy between mesonic radii and mirror nuclear radii. On the other hand, if the mesonic radii are actually in the neighborhood of $r_0=1.30$ fermis, instead of 1.20 fermis, the discrepancy would be removed. It is interesting that the electron-scattering results on nuclei in this region[33,46] lie close to the value $r_0=1.32$.

Carlson and Talmi[93] have also made calculations on pairing effects in Coulomb energies and have related them to determinations of nuclear radii. These authors obtain the r_0 values given in Table V. For nuclei for which $A<11$ and those for which $A>28$, the calculations are less reliable than for those between $A=11$ and $A=28$. The table shows a smooth decrease in radius between C^{13} and Al^{27} from values of $r_0=1.34$ to 1.20 fermis. The results for $A>28$ suggest an increase again in r_0 to values near 1.32 fermis. If these results are substantiated, it appears that local variations of r_0 may be expected to occur in other places and that a smooth variation of r_0 over the whole periodic system is more than can be expected.

TABLE V. Included in this table are the r_0 results of Carlson and Talmi (reference 93) on mirror nuclei.

Nucleus	r_0
Li^7	1.489
Be^9	1.543
B^{11}	1.283
C^{13}	1.340
N^{15}	1.305
O^{17}	1.262
F^{19}	1.259
Ne^{21}	1.248
Na^{23}	1.217
Mg^{25}	1.230
Al^{27}	1.197

These results suggest that generalizations about nuclear radii from a few cases should not be made. Furthermore, as evidenced by the work on electron scattering, more than one single parameter is required to specify a charge distribution and a simple rms radius may not be sufficient for this purpose. Thus, in comparing results of different methods, the often-stated counsel should be heeded; The various methods may measure *different quantities* which are represented as radii, and the results should be compared only with this in mind or under special circumstances. This is, of course, especially true when charge or electromagnetic radii are compared with the nucleonic radii determined by methods involving the range of nuclear forces.

b. The μ-mesonic results appear to be in excellent agreement with electron scattering results for the heavy elements.[94] In the case of lead, the agreement is within 1%. In the case of lighter nuclei, there may be some discrepancies with electron-scattering results although, so far, the mesonic-atom conclusions have less accuracy in this range than for heavy nuclei. There are similar discrepancies of the mesonic data with mirror-nuclei determinations.[8] On the other hand, as stated above, the mirror nuclei radii appear to agree with electron scattering radii.

At present, the μ-meson results ($2P-1S$ transition) measure only one parameter which, for light nuclei, is a mean square radius. For heavy nuclei the parameter measured is not exactly a mean square radius and is somewhat dependent on the density distribution. Higher transitions are also slightly sensitive to the charge distribution. The μ-meson method, therefore, seems promising and should help to elucidate the nuclear size question.

(c) The x-ray fine structure splitting in L-series lines has been carried quite far in recent experiments by Shacklett and DuMond[95,96] but the interpretation of the results is not yet definite. Radii larger than those found by any other method are obtained from the present theoretical interpretation of the data.[96,97] However, the theory is difficult and the interpretation is probably only in its early stages.

d. Isotope shifts will probably turn out to furnish a good method for evaluating nuclear compressibility, but, at present, do not add much information on nuclear sizes.[9,98]

e. From the accurate measurement of the hyperfine structure of hydrogen and a highly accurate value of the fine-structure constant, it is possible to determine the spatial extension of the proton's charge and magnetic moment. A calculation of an upper limit of the *mean* radius (not root-mean-square radius) emerges from the analysis of the hyperfine structure by Moellering *et al.*[99] The value obtained $R_m<2.5(\hbar/MC)\cong 0.5\times 10^{-13}$ cm which is just about at the limit of the electron-scattering result. Further study of this important source of information would be desirable.

[93] B. C. Carlson and I. Talmi, Phys. Rev. **96**, 436 (1954).
[94] Hill, Freeman, and Ford; quoted in reference 9, p. 36.

[95] R. L. Shacklett and J. W. M. DuMond, Bull. Am. Phys. Soc. Ser. II, **1**, 219 (1956).
[96] J. W. M. DuMond (private communication).
[97] A. L. Schawlow and C. H. Townes, Science **115**, 284 (1952); Phys. Rev. **100**, 1273 (1955).
[98] Wilets, Hill, and Ford, Phys. Rev. **91**, 1488 (1953).
[99] Moellering, Zemach, Klein, and Low, Phys. Rev. **100**, 441 (1955). Also, A. C. Zemach (private communication).

f. The experiments with 14–25 Mev neutrons are divided into two casses:

(1) Capture (or absorption) cross sections.
(2) Scattering cross sections.

(1) The experiments related to absorption cross sections were carried out some time ago by Sherr[100] and Amaldi *et al.*[101] The experimental cross sections were equated to the asymptotic limit

$$\sigma_T = 2\pi R^2 \tag{61}$$

and a radius was found from this formula. Of course, R here means the radius at which a nuclear force begins to act and, therefore, includes a "radius" of the neutron. It is not at all clear that the interpretation according to Eq. (61) is valid, and in the 14–25 Mev region of neautron energy it is more likely that the factor 2 in Eq. (61) should be replaced by 2.5 for a medium-heavy nucleus.[102] Substitution of this factor into Eq. (61) will result in radii with $r_0 \cong 1.30$ fermis, whereas the results of Sherr and Amaldi are calculated[102] to give r_0 in the neighborhood of 1.40 fermi. Sherr quoted his results in the form

$$R = b + r_0' A^{\frac{1}{3}}, \tag{62}$$

where $b=1.7$ fermis and $r_0'=1.22$ fermis, but this is essentially equivalent to $r_0 \cong 1.37-1.40$ fermis within the experimental errors. The absorption cross sections, therefore, probably point to smaller values of $r_0 \cong 1.3$ or so when Eq. (61) is corrected.

(2) The neutron scattering cross sections have been measured at 14 Mev by J. H. Coon[103] and interpreted by Culler, Fernbach, and Sherman[104] using the optical model approach of Fernbach, Serber, and Taylor.[105] A two-step potential function, equivalent to a smoothed well, was employed by Culler *et al.* The potential includes, of course, an imaginary part to account for absorption. The radius of the real part of the well was found to be $1.22\,A^{\frac{1}{3}}+0.74$ fermi, but this is equivalent to about $1.4\,A^{\frac{1}{3}}$ for medium range A. J. O. Elliott[106] has also carried out experiments with 14-Mev neutrons on a number of elements and interpreted his results with a simple potential model

$$V = -V_0(1+\zeta) \quad \text{for } r < R_0, \tag{63}$$

where $V_0 = 42$ Mev, $\zeta = 0.15$ and

$$R_0 = 1.32\,A^{\frac{1}{3}} \text{ fermis.} \tag{64}$$

This radius, of course, is an interaction radius and includes the "radius" of the neutron equivalently, the range of nuclear forces. This analysis, therefore, gives rather small radii, not far from the electromagnetic radii, when the range of nuclear forces is allowed for.

g. Fernbach *et al.*[105] developed the use of an "optical model" of the nucleus, in which the nucleus is partially transparent at the higher energies and is imagined to be a uniform sphere characterized by a complex refractive index. Without repeating the details here, these authors interpreted the careful scattering experiments of Cook *et al.*[107] at 90 Mev on a large number of elements and obtained a consistent fit to all the data with a spherical nuclear model of radius R where

$$R = 1.37\,A^{\frac{1}{3}}. \tag{65}$$

This is quite close to the determination of $R_0 = 1.32\,A^{\frac{1}{3}}$ by Elliott,[106] although the models are slightly different. Nevertheless, if the range of nuclear forces is allowed for, say, perhaps 1.0 fermi, the radii will fall close to the electronmagnetic values.

h. Recently, important experiments by Coor *et al.*[108] on the absorption of $\sim$1.4-Bev neutrons by several elements were interpreted with the aid of the optical model and gave a consistent determination of the spherical radius $R = 1.28\,A^{\frac{1}{3}}$ fermis. Thus, these experiments also indicate small radii. The same experiments were analyzed by Williams[109] who showed that the results were consistent with the electron scattering charge distributions and the small electromagnetic size.

i. Proton scattering experiments in the 20-Mev range were carried out by Cohen and Neidigh[110] and by Dayton[111] and others.[112] The scattering cross sections show beautiful diffraction minima and maxima, which offer a splendid opportunity for the eventual determination of much about the structure of nuclei examined in this way. It was not possible to fit the data with an optical model when a square well potential was used.[113] However, Woods and Saxon[114] rounded the edge of the nuclear potential as follows:

$$V(r) = \frac{V + iW}{1 + \exp[(r - r_2)/a_1]}, \tag{66}$$

where r_2 is a parameter measuring nuclear size and a_1 is related to the diffuseness of the surface, in other words, to the nuclear "skin" thickness. This may be seen to be just the Fermi model used by Hahn *et al.*[33] and Yennie *et al.*[18] The Coulomb part of the interaction with the incident proton was taken from a uniformly charged sphere with an r_0 consistent with the electro-

[100] R. Sherr, Phys. Rev. **68**, 240 (1945).
[101] Amaldi, Bocciarelli, Cacciaputo, Trabachi, Nuovo cimento **3**, 203 (1946).
[102] J. M. Blatt and V. W. Weisskopf, *Theoretical Nuclear Physics* (John Wiley and Sons, Inc., New York, 1952), pp. 356, 482.
[103] J. H. Coon (referred to in reference 104).
[104] Culler, Fernbach, and Sherman, AEC DUCRL-4436 (January, 1955); also Phys. Rev. **98**, 273 (1955).
[105] Fernbach, Serber, and Taylor, Phys. Rev. **75**, 1352 (1949).
[106] J. O. Elliott, Naval Research Laboratory Report No. 4640 (October, 1955).
[107] Cook, McMillan, Peterson, and Sewell, Phys. Rev. **75**, 7 (1949).
[108] Coor, Hill, Hornyak, Smith, and Snow, Phys. Rev. **98**, 1369 (1955).
[109] R. W. Williams, Phys. Rev. **98**, 1387 (1955).
[110] B. L. Cohen and R. V. Neidigh, Phys. Rev. **93**, 282 (1954).
[111] I. E. Dayton, Phys. Rev. **95**, 754 (1954).
[112] J. W. Burkig and B. T. Wright, Phys. Rev. **82**, 451 (1951).
[113] D. M. Chase and F. Rohrlich, Phys. Rev. **94**, 81 (1954).
[114] R. D. Woods and D. S. Saxon, Phys. Rev. **95**, 577 (1954).

magnetic values. For platinum, the parameters producing a good fit to the experimental curve of Cohen and Neidigh were $V=38$ Mev, $W=9$ Mev, $r_2=8.24$ fermis, and $a_1=0.49$ fermi. Remembering that $t=4.40\ a_1$, for the Fermi model, t becomes 2.16 fermis, in very good agreement with the value consistently appearing in the electron scattering determinations of Hahn *et al.*[33] The model of Woods and Saxon does not fit experiment quite as well for low Z (e.g., Ni) but it appears as if a spin orbit interaction is also required.[115] However, the radius r_2, above, appears to be larger than the electromagnetic radius. This again may be a reflection of the fact that the range of nuclear forces appears as an effective "radius" of the nucleon whenever the radius is measured by a method involving the nuclear force.

Gatha and Riddell[116] had noted earlier that a rounding-off of the edge of the (optical model) nuclear sphere would be necessary to fit the experimental data[117] on high-energy proton scattering (340 Mev). They also found that an $r_0=1.25$ fermis would provide a better fit of the 340-Mev data than the larger, older, radii.

j. The eleastic scattering of (13—42 Mev) alpha particles by heavy nuclei was studied by Farwell and Wegner[118] and an interpretation of the observed sharp energy breaks has been given by Blair.[119] The theory of such experiments is evidently not simple and probably the estimates of radii should be taken only as upper limits. Allowing for the radius of the alpha particle, the estimate of $r_0=1.5$ fermis was made. It is not clear how reliable this estimate may be.

k. In the Weiszacker semiempirical formula for nuclear binding energies, there is an electrostatic term for a uniformly charged sphere proportional to

$$E_{\mathrm{el}}=\frac{3}{5}\frac{(Ze)^2}{r_0A^{\frac{1}{3}}}, \qquad (67)$$

and so, in principle, a value for r_0 can be found from the packing-fraction curve. Unfortunately, estimates of r_0 from 1.2 fermis to 1.5 fermis can be made consistent with the present data. If a nonuniformly charged model is introduced, the problem becomes more difficult, but, if the shape of the model is known, a new value of r_0 may possibly be found.

l. We shall not delve into the voluminous literature on nuclear radii determined from studied of natural and artificial alpha-particle radioactivities. This is a subject with a historic background and furnished the first evidence for the quantum-mechanical tunneling process. It may be worthwhile, however, to call attention to a recent paper which proposes some changes in the older theories. Tolhoek and Brussard[120] use a nuclear model with a surface of finite thickness, resembling the model of Hahn *et al.*[33] This theory gives a value of $r_0=1.13$ fermis in contrast to the older determinations which gave $r_0=1.4$ to 1.5 for the most part.[102] It is not yet possible to know how good the model of Tolhoek and Brussard may be in practice.

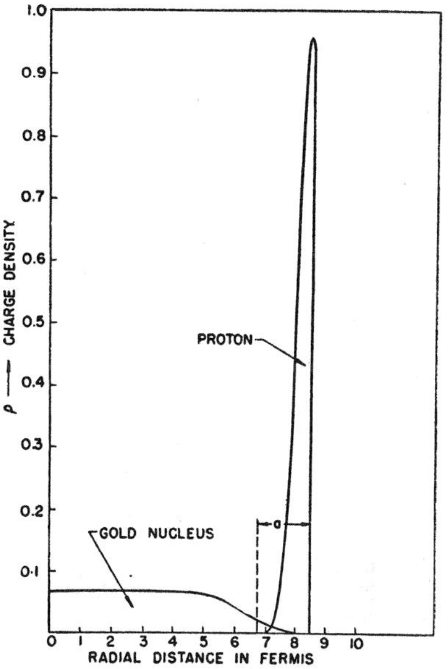

FIG. 52. A proton interacting with a gold nucleus at the old radius for gold, 8.45×10^{-13} cm. Owing to the finite size of the nucleon, there is already some nucleonic interaction at this distance. "a" represents the range of nuclear forces. Note the relatively high charge density of the proton relative to that of the gold nucleus.

Finally, Fig. 52 may serve to remind us that the finite size of the nucleon should be considered when speaking of nuclear radii. This figure shows the charge density (in proton charges per cubic fermi) plotted as ordinate against the distance from the center of a gold nucleus. At the right of the figure a finite Guassian-model proton, with rms radius 0.70 fermi, is shown at a distance of 8.45 fermis between its center and that of the gold nucleus. This distance corresponds to the conventional radius of gold for which $r_0=1.45$ in Eq. (1). In the figure, "a" indicates an approximate value for the range of nuclear forces. It will be seen that there is a fair overlap, both of charge, and of nuclear force fields. It is not surprising that there is a strong interaction at this distance. This figure should be contrasted with Fig. 1 and exhibits clearly the high average density of the proton's charge cloud when compared with that of a representative nucleus such as gold.

In concluding this section, we may note that many of the newer and some of the older determinations are

[115] D. S. Saxon, Brookhaven Report on Statistical Aspects of the Nucleus, BNL 331 (C-21) Brookhaven (January, 1955).
[116] K. L. Gatha and R. J. Riddell, Jr., Phys. Rev. **86**, 1035 (1952).
[117] Richardson, Ball, Leith, and Moyer, Phys. Rev. **83**, 859 (1951).
[118] G. W. Farwell and H. E. Wegner, Phys. Rev. **93**, 356 (1954); **95**, 1212 (1954).
[119] J. S. Blair, Phys. Rev. **95**, 1218 (1954).
[120] H. A. Tolhoek and P. J. Brussard, Physica **XXI**, 449 (1955).

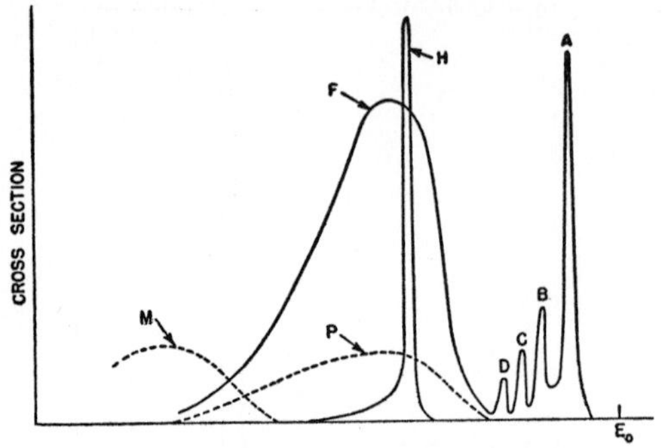

FIG. 53. This figure attempts a summary of the various possible phenomena observed in electron scattering for high momentum transfers. A represents an elastic peak and B, C, D refer to inelastic scattering from nuclear levels. H is the free proton peak observed in hydrogen. P is the incoherent scattering peak of an individual proton (or neutron) in the nucleus. It is broadened with respect to the free proton peak H by motion within the nucleus. F is the simple sum of all such peaks for all the A nucleons in the nucleus. M represents electrons scattered after producing pions. Note that all electrons lie on the low-energy side of E_0 (the incident energy) because of nuclear recoil effects. The figure is not to scale either vertically or horizontally.

consistent with the smaller electromagnetic radii. Still other determinations give stubbornly larger and different figures. Until the nature of the nuclear force is known, many of the "radii" cannot be significantly compared. It is hoped that the constant reference to the quantity r_0 in this section has not focused too much attention on it, since, in reality, nuclei appear to have more than one single parameter (such as r_0) determining their size and shape.

IX. SUMMARY

To summarize in words the results presented in this report would require a lengthy exposition. There would have to be a division of the material into results which are new and need to be checked, and the older, better confirmed results. Some of the older results need not be restated once again. Instead of a repetition of the newer and older conclusions, it is preferable to present the major findings in the form of a single figure and a single table presented below. Each will be inadequate but may serve to suggest new ideas for measurements and theoretical analysis. To accompany the figure and the table, we present the following remarks.

Figure 52 exhibits most of the varied phenomena observed in the electron scattering experiments. This figure is schematic and shows what is seen in a representative nucleus such as carbon at a relatively large scattering angle and at a medium high energy, say, e.g., 70° at 400 Mev. The relative proportions shown in the figure must not be assumed to be accurate.

The incident energy is shown at E_0. The elastic peak appears at A and the inelastic peaks, due to scattering from the nuclear levels, are shown at B, C, D. The bremsstrahlung tail of the elastic peak lies on its left side. Note that the elastic and inelastic peaks are shifted to energies lower than E_0 by recoil effects. At lower energies the inelastic continuum appears at F. The individual nucleons scatter electrons incoherently and all the individual cross sections, such as the one shown for proton P, add up to produce the large peak indicated at F. This broad maximum appears near the free proton peak, H, shown in the figure for reference purposes. But it lies below the peak H because of the binding energy of the protons and neutrons in the nucleus. A good part of the scattering in this incoherent peak is due to the magnetic spin-flip process. In this respect neutron and proton are almost equivalent. The study of how the individual proton and neutron peaks add up to make the continuum at various angles should provide an interesting story. If the experiments start with light nuclei, in which there are only a few components, such as D, H^3, He^3, He^4, Li^6, Li^7, Be^9, etc. and proceed to heavier ones, the interaction of the ejected particle with its surroundings may be studied. Furthermore, the momentum distribution of the nucleons should emerge from such studies.

At still lower energies in Fig. 53, pions will be produced and electrons, labeled M, will be scattered in this production process. The dotted line to the left indicates this in a schematic way. It will be recognized that most of the processes described in our report are incorporated in Fig. 53.

It is not possible to show in Fig. 53 the angular distributions corresponding to each of the various features of the diagram. This would required a many-dimensional plot. In place of this we refer to the figures in the report itself, such as Fig. 38 and Fig. 41 and to Table VI described in the next paragraph.

An analysis of these results is given in Table VI. Two parameters, characterizing the charge distributions, are supplied in those cases in which it is possible to do so. Otherwise, a description of the charge distribution is given as well as an equivalent rms radius and r_0 value. The most general features apparent in Table VI are the approximate constancy of the surface thickness and the shrinking away of the flat region as one proceeds to the lighter elements. A simple prescription does not apply to the extremely light nuclei or to the proton. In general, the average central-charge density of nuclei increases as the atomic number decreases, reaching a maximum in the proton. ρ_U in the table gives the charge density of the equivalent uniform model.

It is interesting to look back into the statistical approach of Jensen and Luttinger[121] who applied the Thomas-Fermi model to the nucleus and calculated mean squared angular momenta. They showed that a constant surface layer of 1.8 fermis would give agree-

[121] J. H. D. Jensen and J. M. Luttinger, Phys. Rev. **86**, 907 (1952).

TABLE VI. This table gives the radial parameters for the nuclei of column 1 and the appropriate charge (and magnetic) distributions. All quantities used in the table are defined in the text, except the parameters of the Hill model (used only for $_{82}Pb^{208}$). All distances are given in units of 10^{-13} cm (one fermi unit). The accuracy in surface thickness parameter is about ±10% and may be somewhat poorer for the lighter elements where it is less well defined. The accuracy of the radial parameters is about ±2% except, possibly, in the case of Ta. The accuracy for gold is better than ±2%. ρ_U in column 9 is the charge density in proton charge per cubic fermi for the equivalent uniform model and may be compared with Fig. 1 (b). The results for lithium and beryllium are to be considered preliminary.

Nucleus (1)	Type of charge distribution (see Table I) (2)	rms radius (3)	Radius of equivalent uniform model (R) (4)	$r_0=\frac{R}{A^{\frac{1}{3}}}$ (5)	Skin thickness (6)	Half-density Radius c (7)	$r_1=\frac{c}{A^{\frac{1}{3}}}$ (8)	ρ_U (9)	$A^{\frac{1}{3}}$ (10)	Comments (11)	Reference number (12)
$^1H^1$	III, IV, VI, VII magnetic distribution similar	0.77±0.10	1.00	1.00	...	...	...	0.239	1.00	The charge distributions in column 2 are equivalent to each other. The rms radius is a mean value for all. The magnetic distribution is the same as that of the charge. The fact that $R=1.00$ in column 4 is accidental.	42, 55, 68
$_1D^2$	Charge distribution calculated from deuteron wave function for Hulthèn, etc., potentials.	1.96	2.53	2.01	...	...	...	0.0147	1.26	...	71
$_2He^4$	III	1.61	2.08	1.31	...	...	...	0.053	1.59	...	42, 49
$_3Li^6$	XII	2.78	3.59	1.98	...	...	...	0.0153	1.82	...	75
$_3Li^7$	XII	2.71	3.50	1.83	...	...	...	0.0167	1.19	...	75
$_4Be^9$	XII	3.04	3.92	1.89	...	...	...	0.0157	2.08	...	75
$_6C^{12}$	XI	2.37	3.04	1.33	~2.0	~2.3	1.00	0.051	2.29	$\alpha=4/3$	77
$_{12}Mg^{24}$	gU	2.98	3.84	1.33	2.6	2.85	0.99	0.051	2.88	...	46
$_{14}Si^{28}$	gU	3.04	3.92	1.29	2.8	2.95	0.97	0.056	3.04	...	46
$_{16}S^{32}$	gU	3.19	4.12	1.30	2.6	3.28	1.03	0.055	3.18	...	46
$_{20}Ca^{40}$	Fermi	3.52	4.54	1.32	2.5	3.64	1.06	0.052	3.42	...	33
$_{23}V^{51}$	Fermi	3.59	4.63	1.25	2.2	3.98	1.07	0.055	3.71	...	33
$_{27}Co^{59}$	Fermi	3.83	4.94	1.27	2.5	4.09	1.05	0.0662	3.89	...	33
$_{49}In^{115}$	Fermi	4.50	5.80	1.19	2.3	5.24	1.08	0.0605	4.87	...	33
$_{51}Sb^{122}$	Fermi	4.63	5.97	1.20	2.5	5.32	1.07	0.0572	4.96	...	33
$_{73}Ta^{181}$	Fermi plus quadrupole	5.50	~7.10	~1.25	~2.8	~6.45	~1.14	0.0491	5.65	The radial distances should be considered "effective" radii in view of the quadrupole effects.	61, 88
$_{79}Au^{197}$	Fermi	5.32	6.87	1.180	2.32	6.38	1.096	0.0581	5.82	...	33
$_{82}Pb^{208}$	Hill *et al.* (reference 9) $n=10$, $s=0$	~5.42	~7.0	1.18	~2.3	~6.5	~1.09	0.057	5.93	The model of Hill *et al.* is similar to the Fermi model	9
$_{83}Bi^{209}$	Fermi	5.52	7.13	1.20	2.7	6.47	1.09	0.054	5.935	...	33

ment with the shell model predictions. This result is suggestive of the data presented in Table VI. It would seem profitable to carry out further work with this model. Additional theoretical approaches are also highly desirable. A few attempts of this kind have been made by various authors.[122–129] It is hoped that some such model will be successful.

X. CONCLUSIONS

In this brief section we wish to remark that the electron-scattering method appears to offer great promise in unraveling the problems of nuclear size and shape and the internal dynamics of nuclei. But it must be emphasized that we do not have complete information on such subjects at the present time. The experiments are just "scratching the surface." Many nuclei still need to be investigated and greater accuracy is needed; absolute cross sections must be obtained. Better resolution between elastic and inelastic scattering should be a fundamental objective and is at present a serious lack. Good electron counters must be made which distinguish high-energy electrons from all other particles having the same momenta. We may summarize these remarks in a familiar way: More and better data are needed. Time is needed to allow the electron scattering results to interact with the results of other methods. Only in this way will it be possible to test the experiments and their findings. It would be desirable to test the validity of electrodynamics by some independent method but this probably requires machines which are not yet built. Time is also needed to improve many of the experimental techniques. New and further development of theoretical ideas appear to be required before a clear picture of many of the detailed findings can be obtained. Some kind of analysis of the many-body problem is a necessity in addition to the prior and more fundamental need of a theory of elementary particles. In this connection everyone awaits the development of a successful, quantitative,

[122] M. Born and L. M. Yang, Nature **166**, 399 (1950).
[123] L. M. Yang, Proc. Phys. Soc. (London) **A64**, 632 (1951).
[124] D. Ivanenko and W. Rodichew, Doklady Akad. Nauk. S.S.S.R. **70**, 605 (1951).
[125] P. Gombas, Acta. Phys. Acad. Sci. Hung. **1**, 329 (1952); **2**, 223 (1952).
[126] S. D. Drell, Phys. Rev. **100**, 97 (1955).
[127] M. Rotenberg, MIT Technical Report, Project D.I.C. 6915, No. 6 (1955).
[128] M. H. Johnson and E. Teller, Phys. Rev. **93**, 357 (1954).
[129] L. Wilets, Phys. Rev. **101**, 1805 (1956).

meson theory. It is hoped that the next few years may see the realization of some of these goals.

XI. ACKNOWLEDGMENTS

The accumulation of the large body of facts presented in this report is due to a large number of individuals. Many of their names appear in the references. Some may not, and in this case the author begs forgiveness on the grounds that their number is so large that oversights are easily made. The author wishes to thank R. Blankenbecler, E. E. Chambers, J. H. Fregeau, R. H. Helm, J. A. McIntyre, M. Lévy, D. G. Ravenhall, J. F. Streib, M. R. Yearian, and D. R. Yennie for kind permission to quote their results prior to publication. He sincerely appreciates the generosity of D. G. Ravenhall and D. R. Yennie in taking a great deal of time to explain their results to the author. He has profited greatly from numerous discussions with his colleagues such as F. Bloch, W. E. Lamb, Jr., and L. I. Schiff. He owes much of the successful operation of the devices used in these experiments to F. Bunker, B. Chambers, L. Franklin, A. Knudsen, V. Prosper, and E. Wright, and to R. Mozley and the accelerator group. Finally he wishes to thank L. Becker, A. L. Berg, F. Bunker, R. Keith, A. Marcum, and E. McWhinney for their willing help in completing the manuscript.

PAPER 34

Structure of the Proton*

E. E. CHAMBERS† AND R. HOFSTADTER
Department of Physics and High-Energy Physics Laboratory, Stanford University, Stanford, California
(Received April 2, 1956)

The structure and size of the proton have been studied by means of high-energy electron scattering. The elastic scattering of electrons from protons in polyethylene has been investigated at the following energies in the laboratory system: 200, 300, 400, 500, and 550 Mev. The range of laboratory angles examined has been 30° to 135°. At the largest angles and the highest energy, the cross section for scattering shows a deviation below that expected from a point proton by a factor of about nine. The magnitude and variation with angle of the deviations determine a structure factor for the proton, and thereby determine the size and shape of the charge and magnetic-moment distributions within the proton. An interpretation, consistent at all energies and angles and agreeing with earlier results from this laboratory, fixes the rms radius at $(0.77\pm0.10)\times10^{-13}$ cm for each of the charge and moment distributions. The shape of the density function is not far from a Gaussian with rms radius 0.70×10^{-13} cm or an exponential with rms radius 0.80×10^{-13} cm. An equivalent interpretation of the experiments would ascribe the apparent size to a breakdown of the Coulomb law and the conventional theory of electromagnetism.

I. INTRODUCTION

SOME time ago deviations from point-charge scattering of electrons against the proton were demonstrated at laboratory energies of 188 Mev and 236 Mev and at laboratory angles between 90° and 140°.[1,2] In those investigations, the cross section varied over approximately a factor of 200 between the forward and backward angles. Yet the deviation of the experimental data from a point-charge, point-moment curve was something less than a factor of two at the largest angles, and the experimental error amounted to perhaps a fourth of the deviation. It was not possible to determine accurately the relative separate proportions of charge structure and moment structure which could give agreement with experiment. However, it was shown that equal form factors for charge and moment agreed excellently with the experimental data and the size was fixed at $(0.74\pm0.24)\times10^{-13}$ cm for the rms radius of the charge and moment distributions. Since the reduced de Broglie wavelength of the probing electrons was larger than the "size" of the protonic distributions, it was not possible to distinguish between different shapes for the density distributions of the charge cloud and moment cloud.

Recently we have completed the construction of a larger analyzing spectrometer for the scattered electrons. This spectrometer can bend and analyze electrons with energies up to 550 Mev. At this energy the reduced de Broglie wavelength approaches one-half the size of the proton determined by the earlier experiments, and the experimental angular distribution is no longer insensitive to the shape of the mesonic clouds in the proton. We have taken advantage of the shape sensitivity and have attempted to find a model of the proton which fits not only the angular distribution at the highest energies, but also those at lower energies where only a size is determined. These matters will be treated in detail below.

II. EXPERIMENTAL METHOD

In many respects the experimental apparatus and method are similar to those reported in earlier papers.[3–5] The new features relate to a larger spectrometer and its accessories in the new installation in the "end station" of the Stanford linear accelerator. The end station and bunker area (beam-switching taking place in the latter) will not be described in this paper since they have already been discussed previously.[6] The details of the linear accelerator are also discussed in reference 6.

Figure 1 shows the experimental arrangement used in the electron-scattering experiments in the end station. The electron beam is deflected and dispersed by the first magnet and passes through the energy-defining slit. After passing through the second magnet, the beam is returned parallel to its original direction and refocused at the target. The beam travels in vacuum from accelerator through the magnets, through a secondary electron monitor, and through a thin window (3-mil aluminum) into air before it strikes the target foil. The secondary monitor is of a type we have used previously[7] and is equivalent to a thickness of 5 mils of aluminum. In future experiments the secondary monitor will be replaced by the large Faraday cup, shown dotted in the figure, which is now nearing completion.

* The research reported here was supported jointly by the Office of Naval Research and the U. S. Atomic Energy Commission, and by the U. S. Air Force, through the Office of Scientific Research of the Air Research and Development Command.

† Lieutenant, U. S. Coast Guard.

[1] R. Hofstadter and R. W. McAllister, Phys. Rev. **98**, 217 (1955).

[2] R. W. McAllister and R. Hofstadter, Phys. Rev. **102**, 851 (1956).

[3] Hofstadter, Fechter, and McIntyre, Phys. Rev. **92**, 978 (1953).

[4] Hofstadter, Hahn, Knudsen, and McIntyre, Phys. Rev. **95**, 512 (1954).

[5] J. H. Fregeau and R. Hofstadter, Phys. Rev. **99**, 1503 (1955).

[6] Chodorow, Ginzton, Hansen, Kyhl, Neal, Panofsky, and Staff, Rev. Sci. Instr. **26**, 134 (1955). See particularly Fig. 6.1 of this paper. See also W. K. H. Panofsky and J. A. McIntyre, Rev. Sci. Instr. **25**, 287 (1954).

[7] G. W. Tautfest and H. R. Fechter, Rev. Sci. Instr. **26**, 229 (1955).

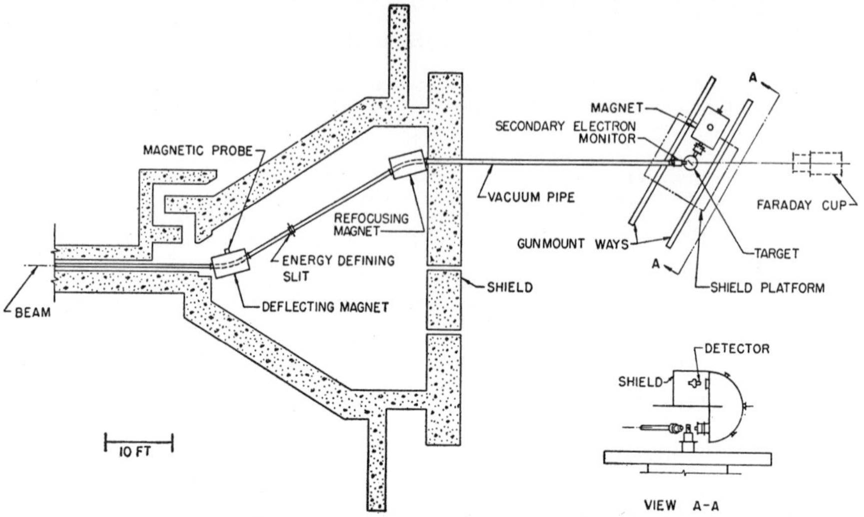

Fig. 1. The installation of the magnetic spectrometer and scattering apparatus.

From the target foil the scattered beam travels through five inches of air, through a thin entrance window (3 mils of aluminum) and then in between the jaws of a lead slit which defines the entrance aperture of the magnetic spectrometer. The target-to-slit distance is usually 26 inches. The pole face of the spectrometer lies at a distance 10.0 inches beyond the lead entrance-slit. The scattered electrons arriving at the magnet are then bent through 180° and double-focused by the magnetic spectrometer. The spectrometer and its mounting will now be described.

The heart of the apparatus is the 180° double-focusing magnetic spectrometer sketched in Fig. 2. The instrument is basically a 30-ton analyzing magnet of a design similar to the smaller $2\frac{1}{2}$-ton magnet used in previous electron-scattering studies.[3] The latter instrument is, in turn, quite similar to the spectrometer of Snyder *et al.*[8] which, itself, is a modification of the original idea of Siegbahn and Svartholm.[9] The presently described spectrometer has been newly designed and is not a scaled-up version of a previous magnet. The radius of curvature of the central trajectory in this magnet is 36 inches and the maximum field obtained on this radius is approximately 20 000 gauss, although the magnet has not often been used in experiments at this maximum field.

In actual practice, electrons with energies up to 510 Mev have been analyzed and studied in these experiments. These correspond to electrons of incident energy 550 Mev in the laboratory, scattered at 30° by protons. Electron trajectories can in principle fill an area of 15×3 inches; these dimensions refer to the pole width and pole gap, respectively. At the present time, a bronze vacuum chamber within the magnet reduces the internal dimensions available to electrons to a cross-sectional area of 14×2 inches. Three radial holes, 4 inches in diameter, pass through the outer yoke of the magnet and communicate with three similar, but smaller, holes in the bronze chamber. Into these holes we have inserted radial magnetic probes to study the field distribution in the median plane of the magnet. These holes lie at the 30°, 90°, 120° azimuths around the magnet circle. The magnetic fields at the 30° and 120° ports have been observed to be 2% smaller than those in the middle of the magnet, at the 90° port. A typical magnetic profile is shown in Fig. 3. Up to 14 000 gauss the field-current curve is essentially linear, and the magnet is unsaturated. 14 000 gauss corresponds to approximately 400 Mev.

Double focusing is achieved by tapering the pole

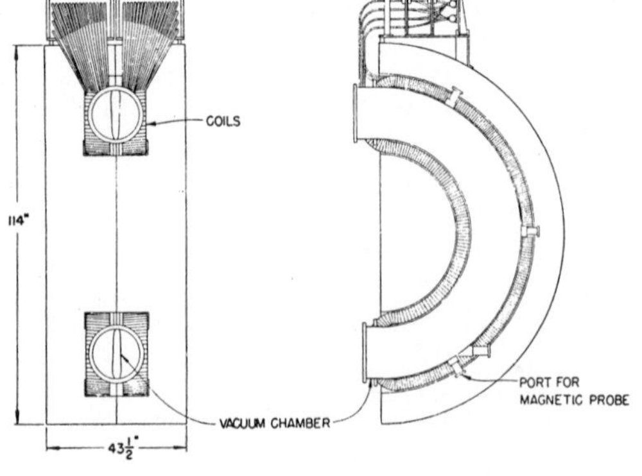

Fig. 2. Details of the magnetic spectrometer.

[8] Snyder, Rubin, Fowler, and Lauritsen, Rev. Sci. Instr. **21**, 852 (1950).

[9] K. Siegbahn and N. Svartholm, Arkiv. Mat. Astron. Fysik **33A**, No. 21 (1946); N. Svartholm, Arkiv. Mat. Astron. Fysik **33A**, No. 24 (1946).

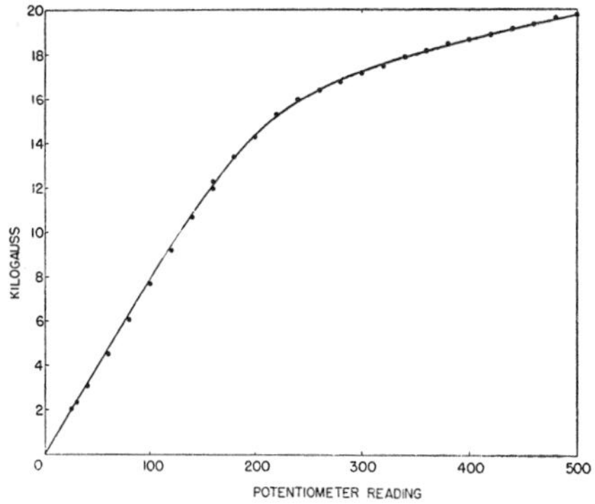

FIG. 3. A typical plot of magnetic field in the median plane *vs* current in the magnetizing coils.

faces so that the field falls off at larger radii in a manner similar to the field in a betatron. The field is required to fall off according to the inverse square root of the radius in this type of instrument. This means that

$$dH/H = -\tfrac{1}{2}dr/r, \tag{1}$$

where H and r refer to the field and the value of the radius on or near the central trajectory in the median plane. In the expectation that the field in the gap would fall off as the reciprocal of the gap itself, or in other words,

$$dH/H = -dy/y = -\tfrac{1}{2}dr/r, \tag{2}$$

where y is the pole gap at any radius, the pole faces were given a linear taper corresponding to Eq. (2). At the edges of the pole, a lip was machined into the steel to prevent a too-rapid decline to zero. The linear taper has proved satisfactory as shown by the radial measurements of the field. The measurements show that up to 400 Mev, relation (1) is well satisfied between radii 33.5 and 38.5 inches. At higher fields this region contracts until at 550 Mev it is only approximately two inches wide. Consequently, up to 400 Mev, the field is as it should be for double focusing. Photographs and visual observation of the exit spot show that focusing does indeed take place in two dimensions, as expected.

Some essential statistics regarding the magnet may prove useful to others.[10] As shown in Fig. 2, the magnet is built in two symmetrical-forged halves, each weighing approximately 15 tons, and having the gross shape of a capital D. Perpendicular to the D plane, the thickness of the iron in each half is 21.75 inches. The outer radius of the D is 57 inches, making the total height of the magnet 9.60 feet. When the two halves are assembled and the magnet is viewed from the input end, an H-like space around the pole gap may be seen accommodating the electrical coils and the bronze vacuum chamber. The coils are constructed of 0.467-inch-square copper tubing, having a round hole of 0.275-inch-diameter, and are water-cooled.[11] There are 256 turns around the poles and the coils are wound four at a time in two bundles to make eight turns per pancake layer. In this way adequate cooling can be provided. All the turns are electrically in series but there are 64 parallel water circuits. The nominal capacity of the magnet is 800 amperes at 250 volts, although as much as 1000 amperes have been put through it. At 800 amperes the coils are barely warm. 400 amperes correspond approximately to 400 Mev on the linear part of the magnet characteristic. The outer return yoke is 11.75 inches thick on each side and 8.5 inches thick radially. The inner return is a half-cylinder 21.75 inches thick and 47 inches in diameter. Each half of the magnet is equipped with a single large handling lug. A fourth hole through the outer return yoke and vacuum chamber permits an x-ray beam to pass through the magnet when desired, the magnetic field itself being used as a clearing field.

Because of the poor duty cycle of the linear accelerator, a heavy shield must guard the detector from background radiation. In this installation a ten-ton shield, constructed of heavy concrete on the outside and lead on the inside, surrounds the Čerenkov detector. The shield is carried on the magnet by means of a massive platform overhanging the target assembly as shown in Fig. 1. As the magnet rotates, the platform and shield are carried with it. The magnet, platform, and shield can also be moved radially to and from the target on two large ways. Within the ways are many cylindrical rollers which take the weight of the 40-odd tons of the spectrometer. The ways are fastened to a modified double five-inch anti-aircraft obsolete gun mount kindly furnished by the Bureau of Ordnance, U. S. Navy, at the request of the Office of Naval Research.[12] The modifications, which transformed the mount from a military device to a scientific instrument, were carried out at the San Francisco Naval Shipyard.[13] The whole gun mount and its assembly can be accurately moved by remote control about the target center. Repeated trials positioning the assembly appear to agree within better than 0.05 degree.

The Čerenkov detector is a truncated Lucite cone 6.0 inches long with a 2.75-inch-diameter input face and a four-inch-diameter termination which couples onto a DuMont 5-inch photomultiplier. The Čerenkov counter is seated behind lead slit jaws which determine the transverse width seen by the detector at the target. Usually a 1.75-inch slit is used to determine the effective target width and the energy slit is, of course, variable

[10] The magnetic spectrometer was designed by L. Rogers and R. Hofstadter. The magnet was constructed by the Bethlehem Steel Corporation at Bethlehem, Pennsylvania. The authors are indebted to Erb Gurney and W. Koegler for assistance in designing and fabricating the forgings.

[11] The coils were wound and installed by the Pacific Electric Motor Company of Oakland, California. Mr. James Allen of this organization worked out the coil design.

[12] We wish to thank Lt. Malcolm Jones and Dr. W. E. Wright for their part in securing for us the use of the gun mount.

[13] We wish to thank Mr. Bernard Smith and his associates at the San Francisco Naval Shipyard for the design and construction of this modification.

but accommodates up to a spread of about 1.3% in energy (strictly speaking, in momentum). The response of the Čerenkov detector is tested before each run and always shows a wide plateau (30 to 40 volts wide) for electrons ranging from less than 200 Mev to the maximum studied (510 Mev). The distribution of Čerenkov counter pulses is checked with a twenty-channel discriminator before each run and has shown insignificant differences at any energy studied: a narrow peak is observed at all energies.

The spot has varied between a width of 0.25 and 0.50 inch in the course of these experiments. The height of the spot has always been less than 0.25 inch and more usually about 0.13 inch.

Although most runs have been taken with polyethylene targets, a few points which check the polyethylene data have been taken with a gas target. In this case the gas target previously described has been used,[2] although its length has been increased to eight inches to allow better observations at small and large angles.

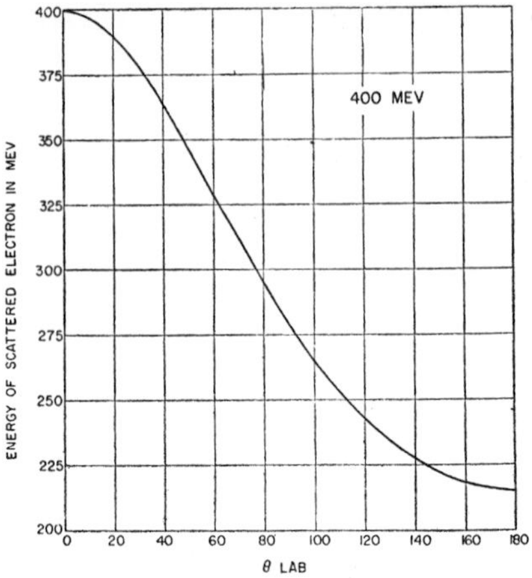

FIG. 5. A theoretical curve found by employing relativistic kinematics of the two-body, electron-proton collision, showing the energy of the scattered electron *vs* angle of scattering in the laboratory frame.

III. RESULTS

The shape and characteristics of an elastic profile taken at 60° at 400-Mev incident energy are shown in Fig. 4. This curve was taken with statistics about four times as numerous as those usually employed in a run in order to determine the characteristic appearance of the profile. Similar curves taken at larger and smaller angles have the same appearance within our experimental errors. Consequently, relatively little error will be obtained by employing the same method at all angles in correcting for the area between *AB* and *CE* which corresponds to the bremsstrahlung tail of the elastic peak. Our method has been to continue the straight line *AC* into the carbon background and calculate the area under the roughly trapezoidal peak. Different and independent methods have been used consistently by each of the two authors to estimate the peak areas, but the results obtained always have agreed within less than the experimental errors. It is to be understood, of course, that the polyethylene-carbon difference is used in obtaining the area under the proton peaks. Excellent agreement is found between such differences and estimations of the areas of the proton peaks obtained by sketching in the relatively flat (or slightly upturned towards lower energies) background in polyethylene alone, on top of which the proton peak "rides."

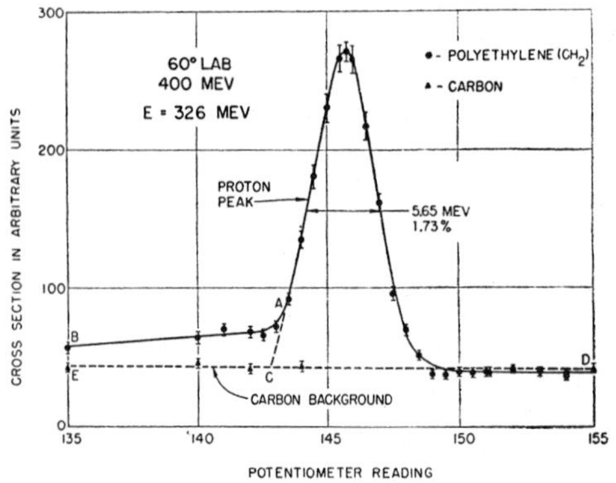

FIG. 4. An elastic profile at 60° and 400 Mev, showing the data taken with polyethylene and the background points due to carbon. The potentiometer reading is proportional to the magnet current, which in this region of the spectrometer characteristic, is proportional to energy.

In finding the area under the proton peak, the half-width of the curve is always expressed in energy units. The conversion from potentiometer readings (magnet current) to an energy scale has been accomplished by (1) using a magnetic probe to find the field in the magnet and assuming the energy is proportional to the field, and (2) using the positions of the centers of the proton peaks and relativistic kinematics to determine the energy of the scattered electrons at any given incident energy and at any given angle. The typical appearance of such a theoretical curve is shown in Fig. 5. Methods (1) and (2) have been combined to give the most consistent calibration curve, using the calibration curve of the deflecting magnet (Fig. 1) to find the incident energy. The two methods agreed so well from the first comparison that it was hardly necessary to make any changes. However, the methods have been merged in a self-consistent way to give what we think is the most accurate final calibration curve. As stated before, this curve tells us that the magnet is essentially linear (energy *vs* magnet current) up to about 400 Mev, which corresponds to 204 units on the potentiometer scale. In almost every measurement we have made, the proton peak has been below 204 on the potentiometer to avoid saturation and possible defocusing prob-

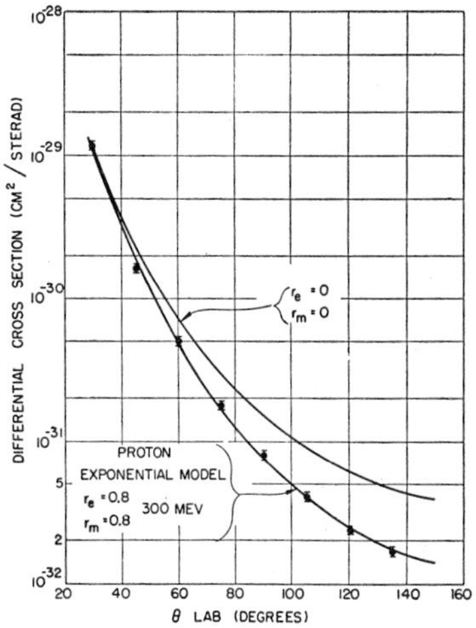

FIG. 6. The experimental points, showing the relative angular data taken at 300 Mev. The point-charge curve ($r_e=0$, $r_m=0$) is shown above. The solid line running through the points is the theoretical curve obtained from Eq. (3) for an exponential proton with rms radii $r_e=0.8\times10^{-13}$ cm and $r_m=0.8\times10^{-13}$ cm, and represents a best fit to the data for an exponential model.

lems. However, in operating at the highest energies and smallest angles, we have occasionally overstepped the 204 limit, but in no way that we believe has caused any serious trouble. Of course, in these cases, as well as in all others, we used the calibration scale to determine the energy width of all peaks. It is not believed that any error larger than 5% can be introduced even at the highest energies and smallest angles. Explicitly, the only cases in which the 204 boundary was passed were at 500 Mev, 45°, and at 550 Mev, angles less than 60°.

Photographic registration of the focused spots at the output of the spectrometer show that the dispersion obtained experimentally is very close to that calculated with Judd's formula.[14] This is further assurance that the calculation of energy width from magnet current is correct. In this connection it should be pointed out that the areas under the proton peaks still need a correction for the constant width of the upper spectrometer slit. The constant slit value was set at 1.3%, which means that, at all momenta, 1.3% intervals are selected for passage into the detector. Thus, at smaller energies of the scattered electrons (larger angles—see Fig. 5), the slit assumes a smaller absolute energy width. This correction varies as the reciprocal of the energy so that at smaller energies the area has been increased by $1/E$ relative to the higher energies. This is the usual correction made in beta-ray spectrographs.

Other small corrections have been made for radiation straggling in the targets and for the radiative calculation of Schwinger.[15] Thickness normalizations have been made where the target thickness varied from angle to angle, because of a half-angle setting as is customary in scattering experiments, or in the case of the gas target. In some experiments the target angle was not varied, although most of the time it was. Consistent results were always obtained.

Thick-target effects were investigated with some care. However, they appear to be absent or at any rate are so small that they do not lie consistently outside our experimental errors. Aside from the normalization due to source thickness, the totals of all corrections to the data were never larger than 10% and were usually considerably smaller. By this we mean, of course, *relative* corrections between the smallest and largest angles. The Schwinger correction itself is approximately a 20% correction in the *absolute* cross section. So far we have confined our attention to relative cross sections exclusively.

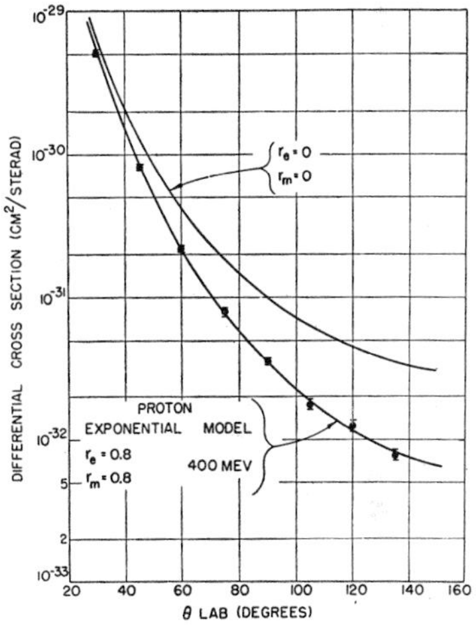

FIG. 7. The experimental points at 400 Mev. Theoretical calculations are similar to those referred to in the legend of Fig. 6.

We have obtained rough absolute cross sections only by knowing the absolute response of the secondary emitting monitor.[7] We shall return to this point after discussing the relative cross sections and the angular distributions which do not require absolute measurements. Thus, in the ensuing material, except where noted, we shall be speaking of relative cross sections only.

By measuring areas under the proton peaks at various angles at a given incident energy, we may prepare relative angular distributions. Such angular distributions are shown in Figs. 6, 7, 8, and 9. The experimental points are the black dots attached to the bars indicating the limits of experimental error, usually not statistical, but primarily due to the type of fluctuation we have mentioned in earlier articles. The data represent in each case the results of at least two separate

[14] D. L. Judd, Rev. Sci. Instr. **21**, 213 (1950). We wish to thank Dr. J. A. McIntyre and Mr. B. Chambers for taking the spot photographs.
[15] J. Schwinger, Phys. Rev. **75**, 898 (1949).

runs, except at 300 Mev where only a single run was taken. We have also made a run at 200 Mev, but since it agrees excellently with the earlier data taken with the smaller spectrometer,[1,2] we do not show it separately here. The 200-Mev data appear in Figs. 11 and 13, along with data of all other energies. In Figs. 6 to 9 there also appear solid lines going through most of the experimental curves. These are not experimental lines, but are actually the result of theoretical calculation which we shall discuss shortly. Also shown in Figs. 6 to 9 are the point-charge curves of Rosenbluth.[16] These are designated $r_e=0$, $r_m=0$, to indicate that the rms radius of the charge and magnetic-moment distributions are each zero, in other words, that the charge and moment are points.

In order to compare the experimental curves with theory, we have employed the same phenomenological

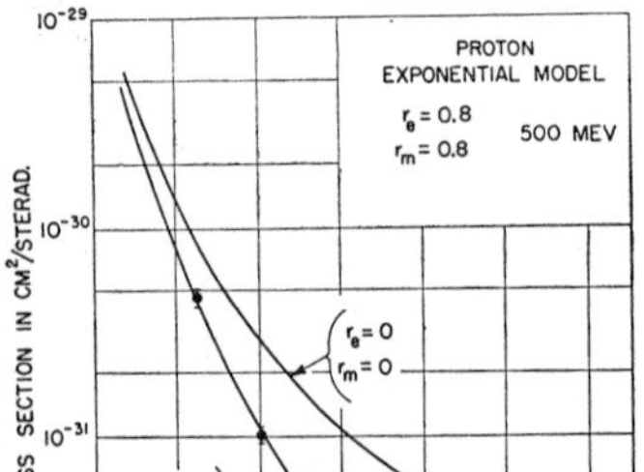

FIG. 8. The experimental points at 500 Mev. The theoretical calculations are similar to those referred to in the legend of Fig. 6.

scheme presented in the earlier paper.[2] This amounts to using a separate form factor F_1 for charge and Dirac moment of the proton, and an additional independent form factor F_2 for the anomalous or Pauli magnetic moment. In the static limit, $F_1=F_2=1$, and the Pauli moment takes on its value, 1.79 nuclear magnetons, compared with the Dirac value, 1.0 nuclear magneton. $F_1\neq 1$ implies a spread-out charge and spread-out Dirac moment and $F_2\neq 1$ implies a spread-out Pauli moment. For reference, the Rosenbluth formula with phenomenological form factors is

$$\sigma = \frac{e^4}{4E^2}\left(\frac{\cos^2(\theta/2)}{\sin^4(\theta/2)}\right)\frac{1}{1+(2E/M)\sin^2(\theta/2)} \times\left\{F_1^2+\frac{q^2}{4M^2}[2(F_1+\mu F_2)^2\tan^2(\theta/2)+\mu^2F_2^2]\right\}, \quad \text{(3a)}$$

[16] M. N. Rosenbluth, Phys. Rev. 79, 615 (1950).

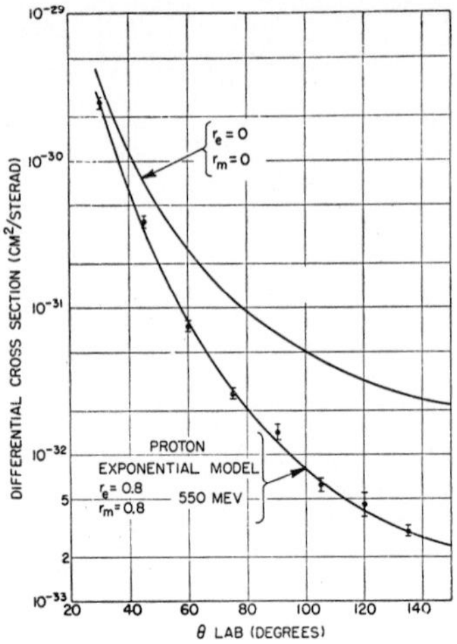

FIG. 9. The experimental points at 550 Mev. The theoretical calculations are similar to those referred to in the legend of Fig. 6.

where

$$q=\frac{(2/\lambda\!\!\!^{-})\sin(\theta/2)}{[1+(2E/M)\sin^2(\theta/2)]^{\frac{1}{2}}}, \quad \text{(3b)}$$

and $\lambda\!\!\!^{-}$ is the de Broglie wavelength of the electron.

The effect of using the form factors is shown in Fig. 10. For this figure an exponential model of the proton is assumed as an example. By this, it is meant that the proton has a charge density given by

$$\rho_{\text{expon}}=\rho_0 e^{-r}. \quad (4)$$

In Eq. (4) as well as in subsequent ones, we shall omit

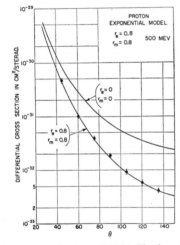

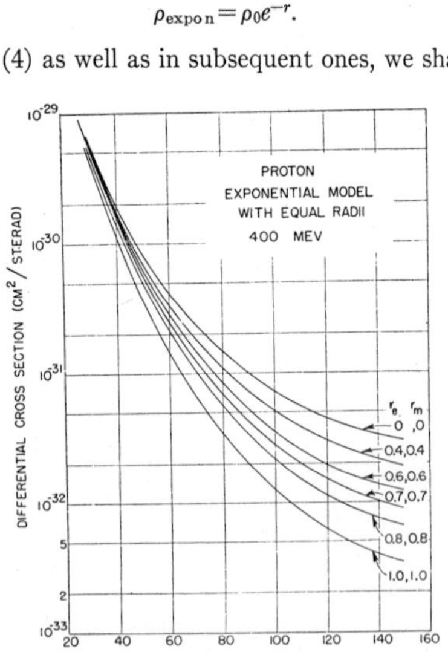

FIG. 10. Shown are the point-charge curve $r_e=0$, $r_m=0$ and various theoretical curves for an exponential proton with equal radii, such as 0.4,0.4 up to 1.0,1.0. These curves were obtained from Eq. (3) and the form factors F_1, F_2 appropriate to an exponential model with the stated rms radii.

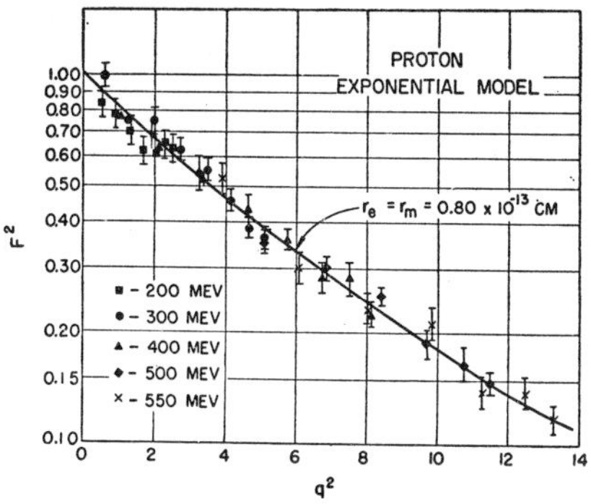

FIG. 11. Summary of the comparison between the exponential model with equal radii (0.8×10^{-13} cm) and the experimental points. The square of the form factor is plotted against q^2, where q is given by Eq. (3). q^2 is given in units of 10^{-26} cm^2.

the parameter corresponding to an rms size, although, of course, the exponential has to be expressed in dimensionless units. For example, ρ_{expon} can be expressed as $\rho_0 \exp(-r/a)$, where $3.48a$ is the rms radius. The assumption that the magnetic-moment distribution has a shape and size equal to that of the charge distribution means that the magnetic-moment density has a distribution of exponential type with the same radius as the charge and points in a single direction everywhere throughout the proton. Under these conditions its form factor will be exactly like that of the charge distribution. The actual computation of explicit form factors has been carried out, for example, by Rose,[17] Smith,[18] Schiff,[19] and others. We shall not reproduce here any of the resultant expressions obtained by integration of the appropriate Born-approximation integral. It is known that the Born approximation is accurate for the proton to better than a few tenths of 1%.[20]

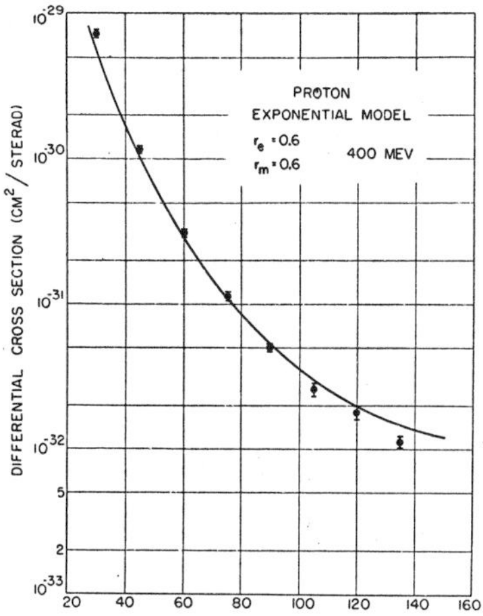

FIG. 12. The comparison of the experimental points with an exponential model with radii equal to 0.6×10^{-13} cm. This is an example of a model which does not fit and shows the tolerance of the fit allowed by experiment.

The features of all other calculations, with different proton models, are similar to those shown in Fig. 10. The general effect is to reduce the scattering below that due to a point charge. At small angles the form factors approach unity and all curves meet with the point-charge curve. Thus, relative fitting of the experimental points to the theoretical curves benefits from the joining-up that must occur at small angles.

When both the shape and size of the protonic model are assumed to be the same, Eq. (3) shows that the square of the form factor may be factored out and the result is a point-charge curve multiplied by the square of a form factor. Such calculations are the easiest to make.

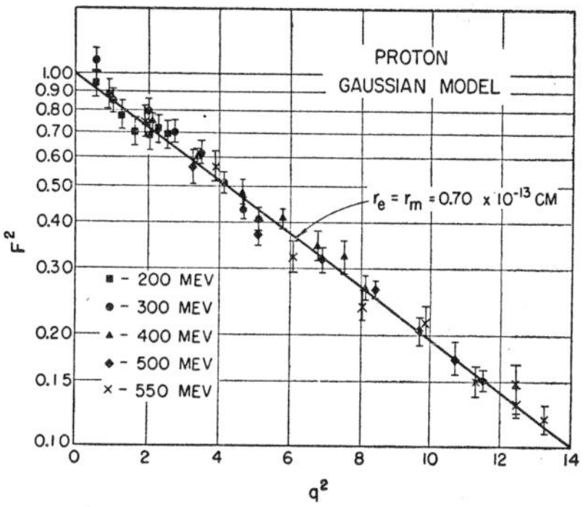

FIG. 13. Summary of a comparison between the Gaussian model with equal radii (0.7×10^{-13} cm) and the experimental points. In this case the theoretical plot is a straight line. q^2 is given in units of 10^{-26} cm^2.

With the models above described, the following shapes have been examined:

$$\rho_a=\rho_1 \exp(-r^2), \quad \text{“Gaussian,”} \quad (5)$$

$$\rho_b=\rho_2(e^{-r}/r^2), \quad \text{Yukawa}_1, \quad (6)$$

$$\rho_c=\rho_3(e^{-r}/r), \quad \text{Yukawa}_2, \quad (7)$$

$$\rho_d=\rho_4 r e^{-r}, \quad (8)$$

$$\rho_e=\rho_5 r^2 e^{-r}, \quad (9)$$

$$\rho_f=\rho_6 r^2 \exp(-r^2), \quad (10)$$

in addition to the exponential model of Eq. (4) and the uniform and shell distributions. These models cover a very wide range, and almost any reasonable shape can be approximated by one of them. The best fits are obtained with models 4, 5, 8, and 9. None of the other models can be made to fit the data at all energies. Each

[17] M. E. Rose, Phys. Rev. **73**, 279 (1948).
[18] J. H. Smith, Ph.D. thesis, Cornell University, 1951 (unpublished); Phys. Rev. **95**, 271 (1954).
[19] L. I. Schiff, Phys. Rev. **92**, 988 (1953).
[20] H. Feshbach, Phys. Rev. **88**, 295 (1952).

model naturally requires a slightly different rms radius for the best fit, but all successful models give a radius very close to 0.75×10^{-13} cm.

For the exponential proton, which we shall take as a typical successful model, the best fit is obtained with the rms radii, $r_e=0.8\times10^{-13}$ cm and $r_m=0.8\times10^{-13}$ cm. Figures 6 through 9 show the quality of the fit at various energies. A summary of all the data taken together can be well presented by plotting the square of the common form factor *vs* q^2, where q is given in Eq. (3b). Such a plot is given in Fig. 11. Since F^2 is a function of q^2, a single theoretical curve suffices for all energies. This is not the case when the charge and moment radii are unequal, for then a separate theoretical curve must be prepared for each energy. Figure 11 shows that the exponential model with radii equal to 0.8×10^{-13} cm is very good at all energies. As an example of the tolerance

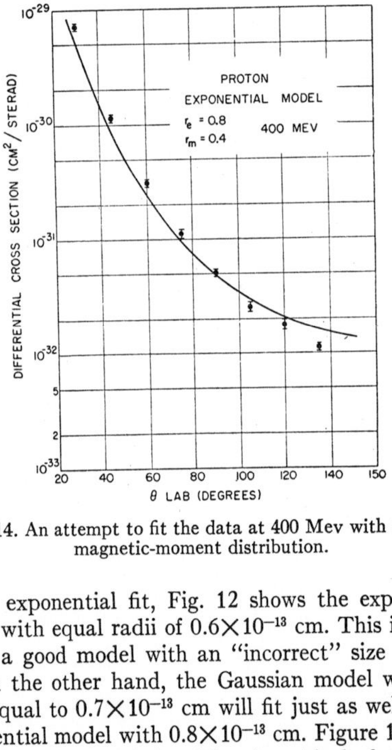

FIG. 14. An attempt to fit the data at 400 Mev with a small magnetic-moment distribution.

of the exponential fit, Fig. 12 shows the exponential model with equal radii of 0.6×10^{-13} cm. This is a case where a good model with an "incorrect" size will not fit. On the other hand, the Gaussian model with rms radii equal to 0.7×10^{-13} cm will fit just as well as the exponential model with 0.8×10^{-13} cm. Figure 13 shows how well this model fits. The theoretical plot in this case is a straight line. The Yukawa model (6) with equal radii cannot be made to fit even with radii as large as 1.5×10^{-13} cm.

The case of two unequal sizes has also been investigated. It has not been possible to find a unique model with two unequal sizes for the charge and moment clouds that will fit the data at all energies (within, of course, the tolerance permitted by experiment). A model with a small magnetic distribution cannot be made to fit under any circumstances. Figure 14 shows a typical case for $r_e=0.8\times10^{-13}$ cm and $r_m=0.4\times10^{-13}$

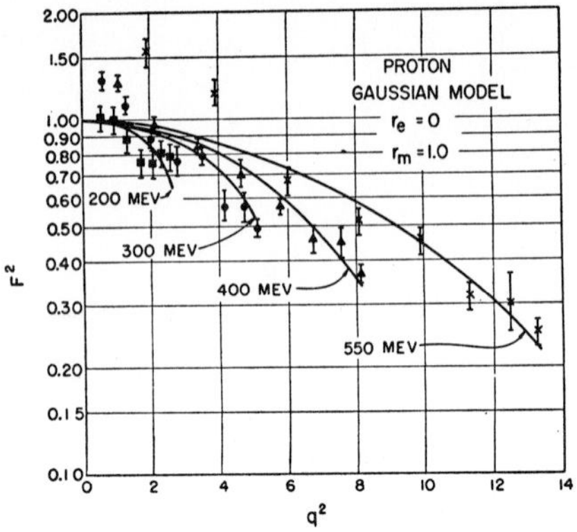

FIG. 15. An attempt to fit the data at all energies with a Gaussian proton having $r_e=0$, $r_m=1.0\times10^{-13}$ cm. The fit is not good and this model can be excluded. Separate curves are required for different energies. q^2 is given in units of 10^{+26} cm^2.

cm. It is possible to find suitable fits by using a larger magnetic-moment size and a smaller charge size. For example, it might be possible to choose $r_e=0.6\times10^{-13}$ cm and $r_m=0.9\times10^{-13}$ cm, and the data at all energies would be satisfied but not quite so well as with the models having equal sizes. On the other hand, a point-charge and spread-out moment will not fit, as shown by the summary graph given in Fig. 15. The results are similar for other models, such as the exponential and uniform. The limit on minimum charge size allowed by these experiments appears to be about 0.6×10^{-13} cm. The maximum is about 1.5×10^{-13} cm. Similar figures apply to the magnetic-moment radii.

The fitting above has been carried out entirely in a relative manner. In other words, each set of data at a given energy was multiplied by a constant factor to obtain the best fit with theory. The data at each energy were thus treated independently. As stated above, the best fit converged on the models 4, 5, 8, and 9 with equal radii. A tabulation of the results is given in Table I.

It is also possible to correlate the data taken at one energy with the data taken at another energy. For example, if a 30° point at 300 Mev can be taken at the same time and under the same conditions as a 75° point at 550 Mev, the lower energy point can be used to normalize the data. The low-energy point has an F^2 value that is essentially unity and thus, except for the

TABLE I. Summary of the models and their values of rms radii which give the best fits. Equal radii for charge and moment are assumed.

Model No.	Shape	rms radius for best fit ($r_e=r_m$) in units of 10^{-13} cm
4	e^{-r}	0.80±0.05
5	$\exp(-r^2)$	0.72±0.05
8	re^{-r}	0.78±0.05
9	r^2e^{-r}	0.75±0.05
		Mean (best fit) 0.77±0.10

TABLE II. Experimental ratios (column 1) at the quoted energies and angles. Columns 2 to 7 list the predicted ratios for the various models represented therein. Where a single radius is given, the value applies to charge and moment. In column 4 the charge radius is zero (a point) and the monent radius is 1.0×10^{-13} cm. All lengths in the table are in units of 10^{-13} cm.

	1	2	3	4	5	6	7
Ratio	Experimental ratio	Model 4 $r=0.80$	Model 5 $r=0.72$	Model 5 $r_e=0$ $r_m=1.0$	Model 8 $r=0.80$	Model 8 $r=0.77$	Model 9 $r=0.75$
$\frac{\sigma\ (300\ \text{Mev},\ 30°)}{\sigma\ (550\ \text{Mev},\ 75°)}$	440 ±10%	381	367	176	425	390	380
$\frac{\sigma\ (300\ \text{Mev},\ 30°)}{\sigma\ (550\ \text{Mev},\ 60°)}$	164 ±10%	128	120	64.8	137	126	124
$\frac{\sigma\ (300\ \text{Mev},\ 60°)}{\sigma\ (550\ \text{Mev},\ 75°)}$	18.9 ±10%	17.2	17.4	9.85	19.2	18.1	17.8
$\frac{\sigma\ (300\ \text{Mev},\ 60°)}{\sigma\ (550\ \text{Mev},\ 60°)}$	6.96±10%	5.80	5.72	3.62	6.15	5.85	5.81

Schwinger correction, the cross section can be obtained absolutely from the Rosenbluth point-charge curve. Now the Schwinger correction varies by only 3% between the two extremes under comparison and can be allowed for with great confidence since the whole effect itself is small. Consequently, the cross section at the larger angle can also be obtained in an absolute way. The absolute cross section at high q values (large-angle, high-energy) is very sensitive to shape and can distinguish between the different models proposed. Table II gives a comparison among the predictions of the different models.

From the comparison it appears that model 8 (column 5) fits best although there is not much to choose between this model and the others. The table shows conclusively, however, that the small-charge cloud and large-moment cloud (column 4) give an unacceptable fit to the data. It may be noticed that the experimental values appear to be a little high. This is probably a result of not knowing the absolute experimental energies precisely.

One of the authors has made an "absolute" determination of cross sections, using the absolute efficiency of the secondary-electron monitor[7] and Judd's[14] calculations of effective solid angle of the spectrometer. These determinations agree excellently with the conclusions of the relative fitting procedure and also with the semiabsolute comparison of large-angle, high-energy, and small-angle, low-energy data. The two authors, have, therefore, independently confirmed the best choices for the charge and moment distributions within the proton.

In Fig. 16 we have displayed the result of these determinations. The ordinate of that figure is $4\pi r^2\rho$, which is a quantity proportional to the amount of charge in a shell at radius r. Three models (4, 5, and 8) are shown. All are good fits to the data at all energies and angles. Of the three, the model 8, the "hollow" exponential, is probably the best. Values of r_e are also given, which represent the best estimate of the rms radius of the charge distribution. The best value for r_m, the rms radius of the magnetic-moment distribution, is equal to r_e. The figure shows that a region is defined which outlines the three best fits and this region in the graph is what the experiments really determine. Any charge distribution lying in this region will define an equally good fit to the data. The region near radius zero is most poorly defined of all because the smallest amount of charge resides there owing to the r^2 factor. In other words, the exponential model, which has a high density at radius zero, cannot be distinguished well from a hollow exponential model in which the charge density is zero at radius zero, for just the reason given above. The fact that the hollow exponential model appears to be a slightly better fit than the exponential or Gaussian

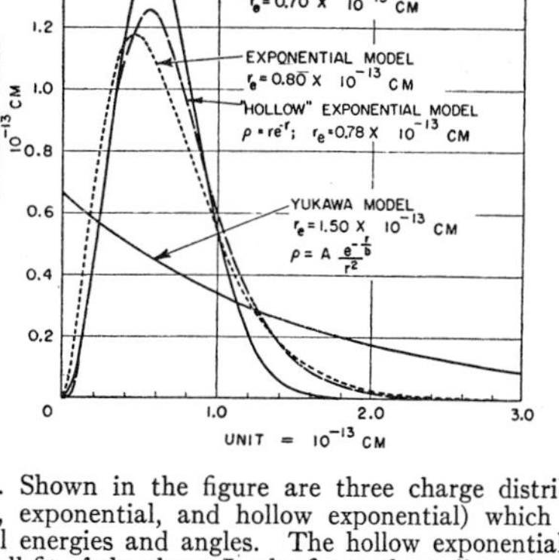

FIG. 16. Shown in the figure are three charge distributions (Gaussian, exponential, and hollow exponential) which fit the data at all energies and angles. The hollow exponential is the best over-all fit of the three. In the figure the ordinate is $4\pi r^2\rho$, a quantity proportional to the amount of charge in a shell at radius r. The Yukawa and uniform models are examples of charge distributions which will not fit the data. In all cases, r_e refers to the best value of the rms radius of the charge distribution. r_m is taken equal to r_e.

may suggest that the density drops a little, or flattens off, as radius zero is approached from larger values. At the moment this remark is rather speculative, but there is no reason why an improvement in the accuracy of the data cannot fix the behavior near zero. In any case, the disagreement with models of type 6 (Yukawa, shown in Fig. 16) and 7, which have large central cores, implies that the center of the proton does not have a dense, charged core. Further improvement in accuracy will also help to clear up this point.

IV. DISCUSSION OF THE RESULTS

We have mentioned in this paper and in the earlier ones[1,2] that the analysis of our results is phenomenological. The analysis determines a charge distribution. From the charge distribution, an electrostatic potential can be calculated, using Poisson's equation in the usual way. Now this potential as a function of radius is the essential meat that can be extracted from the experiments. The basic integral of the Born approximation, containing, in its integrand, the potential multiplied by the product of ingoing and outgoing plane waves, underlies this fact. Consequently, electrostatic and magnetostatic potentials are the end products of these experiments.

One may ultimately determine a protonic model in terms of a meson theory fitting the potentials we have found. These potentials have the feature that they flatten off as radius zero is approached, rather than increasing to infinity as the point-charge Coulomb law would predict. The effective deviations from the Coulomb law due to the flattening-off should be the goals of a meson theory which will then give results consistent with the experimental data. Of course, here we see immediately that the simple assumption that the Coulomb law breaks down (or equivalently, that Maxwell's equations do not hold) at small dimensions (less than 10^{-13} cm), will automatically explain our results and perhaps some other results.[21] This is what we have tried to point out in earlier papers,[1,2] but we have no direct evidence that this breakdown does take place. Phenomenologically the finite-size interpretation and the breakdown of the Coulomb law cannot be distinguished from each other by these experiments. Electron-electron scattering experiments at multi-billion-electron-volts energy could do this. Since we cannot distinguish between these two possibilities, we have talked, for convenience, in terms of the finite-size interpretation. In any case, many of the implications of the two approaches are identical.

A satisfactory meson-theoretic approach to the quantitative explanation of the finite proton size is not yet available, although Rosenbluth[16] has sketched how this may be done. In the absence of such a theory a naive approach would involve assuming that the proton is an undissociated Dirac particle a fraction f of the time and a spread-out meson cloud for the fraction $(1-f)$ of the time. During the latter time, scattering by the overturned value of the magnetic moment of the neutron, into which the proton was changed by emitting the π^+ meson, would take place and appropriate form factors allowing for times f and $1-f$ would have to be employed in the computation. Such calculations are obviously not simple and will depend on the assumptions implicit in the particular meson theory to be used. We shall not consider such an interpretation at this time. However, it may be noted that the simple phenomenological interpretation given in this paper corresponds to a permanently dissociated proton. It is already clear from the experiments that a small dissociation time, corresponding to say, $f=0.9$, will not suffice to fit the experimental facts, because in this case the scattering would be quite close to point-charge scattering.

By comparing cross sections at two energies at the same value of q, the ratio F_1/F_2 can be determined from Eq. (3a). This ratio will be independent of any assumed proton model. The comparison was made between three pairs of energies at a q^2 of about 4×10^{26} cm^{-2} and a value for the ratio was obtained $F_1/F_2=1.1\pm0.2$.

V. ACKNOWLEDGMENTS

We wish to thank Dr. D. R. Yennie, Dr. D. G. Ravenhall, Dr. F. Bloch, Dr. W. E. Lamb, Jr., Dr. J. A. McIntyre, and Dr. L. I. Schiff for many interesting discussions. Mr. H. M. Fried provided some calculations which simplified considerably our computational work, and we are very grateful for his help. We wish to thank Mr. R. Blankenbecler for taking data with hydrogen gas which checked our polyethylene data. Mr. E. deL. Rogers' help was invaluable in designing the magnetic spectrometer. We greatly appreciate the cooperation of the accelerator operating group for providing essentially continuous machine operation. We acknowledge, with many thanks, the work of a great many individuals, too numerous to mention explicitly, who have helped to obtain, construct and install the magnetic spectrometer and associated equipment.

[21] D. R. Yennie and M. Lévy (to be published).

PAPER 35*

Electron Scattering from the Deuteron*

JOHN A. MCINTYRE
High-Energy Physics Laboratory, Stanford University, Stanford, California
(Received April 13, 1956)

The charge distribution of the deuteron has been studied by electron-scattering experiments using 188-Mev and 400-Mev electrons. Both deuterated-polyethylene foils and deuterium gas targets were used. Two different scattering apparatuses were also used. All experiments are consistent with the following results.

The charge of the deuteron is extended over a larger volume than that inferred from low-energy neutron-proton scattering. Specifically, the effective range of the neutron-proton potential is found to be at least $(2.18\pm0.15)\times10^{-13}$ cm as compared with the *n-p* scattering result of $(1.70\pm0.03)\times10^{-13}$ cm. It is possible also to fit the data using a 1.70×10^{-13} cm effective range, and a deuteron consisting of a point neutron and a proton with an rms radius of $(0.82\pm0.17)\times10^{-13}$ cm. This procedure, however, violates the assumption of the charge independence of the internal structure of nucleons. Finally, the 1.70×10^{-13} cm effective range could be preserved by suitably modifying the Coulomb law at small distances.

I. INTRODUCTION

THE scattering of electrons from nuclei gives information about the distribution of charge in the nuclei.[1] Since the charge distribution (wave function) of the deuteron can be calculated directly from a knowledge of the potential between the neutron and the proton, an experimental measurement of this charge distribution by electron scattering would be expected to throw some light on the properties of the neutron-proton potential.

The effective range of this potential has been quite accurately determined from low-energy neutron-proton scattering experiments,[2] and, indeed, the analysis of these experiments is so fundamental and straightforward that it would be surprising if an electron-scattering experiment should give a different result. However, the low-energy, neutron-proton scattering experiments have not yet yielded information about the shape of the nuclear potential between the neutron and proton. It seemed worthwhile, therefore, to do the electron scattering experiment to discover whether any information about the potential shape could be obtained.

II. EXPERIMENTAL PROCEDURES

Scattering from the deuteron has been observed at electron beam energies of 188 Mev and 400 Mev by detecting the elastically-scattered electrons. The 188-Mev data were obtained with the scattering apparatus at the halfway station[3] of the Stanford Mark III linear accelerator. The 400-Mev scattering was performed in the end station of the same accelerator with a larger apparatus similar in principle to that at the halfway station. In addition, a check run at 188 Mev was made in the end station. The scattering was performed also with both solid (CD_2) and gas targets as before.[3] All runs at the two energies, at both stations, and with both kinds of targets are consistent with one another.

A schematic diagram of the end station installation is shown in Fig. 1. The electron beam from the accelerator is deflected and its spread in energy limited by the energy defining slit. A second deflection directs the beam through a secondary-emission monitor[4] and onto either the scattering foil or gas target. The gas target is a cylindrical tube $\frac{3}{4}$ in. in diameter and 8 in. long, with its axis along the beam. The gas pressure is about 2000 psi. The beam striking the target has a cross section of roughly $\frac{1}{4}$ in. by $\frac{1}{4}$ in. The scattered electrons are deflected upward and analyzed by a 36-in. 180° double-focusing magnet spectrometer and then detected by a Lucite Čerenkov counter 4 in. in diameter. A large platform mounted on the spectrometer carries 10 tons of lead and concrete shielding around the counter. The spectrometer and counter are mounted on a twin 5-in. gun mount supplied by the United States Navy; the entire apparatus can be rotated by remote control about the scattering target. The Faraday cup shown in Fig. 1 has not yet been installed.[5]

The 188-Mev data are essentially a more careful rerun of the data published earlier.[3] Improvement in the data results chiefly from better statistics, repeated measurements, and a better understanding of the effects associated with the use of thick targets with the double-focusing magnet spectrometer. Nevertheless, there is still a lack of reproducibility in the data possibly due to hysteresis effects and small drifts in the magnetic field of the magnets. Efforts are being made to install magnetic-field measuring devices to replace the method of deducing the magnetic field from the magnet current.

In the 188-Mev runs at the halfway station, elastic

* The research reported here was supported jointly by the Office of Naval Research and the U. S. Atomic Energy Commission and by the U. S. Air Force, through the Office of Scientific Research of the Air Research and Development Command.

[1] See, e.g., Hahn, Ravenhall, and Hofstadter, Phys. Rev. **101**, 1131 (1956) for recent measurements on large nuclei.

[2] See, e.g., J. M. Blatt and V. F. Weisskopf, *Theoretical Nuclear Physics* (John Wiley and Sons, Inc., New York, 1952), Chap. II.

[3] This apparatus is described in J. A. McIntyre and R. Hofstadter, Phys. Rev. **98**, 158 (1955).

[4] G. W. Tautfest and H. R. Fechter, Rev. Sci. Instr. **26**, 229 (1955).

[5] For details of this apparatus see E. E. Chambers and R. Hofstadter, Phys. Rev. **103**, 1454 (1956), this issue.

See page 684 of this volume for corrections and addenda.

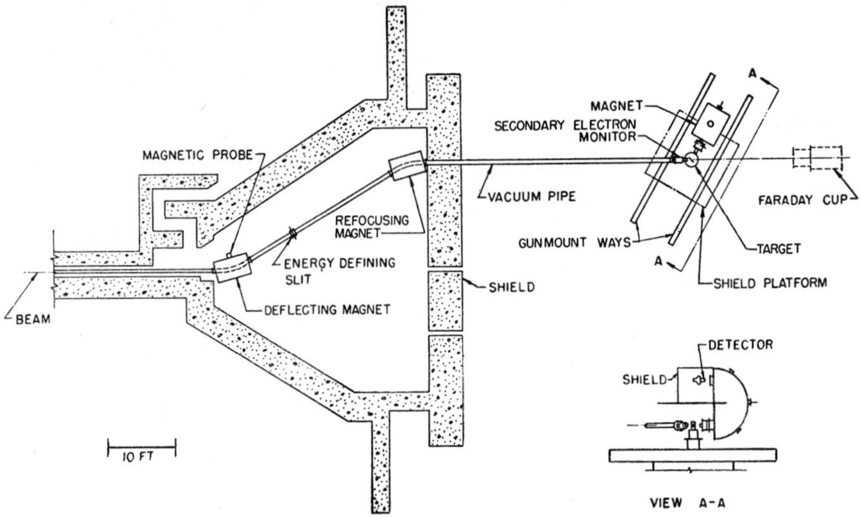

FIG. 1. Schematic diagram showing the end station electron-scattering apparatus.

scattering from the deuteron was observed at angles between 35° and 120°. Five runs were made with the solid target, one with the gas target. One 188-Mev run, covering six angles, also was made in the end station with the gas target. In all runs (except the one in the end station) scattering from the proton also was measured at 50° to give a reference point (using a corresponding solid or gaseous hydrogen target). In all, 36 points were taken at 188 Mev including the proton points.

The 400-Mev deuteron points at the end station were taken at 5° intervals between 30° and 60°. Six runs were made with the gas target, one with the solid target. A proton reference point was taken at 30° in each run. In all, 27 points were taken at 400 Mev including the proton points.

A typical curve, showing the number of 188-Mev electrons scattered by the solid target at 80°, is shown in Fig. 2. Figure 3 shows data at 60° using the gas target. The area between the CD_2 and carbon curves or under the gas curve is then measured to determine a quantity proportional to the number of elastically-scattered electrons at a particular angle. With curves such as these, and their associated areas, the cross sections for elastic scattering at the various angles and energies can be computed.

III. CORRECTIONS TO DATA

A number of corrections must be applied to the areas obtained from the curves such as the ones shown in Figs. 2 and 3. These corrections will now be considered.

1. When using the solid target, the normal to the target is rotated to one-half the scattering angle to equalize energy loss in the target. Thus, the target thickness is $t\sec(\theta/2)$, where t is the thickness normal to the target. With the gas target, on the other hand, the target thickness is $t' \csc\theta$, where t' is the length of the gas target "seen" by the electron counter through the spectrometer magnet.

2. Because of the recoil of the deuteron, the elastically scattered electrons at various angles have different energies. Since the exit-slit width of the spectrometer has a constant value of $\Delta p/p$ (p= electron momentum), the abscissa interval in Figs. 2 and 3 should be changed from dI (I= magnet current) to dp/p. Therefore, the areas obtained are multiplied by $(dp/p)\times(1/dI)=(1/p)\times(dB/dH)$, where dB/dH is the slope of the magnetization curve of the spectrometer (neglecting end effects). Because of the saturation of the halfway-station spectrometer and the significant recoil energy of the deuteron dB/dH varies by 60% for the range of angles

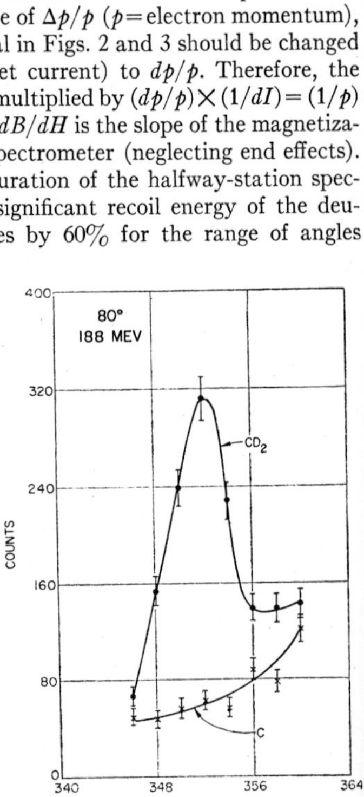

FIG. 2. Elastic electron-scattering data obtained at 80° using the solid CD_2 target. The scattering from a carbon target is shown by the lower curve. The electron beam energy is 188 Mev.

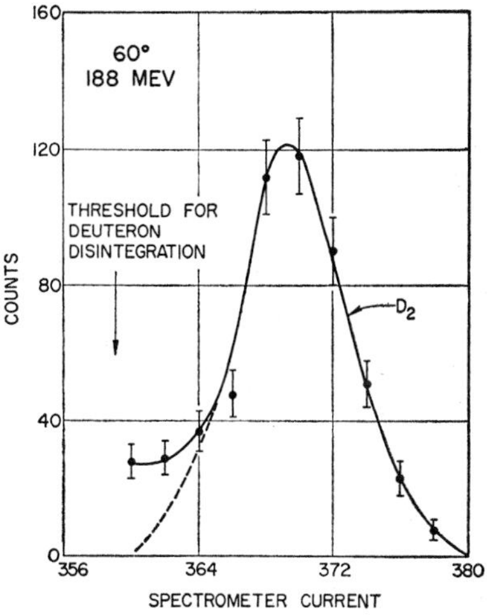

FIG. 3. Elastic electron-scattering data obtained at 60° using the gas target. The electron beam energy is 188 Mev. The points to the left of the dotted line represent electrons which have lost energy in the process of disintegrating the deuteron.

covered in the deuteron experiment. In the end station, dB/dH is constant for the 188-Mev scattering and varies by 15% for the 400-Mev scattering.

3. The number of electrons passing through the target during the counting period must be divided into the area measured under the scattered electron peaks. As mentioned before, the beam is monitored by a secondary-emission monitor. This type of monitor has been found to be stable within a few percent over long periods of time.[4]

4. The scattering cross sections are determined for each run by normalizing the corrected area associated with the hydrogen scattering to the cross section for proton scattering as determined by Chambers and Hofstadter.[5]

5. The radiative correction to the scattering theory[6] has been applied. This amounted to no more than 3% because of the method of normalizing to hydrogen.

6. Correction was made for electrons lost from the experiment due to bremsstrahlung in the target.[7] At most, this was a 3% correction.

IV. EXPERIMENTAL CHECKS

A number of checks was made to determine whether the corrections of the last section were valid. These checks were often not pushed beyond an accuracy of 10% even though better accuracy could have been obtained. This was because the experimental accuracy was already limited to 10% because of lack of reproducibility in the data as already mentioned in Sec. II.

Following are the experimental checks made on the system.

1. The geometrical correction to the target thickness was checked in two ways: First, for scattering at 50°, the solid target was set at 25° and then at 55°. The counting rate varied as $\sec(\theta/2)$ as it should to within a factor of 3%. This result showed not only that the calibration of the target angle was correct but also that the counter beyond the spectrometer magnet could "see" all of the target area struck by the incoming electron beam. This latter conclusion follows from the fact that the horizontal dimension of this active target area depends on the target angle (in this test this dimension changed by 70%).

The second check on the target thickness follows from the agreement between the scattering from the solid and the gas targets. This agreement was on the average better than 5%. Variations among different solid-target runs was sometimes greater than this.

2. The value of dB/dH, the slope of the magnetization curve for the halfway-station spectrometer, was checked by four methods. The first method was to measure the magnetization curve at the center of the spectrometer with a Rawson rotating coil fluxmeter of 2% accuracy. The second method was to measure the voltage induced in a fixed coil when the spectrometer current was changed by a small amount. A ballistic galvanometer was used to measure this voltage. This measurement gave dB/dH directly. The third method was to determine B and H from the recoil energies measured in the hydrogen and deuterium scattering. At a given angle the energy of the scattered electron could be calculated and B was obtained from this energy value. H was obtained at that angle experimentally by noting the magnet current required to bend the scattered electrons through the spectrometer. This method thus determined the magnetization curve over the region used in the scattering experiments. Finally, the fourth method was to relate B and H by measuring the difference in spectrometer current readings between the elastically- and inelastically-scattered electrons from carbon nuclei. Since the nuclear energy levels of carbon are well known, this information provided a 10-Mev section of the magnetization curve at 188 Mev and at 150 Mev, the energies at which the carbon measurements were made. The last two methods measured more nearly the desired quantity as they include the effects of the fringing fields at the entrance and exit of the spectrometer. The four methods agreed with each other within 10%.

For the end-station spectrometer, a rough check of the magnetization curve was made with the Rawson flux meter. The curve used in processing the data, however, was determined from the spectrometer currents associated with the electrons scattered from hydrogen as measured by Chambers and Hofstadter.[5] The electrons scattered from deuterium checked this calibration within a few percent. Since the change in

[6] J. Schwinger, Phys. Rev. **76**, 790 (1949).
[7] H. A. Bethe and J. Ashkin, *Experimental Nuclear Physics*, edited by E. Segrè (John Wiley and Sons, Inc., New York, 1953), p. 272.

the slope is only 15% for the 400-Mev data and is zero for the 188-Mev data at the end station, the slope does not need to be known accurately at these energies.

3. A check was made on the constancy of the dispersion $\Delta p/p$ of the halfway-station spectrometer by placing a double slit at the spectrometer exit. The double peak resulting from the monoenergetic scattered electrons passing through these slits as the spectrometer current was varied gave the change in current required to move the electrons a fixed distance at the exit slit. A check at 186 Mev and at 143 Mev gave a 12% discrepancy. Because the spectrometer current shunt had been damaged and was found later to be in error by 10%, this discrepancy is not viewed seriously and is ignored in processing the data.

A check on the dispersion of the end-station spectrometer using film exposures indicates good agreement with the theory of the magnet. It is known also from film exposures that this spectrometer gives a small focused spot ($\frac{1}{4}$ in. by $\frac{1}{4}$ in.) at the exit slit when analyzing 400-Mev monoenergetic electrons.

4. An over-all check on spectrometer characteristics is provided by performing the 188-Mev scattering experiment at both the halfway station and the end station. Since the magnetization curve of the end-station magnet is linear at this energy, the agreement in scattering data obtained at these two locations gives an excellent check of all of the characteristics of the halfway-station spectrometer. This check provides another reason to doubt the 12% variation found in the dispersion of the halfway-station spectrometer. Finally, the agreement between the 400-Mev data in the end station and the 188-Mev data gives reason for confidence in the characteristics of the end-station spectrometer at 400 Mev. Chambers and Hofstadter[5] have also measured the magnetic field of the end-station spectrometer and its gradient over a wide range of energies and have found the values predicted by the magnet design.

5. The effect of the walls of the gas target has been checked by McAllister and Hofstadter[8] by placing a metal foil comparable in thickness to the target wall between the target and the spectrometer. No change in the area under the elastically scattered electron peaks (such as the peak in Fig. 2) was observed within the accuracy of the measurement (10%).

6. A plateau of Čerenkov-counter pulse heights was taken before each run to determine the discriminator setting of the counter-scaler combination. The counting system was also checked periodically by inserting a radioactive source and crystal in front of the Lucite Čerenkov counter which then acts as a light pipe.

7. There is some uncertainty involved in measuring the areas under the experimental peaks (see Fig. 3). This occurs because there are inelastically-scattered electrons (to the left of the peak) which have disintegrated the deuteron. These electrons must be rejected in the elastic-scattering measurement. Thus, the area is bounded on the left with the dotted line which has been sketched in to make the elastic peak roughly symmetrical. The accuracy of this procedure has been checked in two ways: The first is to sketch in dotted curves that seem to be in limiting possible reasonable positions. The area under the peak as measured by a planimeter is found to vary no more than ±5% for these changes. The second check is to change the abscissa and ordinate scales of the peaks obtained at the various angles so that the peaks will coincide with one another when they are superimposed.[9] The lower left portions of the peaks are ignored when making this superposition so that the problem of the inelastic scattering is circumvented. The abscissa and ordinate compression factors then give the ratios of the areas at the various angles. This procedure gave agreement with the other method of area measurement within ±10%, the variations being on both sides of the first measurements. This shows that there is no large systematic error introduced by the inelastic electrons in measuring the area. This second procedure was not carried out very carefully as it was used only to detect a systematic error.

8. There is little doubt that the above checks, which gave 10% discrepancies, could have been refined to give better consistency. The effort was not made to carry out this refinement because the reproducibility of the data was not better than 10% even when all experimental parameters were held constant. As mentioned before, this lack of reproducibility is thought to be caused by drifts in the field of the beam-deflecting magnet before the energy-selecting slit or in the spectrometer magnet. For example, if a change in field of 0.1% should occur in either of these magnets while the point at current reading 374 in Fig. 3 was being taken, an error of 8% would occur in the number of counts obtained at that point. Such a change is thought to be not unlikely and would account for the 10% lack of reproducibility observed in the data.

V. HANDLING OF DATA

The data from each run were normalized by means of the experimental proton point. The deviation of the proton scattering from the scattering of a point proton has been determined by Chambers and Hofstadter[5] to be $(0.88\pm0.05)\%$ at 50° and 188 Mev and $(0.81\pm 0.05)\%$ at 30° and 400 Mev. Using these deviation factors and the theoretical cross section for scattering from a point proton,[10] the proton scattering cross sections are found to be (omitting the radiative corrections):

$$188 \text{ Mev}, 50°, \quad \sigma=3.23\times10^{-30} \text{ cm}^2 \text{ sterad}^{-1},$$

$$400 \text{ Mev}, 30°, \quad \sigma=5.39\times10^{-30} \text{ cm}^2 \text{ sterad}^{-1}.$$

[8] R. W. McAllister and R. Hofstadter, Phys. Rev. **102**, 851 (1956).

[9] This method was suggested to the author by Professor J. F. Streib.

[10] M. N. Rosenbluth, Phys. Rev. **79**, 615 (1950).

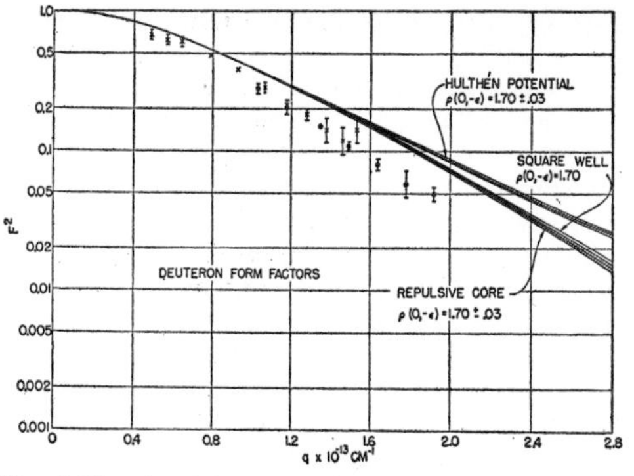

FIG. 4. Experimental points and theoretical F^2 (form factor)^2 curves. The three theoretical curves are for deuterons held together by three types of neutron-proton potentials. The shaded theoretical bands represent the uncertainty in the theoretical curves introduced by the standard deviation in the presently accepted effective range value of $(1.70\pm0.03)\times10^{-13}$ cm.

From these values and the experimental ratios between proton and deuteron scattering, cross sections were obtained for the deuteron points.

This method of determining the deuteron cross sections gives excessive weight to the proton point, however, as a poor proton point will result in all of the deuteron points in a given run being given incorrect cross sections. Consequently, a constant multiplying factor was applied to the cross sections of each run so as to give a least squares fit for all of the data. This adjustment did not change the normalization of any run by more than 2%.

The mean value for the cross section for each deuteron angle was then obtained by averaging the deuteron points from the various runs. The standard deviation of this mean was computed from the different cross-section values used in obtaining the mean. In almost all cases, the deviations between different runs were larger than the statistical deviations. At angles where only one run was made, the deviation was arbitrarily set equal to that for the neighboring angle since that deviation was always larger than the statistical one for the single run.

In order to compare the experimental results with theory, it is convenient to divide the experimental cross sections by the theoretical cross section for the scattering by a point particle with the mass and charge of the deuteron [see Eq. (4)]. This ratio is designated by F^2, (form factor)^2, and is plotted in Fig. 4 as a function of q, the momentum transfer of the scattered electron in the center-of-mass system. The theoretical curves plotted in Fig. 4 will be discussed in the next section.

VI. THEORETICAL CONSIDERATIONS

As mentioned before, there is a simple theory for the deuteron.[2] From low-energy neutron-proton scattering data, an effective range of the neutron-proton potential can be determined which is essentially independent of the shape of the potential. Using Bethe's notation,[11] the effective range of the triplet potential is found to be $\rho(0,-\epsilon)=(1.70\pm0.03)\times10^{-13}$ cm.[12] (ϵ is the binding energy of the deuteron.)

In the work which follows, three types of neutron-proton potentials have been considered: the Hulthén potential, $V(r)=e^{-Kr}/(1-e^{-Kr})$ (which is essentially a Yukawa potential but can be handled more easily mathematically),[13] the square-well potential, and a repulsive-core potential[14] yielding a deuteron wave function of the type

$$\psi=0 \text{ for } r<a,\quad \psi=(1/r)\{e^{-\alpha r}-e^{a(\gamma-\alpha)}e^{-\gamma r}\} \text{ for } r>a.$$

A deuteron binding energy of $\epsilon=2.226$ Mev is used.[15]

For the Hulthén potential, $\rho(-\epsilon,-\epsilon)$ is evaluated in terms of the wave function, $\rho(-\epsilon,-\epsilon)$ then being a function of K, the Hulthén potential parameter. To evaluate K, the value of $\rho(-\epsilon,-\epsilon)$ must be found from $\rho(0,-\epsilon)=1.70$.[16] This is done by combining Eqs. (33), (10), and (13a) from Bethe's article[11] to obtain

$$\rho(\epsilon_2,\epsilon_1)=r_0-2Pr_0^3(k_2^2+k_1^2). \tag{1}$$

For the Yukawa well, Blatt and Jackson[17] give P to be 0.14 so that Eq. (1) above gives $r_0=\rho(0,0)=1.63$ and $\rho(-\epsilon,-\epsilon)=1.77$. For this value of $\rho(-\epsilon,-\epsilon)$, K, the Hulthén potential parameter, is found to be 1.13. The wave function for the deuteron is then determined and also its square, the charge distribution. To obtain the charge distribution in the laboratory system, the lengths given above are divided by two. Using the Born approximation for electron scattering from this distribution,[18] the scattering is found to be[19]

$$F(q)=\frac{1.580}{q}\left(\tan^{-1}\frac{q}{0.930}-2\tan^{-1}\frac{q}{3.19}+\tan^{-1}\frac{q}{5.45}\right), \tag{2}$$

where $q=(2p/\hbar)\sin(\theta/2)[1+(2p/Mc)\sin^2(\theta/2)]^{-\frac{1}{2}}$, p is the incoming electron momentum, θ is the scattering angle in the laboratory, and M is the deuteron rest mass. $F^2(q)$ is defined as the ratio of actual scattering to that expected from a point scatterer. Equation (2) thus gives the theoretically expected modification to point-charge scattering of a deuteron bound together by a Hulthén potential.

Electron scattering from a deuteron with a square-

[11] H. A. Bethe, Phys. Rev. **76**, 38 (1949).
[12] See reference 2, p. 85.
[13] L. Hulthén, Arkiv Mat. Astron. Fysik. **28A**, No. 5 (1942).
[14] V. Z. Jankus, Phys. Rev. **102**, 1586 (1956).
[15] See reference 2, p. 51.
[16] Henceforth, all lengths will be expressed in units of 10^{-13} cm.
[17] J. M. Blatt and J. D. Jackson, Phys. Rev. **76**, 18 (1949).
[18] W. A. McKinley, Jr. and H. Feshbach [Phys. Rev. **74**, 1759 (1948)] have shown that the Born approximation is accurate to better than ½% for scattering from singly-charged particles.
[19] See, e.g., M. E. Rose, Phys. Rev. **73**, 279 (1948), for calculation of form factors.

well potential between neutron and proton has been calculated by Smith.[20] A procedure similar to that used with the Hulthén potential was followed to determine the range and depth of the square well for use in Smith's equation. By using the data in Blatt and Jackson[17] as above, $\rho(0,0)$ was found to be 1.73 for $\rho(0,-\epsilon)=1.70$. The potential range to give this value for $\rho(0,0)$ was found to be 2.04 with a potential depth of 35.2 Mev. Smith's equation then gives the form factor $F(q)$ for scattering from such a deuteron.

Jankus[14] has calculated the scattering from a repulsive-core potential using the repulsive-core wave-function given above. If one investigates instead an extreme repulsive-core model [$\psi=(1/r)e^{-\alpha r}$ beyond the core radius], it may be shown that $\rho(-\epsilon,-\epsilon)=1.67$ for $\rho(0,-\epsilon)=1.70$. The assumption has been made in the following that this is true for Jankus' wave function also. Therefore, the repulsive-core scattering in this paper has been calculated for $\rho(-\epsilon,-\epsilon)=1.67$. A core radius of 0.65 has been used.

The values for $F^2(q)$ are plotted in Fig. 4 for the Hulthén, the square-well, and the repulsive-core deuterons. The 0.03 standard deviation in the effective range value is indicated for the Hulthén and repulsive-core potential by the shaded areas.

Thus far, the deuteron has been considered as consisting solely of a neutral and a charged particle attracted to each other by a central potential and in an S state. The magnetic moments of the neutron and proton and the mixture of D state in the wave function must also be considered as to how they affect the electron scattering. The magnitude of these effects has been investigated by Jankus.[14] He has found that the scattering of electrons from the magnetic moment of the deuteron has a cross section

$$\sigma_{\text{mom}}=\{\tfrac{2}{3}(e^2/Mc^2)^2\mu_D^2[1+\csc^2(\theta/2)]\}\times\{1+(2p/Mc)\sin^2(\theta/2)\}^{-2}\times F_{\text{mom}}^2(q)=\sigma_{\text{point mom}}\times F_{\text{mom}}^2(q), \quad (3)$$

where e is the electronic charge and μ_D is the magnetic moment of the deuteron in nuclear magnetons. This is seen to be negligible, in most cases, when compared to the scattering from the charge of the deuteron which is simply $F_{\text{charge}}^2(q)$ times the Mott scattering from a point charge[21]:

$$\sigma_{\text{charge}}=\left(\frac{e^2}{2pc}\right)^2\csc^4(\theta/2)\cos^2(\theta/2)\times\{1+(2p/Mc)\sin^2(\theta/2)\}^{-1}\times F_{\text{charge}}^2(q)=\sigma_{\text{point charge}}\times F_{\text{charge}}^2(q). \quad (4)$$

For instance, at the largest scattering angle of 120° at 188 Mev, $\sigma_{\text{point mom}}/\sigma_{\text{point charge}}$ is 11% while at 90° it is only 3%. For the 400-Mev scattering at the largest angle, it is 4%.

The small admixture of D state in the deuteron wave function (about 4% of the charge distribution) affects the wave function in two ways: it contributes to the spherically symmetric part of the wave function, and it accounts for the quadrupole moment. The contribution to the electron scattering of these two D-state effects is shown by Jankus[14] to be of the order of no more than a few percent.[22]

Because of the smallness of all of the contributions to the cross section in comparison to the scattering from the charge, it is necessary in the following to consider only the charge scattering. Therefore, the experimental cross sections have been divided by the scattering from a point charge [$\sigma_{\text{point charge}}$ in Eq. (4)] to give the experimental F^2 plotted in Fig. 4 (see Sec. V).

VII. DISCUSSION OF RESULTS

Figure 4 shows that there is a large discrepancy between the theoretical curves and the experimental data. The following possibilities are available to explain this discrepancy:

1. The neglected factors mentioned in the last section should be taken into account. However, these factors all add to the theoretical curve and, hence, make the discrepancy in Fig. 4 larger. Thus, the discrepancy in Fig. 4 results. This feature of the deuteron scattering greatly simplifies the interpretation of the experimental results.

2. The experimental points may be made to agree with theory by increasing the effective range of the neutron-proton potential in the deuteron. If this is done a fit may be obtained for the data as shown in Figs. 5 and 6. For the Hulthén deuteron $\rho(0,-\epsilon)=2.47_{-0.32}^{+0.20}$, and for the repulsive-core deuteron $\rho(0,-\epsilon)=2.18\pm0.15$. The square-well deuteron is in-

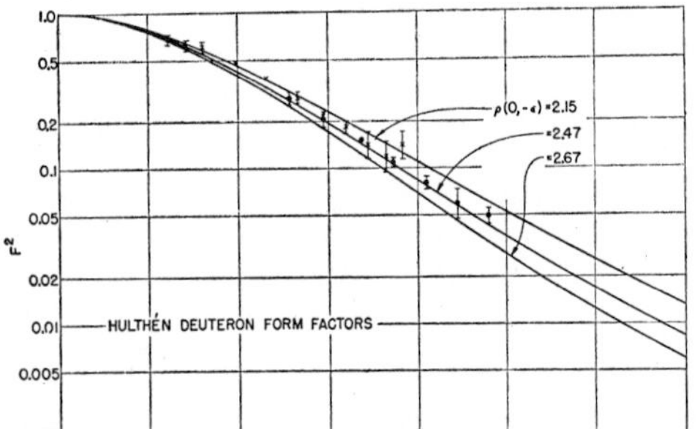

FIG. 5. Experimental points fitted by a theoretical Hulthén deuteron with suitable effective range. The upper and lower curves represent the extremes in effective range values that will still fit the experimental data.

[20] J. H. Smith, Ph.D. dissertation, Cornell University, 1951 (unpublished).

[21] N. F. Mott, Proc. Roy. Soc. (London) A135, 429 (1932).

[22] The effect of the D-state admixture was first calculated by L. I. Schiff, Phys. Rev. 92, 988 (1953).

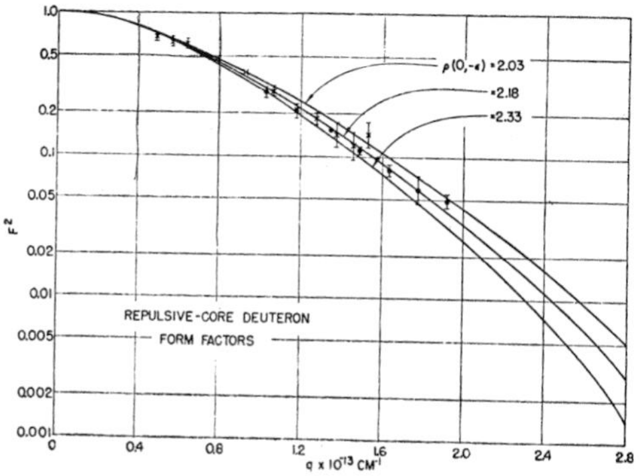

FIG. 6. Experimental points fitted by a theoretical repulsive-core deuteron with suitable effective range. The upper and lower curves represent the extremes in effective range values that will still fit the experimental data.

distinguishable from the repulsive-core deuteron (see, e.g., Fig. 4).

These effective range values are seen to be at least (16±5) standard deviations outside the presently accepted value for the effective range of 1.70±0.03. This latter value for the effective range is based on the simplest assumptions about the neutron-proton potential.[2] It is thus necessary to make a fundamental modification in the present ideas about nuclear forces in order to increase the effective range obtained by low-energy neutron-proton scattering a sufficient amount to agree with the results of the electron-scattering experiments.

3. An agreement between experiment and theory can be obtained by assuming that the charge cloud of the proton in the deuteron is spread out over a root-mean-square radius of about 0.8, while the cloud for the neutron extends over a region much smaller than this. This assumption is in agreement with the electron-proton scattering experiments of Chambers and Hofstadter[5] and the neutron-electron scattering experiments of Melkonian *et al.*[23] and Hughes *et al.*[24,25]

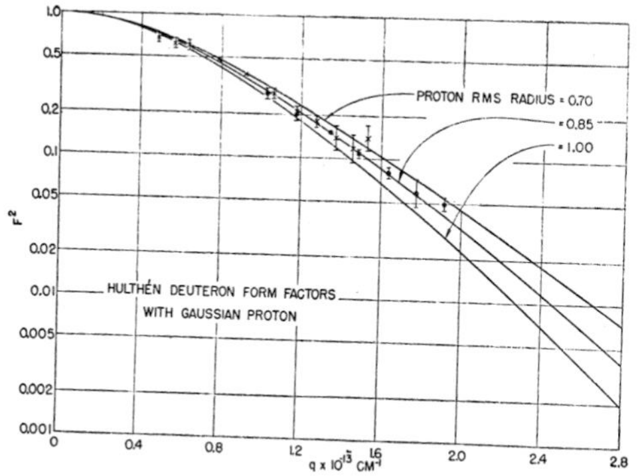

FIG. 7. Experimental points fitted by a theoretical Hulthén deuteron containing a proton with suitably spread-out charge distribution. The radial dependence of the proton charge density is Gaussian.

The form factor of a deuteron which contains a proton with form factor F_P is $F_P \times F_D$, where F_D is the usual deuteron form factor. Figure 7 shows the modified deuteron form factor for a Hulthén deuteron which contains a proton with Gaussian radial charge distribution. The best fit with the experimental data is obtained with a proton rms radius of 0.85. The upper and lower limit proton radius values are 1.00 and 0.70, respectively. Figure 8 shows the repulsive-core deuteron form factor modified by a Gaussian proton. The curves here fit for a proton rms radius of 0.80±0.15.

Some change in these values occurs if the proton radial charge distribution is different from the Gaussian. The change is such as to increase the proton rms radius values required to fit the experimental data. Thus, the proton rms radius values of 0.85±0.15 for the Hulthén

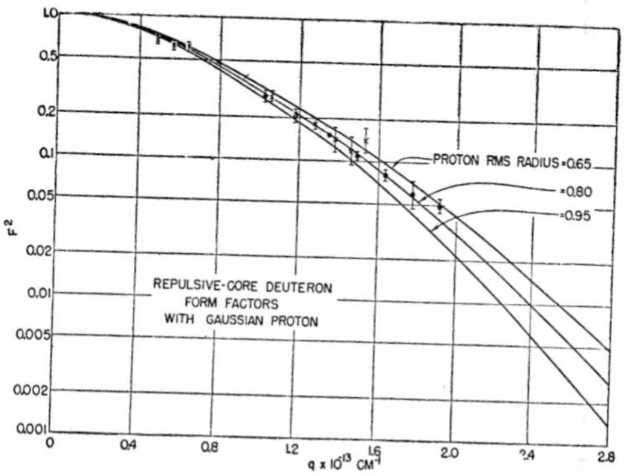

FIG. 8. Experimental points fitted by a theoretical repulsive-core deuteron containing a proton with suitably spread-out charge distribution. The radial dependence of the proton charge density is Gaussian.

deuteron and 0.80±0.15 for the repulsive-core deuteron are minimum values. As mentioned above, the square-well deuteron gives the same result as the repulsive-core deuteron.

Yennie[26] has pointed out that the assumption made here of a proton and neutron of different size existing in the deuteron is almost equivalent to abandoning the property of the charge independence of the internal structure of nucleons. His argument is that, if one assumes charge independence of the neutron and proton in the deuteron, the π^- meson cloud about the neutron and the π^+ meson cloud about the proton will just

[23] Melkonian, Rustad, and Havens, Bull. Am. Phys. Soc. Ser. II, 1, 62 (1956).

[24] Hughes, Harvey, Goldberg, and Stafne, Phys. Rev. **90**, 407 (1953).

[25] For a discussion of the relation between the neutron-electron interaction and the extension of the neutron charge cloud, see, e.g., H. A. Bethe and F. de Hoffmann, *Mesons and Fields* (Row, Peterson, and Company, Evanston, 1955), Vol. 2, pp. 297–299.

[26] D. R. Yennie, Phys. Rev. **100**, 1795 (1955) and Yennie, Lévy, and Ravenhall (to be published).

cancel each other because the wave function for the neutron in the deuteron is the same as that for the proton. Thus, the protonic nucleon core is alone responsible for the charge distribution of the deuteron as measured by the electron-scattering experiments. This argument applies also to the mesons exchanged between the neutron and proton. Therefore, either the nucleon core has an rms radius of 0.8 or the assumption of charge independence is invalid. Since the nucleon Compton wavelength is 0.2, the first possibility seems unlikely. Therefore, it seems necessary to abandon the assumption of charge independence of nucleons if the discrepancy of Fig. 4 is to be removed by postulating a proton rms radius of 0.8 and a smaller neutron in the deuteron.

4. The discrepancy between theory and experiment in Fig. 4 can be removed by assuming a modification of the Coulomb law of interaction between the deuteron and the scattered electrons.[26] This follows from the fact that an electron-scattering experiment measures the potential of the scatterer. A departure of this potential from the Coulomb law has heretofore been interpreted as evidence for a spread-out charge distribution. However, if the Coulomb potential itself is not the correct one at small distances for a point charge, then a different charge distribution would be implied by the electron-scattering experiments. Thus, a suitable modification of the Coulomb potential can be invoked to obtain agreement between experiment and theory in Fig. 4.

VIII. CONCLUSIONS

There is a discrepancy between the charge distribution of the deuteron as determined by the electron-scattering experiments reported here and the charge distribution as inferred from low-energy neutron-proton scattering. This discrepancy is associated only with the charge of the S state of the deuteron. In order to remove the discrepancy, the following three procedures are possible:

1. Increase the effective range of the neutron-proton potential from the presently accepted value of $(1.70 \pm 0.03)\times 10^{-13}$ cm to at least $(2.18\pm 0.15)\times 10^{-13}$ cm. This latter value is 16 ± 5 standard deviations higher than the present value. This procedure entails a re-evaluation of the fundamental nuclear theory used in obtaining the effective range from low-energy neutron-proton scattering experiments.

2. Postulate a point neutron and a proton with rms radius $(0.83\pm 0.17)\times 10^{-13}$ cm as the components of the deuteron. This procedure entails the abandonment of the assumption of the charge independence of the internal structure of nucleons.

3. Assume that the Coulomb law of interaction between the scattered electron and the deuteron is modified at small distances.

Finally, it should be noted that because of the uncertainty in interpreting the experiments, no information can be deduced concerning the shape of the neutron-proton potential.

IX. ACKNOWLEDGMENTS

The author is greatly indebted to Professor Robert Hofstadter, who has conceived and supervised the electron-scattering program at Stanford, for many fruitful discussions and for his continued interest in this problem. Professor D. R. Yennie and Dr. D. G. Ravenhall have been very kind in making clear the theoretical implications of the experiment. Miss Sobhana Dhar has helped greatly in the later stages of taking data and is responsible for a number of the calculations. The author also wishes to thank Mr. V. Z. Jankus for making his deuteron-scattering calculations available as they were obtained, E. E. Chambers, R. W. McAllister, J. H. Fregeau, and B. R. Chambers for information and assistance on experimental problems and Mrs. K. R. Machein for calculating many of the theoretical curves.

The new end-station facilities are the result of the cooperation of many people: Professor R. Hofstadter and Mr. E. L. Rogers designed the magnet spectrometer; Mr. B. Smith of the San Francisco Naval Shipyard supervised the conversion of the gun mount; F. W. Bunker and J. H. Fregeau were responsible for its installation; B. R. Chambers designed and supervised the construction and assembly of the remaining structural components of the system; L. H. Franklin designed and supervised the installation of the electrical system, and E. E. Chambers designed the counting assembly and was responsible for putting the entire system into operation.

Finally, the author thanks the accelerator crew, under the direction of Professor R. F. Mozley, whose efforts have made this experiment possible.

PAPER 36

On the Scattering of High Energy Electrons by Protons.

E. CLEMENTEL and C. VILLI (*)

Istituto di Fisica dell'Università - Padova
Istituto di Fisica dell'Università - Trieste (*)
Istituto Nazionale di Fisica Nucleare - Sezione di Padova

(ricevuto il 10 Settembre 1956)

Recent experiments (1) on the scattering of high energy electrons by protons have given evidence that the measured differential cross-section is larger than that concerning a point proton with no magnetic moment and smaller than the theoretical cross-section for a point proton with anomalous magnetic moment. The two possible explanations of these experimental results are either that the proton is not a point but a structured object or that there is a breakdown of the Coulomb law at short distances (2).

Let us confine ourselves to the former alternative assuming that the proton charge is statistically spread out over a distance of the order of 10^{-13} cm. Because of the extended structure of the proton, a colliding electron feels an effective proton charge e' which is smaller than the natural charge e, as a consequence of the electron penetration into the meson cloud (3). The effective proton charge e' is a decreasing function of the momentum transfer and can be determined from the equation

$$(1) \qquad e' = eF_1(q) ,$$

where

$$(2) \qquad F_1(q) = \int \varrho(\boldsymbol{r}) \exp [i\boldsymbol{q}\cdot\boldsymbol{r}] \mathrm{d}\boldsymbol{r}$$

is the form or penetration factor corresponding to the proton charge density $\varrho(\boldsymbol{r})$ (normalized to 1) and to the momentum q transferred to the recoiling proton. In a system of units where $\hbar = c = 1$, the momentum transfer is given by

$$(3) \qquad q = \frac{2E \sin (\theta/2)}{[1 + (2E/M) \sin^2 (\theta/2)]^{\frac{1}{2}}} ,$$

where E is the energy of the incident electron, θ the scattering angle in the

(1) R. W. MAC ALLISTER and R. HOFSTADTER: *Phys. Rev.*, **102**, 851 (1956).

(2) Proceedings of the Sixth Rochester Conference (1956).

(3) M. N. ROSENBLUTH: *Phys. Rev.*, **79**, 615 (1950).

laboratory system and M the rest mass of the proton.

For sufficiently low energies, i.e. for values of q^{-1} larger than the dimension of the meson cloud, fixed by the density function $\varrho(\boldsymbol{r})$, the exponential in Eq. (2) can be expanded in a rapidly converging series. Assuming $\varrho(\boldsymbol{r})$ as spherically symmetric and taking into account that $(\boldsymbol{q}\cdot\boldsymbol{r})$ is an odd function, the form factor (2), after angular average, can be written as

$$(4)\quad F_1(q) = 1 - \sum_{n=1}^{\infty} (-1)^{n+1} \frac{I_{2n}}{(2n+1)!} q^{2n} ,$$

where I_{2n} is the $2n$-th moment of $\varrho(r)$, i.e.

$$(5)\qquad I_{2n} = \int r^{2n} \varrho(r)\, \mathrm{d}\boldsymbol{r} .$$

It is of interest to see whether the charge density following from the Chew and Low theory ([4]) is in agreement with the electron-proton scattering experiments. To ascertain this point, we have used the proton charge density calculated in one-meson approximation by ZACHARIASEN ([5]) as expectation value $\varrho(r) = \langle\psi|\varrho_{[\mathrm{op}]}|\psi\rangle$ of the meson field charge density operator $\varrho_{[\mathrm{op}]}$ for a static proton in the physical state $|\psi\rangle$. From this distribution ($k_m = 6\mu$) it is found $I_2 = 0.198/\mu^2$ and $I_4 = 0.136/\mu^4$, where $\mu^{-1} = 1.4\cdot10^{-13}$ cm is the Compton wave length of the pion in natural units. The root-mean-square radius of the proton charge distribution is found to be $\langle r^{(2)}\rangle = (I_2)^{\frac{1}{2}} = 0.44/\mu$, a value which is smaller than that determined in ref. ([1]). The charge form factor (4) becomes

$$(6)\quad F_1(q) = 1 - 0.033(q/\mu)^2 + 0.001(q/\mu)^4 .$$

The data of McALLISTER and HOFSTADTER ([1]) at 188 MeV have been compared with the theoretical cross-section

$$(7)\quad \sigma(\theta) = \sigma_{\mathrm{NS}}\{F_1^2 + (q/2M)^2\cdot \cdot[2(F_1 + \mu_P F_2)^2\, \mathrm{tg}^2(\theta/2) + \mu_P^2 F_2^2]\} ,$$

assuming the static magnetic form factor F_2 equal to the charge form factor ([6]). In Eq. (7) $\mu_P = 1.79$ is the proton anomalous magnetic moment and the differential cross-section for a spinless point charge is given by

$$(8)\qquad \sigma_{\mathrm{NS}} = \frac{(e^2/2E)^2\, \mathrm{ctg}^2(\theta/2)\, \csc^2(\theta/2)}{1 + (2E/M)\sin^2(\theta/2)} .$$

The excellent agreement found over all angles between the calculated cross-section and the experimental one gives evidence that the charge density, predicted by the Chew and Low theory, fits the 188 MeV electron-proton scattering experiments with the same value of the coupling constant and the cut-off energy which is needed to fit also the meson-nucleon scattering data. However, since the form factor $F_1(q)$ is almost entirely dependent on the second moment of the charge density, such an evidence is unfortunately weaker than it may appear at first, because the fit obtained using Eq. (6) proves only that the asymptotic behavior of the Zachariasen distribution is in agreement with the data. In fact, inspection of Eq. (5) shows that the factor r^{2n+2} makes the detailed behavior of the charge density less important at short distances than at large ones, where it weights more heavily ([6]). Because of this mathematical circumstance, the influence on the electron-proton differential cross-section of the behavior

([4]) G. CHEW and F. LOW: *Phys. Rev.*, **101**, 1570 (1956).

([5]) F. ZACHARIASEN: *Phys. Rev.*, **102**, 295 (1956).

([6]) This arguments holds also for the electron-neutron interaction since the equivalent square well of depth V_0 and radius r_0 (conventionally) equal to the classical radius of the electron, is proportional to the second moment of the pion cloud charge density: $(-eV_0)_{\pi^-} = (mc^2/2r_0^3)I_2$, where m is the electron rest mass.

at short distances of the proton charge density, predicted by the Chew and Low theory, is practically suppressed in fitting the 188 MeV scattering data. As far as the check of the theory is concerned, it is more significant to examine scattering experiments for which the ratio q/k_m is larger than 1, because obviously in this case the fit cannot be independent of the short distance behavior of the charge distribution. Using in the form factor (2) the Zachariasen distribution, it is found that, at the highest available energy of 550 MeV (2), the agreement between the experimental data and the cross-section (7) ($F_1 = F_2$) is not as good as at 188 MeV. The discrepancy of about 35% for large momentum transfer points out that the experiments do not warrant the examined proton charge density, evaluated in one-meson approximation (7) assuming as negligible the contributions of all meson-nucleon states but the resonant one, and confirms that the successful result obtained at 188 MeV neither involves the physical content of the Chew and Low theory nor the reliability of the approximations used in deriving the charge density, but is largely independent of both.

In view of future more detailed investigations, the following attempt to interpret the high energy electron-proton scattering experiments along a different line, is believed to be of some interest.

Since the conjectured failure of the electrodynamics at short distances or the insufficiency of the assumption that the interacting particles are structureless can be accounted for by properly modifying the photon propagation function, we summarize these two alternatives assuming, in the spirit od STUECKELBERG's idea of compensation (8), that the Coulomb potential, experienced by the electron colliding with a proton, is given by

$$V(r) = (e/r)\{1 - \eta \exp[-k_m r]\}\,, \tag{9}$$

where η and k_m are two unknown parameters (9). For $\eta = 1$, the cut-off for the photon propagation function implied by the static potential (9) readily follows from the one suggested by FEYNMAN (10).

Let us indicate with e'' the effective electron charge, which accounts for radiative corrections to scattering (11), and assume $e''V(r)$ as the electron-proton interaction energy. The Born approximation cross-section, calculated with this interaction energy, identifies with the Mott-Rutherford formula, modified by ROSENBLUTH (3), provided we define the effective proton charge according to Eq. (1), where the form factor in this case turns out to be

$$F_1(q) = \frac{k_m^2 + (1-\eta)q^2}{k_m^2 + q^2}\,. \tag{10}$$

The potential (9) does not necessarily imply a failure of the electrodynamics at distances $r < k_m^{-1}$ if one assumes that the extended structure of the proton is ruled by the unknown parameter k_m according to the following relation

$$\varrho(\boldsymbol{r}) = (\eta k_m^2/4\pi r)\cdot \exp[-k_m r] - (\eta - 1)\,\delta(\boldsymbol{r})\,. \tag{11}$$

Let us consider the case $\eta = 1$. Then, from Eq. (10), or substituting into Eq. (4) the $2n$-th moment $I_{2n} = (2n+1)!\cdot(\eta/k_m^{2n})$ of the proton charge density (11),

(7) The reliability of this approximation is discussed by M. CINI and S. FUBINI: *Nuovo Cimento*, **3**, 764 (1956).

(8) B. STUECKELBERG: *Helv. Phys. Acta*, **14**, 51 (1941); A. PAIS: *Phys. Rev.*, **69**, 125 (1946); S. SAKATA and H. UMEZAWA: *Progr. Theor. Phys.*, **5**, 682 (1950).

(9) This potential has been used also by VACHASPASTI in connection with the scattering of electrons by nuclei (*Phys. Rev.*, **93**, 502 (1954)).

(10) R. P. FEYNMAN: *Phys. Rev.*, **76**, 769 (1949).

(11) J. SCHWINGER: *Phys. Rev.*, **76**, 813 (1949).

it is found for $q/k_m < 1$

$$(12) \qquad F_1(q) = 1 - \sum_{n=1}^{\infty} (-1)^{n+1} (q/k_m)^{2n} ,$$

which identifies with the form factor (6) assuming $k_m \cong 5.6\ \mu$; i.e. using the charge density (11) with $\eta = 1$, it is not only possible to fit the electron-proton scattering data at 188 MeV equally well as with the Zachariasen distribution, although the considered charge density diverges at the origin, but the fit itself can be obtained provided the unknown parameter k_m assumes a cut-off value very close to that required by the Chew and Low theory. However, the charge density (11) with $\eta = 1$ is in disagreement over all angles with the 550 MeV data, because of the too slow decrease of the form factor (10) with increasing momentum transfer [12].

A consistent picture of the experimental data both at 188 MeV and at 550 MeV can be obtained assuming $\eta \neq 1$. The 188 MeV data are fairly well reproduced with $k_m = 6\ \mu$ and $\eta = 1.5$. The root-mean-square radius of the proton charge density (11) turns out to be $\langle r^{(2)} \rangle = (I_2)^{\frac{1}{2}} = 0.7 \cdot 10^{-13}$ cm, in close agreement with the value given by MacAllister and Hofstadter [1]. Using the same value of k_m and η, the 550 MeV data are also very well reproduced. The Stanford scattering experiments seem therefore to suggest that the electron-proton potential changes sign at the interparticle separation $r^* \cong 0.07/\mu$ and that the spatial extension of the proton charge is ruled by the parameter k_m^{-1}, which is closer to the Compton wave length of the nucleon rather than of the pion.

Whether the electron-proton interaction can be realistically described in terms of the potential (9), could be tested experimentally when higher electron energies will become available. In fact, from the form factor (10) it appears clearly that for momentum transfer $q = q_c = k_m/(\eta - 1)^{\frac{1}{2}}$ a very peculiar situation is to be expected, namely, the electron-proton differential cross-section will appear as a monotonically decreasing function of the angle θ for $q < q_c$, reaching the value zero for $q = q_c$, and then *increasing* slowly afterwards. For electron energies higher than a critical energy E_c, the condition $q = q_c$ fixes a critical angle θ_c at which $\sigma(\theta_c) = 0$. This critical angle is a decreasing function of

---

[12] For $\eta = 1$, the potential (9) may formally be derived either from the Bopp generalized electrodynamics (V. F. Bopp: *Ann. der Phys.*, **38**, 345 (1940); P. Podolsky and R. Schwed: *Rev. Mod. Phys.*, **20**, 40 (1948)) or from the de Broglie's theory of mixed fields (*Journ. de Phys. et Rad.*, **11**, 481 (1950)). The electron-proton data at 550 MeV give therefore evidence against these generalizations of electrodynamics. It is however interesting to point out that the fourth order Bopp equation for a point source is formally equivalent to the second order Poisson equation for a Yukawa density function (Eq. (11); $\eta = 1$). The important point is that a generalized electrodynamics leads to a charge form factor although the source is assumed to be a δ-function. This can be easily seen assuming that the potential $V(r)$ is spherically symmetric. In this case the form factor can be written in the following general form

$$F_1(q) = (1/4\pi e) \int \nabla^2 V(r) \exp [i\boldsymbol{q} \cdot \boldsymbol{r}]\, \mathrm{d}\boldsymbol{r} .$$

Eq. (2) is therefore a special case valid when $\nabla^2 V(r) = 4\pi e \varrho(r)$. For instance, in case of the Bopp equation the form factor is given by

$$F_1(q) = 1 + (k_m^{-2}/4\pi e) \int \nabla^2 \nabla^2 V(r) \exp [i\boldsymbol{q} \cdot \boldsymbol{r}]\, \mathrm{d}\boldsymbol{r} ,$$

from which Eq. (10) can be derived using the potential (9). Because of the equivalence between a point source field obeying a generalized (linear or non-linear) equation and an extended source field obeying a second order differential equation, the electron-proton scattering experiments will hardly discriminate the two possible alternatives: (*a*) point-like source and failure of the electrodynamics, (*b*) extended source and validity of electrodynamics.

the electron energy. For instance, assuming as above $k_m = 6\mu$ and $\eta = 1.5$, it is found $E_c \simeq 1.05$ GeV; for $E = 1.1$ GeV and $E = 1.3$ GeV the electron-proton differential cross-section goes to zero at $\theta_c = 140^\circ$ and at $\theta_c = 90^\circ$ respectively. The critical condition implying the proton effective charge e' to be zero, is in this case $q_c = 1.4 k_m$. This result is in many ways interesting, mainly because this value of q_c is very close to the cut-off $(= 1.4M)$ for the photon propagation function required to reproduce the proton-neutron mass difference [13].

Note added in proof: In a paper appeared recently in the *Rev. Mod. Phys.*, **28**, 214 (1956) ideas similar to those suggested in this note have been extensively discussed albo by prof. R. HOFSTADTER.

---

(13) R. P. FEYNMAN and G. SPEISEMAN: *Phys. Rev.*, **94**, 500 (1954).

PAPER 37

Inelastic and Elastic Scattering of 187-Mev Electrons from Selected Even-Even Nuclei*

RICHARD H. HELM†
High-Energy Physics Laboratory, Stanford University, Stanford, California
(Received August 27, 1956)

A survey has been made of the differential scattering cross sections for 187-Mev electrons on the even-even nuclei $_{12}Mg^{24}$, $_{14}Si^{28}$, $_{16}S^{32}$, $_{18}A^{40}$, and $_{38}Sr^{88}$. It has been possible to separate the elastic scattering from the inelastic in all cases and to resolve the inelastic groups from specific nuclear levels for at least one level in all cases. A simple Born-approximation analysis of the elastic data yields values of the effective radii and surface thicknesses of the nuclear charge densities which (if suitably corrected for failure of the Born approximation) are in substantial agreement with the results of Hahn, Ravenhall, and Hofstadter; i.e., a radius parameter of $c \cong 1.08\ A^{\frac{1}{3}} \times 10^{-13}$ cm (radius to half-maximum of the charge distribution) and a surface thickness of $t \cong 2.5 \times 10^{-13}$ cm (thickness from 10% to 90% of the maximum of the charge distribution). Phenomenological analysis of the inelastic scattering along the lines laid down by Schiff yields some tentative multipolarity assignments, and application of some results of Ravenhall yields estimates of (radiative) partial level widths; for the $E2$ transitions these correspond to lifetimes of $\sim 19 \times 10^{-13}$ sec (Mg 1.37 Mev) to $\sim 1.4 \times 10^{-13}$ sec (Sr 1.85 Mev). The observed strengths of the transitions are compared to those predicted by Weisskopf theory.

I. INTRODUCTION

THE elastic scattering of high-energy electrons by atomic nuclei has been the subject of considerable experimental study.[1–8] Recently it has been possible in this laboratory to observe certain examples of inelastic scattering[9–11] in which the incident high-energy electron is scattered with the loss of a discrete quantum of energy corresponding to the excitation of a level in the target nucleus.

The present experiments were initiated as a survey of the inelastic and elastic scattering from even-even nuclei in the region of intermediate atomic numbers. These target materials were chosen for a number of reasons: First, most of them are known from gamma-ray spectroscopy, angular correlations, etc., to have easily excited low-lying levels with spacings on the order of a few Mev, which should be resolvable in an experiment of the type of Fregeau and Hofstadter.[11] Second, the principal isotope of most of these elements occurs in high abundance, so that the natural form may be used in the targets. Third, the ground state has zero spin and even parity in the known cases (see, e.g., Endt and Kluyver[12] and probably in all cases (i.e., from shell-structure arguments); furthermore, it usually happens[12–14] that one or more or the lower levels has known total angular momentum and a parity consistent with electric-type multipole transitions from the ground state. This last point is important because the

* The research reported in this document was supported jointly by the U. S. Navy (Office of Naval Research) and the U. S. Atomic Energy Commission, and by the U. S. Air Force through the Air Force Office of Scientific Research, Air Research and Development Command.

† Now at the University of California Los Alamos Scientific Laboratory, Los Alamos, New Mexico.

1 Hanson, Lyman, and Scott, Phys. Rev. **84**, 626, 638 (1951).
2 H. R. Fechter (unpublished).
3 Hofstadter, Fechter, and McIntyre, Phys. Rev. **91**, 422 (1953).
4 Hofstadter, Fechter, and McIntyre, Phys. Rev. **92**, 978 (1953).
5 Hofstadter, Hahn, Knudsen, and McIntyre, Phys. Rev. **95**, 512 (1954).
6 R. Hofstadter and R. W. McAllister, Phys. Rev. **98**, 217 (1955).
7 R. W. Pidd and C. L. Hammer, Phys. Rev. **99**, 1396 (1955).
8 Hahn, Ravenhall, and Hofstadter, Phys. Rev. **101**, 1131 (1956).
9 McIntyre, Hahn, and Hofstadter, Phys. Rev. **94**, 1084 (1954).
10 J. A. McIntyre and R. Hofstadter, Phys. Rev. **98**, 158 (1955).
11 J. H. Fregeau and R. Hofstadter, Phys. Rev. **99**, 1503 (1955).
12 P. M. Endt and J. C. Kluyver, Revs. Modern Phys. **26**, 94 (1954).
13 F. Ajzenberg and T. Lauritsen, Revs. Modern Phys. **24**, 321 (1952).
14 B. B. Kinsey and G. A. Bartholomew, Can. J. Phys. **31**, 1051 (1953); G. R. Bishop and J. P. Perez y Jorba, Phys. Rev. **98**, 89 (1955).

electric transitions should be particularly easily interpreted theoretically,[15,16] at least phenomenologically, and therefore should be valuable in checking the theory.

While this work was intended primarily to be a preliminary survey, it was anticipated that considerable information could be derived from the results. The elastic-scattering angular distribution should give information as to the radial dependence of the nuclear charge distributions.[3–5,8,17–23] The inelastic cross sections, if measured accurately enough over wide enough ranges of scattering angle and energy of the incident electrons, should enable one (a) to determine the multipolarity and electric or magnetic character of the transitions[24] which will supplement γ- and β-ray work and Coulomb excitation in assigning angular momentum and parity to the various states; (b) to determine the magnitude and shape of the transition charge density and hence obtain considerable information about the various wave functions; (c) to derive a number of interesting parameters such as the transition probabilities (or level widths). Such a complete analysis is beyond the scope of the present work. However, it has been possible to decide with fair certainty that several observed transitions are electric monopole, quadrupole, or octupole where this was not previously known, and to estimate the transition probability and certain gross features of the transition charge density in the known electric-quadrupole cases.

II. EXPERIMENTAL METHOD

The experiments were performed at the first halfway station of the Stanford Mark III linear accelerator, using the magnetically analyzed and deflected electron beam and the 16-in. magnetic spectrometer. The accelerator,[25] and the spectrometer and its associated counting and beam monitoring equipment including a number of recent improvements are described in earlier articles.[2–6,8–11]

The important physical properties of the various targets are summarized in Table I. With the exception

TABLE I. Target parameters.

Element	Principal isotope: Mass No.	Principal isotope: Percent abundance	Target thickness, gross: Inches	Target thickness, gross: g/cm^2	Target thickness, gross: Radiation lengths	$10^{-22}\times$No. atoms per cm^2	$10^{-22}\times$No. atoms/cm^2, principal isotope
$_{12}Mg^{24}$	24	78.8	0.13	0.570	1.93×10^{-2}	1.42	1.12
$_{14}Si^{28}$	28	92.2	0.70	0.41	1.62×10^{-2}	0.885	0.816
$_{16}S^{32}$	32	95.0	0.118	0.588	2.64×10^{-2}	1.11	1.05
$_{38}Sr^{88}$	88	82.7	0.050	0.33	2.94×10^{-2}	0.23	0.19
			0.100	0.66	5.96×10^{-2}	0.46	0.38
$_{18}A^{40}$	40	99.6	...	...	...	...	...
CH_2	1	14.3	0.119	0.275	0.55×10^{-2}	...	2.38

of the argon, which was used in a high-pressure gas target chamber,[26] all the targets were in the form of wafers, roughly 1 in. by 2 in. in size. Surface densities were found by weighing and measuring with a precision of a few percent; the uncertainty in the Si target thickness was slightly greater, possibly 5% because of visible pits in the material. The CH_2 (polyethelene) target was used for an "absolute" cross-section calibration in the manner described by Fregeau and Hofstadter.[11]

The spectra of electrons scattered at various angles were taken as described in previous publications.[2–6,8–11] Typical spectrometer curves are shown in Fig. 1. They are seen to be characterized by an elastic peak and one or more resolved or partially resolved inelastic peaks, shifted downward from the elastic peak by the characteristic excitation energies of the corresponding nuclear levels. The widths of the peaks (i.e., with at half-maximum) are well explained by the combined effects of beam energy spread, spectrometer resolution setting, beam size, and ionization straggling in the target; however, while the fold of these effects is an essentially Gaussian shape, the observed peaks are broader at the base than is a Gaussian (probably because of scattering from the spectrometer vacuum chamber, exit port, etc.) and have a long, low-energy tail resulting from radiation processes in the target. In subtracting the tail of the elastic peak from the inelastic peaks it usually has been sufficient to fit an empirical tail of the form $A(E_0-E)^{-1}+B(E_0-E)^{-2}$ and to adjust the parameters until the various peaks of a given spectrometer curve have the same shape after the subtraction.

In principle, the relative intensities of the peaks should be subject to a number of corrections: (1) correction for isotopic abundance, since all isotopes will contribute to the elastic peak but only the principal isotope will contribute to the inelastic peaks; (2) the variation of spectrometer "window width" with energy setting should be taken into account (i.e., $\Delta E\sim E$); (3) the effects of finite resolution in angle ($\sim\pm1.8°$) and energy (0.5–1.0 Mev) on the angular distributions; (4) effects of plural scattering (the $n=2,3\cdots$ terms in

[15] L. I. Schiff, Phys. Rev. **96**, 765 (1954).
[16] C. J. Mullin and E. Guth, Phys. Rev. **98**, 277(A) (1955).
[17] E. Guth, Anz. Akad. Wiss. Wien, Math.-naturw. Kl. **24**, 299 (1934); Thie, Mullin, and Guth, Phys. Rev. **87**, 962 (1952).
[18] M. E. Rose, Phys. Rev. **73**, 279 (1948).
[19] J. H. Smith, Cornell University, Ph.D. thesis, 1951 (unpublished).
[20] L. R. B. Elton, Proc. Phys. Soc. (London) **A63**, 1115 (1950); **A65**, 481 (1952); Phys. Rev. **79**, 412 (1950).
[21] Yennie, Ravenhall, and Wilson, Phys. Rev. **95**, 500 (1954).
[22] L. I. Schiff, Phys. Rev. **92**, 988 (1953).
[23] G. E. Brown and L. R. B. Elton, Phil Mag. **46**, 164 (1955).
[24] D. G. Ravenhall (to be published).
[25] R. B. Neal, Stanford University Microwave Laboratory Technical Report No. 185 (unpublished); Chodorow, Ginzton, Hansen, Kyhl, Neal, and Panofsky, Rev. Sci. Instr. **26**, 134 (1955); McIntyre, Kyhl, and Panofsky, Stanford University Microwave Laboratory Technical Report No. 202 (unpublished); W. K. H. Panofsky and J. A. McIntyre, Rev. Sci. Instr. **25**, 287 (1954); G. W. Tautfest and H. R. Fechter, Phys. Rev. **96**, 35 (1954).
[26] Hofstadter, McAllister, and Wiener, Phys. Rev. **96**, 854(A) (1954).

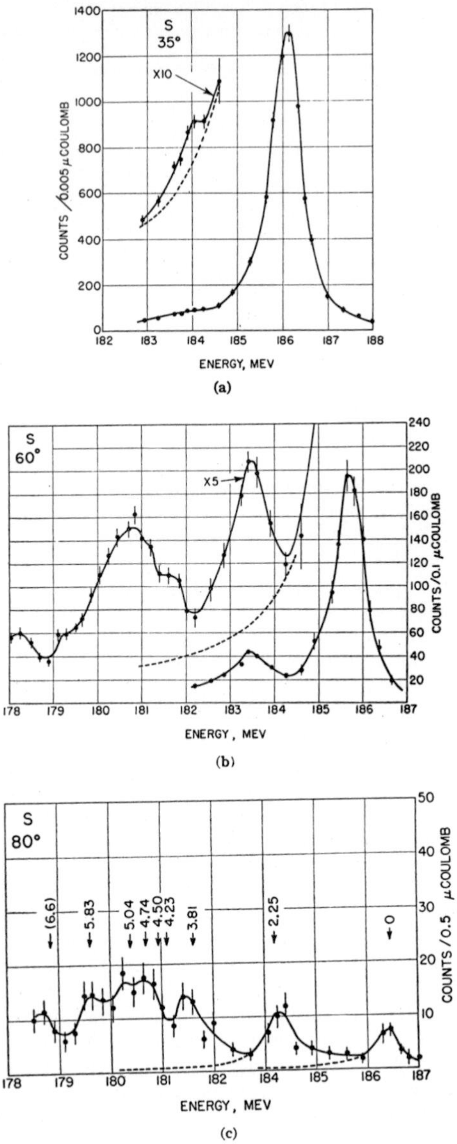

FIG. 1. Spectrometer curves: 187-Mev electrons on S.

the Molière[27] series); (5) corrections for Schwinger[28] and bremsstrahlung radiation. Effect (1) amounts to up to 26% (Mg). Effect (2) is generally negligible in view of the small shifts of inelastic peaks relative to the incident energy. Effect (3) estimated in the manner of Hanson, Lyman, and Scott[1] amounts to perhaps 5% in the region of the diffraction minima and has been been ignored. Plural scattering (4) is estimated[29] to contribute <1% to the observed scattered intensities.

Of the radiation corrections (5), the Schwinger effect is estimated to decrease the observed intensity by ~8% at small angles to ~20% at large angles, and the bremsstrahlung in typical cases is estimated[30] to decrease the intensities by ~20% at small angles to ~40% at large angles. The radiation corrections have not been applied in analyzing the data, and the following remarks should be made: (a) the corrections vary slowly with angle and therefore will affect mainly the absolute cross sections; (b) the bremsstrahlung correction should be applied to both the "measured" and "calculated" cross sections (see Table II for explanation) but the "measured" cross sections already have been corrected for Schwinger effect (because the proton cross sections used in this calibration have been corrected) while the "calculated" cross section has not; (c) the main effect of ignoring the angular dependence of the radiation corrections will be a slight overestimate of the surface thickness parameters of the nuclear charge densities (see Secs. III, IV).

III. ANALYSIS OF ELASTIC DATA

It is convenient to analyze the scattering cross sections by means of the Born approximation.[31] The exact calculations of Yennie, *et al.*[21] show that although the Born approximation is considerably in error for high-energy electrons in medium-to-high atomic-numbered elements, it is probably still accurate enough to account for most of the important features of the scattering.

The Born approximation result, as used here, is given in terms of a nuclear form factor, F:

$$d\sigma/d\Omega=(d\sigma/d\Omega)_{\text{point}}|F|^2, \tag{1}$$

$$F(\mathbf{q})=\int \rho(\mathbf{r})e^{i\mathbf{q}\cdot\mathbf{r}}d^3\mathbf{r}. \tag{2}$$

Here $(d\sigma/d\Omega)_{\text{point}}$ is the differential scattering cross section of a point charge Ze; $\mathbf{q}$ is the momentum transfer of the electron in the scattering process; and $\rho(\mathbf{r})$ is the probability density of the charge distribution, normalized so that $\int\rho(\mathbf{r})d^3\mathbf{r}=1$.

For the point-charge cross section, it is not clear whether one should use the Born-approximation, or an exact calculation of the type made by Feshbach.[32] As suggested by Schiff,[22] the correct function may be something between these. In the present case, the

[27] G. Molière, Z. Naturforsch. **3a**, 78 (1948).

[28] J. Schwinger, Phys. Rev. **75**, 898 (1949); H. Suura, Phys. Rev. **99**, 1020 (1955).

[29] H. A. Bethe and J. Ashkin, *Experimental Nuclear Physic* edited by E. Segrè (John Wiley and Sons, Inc., New York, 1953 Vol. I, p. 290.

[30] Using the radiation straggling expressions given by W. Heitler, *The Quantum Theory of Radiation* (Clarendon Press, Oxford, 1954), third edition, p. 378.

[31] For bibliography of Born approximation in electron scattering, see reference 22.

[32] H. Feshback, Phys. Rev. **88**, 295 (1952).

TABLE II. "Calculated cross sections": experimental angular distributions, expressed in absolute units by fitting elastic data to cross sections calculated from the gU charge distributions (Sec. III).

(a) Calculated cross sections in Mg^{24} and Si^{28} in units of 10^{-30} cm². To convert to the measured cross sections (Sec. IV), multiply the Mg data by 1.28 (±10%) and the Si data by 1.06 (±10%).

Angle	$_{12}Mg^{24}$ Elastic	$_{12}Mg^{24}$ 1.37 Mev	$_{14}Si^{28}$ Elastic	$_{14}Si^{28}$ 1.78 Mev
40°	426 ±14	22.2 ±3.2	382 ±11	6.5 ±0.8
50°	74.5 ± 1.0	8.9 ±1.3	61 ± 3	4.50 ±0.60
60°	15.0 ± 0.5	3.9 ±0.7	10.3 ± 0.2	2.39 ±0.14
70°	1.61 ± 0.10	1.44 ±0.11	1.13 ± 0.08	0.76 ±0.08
80°	0.24 ± 0.02	0.52 ±0.04	0.11 ± 0.02	0.24 ±0.02
90°	0.065± 0.029	0.15 ±0.03	0.012 ± 0.006	0.074±0.012
100°	0.014± 0.003	0.042±0.006	...	...
110°	...	...	0.0075± 0.0019	0.012±0.002

(b) Calculated cross sections in S^{32} in units of 10^{-30} cm². To convert to measured cross sections, multiply by 1.41 (±10%).

Angle	Elastic	2.25 Mev	3.81 Mev	5.83 Mev	6.6 Mev[a]
35°	1250 ±23	17 ±3	...	...	...
40°	480 ±15	10.3 ±1.2	3.5 ±1.2	4.1 ±0.9	...
50°	69 ± 1.5	4.4 ±0.4	...	...	...
60°	8.55 ± 0.35	1.22 ±0.08	0.34 ±0.05	0.27 ±0.06	0.13 ±0.05
70°	0.81 ± 0.06	0.225 ±0.032	0.17 ±0.06	0.14 ±0.06	0.12 ±0.05
80°	0.050± 0.007	0.083 ±0.012	0.076±0.024	0.059±0.024	0.047±0.024
85°	0.060± 0.008	0.052 ±0.008	...	...	...
90°	0.055± 0.005	0.026 ±0.006	0.012±0.006	0.028±0.011	0.014±0.007
100°	0.040± 0.006	0.0079±0.0024	0.006±0.003	0.015±0.005	0.019±0.005
110°	0.011± 0.003	...	...	...	...

(c) Calculated cross sections in A^{40} in units of 10^{-30} cm². To correct to measured cross sections, multiply by 1.1 (±14%).

Angle	Elastic	1.46 Mev	2.4 Mev
50°	57	10.5 ±1.9	1.6 ±0.9
60°	5.9	1.4 ±0.1	0.63±0.08
70°	0.36	0.32±0.07	...

(d) Calculated cross sections in Sr^{88} in units of 10^{-33} cm². To convert to measured cross sections, multiply by 2.05 (±10%).

Angle	Elastic	1.85 Mev	2.76 Mev	4.3 Mev[a]
35°	2640 ±100	...	...	...
40°	538 ± 16	17.2 ±1.4	13.5 ±1.3	3.7 ±0.7
45°	158 ± 8	...	...	...
50°	35.7 ± 1.7	3.1 ±0.4	5.1 ±0.4	1.27±0.24
55°	18.0 ± 1.1	...	...	...
60°	10.8 ± 0.5	0.41±0.12	1.81 ±0.13	0.74±0.12
70°	5.0 ± 0.3	0.30±0.11	0.53 ±0.10	0.37±0.10
80°	1.38± 0.10	0.11±0.05	0.168±0.048	0.12±0.04

[a] This level has not been reported previously, and may represent impurities (see Sec. VI).

choice is not critical, and the Feshbach results have been used (see Figs. 2 and 3).

In fitting the experimental data, it has proved convenient to use a "folded" charge distribution, given by

$$\rho(\mathbf{r})=\int \rho_0(\mathbf{r}')\rho_1(\mathbf{r}-\mathbf{r}')d^3\mathbf{r}', \quad (3)$$

where

$$\int \rho(\mathbf{r})d^3\mathbf{r}=\int \rho_0(\mathbf{r})d^3\mathbf{r}=\int \rho_1(\mathbf{r})d^3\mathbf{r}=1.$$

When (3) is substituted in (2), it follows that

$$F(\mathbf{q})=F_0(\mathbf{q})F_1(\mathbf{q}), \quad (4)$$

where F_0 and F_1 result from the substitution of ρ_0 and ρ_1, respectively, in Eq. (2). The advantage of this is that one can use trial functions of such a form that, for example, ρ_0 essentially defines the nuclear radius and ρ_1 a surface thickness; the resulting form factor is then readily calculated for different ratios of the two parameters.

As is shown by Hahn *et al.*,[8] the scattering at these energies depends mainly on the shape of the charge distribution near the surface and is relatively insensitive to the distribution at the center of the nucleus. Hence, it is sufficient to take for $\rho_0(r)$ a uniform distribution of radius $R\sim r_0A^{\frac{1}{3}}$, where $r_0\sim 1.2\times 10^{-13}$ cm; it is then assumed that $\rho_1(r)$ is a (spherically symmetric) distribution of effective radius $\sim r_0$. The following two models will be considered:

$$\rho_0=\begin{cases}3/4\pi R^3, & r<R\\ 0, & r>R,\end{cases} \quad (5)$$

and

$$\rho_1(r)=(2\pi g^2)^{-\frac{3}{2}}\exp(-r^2/2g^2), \quad (6)$$

or

$$\rho_1(r)=\begin{cases}3/4\pi u^3, & r<u\\ 0, & r>u.\end{cases} \quad (7)$$

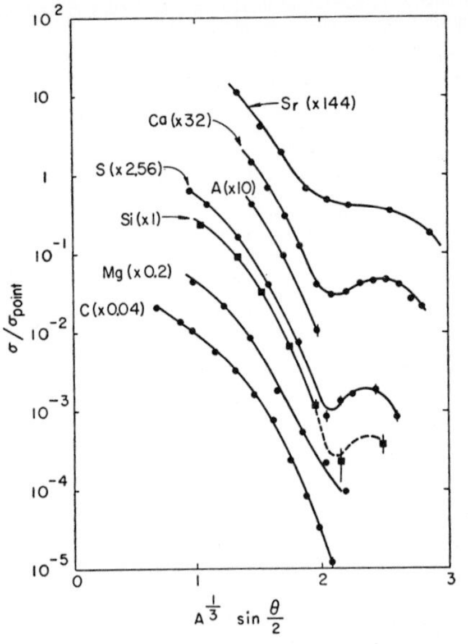

FIG. 2. Elastic angular distributions (observed cross sections divided by Feshbach point-charge cross sections). The results of Hahn *et al.* (reference 8) for Ca and of Fregeau and Hofstadter (reference 11) for C are included for comparison.

Substitutions of (5) and (6) in (3) will be termed a "Gaussian-uniform" or gU distribution, and substitution of (5) and (7) will be termed "uniform-uniform" or uU.

For comparison with other work, the rms radii will be calculated and expressed in terms of r_0[33]:

$$r_0 = A^{-\frac{1}{3}} R_0,$$

$$R_0^2 = (5/3)\int r^2\rho(r)d^3\mathbf{r} = (5/3)(\langle r^2\rangle_0 + \langle r^2\rangle_1), \quad (8)$$

where

$$\langle r^2\rangle_{0,1} = \int r^2\rho_{0,1}(r)d^3\mathbf{r}.$$

It is known from the work of Yennie *et al.*[21] that, while the Born approximation fails completely in the region of the zeros predicted by discontinuous distributions such as (5), it is quite accurate for values of $qR < 90\%$ of its value at the first zero, and again in the region midway between the successive zeros.

The data-fitting procedure which has been adopted consists of choosing several values of R, and for each one picking the value of R/g or R/u which best fits the calculated $|F|^2$ to the experimental $|F|^2$. Because the data are rather scanty and because the Born approximation is not very accurate, least-square fits were not attempted; the best fits were chosen by inspection. It is felt that the subjective bias introduced by this procedure is at least qualitatively unimportant in showing how the parameters vary from element to element. Typical "best fits" of the form factors of two charge distributions to the data are shown in Fig. 4.

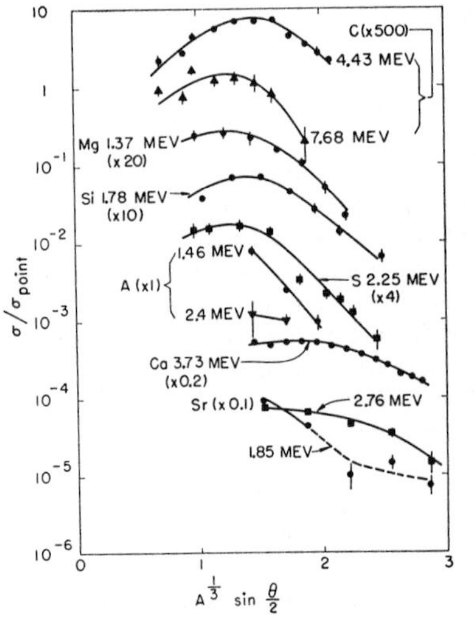

FIG. 3. Inelastic angular distributions (observed cross section divided by Feshback point-charge cross sections). The results of Hahn *et al.* (reference 8) for Ca and of Fregeau and Hofstadter (reference 11) are included for comparison.

IV. RESULTS: ELASTIC DATA

(The data of Hahn, *et al.*[8] for calcium and of Fregeau and Hofstadter[11] for carbon are included for purposes of comparison.) It is seen from Table III that the radial and surface-thickness parameters differ appreciably with choice of model but are quite constant as a function of A and Z for a given model. Thus, for the gU model, $r_0 \cong (1.35 \pm 0.04)\times 10^{-13}$ cm, and $g \cong (1.0 \pm 0.1)\times 10^{-13}$ cm for all elements investigated; for the uU model, $r_0 \cong (1.32 \pm 0.04)\times 10^{-13}$ cm and $u \cong (2.0 \pm 0.3)\times 10^{-13}$ cm. The variations of the surface-thickness parameter from element to element (Table III), are greater than the estimated errors, have roughly the same form for both models, and may be real. The rms radius possibly varies slowly with A and Z but the variation is smooth within the estimated experimental accuracy. It should be noted, of course, that any smooth variation of the parameters with Z and A may be related to the worsening of the Born approximation in heavier nuclei.

It is interesting to note the remarkable agreement between the two models for the values of the parameters r_1 and t (see Table IV). Hahn *et al.*[8] also noticed that these parameters are nearly independent of the model used.

Some insight as to the validity of using the Born

[33] This definition is equivalent to the r_0 of Hahn *et al.*, reference 8.

approximation to derive these parameters can be gained by comparison with the exact calculations of Hahn *et al.*[8] Note that the Fermi smoothed-uniform shape

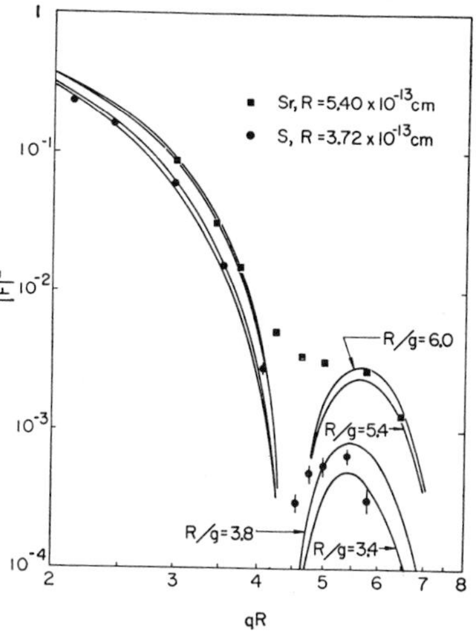

(a)

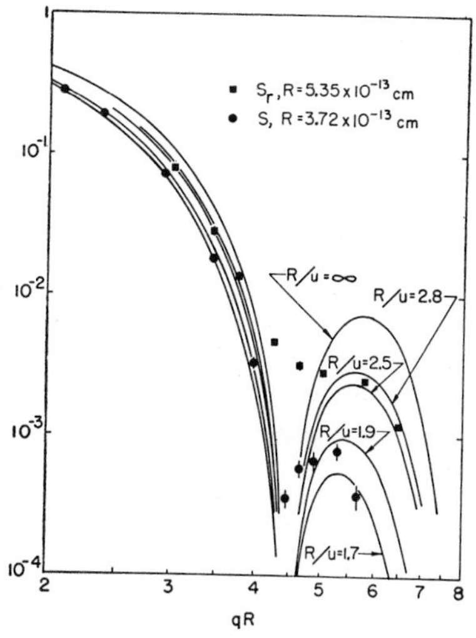

(b)

FIG. 4. Typical "best fits" of squared experimental form factors to calculated squared form factors, showing how a variation of 5–10% of the surface-thickness parameter from its "best" value gives noticeably worse fits. Variation of the radial parameter R by 2–3% either way also makes the fit worse for all choices of the surface-thickness parameter.

used by Hahn *et al.* somewhat resembles the models used in the present analysis. Thus for calcium, using the scattering data of Hahn *et al.*,

TABLE III. Parameters for gU and uU charge distributions.

(a) Parameters for gU charge distribution. The quantities R and g are defined in Sec. IV; r_0, r_1, and t as in Hahn *et al.* (reference 8): $r_0 = A^{-1/3} \times \langle (5/3) r^2 \rangle^{\frac{1}{2}}$; $r_1 = A^{-1/3} c$; where c is the radius to half-maximum of charge distribution, t is the surface thickness from 10% to 90% of maximum of charge density. Accuracy: R, r_0, and r_1, ~2–3%; g and t, ~5–10%. Values are given in units of 10^{-13} cm.

Element	$A^{-1/3}R$	g	r_0	r_1	t	Corrected for Born approximation[a] r_0	r_1	t
C^{12}	1.10	0.90	1.39	0.97	2.3	1.35	0.95	2.2
Mg^{24}	1.14	1.03	1.39	1.03	2.7	1.33	0.99	2.6
Si^{28}	1.12	1.07	1.35	1.01	2.9	1.29	0.97	2.8
S^{32}	1.17	1.01	1.37	1.08	2.7	1.30	1.03	2.6
Ca^{40}	1.20	0.93	1.85	1.14	2.5	1.28	1.08	2.4
Sr^{88}	1.20	0.95	1.30	1.17	2.5	1.20	1.08	2.3

(b) Parameters for uU charge distribution. The quantities R and u are as defined in Sec. IV; r_0, r_1, and t as in Hahn *et al.* [reference 8, and (a) of this table]. Values are given in units of 10^{-13} cm. Accuracy: R, r_0, and r_1, ~2–3%: u and t, ~10%.

Element	$A^{-1/3}R$	u	r_0	r_1	t	Corrected for Born approximation[a] r_0	r_1	t
C^{12}	1.11	1.7	1.33	0.96	2.1	1.29	0.93	2.0
Mg^{24}	1.13	2.3	1.35	0.97	2.85	1.30	0.93	2.0
Si^{28}	1.14	2.2	1.35	1.03	2.7	1.29	0.99	2.6
S^{32}	1.17	2.1	1.34	1.08	2.6	1.28	1.03	2.5
Ca^{40}	1.20	2.0	1.34	1.14	2.5	1.27	1.08	2.4
Sr^{88}	1.20	2.0(5)	1.28	1.15	2.4	1.18	1.06	2.3

[a] Correction factor $[1+(3Z\alpha/2kR)]^{-1}$; see Sec. IV.

(i) gU and uU model (Born approximation):

$$r_1 = (1.14 \pm 0.02) \times 10^{-13} \text{ cm},$$

$$t = (2.5 \pm 0.1) \times 10^{-13} \text{ cm};$$

(ii) Fermi smoothed-uniform (exact calculation)[8]:

$$r_1 = (1.06 \pm 0.02) \times 10^{-13} \text{ cm},$$

$$t = (2.5 \pm 0.1) \times 10^{-13} \text{ cm}.$$

The greater-than-probable difference in r_1 may be due in part to the use of different models, but probably also is related to the use of the Born approximation, which, because its neglects the modifications of the incident plane wave by the attractive potential of the nucleus, tends to give slightly larger values of the nuclear radii than do exact calculations. An estimate of this effect based on a uniform charge distribution shows

TABLE IV. Parameters associated with inelastic scattering. Indicated errors in β_l have been estimated roughly in fitting calculated squared form factors to the data (see Sec. V). Relative errors of Γ, τ and $|M|^2$ are roughly the same as for β_l. See Sec. V for definitions.

Element	Energy Mev	J, parity	$\beta_l(I_i,I_f)$	$\Gamma_l(I_f \to I_i)$ millivolts	τ_r seconds	$\|M\|^2$
C^{12}	4.43	2+	0.40 ±0.08	12.5	0.53×10^{-13}	2.3
Mg^{24}	1.37	2+	0.34 ±0.03	0.34	19×10^{-13}	9.1
Si^{28}	1.78	2+	0.18 ±0.03	1.1	6.0×10^{-13}	6.1
S^{32}	2.25	(2+)[a]	0.11 ±0.01	4.0	1.6×10^{-13}	5.8
A^{40}	2.4	(2+)[b]	0.025±0.005	2.0	3.3×10^{-13}	1.8
Ca^{40}	3.73	(3−)[a]	0.125±0.005	0.0093	0.71×10^{-10}	7.7
Sr^{88}	1.85	2+	0.014±0.001	4.7	1.4×10^{-13}	4.6
Sr^{88}	2.76	3−	0.033±0.003	0.0061	1.08×10^{-10}	7.1

[a] Probable.
[b] Assumed.

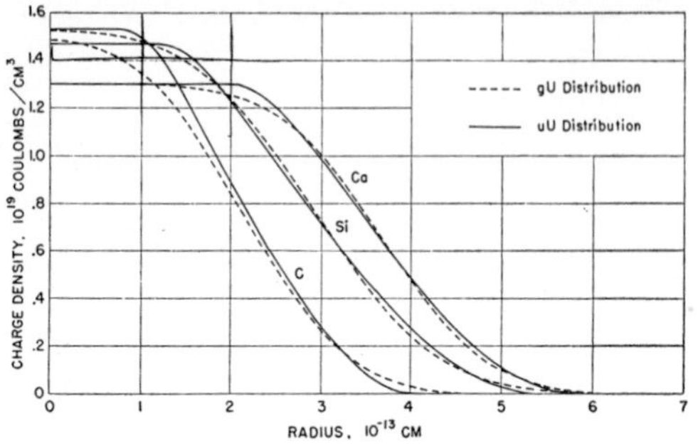

(a)

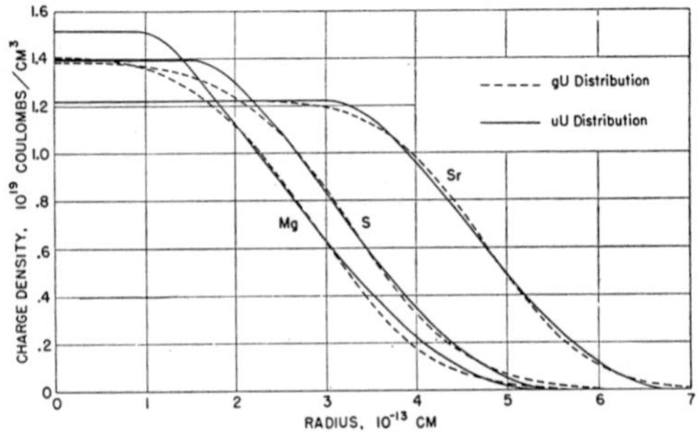

(b)

FIG. 5. Charge distributions calculated for the parameters given in Table III. The radius and surface-thickness parameters have been corrected by the factor $(1+3Z\alpha/2kR)^{-1}$.

that the Born-approximation radii should be reduced by the factor $[1+(3Z\alpha/2kR)]^{-1}$; for calcium in the present experiment this amounts to a 6% correction, giving r_1 (corrected)$=1.08\times10^{-13}$ cm, in excellent agreement with Hahn *et al.* Figure 5 shows the charge distributions defined by the parameters of Table III.

It will be noticed that the conversion factors from "calculated" to "measured" cross sections, given in Table II, differ considerably from unity, ranging up to factor of 2 for Sr. This discrepancy probably is due partly to some undetected experimental error in one of the hydrogen calibration points (Sec. II); it is possible also that using the Feshbach rather than the Born-approximation point-charge cross section was the wrong choice. (Thus the Feshbach point-charge cross section for Sr is 40% larger than the Born approximation, which could account for nearly half the discrepancy.) This error, although it seriously affects the magnitude of the absolute cross sections, will have have little effect on the radius and surface-thickness parameters.

V. ANALYSIS OF INELASTIC DATA

The inelastic cross sections also may be discussed in terms of Born-approximation form factors, at least in the case of electric-multipole transitions. As is shown by Schiff,[15] Eq. (1) again holds in these cases, if the inelastic form factor is properly defined.

Writing out the general form of Eq. (25) of reference 15, the form factor for inelastic scattering involving an electric l-pole transition between an initial nuclear state I_i and a final state I_f is given by

$$|F_l(I_i,I_f)|^2=\frac{4\pi(2l+1)}{2I_i+1}\sum_{m_i,m_f}\times\left|\int j_l(qr)Y_{l0}\rho_l(I_im_i;I_f,m_f)d^3\mathbf{r}\right|^2 \quad (9)$$

$$=\beta_l(I_i,I_f)\left|4\pi\int j_l(qr)\rho_l{}^{i,f}(r)r^2dr\right|^2$$

$$=\beta_l(I_i,I_f)|f_l{}^{i,f}|^2$$

where

$$f_l{}^{i,f}(q)=4\pi\int j_l(qr)\rho_l{}^{i,f}(r)r^2dr; \quad (10)$$

here $\rho_l(I_i,m_i;I_f,m_f)$ is the transition matrix element between the initial and final states. The second equality holds because all the ρ_l are assumed to have the same radial dependence, so that the radial integral may be factored out. The quantity $\beta_l(I_i,I_f)$, then, brings together all the terms of the summations over nuclear orientation and in general will depend strongly on the details of the nuclear model. For the treatment that follows, the normalization of $\rho_l{}^{i,f}(r)$ will be unimportant, but will be taken arbitrarily so that $\langle r^l\rangle_{i,f}=R^l$ [see Eq. (12) below].

Now if we made an assumption as to the form of $\rho_l{}^{i,f}(r)$, and evaluate the integral in Eq. (10), and if we already know l or can infer it from the experimental shape of F_l then we can evaluate $\beta_l(I_i,I_f)$ by comparing $f_l{}^{i,f}$ with the experimental form factors. We may relate $\beta_l(I_i,I_f)$ to the width of the inverse γ-ray transition in the following way:

Expanding the Bessel function for small values of q, we obtain

$$|F_l(I_i,I_f)|^2_{q\to0}=\beta_l(I_i,I_f)q^{2l}\left[\frac{\langle r^l\rangle_{i,f}}{1\cdot3\cdots(2l+1)}\right]^2, \quad (11)$$

where

$$\langle r^l\rangle_{i,f}=4\pi\int r^l\rho_l{}^{i,f}(r)r^2dr. \quad (12)$$

This may be combined with an expression given for the γ-transition width by Ravenhall,[24] giving

$$\Gamma_l(I_f\to I_i)=\frac{2I_i+1}{2I_f+1}\frac{\beta_l(I_i,I_f)}{[1\cdot3\cdots(2l+1)]^2}\times4Z^2k^{2l}\langle r^l\rangle^2_{i,f}\frac{e^2}{hc}\frac{l+1}{2l}\left(\frac{\epsilon}{E}\right)^{2l}\epsilon, \quad (13)$$

where ϵ is the transition energy. It will be noticed that in the special case of $I_i = I_f = 0$, $l=0$, Eqs. (9) and (10) should be replaced by

$$|F(0,0)|^2_{q\to 0} = \beta(0,0)[q^2 r^2_{0,0}/3]^2 \quad (14)$$

$$\langle r^2 \rangle_{0,0} = 4\pi \int r^2 \rho_0^{0,0}(r) r^2 dr. \quad (15)$$

This is because orthogonality of the excited- and ground-state wave functions requires that $4\pi \int \rho_0^{0,0}(r) r^2 dr = 0$.[15] Also, Eq. (13) does not apply, but should be replaced by expressions for $\Gamma_{\text{i.c.}}$ and $\Gamma_{\text{i.p.}}$, the internal-conversion and internal-pair transition widths.

Following the suggestion of Bohr and Mottleson[34] and of Schiff,[15] it will be assumed tentatively that a trial function for $\rho_l^{i,f}(r)$ may be taken as a delta function $\delta(r-R_l)$ when $l \neq 0$. When this is done, it may be seen (Fig. 6) that R_l must be some 20–30% larger than the value of R obtained for the static charge from the elastic data. However, if one smears out the delta function by the folding technique of Eq. (13) using the value of the parameter g or u [Eqs. (6) and (7)] found from the elastic data, then one finds that R_l (at least in the electric-quadrupole case) can be taken as equal to R.

In this connection it should be pointed out that Eq. (14) applies whether or not the $\rho(r)$ are spherically symmetric. Thus, if we assume $\rho_1(r)$, and, hence, $F_1(q)$ to be spherically symmetric, then the lth term of a multipole expansion of (r) will have the same form as the F_l in (9) with an additional factor $F_k(q)$:

$$|F_l(I_i,I_f)|^2 = \beta_l(I_i,I_f) \left| 4\pi \int j_l(qr) \rho_l^{i,f}(r) r^2 dr \right|^2 |F_1(q)|^2. \quad (16)$$

Equations (12) through (15) will be unchanged because $\text{Lim}_{q\to 0}[F_1(q)]^2 = \int \rho_1(r) d^3\mathbf{r} = 1$.

In interpreting the results, it is useful to compare the experimental inelastic form factors to the functional form of Eq. (16). This has been done in Fig. 6.

It is of some interest to compare the predictions of the Weisskopf[35] single-particle model to the present results. Here the Weisskopf[35] wave functions for all states of the excited nucleon are taken to be constant out to radius R_w, and zero from R_w to infinity. Then, using the results of Ravenhall[24] for the inelastic-scattering cross section for the single-particle model, it follows that

$$|M|^2 = \left[\frac{(d\sigma/d\Omega)_l^{i,f}}{(d\sigma/d\Omega)_{\text{Weisskopf}}}\right]_{q\to 0} = \frac{\Gamma_l(I_f \to I_i)}{\Gamma_{\text{Weisskopf}}}$$

$$= \left(Z\frac{l+3}{3}\right)^2 \left(\frac{R}{R_w}\right)^{2l} \frac{\beta_l(I_i,I_f)}{2l+1}, \quad (17)$$

[34] A. Bohr and B. R. Mottleson, Kgl. Danske Videnskab. Selskab, Mat.-fys. Medd. 27, No. 16 (1953).

[35] V. F. Weisskopf, Phys. Rev. 83, 1073 (1951).

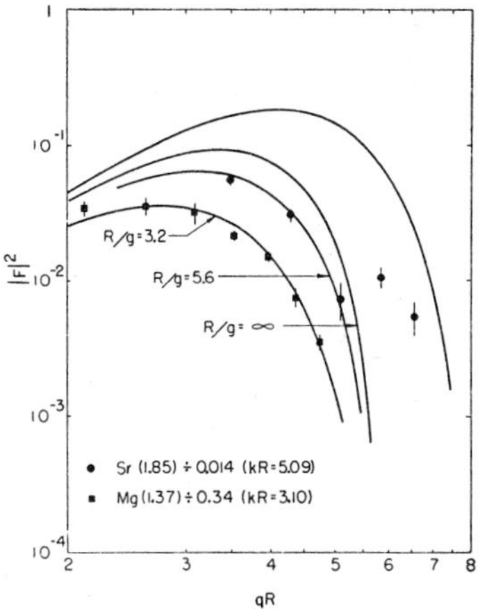

FIG. 6. Comparison of typical experimental and calculated squared inelastic form factors. Both the Sr (1.85 Mev) and Mg (1.37 Mev) are known to be 2+ levels. The calculated curves are for a "smeared δ-function" transition charge density (see Sec. V) with values of R/g taken from the elastic results. The abscissae for the experimental data are scaled by values of R taken from the elastic results [Table III (a)]. Shown for comparison (upper curve) is a squared form factor calculated from a quadrupole transition charge density whose radial dependence is constant for $r<R$, zero for $r>R$. This would give a poorer fit to the data than the δ-function distribution, indicating that the quadrupole vibrational mode is approximated better by a transverse wave in an incompressible nuclear fluid than by some sort of a compressional body wave.

where the numerator of the first quotient is the inelastic cross section, as extrapolated to the forward direction, from the present type of experiment. Note that $|M|^2$ is defined in the same way as $|M|^2$ of Wilkinson.[36]

Since the absolute cross sections are not known with great accuracy (Sec. II), the experimental values of $\beta_l(I_i,I_f)$ are based on a calibration of absolute cross section obtained by fitting the elastic curves to the calculated elastic form-factors. An alternate and very convenient method would be to obtain $\beta_l(I_i,I_f)$ by normalizing the ratio $|f_l^{i,f}|^2/|F|^2_{\text{elastic}}$ to the experimental ratio of inelastic to obtain elastic scattering; this method is applicable if the measurements go to values of q sufficiently below the first diffraction minimum. Table IV summarizes the inelastic results in terms of the values of $\beta_l(I_i,I_f)$, $\Gamma_l(I_f \to I_i)$, and other related parameters.

VI. RESULTS—INELASTIC DATA

In addition to the inelastic scattering observed in the present work in $_{12}Mg^{24}$, $_{14}Si^{28}$, $_{18}A^{40}$, and $_{38}Sr^{88}$, the 4.43-Mev 2+ and 7.68-Mev 0+ levels in $_6C^{12}$, reported by Fregeau[37] and Hofstadter[11] and the 3.73-Mev level in $_{20}Ca^{40}$, reported by Hahn *et al.*,[8] will be considered.

[36] D. H. Wilkinson, Phil. Mag. (to be published).

[37] Through the generosity of Mr. Fregeau, some data on carbon more recent than those of reference 11 are included here.

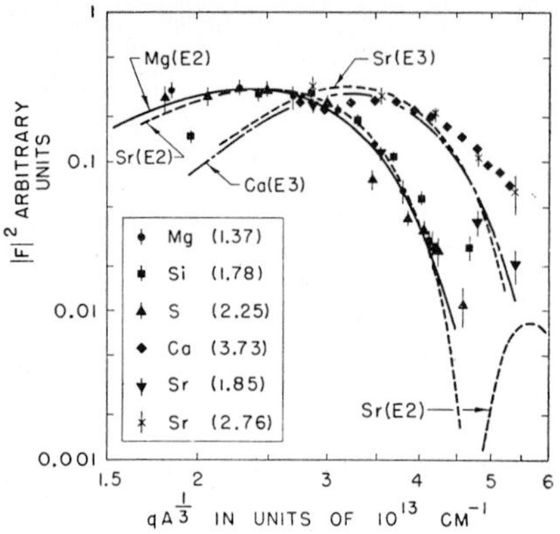

FIG. 7. Inelastic "universal curves." A composite plot of inelastic data from Mg, Si, S, Ca, and Sr against $qA^{\frac{1}{3}}$. The various form factors are arbitrarily normalized to minimize the spread of points. The point from sulfur and the point from silicon which seem to deviate from the "universal curve" are assumed to contain undetected experimental errors. The curves labeled Mg($E2$), Sr($E2$), Ca($E3$), and Sr($E3$) are calculated for electric-quadrupole and-octupole transitions using the "smeared δ-function" transition charge densities of Sec. V, and are arbitrarily normalized.

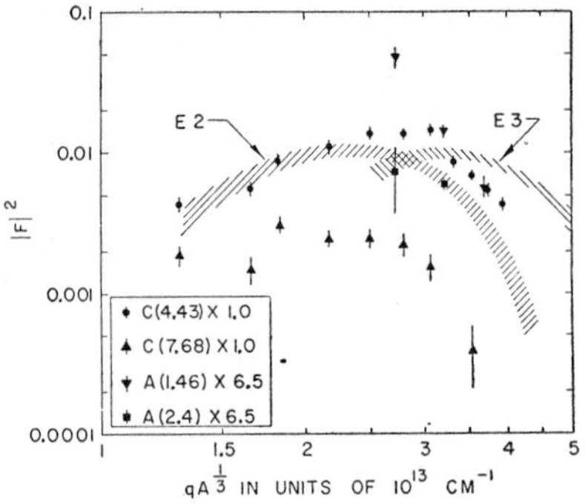

FIG. 8. Comparison of carbon (reference 11) and argon inelastic data to the "universal curves." The shaded areas, arbitrarily normalized, represent the envelopes of the experimental points of Fig. 7. $E2$ refers to quadrupole and $E3$ to octupole transitions. It is evident that the known quadrupole cases (4.43 Mev) deviates somewhat from the "universal curve" of the heavier elements, while the C (7.68 Mev) would, if appropriately normalized, fit the "universal curve" almost as well as the 4.43 Mev. The argon data are normalized to make the 2.4 Mev fall on the $E2$ curve, although it could equally well fit the $E3$ or possibly the monopole curves. The A (1.46 Mev) curve clearly has too steep a slope to fit either the $E2$ or $E3$, and therefore is very probably a monopole.

It is found that when the various experimental form factors are plotted against $qA^{\frac{1}{3}}$ and are arbitrarily normalized together in the region where the form factors are maximum, then practically all the points fall (within experimental accuracy) onto several "universal" curves, (see Fig. 7). Assuming that all the levels observed are electric multipoles,[38] then one is tempted to conclude that there is a distinct universal curve for each value of $l=0, 2, 3 \cdots$, at least for the lower levels in even-even nuclei. This is partially borne out by what is known about the levels: thus, Mg (1.37 Mev), Si (2.25 Mev), and Sr (1.85 Mev), all of which are known 2+ levels,[12,14] fall on essentially the same curve; also, Sr (2.76 Mev), which is known[14] to be 3+, gives a distinctly different curve. Carbon, however, seems to be an exception; the data on the 7.68-Mev, 0+ level fit with the Mg-Si-Sr 2+ data about as well as do the carbon 4.43-Mev 2+ data (see Fig. 8). Also, the Mg, Si, and Sr 2+ curves are fitted fairly well by the calculated (smeared δ-function) form factors using R and g from the elastic data, while the carbon curve is not (i.e., carbon 2+ would require a slightly smaller g or larger R).

Undoubtedly, the exact shapes of the form factors are dependent on the details of the actual nuclear wave functions, and it seems plausible that "universal" curves will apply only in nuclei that are heavy enough so that a truly collective model is a good approximation. (It might also be expected that for the shell model the *form*, but not necessarily the magnitude, of the form factor would be the same for all the heavier nuclei.)

[38] Most of the observed transitions are known to be electric because of the spins and parities of the levels; also, according to the estimates of Schiff (reference 15) magnetic transitions should be excited with much lower probability.

With these considerations in mind, it is felt that some tentative multipolarity assignments still can be made by comparison of the form factors with known cases. The following are considered highly probable[39] (refer to Fig. 7)[40]:

$$S^{32}(2.25 \text{ Mev}), \quad J=2(+);$$
$$Ca^{40}(3.73 \text{ Mev}), \quad J=3(-).$$

The following are possibilities that need further investigation (Fig. 8):

$$A^{40}(1.46 \text{ Mev}), \quad J=0(+);$$
$$A^{40}(2.4 \text{ Mev}), \quad J=2(+).$$

The quantities β_l (defined in Sec. V), Γ_l, $|M|^2$, and the mean life τ_r for radiative decay to the ground state are listed in Table IV. The transition widths (and mean lives), because of their ϵ^{2l+1} dependence, vary widely; but β_l, which essentially measures the excitation probabilities, is much more uniform from element to element.

The values of $|M|^2$ (based on $R_w=1.5A^{\frac{1}{3}}\times 10^{-13}$ cm, and with R from Table III) range from $\sim$1.8 to $\sim$9; the results suggest vaguely that the single-particle model is best for nuclei that come just before a magic number (i.e., C and A), and is better for quadrupole than for octupole transitions.

The estimates of the transition widths turn out to be on the order of 0.006 mv for the Sr (2.76 Mev, 3−), to 12.5 mv for the C (4.43 Mev, 2+), corresponding

[39] Total angular momentum J [referred to as I_f in Eqs. (11) and (17)] is equivalent to the multipolarity l of the transition by virtue of the 0+ nature of the ground state.

[40] This was suggested also by Dr. G. Ravenhall and B. Hahn (private communication) from an earlier, cursory examination of the data.

to mean lives for γ decay of 1.08×10^{-10} to 0.53×10^{-13} sec. It seems probable that cases will be found among the $0+ \rightarrow 0+$ transitions and some of the higher multipoles for which the lifetime estimated by this means can be compared to that found directly from the decay of the metastable state. [The 10^{-10}-sec lifetime quoted for Sr probably is not such a case, since the competing (2.76-Mev, 3−) →(1.85-Mev, 2+), dipole transition would make the actual lifetime much shorter.]

Several partially-resolved levels were seen, especially in sulfur. The data on these are not considered reliable enough to warrant analysis; for example, it appears that the partially resolved 3.8- and 5.8-Mev levels in sulfur could be 2+, 3−, or 4+. Also, two levels not previously reported were seen, one at ~6.6 Mev in sulfur and one at ~4.3 Mev in strontium. Since it is uncertain that these are not caused by impurities, further investigation is needed to establish this point.

VII. CONCLUSIONS

Within the known limitations of the Born approximation, it has been confirmed that the elastic scattering in the range of Z investigated here can be interpreted fairly well in terms of a nuclear radius and surface thickness. The rms radius is found to vary quite accurately as $A^{\frac{1}{3}}$ for the models used, and the surface thickness is quite constant but may have appreciable variation associated with shell structure. The use of the "folded" charge distribution is suggested as a convenient means of obtaining preliminary estimates of the charge radius and surface-thickness parameters.

Measurement of the inelastic scattering angular distributions has been shown to be a promising method for investigating the properties of certain excited states, in particular those levels that give rise to electric transitions. Angular momentum assignments are proposed for several levels where this was not known previously, and the transition widths or radiative lifetimes are calculated. It is difficult, in view of the obviously crude transition charge densities used, to estimate the absolute accuracy of these measurements; but except in cases where the J value is in doubt, it seems certain that subsequent work will not alter these answers by as much as an order of magnitude.

ACKNOWLEDGMENTS

The author is greatly indebted to Professor Robert Hofstadter for suggesting this project and for his invaluable help, encouragement, and advice in all phases of the work. Thanks also go to the operating and maintenance crews of the linear accelerator, whose skillful and devoted execution of their duties made the experiments possible; to the members of the electron-scattering group, especially Professor Hofstadter, Dr. J. A. McIntyre, Dr. Beat Hahn, A. W. Knudsen, J. H. Fregeau and R. W. McAllister, for cooperation and material assistance; to B. G. Stuart, of the Stanford University Physics Department, for careful fabrication of the silicon, sulfur, and strontium targets. A special word of appreciation goes to Dr. D. G. Ravenhall for a number of worthwhile discussions, for many suggestions and corrections in the introductory and analytical portions of the manuscript, and for making available formulas from papers which have not yet been published.

PAPER 38

Absolute Cross Section for Electron Scattering from Protons*

ROBERT W. MCALLISTER†
Department of Physics and High-Energy Physics Laboratory, Stanford University, Stanford, California
(Received October 12, 1956)

WITH apparatus described in part previously,[1–3] 189.6-Mev electrons have been scattered through 60° in the laboratory frame from polyethylene and carbon targets. Results of this investigation have yielded an absolute cross section for scattering from protons under these conditions.

Electron scattering from protons in the energy range 100 Mev to 550 Mev has been studied previously,[4–6] but absolute cross sections have been obtained only approximately. Results of the relative scattering are compared with the Rosenbluth[7] formula interpreted as if the proton had a diffuse charge and a diffuse magnetic moment.[5] In this manner shapes and sizes of the charge and magnetic moment distributions are obtained. The radiative correction calculated by Schwinger[8] does not enter in a sensitive manner into such a relative comparison since its angular dependence is very small. The present determination of an absolute cross section eliminates one degree of freedom in the comparison with theory and provides a check on the radiative correction.

The choice of conditions (189.6 Mev, 60°) for this determination was convenient. Thus, scattering from the proton's magnetic moment contributes only ~7% to the cross section under these conditions. Hence the interpretation of the experiment is not sensitive to existing uncertainties in the size of the magnetic moment distribution ($d\sigma/\sigma \cong 0.02 dR_2/R_2$), which makes only a small uncertainty in the 7% contribution. In addition, values of the momentum transfer q in the center-of-mass system are small enough, so that the squares of the form factors are determined to within 1% by the rms radius of the distributions ($F^2 \cong 1-\frac{1}{3}q^2R^2$). The shapes of the density distributions thus need not be known accurately in order to interpret the experiment. The recoil energy of the proton is ~17 Mev, so that the hydrogen and carbon scattering peaks present in the scattering from polyethylene are well separated. For this reason the carbon contributes only a 15% background to the hydrogen peak area.

Now charge scattering contributes ~93% to the cross section, and, since the finite size makes an ~17% contribution to the square of the charge form factor (F_1^2), the cross section is somewhat sensitive to the charge radius ($d\sigma/\sigma \cong -0.3 dR_1/R_1$). This fact is desirable from the standpoint of obtaining information about the size of the charge distribution alone. It is undesirable from the standpoint of checking the radiative correction. The interpretation of the experiment consists in determining whether or not the experimental cross section is consistent with the radiative correction and existing values of the charge radius.

A preliminary analysis of the data yields a differential cross section of $(1.20 \pm 0.07) \times 10^{-30}$ cm^2. The fractional energy resolution, $\Delta E/E$, required for the radiative correction is approximately just the peak width observed in the experiment. However, the radiative correction is very insensitive to $\Delta E/E$ for values in this range. The experimental peak widths are very nearly 1% so that a value 0.01 can be assumed for $\Delta E/E$, yielding a radiative correction of 0.836. This correction is applied to the Rosenbluth formula for a diffuse proton,[5] assuming a magnetic moment rms radius of 0.77×10^{-13} cm. The result is compared with the above central experimental value, and an rms radius of 0.75×10^{-13} cm is determined for the charge. This radius is consistent with existing values.[6]

The details of the experimental arrangement and procedure and a more thorough analysis of the data will be presented in a paper to be submitted soon to the Physical Review. It may be possible at that time to establish smaller limits of uncertainty on the experimental cross section.

The author wishes to thank Dr. Robert Hofstadter for suggesting this problem and for making many valuable suggestions contributing toward its solution. Dr. J. A. McIntyre and Mr. A. W. Knudsen have presented many worthwhile ideas. Miss Monica Eder has been very helpful in taking data.

* The research reported in this document was supported jointly by the U. S. Navy (Office of Naval Research) and the U. S. Atomic Energy Commission, and by the U. S. Air Force through the Air Force Office of Scientific Research, Air Research and Development Command. It was also aided by a grant from the Research Corporation.

† Now at the University of Zurich, Zurich, Switzerland.

1 Hofstadter, Fechter, and McIntyre, Phys. Rev. **92**, 978 (1953).
2 Hofstadter, Hahn, Knudsen, and McIntyre, Phys. Rev. **95**, 512 (1954).
3 J. H. Fregeau and R. Hofstadter, Phys. Rev. **99**, 1503 (1955).
4 R. Hofstadter and R. W. McAllister, Phys. Rev. **98**, 217 (1955).
5 R. W. McAllister and R. Hofstadter, Phys. Rev. **102**, 851 (1956).
6 E. E. Chambers and R. Hofstadter, Phys. Rev. **103**, 1454 (1956).
7 M. N. Rosenbluth, Phys. Rev. **79**, 615 (1950).
8 J. Schwinger, Phys. Rev. **76**, 790 (1949).

PAPER 39

Electromagnetic Structure of Nucleons*

D. R. YENNIE, M. M. LÉVY,† AND D. G. RAVENHALL, *Stanford University, Stanford, California*

The theoretical implications of various experiments relating to the electromagnetic structure of nucleons are examined in the light of current field theory. It is concluded either that the nucleon core is about three times as large as would be expected from intuitive considerations of meson theory, or that there is some inconsistency in the present field theory.

1. INTRODUCTION

INFORMATION about the internal structure of individual nucleons is contained in the results of a variety of experiments performed in recent years.[1] Those experiments in which the interaction with the nucleon is electromagnetic (or is thought to be so) are susceptible of a considerably more precise and unambiguous interpretation than those involving meson interactions. Of the former type (which alone will concern us here) the best known is that involving neutron scattering by atoms, which, when analyzed, gives information about the electron-neutron interaction (to be specific, its volume integral). The Lamb shift and the hyperfine splitting can also give such information, although much less precisely. The fact that the anomalous magnetic moments of the nucleons are equal and opposite has important implications for a meson model of the nucleons, of course. Recent experiments on the scattering of high-energy electrons by hydrogen and deuterium now give considerably more detailed and complete information about the proton and, to some extent, about the neutron. The aim of this paper is to examine the extent to which the results of the separate experiments can be combined into a consistent picture of nucleons as charge-current distributions. We make no claim for the originality of most of the theoretical ideas presented here; they have all appeared in various forms in the literature, and we have brought them together for the purpose of discussing these experiments. In Sec. 2 we present the phenomenology of the electromagnetic interaction of electrons and nucleons. This is interpreted in Sec. 3 in terms of a simple meson model of nucleon structure in which it is assumed that the "physical" nucleon is made up of "bare" nucleons and pions interacting in a charge-symmetrical manner. In Sec. 4 other, more speculative, ways of interpreting these results are suggested, and the implication of these ideas, and their effects on the interpretation of other experiments, are commented on. The Appendix, due to one of us (D. R. Y.), gives a general treatment of the charge-current density of particles of general spin.

* This work was supported in part by the U. S. Air Force through the Air Force Office of Scientific Research, Air Research and Development Command.

† The work was completed while this author was at the University of Paris.

[1] Some of the topics we shall discuss have been reviewed in Bethe and de Hoffmann's book *Mesons and Fields Vol. II* (Row, Peterson and Company, Evanston, 1955), pp. 289–299. In many cases we shall refer the reader to this excellent book for bibliographies.

2. PHENOMENOLOGY OF ELECTRON-NUCLEON INTERACTION

The scattering of an electron from a nucleon caused by their electromagnetic interaction[2] is represented by the Feynman diagram of Fig. 1. We write the matrix element for the process as

$$-4\pi i j_\mu^{p,n}(P',P)(1/q^2)j_\mu^e(k',k), \qquad (2.1)$$

which includes both the Coulomb interaction and the effect of the exchange of transverse photons.[3] The interpretation of this expression is as follows: the factor $(1/q^2)$ represents the propagation of a virtual photon of four-momentum q_μ between the electron and the nucleon where q_μ is the recoil momentum,

$$q_\mu = P_\mu' - P_\mu = -(k_\mu' - k_\mu). \qquad (2.2)$$

In the center-of-momentum frame ($q_0=0$), q^2 is given by

$$q^2 = (2k_c \sin\tfrac{1}{2}\theta_c)^2, \qquad (2.3)$$

where k_c and θ_c are the electron's momentum and scattering angle in this frame. The factor j_μ^e is the electron's charge-current density, which, assuming no internal structure, is given simply by

$$j_\mu^e(k',k) = -ie\bar{u}(k')\gamma_\mu u(k), \qquad (2.4)$$

where $u,\bar{u}$ are Dirac spinors for the electron. The charge-current density of the nucleon $j_\mu^{p,n}(P',P)$ (proton or neutron) includes all of the effects of the internal structure.[4] The purpose of the experiments we are discussing

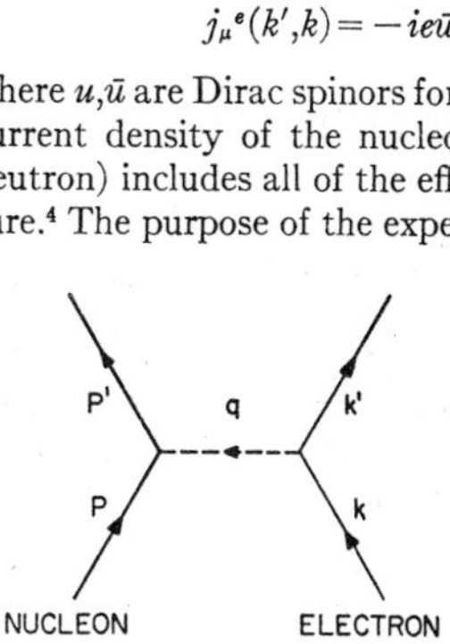

FIG. 1. Feynman diagram of the scattering of an electron by a nucleon caused by the exchange of a virtual photon.

[2] Scattering due to nonelectromagnetic interactions is discussed later in this Section.

[3] R. P. Feynman, Phys. Rev. 74, 939 (1948). Our notation differs from Feynman's somewhat, in that e, the electric charge, is given in unrationalized units, and the four-vector product $a\cdot b$ means $\mathbf{a}\cdot\mathbf{b}-a_0b_0$. Usually we put $\hbar=c=1$.

[4] Technically this is the vertex operator evaluated between free nucleon states.

is to determine information about this charge-current distribution beyond what is already well known from static experiments (the total charge and magnetic moment).

The problem has been simplified by Foldy,[5] and later, in more generality, by Salzman.[5] They show that the nucleon charge-current density must have the form

$$j_\mu{}^{p,n}(P',P)=ie\bar{v}(P')[\gamma_\mu F_1{}^{p,n}(q^2)+(\kappa^{p,n}/2M)\sigma_{\mu\nu}q_\nu F_2{}^{p,n}(q^2)]v(P). \quad (2.5)$$

The assumptions are (i) relativistic covariance, which means that $j_\mu{}^{p,n}$ transforms as a four-vector; (ii) a differential law of current conservation, which in momentum space is expressed as

$$(P'-P)_\mu j_\mu{}^{p,n}(P',P)=0; \quad (2.6)$$

and (iii), that the nucleon is a Dirac particle.[6] In Eq. (2.5), the quantities $v,\bar{v}$ are Dirac spinors for the nucleon, $\kappa^{p,n}$ is the anomalous magnetic moment of the nucleon in nuclear magnetons, and the rest of the symbols have their usual meanings. The functions $F_{1,2}{}^{p,n}(q^2)$ describe the internal structure, and in the static limit $(q^2\rightarrow 0)$ take the value unity, except for $F_1{}^n(0)$, which is zero. As regards the uniqueness of the form of Eq. (2.5), it should be mentioned that there are other covariant expressions satisfying Foldy's assumption, e.g., the convection-current term $(P'+P)_\mu\bar{v}(P')v(P)$. However, such terms always can be expressed in the form (2.5) by the use of the Dirac equation,

$$(\gamma_\mu P_\mu-M)v(P)=0,$$
$$\bar{v}(P')(\gamma_\mu P_\mu'-M)=0. \quad (2.7)$$

The functions F_1 and F_2 are relativistic generalizations of the form factors characteristic of finite extension occurring in other experiments, for example, in the scattering of electrons from nuclei.[7] There, the form factor is simply the Fourier transform of a radial density function,

$$F(q^2)=\int f(r)\exp(i\mathbf{q}\cdot\mathbf{r})d^3r. \quad (2.8)$$

The function $f(r)$ comes from the product of the initial wave function of the scatterer at rest and the final wave function of the scatterer after it has absorbed the recoil momentum $\mathbf{q}$. For heavy nuclei, where the recoil velocity is negligible compared with c, nonrelativistic wave functions are sufficient, and $f(r)$ is just the static charge or magnetic-moment distribution. For the scattering from a nucleon, however, the situation is qualitatively different, in that for values of $\mathbf{q}$ large enough that the finite nucleon size may be detected, the recoil velocity is comparable with c. It should be emphasized, however, that it is always possible to analyze the experiments in terms of the invariant functions $F_1(q^2)$ and $F_2(q^2)$, and for intuitive convenience to define structure functions $f(r)$ as their Fourier transforms.[8] An accurate calculation of $f(r)$ from some theory would require a correct relativistic description of the internal state of the nucleon. Physically, $f(r)$ would contain the overlap of two wave functions, each Lorentz-contracted, but in different directions. (Actually the structure will be described by a relativistic many-body wave function, so the problem is in fact more complicated than this.) Thus, in relating f to the nucleon wave functions, effects of order v^2/c^2 (or q^2/M^2) are introduced. Consequently there will be a dependence of F on q^2 which is in a sense kinematic in origin, in addition to that coming from the finite extent of the internal wave functions. The essential point is that measurement of structure to within a distance d requires values of $|\mathbf{q}|$ of order $1/d$, and if absorption of this momentum causes relativistic recoil (i.e., if $|\mathbf{q}|>Mc/\hbar$) then intuitive concepts of static charge and current distributions are no longer vaild. Since we expect nuclear structure to extend a distance of order $\hbar/\mu c$, there should be a range of $|\mathbf{q}|$ values $(\mu c/\hbar<|q|<Mc/\hbar)$ for which the interpretation in terms of static distributions has some validity. A correct relativistic theory for nucleon structure would, of course, avoid these difficulties by allowing a direct calculation of F as a vertex operator.

To the extent that it is possible to interpret F in terms of static charge-current distributions, it is instructive to make a nonrelativistic reduction of (2.5). This is done in the usual way by expressing the small components of the nucleon spinors in terms of the large components ϕ, which are independent of momentum. In the center-of-momentum frame, and for $|\mathbf{q}|\ll Mc/\hbar$, the components of $j_\mu{}^{p,n}$ become

$$j_0\simeq e(E/M)\phi_2{}^*\phi_1[F_1-(q^2/8M^2)(F_1+2\kappa F_2)], \quad (2.9a)$$

$$\mathbf{j}\simeq e[(\mathbf{P}'+\mathbf{P})/2M]\phi_2{}^*\phi_1F_1+(e/2M)\phi_2{}^*(i\boldsymbol{\sigma}\times\mathbf{q})\phi_1(F_1+\kappa F_2). \quad (2.9b)$$

In (2.9b), the first term represents the convection current, and the second the effect of the magnetic moment. In the expression for j_0, in (2.9a), there is, in addition to the expected term F_1, a kinematic term of order q^2 arising from the overlap of the two spinors. The importance of this term in connection with electron-neutron scattering was noted by Foldy.[9]

[5] L. L. Foldy, Phys. Rev. **87**, 688 (1952); G. Salzman, Phys. Rev. **99**, 973 (1955). An even more general derivation has been given by A. C. Zemach, reference 35. We thank Dr. Zemach for informing us of this work.

[6] This last restriction can be relaxed, as is shown in the Appendix so that Eq. (2.5) holds for any spin one-half particle, e.g. C^{13}. The Dirac spinors are used merely for convenience in representing j_μ in a covariant form.

[7] Hofstadter, Fechter, and McIntyre, Phys. Rev. **92**, 978 (1953); L. I. Schiff, Phys. Rev. **92**, 988 (1953).

[8] We mean here the three-dimensional Fourier transform, obtained by inverting Eq. (2.8).

[9] L. L. Foldy, Phys. Rev. **88**, 693 (1952). It might seem natural to define the spatial distribution of charge as the Fourier transform of the expression in square brackets in j_0. This is not unambiguous, however, as can be seen from Eqs. (A-22) and (A-23).

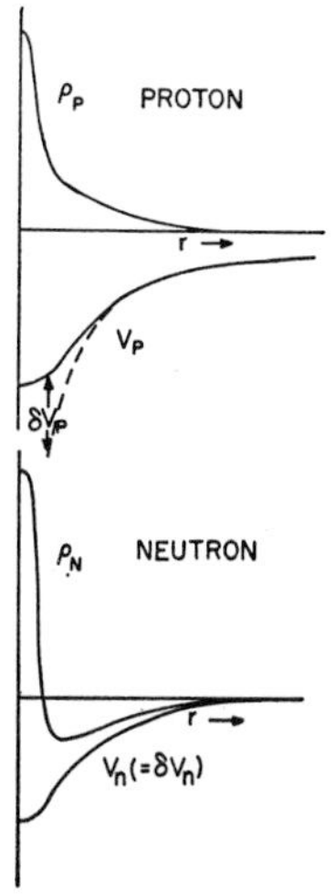

FIG. 2. Intuitive concepts of the neutron and proton charge densities and of the interactions potential between these particles and an electron. The quantities δV represent the departure of these potentials from their values for point nucleons.

For convenience, the functions F can be expanded in powers of q^2. The coefficient of q^2 is simply related to the mean-square radius of the distribution[10]:

$$F(q^2)\simeq 1-q^2\langle r^2\rangle/6+\cdots,\quad \langle r^2\rangle=\int r^2 f(r)d^3r. \tag{2.10}$$

Because of the relativistic complications discussed previously, there may be contributions to the coefficient of q^2 other than those coming from the finite extension. If this extension is of order $\hbar/\mu c$, they will not completely invalidate intuitive considerations based on static models. With these limitations in mind, we note that the mean-square radii of charge and moment distributions of the nucleons are, from Eqs. (2.9),

$$\begin{aligned}\langle r^2\rangle_{\mathrm{ch}}&=\langle r^2\rangle_1+(3/4M^2)[F_1{}^{p,n}(0)+2\kappa],\\ \langle r^2\rangle_{\mathrm{m}}&=[\langle r^2\rangle_1+\kappa\langle r^2\rangle_2]/(1+\kappa).\end{aligned} \tag{2.11}$$

In Fig. 2 are shown the usual concepts of the proton and neutron charge densities, and the interaction potentials between those particles and an electron. The quantities δV represent the departure of these potentials from their values for point nucleons, and they can be related to the mean-square radius by Poisson's equation,

$$\begin{aligned}\int \delta V d^3r&=(2\pi e/3)\int r^2\rho(r)d^3r\\ &=(2\pi e^2/3)\langle r^2\rangle_{\mathrm{ch}}.\end{aligned} \tag{2.12}$$

Electron-Neutron Interaction

Aside from the static limits, the first information about nucleon structure was obtained from experiments on the scattering of neutrons by atoms. Analysis of the results yields the volume integral of the electron-neutron interaction potential, Eq. (2.12). This quantity is conventionally represented by a constant potential, of strength V_0, extending out to a radius $r_0=e^2/mc^2$, the classical electron radius. (This convention is rather confusing since r_0 has nothing to do with this particular interaction.) Hughes *et al.*[11] find for V_0 the value -3860 ± 370 ev, and more recently Melkonian *et al.*[12] report the value -4165 ± 265 ev. Using the mean of these two results, and expressing it in terms of a radius by means of Eqs. (2.11) and (2.12), we find that $\langle r^2\rangle_{\mathrm{ch},n}=-(0.35\times10^{-13}\text{ cm})^2$. This is accounted for completely by the magnetic term of Eq. (2.11), so that

$$\langle r^2\rangle_{1,n}=(0.000\pm0.006)\times10^{-26}\text{ cm}^2. \tag{2.13}$$

Expressed in terms of potentials, as is customary, the magnetic contribution, first calculated by Foldy,[9] is -4070 ev, leaving for the V_0 associated with $\langle r^2\rangle_{1,n}$ the value 0 ± 200 ev. Had the neutron structure been comparable in extent to that found for the proton, a value of about 0.7×10^{-13} cm would be obtained for $\langle r^2\rangle_{1,n}{}^{\frac{1}{2}}$, or for V_0 about 16 000 ev! The conventional interpretation of this very surprising result is either that the radius associated with the Dirac term is very small, or that the structure, if extended, is almost neutral. In the light of our previous remarks on the meaning of $f(r)$, it is also possible (although perhaps unlikely) that the static charge-current distribution is extended, but that its contribution to $f(r)$ has been canceled fortuitously by relativistic corrections.

Another method for examining neutron structure has been suggested, and is being carried out, by Hofstadter.[13] In the inelastic scattering of electrons from the deuteron at high energies and large angles, binding effects are unimportant, and the neutron and proton scatter independently. Since the electron-proton scattering has been measured separately, the electron-neutron cross section can be deduced. This method can give information about $F_2{}^n$, and possibly also about $F_1{}^n$.

Electron-Proton Scattering

The extensive experiments on the scattering of high-energy electrons by hydrogen of Hofstadter *et al*,[14,15] have given much detailed information about the structure functions of the proton. The analysis uses the formula, first derived by Rosenbluth,[16] for the cross section for the scattering of a relativistic electron by a proton.

[10] Except for $f_{1,n}(r)$, all of the f's have unit volume integral because the corresponding $F(0)$ is unity. Because $F_{1,n}(0)=0$, the quantity $\langle r^2\rangle_{1,n}$ depends on the amount of charge displaced as well as on its radius. For reasonable distributions $\langle r^2\rangle_{1,n}$ will be negative, and the other quantities positive.

[11] Hughes, Harvey, Goldberg, and Stafne, Phys. Rev. **90**, 497 (1953).

[12] Melkonian, Rustad, and Havens, Bull. Am. Phys. Soc. Ser. II, **1**, 62 (1956).

[13] R. Hofstadter, Revs. Modern Phys. **28**, 214 (1956).

[14] R. N. McAllister and R. Hofstadter, Phys. Rev. **102**, 851 (1956).

[15] E. E. Chambers and R. Hofstadter, Phys. Rev. **103**, 1454 (1956).

[16] M. Rosenbluth, Phys. Rev. **79**, 615 (1950).

In the laboratory frame this can be expressed as

$$\sigma(\theta)=\sigma_{NS}(\theta)\{(F_1{}^p)^2+(q^2/4M^2)[2(F_1{}^p+\kappa^pF_2{}^p)^2 \times\tan^2\tfrac{1}{2}\theta+(\kappa^pF_2{}^p)^2]\}, \quad (2.14)$$

where σ_{NS} is the cross section for scattering by a point, spinless particle of mass M:

$$\sigma_{NS}(\theta)=e^4\cos^2\tfrac{1}{2}\theta/\{4k^2[1+2(k/M)\sin^2\tfrac{1}{2}\theta]\sin^4\tfrac{1}{2}\theta\}.$$

The terms in the square bracket in (2.14) arise from the magnetic moment of the proton. The interesting fact that one term involves the total moment while the other contains only the anomalous moment is related to the mixing of F_1 and F_2 in the expressions for charge and current density (2.9).

At the present experimental energies $F_1{}^2$ and $(F_1+\kappa F_2)^2$ are the dominant terms of Eq. (2.14). Since the dependence on angle and energy of the quantity in the curly brackets cannot be expressed in terms of $q(=2k_c \sin\frac{1}{2}\theta_c)$ alone, it is possible to separate the contributions from F_1 and F_2 by performing experiments at various energies and angles. If finite size effects are ignored, so that $F_1=F_2=1$, the first term has the very strong angular dependence and k^{-2} energy dependence characteristic of scattering in a Coulomb field. In contrast, the second term is approximately a constant, independent of energy and angle. Thus the charge scattering and hence the effect of finite charge extension is seen at small angles, while the magnetic moment size is apparent at large angles. The situation is illustrated in Figs. 3. and 4. The "total form factor" $\mathfrak{F}(\theta,k)$ defined by

$$\sigma(\theta)=\sigma_{\text{point}}(\theta)[\mathfrak{F}(\theta,k)]^2, \quad (2.15)$$

where σ_{point} is given by Eq. (2.14) with $F_1=F_2=1$, is plotted as a function of q^2. The three different proton models used for illustration assume either equal charge and moment radii, or else that one of these radii is zero.

McAllister and Hofstadter[14] have measured the elec-

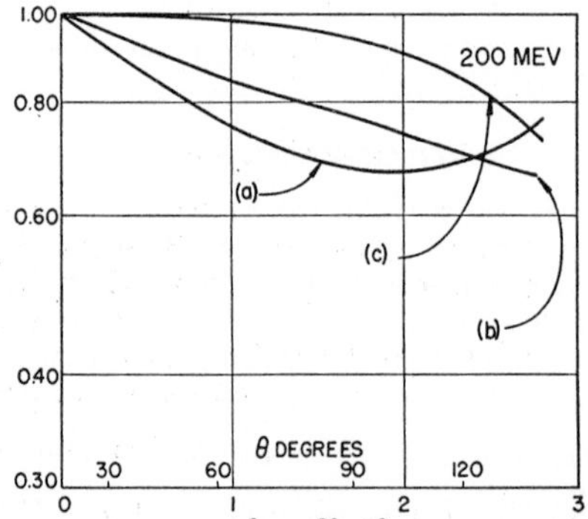

FIG. 3. A plot of the square of the total form factor $\mathfrak{F}$, defined by Eq. (2.15), *vs* q^2, at 200 Mev. Three different proton models are illustrated, corresponding to the following choices for the values of $\langle r^2\rangle_{1,p}{}^{\frac{1}{2}}$ and $\langle r^2\rangle_{2,p}{}^{\frac{1}{2}}$, in 10^{-13} cm: (a) 1.00 and 0.00; (b) 0.70 and 0.70; (c) 0.00 and 0.85.

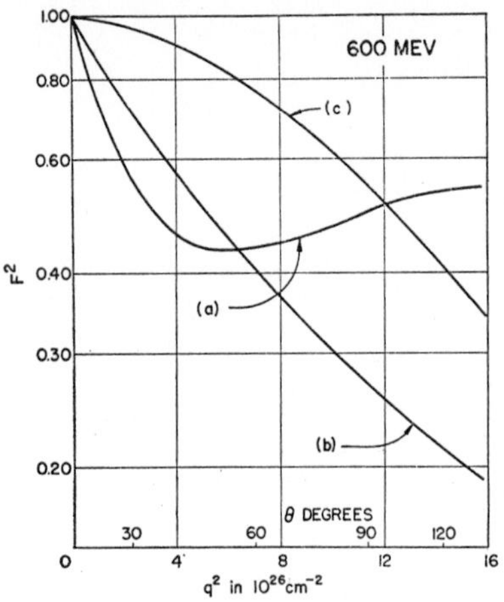

FIG. 4. A plot of $\mathfrak{F}^2$ *vs* q^2 at 600 Mev, for the same cases as in Fig. 3.

tron-proton scattering cross section at 100, 188, and 236 Mev, while more recently experiments at 200, 300, 400, 500, and 550 Mev have been carried out by Chambers and Hofstadter.[15] The detailed analysis of the experiments in terms of F_1 and F_2, and their associated distributions $f_1(r)$ and $f_2(r)$, has been carried out by Hofstadter and his colleagues, and here we shall quote from their results. A feature which makes the fitting with theory a little more flexible than Figs. 3 and 4 might indicate is that the absolute values of the experimental cross sections are not known, although the relative normalization of results for the various energies is known for the latter series of runs. In their analysis, the above authors use the simplifying assumption that the analytic forms of $f_1(r)$ and $f_2(r)$ are identical. The best agreement is found to occur for shapes which are not singular at the center, and which drop off fairly rapidly at large radius. The best fit is then given for equal radii; their actual value depends a little on the choice of shape, but an average value is

$$(\langle r^2\rangle_{1,p})^{\frac{1}{2}}=(\langle r^2\rangle_{2,p})^{\frac{1}{2}}=(0.77\pm0.10)\times10^{-13}\text{ cm}. \quad (2.16)$$

It is possible to have slightly different radii, but neither can be less than about 0.6×10^{-13} cm, or greater than about 1.5×10^{-13} cm. For the case of equal radii the results are illustrated in Fig. 5, where $4\pi r^2 f(r)$ is plotted against r. Chambers[17] has also considered the possibility of different analytic forms for $f_1(r)$ and $f_2(r)$. He finds that it is still not possible to relax the above limits on the radii. The general conclusions are that the proton radii are as given in Eq. (2.16), and that there is no concentration of charge or magnetic moment at the center.

There are possible corrections that might be made to the above analysis, but they are quite unimportant. By

[17] E. E. Chambers, Ph. D. dissertation, Stanford University (1956) (unpublished).

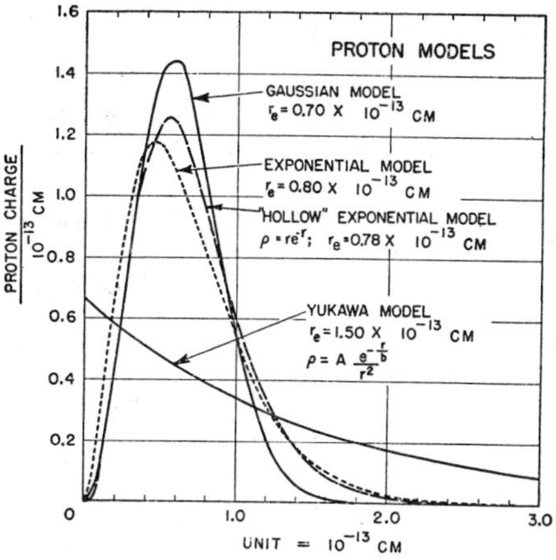

FIG. 5. Graphical representation of proton distribution functions, from the analysis of Chambers and Hofstadter.[15] For the assumption that $f_1(r)=f_2(r)$, these authors find that the Gaussian, exponential and hollow exponential models all give a good fit to the experiments. The Yukawa model, which is suggested by the theory of scalar mesons weakly coupled to nucleons, is given for comparison only; it is in fact inadmissible as a fit to the data. What is plotted *vs* radius r is $4\pi r^2 f(r)$, so that these curves have equal area.

comparing with the results of a partial wave analysis of the scattering process,[18] it is found that the Born approximation used by Hofstadter *et al.* gives cross sections accurate to about 0.25%. The effect on predicted radii is completely negligible. A complication which might influence the interpretation of the form factors F arises from the possibility of virtual excitation of an isobaric state of the proton, corresponding to the resonance in the cross section for photoproduction of mesons. Drell and Ruderman[19] have estimated that the effect of this on the predicted radii is less than about half a percent. The radiative correction of Schwinger[20] has of course been taken into account by Hofstadter *et al.* in their handling of the experimental data.[21] Throughout the analysis it has been assumed that the functions $F(q^2)$ are analytic and "smooth" over the regions of q examined. The electron-proton and electron-neutron experiments are made over completely different ranges of q. It is conceivable, therefore, that the functions F are so peculiar that extrapolation from the one range of q to the other in the simple way that has been assumed is unjustified. A theory that would predict such functions would itself be very peculiar, and we do not consider the possibility further.

[18] Yennie, Ravenhall, and Wilson, Phys. Rev. **95**, 500 (1954), and unpublished calculations.

[19] S. D. Drell and M. A. Ruderman, Phys. Rev. (to be published).

[20] J. Schwinger, Phys. Rev. **76**, 790 (1949).

[21] As in other electron-scattering experiments, the radiative correction is quite large (~20%) but its variation over the angular range used is small (~3%), so that it is not an important correction. The physical situation is different from that considered by Schwinger, in that the proton can emit and absorb photons; but the extra contributions due to this, even that arising from interference with the electron contributions, are negligible.

Electron-Deuteron Scattering

There exists at present no relativistic theory for the binding of nucleons of finite size to form a nucleus. In the nonrelativistic limit, the solution of the Schrödinger equation describing the interaction of a group of point nucleons is presumably to be interpreted as giving the distribution in space of the centers of mass of the extended nucleons. A difference between this calculated distribution and the measured charge distribution could then be ascribed to finite nucleon size. Use of the nonrelativistic theory unfortunately forces us to ignore the relativistic effects discussed at the beginning of this section.

Experiments on the elastic and inelastic electron-deuteron scattering have been carried out by McIntyre and Hofstadter.[22,23] Following the analysis of Schiff,[24] Jankus[25] has made extensive calculations of both processes, investigating the effect of various assumptions about the neutron-proton potential, and taking into account the effects of magnetic dipole and electric quadrupole moments. Calculations of elastic scattering for particular potentials have been carried out by McIntyre,[23] Bernstein,[26] and Ravenhall.[27] For the detailed comparison of the experiments with these calculations, we quote from the work of McIntyre. He finds that even with the most favorable choice of potential, the experimentally observed charge distribution is significantly more extended than that given by the above calculations. His results are illustrated in Fig. 6.

In the nonrelativistic approximation these calculations give the distribution in space $|\psi_D(r)|^2$ of the centers of mass of the neutron and proton. Neglecting distortions of the nucleon structure due to the binding, the observed deuteron charge density is then

$$\rho(r)=\int [f_{1,p}(|r-r'|)+f_{1,n}(|r-r'|)] \times |\psi_D(r')|^2 d^3r'. \quad (2.17)$$

The form factor for electron-deuteron scattering is thus

$$F(q^2)=[F_1^p(q^2)+F_1^n(q^2)]F_D(q^2), \quad (2.18)$$

where $F_D(q^2)$ is the form factor calculated directly from $|\psi_D(r)|^2$. The factor contributed by the nucleon structure is for small q just

$$[\cdots]\simeq[1-(q^2/6)(\langle r^2\rangle_{1,p}+\langle r^2\rangle_{1,n})+\cdots]. \quad (2.19)$$

On the basis of the naive meson theory discussed in the next section, it was expected that the proton and

[22] J. A. McIntyre and R. Hofstadter, Phys. Rev. **98**, 158 (1955).

[23] J. A. McIntyre, Phys. Rev. **103**, 1464 (1956).

[24] L. I. Schiff, Phys. Rev. **92**, 988 (1953).

[25] V. Z. Jankus, Phys. Rev. **102**, 1586 (1956).

[26] J. Bernstein, unpublished calculations. We thank Dr. Bernstein for communication of these results.

[27] Unpublished calculations.

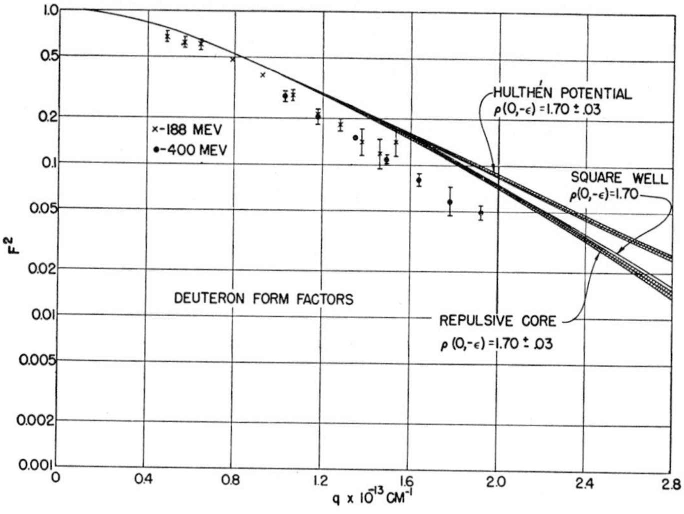

FIG. 6. Experimental and theoretical results of McIntyre on elastic electron-deuteron scattering at 188 and 400 Mev. The theoretical curves include only deuteron S-state contributions; magnetic dipole and electric quadrupole effects are small and would in any case increase F^2. This figure illustrates the fact that the experimental results predict a more extended charge than that obtained assuming point nucleons.

neutron contributions to the q^2 term would cancel, leaving no correction to (2.18) due to the nucleon structure. On the other hand, use of the results of the experiments on the free nucleons means that Eq. (2.19) reduces to the proton form factor. In fact, the analysis of McIntyre strongly favors the latter choice, and can thus be regarded as confirming the difference in size of the neutron and proton. Alternatively, the assumption of nucleon sizes as obtained from the other experiments would give valuable information about the deuteron wave functions.

A possible source of error in the above treatment, associated with the use of the first Born approximation, has been studied by Schiff.[28] In the second Born approximation there is, as well as the usual contribution in which the nucleus stays in its ground state, also a dispersion contribution associated with the possibility of virtual excitation. He shows that the sum of these two effects is of order 1/137 of the elastic scattering, and so is quite unimportant. For the special case of the deuteron, a more exact calculation has been carried out by Volk and Malenka,[29] which confirms his result for the total second Born contribution.

At present, little is known about the accuracy of the nonrelativistic approximation, and of the effect of binding on the nucleon structure. A start to the calculation of relativistic corrections has been made by Blankenbecler,[30] who has treated the deuteron phenomenologically as an elementary vector particle, in analogy with the electron-proton calculation of Rosenbluth.[16] Estimates of mesonic corrections by Bernstein[31] will be discussed in the next section.

[28] L. I. Schiff, Phys. Rev. **98**, 756 (1955).
[29] H. S. Volk and B. J. Malenka, Phys. Rev. (to be published).
[30] R. Blankenbecler, unpublished calculation.
[31] J. Bernstein, Phys. Rev. (to be published).

Hydrogen Spectra

There is known to be a discrepancy of 0.6 Mc between the experimental and theoretical values of the Lamb shift for the $2s_{\frac{1}{2}}$ and $2p_{\frac{1}{2}}$ levels of hydrogen and deuterium.[32,33] Part of this can be ascribed to the finite proton size: according to Eqs. (2.11), (2.16), and (2.12), this produces a shift in the $2s_{\frac{1}{2}}$ level of 0.1 Mc,[34] reducing the discrepancy to 0.5 Mc. In deuterium most of the effect of finite size has already been taken into account with a term corresponding to $F_D(q^2)$ of Eq. (2.18).[33] Because of the small neutron size, the finite proton size gives an additional shift of 0.1 Mc in deuterium, the same as in hydrogen.

According to Zemach,[35] the hydrogen hyperfine structure can be used in combination with other experiments to determine a mean electromagnetic radius $\langle r\rangle_{\text{em}}$ of the proton: present experimental values lead to the result that $\langle r\rangle_{\text{em}}<0.5\times10^{-13}$ cm. This mean radius depends on both the charge and the moment distributions, the relationship among the distributions being

$$\langle r^2\rangle_{\text{em}}=\langle r^2\rangle_{\text{ch}}+\langle r^2\rangle_{\text{m}}.$$

For the shapes predicted by the electron-scattering experiments, which are not peaked at the center, $\langle r\rangle_{\text{em}}$ should not be much smaller than $(\langle r^2\rangle_{\text{em}})^{\frac{1}{2}}$. The electron-scattering values for the radii predict, however, that $(\langle r^2\rangle_{\text{em}})^{\frac{1}{2}}$ is approximately 1.0×10^{-13} cm. There is an apparent disagreement between these two

[32] Triebwasser, Dayhoff, and Lamb, Phys. Rev. **89**, 98 (1953); this paper contains references to the earlier work of Lamb and co-workers in this field.
[33] E. E. Salpeter, Phys. Rev. **89**, 92 (1953).
[34] The reliability of the perturbation theory has been confirmed by considering exact solutions of the Dirac equation containing a potential of the kind shown in Fig. 2.
[35] A. C. Zemach, Phys. Rev. (to be published). We thank Dr. Zemach for informing us of this work.

determinations of the proton size. We regard electron scattering, however, as an inherently more accurate method for examining nucleon structure.

Nonelectromagnetic Interactions

The preceding discussion, and in fact all previous analyses of electron scattering, have assumed a purely electromagnetic interaction between the electron and the scatterer. Although the agreement between experiment and this theory is remarkably close,[13] it is still desirable to consider the possibility of nonelectromagnetic interactions. As is well known, there are five possible nonderivative interactions,

$$\begin{aligned} &\bar{u}uV^s && \text{(scalar)},\\ &\bar{u}\gamma_\mu uV^v && \text{(vector)},\\ &\bar{u}\gamma_\mu\gamma_\nu uV^t && \text{(tensor)}, \qquad (2.20)\\ &\bar{u}\gamma_5\gamma_\mu uV^{pv} && \text{(pseudovector)},\\ &\bar{u}\gamma_5 uV^{ps} && \text{(pseudoscalar)}, \end{aligned}$$

where the potentials V are of short range. The presence of the vector interaction would not modify the preceding phenomenological analysis, since the finite size effects appear in just this form. For example, the potentials δV of Fig. 2 are $\bar{u}\gamma_4 uV^v$ in this notation. It would alter, however, the interpretation of F_1 and F_2 in terms of nucleon structure; we shall return to this point later. An example of the tensor interaction is given by the electron's anomalous magnetic moment; the Schwinger radiative correction to scattering includes it automatically. For simplicity we will consider first the scalar interaction.

The scalar interaction differs from the interaction with an electrostatic potential by the factor of the Dirac matrix β. For low energy electrons β is effectively unity, and the two interactions will have the same effect. For example, a change of 0.5 Mc in the Lamb shift, mentioned earlier, would require a volume-integral for V^s of 8×10^{-39} Mev cm^3. At high energies ($E\gg Mc^2$) it turns out that there is no interference between the two interactions, and the scattering cross section can be written

$$\sigma(\theta)=\sigma_{\text{em}}(\theta)+\sigma_s(\theta),$$

$$\sigma_s(\theta)=\left[\int V^s d^3r/4\pi\hbar c\right]^2 q^2[F(q^2)] \times[1+2(\hbar k/Mc)\sin^2\tfrac{1}{2}\theta]^{-2}, \qquad (2.21)$$

where $F(q^2)$ is the form factor for V^s. By comparing (2.21) with (2.14), we see that σ_s has the same form as the term in σ_{em} involving the total moment, except for an extra factor of q^2. Thus the effect of σ_s is to reduce the observed magnetic moment size. For example, a scalar interaction with the above volume integral would reduce $\langle r^2\rangle_{\text{m}}$ by $(1.7\times10^{-13}\text{ cm})^2$! If, more plausibly, we were to assume that $\langle r^2\rangle_{\text{m}}$ is really $(1.0\times10^{-13}\text{ cm})^2$, then the fact that the phenomenological analysis has given its value as $(0.8\times10^{-13}\text{ cm})^2$ could be ascribed to the presence of a scalar interaction with volume-integral 3×10^{-39} Mev cm^3.

It is probably true that all of the interactions (2.20) behave similarly, i.e., they would all have effects on the cross section indistinguishable from those coming from the finite electromagnetic sizes. It seems clear that there is no interference between the vector interaction and any of the others. Thus, except for a possible anomalous vector interaction, the effect of the interactions (2.20) is to increase the cross section, and, therefore, to reduce the apparent electromagnetic size. From a theoretical point of view, such interactions would be very unpleasant, and we do not regard the possibility very seriously.

3. MESON-THEORETICAL IDEAS ABOUT NUCLEON STRUCTURE

The discussion of this section will be based on the assumption that "physical" nucleons are made of "bare" nucleons and pions interacting in a charge-symmetrical manner. The results of the phenomeonlogical analysis of the previous section will be examined from this point of view in as general a way as possible. Various calculations of nucleon structure, based on particular meson theories, can then be compared with these conclusions. Some effects associated with the presence of K mesons will also be discussed.

The assumption of charge symmetry implies a relationship between proton and neutron structure. Some of the component states of physical nucleons are represented pictorially in Fig. 7. Charge symmetry requires that, whenever a proton state contains a charged meson, there is a corresponding neutron state with a meson of the opposite sign of the charge. (If the interaction is also *charge-independent*, the amplitudes of the states

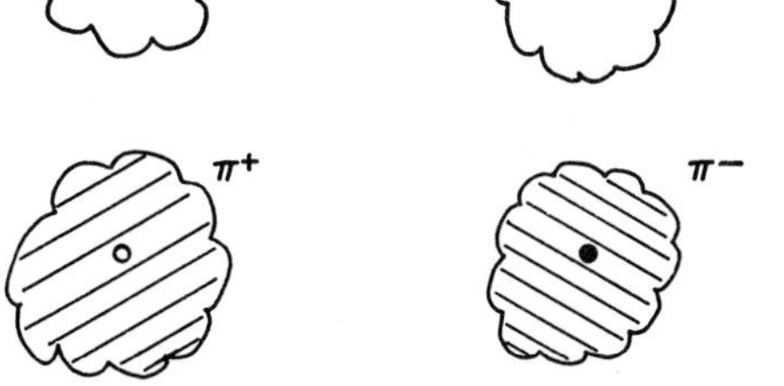

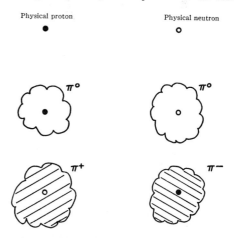

FIG. 7. A pictorial representation of some of the component states of physical nucleons, following the ideas of weak-coupling meson theory. The bare proton is indicated by the black dot, the bare neutron by the open circle.

containing neutral mesons are related to those for the charged mesons.) This is clearly true not only for those component states containing one meson, but for all states. Following Sachs,[36] we can use this result to eliminate the meson part of the nucleon charge density; if we add the proton and neutron charge densities, the meson part cancels completely. The resulting charge distribution, which is a combination of the bare nucleon parts of the proton and neutron charge densities, is called the core distribution;

$$\rho_c(r)=\rho_{c,p}(r)+\rho_{c,n}(r)$$
$$=\rho_p(r)+\rho_n(r). \tag{3.1}$$

It includes nucleon pairs as well as single nucleons. From (2.11), the mean square radius of ρ_c is given by

$$\langle r^2\rangle_c=\langle r^2\rangle_{1,p}+\langle r^2\rangle_{1,n}+(3/4M^2)[1+2(\kappa^p+\kappa^n)]. \tag{3.2}$$

There may be some doubt about the treatment of the Foldy terms, but fortunately they tend to cancel each other. The experimental values discussed in Sec. 2 then give

$$\langle r^2\rangle_c^{\frac{1}{2}}=0.77\times10^{-13}\text{ cm}. \tag{3.3}$$

For comparison, the nucleon compton wavelength is 0.21×10^{-13} cm, and the charge radius of the proton calculated in the above way is 0.84×10^{-10} cm. Thus the core radius is three and one-half times the nucleon Compton wavelength! The results of Chambers and Hofstadter[15] on the shape of the proton charge distribution, which indicate no concentration of charge at small distances, are consistent with this result, and would be inconsistent with a small core radius.

It is very difficult to understand this result. The picture we are considering for nucleon structure would attribute core size to the recoil of the nucleon upon emission of mesons, since the bare particles are assumed to have no intrinsic extension. If the momenta of the emitted mesons are small compared with Mc, by a simple velocity argument the core size will be about one-seventh ($1/7\simeq\mu/M$) of the size of the meson cloud. Under these circumstances the meson cloud extends a distance $\hbar/\mu c$, so that the core should be no bigger than $\hbar/Mc$. If, on the other hand, the virtual mesons are emitted with momenta comparable with Mc, then, because of the relativistic increase in the meson's mass, the core and the meson cloud will be about equal in size, this size being, however, around $\hbar/Mc$. For the states with more than one meson present, the situation is not clear to us. From a semiclassical standpoint, there seem to be a number of possibilities, of which we give two ex-extremes. As a starting point we assume a recoilless theory in which all of the mesons have the same wave function, centered about the fixed source. A possible approximation to the problem with recoil is to neglect its effect on the state function, and to calculate the core radius by assuming the relation

$$MR+\mu(r_1+r_2+\cdots+r_n)=0, \tag{3.4}$$

where R is the coordinate of the bare nucleon, and r is the coordinate of the ith meson, all measured from the position of the center of mass. It is then easy to show that

$$\langle R^2\rangle=\bar{n}(\mu/M)^2\langle r^2\rangle_{\text{meson}}, \tag{3.5}$$

where $\bar{n}$ is the average number of mesons present. Clearly this result cannot be correct if $\bar{n}$ is large. It seems to us that a more reasonable assumption is that the meson wave functions are centered on the instantaneous position of the bare nucleon. The result is to replace $\bar{n}$ of Eq. (3.5) by the average value of

$$n/(1+n\mu/M)^2. \tag{3.6}$$

Since this quantity has an upper limit of about $M/4\mu$, $\langle R^2\rangle$ is close to $(\hbar/Mc)^2$. Although these semiclassical arguments are difficult to justify, the second seems to us the more valid. A correct quantum-mechanical version of Eq. (3.4) will contain field operators, which may link states containing different numbers of mesons, so that the final result may differ from what we have given here. A similar situation with regard to the meson cloud has been pointed out by Sachs.[36] On the other hand, many-meson effects on the meson cloud in the Chew-Low theory do not change the one-meson results qualitatively,[37] and the same result may hold with respect to the core.[38]

[36] R. G. Sachs, Phys. Rev. 87, 1100 (1952).

[37] S. B. Treiman and R. G. Sachs, Phys. Rev. (to be published); S. Fubini, Nuovo cimento 3, 1425 (1953); H. Suura (private communication). We are informed by Dr. F. Zachariasen that, due to a computational error, the numerical values given in his calculation [Phys. Rev. 102, 295 (1956)], which are in disagreement with those of the aforementioned authors, are incorrect.

[38] A different opinion on the size of the nucleon core has been put forward by Tamm [I. Tamm, International Congress on Theoretical Physics, University of Washington (1956), reported by N. N. Bogoliubov] and is as follows. In strong-coupling theory the spatial distribution of nucleon-antinucleon pairs will be closely the same as the meson distribution. If a pair annihilates again, it will not contribute to the nucleon core. Those processes in which the antinucleon of the pair annihilates with the original nucleon do contribute, however, and the large cross section for antiproton annihilation in nuclei observed at Berkeley suggests that they can happen even for pairs created relatively far out in the meson distribution. Thus the presence of many bare-nucleon pairs in the physical nucleon can explain a core distribution which is as large as the meson distribution. These qualitative arguments are, we think, open to question on several counts. That the pair distribution follows the meson distribution will only be true for very strong coupling, where there are so many virtual mesons present that an additional amount of many times $2Mc^2$ added to the energy denominator is inappreciable. Yet the work done on the Chew-Low theory would suggest that the coupling is weak. The application of the experimental results relating to physical nucleon pairs to the annihilation of bare nucleons is not obviously justifiable. Also, it is difficult to believe that the pair contribution can be so closely the same as the meson distribution that the electron-neutron interaction cancels from an expected 10 000 volts down to 200 volts. To settle these questions, it is very necessary to make reliable calculations of the core size. As a final note of comfort, it can be pointed out that if Tamm's suggestion is correct, the true theory is a strong-coupling theory involving the emission of many nucleon pairs, and all meson calculations which have neglected pairs are of little value.

From a theoretical point of view, the correct procedure would be to calculate the appropriate vertex operator with a relativistic field theory, taking account of renormalization. The resulting form factor would include all of the relativistic effects discussed in the last section, and which the above physical arguments ignore. Unfortunately, present techniques allow calculation only in the lowest orders of perturbation theory. A summary of the results of such calculations is contained in Sec. 46 of reference 1. Fried[39] has examined the electron-neutron interaction using pseudoscalar coupling in second order perturbation theory. Using $g^2/\hbar c=13.5$, a "reasonable" value, one finds his formula gives 1300 ev for the specific interaction. Combining this work with Rosenbluth's calculations of electron-proton scattering using the same theory and approximation,[16] one obtains for this value of $g^2/\hbar c$ a core radius of 0.38×10^{-13} cm. Thus the theory to this approximation predicts a not unreasonable value for the electron-neutron interaction, but the core radius is too small by a factor two. The reliability of such calculations can be gauged by looking at their predictions for the anomalous nucleon magnetic moments. There the second-order calculation gives for the ratio $-\mu_n/(\mu_p-1)$ about seven, instead of its observed value close to unity. Although the fourth-order calculations improve the situation somewhat, the results are so different from those in second order as to indicate that no valid conclusions can be drawn from such low-order calculations. It is conceivable that if a correct calculation could be done the results would agree with the experiments. We feel, however, that this is unlikely, and that either the physical model used is basically wrong, or the phenomena can be explained in some other way.

Various calculations of neutron and proton form factors have been made using current cut-off meson theories. In these theories the bare nucleon is treated as a fixed source, and the meson-nucleon interaction is modified to include a cut-off function which suppresses the high momenta. Because the mesons, being pseudoscalar, are emitted into p states, their wave function falls off rapidly outside the source, and its size depends sensitively on the source or cut-off distribution. The cut-off function found by Chew[40] to give agreement with other meson experiments (e.g., meson-nucleon scattering meson photoproduction, etc.) leads to a meson cloud of reasonable size ($\sim0.7\times10^{-13}$ cm). In order to obtain agreement with the observed nucleon sizes, Salzman[41] has assumed arbitrarily that the core extends as far as the meson cloud. As our previous arguments suggest, it seems unlikely that present meson theories can lead to such a large core. A very necessary improvement, which has not yet been made to our knowledge, is the calculation of the core size with this theory. As a first step it may be sufficient to treat the nucleon nonrelativistically.

It has been assumed previously that these static theories do not include the Foldy terms. A proof of this, given by Salzman,[41] involves a two-component reduction of Dirac spinors, taken in the limit as M tends to infinity, but with the anomalous nucleon moment held at its observed value. A different treatment of the charge-current density, given in the appendix, considers charge and magnetic moment as independent quantities. From this point of view the static calculation of the charge density should give all of the interaction, including what from the other viewpoint are called the Foldy terms. It seems to us that all nonrelativistic theories are ambiguous in their treatment of these terms.

An interesting suggestion about the effect of heavy mesons on nucleon structure has been made by Sandri.[42] Because of the "strangeness" selection rule, the K-meson cloud surrounding the nucleon will contain only positively-charged and neutral particles. Thus in adding proton and neutron charge densities to make the core distribution, the K-meson contributions do not cancel. As Sandri points out, s-state mesons extend further than p-state mesons of the same mass. However, the relatively large K-meson mass together with the small coupling constant lead to only a small addition to the core size [about $(\hbar/Mc)^2$ to $\langle r^2\rangle_c$].

The conclusions about the nucleon core are confirmed by the electron-deuteron scattering. In fact, from Eqs. (2.18) and (3.1), we see that the elastic scattering is a process which, so far as its dependence on nucleon size is concerned, automatically measures just ρ_c. Of the various corrections to this simple nonrelativistic picture, Bernstein[31] has considered the fact that the binding is due to the exchange of mesons, rather than to an instantaneous potential. He identifies the state of two physical nucleons, with no mesons being exchanged, with the phenomenological wave function. The additional contribution to the scattering comes from the state in which one meson is being exchanged. The scattering from the exchanged mesons vanishes by charge symmetry; the effect comes from scattering by the nucleons in this state. The nucleon distribution in the one-meson state is much more peaked at the center than for the no-meson state, and as a result the cross section is enhanced for large q. Bernstein calculates the effect to be more than 10% at the largest q values shown in Fig. 6. It is not clear to us what the phenomenological Schrödinger wave functions are an approximation to, and even if the identification with the no-meson state is valid, the calculation has neglected the effect of states containing two mesons on the one-meson state, which is presumably as important as the effect Bernstein has examined. There may well be an effect of this kind, however.

[39] B. D. Fried, Phys. Rev. **88**, 1142 (1952).
[40] G. Chew, Phys. Rev. **95**, 1669 (1954).
[41] G. Salzman, Phys. Rev. **99**, 973 (1955); Phys. Rev. (to be published).
[42] G. Sandri, Phys. Rev. **101**, 1616 (1956).

4. ALTERNATIVE INTERPRETATIONS OF THE EXPERIMENTS

Since it is not clear that orthodox meson theory will be able to explain the experimental results, we consider in this section possible alternative interpretations.

Charge Symmetry

Present experimental evidence for belief in charge symmetry and charge independence is discussed in Sec. 30 of reference 1. Charge symmetry is a very plausible hypothesis that, according to experimental results, is clearly true to a good approximation, although it is impossible to make a very accurate quantitative check. A possible solution to the dilemma about nucleon structure is that charge symmetry holds for interactions over large distances, but breaks down completely for short distances. This would imply that the fundamental interaction is not charge symmetric; that the large distance effects are charge symmetric is then difficult to understand. The stronger assumption of charge independence contains charge symmetry. It is used in all current theories of phenomena involving nucleon and pions, and plays a fundamental role in theories of the strange particles. It would be a pity to throw out such a beautiful and simplifying hypothesis if any other way can be found out of the difficulty.

Current Conservation

In deriving Foldy's result, Eq. (2.5), it was necessary to assume a differential law of current conservation. Now we might imagine that, since the nucleon has a complicated structure, charge may not be conserved in small regions, but only as a whole. Although such a modification is objectionable because it violates gauge invariance, for the sake of completeness we consider it briefly.

Current conservation is expressed by Eq. (2.6), which in momentum space says that j_μ should be orthogonal to the momentum transfer q_μ. The simplest and most general charge-current density which violates this condition is

$$j_\mu' = -ieq_\mu \bar{v}(P')v(P). \tag{4.1}$$

In the static limit this implies a radial current flow, but gives no contribution to the charge density. If (4.1) is inserted into the matrix element (2.1), the result is zero because of the conservation law obeyed by the electron. Thus, in order to obtain an electron-proton interaction, we must assume that the electron also violates current conservation. Following this through, we arrive at an additional cross section of the same form as $\sigma_s(\theta)$, shown in Eq. (2.21). Thus, as with the anomalous interactions discussed in Sec. 2, violation of charge conservation will not help in interpreting the experiments.

Electromagnetic Interaction

We can easily explain all of the experiments in terms of a modification of quantum electrodynamics at small distances. The high-momentum cutoffs introduced into the theory by Feynman[43] to suppress the ultraviolet divergences have just this effect. Following Feynman, we may introduce this cutoff as a modification in the photon propagator,

$$1/q^2 \rightarrow C(q^2)/q^2. \tag{4.2}$$

From Eqs. (2.1) and (2.5), the effect on the phenomenological analysis is seen to be the replacement of any form factor F by CF; hence these experiments cannot be used to separate finite size effects from those of a possible modification in the Coulomb law. The physical reason for this is that the scattering involves not the charge distribution, whose extension is characterized by F, but its electromagnetic potential V, which depends also on the force law; with the modification (4.2), even a point charge could give a potential of the form shown in Fig. 2.

Because the observed form factors CF_1 and CF_2 in the electron-proton scattering are essentially the same, it is possible to ascribe all of the effects to C, although we expect some intrinsic nucleon size. (If the form factors had been unequal, the two effects would be to some extent distinguishable, in that an upper limit could be put on the radius associated with C, and a lower limit on the actual finite extension.) The modification does not affect the results for the neutron charge radius, since the product $C(q^2)F_{1,n}(q)^2$ is still approximately $(1/6)q^2\langle r^2\rangle_{1,n}$ for small q. For the other experiments—electron-deuteron scattering, Lamb shift, and hyperfine splitting—the effects of finite nucleon size can be reinterpreted as being caused partly or entirely by a modification in the Coulomb law. Such an interpretation makes the reconciliation of the various nucleon properties much easier. With the assumption that, for example, the meson cloud extends only to about $\hbar/Mc$, it is quite plausible that the core and meson distributions are similar enough that the electron-neutron interaction can be as low as 200 ev, especially since the effect of K mesons can be important at this small distance. At the same time the meson clouds in the neutron and proton are charge symmetric, so the near equality of κ^p and $-\kappa^n$ is maintained.

It is hard to devise experiments which would clearly distinguish between a modification in quantum electrodynamics and the effect of finite nucleon size. The most obvious possibility is high-energy electron-electron scattering, but the laboratory energy required to obtain a center-of-momentum energy of 100 Mev is 40 Bev! Processes which involve only real photons, such as Compton scattering, are not affected by a change in the photon propagator [since $C(k^2=0)=1$], although

[43] R. P. Feynman, Phys. Rev. 74, 939 (1948).

particle structure will alter the process. Other electrodynamic processes, such as bremsstrahlung and pair production, usually involve such a small momentum transfer that nuclear size itself is unimportant. In estimating the electromagnetic effects in proton-proton scattering, and in the properties of light nuclei, the two alternatives have slightly different effects, but they would be masked by the greater uncertainty in our knowledge of nuclear forces.

A modification in the Coulomb law would alter slightly the results of other experiments. For example, the radii of nuclear charge distributions deduced from mu-mesic atom level structure and high-energy electron-nucleus scattering would be reduced slightly. For mean square radii the effect is given by

$$\langle r^2\rangle_{\text{obs}}=\langle r^2\rangle_{\text{charge}}+\langle r^2\rangle_c.$$

There would also be some alteration in the nuclear surface thickness.[44]

The theoretical implications of such a modification in quantum electrodynamics have been discussed by Feynman,[45] in an article reviewing the present situation in fundamental theoretical physics, and we will recapitulate some of the points discussed. The renormalization view of the theory regards the cutoffs as mathematical devices to eliminate divergences, with no physical consequences. In contrast to this, Feynman's viewpoint is that they are the manifestation of effects not included in the present theory, which we do not know how to describe in a more fundamental way. According to the former view the theory cannot be used to calculate quantities which depend sensitively on the cutoff—the neutron-proton mass difference, for example. From the latter view, such quantities can be used to give information about the cutoff. Feynman's results for the $N-P$ mass-difference correspond to a cutoff of the same order of magnitude as that required for the electron scattering.

Vacuum polarization affects the photon propagator in the manner indicated by Eq. (4.2), but in the opposite direction to that of a finite size. Feynman brings about the finite size modification described by Eq. (4.2) by introducing "heavy photons." Because their potential must at short distances cancel the Coulomb potential, it is unfortunately necessary that their coupling constant be imaginary. As has been discussed by Feynman, this leads to very fundamental difficulties with regard to conservation of probability. In fact it seems to be impossible to obtain the finite-size effects required from a consistent, point-interaction theory. General arguments lead to an expression for the renormalized photon propagator of the form[46]

$$D_F(q^2)=q^{-2}\left\{1-q^2\int_0^\infty \sigma(\kappa^2)d\kappa^2/\kappa^4(q^2+\kappa^2)\right\}^{-1}, \quad (4.3)$$

where $\sigma(\kappa^2)\geqslant 0$. The form factor must then be of the general form

$$C(q^2)=\left\{1-\int_0^\infty \sigma(\kappa^2)d\kappa^2/\kappa^4 + \int_0^\infty \sigma(\kappa^2)d\kappa^2/\kappa^2(q^2+\kappa^2)\right\}^{-1}. \quad (4.4)$$

Even though it may not be possible to expand the integral of Eq. (4.4) in ascending powers of q^2, it is clear that the whole expression is an increasing function of q^2, and so cannot represent a finite-size effect.

Thus, unless it is possible for pion-nucleon theory to explain the large core size, it seems necessary to make a fundamental revision of present electrodynamic theory. Theoretical arguments concerned with the consistancy of the theory have been advanced by many authors[47] for such a revision, and the nucleon-size experiments may be the first experimental manifestation of this need. It may be necessary to describe nucleons by nonlocal fields, or even to alter our usual concepts of space at small distances.‡

Finite Electron Size

As can be seen from Eq. (2.1), the experiments could also be explained in terms of a finite electron size. Most of the remarks made in connection with the modification of the Coulomb law apply here also. In particular, electron-electron scattering at ultra-high energies would distinguish this possibility from the others. The main objection to this explanation is that there is no reason why the Dirac electron theory should break down at this particular wavelength, since it is clearly valid to wavelengths considerably shorter than $\hbar/mc$, its natural length. We do not regard it as a very likely explanation of the experiments.

---

[44] For the nuclei examined in Hahn, Ravenhall, and Hofstadter [Phys. Rev. **101**, 1131 (1956)], the nuclear surface thickness is decreased by about 13%, while the value of c (the point where the charge distribution has dropped to a half of its central value) is increased by about one percent.

[45] R. P. Feynman, Anais acad. brasil. Ciênc. **26**, 1 (1954).

[46] Section 25c of reference 1; G. Källén, Helv. Phys. Acta **25**, 417 (1952); H. Lehmann, Nuovo cimento **11**, 342 (1954); J. S. Schwinger, Lectures at Stanford, 1956. We would like to acknowledge the clarification of these points produced by Professor Schwinger's stimulating lectures.

[47] G. Källén, *Proceedings of the CERN Symposium* (Geneva, Switzerland, 1956), Vol. 2, p. 187; L. Landau and I. Pomeranchuk, Doklady Akad. Nauk. U. S. S. R. **102**, 489 (1955) [a review of the work of Landau and colleagues on this subject is given in Pomeranchuk, Sudakov, and Ter-Martirosyan, Phys. Rev. **103**, 784 (1956)]; J. S. Schwinger, reference 46.

‡ *Note added in proof.*—A recent determination of the electron's magnetic moment by P. A. Franken and S. Liebes, Jr. [Phys. Rev. **104**, 1197 (1956)] gives the result that $(\mu_e/\mu_0)_{\text{exp}}=1+(\alpha/2\pi)+(0.7\pm2.0)(\alpha^2/\pi^2)$. The value of the third term predicted by quantum electrodynamics [R. Karplus and N. Kroll, Phys. Rev. **77**, 536 (1950)] is -2.973 (α^2/π^2). The discrepancy may perhaps be another indication of the breakdown of quantum electrodynamics.

5. SUMMARY

An examination has been made of the present experimental situation regarding the electromagnetic structure of nucleons. It is difficult to understand the remarkable difference in charge radius between the neutron and the proton. Relativistic effects are not expected to be too important, and current meson theories which are charge symmetric seem to us unable to explain the difference. It may be that our physical considerations have leaned too heavily on weak-coupling concepts and results, but a calculation which does not make this approximation, and which at the same time does not neglect recoil, has not yet been made. Apart from this, there seem to be two relatively simple explanations: (i) that charge symmetry does not hold for very small distances; or (ii), that quantum electrodynamics fails at high energies—in other words, that the interaction between two charges is not $(1/r)$ at very small distances. The first alternative would destroy the simplicity of present charge-independent field theories. The second would require a fundamental alteration of present field theory.

ACKNOWLEDGMENTS

In collecting the ideas which form the body of this paper we have benefited greatly from discussions with very many people, both at Stanford and elsewhere. We should like to acknowledge particularly the interest of Professor Robert Hofstadter and Dr. J. A. McIntyre, whose experiments stimulated this investigation. We wish to thank also Professor L. I. Schiff and Professor W. E. Lamb, Jr., for several helpful conversations and Professor Sidney D. Drell for a critical reading of the manuscript.

APPENDIX. GROUP-THEORETICAL TREATMENT OF CHARGE-CURRENT DISTRIBUTIONS OF RELATIVISTIC PARTICLES

There are well-known group-theoretical arguments that nonrelativistic particles of definite spin and parity can possess only certain electric and magnetic multipole moments. In this appendix those arguments will be extended to relativistic particles, and it will be shown in particular that for a spin one-half particle the most general expression of the current density is given by Eq. (2.5).

We shall be interested primarily in matrix elements of the current-density operator between states of definite momentum and spin projection

$$J_\mu(\mathbf{P}',m';\mathbf{P}m)\delta(P'-P-q)=\langle\mathbf{P}',m|j_\mu(q)|\mathbf{P},m\rangle. \quad \text{(A-1)}$$

The physical states of the particle, $|\mathbf{P}m\rangle$, $|\mathbf{P}'m'\rangle$, include all of the effects of the interaction which produces its internal structure; here we need use only the information that these states form a basis for a representation of the inhomogeneous Lorentz group corresponding to a definite spin. The operator $j_\mu(q)$ is the Fourier transform of the current-density operator

$$j_\mu(q)=(2\pi)^{-4}\int j_\mu(x)e^{-iq_\lambda x_\lambda}d^4x. \quad \text{(A-2)}$$

The δ function representing energy and momentum conservation arises from the fact that $j_\mu(x)$ may be expressed

$$j_\mu(x)=e^{iP_\lambda x_\lambda}j_\mu(0)e^{-iP_\lambda x_\lambda}, \quad \text{(A-3)}$$

where P_λ is the energy-momentum operator for the system. In momentum space, charge conservation is expressed by

$$q_\mu j_\mu(q)=0. \quad \text{(A-4)}$$

This imposes a condition on the matrix elements of j_μ

$$(P'-P)_\mu J_\mu(\mathbf{P}'m';\mathbf{P}m)=0. \quad \text{(A-5)}$$

Under a homogeneous Lorentz transformation the state vectors $|\mathbf{P}m\rangle$ and the operators $j_\mu(q)$ transform in a definite way (which fortunately we need consider explicitly only in special simple cases). Thus a knowledge of $J_\mu(\mathbf{P}'m';\mathbf{P}m)$ for one pair of momenta $\mathbf{P}$, $\mathbf{P}'$ and all m, m' will determine J_μ for all other $\mathbf{P}m$, $\mathbf{P}'m'$ that can be reached from the first set by a Lorentz transformation. The totality of such pairs is given by

$$(\bar{P}'-\bar{P})^2=(P'-P)^2=q^2. \quad \text{(A-6)}$$

Thus, for a given q^2, the current density is characterized by at most $4(2s+1)^2$ independent constants: in fact, as we shall see, the actual number of such constants is $(2s+1)$. For a given value of q^2 it now seems appropriate to study the properties of the current density for some particularly simple values of $\mathbf{P}$, $\mathbf{P}'$. The simplest choice seems to be

$$\mathbf{P}'=-\mathbf{P}=\tfrac{1}{2}\mathbf{q}. \quad \text{(A-7)}$$

For simplicity we orient the z axis along $\mathbf{q}$; then since q_0 necessarily vanishes for this combination of momenta, Eq. (5) reduces to

$$J_z(\tfrac{1}{2}\mathbf{q},m';-\tfrac{1}{2}\mathbf{q},m)=0. \quad \text{(A-8)}$$

It will also be convenient to take the direction of spin quantization along the z axis. Then under a rotation about the z axis through an angle ϕ, the states and the operators j_μ will transform according to

$$R_z(\phi)|\pm\tfrac{1}{2}\mathbf{q},m\rangle=e^{im\phi}|\pm\tfrac{1}{2}\mathbf{q},m\rangle \quad \text{(A-9)}$$

$$R_z(\phi)j_0(q)R_z^{-1}(\phi)=j_0(q) \quad \text{(A-10a)}$$

$$R_z(\phi)[j_x(q)\pm ij_y(q)]R_z^{-1}(\phi)=e^{\pm i\phi}[j_x(q)\pm ij_y(q)]. \quad \text{(A-10b)}$$

From this we can easily deduce that (displaying only the m dependence)

$$J_0(m',m)=A(m)\delta_{mm'} \quad \text{(A-11a)}$$

$$J_\pm(m',m)=J_x(m',m)\pm iJ_y(m',m)=B_\pm(m)\delta_{m'm\pm1}. \quad \text{(A-11b)}$$

Further information can be obtained by making the following combination of transformations: (i) space inversion, which leaves m, m' unchanged, but reverses the sign of $\mathbf{q}$ and the spatial components of j_μ; (ii) rotation of 180° about the y axis, which reverses the sign of m, m', but restores the original sign of $\mathbf{q}$ and the x component of j_μ. Since this combination of operations must leave the matrix element unchanged (the specific effect of the parity operation on the states of the particle cancels out because the particle has definite parity), we find the relations

$$A(m)=A(-m)=A(|m|) \qquad \text{(A-12a)}$$

$$B_\pm(m)=-B_\mp(-m). \qquad \text{(A-12b)}$$

The minus sign arises from the fact that $R_y(\pi)|\frac{1}{2}\mathbf{q},m\rangle=(-1)^{s+m}|-\frac{1}{2}\mathbf{q},-m\rangle$, according to the usual conventions. The reality properties of the operators

$$j_0^*(\mathbf{q})=j_0(-\mathbf{q});\ \mathbf{j}^*(\mathbf{q})=\mathbf{j}(-\mathbf{q}), \qquad \text{(A-13)}$$

in combination with a space inversion, lead to the further relations

$$A^*(m)=A(m) \qquad \text{(A-14)}$$

$$B_\pm^*(m)=-B_\mp(m+1). \qquad \text{(A-15)}$$

Thus the A's are real. The reality properties of the B's are not fixed by the present considerations alone, but it can be shown by time-reversal arguments[48] that $B_+(m)=B_+[(m+1)$ for the usual choice of phase of the angular momentum states. When this is combined with Eqs. (A-12b) and (A-15), it is seen that the B's are also real. No additional information can be obtained by considering rotations about the x and y axes since, in contrast to the situation in the nonrelativistic case, a preferred axis ($\mathbf{q}$) enters the definition of the spin states.

We may now illustrate these results for the few lowest spins.

Spin Zero

The m label may be omitted, and for the special choice of momenta we have simply

$$J_0=A(q^2), \qquad \text{(A-16)}$$
$$\mathbf{J}=0.$$

These may be expressed in covariant form,

$$J_\mu(P';P)=(1/2M)(P+P')_\mu F(q^2), \qquad \text{(A-17)}$$

where

$$F(q^2)=[M/(M^2+\tfrac{1}{4}q^2)^{\frac{1}{2}}]A(q^2). \qquad \text{(A-18)}$$

This is just the form for the current density of a Klein-Gordon particle modified by a form factor $F(q^2)$, which may represent possible internal structure. We emphasize again that it is not necessary to assume the particle to be a Klein-Gordon particle, but only that it is a spin-zero particle.

[48] This possibility was suggested by Professor S. D. Drell. For a discussion of time reversal, see S. Watanabe, Revs. Modern Phys. **27**, 40 (1955). See also F. Coester, Phys. Rev. **89**, 619 (1953).

Spin One-Half

The nonvanishing matrix elements may be written out explicitly

$$J_0(\tfrac{1}{2};\tfrac{1}{2})=J_0(-\tfrac{1}{2};-\tfrac{1}{2})=A(q^2), \qquad \text{(A-19)}$$

$$J_+(-\tfrac{1}{2};\tfrac{1}{2})=-J_-(\tfrac{1}{2};-\tfrac{1}{2})=B(q^2). \qquad \text{(A-20)}$$

In order to write these in covariant form, it is convenient to introduce Dirac spinors which transform in the same way as the states $|\mathbf{P}m\rangle$; these are the usual quantities $v_{\mathbf{P}m}$, which for convenience we take to have the relativistic normalization

$$\bar{v}_{\ m}v_{\mathbf{P}m}=1. \qquad \text{(A-21)}$$

The form of current density given in Eq. (2.5) has the right transformation properties and the arbitrarines necessary to fit the two functions A and B; it is therefore one possible way of writing Eqs. (A-19) and (A-20) covariantly. Any other covariant forms can always be reduced to Eq. (2.5); this analysis shows also that the most general covariant expression for a current which is not conserved is given by Eq. (4.1). The relation between A, B and F_1, F_2 is

$$\begin{aligned} A(q^2)&=e[F_1(q^2)-\kappa(q^2/4M^2)F_2(q^2)],\\ B(q^2)&=2e(|q|/2M)[F_1(q^2)+\kappa F_2(q^2)]. \end{aligned} \qquad \text{(A-22)}$$

We may also define a "charge" form factor by

$$F_{\rm ch}(q^2)=[M/(M^2+\tfrac{1}{4}q^2)^{\frac{1}{2}}]\times[F_1(q^2)-\kappa(q^2/4M^2)F_2(q^2)]. \qquad \text{(A-23)}$$

The factor $M/(M^2+\frac{1}{4}q^2)^{\frac{1}{2}}$ is the reciprocal of the usual E/M factor in the relativistic charge density [see Eqs. (A-17) and (A-18)].

We can now see why there is an ambiguity in calculating the nucleon's charge distribution according to a fixed source meson theory. In the limit $M\rightarrow\infty$, there is no distinction between $A(q^2)/e$, $F_1(q^2)$ and $F_{\rm ch}(q^2)$; however, for finite M we do not know with which quantity the static charge distribution is to be associated. The difference between the first and second possibilities is just the Foldy term, which is not negligible. The difference between the first and third possibilities is associated with the Lorentz contraction of the charge and it is comparatively unimportant for the analysis of the present paper.

Spin One

A new feature arises in the case of spin one in that it is now necessary to specify two constants in order to determine the charge density completely. The new constant is clearly associated with the possibility of an electric quadrupole moment, so we write the charge density in the form

$$J_0(m';m)=A_1(q^2)\delta_{m'm}+A_2(q^2)(m^2-\tfrac{2}{3})\delta_{m'm}. \quad \text{(A-24)}$$

The second term has been so chosen that it vanishes upon averaging over m. Only one constant is needed to specify the current density in the special Lorentz frame.

This result has applications to electron scattering from deuterium. R. Blankenbecler[30] has performed such a calculation by expressing the current density in a covariant form using the β-matrix formalism.

Spin Three-Halves and Higher

One new constant is needed to describe the current density of a spin three-halves particle. It is associated with the possibility of a magnetic octupole moment and occurs explicitly because $J_+(\frac{3}{2},\frac{1}{2})$ and $J_+(\frac{1}{2},-\frac{1}{2})$ are not related to each other by group-theoretical considerations. In this way, every increase of the spin by one-half will result in the possible addition of an electric or magnetic multipole moment.

Cross-Section Formula

In practical applications we often have to evaluate quantities of the form

$$\langle J_\mu{}^*J_\nu\rangle_{\text{Av}}=\frac{1}{2s+1}\sum_{mm'} \times J_\mu{}^*(\mathbf{P}m;\mathbf{P}'m')J_\nu(\mathbf{P}'m';\mathbf{P}m). \quad \text{(A-25)}$$

In the special Lorentz frame it is easy to see that

$$\langle J_0{}^*J_0\rangle_{\text{Av}}=\bar{A}^2,$$
$$\langle J_0{}^*J_i\rangle_{\text{Av}}=0, \quad \text{(A-26)}$$
$$\langle J_i{}^*J_j\rangle_{\text{Av}}=\begin{cases}\bar{B}^2\delta_{ij}, & i=x,y,\\ 0, & i=z,\end{cases}$$

where

$$A^2=\frac{1}{2s+1}\sum_m |A(m)|^2,$$
$$B^2=\frac{1}{2}\frac{1}{2s+1}\sum_m |B_+(m)|^2. \quad \text{(A-27)}$$

Defining $\bar{P}_\mu=P_\mu+P'_\mu$, Eq. (A-26) may be expressed in the covariant form

$$\langle J_\mu{}^*J_\nu\rangle_{\text{Av}}=\bar{A}^2[\bar{P}_\mu\bar{P}_\nu/(-\bar{P}^2)] +\bar{B}^2[\delta_{\mu\nu}-(q_\mu q_\nu/q^2)-(\bar{P}_\mu\bar{P}_\nu/\bar{P}^2)]. \quad \text{(A-28)}$$

In order to calculate the cross section, a similar sum must be carried out over the electron spins; the result is

$$\langle j_\mu{}^*j_\nu\rangle_{\text{Av}}\langle J_\mu{}^*J_\nu\rangle_{\text{Av}}=(e^2/2m^2)\{(\bar{A}^2+\bar{B}^2) \times[-q^2-(\bar{P}\cdot\bar{k})^2/\bar{P}^2]+2\bar{B}^2q^2\}, \quad \text{(A-29)}$$

where $\bar{k}_\mu=k_\mu+k_\mu'$. From this the cross section may be obtained directly in any coordinate system by inserting the proper expressions for incident flux, density of final states, etc.

Possible Extensions of the Method

The same method may be applied to the matrix elements for pair production with only changes of detail. In this case $q^2<0$ and it is convenient to choose the frame in which $\mathbf{q}=0$. Then the matrix elements of j_0 vanish, while those of j_z do not. Because the range of q^2 is different from that for scattering, group theory seems to impose no relationship between pair production and scattering. However, if these matrix elements are used directly in higher order perturbation calculations, the result will not usually be gauge invariant (in spite of charge conservation!), and it will be necessary to introduce extra terms to maintain gauge invariance. At present the method seems fruitful only in lowest order perturbation theory.

We may also employ these techniques to calculate the form of the matrix element for systems making a transition (for example, a nuclear transition or photoproduction of pions). For any specific case the procedure would be quite clear, so we shall not present any general rules. Suffice it to say that the result is the relativistic generalization of the usual multipole description of radiative transitions.

PAPER 40*

Electron Scattering from Nonspherical Nuclei*†

B. W. Downs,‡ D. G. Ravenhall, and D. R. Yennie
Stanford University, Stanford, California
(Received March 5, 1957)

To explain the anomalously smooth cross sections observed in electron scattering from certain nuclei (Hf, Ta, W, U), the contributions to the cross section arising from the nonspherical character of those nuclei have been examined. Approximations are developed for the calculation of these contributions, and for a sample case, Ta, numerical results are given; the value required for the nuclear distortion in order to obtain agreement with experiment in this case is in good agreement with the spectroscopic and Coulomb-excitation values. The results suggest that in certain cases electron scattering will be a useful new method for measuring both the magnitude and the radial shape of nuclear deformations.

1. INTRODUCTION

EXPERIMENTS on high-energy electron scattering by some heavy nuclei (e.g., gold, lead, bismuth) yield differential cross sections with pronounced diffraction structure.[1] On the assumption of elastic scattering from a spherically symmetric nuclear charge distribution these cross sections have been found to indicate distributions approximately uniform in the center, with a relatively sharp surface. Another group of elements (hafnium, tantalum, tungsten, uranium) show, however, markedly different differential cross sections: as can be seen from Fig. 1, they have roughly the same slope (on a semilog plot) but show no diffraction dips. In an attempted analysis of the latter experiments it was found to be not possible to alter the radius and surface thickness of the smoothed uniform charge distribution so as to fit both the lack of diffraction structure and the rather shallow slope. In search of a reason for this strange behavior, one notices that the first-mentioned group of nuclei are at or close to closed nucleon shells, whereas the second group occupies positions in the middle of a shell. Using a collective nuclear model, Bohr and Mottelson[2] have characterized nuclei in the first group as essentially spherically symmetric, while those in the second group have equilibrium shapes far from spherical, having, as a consequence, low-lying levels corresponding to a collective rotation of the outer nucleons. The energy resolution of the electron-scattering experiments does not distinguish between elastic scattering and inelastic scattering corresponding to excitation of such levels. In an attempt to explain the observed smooth cross section, an approximate calculation has been made of differential cross sections for scattering from such a deformed nucleus. It is found that agreement can be obtained by suitable choice of the parameters involved. The method, with more extensive analysis, may possibly be used to give information about both the magnitude and radial shape of nuclear deformations.[3,4]

* Supported in part by the United States Air Force through the Air Force Office of Scientific Research, Air Research and Development Command.

† Part of a thesis submitted by one of us (B.W.D.) in partial fulfillment for the Ph. D. degree, Stanford University, June 1955.

‡ Present address: Laboratory of Nuclear Studies, Cornell University, Ithaca, New York.

[1] Hahn, Ravenhall, and Hofstadter, Phys. Rev. **101**, 1130 (1956). For a complete bibliography of electron scattering, see R. Hofstadter, Revs. Modern Phys. **28**, 214 (1956).

[2] A. Bohr and B. R. Mottelson, Kgl. Danske Videnskab. Selskab, Mat.-fys. Medd. **27**, No. 16 (1953).

[3] A preliminary account of this work was given at the 1954 Winter Meeting of the American Physical Society, reported in Phys. Rev. **98**, 277(A) (1954).

[4] A more detailed account of the analysis and results of this calculation is contained in the Ph. D. dissertation of one of us: B. W. Downs, Ph. D. dissertation, Stanford University, 1955 (unpublished).

* *See page 684 of this volume for corrections and addenda.*

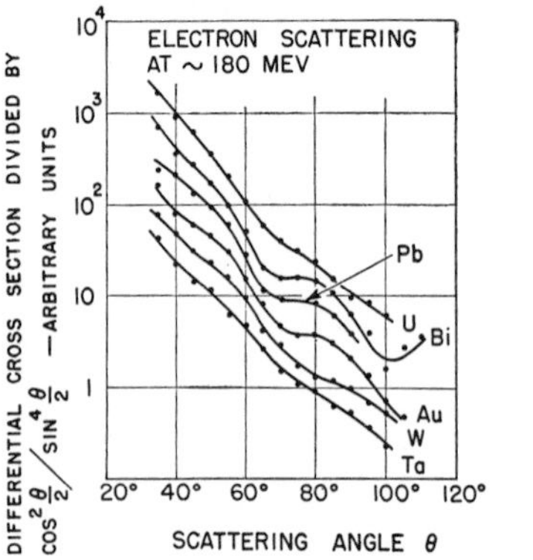

FIG. 1. Experimental cross sections for scattering of 180-Mev electrons by some heavy nuclei. To display the diffraction structure more prominently, the cross section has been divided by $[\cos^2(\frac{1}{2}\theta)/\sin^4(\frac{1}{2}\theta)]$, which is proportional to the point-scattering cross section in first Born approximation.

The system to be investigated is that of a very energetic electron scattered by the Coulomb field of a heavy, nonspherical nucleus, with the possibility of nuclear excitation. It has been shown previously, for the spherically symmetrical case with no excitation, that a solution accurate enough for detailed comparison with the experiments requires a complete phase-shift analysis of the Dirac equation for the system.[5] Such an analysis would be impossible for the system of interest here since the Dirac equation cannot be separated into partial waves. It has therefore been necessary to make a number of approximations. These are as follows:

(a) The interactions additional to the spherically symmetric interaction (that is, the fields of higher multipole order caused by the nonspherical charge distribution and by the nuclear excitation) are assumed small, and are treated by first-order perturbation theory.

(b) The electron wave functions used in the above perturbation theory, which describe scattering in the spherically symmetric part of the charge distribution, will be approximated by distorted plane waves (the zero-order scattering by the spherically symmetric part of the charge distribution is *not* approximated: it is calculated by the phase-shift analysis described previously).

(c) A model of the nucleus which is essentially an extension of Bohr's collective model in the strong-coupling limit will be assumed.

Approximation (a) is necessary in order to be able to do the calculation at all. We feel that this is a plausible approximation, although at present it cannot be strictly justified. We shall discuss it at the end of Sec. 2, after the formalism has been developed. Approximation (b) is not mandatory, since it is feasible to use as zero-order wave functions the exact partial-wave expansion of the elastically scattered wave. In the case of interest here it would be necessary to evaluate and combine about sixty radial matrix elements. The alternative we have chosen is to find for the wave function describing the elastic scattering a three-dimensional approximation which is reliable close to the nucleus. The complete matrix element can then be evaluated analytically. With approximation (c) the sum of elastic and inelastic scattering due to the deformed part of the charge distribution turns out to be independent of the nuclear spin, and is identical with what would be obtained from a classical, deformed charge distribution oriented at random.[6] That this should be so can be understood by uncertainty principle arguments, since the energy is not resolved. We assume, with Bohr,[2] that the radial matrix element is the same for all transitions; instead of the surface delta function, however, we use a smooth transition density approximately proportional to $\partial\rho_0/\partial r$, where ρ_0 is the spherically symmetric part of the charge distribution. The use of the Bohr model for the nuclear matrix elements thus simplifies the analysis, but it is not essential. Since, however, comparison with experiment does not allow complete determination of the parameters of even this simplified model, it would be unprofitable at this stage to consider more complex matrix elements.

2. ANALYSIS

The development of the three-dimensional approximation to the wave function describing the elastic scattering will be given in a later paper,[7] and we summarize it here. It is based on two observations concerning the behavior of the exact partial waves near the nucleus: the radial wave functions are to a good approximation spherical Bessel functions with modified argument; and the total phase shifts are connected for small j by the relation

$$\eta_j = a + bj(j+1), \quad (1)$$

where $j(j+1)\hbar^2$ is the eigenvalue of the square of the total angular momentum J. Thus the total scattering wave function $\varphi^{(\pm)}(\mathbf{r})$ [where (+), (−) refer, respectively, to outgoing and incoming scattered waves], which rigorously is an expansion in terms of the exact radial wave functions $F_j(r)$ and $G_j(r)$ and the spin-angular functions χ_j^1 and χ_j^2,

$$\varphi^{(\pm)}(\mathbf{r}) = \sum_j (kr)^{-1} i^{j-\frac{1}{2}} e^{\pm i\eta_j} [G_j\chi_j^1 + iF_j\chi_j^2], \quad (2)$$

can be approximated at small distances by

$$\varphi^{(\pm)}(\mathbf{r}) \simeq (k'/k) e^{\pm i\eta} \sum_j i^{j-\frac{1}{2}} [j_{j-\frac{1}{2}}(k'r)\chi_j^1 + i j_{j+\frac{1}{2}}(k'r)\chi_j^2]$$
$$= (k'/k) e^{\pm i\eta} e^{i\mathbf{k}'\cdot\mathbf{r}} \begin{pmatrix} \cos\frac{1}{2}\theta \\ \sin\frac{1}{2}\theta \exp(i\phi) \end{pmatrix}, \quad (3)$$

where k' is the electron's wave number in the vicinity

[5] Yennie, Ravenhall and Wilson, Phys. Rev. 95, 500 (1954).

[6] L. I. Schiff, Phys. Rev. 96, 765 (1954).

[7] D. R. Yennie and D. G. Ravenhall (to be published).

of the nucleus and η is now the operator

$$\eta=a+b[i^{-1}\mathbf{r}\times\nabla+\tfrac{1}{2}\boldsymbol{\sigma}]^2. \qquad (4)$$

The simple form of Eq. (3) arises from the physical situation that an incident plane wave, after traveling through the weak, slowly varying Coulomb field, arrives at the nucleus with modified argument, amplitude, and phase, and with curved wave fronts [due to the factor $\exp(ibJ^2)$]. For the case of interest here, scattering of 182-Mev electrons by tantalum ($Z=73$), b turns out to be -0.0080 which is small enough for us to expand the exponential in powers of b and retain only the first few terms.

The application of the Born approximation to this physical situation has been made by Schiff in some detail.[6] He obtains the results, mentioned in the Introduction, that the total contribution to the scattering from the intrinsic nuclear deformation is independent of the nuclear spin, and is equivalent to scattering from a classical deformed charge distribution. The corresponding arguments in the present case with the more accurate wave functions (2) are essentially the same as Schiff's, but we give them for the sake of completeness.

The essential feature of the Bohr-Mottelson model is the close connection between the static quadrupole moment and the $E2$ transition matrix elements among the rotational levels. These matrix elements of the charge density operator $\rho_{\text{op}}(\mathbf{r})$,

$$\rho_{\text{op}}(\mathbf{r})=\sum\nolimits_{\text{protons}} e\delta(\mathbf{r}-\mathbf{r}_p),$$

are related as follows:

$$\begin{aligned}\langle I'M'|\rho_{\text{op}}(\mathbf{r})|IM\rangle &=\delta_{II'}\delta_{MM'}\rho_0(r)+(2I+1)^{\frac{1}{2}}[\textstyle\sum_m \gamma_{II'}^{(2)}\\ &\quad\times C_{II'}(2m;-M'M)Y_{2m}(\theta,\phi)]\rho_2(r)+\cdots. \end{aligned}\qquad (5)$$

The dependence on the Clebsch-Gordan coefficients C is a consequence of rotational invariance. The factors $\gamma_{II'}^{(2)}$ are peculiar to the Bohr-Mottelson model; for $I\neq\frac{1}{2}$ they are given by

$$\begin{aligned}[\gamma_{II}^{(2)}]^2&=I(2I-1)/(I+1)(2I+3),\\ [\gamma_{II+1}^{(2)}]^2&=3I/(I+1)(I+2),\\ [\gamma_{II+2}^{(2)}]^2&=6/(I+2)(2I+3).\end{aligned}$$

They have the property, observed by Schiff,[6] that

$$\textstyle\sum_{I'}[\gamma_{II'}^{(2)}]^2=1. \qquad (6)$$

In calculating the electron scattering due to these static and transition charge densities, we shall treat the ρ_0 term exactly by using the partial-wave analysis, i.e., we solve exactly the Dirac equation containing the electrostatic potential generated by $\rho_0(r)$. The potential due to ρ_2 is then treated by perturbation theory. The scattering amplitude for elastic collisions is the sum of the ρ_0 term and a part of the ρ_2 term. It is easy to show that the interference term vanishes for an unpolarized target.

The total quadrupole contribution to the cross section is simplified because of (6), so that the total cross section, including all transitions, is given by

$$\sigma(\theta)=\sigma_0(\theta)+\sigma_2(\theta); \qquad (7)$$

for σ_2 we have the simple expression

$$\sigma_2(\theta)=(E/2\pi\hbar^2c^2)^2\textstyle\sum_m\left|\displaystyle\int\rho_2(r)Y_{2m}(\theta,\phi)V(\mathbf{r})d^3r\right|^2, \qquad (8)$$

where $V(\mathbf{r})$ is the potential due to the passing electron:

$$V(\mathbf{r})=e\int\frac{1}{|\mathbf{r}-\mathbf{r}'|}\varphi_{\mathbf{k}'}^{(-)*}(\mathbf{r}')\varphi_{\mathbf{k}}^{(+)}(\mathbf{r}')d^3r'. \qquad (9)$$

We observe that the cross section (8) is just what could be obtained from a classical deformed charge distribution, oriented at random.

A natural way to introduce this classical deformation is to write

$$\rho_d(\mathbf{r})=\rho(r[1-\alpha P_2(\cos\gamma)]), \qquad (10)$$

where α is a deformation parameter, and γ is the angle measured from the symmetry axis. Surfaces of constant charge density are give by the relation

$$r[1-\alpha P_2(\cos\gamma)]=\text{constant},$$

i.e., they are concentric and roughly spheroidal. A multipole expansion of (10) gives the result, accurate for small α, that

$$\rho_d(\mathbf{r})=\rho_0(r)+\rho_2(r)P_2(\cos\gamma)+\cdots, \qquad (11)$$

where

$$\begin{aligned}\rho_0(r)&=\rho(r)+(1/10)\alpha^2r^2\rho''(r)+\cdots,\\ \rho_2(r)&=-\alpha r\rho'(r)+(1/7)\alpha^2r^2\rho''(r)+\cdots.\end{aligned} \qquad (12)$$

If for $\rho(r)$ we use any "smoothed uniform" distribution with radius c (distance to the half-point) and surface thickness t (the 90% to 10% distance), then $\rho_0(r)$ is also a smoothed uniform distribution with parameters c_0, t_0 given by

$$\begin{aligned}c_0&\simeq c(1+\alpha^2/5),\\ t_0^2&\simeq t^2(1+3\alpha^2/5)+\lambda^2\alpha^2c^2.\end{aligned} \qquad (13)$$

For the Fermi distribution,

$$\rho(r)=\rho(0)\{1+\exp[(r-c)/0.228t]\}^{-1}, \qquad (14)$$

the parameter λ in (13) is 1.08. A result of this plausible assumption about the form of the deformation is that $\rho_2(r)$ is not independent, but is given by $\rho(r)$. It is in fact a smooth function with a maximum at $r\simeq c$, and width of order t. The intrinsic quadrupole moment Q_0, as defined by Bohr and Mottelson,[2] is given by

$$eQ_0=(8\pi/5)\int_0^\infty\rho_2(r)r^4dr. \qquad (15)$$

With a deformation of the type (10) this relation can be

simplified to

$$Q_0 = 2Z\langle r^2\rangle_d[1+6\alpha/7+O(\alpha^3)],$$

where $\langle r^2\rangle_d$ is the mean-square radius of $\rho_d(r)$; for the particular shape (14), $\langle r^2\rangle_d$ can be expressed in terms of c_0 and t_0 by the use of Eqs. (13) and the relations

$$\langle r^2\rangle_d = \langle r^2\rangle[1+9\alpha^2/5+\cdots],$$

$$\langle r^2\rangle = \tfrac{3}{5}c^2[1+1.70(t/c)^2+0.61(t/c)^4]/[1+0.58(t/c)^2]. \quad (16)$$

The remaining problem is to evaluate (9) and (8), using for the eigenstates of the ρ_0 scattering which appear in (9) the approximation (3). To do this it is necessary to expand $\exp(ibJ^2)$ in powers of b. The justification for this is that the j values that are important in the matrix element are of order $k'c$, which at this energy is about 6.4. Thus the exponent will be of order 0.4, so that an expansion which keeps terms up to b^2 should be reasonably accurate. At this point it should also be remembered that the representation (1) for η is itself an approximation; for the present situation it is accurate up to j values of about 6 or 7, however. In the expansion in powers of b, the first term, which is independent of b, results in an expression for (8) which is closely similar to the Born approximation, the only differences being in the modified amplitude and wave number. To this approximation $\sigma_2(\theta)$ still has the zeros typical of the first Born approximation. Because the term linear in b in the matrix element is $\pi/2$ out of phase with the Born-approximation term, the next contribution to $\sigma_2(\theta)$ is of order b^2. We calculate the b^2 term only at the zeros, since at these angles only the b term in the matrix element contributes to the cross section. The evaluation of this term is simplified by noting that

$$\mathbf{r}\times\nabla e^{i\mathbf{k}'\cdot\mathbf{r}} = -\mathbf{k}'\times\nabla_{k'}e^{i\mathbf{k}'\cdot\mathbf{r}}.$$

It can be expressed in terms of derivatives of the Born-approximation matrix element.

We return to the question of the validity of approximation (*a*), that the quadrupole contributions can be treated by first-order perturbation theory. Some measure of the reliability of this approximation is given by the ratio of quadrupole to monopole potentials. The maximum value of this ratio, attained at the surface, is $\epsilon = \tfrac{3}{5}\alpha[1-0.8(t/c)+\cdots]$. For the values of α needed to fit the experiments, ϵ is at most about 0.1. In fact ϵ probably overestimates the importance of the quadrupole effects, because the quadrupole potential has a short range, whereas the central potential has a long range. In any case, the smallness of ϵ implies that higher-order contributions in ϵ can be neglected. However, there are two contributions to the cross section of order ϵ^2, of which we include only σ_2. The other term of this order in ϵ^2 is the dispersion contribution to the monopole scattering, arising from virtual excitation of the rotational levels. To order ϵ^2 the monopole scattering amplitude is actually of the form

$$F_0(q)+\epsilon^2 F_{\text{disp}}(q).$$

We have not calculated $F_{\text{disp}}(q)$, but Schiff's closure estimate of this term[8] for the general case of nuclear excitation suggests that it is of the same order of magnitude as $F_0(q)$, so that the resulting contribution to the monopole cross section is only ϵ^2 of the part we use, and thus can safely be neglected.

3. RESULTS

The results of calculations for a typical case are illustrated in Fig. 2.[4] It has been made for tantalum ($Z=73$), at an energy of 182 Mev. It is seen that the quadrupole scattering does tend to fill in the diffraction minima of the ρ_0 scattering. That this should be so is clear from the simple Born-approximation argument that the form factors for the two contributions vary with q as $j_2(qc)$ and $(3/qc)j_1(qc)$, respectively, and j_1 and j_2 are $\pi/2$ out of phase. Figure 2 also illustrates the rather crude way in which we have estimated the quadrupole cross section. We have calculated the b^2 term only at the diffraction minimum of $\sigma_2(\theta)$ and have assumed that it is negligible at the diffraction maximum. From these points and from the term independent of b^2, which is easier to calculate, we have sketched in an estimated $\sigma_2(\theta)$. To the accuracy with which we wish to

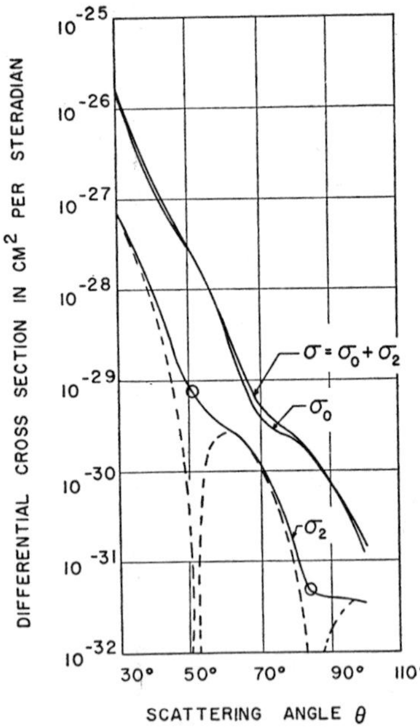

FIG. 2. A plot of the separate contributions $\sigma_0(\theta)$ and $\sigma_2(\theta)$ and the total differential cross section $\sigma(\theta)$, for electron scattering from tantalum ($Z=73$) at 182 Mev.

[8] L. I. Schiff, Phys. Rev. **98**, 756 (1955). See also B. W. Downs, Phys. Rev. **101**, 820 (1956).

compare the calculations with the experiments, this crudeness does not affect our conclusions appreciably. For a more precise comparison it is possible to calculate the b^2 term at all angles, but the evaluation is rather lengthy.

With the limitation on $\rho_2(r)$ imposed by (10), the model contains three parameters, c, t, and α, or, as has proved more convenient, c_0, t_0, and α. It is *a priori* unlikely that we can do better here than was possible with the spherically symmetric nuclei, where the pronounced diffraction structure enabled us to determine c and t. We first observe that it is not possible to fit these experimental results with $\alpha=0$ and a distribution ρ of the type exemplified by (14). Although a distribution of this type can, with large enough t, yield a cross section with little diffraction structure, the slope of the cross section is then much too steep. We next admit that since the experimental results contain very little diffraction structure, it is not possible to determine c_0 with any accuracy; we assume a value for c_0 scaled down from the result obtained for the spherically-symmetric nuclei, lead and gold, by the relation $c=1.09A^{\frac{1}{3}}\times10^{-13}$ cm, and increased a little to allow for the α^2 term in Eq. (13). If now a value of t_0 is assumed, α can be chosen to give a smooth cross section, but this cross section will not in general have the correct slope. Thus by fitting the slope also we can determine both α and t_0. Figure 3 illustrates our results for various values of α, with $c_0=6.38\times10^{-13}$ cm and $t_0=2.80\times10^{-13}$ cm. The experimental values are for Ta^{181}, at 182 Mev.[1] We estimate that the curve for $\alpha=0.19$ is smooth and is a reasonable fit to the experimental points. The intrinsic surface thickness t is from Eq. (13) equal to 2.5×10^{-13} cm, which is close to the value obtained for the spherically symmetric nuclei.[1] With the assumed radius, this value of α leads to an intrinsic quadrupole moment Q_0 of 10×10^{-24} cm², which is roughly midway between the spectroscopic and Coulomb excitation values.[9]

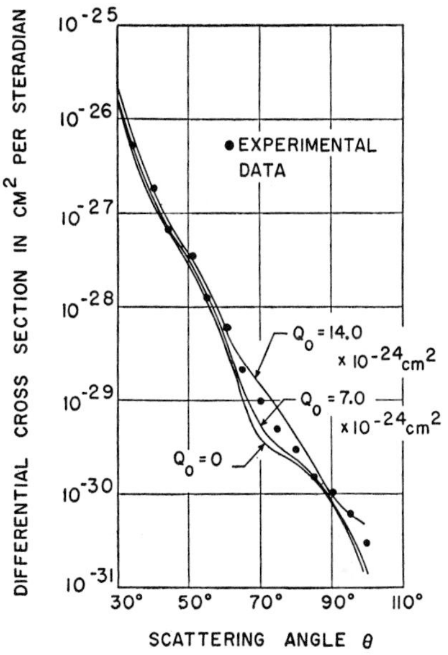

FIG. 3. Theoretical cross sections for various values of Q_0 compared with the experimental values, all for tantalum ($Z=73$) at 182 Mev.

SUMMARY

An approximate calculation has been made of quadrupole contributions to electron scattering from heavy, distorted nuclei. The general features of the results are qualitatively reliable, we feel, although inability to calculate the errors involved in the approximations does not allow us to quote accurate numerical results. The nuclear model employed contains three parameters, of which one, the radius c, cannot be determined. Assuming a reasonable value for c, comparison of the theoretical cross sections with the experiments then determines the parameter t, the surface thickness, and α, the distortion parameter. For the case of Ta^{181}, at 182 Mev, a rough comparison with experiment of our approximate calculations indicates values $t=2.5\times10^{-13}$ cm and $\alpha=0.19$. The intrinsic quadrupole moment Q_0 is then roughly 10 barns.

It is practicable, although tedious, to improve the theoretical analysis to the stage where reliable numerical values can be obtained for t and α, and consequently Q_0. Information about the shape of ρ_2 may also be found by considering it as independent of ρ_0.[4] Considerably more information could be extracted from the very difficult experiment of electron scattering from aligned tantalum nuclei, since there would then be interference between the quadrupole and monopole scattering amplitudes.

ACKNOWLEDGMENTS

We acknowledge with thanks stimulating discussions of the experiments with Dr. Beat Hahn and Professor Robert Hofstadter, and helpful conversations with Professor L. I. Schiff concerning the theory. The partial wave analyses used in this work were performed by the computer Univac of the University of California Radiation Laboratory at Livermore. We wish to thank the authorities of this Laboratory, particularly Dr. S. Fernbach, for the use of this computer.

[9] McClelland, Mark, and Goodman, Phys. Rev. **97**, 1191 (1955). These authors give Q_0 (spectroscopic) = 12.9 barns, Q_0 (Coulomb excitation yield) = 6 barns.

Possible Existence of a Heavy Neutral Meson*

YOICHIRO NAMBU
The Enrico Fermi Institute for Nuclear Studies, The University of Chicago, Chicago, Illinois
(Received April 25, 1957)

IN an attempt to account for the charge distributions of the proton and the neutron as indicated by the electron scattering experiments,[1] we would like to consider the possibility that there may be a heavy neutral meson which can contribute to the form factor of the nucleon. We assume that this meson, ρ^0, is a vector field with isotopic spin zero and a mass two to three times that of the ordinary pion, coupled strongly to the nucleon field. An isolated ρ^0 would decay through virtual nucleon pair formation according to the following schemes:

(a) $\rho^0 \to \pi^0 + \gamma, \quad 2\pi^0 + \gamma, \quad \pi^+ + \pi^- + \gamma;$

(b) $\rho^0 \to e^+ + e_-, \quad \mu^+ + \mu^-;$

(c) $\rho^0 \to \pi^+ + \pi^-.$

The process (a) would have a decay probability roughly of the order of $P_a \sim (\mu c^2/\hbar)(G^2/\hbar c)(e^2/\hbar c)(\mu/M)^2$, where G is the nuclear coupling constant, μ and M the ρ^0 and the nucleon masses, respectively. For the process (b), the probability would be $P_b \sim (\mu c^2/\hbar)(G^2/\hbar c)(e^2/\hbar c)^2 \times (\mu/M)^2$. The process (c) is a forbidden transition, so that it can take place only in violation of the isotopic spin conservation, with a decay rate comparable to that for (b).

Now the process (b) gives rise to a short-range interaction between a nucleon and an electron (or a muon) by exchange of a ρ^0. This will contribute a form factor $F'(k^2) \sim Gg/(\mu^2+k^2)$ to the electron-nucleon scattering, where g is the effective ρ^0-electron coupling, $g^2/\hbar c \sim (G^2/\hbar c)(e^2/\hbar c)^2(\mu/M)^2$. Since ρ^0 is an isotopic scalar, F' has the same sign for both proton and neutron, whereas the corresponding form factor F due to the pion cloud should change sign. Relativistic field theory shows on general grounds that $F(k^2)$ has the form

$$F(k^2) = \int_{2m_\pi}^{\infty} \frac{\rho(m)}{m^2+k^2} dm,$$

where the lower limit of integration corresponds to the threshold for pion pair creation by an external electromagnetic field. With our assumptions about ρ^0, it is thus possible that the two form factors F and F' cancel approximately for the neutron but reinforce for the proton, in agreement with observation. If we equate tentatively the mean square radius of the proton with the one due to ρ^0:

$$Gg/\mu^2 \sim e^2\langle a^2\rangle/b,$$

we get

$$(G^2/\hbar c)(g^2/\hbar c) \sim [(e^2/\hbar c)/b]^2 \sim 10^{-6},$$

which checks with the previous estimate since $G^2/\hbar c$ would be of the order one. The decay lives become, very approximately,

$$\tau_a \sim 10^{-19} - 10^{-20} \text{ sec},$$

$$\tau_b \sim \tau_c \sim 10^{-17} - 10^{-18} \text{ sec}.$$

We can pursue further consequences of our assumption.

(1) ρ^0 could be produced by any strong nuclear reactions, but it would instantly decay mostly into a high-energy $\gamma(\gtrsim 140$ Mev) and a ρ^0. The ratio of charged to neutral components in high-energy reactions should accordingly be influenced.

(2) The second maximum of the pion-nucleon scattering around 1 Bev[2] could be attributed to the reaction

$$\pi^- + p \to n + \rho^0,$$

if a resonance should occur for such a system.

(3) ρ^0 would contribute a repulsive nuclear force of Wigner type and short range ($\lesssim 0.7 \times 10^{-13}$ cm), more or less similar to the phenomenological hard core.

(4) The anomalous moment of the nucleon[3] should be affected by ρ^0. The main effect seems to be that ρ^0 and the usual pion give opposite contributions to the isotopic scalar part of the core moment, thus tending to bring better agreement between theory and experiment.

(5) If it is energetically possible, we ought to expect that K mesons and hyperons would sometimes decay by emitting a ρ^0.

It should perhaps be added that the neutral meson considered here is similar in nature to the one introduced by Teller for quite different purposes.[4]

* This work was supported by the U. S. Atomic Energy Commission.

[1] R. Hofstadter, Revs. Modern Phys. **28**, 214 (1956). Other references are given in this paper. Also E. E. Chambers and R. Hofstadter, Phys. Rev. **103**, 1456 (1956); J. A. McIntyre, Phys. Rev. **103**, 1464 (1956); R. W. McAllister, Phys. Rev. **104**, 1494 (1956); Hughes, Harvey, Goldberg, and Stafne, Phys. Rev. **90**, 497 (1953); Melkonian, Rustad, and Havens, Bull. Am. Phys. Soc. Ser. II, **1**, 62 (1956). For theoretical interpretations, see Yennie, Lévy, and Ravenhall, Revs. Modern Phys. **29**, 144 (1957).

[2] Shapiro, Leavitt, and Chen, Phys. Rev. **92**, 1073 (1953); Cool, Madansky, and Piccioni, Phys. Rev. **93**, 637 (1954); O. Piccioni and other authors, *Proceedings of the Sixth Annual Rochester Conference on High-Energy Physics 1956* (Interscience Publishers, Inc., New York, 1956). See also F. Dyson, Phys. Rev. **99**, 1037 (1955); G. Takeda, Phys. Rev. **100**, 440 (1955).

[3] H. Miyazawa, Phys. Rev. **101**, 1564 (1956); see also G. Sandri, Phys. Rev. **101**, 1616 (1956).

[4] M. H. Johnson and E. Teller, Phys. Rev. **98**, 783 (1955); H. Duerr and E. Teller, Phys. Rev. **101**, 494 (1956); E. Teller, *Proceedings of the Sixth Annual Rochester Conference on High-Energy Physics 1956* (Interscience Publishers, Inc., New York, 1956); H. Duerr, Phys. Rev. **103**, 469 (1956).

PAPER 42*

NUCLEAR AND NUCLEON SCATTERING OF HIGH-ENERGY ELECTRONS[1,2]

By Robert Hofstadter

Department of Physics, Stanford University, Stanford, California

I. INTRODUCTION

The author recently prepared a review article (1) on high-energy electron scattering and its relation to nuclear structure. In that paper various types of phenonema were discussed, important formulas of scattering theory were given, and experimental results on the sizes of nucleons and nuclei were summarized.

The purpose of the present article is somewhat different, although it, too, will be in the nature of a review and summary. In the first paper the principal results of scattering theory were collected together but not derived. In this paper the intention is threefold: (*a*) To convey to the reader the fundamental ideas of the important scattering formulas by working out sample derivations. (*b*) To collect useful results in scattering theory. (*c*) To bring the experimental and theoretical results up-to-date.

It is almost impossible to keep up with the rapid progress involved in Item (*c*), and so the present paper makes no claim to be complete.

II. THEORY OF THE SCATTERING PROCESS

A. Kinematics

In scattering electrons from massive particles such as nucleons or nuclei, the kinematic relations play a crucial role. For this reason, and because we shall use the kinematic relations in later sections, we wish to present some of the useful results below. The derivation of such purely kinematic results will not be given here, because only the well-known ideas of relativistic dynamics, employing the conservation theorems of energy and momentum, are needed to obtain complete solutions. In fact, for an elastic collision, the energy, momentum, and angular relations are similar to those used in the Compton effect. Since the rest mass of the electron is negligible compared to any nuclear mass, the high-energy incident electron of scattering theory plays the role of the incident γ-ray in the Compton effect and the scattered electron represents the outgoing degraded γ-ray. The struck nucleus is the counterpart of the ejected electron of the Compton effect (2).

Figure 1 shows the essential nature of an elastic collision. The incident

[1] The survey of the literature pertaining to this review was completed in June, 1957.

[2] The research reported here was supported jointly by the Office of Naval Research and the U. S. Atomic Energy Commission and by the U. S. Air Force, through the Office of Scientific Research of the Air Research and Development Command.

See page 684 of this volume for corrections and addenda.

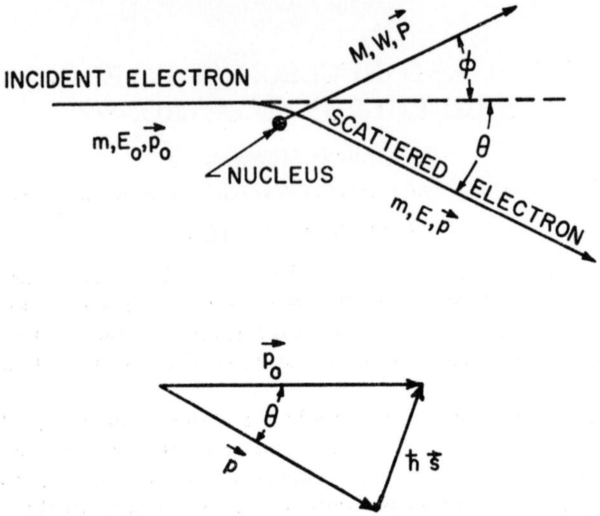

FIG. 1. Electron-scattering diagrams and definitions of symbols.

electron (energy E_0) suffers an energy loss $E_0 - E$ and loses momentum $\hbar \mathbf{s}$ in the process, the latter being transferred to the nucleus. If the nucleus, of mass M, was originally at rest, it picks up momentum

$$P = \hbar s = p_0 - p \qquad 1.$$

$$E_0 = cp_0; \qquad E = cp; \qquad E_0 - E = \Delta E \qquad 2.$$

with negligible error and thus

$$p = \frac{p_0}{1 + \frac{2E_0}{Mc^2}\sin^2 \theta/2} \qquad 3.$$

The kinetic energy (T) of the struck nucleus becomes

$$T = \frac{E_0{}^2}{Mc^2}\,\frac{2\sin^2 \theta/2}{1 + \frac{2E_0}{Mc^2}\sin^2 \theta/2} = \Delta E \qquad 4.$$

If the nucleus is nonrelativistic, this expression will also be represented by

$$T = \frac{P^2}{2M} = \frac{\hbar^2 s^2}{2M} \qquad 5.$$

Otherwise the relativistic expression for the total energy will apply:

$$W^2 = M^2c^4 + c^2P^2 \qquad 6.$$

Also

$$\hbar s = \frac{2p_0 \sin \theta/2}{\left(1 + \frac{2E_0}{Mc^2} \sin^2 \theta/2\right)^{1/2}} \left[1 + \frac{\frac{E_0^2}{M^2c^4} \sin^2 \theta/2}{1 + \frac{2E_0}{Mc^2} \sin^2 \theta/2}\right]^{1/2} \qquad 7.$$

and a new four-vector $\hbar q$ is defined such that:

$$q^2 = s^2 - \left(\frac{\Delta E}{\hbar c}\right)^2 = \frac{1}{\hbar^2} | p_0 - p |^2 - \frac{1}{\hbar^2}(p_0 - p)^2 = 4 \frac{pp_0}{h^2} \sin^2 \theta/2 \qquad 8.$$

Other useful results involving q are:

$$\Delta E = \frac{\hbar^2 q^2}{2M} \qquad 9.$$

and

$$c^2P^2 = \frac{\hbar^2 q^2}{2M}(W + Mc^2) \qquad 10.$$

The vector q is the four-dimensional momentum-energy transfer and the vector $\boldsymbol{s}$ is its spatial part which is the three-dimensional momentum transfer. The magnitude q is an invariant and the four-vector q is the difference between the four-dimensional momentum-energy vectors ($\boldsymbol{p}_0$, E_0) and ($\boldsymbol{p}$, E). From Eq. 3 and 8 it follows that

$$| q | = \frac{2 \frac{p_0}{\hbar} \sin \theta/2}{\left[1 + \frac{2E_0}{Mc^2} \sin^2 \theta/2\right]^{1/2}} = \frac{2/\lambda\!\!\!^{-} \sin \theta/2}{\left[1 + \frac{2E_0}{Mc^2} \sin^2 \theta/2\right]^{1/2}} \qquad 11.$$

where $\lambda\!\!\!^{-}$ is the de Broglie wavelength of the electron in the laboratory system. It may be noted that, even for 1-Bev incident electrons scattering against a proton, $|q|$ and $|s|$ differ only by 15 per cent at most when $\theta = \pi$. For nuclei heavier than a proton or for smaller angles, the difference is smaller. It will be seen later that q is the more fundamental quantity of the two, appearing in form factors as an invariant. However, in occasional cases, we may refer to $\boldsymbol{s}$ in partially relativistic calculations, for which the more complete relativistic solution would contain q. In those cases, where the difference between s and q is small, we shall always use q in the final formulas.

For reference, the kinetic energy of the recoiling nucleus, in terms of the an gle ϕ in Figure 1, is given by

$$T = E_0 \frac{2\left(\frac{E_0}{Mc^2}\right) \cos^2 \phi}{\left(1 + \frac{E_0}{Mc^2}\right)^2 - \frac{E_0^2}{M^2c^4} \cos^2 \phi} \qquad 12.$$

as well as by Eq. 4, which is written in terms of the electron's scattering angle.

B. Scattering Results

In this part it will be our aim to set forth three basic methods and the corresponding physical ideas, which appear frequently and are of great utility in understanding the various electron-scattering phenomena. Our program is as follows: In section 1 we shall discuss the underlying concepts which justify the use of electrons in probing the charge density in nucleons and nuclei. In section 4 we shall consider magnetic scattering. In section 12 we shall illustrate the method by which the exact scattering calculations can be carried out, that is, the phase-shift method. We shall also illustrate the various processes with examples taken from experiment and this procedure will permit us to bring the results up-to-date.

1. *The first Born approximation for the scattering of an electron without spin from a nucleus without spin.*—In order to illustrate the method and physical ideas behind the size determinations, we wish to make some simplifications that may render the physical analysis more transparent. To do this we shall employ the first Born approximation (3), and we shall further assume that the incident electrons do not have spin. We shall show later how the spin may be put back on the incident particle and how more exact methods may be used where needed. Though not exact, the Born approximation supplies a very powerful tool in understanding the physical ideas in the scattering patterns for light nuclei and in giving a qualitative picture of diffraction phenomena for heavier nuclei.

Let us assume that the target nucleus contains Z point-protons, each of charge e, but, like the electron, also without spin. We assign wave functions $\Phi_i(i=0, 1, 2 \cdots)$ to the nucleus containing the coordinates $\boldsymbol{R}_k(k=1, \cdots Z)$ of all the protons in the nucleus. Φ_0 is the wave function in the ground state. Let $\boldsymbol{r}$ be the electron's position vector. For many purposes it will prove convenient to assume that the target nucleus is very heavy compared to the incident electron. This is true in most cases studied by experiment. However, we shall later also relax this condition.

Now we shall employ one version of the Born approximation given by the first-order time-dependent perturbation theory (4, 5, 6). According to this theory, the transition probability per unit time (w') for an electron to make a jump from its initial state of momentum $\boldsymbol{p}_0$ (energy E_0) to a final state $\boldsymbol{p}$(energy E) under the influence of a perturbation, V, is given by:

$$w' = \frac{dw}{dt} = \frac{2\pi}{\hbar} | H|^2 \frac{dn}{dE_f} \qquad 13.$$

where H is the matrix element of V, causing the transition. In this equation dn/dE_f is the density of final energy states in the continuum. In order to avoid the infinite densities of the continuum, we shall confine the electron, in a standard manner, to a large cubic box of side L, which we may later allow to approach an infinite size. (As is well-known, it will turn out that the dimensions of the box cancel out and later, in another context, we may assume the box to have a unit side.)

We shall write the perturbing interaction in the form

$$H_1 = eV = e^2 \sum_{k=1}^{Z} \frac{1}{|r - R_k|} \qquad 14.$$

which is the usual Coulomb energy of interaction of two point charges. The matrix element H then becomes

$$H = e^2 \int \Phi_f^*(R_k) \frac{1}{L^{3/2}} \exp -(i/\hbar)(p \cdot r) \sum_1^Z \frac{1}{|r - R_k|} \Phi_0(R_k) \frac{1}{L^{3/2}} \cdot \exp (i/\hbar)(p_0 \cdot r) d^3r d^3R_k \qquad 15.$$

The electron's incident and final wave functions were inserted into Eq. 15 as normalized plane waves

$$\psi(r) = \frac{1}{L^{3/2}} \exp (i/\hbar)(p \cdot r) \qquad 16.$$

and this step is characteristic of the Born approximation. Now introduce the momentum transfer vector s, of Figure 1, and H becomes

$$H = \frac{e^2}{L^3} \int \Phi_f^* \Phi_0 \sum_1^Z \frac{1}{|r - R_k|} \exp is \cdot r d^3r d^3R_k \qquad 17.$$

When integrating over the electron's coordinates, choose polar coordinates for which the Z axis lies along the direction s. Furthermore, it is convenient to use a simple shielded potential, V_a,

$$eV_a(r - R_k) = \sum_1^Z \frac{e^2}{|r - R_k|} \exp - \frac{|r - R_k|}{a} \qquad 18.$$

in place of Eq. 14, to take care of shielding by the atomic electron cloud and to make the integration converge. In Eq. 18 a is a parameter of atomic size and is not critical, nor is the shape of the shielding function critical. Thus it is merely necessary to have $a \gg R$, where R is a nuclear dimension. Also place

$$r = R_k + (r - R_k) \qquad 19.$$

and substitute Eq. 18 and 19 into the part of the integral in Eq. 17 having to do with electron coordinates. Thus the integration

$$\varphi(R) = e \sum_1^Z \int (\exp is \cdot R_k)(\exp is \cdot (r - R_k)) \left(\exp - \frac{|r - R_k|}{a}\right) \frac{1}{|r - R_k|} d^3r \qquad 20.$$

may be carried out over the electron's coordinates for each separate proton as an origin, and let polar coordinates ρ', θ', ϕ' be used where θ' is measured relative to s. Then $\varphi(R)$ becomes

$$\begin{aligned} \varphi(R) &= e \sum_1^Z \exp is \cdot R_k \int \exp is\rho' \cos\theta' \frac{\exp - \rho'/a}{\rho'} \rho'^2 d\rho' \sin\theta' d\theta' d\varphi' \\ &= e \sum_1^Z \exp is \cdot R_k \frac{2\pi}{s} \int_0^\infty 2 (\exp - \rho'/a) \sin (s\rho') d\rho' = e \sum_1^Z \exp is \cdot R_k \frac{4\pi}{s^2 + 1/a^2} \\ &= \frac{4\pi e}{s^2} \sum_1^Z \exp is \cdot R_k \end{aligned} \qquad 21.$$

since $a \gg 1/s$ for the interesting scattering events not close to $\theta = 0$. We may then write

$$H = \frac{4\pi e^2}{L^3 s^2} \int_{\text{N.V.}} \Phi_f^* \Phi_0 \sum_1^Z \exp i\mathbf{s} \cdot \mathbf{R}_k d^3 R_k = \frac{4\pi e^2}{L^3 s^2} M_{f0} \qquad 22.$$

where N.V. stands for integration over the nuclear volume and where

$$M_{f0} = \int_{\text{N.V.}} \Phi_f^*(R_k)\Phi_0(R_k) \left(\sum_1^Z \exp i\mathbf{s} \cdot \mathbf{R}_k \right) d^3 R_k \qquad 23.$$

$| M_{f0} |$ measures the interference effects between the waves from the various protons. The transition probability w' then becomes

$$w' = \frac{32\pi^3 e^4}{\hbar L^6 s^4} | M_{f0} |^2 \frac{dn}{dE_f} \qquad 24.$$

and it is only necessary to evaluate dn/dE_f to obtain the differential cross section for scattering.

If the electrons were free, the density of states would be

$$\left(\frac{dn}{dE_f} \right)_{free} = \frac{p^2 d\Omega L^3}{ch^3} \qquad 25.$$

where $d\Omega$ is the elementary solid angle and $p^2 dp d\Omega$ is the momentum contribution to the elementary volume of phase space. c is necessary to trans-from momentum density to energy density. Since the nuclei are assumed to be massive and to suffer little recoil, like the walls of a box in kinetic theory, we could use Eq. 25 if we wished to. However, it is just as simple, and more convenient for the future, to allow the nuclei to recoil. In this case, Eq. 25 will be changed just as in the recoil of the struck particle in the Compton effect. In this case it is easy to show (7) that

$$\left(\frac{dn}{dE_f} \right) = \frac{p^2 d\Omega L^3}{ch^3} \left(\frac{p}{p_0} \right) \left(\frac{W}{Mc^2} \right) \qquad 26.$$

by using the expressions 3 and 6 as in the Compton effect. For our purposes

$$\frac{W}{Mc^2} = 1 + \frac{2\left(\frac{E_0}{Mc^2} \right)^2 \sin^2 \theta/2}{1 + 2\left(\frac{E_0}{Mc^2} \right) \sin^2 \theta/2} \cong 1 \qquad 27.$$

if the nucleus is massive, and by using 3 we find that

$$\left(\frac{dn}{dE_f} \right) = \frac{p^2 d\Omega L^3}{ch^3} \frac{1}{1 + \frac{2E_0}{Mc^2} \sin^2 \theta/2} \qquad 28.$$

We shall see below that when the electron scatters against a relativistic particle, such as a proton, the factor W/Mc^2 of Eq. 26 is cancelled exactly, resulting in a formula like Eq. 28. Eq. 24 becomes therefore

$$w' = \frac{64\pi^4 e^4 d\Omega}{ch^4 L^3 s^4} \frac{p^2}{1 + \frac{2E_0}{Mc^2} \sin^2 \theta/2} | M_{f0} |^2 \qquad 29.$$

To obtain the differential scattering cross section, we must divide this transition probability by the probability current in the incident beam, which is c/L^3. Carrying out this operation and substituting $\hbar = h/2\pi$, we have

$$\frac{d\sigma}{d\Omega} = 4\left(\frac{e^2}{\hbar^2 c}\right)^2 \frac{p^2}{s^4} \frac{1}{1+\frac{2E_0}{Mc^2}\sin^2\theta/2} |M_{f0}|^2 \qquad 30.$$

For a target nucleus that is massive and therefore undergoes little recoil, $\Delta E = E_0 - E$ is small, $p = p_0$, etc., and

$$\hbar^2 s^2 = \hbar^2 q^2 = 4pp_0 \sin^2\theta/2 = 4p_0^2 \sin^2\theta/2 \qquad 31.$$

by Eq. 8. Hence Eq. 30 becomes finally

$$\frac{d\sigma}{d\Omega} = \left(\frac{e^2}{2E_0}\right)^2 \frac{1}{\sin^4\theta/2} \frac{1}{1+\frac{2E_0}{Mc^2}\sin^2\theta/2} | M_{f0}|^2 \qquad 32.$$

This result is educational, but it should not be used for real electrons with spin. However, light bosons would scatter according to this formula. We pass on to a more realistic case.

2. *Scattering of electrons with spin.*—Now let us go to the case of electrons carrying spin. For this we need the Dirac equation (5)

$$(\boldsymbol{\alpha}\cdot \boldsymbol{p}c + \beta mc^2 + eV)\psi = E\psi \qquad 33.$$

where the ψ's are spinor quantities and where $\boldsymbol{\alpha}$ is the current density Dirac operator and β the fourth abbreviated Dirac operator. Thus

$$\boldsymbol{\alpha} = \begin{pmatrix} 0 & \boldsymbol{\sigma} \\ \boldsymbol{\sigma} & 0 \end{pmatrix}; \quad \beta = \begin{pmatrix} 1 & 0 \\ 0 & -1 \end{pmatrix} \qquad 34.$$

and $\boldsymbol{\sigma}$ represents the usual set of Pauli spin matrix operators:

$$\sigma_x = \begin{pmatrix} 0 & 1 \\ 1 & 0 \end{pmatrix}, \quad \sigma_y = \begin{pmatrix} 0 & -i \\ i & 0 \end{pmatrix}, \quad \sigma_z = \begin{pmatrix} 1 & 0 \\ 0 & -1 \end{pmatrix} \qquad 35.$$

eV in Eq. 33 is still given by (14) and the four components of ψ, for plane wave solutions, are abbreviated by the column matrix

$$\psi(r, t) = \begin{bmatrix} \psi_1(r, t) \\ \psi_2(r, t) \\ \psi_3(r, t) \\ \psi_4(r, t) \end{bmatrix} \qquad 36.$$

where each ψ can be expressed as

$$\psi_j(r, t) = u_j \exp \frac{i}{\hbar}(\boldsymbol{p}\cdot \boldsymbol{r} - Et); \qquad j = 1, 2, 3, 4 \qquad 37.$$

with similar equations for the ground state $\psi_{0j}(r, t)$.

It is well known in Dirac theory that there are two sets of solutions corresponding to the positive and negative energy states. We shall deal only with the positive energy solutions. Furthermore, among the positive set there are two linearly independent solutions corresponding to two possible spin orientations of the electron. In this case

$$u_1 = -\frac{cp_z}{E + mc^2}, \qquad u_2 = -\frac{c(p_x + ip_y)}{E + mc^2}, \qquad u_3 = 1,\ u_4 = 0$$

and

$$u_1 = -\frac{c(p_x - ip_y)}{E + mc^2}, \qquad u_2 = \frac{cp_z}{E + mc^2}, \qquad u_3 = 0,\ u_4 = 1 \qquad 38.$$

or when $mc^2 \ll E$ and $E \cong cp$, as in our case,

$$u_1 = -\frac{p_z}{p}, \qquad u_2 = -\frac{p_x + ip_y}{p}, \qquad u_3 = 1,\ u_4 = 0$$

$$u_1 = -\frac{p_x - ip_y}{p}, \qquad u_2 = \frac{p_z}{p}, \qquad u_3 = 0,\ u_4 = 1 \qquad 39.$$

If each u is multiplied by $1/\sqrt{2}$, the solutions are normalized so that $\psi^*\psi = \sum(\psi_j{}^*\psi_j) = 1$. The probability density and probability current density are written:

$$\psi_f{}^*\psi_0 = \text{probability density}$$
$$-c\psi_f{}^*\alpha\psi_0 = \text{probability current density.} \qquad 40.$$

where ψ^* stands for the Hermitian adjoint matrix corresponding to Eq. 36.

When the Dirac plane wave solutions are substituted in the matrix element H, the calculation proceeds exactly as in the spin-less case, except that the four-component character of the electron's wave functions requires that the probability of the transition be proportional to the sum of the four terms:

$$u_f{}^*u_0 = \sum_1^4 \psi^*{}_{fj}\psi_{0j} = u_1{}^*{}_f u_{10} + u_2{}^*{}_f u_{20} + u_3{}^*{}_f u_{30} + u_4{}^*{}_f u_{40} \qquad 41.$$

in accordance with Eq. 40. The square modulus of the matrix element (23) is then modified by the relativistic considerations so that it contains $|u_f{}^*u_0|^2$ as a multiplicative factor.

The calculation is then further complicated by the new possibilities for the spins of the ingoing and scattered electrons. If we let I refer to spin-up and II to spin-down, then four transitions are possible thus: I_fI_0, I_fII_0, II_fI_0, II_fII_0. However, in a normal scattering experiment, we do not start with a polarized electron beam nor do we examine the spins of the scattered particles. Hence we must carry out an averaging procedure over the initial and final spin orientations. This means that we must evaluate $|u_f{}^*u_0|^2$ for each of the four combinations, I_fI_0, I_fII_0, etc., and then take an average over the initial states and a sum over the two final states. This may be done easily with Eq. 38 and 39 by calling them appropriately the initial and final states. Carrying out this algebraic procedure, we obtain for the result:

$$\frac{1}{2EE_0}\left[m^2c^4 + EE_0(1 + \cos\theta)\right] \qquad 42.$$

In practice, where E, $E_0 \gg mc^2$ and θ is not extremely close to $\theta = \pi$, this expression is simply $\cos^2 \theta/2$. Thus the cross section corresponding to Eq. 32 now becomes:

$$\frac{d\sigma}{d\Omega}=\left(\frac{e^2}{2E_0}\right)^2\frac{\cos^2\theta/2}{\sin^4\theta/2}\frac{|M_{f0}|^2}{1+\frac{2E_0}{Mc^2}\sin^2\theta/2} \qquad 43.$$

The more elegant trace methods (4, 8) may also be used and one obtains the same result. Writing the final result in detail, we have

$$\frac{d\sigma}{d\Omega}=\left(\frac{e^2}{2E_0}\right)^2\frac{\cos^2\theta/2}{\sin^4\theta/2}\frac{\left|\int_{\mathrm{N.V.}}\Phi_f^*(R_k)\Phi_0(R_k)\sum_1^Z \exp i\boldsymbol{q}\cdot\boldsymbol{R}_k d^3R_k\right|^2}{1+\frac{2E_0}{Mc^2}\sin^2\theta/2} \qquad 44.$$

where we have replaced $\boldsymbol{s}$ by $\boldsymbol{q}$, as explained previously. Now we shall apply this equation.

3. *Elastic scattering.*—For elastic scattering, the conditions are

$$\left.\begin{aligned}&\Phi_f=\Phi_0, \qquad p=p_0\Big/\left(1+\frac{2E_0}{Mc^2}\sin^2\theta/2\right)\\ &\hbar s\cong\hbar q=2p_0\sin\theta/2\Big/\left[1+\frac{2E_0}{Mc^2}\sin^2\theta/2\right]^{1/2}\end{aligned}\right\} \qquad 45.$$

as given by Eq. 11 and 31. Eq. 44 then takes the form:

$$\frac{d\sigma_{el}}{d\Omega}=\left(\frac{e^2}{2\mathrm{E}_0}\right)^2\frac{\cos^2\theta/2}{\sin^4\theta/2}\frac{1}{1+\frac{2E_0}{Mc^2}\sin^2\theta/2}\left|\int_{\mathrm{N.V.}}|\Phi_0|^2\sum_1^Z\exp i\boldsymbol{q}\cdot\boldsymbol{R}_k d^3R_k\right|^2 \qquad 46.$$

When the nuclear dimensions are small compared to the de Broglie wavelength of the electrons,

$$\boldsymbol{q}\cdot\boldsymbol{R}_k\cong 0 \qquad 47.$$

and the volume integral is simply the sum of Z charges integrated over the nuclear volume, since $|\Phi_0|^2$ is normalized to unity over the nucleus. The condition given in Eq. 47 means essentially that, for the momentum transfer considered, the nucleus cannot be distinguished from a point of charge Ze. Under such conditions, Eq. 46 may be written

$$\left(\frac{d\sigma_{el}}{d\Omega}\right)_{\mathrm{point}}=\left(\frac{Ze^2}{2E_0}\right)^2\frac{\cos^2\theta/2}{\sin^4\theta/2}\frac{1}{1+\frac{2E_0}{Mc^2}\sin^2\theta/2}=\sigma_{NS} \qquad 48.$$

where σ_{NS} stands for scattering from a point charge Ze with "no spin."

This simple Born-approximation scattering formula is the justly famous "Mott-scattering formula" and represents the relativistic scattering of Dirac electrons from a massive point nucleus of charge Ze. (The Mott formula is generally written without the center-of-mass correction

$$\frac{1}{1+\frac{2E_0}{Mc^2}\sin^2\theta/2},$$

since this term is very close to unity.)

In the event that $\boldsymbol{q}\cdot\boldsymbol{R}$ is not zero, nor small compared to unity, the scattering formula 46 may be written

$$\frac{d\sigma_{el}}{d\Omega} = \left(\frac{e^2}{2E_0}\right)^2 \frac{\cos^2\theta/2}{\sin^4\theta/2} \frac{|F(q)|^2}{1 + \frac{2E_0}{Mc^2}\sin^2\theta/2} \qquad 49.$$

where we have introduced the quantity

$$F(q) = \int_{\text{N.V.}} |\Phi_0|^2 \sum_1^Z \exp i\boldsymbol{q}\cdot\boldsymbol{R}_k d^3\boldsymbol{R}_k \qquad 50.$$

$F(q)$ is a type of quantity well known from atomic studies of electron diffraction and x-ray diffraction and is the analog of the so-called "form factor" or "structure factor" of those disciplines. In our work we shall refer to $F(q)$ as the nuclear form factor.

Now in Eq. 50 $|\Phi_0|^2$ contains all the proton-configuration coordinates symmetrically, and so each integral of the sum is like any other. Hence the square modulus of the integral $F(q)$ in Eq. 50 is (9)

$$|F(q)|^2 = Z^2 \left| \int \varphi_0^* \varphi_0 \exp i(\boldsymbol{q}\cdot\boldsymbol{R}) d^3\boldsymbol{R} \right|^2 \qquad 51.$$

since $F(q)$ adds up to Z similar integrals. As in Eq. 51 each of these integrals has an integrand of the form

$$|\varphi_0|^2 = \varphi_0^*\varphi_0 = \int_{\text{N.V.}} |\Phi_0|^2 \sum_{k=1}^{Z} d^3\boldsymbol{R}_k \qquad 52.$$

and $|\varphi_0|^2 d^3\boldsymbol{R}$ is the probability that there is one proton in $d^3\boldsymbol{R}$, and all other proton positions are arbitrary. Integration of $|\varphi_0|^2$ over $d^3\boldsymbol{R}$ will give unity because of the normalization of the wave functions. Thus the effective or "static" nuclear-charge density $\rho_0(\boldsymbol{R})$, in the ground state of the nucleus, is Ze times expression Eq. 52 or

$$\rho_0(\boldsymbol{R}) = Ze|\varphi_0|^2 \qquad 53.$$

and integration of ρ_0 over $d^3\boldsymbol{R}$ will yield Ze. We may normalize a density, defined slightly differently and called $\rho(\boldsymbol{R})$, to unity in the sense that

$$\int \rho(\boldsymbol{R}) d^3\boldsymbol{R} = 1; \qquad \rho = \frac{\rho_0}{Ze} \qquad 54.$$

instead of to Ze. This is convenient for many calculations. $\boldsymbol{R}$ is then the position vector of a charged volume element in the nucleus measured from its center of mass. We can write

$$F(q) = \int_{\text{N.V.}} \rho(\boldsymbol{R}) \exp i\boldsymbol{q}\cdot\boldsymbol{R} d^3\boldsymbol{R} \qquad 55.$$

and Eq. 49 becomes

$$\frac{d\sigma_{el}}{d\Omega} = \left(\frac{Ze^2}{2E_0}\right)^2 \frac{\cos^2 \theta/2}{\sin^4 \theta/2} \frac{|F(q)|^2}{1 + \frac{2E_0}{Mc^2} \sin^2 \theta/2} \tag{56.}$$

which is like Eq. 49 except for the factor Z and the new normalized definition of $F(q)$ given in Eq. 55.

From Eq. 48 and 56 we then observe that

$$\frac{\dfrac{d\sigma_{el}}{d\Omega}}{\left(\dfrac{d\sigma}{d\Omega}\right)_{\text{point}}} = |F(q)|^2 \tag{57.}$$

This amounts to the generally accepted definition of $|F(q)|^2$ as the ratio of the experimental cross section to the point-charge cross section. It may easily be shown by integrating over angle, with $q \cong (2p_0|\hbar)\sin \theta/2$, that Eq. 55 can be reduced to the form

$$F(q) = \frac{4\pi}{q} \int_0^\infty \rho(r) \sin (qr) r dr \tag{58.}$$

for a spherically symmetric charge distribution. In future applications of Eq. 58 to high energies it may be necessary to make a small allowance for the center of mass motion.

While Eq. 46 represents elastic scattering, the more general Eq. 44 contains the inelastic scattering formulas in Born approximation. In this case $\Phi_f \neq \Phi_0$ and the so-called transition matrix elements arise from the integral in Eq. 44. We shall return to this problem later.

Many nuclear form-factor results have been given for elastic scattering (1, 9). Figure 2 shows a typical form-factor curve for a charge distribution due to an independent particle shell model of a nucleus for an infinite harmonic well potential. Figure 3 shows the appropriate charge distribution corresponding to $C^{12}(\alpha = 4/3)$ in this shell-model picture, to $O^{16}(\alpha = 2)$, and to other p-shell nuclei. (The abscissa scale is correct only for carbon.) It is typical of many Born-approximation form factors that they show diffraction zeroes such as the one at $x = qa = 4.4$ in Figure 2. (a is the root-mean-square value of the radius of the charge distribution.) On a semi-logarithmic plot, at a true zero, the curve goes to $-\infty$. Experimental data do exhibit minima, as illustrated in Figure 4. In this figure, the experimental points represent electron-scattering restults in C^{12} at 420 Mev, obtained by Sobottka & Hofstadter (10), but, of course, the experimental curves do not show true zeroes. The question of minima versus true zeroes has been discussed in some detail (1) and is connected with the fact that the Born approximation is not accurate near diffraction minima and fails also for elements of high atomic number. This problem will be discussed at length in section (12) which is concerned with the exact phase-shift calculations. On the other hand, many charge distributions, such as a Gaussian or an exponential, do not show dif-

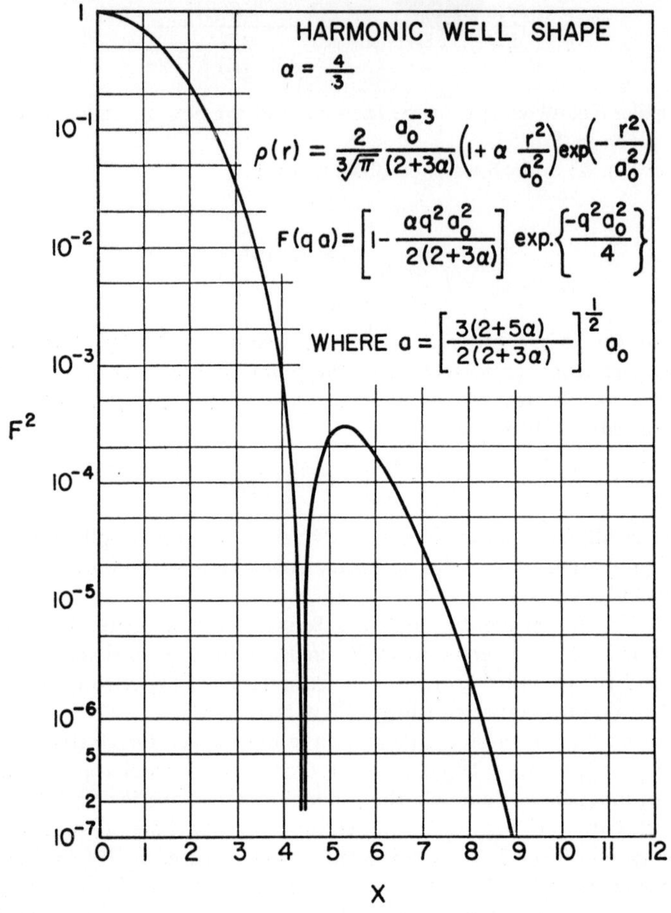

FIG. 2. Born approximation for the absolute square of the form factor associated with the harmonic-well shape in the case, $\alpha = 4/3$, which is appropriate to carbon. $x = qa$.

fraction zeroes, and, for these models, the Born approximation is much more accurate than for models yielding diffraction zeroes, or minima even for nuclei of moderate Z. Figure 4 also shows the Born-approximation results (dotted line) for the same model which gives the exact phase-shift calculations (solid line). Except for the region about the minimum, the Born approximation is surprisingly good, even for this simple model of the carbon nucleus. The exact phase-shift curve in Figure 4 is due to D. G. Ravenhall.

4. *Magnetic scattering of a point.*—At the higher electron energies and at large angles, scattering by the magnetic moment of the target nucleus

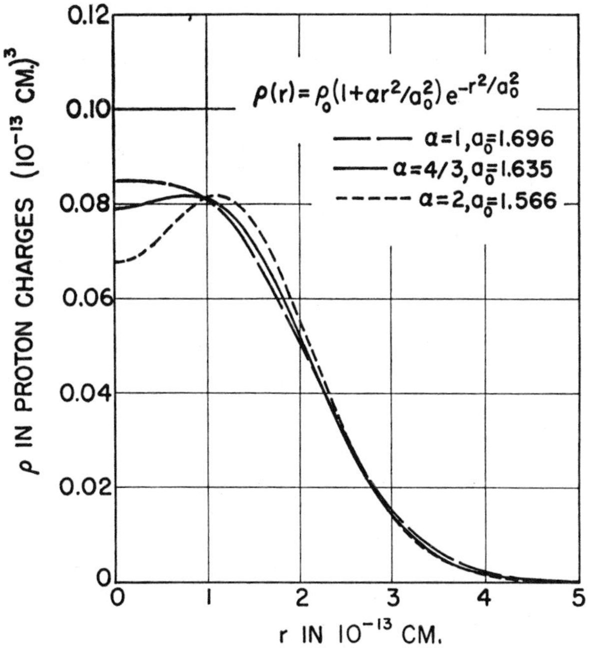

FIG. 3. The charge-density distribution for the harmonic-well nuclear model for three different values of α. The abscissa is correct only for the case of carbon, for which $\alpha = 4/3$.

becomes important. We shall try to demonstrate the basic type of analysis involved in this phenomenon by carrying out the calculational details for the case when the target is a proton. We shall consider the fully relativistic treatment for the proton which means that we shall take the proton to be a Dirac particle.

Like the calculations in the preceding sections, this derivation is based on the first Born approximation. There are many equivalent ways of working out a solution, but we shall choose a method involving the Møller potentials (11) because the physical ideas then become rather clear.

We have seen that the transition probability depends on the square modulus of the matrix element H of the perturbing potential, as in Eq. 13. The matrix element is given by Eq. 17, except that we shall now specialize to the case of a single proton, and the summation in Eq. 17 is therefore not required. We shall assume that the box "L" has sides equal to unity, and so it will not be necessary to carry L in the calculations.

Following Møller, we shall first deal with the partially relativistic problem as an example. The integration in Eq. 17 or 20 over the electron's coordinates:

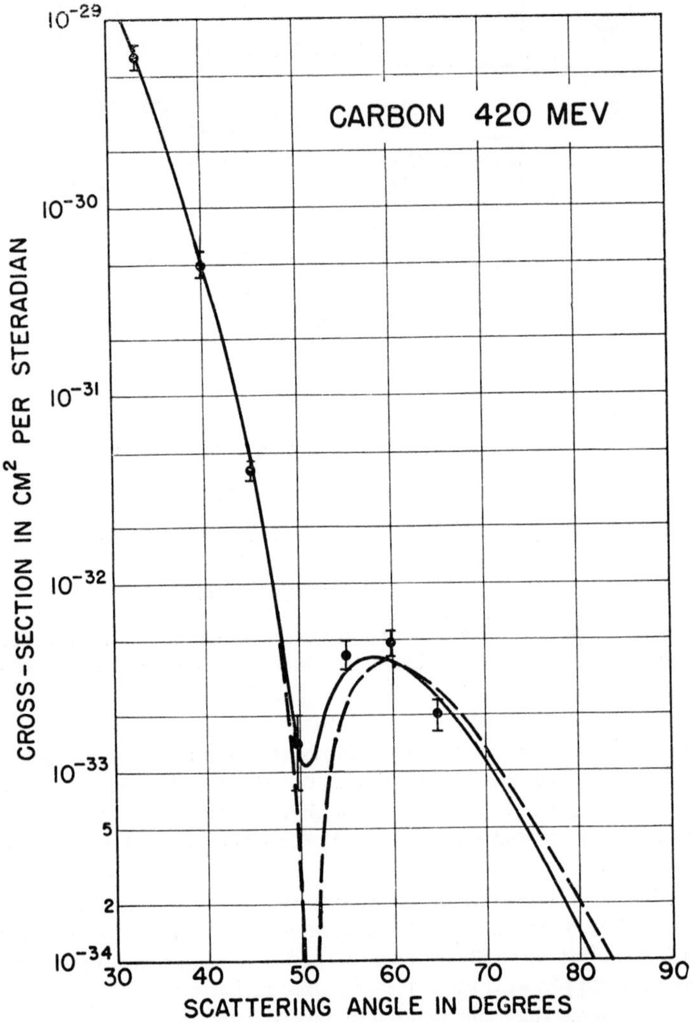

FIG. 4. Recent data in C^{12} observed by Sobottka & Hofstadter (10) at an incident electron energy of 420 Mev. Two theoretical curves are presented for comparison. The dashed curve is the Born approximation for a harmonic-well charge distribution corresponding to Fig. 3 ($\alpha=4/3$). The solid line is the accurate phase-shift calculation of D. G. Ravenhall, which appears to fit the experimental points rather well.

$$\varphi(R) = e\int \frac{\exp i/\hbar(p_0 - p)\cdot r}{|R - r|} d^3r = e\int \frac{\exp is\cdot r}{|R - r|} d^3r \qquad 60.$$

yields by the method first given by Bethe (12, 13) (similar to our earlier derivation of equation 21) a scalar potential, $\varphi(R)$, which can be written

$$\varphi(R) = 4\pi e \frac{\exp is\cdot R}{|s|^2} = \frac{e\hbar^2}{\pi} \frac{\exp i/\hbar(p_0 - p)\cdot R}{|p_0 - p|^2} \qquad 61.$$

where R is the position vector of the proton, and where the scalar potential, $\varphi(R)$, satisfies the Poisson equation

$$\nabla^2\varphi = -4\pi\rho \qquad 62.$$

In the latter equation

$$\frac{\rho}{e} = \exp is\cdot R = \exp i/\hbar(p_0 - p)\cdot R \qquad 63.$$

and has been called a "transition-charge density." For the matrix element involving the interaction with a single proton, insertion of the potential φ gives

$$H = \int \Phi_f^*(R)e\varphi(R)\Phi_0(R)d^3R \qquad 64.$$

which is the contraction of H in Eq. 17 to the case of a single proton. We may say that the potential φ corresponds to the transition charge density ρ and acts to make transitions between the states of Φ of the heavy particle.

Now let the electrons satisfy the Dirac Eq. 33 and let their wave functions be represented by Eq. 36 and 37. The solutions corresponding to negative energy states are small and need not be considered. According to the method of Møller, when the treatment is fully relativistic, the transition charge density becomes

$$\rho = -eu_f^*u_0 \exp i\left[s\cdot R - \frac{1}{\hbar}(E_0 - E)t\right] \qquad 65.$$

in analogy with Eq. 63, and the "transition current density" j is given by

$$j = eu_f^*\alpha u_0 \exp i\left[s\cdot R - \frac{1}{\hbar}(E_0 - E)\cdot\right] \qquad 66.$$

where $e\alpha$ is the Dirac current density operator of Eq. 33. The potentials corresponding to Eq. 61 and 62 then satisfy

$$\nabla^2\varphi - \frac{1}{c^2}\frac{\partial^2\varphi}{\partial t^2} = -4\pi\rho \qquad 67.$$

$$\nabla^2 A - \frac{1}{c^2}\frac{\partial^2 A}{\partial t^2} = -4\pi\frac{j}{c} \qquad 68.$$

where A is the vector potential corresponding to the current sources j. The latter two equations may be solved as in Eq. 61 and 62 to give

$$\varphi(R) = -4\pi e \frac{u_f{}^* u_0 \exp i\left[s\cdot R - \frac{1}{\hbar}(E_0 - E)t\right]}{s^2 - \left(\frac{\Delta E}{\hbar c}\right)^2} \qquad 69.$$

$$A(R) = -4\pi e \frac{u_f{}^* \alpha u_0 \exp i\left[s\cdot R - \frac{1}{\hbar}(E_0 - E)t\right]}{s^2 - \left(\frac{\Delta E}{\hbar c}\right)^2} \qquad 70.$$

The potentials φ, A of Eq. 69 and 70 are the so-called Møller potentials produced by the passing electron.

The perturbing interaction applied to the proton, when written in terms of these potentials, would be given by

$$e\int [\rho_P \varphi(R) + \alpha_P \cdot A(R)] d^3R \qquad 71.$$

where the assumption has been made that the proton obeys the Dirac equation with no anomalous magnetic moment, and where ρ_P and α_P are its corresponding charge and current-density operators, respectively. Then ρ_P must be replaced by the relativistic spinor matrix element

$$eU_f{}^* U_0 \exp i\left[S_P\cdot r - \frac{1}{\hbar}(W_0 - W)t\right] \qquad 72.$$

and the vector α_P by

$$eU_f{}^* \alpha_P U_0 \exp i\left[S_P\cdot r - \frac{1}{\hbar}(W_0 - W)t\right] \qquad 73.$$

where the capital U's refer to the proton's spin amplitudes, and where the other heavy particle symbols are self-explanatory. Then the scalar product given in Eq. 71 can be written, as shown by Møller,

$$H = -\frac{4\pi e^4}{q^2}\{(u_f{}^* u_0)(U_f{}^* U_0) - (u_f{}^* \alpha u_0)(U_f{}^* \alpha_P U_0)\} \qquad 74.$$

and exhibits complete symmetry between the electron and the proton. q is given by Eq. 8. In obtaining Eq. 74, the exponential factors are eliminated by well-known methods equivalent to the conservation theorems:

$$\begin{gathered} S_P + s = P_0 - P + p_0 - p = -P + p_0 - p = 0 \\ W_0 - W + E_0 - E = 0 \end{gathered} \qquad 75.$$

and where $P_0 = 0$ and $W_0 = Mc^2$ represent the proton's initial conditions in the laboratory frame.

The matrix element H, given by Eq. 74, lies at the heart of the electron-proton scattering theory. In recent times it has proved convenient to write the interaction in a completely covariant manner (8, 14), and in this language the matrix element H is given by

$$H = -2\pi i j_\mu{}^P(P, P_0)\frac{1}{q^2} j_\mu{}^e(p, p_0) \qquad 76.$$

where j_μ^e is the electron's charge-current density, and where

$$q_\mu = P_\mu - P_{\mu_0} = -(p_\mu - p_{\mu_0}) \qquad 77.$$

is the recoil four-momentum, and where $1/q^2$ represents the propagation of a virtual photon with four-momentum q_μ between the electron and the proton. Repeated Greek indices indicate the usual summation convention. In covariant notation

$$j_\mu^e(p, p_0) = -ie\bar{u}(p)\gamma_\mu u(p_0) \qquad 78.$$

and this density is equivalent to Eq. 65 and 66. The bar over the Dirac spinors will refer to the "adjoint" functions [defined in ref. (8), Eq. 46]. A Dirac proton will have a charge-current density similar to Eq. 78. The γ_μ operators are given in terms of a single vector equation

$$\gamma_\mu = (-i\beta\alpha, \beta) \qquad 79.$$

β and α are given in Eq. 34 and 35. The above formalism is very useful in extending the scattering theory to a proton with an anomalous magnetic moment. We shall consider this topic later.

Not let us return to the actual evaluation of the matrix element (74). This calculation may be carried out by methods similar to those used in the evaluation of Eq. 41. However, now the spin transitions are more numerous since the proton has also been assumed to have a spin. Thus combinations such as $(I_L I_H)_f(I_L I_H)_0$; $(I_L II_H)_f(II_L, I_H)_0$, etc., need to be considered, where L stands for the light particle (electron) and H for the proton (heavy particle). Sixteen such combinations can be formed, of which eight are equal pairs. The corresponding scalar products in the bracket of equation 74 are formed and the square modulus found for each combination. The square moduli are then added and an average over initial states and a sum over final states is finally taken. The results before averaging are as follows:

$$\left(\frac{W + Mc^2}{2W}\right)(4\cos^2\theta/2) \text{ for the } |(u_f{}^*u_0)(U_f{}^*U_0)|^2 \text{ terms} \qquad 80.$$

and

$$\left(\frac{W + Mc^2}{2W}\right)\left(\frac{4\Delta E\cos^2\theta/2}{(W + Mc^2)}\right)(2\tan^2\theta/2 + 1) \text{ for the } |(u_f{}^*\alpha u_0)U_f{}^*\alpha_p U_0|^2 \text{ terms} \qquad 81.$$

and

$$-\left(\frac{W + Mc^2}{2W}\right)\left(\frac{4}{W + Mc^2}\cdot 2\Delta E\cos^2\theta/2\right) \text{ for the cross terms} \qquad 82.$$

When the average over initial spins is taken, one obtains

$$\frac{Mc^2}{W}\cos^2\theta/2\left\{1 + \frac{\hbar^2 q^2}{4M^2c^2}\cdot 2\tan^2\theta/2\right\} \qquad 83.$$

for the averaged sum. In obtaining this result, use is made of Eq. 9 and 10. The corresponding square of the matrix element H is then $(4\pi)^2e^4/q^4$ times the result (83) as indicated by Eq. 74. Finally we obtain the cross section through the use of Eq. 3, 8, 13, and 26 and find:

$$\left(\frac{d\sigma}{d\Omega}\right)_d = \left(\frac{e^2}{2E_0}\right)^2 \frac{\cos^2\theta/2}{\sin^4\theta/2} \frac{1}{1+\dfrac{2E_0}{Mc^2}\sin^2\theta/2}\left\{1+\frac{\hbar^2q^2}{4M^2c^2}(2\tan^2\theta/2)\right\} \quad 84.$$

where $(d\sigma/d\Omega)_d$ stands for "Dirac" scattering of an electron against a "Dirac" proton whose magnetic moment would be

$$\mu_d = \frac{e\hbar}{Mc} \quad 85.$$

or one nuclear magneton. Eq. 84 is the prototype of all scattering formulas involving magnetic as well as electric scattering and is therefore a generalization of Eq. 48.

The calculation of $(d\sigma/d\Omega)$ can be simplified by the use of trace methods and projection operators (8), although for some purposes, such as those for which polarization properties are of interest, the method outlined is probably simplest, although tedious.

Now the scattering formula 84 has been calculated for an artificial proton since in reality a physical proton's magnetic moment is 2.79 nuclear magnetons of which 1.0 nuclear magneton (Eq. 85) is the Dirac contribution and the remainder ($K=1.79$ n.m.) is often called the "Pauli" part of the magnetic moment. The name derives from the fact that Pauli (15) showed that a new term can be added to the Dirac equation, endowing a Dirac particle with an additional magnetic moment, sometimes also called the "anomalous" moment. In the covariant notation, corresponding to Eq. 78 (which is written for an electron without structure), the proton's current density can be generalized to

$$j_\mu^P(P, P_0) = ie\overline{U}(P)\left[\gamma_\mu + \frac{K}{2Mc}\gamma_\mu\gamma_\nu q_\nu\right]U(P_0) \quad 86.$$

in which $\overline{U}$ and U are the usual heavy particle spinor amplitudes and q_ν is the four-component momentum-energy transfer given in Eq. 77. Further calculation, similar to that leading to Eq. 80 to 84, shows that the resulting scattering cross section now contains some additional terms relative to Eq. 84 as follows:

$$\left(\frac{d\sigma}{d\Omega}\right)_R = \left(\frac{e^2}{2E_0}\right)^2 \frac{\cos^2\theta/2}{\sin^4\theta/2} \frac{1}{1+\dfrac{2E_0}{Mc^2}\sin^2\theta/2}\left\{1+\frac{\hbar^2q^2}{4M^2c^2}\left[2(1+K)^2\tan^2\theta/2+K^2\right]\right\} \quad 87.$$

and this represents what we may call "Rosenbluth scattering" (16) by a point-charge and point-magnetic moment.

In Figures 5, 6, and 7, we show representative scattering curves in the laboratory system for a point-proton without nuclear spin (Fig. 5), for a "Dirac" point-proton with spin 1/2 and with a Dirac moment (1.0 n.m.) (Fig. 6), and for a point-proton having a real magnetic moment and Rosenbluth scattering ($\mu_P=1+K=2.79$ n.m.) (Fig. 7).

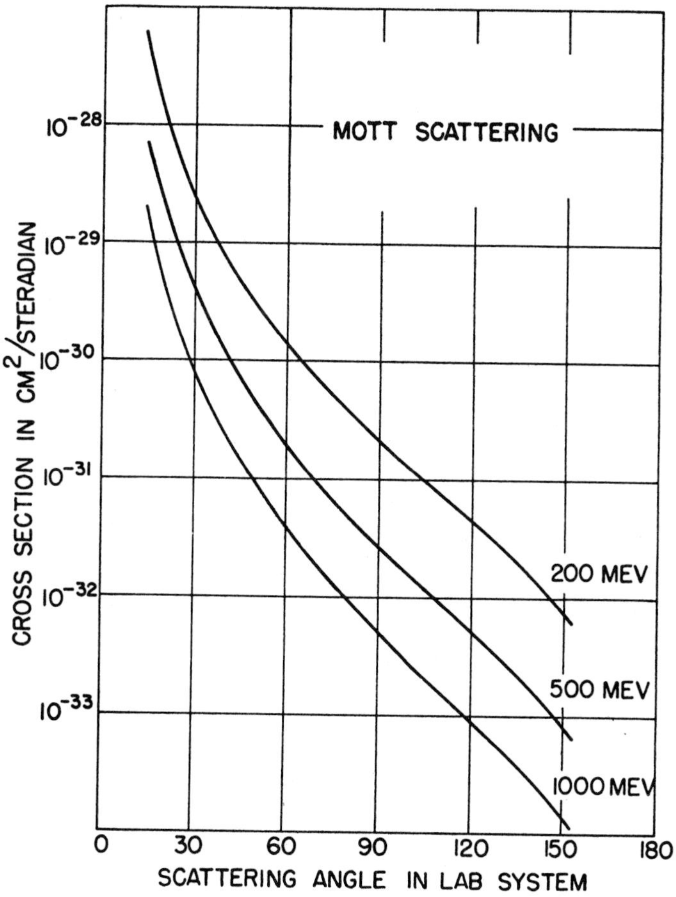

FIG. 5. The Mott-scattering curves for the energies 200, 500, 1000 Mev in the laboratory system. The appropriate cross section is given in Eq. 48 with $Z=1$ and represents electron scattering against a point-proton with zero spin and zero nuclear magnetic moment.

An important feature of magnetic-moment scattering is connected with the $\tan^2 \theta/2$ term since this term becomes dominant at large angles and high energies. The reason the Rosenbluth curves hold up at large angles (Fig. 7) is due to the magnetic-moment term. In principle this fact permits a magnetic-form factor (see below) to be distinguished from a charge-form factor.

5. *Magnetic scattering from a finite nucleon.*—It has been demonstrated experimentally (17, 18, 19) that the physical proton shows deviations from the scattering given by the point proton of Eq. 87. The observed scattering can be accounted for satisfactorily by introducing phenomenological form

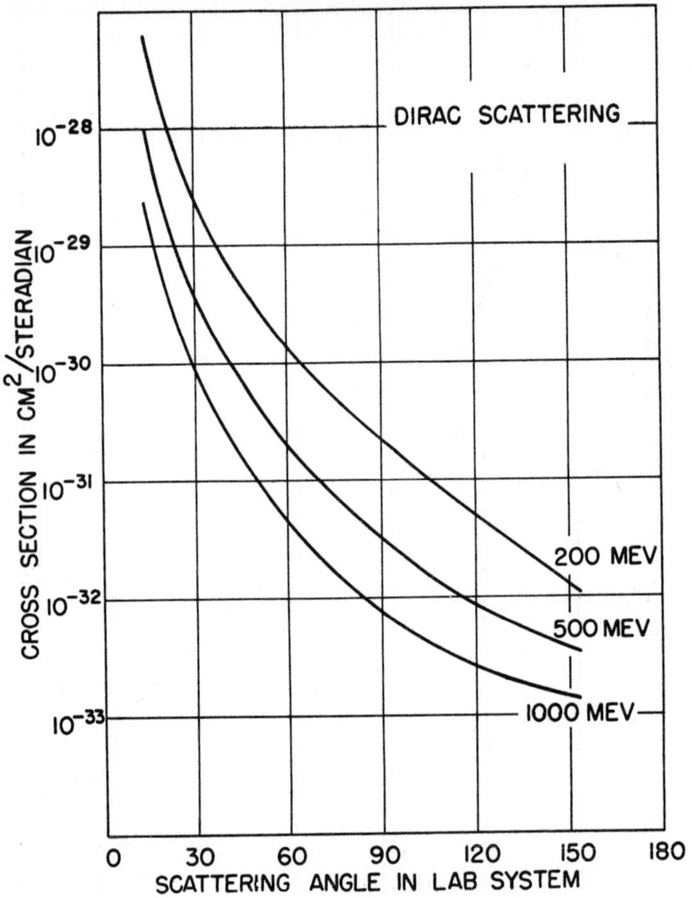

FIG. 6. The "Dirac"-scattering curves for a "Dirac" point-proton with spin $\frac{1}{2}\hbar$ and with a Dirac moment (1.0 nuclear magneton). The appropriate cross section is given by Eq. 87 with $K=0$, or equivalently by Eq. 84.

factors (14, 17), which imply either structure in the proton or a breakdown of electrodynamics at small distances (1, 14). Whichever interpretation applies, it has been shown by Foldy (20) and by Salzman (21) that the most general form of a nucleon's charge-current density must look like:

$$j_\mu^{p,n}(P, P_0) = ie\overline{U}(P)\left(\gamma_\mu F_1^{p,n}(q^2) + \frac{\hbar K^{p,n}}{2Mc}\gamma_\mu\gamma_\nu q_\nu F_2^{p,n}(q^2)\right)U(P). \qquad 88.$$

where j_μ^p, etc. applies to a proton and j_μ^n, etc. applies to a neutron. A finite proton would then be described by the phenomenological form factors F_1 and F_2 in Eq. 88. The assumptions behind Eq. 88 are (a) $j_\mu^{p,n}$ must be relativistically covariant, (b) the differential law of current conservation

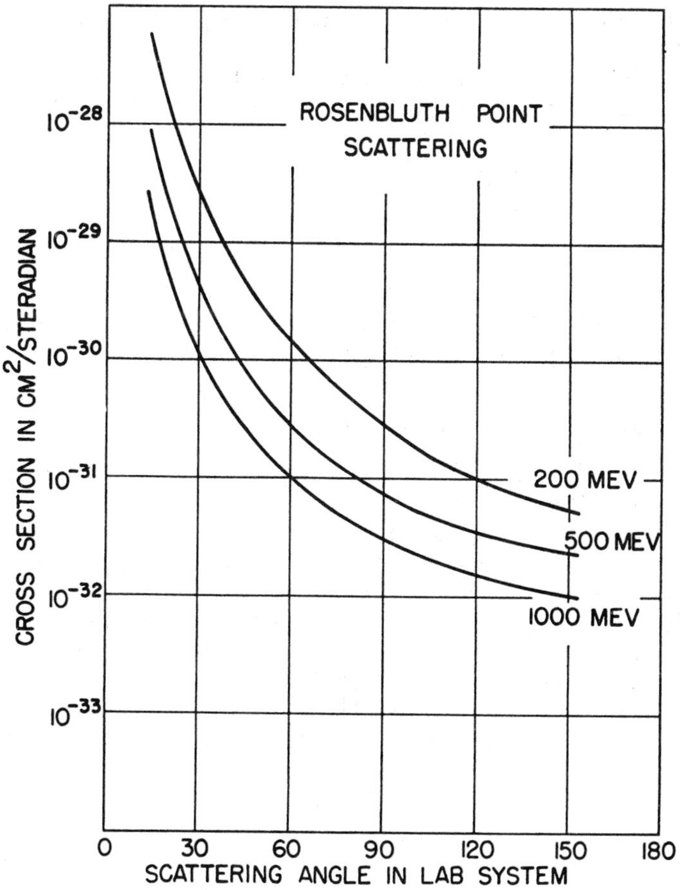

FIG. 7. Rosenbluth-point scattering for point-protons with real values of the nuclear spin and magnetic moment. The appropriate cross section is given by Eq. 87 with $K=1.79$ nuclear magnetons. ($\mu_p=2.79$ *n.m.*)

must hold, and (*c*) the nucleon behaves according to the Dirac equation [see also ref. (14), footnote 6]. Rosenbluth's calculation (16) had already included form factors of the type given in Eq. 88. In his calculation F_1 and F_2 were obtained from a weak-coupling meson theory.

In Eq. 88 $F_1(q^2)$ clearly should be associated with the proton's charge and Dirac magnetic moment (1.0 n.m.), while $F_2(q^2)$ is to be associated with the Pauli moment (1.79 n.m.). The F_1 and F_2 may be thought of as the relativistic extensions of the form factors of Eq. 50 and 55. For moderate values of the momentum transfer q, this interpretation is quite satisfactory. When the proton or neutron obtains a velocity comparable with c, the simple structural interpretation of F_1 and F_2 may have to be abandoned (14), although the formulations of $j_\mu^{p,n}$ in terms of the phenomenological values of F_1, F_2, as in Eq. 88, are still valid.

On applying F_1 and F_2 to j_μ, it is now clear that Eq. 87 for a point will have a counterpart for finite nucleons. For a physical proton the elastic scattering will have the appearance

$$\frac{d\sigma}{d\Omega} = \left(\frac{e^2}{2E_0}\right)^2 \frac{\cos^2\theta/2}{\sin^4\theta/2} \frac{1}{1+\frac{2E_0}{Mc^2}\sin^2\theta/2} \cdot \left\{F_1^2 + \frac{\hbar^2 q^2}{4M^2c^2}\left[2(F_1+KF_2)^2\tan^2\theta/2 + K^2F_2^2\right]\right\} \qquad 89.$$

where F_1 and F_2 are functions of q and the latter is given by Eq. 11.

If now F_1 and F_2 happen to have the same functional form:

$$F_1 = F_2 = F_P \qquad 90.$$

then Eq. 89 would have the simple appearance:

$$\frac{d\sigma}{d\Omega} = F_p^2 \times \left(\frac{d\sigma}{d\Omega}\right)_R = F_P^2 \times \text{(scattering by a point)} \qquad 91.$$

where $(d\sigma/d\Omega)_R$ is given by Eq. 87.

Now the experiments (1) show that the proton may indeed be described consistently up to an energy of 550 Mev and a laboratory scattering angle of 135° by the choice, $F_1 = F_2 = F_P$, where F_P can be represented, not perfectly uniquely but within certain limits, by a behavior similar to that shown in Figure 8. These results are obtained chiefly from relative data on angular shapes but also from rough absolute measurements (19). In this particular example, the charge distribution in the proton, ρ_P, is given by the exponential

$$\rho_P(r) = \rho_0 e^{-r/a_1} \qquad 92.$$

where

$$F_P(qa) = (1 + q^2a_1^2)^{-2} \qquad 93.$$

and where

$$a = \langle r^2 \rangle^{1/2} = a_1\sqrt{12} \qquad 94.$$

in which a is the root-mean-square radius of the charge distribution. This particular charge distribution with $a = 0.80 \times 10^{-13}$cm. is meant only to be typical of charge distributions which fit the proton within experimental error. Other distributions, such as a gaussian with a slightly smaller rms radius and a hollow exponential (19) with rms 0.78×10^{-13} cm., fit equally well. This is shown in Figure 9, where three typical distributions ($4\pi r^2\rho$) are shown that provide good fits. A sharply peaked distribution, such as a Yukawa *II* distribution (1, 19), will not fit, nor will a uniform distribution (not shown). Thus a band of suitable distributions lying near the three satisfactory curves is mapped out. It would be desirable to fix the limits of this region in more detail. Such experiments are now in progress. From the experiments described above, a "best" rms radius of the proton could be obtained and was found to be 0.77×10^{-13} cm. This radius is rather independent of shape and appears to be closely the same for F_1 and F_2. For further details the original paper (19) may be consulted. R. W. McAllister (109) has recently made an absolute measurement of the electron-proton elastic scattering cross section at 189.6 Mev and 60° and finds that the above radius is in good agreement with the measured cross section. In McAllister's

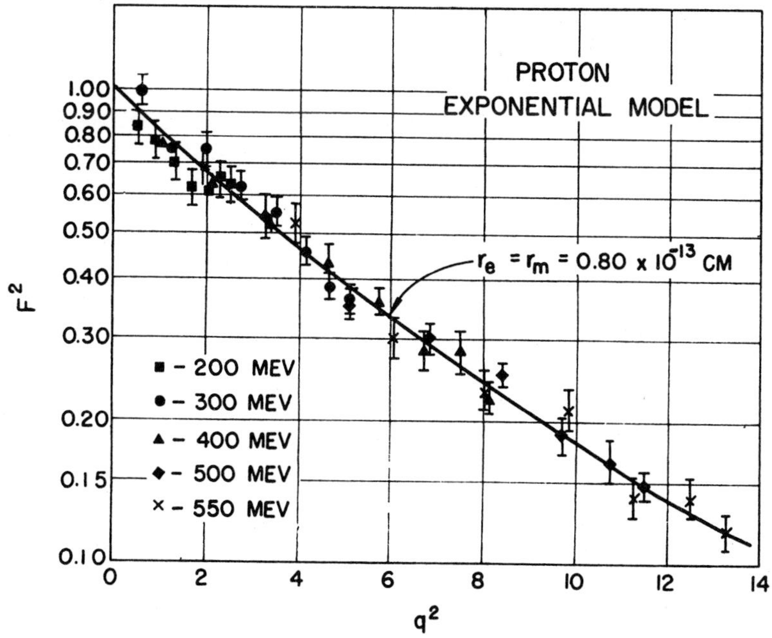

FIG. 8. An example of a model which fits the experimental values of F^2. This model gives the proton an exponential charge density and an exponential magnetic-moment density with rms radii 0.80×10^{-13} cm. Other close models fit equally well.

work the finite size produces an ~ 17 per cent effect in the cross section. In other recent work of Tautfest & Panofsky (110), the finite size effect is only ~3 per cent and is too small to be a test of the size effect.

Clementel & Villi (22) have recently proposed a proton model consisting of a negative δ function for the charge density at the center of the proton together with a Yukawa *II* (c.f. ref. 1) type positive cloud surrounding the negative core. The fit with experiment is not as good as the best models discussed (19), but is still satisfactory. This proposed model predicts that the electron-proton cross section should have a diffraction zero at 140° for an incident energy of 1.1 Bev. Beyond the zero the cross section increases slowly.

The significance of the findings on the finite size of the proton is not yet clear. There is undoubtedly a correlation of the proton's size with the

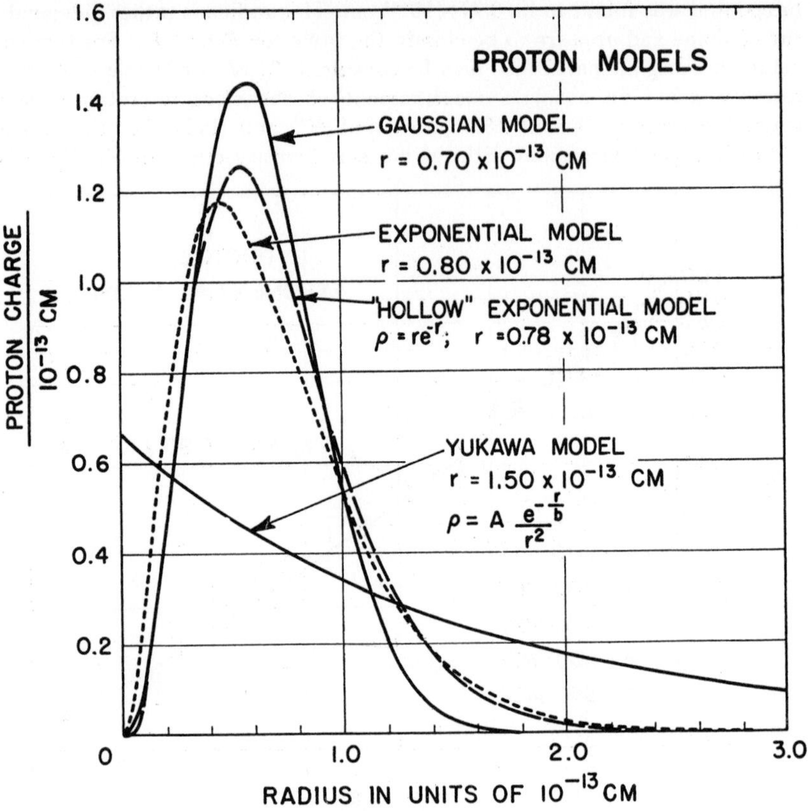

FIG. 9. This graph shows the latitude in the charge and moment distributions allowable in fitting the experiments on the proton (1, 19). The three models: gaussian, exponential, and hollow exponential are equally good. The Yukawa model will not fit, nor will a uniform model (not shown). For the above models, $F_1 = F_2$ for all q values. The ordinate is $4\pi r^2 \rho(r)$.

neutron's mesonic structure (see below), but the investigations are only beginning now, and it is too early to draw definite conclusions. The large size of the proton core is especially difficult to understand. For further comments on the interpretation of proton and neutron structure, see ref. 14 and the papers referred to in that article.

6. *Electron scattering from a deuteron.*—A completely relativistic theory of electron scattering from the deuteron has not appeared in the literature, and for a deuteron composed of finite nucleons such a complete theory can probably not be given at this time. However, certain close approximations can be made. A recent theoretical investigation of electron-deuteron scattering has been presented by Jankus (23). Earlier calculations, applying to lower

energies, were made by several authors (9, 24 to 28) but do not take into account the effects of higher multipoles, which are important for inelastic scattering at large values of the momentum transfer.

As pointed out by Jankus, the matrix elements in electron-deuteron scattering are similar to those involved in the photodisintegration of the deuteron. However, in the photoprocess only real, transverse photons are effective while, in the inelastic-deuteron scattering (electrodisintegration), the main part of the cross section arises from the longitudinal part of the electromagnetic field. Furthermore, it is well known (29) that excitation or disintegration by electrons is quite different from that due to photons. This occurs because in the lowest order processes the photon disappears entirely, that is, it is absorbed. Upon absorption, if it produced a large momentum transfer, it also produced a corresponding large energy change. But in electro-excitation or electro-disintegration processes a large momentum transfer may cause only a small energy transfer. This may be seen, for example, in the excitation of nuclear levels in carbon (30). Thus the photodisintegration results may not easily be applied to the deuteron, e.g., by using the Weizsacker-Williams method with the matrix elements known from the photoprocesses.

The deuteron will be considered below in a nonrelativistic heavy particle approximation used by Jankus although, of course, in the calculations, the electron will be treated in a fully relativistic manner. Like other computations for low Z elements, the first Born approximation is used in this case also. We employ once again the electron's Møller potentials, Eq. 69 and 70. However, in place of terms for the proton and neutron like those in Eq. 71, the nonrelativistic heavy-particle treatment involves the perturbing interaction:

$$H = e\int\left[\rho_D\varphi - \frac{1}{c}\boldsymbol{j}_D\cdot\boldsymbol{A} - \boldsymbol{M}_D\cdot(\nabla\times\boldsymbol{A})\right]d^3R \qquad 95.$$

which is perhaps more familiar than Eq. 71. In Eq. 95 the three-dimensional vector $\boldsymbol{M}_D$ is the magnetization density due to the spin-current densities in the deuteron, and $\boldsymbol{j}_D$ is the convection-current density due to the motion of the nucleons within the deuteron. These densities, and also ρ_D, the charge density in the deuteron, compose the perturbation H of Eq. 95.

In Eq. 95 the spin effects ($\boldsymbol{M}_D$) are separated from those due to the convection-current density ($\boldsymbol{j}_D$). Although this separation agrees with the more familiar nonrelativistic treatments of electromagnetic interactions, the splitup in Eq. 95 is only an approximation. The degree of approximation can be understood from the physical interpretation of the Dirac equation given by Foldy (20) who shows that "spin-orbit" coupling, the Darwin term and higher order terms, have been dropped in Eq. 95. These terms are of the order (P^2/M^2c^2) and are small compared to the principal term of Eq. 95. At higher energies, however, they must not be neglected. Further, if the exchange currents are neglected and the nucleons are thought of as point charges and point-magnetic moments, the interaction Eq. 95 becomes

$$H = \sum_{k=1,2} \left\{ e_k\varphi(R_k) + \frac{i}{2}\frac{e_k\hbar}{Mc}\left[A(R_k)\cdot\nabla_k + \nabla_k\cdot A(R_k)\right] - \frac{ie\hbar}{2Mc}\mu_k\sigma_k\cdot[\nabla\times A(R_k)]\right\} \quad 96.$$

in which R_k is the position coordinate of the kth nucleon, e_k its charge, and μ_k its magnetic moment in terms of a nuclear magneton ($\mu_p = 2.79$, $\mu_n = -1.91$). This expression can be shown to follow from the quantum mechanical operator for current density.

The resulting calculation for elastic scattering is lengthy but straightforward and is carried out in detail in Jankus' thesis (31). The elastic-scattering result is given by the expression

$$\frac{d\sigma}{d\Omega} = \left(\frac{e^2}{2E_0}\right)^2 \frac{\cos^2\theta/2}{\sin^4\theta/2} \frac{1}{1+\dfrac{E_0}{Mc^2}\sin^2\theta/2}\cdot G^2 \quad 97.$$

where

$$G^2 = \left[\int_0^\infty (u^2+w^2)j_0\left(\frac{1}{2}qr\right)dr\right]^2 + \left[\int_0^\infty 2w(u - 8^{-1/2}w)j_2\left(\frac{1}{2}qr\right)dr\right]^2$$
$$+ \frac{2}{3}\frac{\hbar^2q^2}{4M^2c^2}[2\tan^2\theta/2+1]$$
$$\times\left[\int_0^\infty\left\{\left[(\mu_p+\mu_n)(u^2+w^2) - \frac{3}{2}(\mu_p+\mu_n-\frac{1}{2}w^2)\right]j_0\left(\frac{1}{2}qr\right)\right.\right.$$
$$\left.\left. + 2^{-1/2}w[(\mu_p+\mu_n)(u+2^{-1/2}w) + 3\times 8^{-1/2}w]j_2\left(\frac{1}{2}qr\right)\right\}dr\right]^2 \quad 98.$$

and where the integral in the second bracket, with j_2 replaced by r^2, is equal to the quadrupole moment of the deuteron, except for a constant of proportionality. It is to be noted that the coefficient of $E_0/Mc^2 \sin^2\theta/2$ in Eq. 97 is unity and not two, as in the corresponding center-of-mass term for a proton. This is, of course, because of the doubled mass of the deuteron with respect to that of the proton. The expression for q (Eq. 11) will also be modified in the same way. Although Jankus' result (23) is really expressed in terms of s instead of our q, it is probable that a relativistic generalization would contain q, and so we have made the appropriate changes. In any case, for the present accuracy, the difference is not important.

The result for G^2 may be broken down into three parts. The first bracket gives the scattering from that part of the charge distribution which is spherically symmetric in the deuteron, and the square of the corresponding bracket can be called G_a^2. The second term is associated with the quadrupole scattering from the deuteron and may be called G_b^2. The lengthy third term corresponds to the scattering from the magnetic moment of the deuteron and can be recognized by the factor involving $q^2\tan^2\theta/2$. The third term will be called G_c^2. Consequently Eq. 98 can also be expressed in the form

$$G^2 = G_a^2 + G_b^2 + G_c^2 \quad 99.$$

which is suitable for easy reference to the various terms. In Eq. 98

$$j_0(x) = \frac{\sin x}{x} \quad \text{and} \quad j_2(x) = \left(\frac{3}{x^3} - \frac{1}{x}\right) \sin x - \frac{3}{x^2} \cos x \qquad 100.$$

and are two spherical Bessel functions [see for example ref. (2), p. 868]. The wave functions for the ground state of the deuteron involve the ^3S-state component $u(r)$, and $w(r)$, the ^3D-state component, and thus the ground state wave function is generally written (28, 32)

$$\psi_m = (4\pi)^{-1/2} r^{-1} [u(r) + 8^{-1/2} S_{np} w(r)] \chi_m \qquad 101.$$

for $m = 0$ and ± 1, where χ_m is the usual triplet-spin function. S_{np} is the tensor operator (32)

$$S_{np} = 3r^{-2}(\boldsymbol{\sigma}_n \cdot \boldsymbol{r})(\boldsymbol{\sigma}_p \cdot \boldsymbol{r}) - (\boldsymbol{\sigma}_n \cdot \boldsymbol{\sigma}_p) \qquad 102.$$

and where $1/2\, \boldsymbol{r}$ is the position of the charged proton with respect to the center of mass of the deuteron. $\boldsymbol{\sigma}_n$ and $\boldsymbol{\sigma}_p$ are the Pauli spin-matrix operators for the neutron and proton and are given by Eq. 35.

Since $u(r)$ and $w(r)$ are determined principally from the low-energy theory of the deuteron and depend in large measure on properties outside the range of nuclear forces, Jankus was able to calculate the quadrupole term approximately without assuming a detailed model. The quadrupole term is found to be $8/9(\hbar q/4Mc)^4 Q^2$ for small values of q, where $Q(\hbar/2Mc)^2 = 0.274 \times 10^{-26}$ cm^2. and is the deuteron's quadrupole moment. For larger values of q, the quadrupole term reaches a maximum value of about 0.002 for a Hulthén potential and about 0.006 for a repulsive-core potential. In either case it remains near these values for $q < 4 \times 10^{13}$ cm^{-1}. Evidently the quadrupole term is rather small. The magnetic-moment term and the spherically symmetric term are much more important for values of $q < 3 \times 10^{13}$ cm^{-1} at low energies.

Jankus (23) shows that, if the quadrupole term is neglected and if other small terms involving w and w^2 are neglected, the expression for eq. 98 may be simplified considerably and becomes

$$G^2 = f_D^2 \left\{ 1 + \frac{2}{3} \frac{\hbar^2 q^2}{4M^2 c^2} (\mu_p + \mu_n)^2 [2 \tan^2 \theta/2 + 1] \right\} \qquad 103.$$

where

$$f_D = \int (u^2 + w^2) j_0 \left(\frac{1}{2} qr\right) dr \qquad 104.$$

The bracket in Eq. 103 bears a resemblance to the bracket of Eq. 87. The factor 2/3, in front of the magnetic term in Eq. 103, comes from the spin sums associated with spin 1 in the deuteron. f_D is the spherically symmetric form factor of the deuteron's charge distribution. Because the tensor, or ^3D part (w) of the charge distribution, is approximately 4 per cent of the ^3S part (u), the w^2 term in Eq. 98 can be neglected with only a small error. In this event the function $u(r)$ determines the main features of the scattering cross section. The function f_D^2 (with w^2 neglected) is plotted in Figure 10, and the graph shows how a repulsive-core potential (curve (c) of the Figure) prevents charge from accumulating at the center of the deuteron, therefore

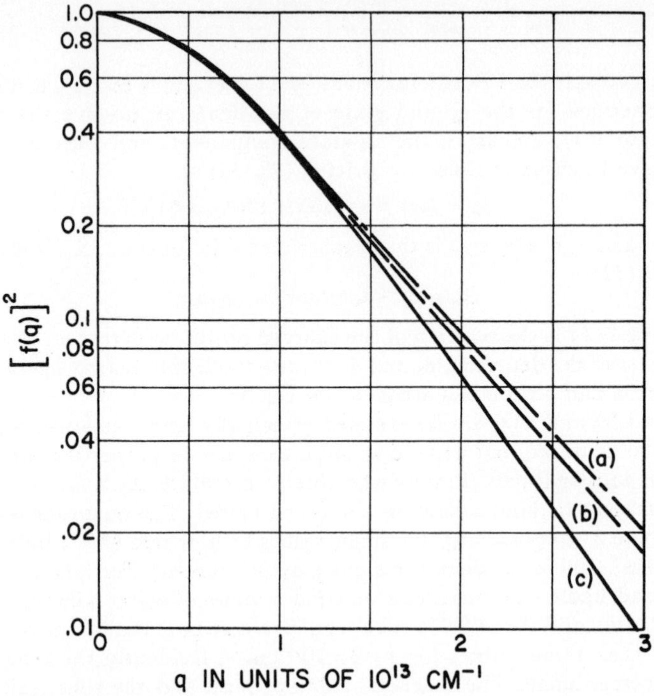

FIG. 10. Three approximate (form factors)² for the deuteron calculated by Jankus (23). Curves (a) and (b) refer to Hulthén distributions with effective range values of 1.77×10^{-13} cm. and 1.88×10^{-13} cm., respectively, while curve (c) refers to a suitable repulsive-core potential.

resulting in less scattering at large angles. This type of behavior is characteristic of all form factors with charge distributions pushed away from the center of a nucleus. Curves (a) and (b) refer to Hulthén distributions for effective ranges of 1.77×10^{-13} cm. and 1.88×10^{-13} cm., respectively.

Figure 11 shows the results of a numerical calculation of form factors made by McIntyre & Dhar (33) with Jankus' formulas (97) and (98) for a typical repulsive-core potential in the deuteron. In this case the w^2 term is retained. The various contributions G_a^2, G_b^2, G_c^2 are shown for several different incident electron energies. Since G_b^2 is a function only of q and of the type of interaction (Hulthén, etc.) potential, it has the same appearance at all energies.

The kind of charge distribution which gives the form factors of Figure 11 is illustrated in Figure 12 and has also been calculated by the above authors and independently by Smythe (34). As may be seen from Eq. 101, the sum u^2+w^2 is proportional to the charge in a shell at radius r from the center of mass in the deuteron. The curve for the repulsive-core potential corresponds to Figure 11. Smoother potentials of the Yukawa variety (32), with differing

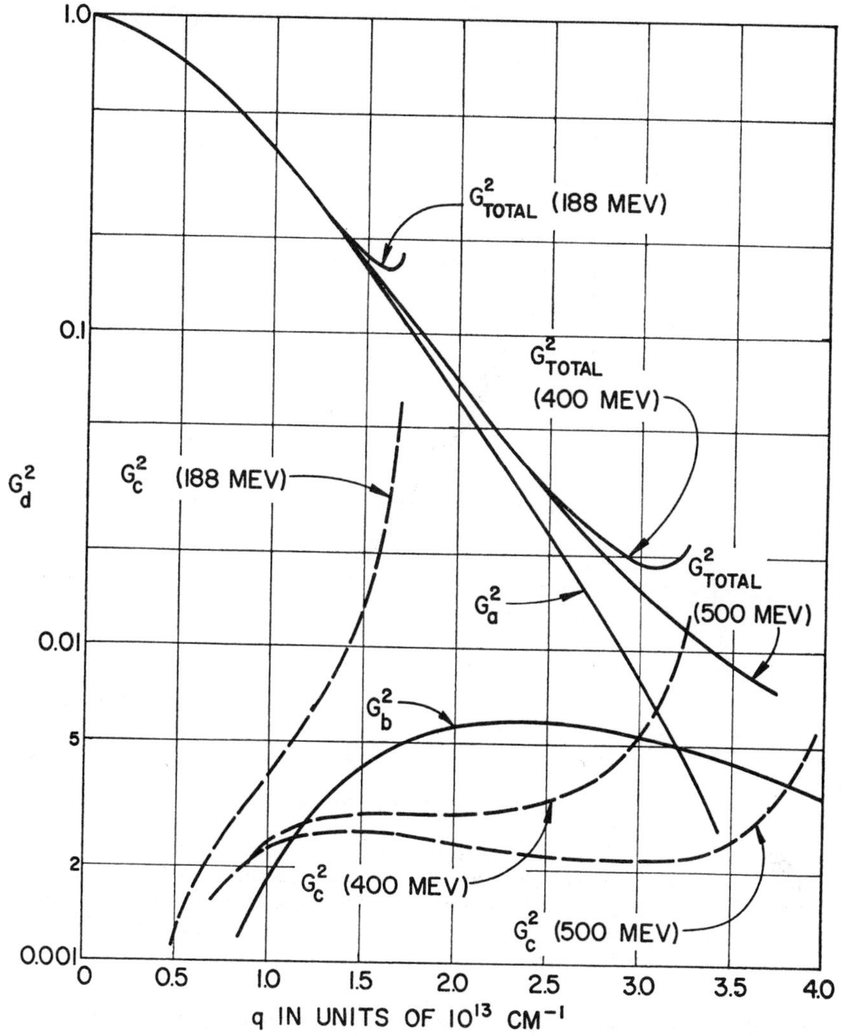

FIG. 11. The calculations of McIntyre & Dhar (33) based on Jankus' Eq. 97 and 98 for a repulsive-core potential in the deuteron. The general appearance is similar to (c) of Fig. 10, except that the quadrupole and magnetic-moment terms are included.

amounts of ^3D state contributions, give other charge distributions with more charge at the center of the deuteron. We shall turn later to a comparison with experiment of form factors such as shown in Figure 10 and 11.

A new and interesting theoretical treatment of the problem of elastic scattering from the deuteron has been given by Blankenbecler (35). His analysis is patterned after the corresponding relativistic calculation of

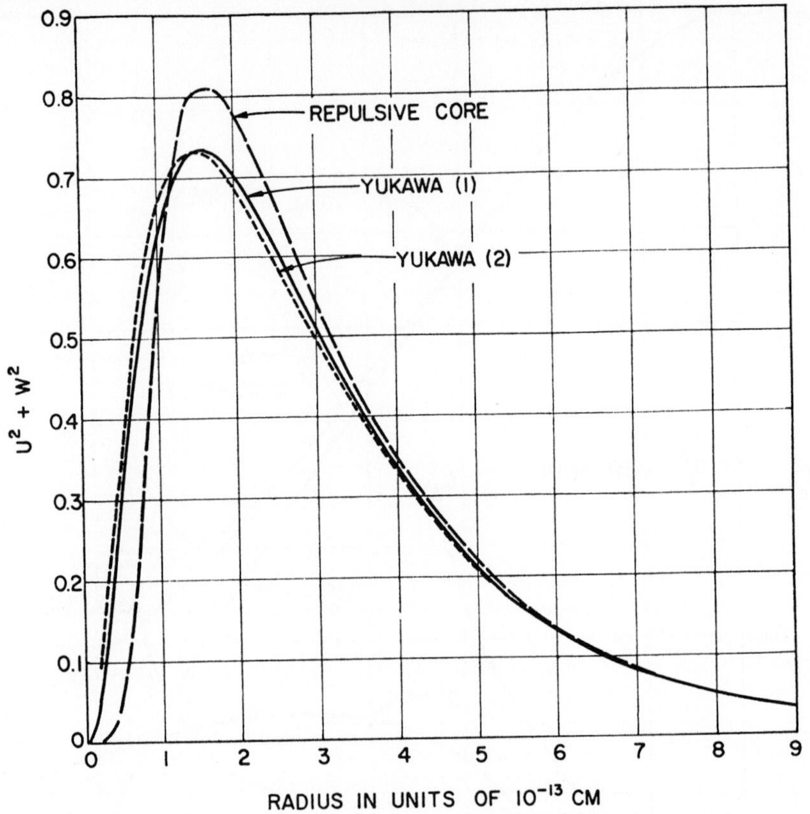

FIG. 12. These curves are proportional to $4\pi r^2\rho$ for the deuteron and show the differences between the repulsive core and Yukawa type potentials in the deuteron. The small charge densities in the deuteron may be appreciated by referring to Fig. 9, which shows a similar plot in the proton where the radius scale is expanded. The total charge is the same in both cases.

Rosenbluth for electron-proton scattering. Blankenbecler considers the deuteron to be a point particle with spin unity, with a charge e and a magnetic moment $\delta e\hbar/2Mc$ and with a quadrupole moment Q (M is the nucleon mass). This means that in covariant notation the current has three parts:

$$j_{\mu(\text{deuteron})} = j_{\mu(\text{charge})} + j_{\mu(\text{mag. mom})} + j_{\mu(\text{quad. mom.})} \qquad 105.$$

He then shows that the electron-deuteron cross section is given by

$$\left(\frac{d\sigma}{d\Omega}\right)_D = \left(\frac{d\sigma}{d\Omega}\right)_{Mott} F^2 = \sigma_{NS}F^2 \qquad 106.$$

where σ_{NS} is given by Eq. 48 and

$$F^2 = \left(1 - \frac{(\delta - \frac{1}{2})}{2} \frac{\hbar^2 q^2}{4M^2c^2}\right)^2 + \frac{2}{3}\delta^2 \frac{\hbar^2 q^2}{4M^2c^2}\left(2 \tan^2 \theta//2 + 1 + \frac{2E^2}{4(E + Mc^2)^2} \tan^2 \theta/2 \sin^2 \theta/2\right) + \frac{Q^2}{18}\frac{q^4\hbar^4}{16M^4c^4} \qquad 107.$$

and where the mass of the deuteron, $2M$, appears in the denominator in the center-of-mass term in σ_{NS}. The various terms in Eq. 107 have the following significance: The first term represents the charge scattering and an interference term between the charge and the "anomalous" magnetic moment. (A "normal" magnetic moment of a spin-one deuteron is $\delta = \frac{1}{2}$.) The first term is analogous to the proton case where the first and last terms of the bracket in Eq. 87 are to be compared with the first bracket of Eq. 107. However, in the latter case, the bracket is squared while in the proton case the bracket appears to the first power. This is due to the higher spin.

The second term in Eq. 107 represents the magnetic-moment scattering and bears a direct resemblance to the magnetic term in Eq. 87, containing $(2K^2 \tan^2 \theta/2)$. However the factor 2/3 occurs in the deuteron case because of the unit value of spin (see Eq. 103). The $\tan^2 \theta/2 \sin^2 \theta/2$ term in Eq. 107 has little similarity with the cross term involving $2K \tan^2 \theta/2$ in Eq. 87.

The third term containing Q^2 is similar to the quadrupole scattering obtained by Jankus (Eq. 98) and the approximation considered above.

In the spirit of Rosenbluth's calculation, or of the introduction of phenomenological form factors for the proton (1, 14, 17), the constants e, δ, Q may be made functions of q^2. However the interpretation of these form factors in terms of a physical model of the deuteron is not clear.

7. *Elastic scattering from a deuteron containing finite nucleons.*—The previous section has considered the elastic scattering from a deuteron containing a point proton and a point neutron. The experimental work on the proton (1) shows that it is a spread-out entity and presumably the neutron is spread out also insofar as its meson cloud is concerned. The obvious question may be asked: How do these spread-out particles affect the elastic scattering in the deuteron? Naive considerations would suggest that a folding of the nucleon's charge and moment distributions into the density distributions already given by deuteron theory (section 6), would yield a further spreading of the deuteron. Thus the larger deuteron would scatter less at large angles and high energies than a deuteron containing a point proton and a point neutron. These considerations prove to be correct as we shall see below.

The charge distribution in the deuteron implicit in u and w of Eq. 104 is

$$\rho_D(r) = |\psi_m(r)|^2 \qquad 108.$$

where ψ_m is the wave function in the ground state, Eq. 101, and corresponds to a deuteron containing point nucleons. If we make the assumption that the nucleons themselves are not distorted appreciably by the nuclear force in the deuteron and that the heavy particles may be treated nonrelativistically, then the folded charge distribution corresponding to finite nucleons, $\rho_f(r)$, may be represented by

$$\rho_f(r) = \int [\rho_P(|r - r'|) + \rho_N(|r - r'|)] \frac{1}{e} \rho_D(r') d^3r' \qquad 109.$$

where ρ_P, ρ_N, and ρ_D are, respectively, the charge density in a finite proton, the charge density in a finite neutron, and the charge density in a deuteron, given by Eq. 108. e In Eq. 109 is the absolute value of the charge of the proton. A folded charge distribution formed from a product of the type of equation 109 may be integrated directly to give a resultant form factor $F_D(q)$ similar to Eq. 55. The resultant $F_D(q)$ is then simply a product of form factors (14, 36)

$$F_D(q) = [F_P(q) + F_N(q)] f_D(q) \qquad 110.$$

where f_D is given by Eq. 104 and where $F_P = F_1$ is given by Eq. 90. A typical but not the only form of F_P is shown in Eq. 93. F_N is at present unknown except for indications from experiments on the neutron-electron interaction (37) that $F_N(q) \approx 0$ for small q, since the overall charge on the neutron is zero and since the mean square of the neutron's radius, weighted according to charge, is very small or zero according to those experiments. In principle, it is possible to find $F_N(q)$ if all other quantities in Eq. 110 are known.

It must be noted that only the charge distribution matters in Eq. 110. In actuality, when dealing with the deuteron, the complete expression for the form factor, G, of Eq. 97 and 98 must be used to compare theory with experiment. Fortunately, the quadrupole terms are rather small and this is true also of the magnetic scattering. In the latter case, $\mu_p + \mu_N = 0.857$ n.m., and the magnetic scattering is

$$\sim \frac{2}{3} \times \left(\frac{0.86}{2.79}\right)^2 = 0.063$$

or only about 1/16 as important as in the case of the proton where the magnetic effects are dominant at large angles and high energies. This fortunate circumstance may make it possible to find details of the neutron-proton potential when very accurate elastic-scattering experiments on the deuteron can be performed. In this case, however, it is probable that the quadrupole scattering will need to be known to higher accuracy than it is now known. By the same arguments, it will be difficult to learn about the shape or size of the neutron's magnetic cloud through elastic scattering, because the magnetic term enters only in a minor way into the elastic scattering formulas at presently attainable energies. (The next section will describe how it is possible by another method to determine the shape and size of the magnetic cloud in the neutron.)

Recent experimental work by McIntyre & Dhar (33, 38) on the deuteron shows clearly the effects of the finite size of the proton. Figure 13 provides a comparison of the experimental points showing the ratio of the deuteron's elastic scattering to that from a deuteron with point nucleons. Thus the experimental value of F_D^2 is shown in Figure 13. This is slightly different from F_D of Eq. 110, because, as explained above, only the charge was taken into account in that equation. However, if f_D of Eq. 110 is taken to be the G of Eq. 98 or its approximation Eq. 104, a direct comparison can be made with the experimental form factor. Then

$$F_{D(\text{exp})} = (F_P + F_N)G \qquad 111.$$

In these experiments $F_N \cong 0$ so that

$$F_{D(\text{exp})}^2 = F_P^2 G^2 \qquad 112.$$

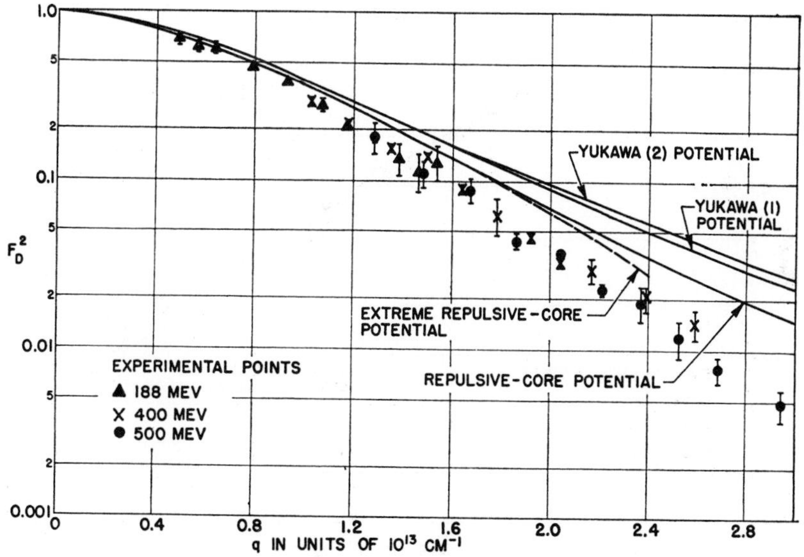

FIG. 13. The experimental value of F_D^2 is compared with theoretical calculations for F_D^2 for a deuteron composed of point nucleons. No allowable stretching of the constants of the theory will permit a good fit with the experiments (33).

and since in Figure 13 F_P^2 has not been allowed for, the experimental curve departs from the scattering expected from a deuteron with a point proton. Neither Yukawa potentials nor a repulsive-core potential, satisfying the parameters found from low-energy studies of the deuteron, are adequate to fit the experimental scattering without the introduction of a finite proton. On the other hand, Figure 14 shows that a repulsive-core deuteron, with a finite proton close to the size found previously (17, 18, 19), will fit the experimental points suitably, and this result confirms those findings. Once again the choice is not unique since an excellent fit is also obtained with a Yukawa potential and the rms proton size 0.78×10^{-13} cm. found by Chambers & Hofstadter (19). The "shape" of the proton was taken to agree with a hollow exponential (re^{-r}) model (ref. 19).

Thus the present conclusion is that the experiments on elastic electron scattering from the deuteron (33, 38) agree with those on the proton and give essentially the same proton size. This fact may be understood as a verification of the assumption that $F_N \cong 0$, and in this respect it is consistent with the experiments on the neutron-electron interaction (14). On the other hand, the present accuracy of the experiments does not permit conclusions to be drawn about the shape of the neutron-proton potential.

At small angles and lower energies ($\sim 40°$, 192 Mev), the form factors are close to unity and the electron-deuteron scattering (39) shows good agree-

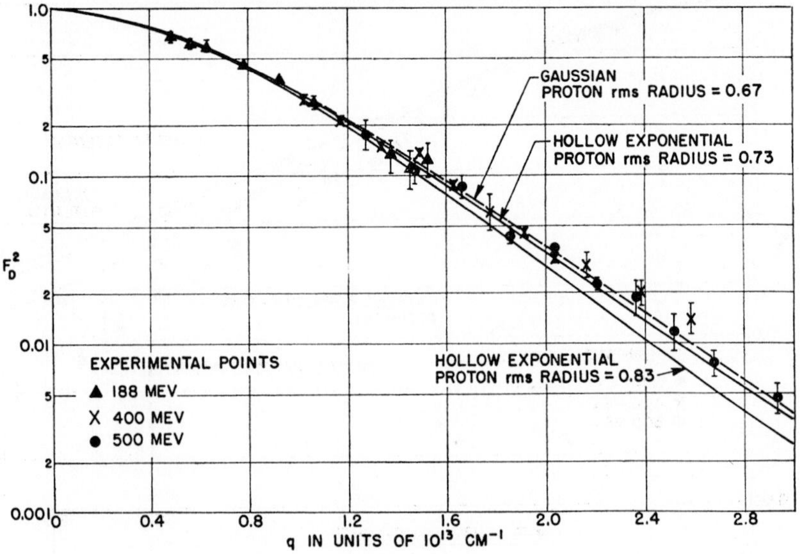

FIG. 14. This plot shows that the experimental values of the deuteron's (form factors)^2 can be made to agree with the conventional deuteron theory if allowance is made for a finite proton of the type presented in Fig. 9.

ment with the expected behavior for point nucleons and with the usual theory of the deuteron. This is consistent with the corrections for finite size now known.

8. *Inelastic scattering from the deuteron* (*electrodisintegration*).—In the first of the papers on electron scattering from the deuteron (39), an inelastic continuum was found on the low-energy side of the elastic-scattering peak. The general character of such an inelastic continuum (for complex nuclei) was pointed out by Amaldi *et al.* (40) and later, qualitatively by Feshbach (41). Physically, this type of scattering can be understood qualitatively (1) as elastic scattering of electrons from moving nucleons in a nucleus if the momentum transfer is sufficiently large so that the binding effects in the nucleus can be neglected. This is equivalent to the idea of an electrodisintegration, and an analysis of the cross section can yield the momentum distribu-

tion of nucleons within the nucleus. The experimental realization of such scattering has been illustrated (1) for deuterium and also for helium.

Figure 15, due to Jankus (23), shows the type of inelastic scattering to be expected from the theory for the deuteron at 350 Mev and at 60° in the laboratory system. The elastic cross section, whose size is not indicated in the Figure, is shown at 320.2 Mev. An inelastic cross section in the deuteron arises from terms such as

$$\left(\frac{d\sigma}{d\Omega}\right)_{in} = (4\pi)^{-3}\left(\frac{e^2}{E_0}\right)^2 \frac{1}{\sin^4\theta/2}\, kdpd\Omega_k$$
$$\times\left|\left\langle fin\left|\left[a_0 - i\nabla\cdot\boldsymbol{a} + \frac{1}{2}i\frac{\hbar}{Mc}\mu_p\sigma_p\cdot(\boldsymbol{q}\times\boldsymbol{a})\right]\exp\frac{1}{2}i\boldsymbol{q}\cdot\boldsymbol{r}\right.\right.\right. \qquad 113.$$
$$\left.\left.\left. + \frac{1}{2}i\frac{\hbar}{Mc}\mu_n\sigma_n\cdot(\boldsymbol{q}\times\boldsymbol{a})\exp -\frac{1}{2}i\boldsymbol{q}\cdot\boldsymbol{r}\right| init\right\rangle\right|$$

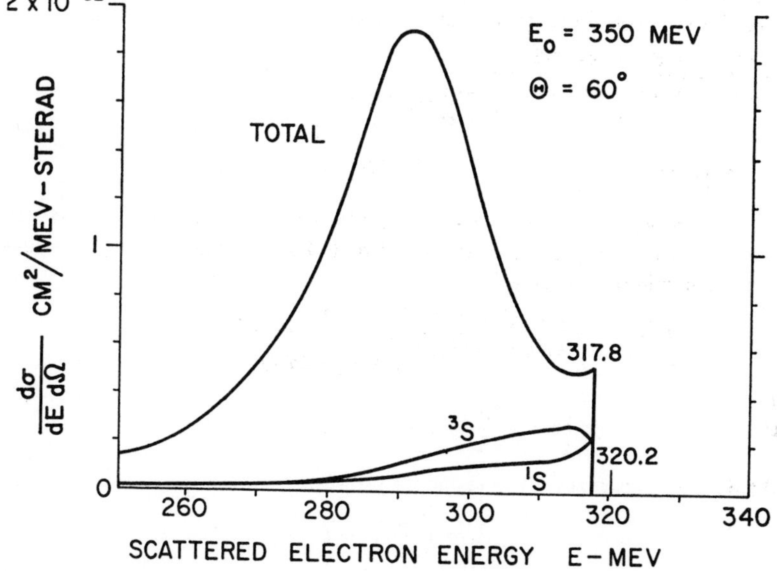

FIG. 15. A typical plot of the inelastic continuum in the deuteron obtained from the Jankus theory (23). The ^{3}S and ^{1}S contributions are also shown.

where $\boldsymbol{k}$ represents the final momentum of the proton with respect to the center of mass of the recoil deuteron, and where $\boldsymbol{a}$ and a_0 are the matrix elements of the Dirac $\boldsymbol{\alpha}$ and $\boldsymbol{\beta}$ operators. $d\Omega_k$ is the relevant proton solid angle and p refers to the momentum of the scattered electron. The above expression has been obtained by Jankus from Eq. 96.

The general evaluation of Eq. 113 is quite complex but, when completed, does provide the continuous energy spectrum of electrons scattered into any energy interval at a given angle. As shown experimentally at 500 Mev, 135° (42), the distribution has a rather narrow width at half-maximum (~44 Mev). The same behavior is also apparent from theory in Figure 15, due to Jankus. At 350 Mev and 60°, the width is about 23 Mev. (The change in width with incident energy is easily seen to be consistent with relativistic kinematics.) Thus, as a crude approximation, the momentum transfer, q, does not vary very much over the important region in the inelastic peak where the cross section accumulates most of its value. The rough approximation can then be made that q is constant and may be taken out of the integral (over dp) involving the differential cross section Eq. 113. Using the closure property of the deuteron's final wave functions, a total cross section at a given angle can be found. Then the elastic cross section, given approximately by Eq. 97 and 103, may be subtracted from the total cross section just found and the difference yields the inelastic cross section at a given angle. This procedure led Jankus to an important approximate formula[3] for large q, giving the total inelastic cross section of the deuteron at a given angle:

$$\left(\frac{d\sigma}{d\Omega}\right)_{in} = \left(\frac{e^2}{2E_0}\right)^2 \frac{\cos^2\theta/2}{\sin^4\theta/2} \frac{1}{1+\dfrac{2E_0}{Mc^2}\sin^2\theta/2} \times \left\{(1-f_D{}^2) + \frac{\hbar^2 q^2}{4M^2c^2}\left[2(\mu_P{}^2+\mu_N{}^2-3f_D{}^2)\tan^2\theta/2 + \mu_P{}^2+\mu_N{}^2-3f_D{}^2\right]\right\} \qquad 114.$$

which can be used only when $q > \alpha$, where $1/\alpha$ is the usual size of the deuteron $[(1/\alpha) \cong 4 \times 10^{-13}$ cm$]$. Examination of Eq. 114 shows that for larger values of q, that is, where f_D is small,

$$\left(\frac{d\sigma}{d\Omega}\right)_{in} = \left(\frac{e^2}{2E_0}\right)^2 \frac{\cos^2\theta/2}{\sin^4\theta/2} \frac{1}{1+\dfrac{2E_0}{Mc^2}\sin^2\theta/2} \times \left\{1 + \frac{\hbar^2 q^2}{4M^2c^2}\left[2(\mu_P{}^2+\mu_N{}^2)\tan^2\theta/2 + \mu_P{}^2+\mu_N{}^2\right]\right\} \qquad 115.$$

and this is approximately the same, for point nucleons, as

$$\left(\frac{d\sigma}{d\Omega}\right)_{in} = \left(\frac{d\sigma}{d\Omega}\right)_{P} + \left(\frac{d\sigma}{d\Omega}\right)_{N} \qquad 116.$$

Now the theory of Jankus makes certain nonrelativistic approximations referred to previously. Blankenbecler (43) has avoided making some of these assumptions and arrives at an expression indentical with Eq. 116 except for small correction terms of the order of a few per cent.

Further details on the shape of the inelastic spectrum of electrons scattered against deuterium must be left to the original paper of Jankus, since

[3] Jankus' (31) result for inelastic scattering, given in his Eq. 7, contains the factor $[1+(E_0/Mc^2)]^{-1}$ instead of $[1+(2E_0/Mc^2)]^{-1}$. Although the former factor is correct for elastic scattering, it is not correct for inelastic scattering. [The correct result was given in ref. 1, Eq. 59 and has been proved by Blankenbecler (43)].

the computations are quite intricate. However, we should not fail to note in passing that the interaction between the neutron and proton in the final state must be taken into account. This has been done approximately by Jankus for a Yukawa potential. He shows that there is an effect of the order of 10 per cent on the shape of the inelastic continuum of Figure 15. The change in the total cross section at a given angle appears to cancel out, at least approximately, although the spectrum suffers slight changes. Thus it may be expected that the effect of the interaction on equation 116 will be small. It would be interesting to carry out a similar calculation for a repulsive-core potential where the effect might be larger. To the author's knowledge this calculation has not been made.

9. *The neutron.*—Inelastic electron scattering from the deuteron is extremely interesting from the viewpoint of determining the neutron's structure. It was previously suggested (1) that by examining the inelastic scattering in the deuteron at large values of the momentum transfer, it might be possible to separate the scattering effects of the neutron and proton and thus to measure the form factor of the neutron. The basic equation 116 would permit a determination of the neutron's cross section by a subtractive method

$$\sigma_N = \sigma_{in}{}^D - \sigma_P \qquad 117.$$

in which it would be necessary to know the proton's cross section. For convenience we have replaced the differential cross-section symbols by the corresponding σ's. These σ's are integrals over the spectrum of the inelastic-deuteron peak and the proton's elastic peak at a given angle.

Now Eq. 117 or 116 have been worked out for point nucleons, and it might be expected that finite-nucleon size could have a very large effect on the magnitude of the scattering cross sections. We have already seen in section 7 how the elastic scattering is modified by the effect of finite-proton size. If the scattering from proton and neutron are independent and incoherent as suggested by Eq. 117, our crude expectation would be that the point-nucleon cross sections would be multiplied by their respective (form factors)^2 when the nucleons are permitted to have finite dimensions. Our assumptions would involve the notions: (*a*) that the nucleons are not distorted by the presence of each other, (*b*) that exchange effects are small, and (*c*) that polarizability effects between the electron and the nucleons' mesonic clouds are also small. With respect to (*a*), nothing is now known of such effects. In case (*b*), Jankus suggests that exchange effects are small (23). For (*c*), Drell & Ruderman (44) show that below 500 Mev electron-induced polarization in the proton is small, corresponding to a 0.5 per cent effect at 400 Mev and 90° scattering.

Consequently, it appears reasonable to assume that mesonic effects will not influence the interpretation of Eq. 117 in an important manner when it is applied to nucleons of finite dimensions. Blankenbecler (35) has considered the modifications of Eq. 117 required by a relativistic treatment of the sum rule from which Eq. 117 was derived and includes the effect of finite size of the nucleons. Thus his treatment considers the variation of q over the energy spectrum of the inelastic continuum and the variation of the free nucleons' form factors over the same region. Mesonic corrections due to the exchange of charged mesons or other corrections discussed above are not included in his work.

Blankenbecler's result is given below:

$$\sigma_{in}{}^D = A\left[\sigma_P{}^F + \sigma_N{}^F\right]_{p_f - \bar{p}_f + B/A - \epsilon} \qquad 118.$$

where

$$\begin{aligned} A &= 1 + 0.847\langle p^2 \rangle = 1.017 \\ B &= 0.574\langle p^2 \rangle = 0.0115. \end{aligned} \qquad 119.$$

A and B are correct up to $\langle p^2 \rangle \rightarrow (v^2/c^2)$ but not including $\langle p^4 \rangle \rightarrow (v^4/c^4)$ at angle of 135° and incident energy of 470 Mev, and a value of $\langle p^2 \rangle = 0.02$. The mean-square value of the momentum spread is $\langle p^2 \rangle = 0.04$ for a repulsive core and 0.015 for a Hulthen potential, p is measured in units of the rest energy of a nucleon and thus B corresponds to about 10 Mev when $\langle p^2 \rangle$ corresponds to about 19 Mev. The value of the bracket in equation 118 is to be found at a final scattered energy corresponding to the free proton-recoil energy ($\bar{p}_f$) plus approximately 10 Mev (B/A) minus the binding energy of the deuteron ($\epsilon = 2.2$ Mev). The superscript F stands for the free proton and free neutron cross sections including the effects of their form factors. The final state attraction is taken into account and influences the value and sign of B. Eq. 118 allows for the fact that the deuteron is a bound structure and hence the electron scatters at an effectively different mean energy from the incident energy. The variation of the form factors of the nucleons over the momentum spectrum of the moving nucleons is also included in this equation. It is as if the electron were scattering against nucleons sometimes moving with momentum components along its direction and sometimes against its direction. When the terms of Eq. 118 are evaluated, the result is that $\sigma_{in}{}^D = \sigma_p{}^F + \sigma_N{}^F$ with an error of less than 8 per cent for the stated conditions. The sign of the correction is positive so that the resulting $\sigma_{in}{}^D$ is 8 per cent greater than would correspond to Eq. 117 when applied to nucleons of finite size.

Figure 16 shows an experimental realization of the inelastic scattering in the deuteron and represents recent data obtained by Yearian & Hofstadter (45). The data were obtained at 135° at an incident energy of 500 Mev and were found by direct comparison between a liquid-deuterium target and a liquid-hydrogen target. In this figure one sees the slight shift (C) to lower energies of the maximum of the inelastic spectrum compared to the electron-proton peak (A). At low-energy settings (D) ($\sim$139 Mev) one observes the scattering of electrons which have produced mesons in the deuteron. The bremsstrahlung tail of the free-proton peak is also clearly shown at (B).

In order to subtract the deuteron and proton cross sections, it is necessary to find the area under each peak. In this calculation a correction must be made for the radiative effect, that is, for electrons not counted because

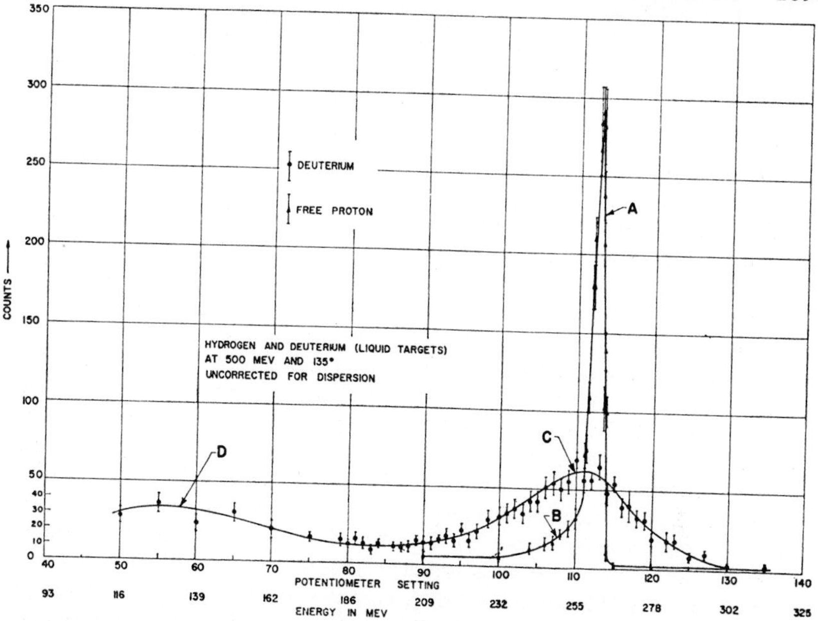

FIG. 16. The experimental comparison of the scattering from the moving proton and neutron in the deuteron (C) and the scattering associated with free protons (A). The data are taken from Yearian and Hofstadter (45). At (D) there is a peak belonging to electrons which have been scattered after producing pions in deuterium. From the scattering data in this figure, the magnetic form factor of the neutron can be obtained. It is found to be larger than that of a proton for a similar momentum transfer.

they radiated high-energy photons and appeared at very low final energies. This correction may be evaluated using the Schwinger formula straggling, etc. (1). Furthermore, the usual $(1/E)$ instrumental correction corresponding to the use of constant-width energy slit must be made. When these corrections are applied, the resulting ratio, σ_N/σ_P, comes out to be 1.0 ± 0.20.

Except for Blankenbecler's correction, the actual calculation of a neutron form factor may be made with the help of Eq. 89. When applied to a neutron, for which we may take $F_1 = 0$, at least approximately, we obtain

$$\sigma_N = \sigma_{NS} F_{2N}^2 K_N^2 \frac{\hbar^2 q^2}{4M^2c^2} \{2 \tan^2 \theta/2 + 1\} \qquad 120.$$

whereas, from the result of Chambers & Hofstadter (19), Eq. 90, $F_1 = F_2 = F_P$, holds and thus

$$\sigma_P = \sigma_{NS} F_P^2 \left\{ 1 + \frac{\hbar^2 q^2}{4M^2c^2} [2(1 + K_P)^2 \tan \ \theta/2 + K_P^2 \right\} \qquad 121.$$

Then

$$\frac{\sigma_N}{\sigma_P} = \frac{F_{2N}^2}{F_P^2} \frac{\frac{K_N^2\hbar^2q^2}{4M^2c^2}[2\tan^2\theta/2 + 1]}{1 + \frac{\hbar^2q^2}{4M^2c^2}[2(1 + K_P)^2\tan^2\theta/2 + K_P^2]} \qquad 122.$$

The ratio depends on incident energy and angle since q depends on both of these quantities. Further, F_{2N} and F_P are functions of q.

As we have seen, the experimental ratio, σ_N/σ_P, is in the neighborhood of unity. Placing the right-hand side of Eq. 122 equal to unity, we may solve for F_{2N}^2/F_P^2. The solution is found to be approximately $F_{2N}^2/F_P^2 = 2.2$. This ratio differs from σ_N/σ_P not so much because of the proton charge, which makes a small contribution at these momentum transfers, but because of the differing magnetic moments of neutron and proton. Now it is possible to find F_{2N}^2, since F_P^2 is known to be 0.15. The approximate value is found to be $F_{2N}^2 = 0.33$. From these results we find that F_N and F_P are unequal for virtually the same value of q. Thus, if it can be assumed that mesonic effects involve only small correction and if Blankenbecler's expansion is rapidly convergent, the dimensions and magnetic structure of the neutron are somewhat different from those of the proton. This would mean that a failure of electrodynamics cannot be wholly responsible for the size effects found in the proton and neutron, and this would be a major conclusion from the experiments on the size of nucleons (1, 17, 18, 19, 45). On the other hand, if the corrections in the Blankenbecler expansion are positive and not negligible, the form factors of neutron and proton can be the same. It should be emphasized that a complete form-factor curve must be obtained in order to be certain about these facts; *i.e.*, the consistency of the results at different values of q must be examined. Such a program is now in progress, but it is too early to give a definite answer to the problem. Thus, although the experiments are definite, the precise neutron structure question now awaits a more detailed calculation for the nuclear two-body problem. Even though there are some theoretical uncertainties, the observed cross sections definitely rule out a point magnetic moment for the neutron and the neutron size is crudely the same as that of the proton. Taking the data at face value, the neutron's rms magnetic radius is $(0.61 \pm 0.10) \times 10^{-13}$ cm.

One bit of experimental evidence that indicates that mesonic effects are not important may be obtained from the shape of the inelastic deuteron peaks at different mean values of q, such as those obtained at 75°, 90°, 105°, 120°, and 135° at 500 Mev. It is found (45) that all the peaks have essentially the same shape and half-width. If mesonic effects are important, it might be expected that the shapes would vary, particularly for such q's that the isobaric state of the nucleon is excited. There appears to be no large effect of this kind.

Simple relativistic calculations for a collision between an electron and nucleons in motion have been made by the author. These show that, at a given energy at large angles, the scattered electrons resulting from electro-

For helium the experimental rms radius, $a=1.61\times10^{-13}$ cm., yields, according to expression (128), $a=1.223\ a_0$ or $a_0(\mathrm{He})=1.31\times10^{-13}$ cm. If corrected for the finite size of the proton, a corresponding value of a_0, called a_0', would equal 1.15×10^{-13} cm., since $a=1.41\times10^{-13}$ cm. in this case.

(*b*) Lithium. Li^6 belongs to a $(1s)^2(1p)^1$ proton configuration. For this nucleus, $Z=3$ gives $\alpha=1/3$. Now, Streib's (1) preliminary value of the rms radius for Li^6 was given as 2.78×10^{-13} cm, and the model used was a modified exponential [model XII (1)]. Further independent studies by Streib and the author show that other models with smaller rms radii also fit the data as well. A gaussian, with rms radius 2.37×10^{-13} cm and a uniform charge distribution with rms radius 2.10×10^{-13} cm, will provide satisfactory fits. If a harmonic-well *p*-shell type model is used, a is found to be about 2.44×10^{-13} cm and $a_0=1.80\times10^{-13}$ cm. Unfortunately there are no data at lower or higher energies, or absolute values of the cross section, to fix which of these models is correct. Higher energy experiments to settle these questions are now in progress. Thus, at present, it is not possible to decide between the larger and smaller sizes. However, as we shall see, the evidence from nearby nuclei probably favors the smaller size. Of course, with precise data, it is possible to decide between the shapes and sizes unequivocally. (Newer data at 420 Mev taken by G. Burleson and the author support the smaller size and give a in the neighborhood of 2.1×10^{-13} cm.)

(*c*) Beryllium. This nucleus has the proton configuration $(1s)^2(1p)^2$. The early data of Hofstadter *et al.* (60) at 125 Mev were analyzed by these authors and yielded best fits for the rms radius of uniform and gaussian models of 1.90×10^{-13} cm and 1.96×10^{-13} cm, respectively. However, the early data were corrected for the "anomalous" width of the elastic profiles. [See Fig. 6 and 10 of ref. (60).] This width at large angles was later shown to be due to the partial inclusion in the elastic profile of the first inelastic peak (61). By using the original data, instead of the "corrected" data, of Figure 10 (60), one easily finds that the rms radii for the uniform and gaussian models are 2.17 and 2.28×10^{-13} cm, respectively. The independent data at 190 Mev (61) can also be analyzed and the results in this case are found to give corresponding values of 1.99 and 2.39×10^{-13} cm for the uniform and gaussian models, respectively.

The harmonic-shell charge distribution Eq. 127 with $\alpha=2/3$ $(Z=4)$ may also be fitted to the two angular distributions at 125 Mev and 190 Mev (60, 61) and yields, since $a=\sqrt{2}a_0$ for $Z=4$, the value $a=2.2\times10^{-13}$ cm or $a_0=1.56\times10^{-13}$ cm. It is to be noted that the energy 125 Mev is low enough so that there is little effect on the rms size because of a choice of different models. Thus the rms size is uniquely found to be $2.2\pm0.2\times10^{-13}$ cm. All the above results are consistent with this value. The preliminary data of Streib (62) are also in agreement with the above conclusions. Gatha *et al.* (63) and Tassie (59) have analyzed the Be scattering data of references 60 and 61 and find agreement with the above conclusions within the experimental error.

(*d*) Carbon. The details of obtaining the best fit between experiment and theory for this $(1s)^2(1p)^4$ proton configuration will be found in the original papers and have been discussed (1). In this section we shall merely point out that a harmonic-well model (Eq. 127) with $\alpha = 4/3$ fits the elastic-scattering data extremely well. It is not possible to distinguish convincingly between $\alpha = 4/3$ and other close values such as $\alpha = 1$ and $\alpha = 2$, provided that appropriate choices of a are also made. However, $\alpha = 4/3$ gave the best fit of all models tried.

Now in the case of C^{12} there are new data at higher energy to compare with the predictions of the older models. In Figure 4 we have already shown the new data of Sobottka & Hofstadter (10). The data can be analyzed by the Born approximation shown as a dashed line in Figure 4. However, the minimum is not properly reproduced, as expected. The solid line in Figure 4 represents the results of the accurate phase-shift method to be discussed in section 12. The exact calculation shown in the figure has been made by D. G. Ravenhall for the model of eq. 127 with $\alpha = 4/3$ and $a = 2.40 \times 10^{-13}$ cm. or equivalently $a_0 = 1.64 \times 10^{-13}$ cm. These are essentially the same parameters which are used to fit the low-energy data (187 Mev) (51, 52). The fit is seen to be very good, and the position and depth of the minimum are reproduced within experimental error. Since the low-energy analysis did not have the advantage of working with the diffraction minimum of Figure 4, the good fit must be counted as a strong justification for the method and confirms many of the assumptions which have gone into the theory. In particular, the static model of the charge distribution in the nucleus appears to be quite faithful, and dispersion corrections to this model must be very small.

It should be mentioned that when the proton size is allowed for, the parameter of the best fit, such as $a_0 = 1.64$, will be changed slightly, but the phenomenological shell-type charge distribution given by Eq. 127 still describes the experimental scattering. Folding-in of the proton charge distribution will multiply the form factor of Eq. 129 by exp $(-q^2a_0^2(p)/4)$, thus giving

$$F(qa) = \left[1 - \frac{\alpha q^2 a_0^2}{2(2+3\alpha)}\right] \exp\left[-\frac{q^2}{4}\left(a_0^2 + a_0^2(P)\right)\right] \qquad 132.$$

where

$$a_0(P) = \frac{0.72}{1.224} \times 10^{-13} \text{ cm.} = 0.59 \times 10^{-13} \text{ cm.}$$

if a gaussian model with $a = 0.72 \times 10^{-13}$ cm. is chosen for the proton.

(*e*) Oxygen. The same type of shell-model calculation can be applied to O^{16}, where shell theory predicts a value $\alpha = 2$, since O^{16} is expected to have the proton configuration $(1s)^2(1p)^6$. The Born-approximation form factor for this case is quite similar to the curve shown in Figure 2 for $\alpha = 4/3$, except that the $O^{16}(\alpha = 2)$ minimum occurs at a value of $x = qa = 4.24$ instead of 4.42 for C^{12} $(\alpha = 4/3)$. The maximum near $x = 5.3$ is also slightly higher for $\alpha = 2$ than for $\alpha = 4/3$. Figure 17 shows new experimental data in O^{16} of Ehrenberg, Meyer-Berkhout, and the author (64), obtained at 420 Mev with the

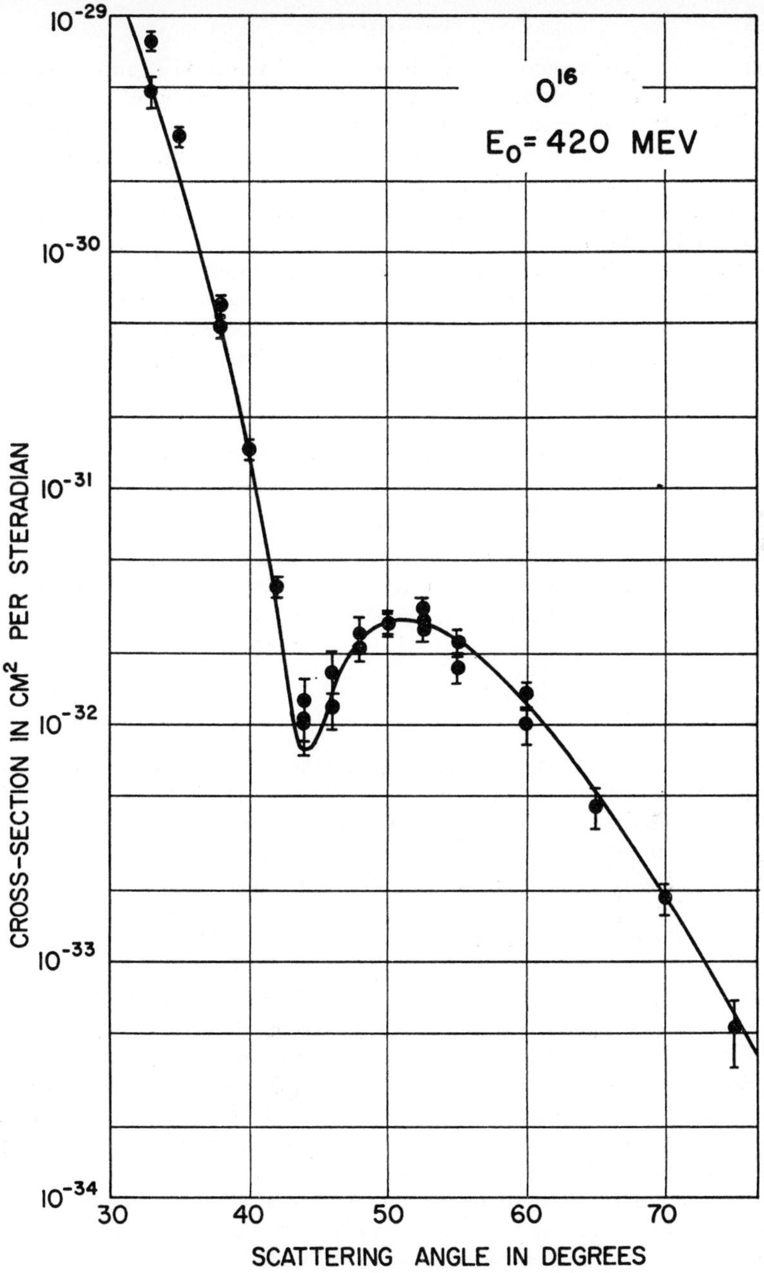

FIG. 17. New experimental data of Ehrenberg *et al.* (64) obtained at 420 Mev for the O^{16} nucleus. The figure also shows the exact calculations of D. G. Ravenhall for the harmonic-well model for which $\alpha = 2.0$ and $a_0 = 1.75 \times 10^{-13}$ cm.

Stanford 36″ spectrometer. The minimum occurs near 43.7° and when used with the Born-approximation form factor, Eq. 129, gives a value of $a = 2.64 \times 10^{-13}$ cm. or $a_0 = 1.77 \times 10^{-13}$ cm. Again, if a correction is made for the finite size of the proton, the value of a_0 would be slightly smaller for a given value of a. Figure 17 shows also the exact phase-shift calculation of D. G. Ravenhall for the harmonic-well model ($\alpha = 2$) and the parameter $a_0 = 1.75 \times 10^{-13}$ cm. As in the case of carbon, the fit is very good.

Summary.—We may summarize the above results for a_0 in Table I. No correction has been applied for a finite proton size in the table.

Thus, except for the Li^6 result, which is questionable, there is a slight tendency for ϵ to decrease as the p-shell is filled in. We must await more

TABLE I

PARAMETERS FOR p-SHELL NUCLEI

Nucleus	Proton Configuration	$a(10^{-13}$cm.)	$a_0(10^{-13}$cm).	ϵ(Mev)
He^4	$(1s)^2$	1.61	1.31	18.7
Li^6	$(1s)^2(1p)^1$	2.44(?)	1.80(?)	9.9(?)
Be^9	$(1s^2)(1p)^2$	2.2	1.56	13.3
C^{12}	$(1s^2)(1p^4)$	2.40	1.64	12.0
O^{16}	$(1s^2)(1p^6)$	2.64	1.77	10.3

accurate data to substantiate these results but the tendency already seems clear. The newer data on Li^6 ($a = 2.1$) confirms the tendency.

12. *Heavier nuclei: The phase-shift calculations for elastic scattering*

(*a*) Lower energies.—We have seen in section II, B, 3 that the experimental results for nuclei heavier than the proton or deuteron, such as C^{12}, could not be analyzed precisely by the Born approximation because of inaccuracy near the diffraction features of the scattering pattern. On the other hand, the Born approximation is quite good for C^{12} and for other light nuclei in regions more remote from the diffraction zeroes, and it has been useful in describing the coarse features of electron scattering even for nuclei as heavy as copper ($Z = 29$). The same kind of relationship exists also for the point-nuclear-model, and it was recognized early by Bartlett & Watson (65) and by Feshbach (66) that the accurate calculations for high Z differed widely from the Born results. Nowadays the model of a point-nucleus of high-atomic number is of more-or-less academic interest in its own right, but because of its relevance to low-energy scattering (0–10 Mev) and also because the more exact methods make phase-shift comparisons with the point-charge wave functions, the point-charge calculations have considerable value.

For low values of Z, McKinley & Feshbach (67) have carried out an evaluation of the conditionally convergent, infinite series of Mott (67a) and have derived a scattering formula for cases when $Z/137$ is not large and when

$$\beta = \frac{v}{c} \cong 1 \qquad 133.$$

This formula applies with relatively small errors for nuclei up to values of $\alpha \cong 0.2$ where

$$\alpha = \frac{Ze^2}{\hbar c} = \frac{Z}{137} \qquad 134.$$

thus up to about copper. The McKinley-Feshbach formula for elastic scattering may be represented in closed form as

$$\left(\frac{d\sigma}{d\Omega}\right)_F = \left(\frac{Ze^2}{2E_0}\right)^2 \frac{\cos^2 \theta/2}{\sin^4 \theta/2}\left[1 + \frac{\pi Z}{137} \frac{(\sin \theta/2)(1 - \sin \theta/2)}{\cos^2 \theta/2}\right] \qquad 135.$$

where the center-of-mass correction has been omitted since it is so very small.

However, this formula fails for higher values of Z and an accurate closed formula for such scattering is unknown. [For a closed-formula approximation, see ref. (131).] McKinley & Feshbach also developed an expansion which yields the scattering up to terms in α^4, but these results must be expressed numerically (67). R. M. Curr (68) has extended these calculations to energies greater than 0.5 Mev ($\alpha \cong 1$) up to and including terms in α^8. Thus, for $Z \cong 82$ ($\alpha = 0.6$), the error of these solutions is less than 1 per cent. The power series of Curr, which is expressed as a ratio

$$R = \frac{\sigma}{\sigma_R} \qquad 136.$$

of σ to the Rutherford cross section,

$$\sigma_R = \left(\frac{Ze^2}{2mv^2}\right)^2 (1 - \beta^2) \csc^4 \theta/2 \qquad 137.$$

is given in the form of a single power series. Curr compares his approximation with an exact calculation of Yadav (69) for uranium. The results are shown in Figure 18. Thus we may say that for energies >0.5 Mev, the point-charge scattering problem for unpolarized electrons has been solved to a high degree of accuracy for all elements. Tables of the desired scattering cross sections are to be found in Curr's paper. (See also footnote on p. 201 of ref. 73).

The question of experimental verification of the low-energy electron scattering theory is a long and involved one. Recent work, in which references to the early papers are given, has been reported by Chapman *et al.* at 0.4–0.5 Mev (70), Brown *et al.* at 0.4–0.5 Mev (71), Bayard & Yntema at about 1 Mev (72), and Damodaran & Curr (73). The new results in Al, Au, and U are in quite good agreement with Curr's theoretical work, and there seems to be little doubt that the Curr theory gives a correct representation of all the experiments. The early work by Van de Graaff *et al.* (74, 75) also gave excellent agreement with theory. [See Figure 5 of ref. (67).] A review of these and other pertinent electron-scattering results up to 1955 has been given by Urban (76).

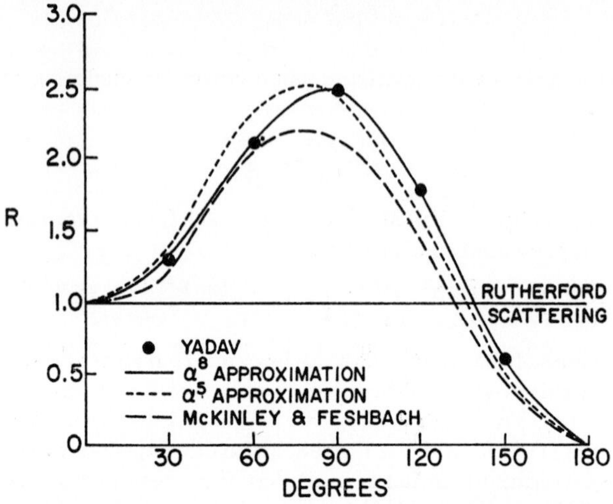

FIG. 18. Comparison of the results of the Curr approximation (68) with the exact calculations of Yadav (69) for point-uranium nuclei. The results of the McKinley-Feshbach calculation are also shown. The value of R is given in Eq. 136.

At energies even lower than those discussed above, exact calculations have been made by Doggett & Spencer (77) and by Sherman (78). The latter work also presents data on polarization. Doggett & Spencer's calculation covers the energy range (0.05 to 10 Mev) and provides positron-scattering results as well as electron-scattering data.

For the heavier nuclei of finite size, the phase-shift methods must be employed (79, 80). Elton (81) and Parzen (82) appear to have been the first investigators to look into the effects of finite nuclear size on the exact phase-shift scattering formulas, although, as is well known, the Born approximation was first applied to problems of finite nuclei by Guth (83) and independently by Rose (26). Elton was successful in finding such effects at electron energies in the neighborhood of 20 Mev for gold nuclei, and offered an explanation of the experimental results at 15.7 Mev of Lyman *et al.* (84) in terms of uniform and spherical-shell charge distributions with radii $R = 1.41 \times A^{1/3} \times 10^{-13}$ cm. Elton showed also that only the zero-order phase shift was important for the calculations at an energy of 20 Mev, unless very high experimental accuracy could be obtained.

Acheson (85) and Feshbach (86) made further developments along these lines for various values of Z at energies between 15 and 40 Mev. Acheson showed that at such energies the rest mass of the electron could be ignored in the basic differential equations, and the resulting calculations could be greatly simplified. All succeeding authors employ this approximation. Acheson and Feshbach demonstrated further that the phase shifts at high energies essentially depend only on a product of the incident electron energy and a radial parameter of the nucleus and not separately on these quantities.

The scattering depends also, to be sure, on the nuclear charge Z. At energies for which the energy-radius product is small compared with unity, Feshbach showed that the zero-order phase shift involves only the volume integral over the nucleus of the deviation of the electrostatic potential from that of a point charge. This kind of result let to the term "model independence" of the nuclear charge distribution (87, 88) in connection with low-energy (20 Mev for heavy nuclei) electron scattering experiments. For such energies, the scattering cross section is essentially the same for two different models whose mean-square radii are chosen to be equal. An exact statement of this result is given in Eq. 26 of Feshbach's article (86) in terms of the electrostatic potentials of the respective charge distributions. Further work on Feshbach's low-energy theorem will be found in an investigation by Bodmer (89).

On the other hand, Elton (87) and Bodmer (89) show already that at ~40 Mev for heavy nuclei model independence begins to break down. Again, Glassgold (90) has made exact phase shift calculations with various models to test the idea of model independence at higher energies, and finds, in agreement with Elton and Bodmer, that at 30 to 45 Mev for heavy nuclei, shell and uniform distributions give different scattering cross sections at large angles. Thus the idea of model independence has limited applicability and only in those cases for which not more than one or two phase shifts are important for the calculation of the cross sections, or essentially where $R < \lambda\!\!\!^{-}$. R is the "radius" and $\lambda\!\!\!^{-}$ is the reduced de Broglie wavelength of the incident electrons.

There appears to be a fair amount of confusion in the literature regarding model independence at higher energies. For example, it has been stated (91) that if the scattering experiments "are used to derive as detailed a picture as possible of the density distribution, the electron energy ought not to be taken too large," and therefore it is suggested that the greatest sensitivity should be obtained at about 70 Mev. The basis of the statement is attributed to work of Fowler (92) and Reignier (93, 94). However, it must be pointed out that Fowler's work considers only *s*, *p*, and *d* phase shifts. Of these, the *d* phase-shift correction is made model independent by a proper choice of the ratio of sizes of shell and uniform charge-density models. Actually, however, the *s* phase shift is observed to be "model dependent" and no calculation is presented for the *p* phase shift. Reignier's work also shows that all phase shifts cannot be simultaneously made model independent by a proper choice of radii. In fact, as we shall now see, and this seems to be not properly appreciated by many authors, the exact phase shift methods at the higher energies ($E > 100$ Mev) demonstrate unequivocally that the higher phase shifts are very important and must not be neglected. Even the smallest differences in phase shifts make very appreciable changes in cross section because of a very delicate cancellation which takes place in the sum of the partial wave contributions at the larger scattering angles. In the next sections we shall deal with the exact method at high energies and shall illustrate this very great sensitivity to small variation in phase shift (116).

(*b*) Higher energies. At higher energies nuclei no longer appear as points and their various shapes and sizes may be delineated by the methods of electron scattering. Several independent calculations have been carried out with the Dirac electron theory for nuclei of finite size at higher energies ($E > 100$ Mev) by the exact phase-shift methods. Among these, we may enumerate the works of Yennie, Ravenhall & Wilson (95, 96), Brenner, Brown & Elton (97), Ravenhall & Yennie (98), Brown & Elton (99), Hill & Freeman & Ford (100), Hahn, Ravenhall & Hofstadter (101). Most of these calculations are not different in principle. Some differ in computational details, others differ because they are applied to different nuclear models. Furthermore, all methods are similar to those developed by Elton (81) and Parzen (82) for the lower energies. The newer calculations require the use of more numerous phase shifts.

Many of the recent calculations are similar to those of Yennie *et al.* (96) and since that paper gives a straightforward account of the general method, we choose below to follow their outline of theory. We shall omit computational details but shall retain enough of the method to permit a basic understanding of the mode of calculation required for finite nuclei at high energies.

Before we study the method itself, a few remarks about its limitations should be stated. The finite nucleus will be treated in the elastic-scattering approximation in which granular structure is ignored. Instead, the nuclear charge distribution will be represented by a smoothed static potential. Furthermore, we shall restrict the calculations to cases where the density distribution is known to be spherically symmetric, or nearly so. In the literature, as far as the author knows, there is no evidence that the outlined method of approach is not satisfactory for elastic scattering at the energies under consideration, say less than 500 Mev.

Effects of granularity do appear in the inelastic-scattering continua observed from all nuclei at high energies, and can thus indirectly affect the elastic scattering. [See section 8 and refs. (1), (40), and (41).] An estimate of the effect of the totality of all kinds of (nonradiative) inelastic processes on the magnitude of the elastic-scattering process has been carried out by Valk (102), according to a phenomenological first Born-approximation theory. Valk's theory describes the inelastic processes by the addition of an imaginary term to the interaction Hamiltonian responsible for elastic scattering and is thus similar in approach to nuclear-reaction theory. The theory is applied to electron-proton and electron-deuteron elastic scattering. Up to reasonably high energies and large angles (450 Mev, 120°), the corrections are less than a few per cent and practically zero for the proton. Ravenhall (103) has estimated that for heavier nuclei the corrections still remain small.

The effects of granularity are related to correlations in the nucleons' coordinates and these in turn are related to "dispersion effects." Thus a limitation of the method is that dispersion scattering is not included. The dispersion process refers to a double interaction in which a nucleus may be raised virtually to an excited state by the incident electron. The nucleus, during a subsequent transition and scattering process, returns the excitation to the electron. Thereby the nucleus is returned to its ground state. Since the process involves two steps, it may understandably be smaller than the direct interaction of the electron with the ground state of the nucleus. With the Born approximation, Schiff (104) and Valk & Malenka (105) have shown that the contribution of dispersion scattering, due to virtual excitation, is only of the order of 1/137 of the usual elastic scattering from the ground state. No experimental test of this conclusion is as yet available. (For a further discussion of correlation effects, see section 15.)

The radiative correction of Schwinger (106) and Suura (107) will only be mentioned briefly at this point, because the correction itself is small for relative measurements. When absolute cross sections are to be compared with theory, the correction must be included and is of the order of 10 to 20 per cent. A discussion of the radiative correction has been given in reference 1,[4] and since the theory of the radiative process will not be entered into in this review, it appears wiser to omit further discussion of the theory.

Reference should be made however to a recent suggestion by Lomon (108) for a test of the radiative correction at high energies, and to recent articles by McAllister (109) and Tautfest & Panofsky (110), who have shown that there is no outstanding violation of the Schwinger-Suura result. However, these recent results do not furnish a sensitive test of the theory of the radiative corrections.

Subject to the limitations and corrections just described, the representation of Yennie *et al.* (96) of the Dirac electron-finite-nucleus scattering theory will be treated below. As pointed out by Acheson (85), the rest-mass of the electron may be eliminated from the basic equations of high energy electron scattering theory without introducing relative errors greater than $(mc^2/E_0)^2$, which is exceedingly small. The elimination of the mass-term results in a great simplification of the theory, and the Dirac Eq. 33 can be written

$$(\alpha \cdot pc + W)\psi = E\psi \tag{138.}$$

where

$$W = eV \tag{139.}$$

and is the electrostatic potential energy of the smoothed density distribution. It proves advisable to choose a representation for the Dirac matrices which is slightly different from the one given by Eq. 34:

$$\alpha_1 = \begin{bmatrix} 0 & 1 & 0 & 0 \\ 1 & 0 & 0 & 0 \\ 0 & 0 & 0 & -1 \\ 0 & 0 & -1 & 0 \end{bmatrix}; \quad \alpha_2 = \begin{bmatrix} 0 & -i & 0 & 0 \\ i & 0 & 0 & 0 \\ 0 & 0 & 0 & i \\ 0 & 0 & -i & 0 \end{bmatrix}; \quad \alpha_3 = \begin{bmatrix} 1 & 0 & 0 & 0 \\ 0 & -1 & 0 & 0 \\ 0 & 0 & -1 & 0 \\ 0 & 0 & 0 & 1 \end{bmatrix};$$
$$\beta = \begin{bmatrix} 0 & 0 & 1 & 0 \\ 0 & 0 & 0 & 1 \\ 1 & 0 & 0 & 0 \\ 0 & 1 & 0 & 0 \end{bmatrix} \tag{140.}$$

[4] Typographical errors were made in equation 31 (1). The fraction $\frac{17}{12}$ should be replaced by $\frac{17}{72}$, and the capital M should be replaced by small m.

This set of matrix operators may be represented more conveniently as

$$\alpha_i = \rho_3\sigma_i \qquad \beta = \rho_1 \tag{141.}$$

in terms of Dirac's nomenclature (111). The Dirac matrices σ_1, σ_2, σ_3 may be identified with (4×4) matrices in which the Pauli (2×2) matrices σ_x, σ_y, σ_z of Eq. 35 are repeated along the diagonals (111). The representation in Eq. 141 is especially useful for working with the double set of two-component wave functions,

$$\begin{pmatrix}\phi_1\\ \phi_2\end{pmatrix}, \quad \begin{pmatrix}\chi_1\\ \chi_2\end{pmatrix},$$

thus

$$(\boldsymbol{\sigma}\cdot\boldsymbol{p}c + W - E)\begin{pmatrix}\phi_1\\ \phi_2\end{pmatrix} = 0 \tag{142.}$$

$$(-\boldsymbol{\sigma}\cdot\boldsymbol{p}c + W - E)\begin{pmatrix}\chi_1\\ \chi_2\end{pmatrix} = 0 \tag{143.}$$

where $\boldsymbol{\sigma}$ refers to the Pauli matrices of Eq. 35. This is clear since β may be neglected in Eq. 33, because of the small electron rest mass, and then the α matrices break down into the smaller Pauli matrices.

When the potential is removed, thus for free waves,

$$\begin{pmatrix}\phi_1\\ \phi_2\end{pmatrix} = \begin{pmatrix}u_1\\ u_2\end{pmatrix}\exp i\boldsymbol{k}\cdot\boldsymbol{r}; \quad \begin{pmatrix}\chi_1\\ \chi_2\end{pmatrix} = \begin{pmatrix}v_1\\ v_2\end{pmatrix}\exp i\boldsymbol{k}\cdot\boldsymbol{r} \tag{144.}$$

where

$$\boldsymbol{k} = \frac{\boldsymbol{k}_0}{\lambda} \tag{145.}$$

and $\boldsymbol{k}_0$ is a unit vector in the direction of the incident wave (polar angles θ, φ). The solutions for ϕ and χ may then be found by substitution in Eq. 142 and 143 and are

$$\begin{pmatrix}\phi_1\\ \phi_2\end{pmatrix} = \begin{pmatrix}\cos\theta/2\\ \sin\theta/2e^{i\varphi}\end{pmatrix} \tag{146.}$$

$$\begin{pmatrix}\chi_1\\ \chi_2\end{pmatrix} = \begin{pmatrix}-\sin\theta/2e^{-i\varphi}\\ \cos\theta/2\end{pmatrix} \tag{147.}$$

The solutions ϕ, χ correspond to the two spin states of the electron relative to the direction of the electron's momentum. In the first state the spin vector may be thought of qualitatively as precessing tightly about the incident momentum vector with a positive component along that direction, and in the second state the component will be negative along $\boldsymbol{k}_0$. The solutions corresponding to Eq. 146 and 147 may be written equivalently as

$$\phi = \begin{pmatrix}1\\ \tan\theta/2e^{i\varphi}\end{pmatrix} \tag{148.}$$

$$\chi = \begin{pmatrix}-\tan\theta/2e^{-i\varphi}\\ 1\end{pmatrix} \tag{149.}$$

where the normalization factor is modified by dividing by cos $\theta/2$. Now, when the potential energy W is put back into the Dirac equation, the asymptotic form of the solutions will have to resemble the free wave situation, Eq. 148 and 149, except for the radial spreading factor $r^{-1}e^{ikr}$ and angular factors f_1, f_2 which determine the angular distribution of scattered electrons. Putting $\theta=0$ for the incident state vector (first term in Eq. 150 and 151), we may write for the complete asymptotic wave functions

$$\phi \rightarrow \begin{pmatrix} 1 \\ 0 \end{pmatrix} e^{ikz} + r^{-1}f_1(\theta, \varphi) \begin{pmatrix} 1 \\ \tan \theta/2 e^{i\varphi} \end{pmatrix} e^{ikr} \qquad 150.$$

$$\chi = \begin{pmatrix} 1 \\ 0 \end{pmatrix} e^{ikz} + r^{-1}f_2(\theta, \varphi) \begin{pmatrix} -\tan \theta/2 e^{i\varphi} \\ 1 \end{pmatrix} e^{ikr} \qquad 151.$$

where the direction of the original beam lies along the z axis. It may be shown (96) that at the high energy in this problem there is nothing physical to distinguish between the scattering of the two spin states for a spherically symmetric potential. Hence in the scattering problem only the first wave, ϕ, needs to be considered. χ adds nothing new.

The phase-shift method now proceeds to decompose the solutions ϕ of the scattering Eq. 142 into a set of partial waves which are simultaneous eigenfunctions of the total angular momentum operator (squared), J^2, and its z-component, J_z. The operator J can be written as

$$J = r \times p + \tfrac{1}{2}\hbar\sigma \qquad 152.$$

and the z component

$$J_z = xp_y - yp_x + \frac{\hbar}{2}\sigma_z = \frac{\hbar}{i}\left(x\frac{\partial}{\partial_y} - y\frac{\partial}{\partial_x}\right) + \frac{\hbar}{2}\sigma_z \qquad 153.$$

The eigenvalues of J^2 and J_z are $j(j+1)\hbar^2$ and $m\hbar$ according to the well-known behavior:

$$J^2\phi_{jm} = j(j+1)\hbar^2\phi_{jm}; \qquad J_z\phi_{jm} = m\hbar\phi_{jm} \qquad 154.$$

where the wave function ϕ is now broken down into its partial waves ϕ_{jm}

$$\phi = \sum a_{jm}\phi_{jm} \qquad 155.$$

For the incident plane wave, that is, the first term in equation 150, $m=+\frac{1}{2}$, and since we shall consider only one spin orientation, the only states of concern are those designated as $\phi_{j,1/2}$. It may be noticed that the decomposition of Eq. 155 into states of given j is a bit unlike the usual treatment (13). In Eq. 155, states of a given $\phi_{j,1/2}$ do not have a definite parity. On the other hand, the usual decomposition into states of given orbital-angular momentum gives them a definite parity.

The scattered angular-wave-parts of the complete wave functions (of which Eq. 150 and 151 are the asymptotic forms) are

$$\chi_j^{(1)} = \begin{pmatrix} (j+\frac{1}{2})P_{j-1/2}(\cos\theta) \\ -P^1_{j-1/2}(\cos\theta)e^{i\varphi} \end{pmatrix} \qquad 156.$$

$$\chi_j^{(2)} = \begin{pmatrix} (j+\frac{1}{2})P_{j+1/2}(\cos\theta) \\ P^1_{j+1/2}(\cos\theta)e^{i\varphi} \end{pmatrix} \qquad 157.$$

where $\chi^{(1)}$ and $\chi^{(2)}$ are not to be confused with the χ of Eq. 143, corresponding to the second spin state. Two sets of Legendre functions $P_{j-1/2}$ and $P_{j+1/2}$ are now required, corresponding to the fact that two values of the orbital-angular momentum are associated with a given value of j. One has even and the other had odd parity. The associated Legendre functions $P^1{}_{j-1/2}$ or $P^1{}_{j+1/2}$ are to be found in many sources [p. 127 of ref. (112)]. The partial wave functions $\chi_j^{(1)}$ and $\chi_j^{(2)}$ are essentially like those found originally by Darwin (113), but the notation is not the same. [The difference in notation is explained in detail in Appendix 1 of ref. (96).]

The partial wave, now containing the radial behavior as well as the angular part of Eq. 156 and 157, becomes

$$\phi_{j,1/2} = r^{-1}(G_j(r)\chi_j^{(1)} + iF_j(r)\chi_j^{(2)}) \tag{158.}$$

which is really a double equation, corresponding to the two rows of each of Eq. 156 and 157. F_j and G_j are the radial wave functions satisfying the Dirac equation and both F_j and G_j will depend on the exact nature of the potential V and hence on the assumed distribution of charge density in the nuclear model. The equations for F and G, corresponding to the Darwin treatment [see ref. (13), p. 75], can be obtained as shown in reference 96, by the use of appropriate simplifications, in the following form.

$$\frac{dG_j}{dr} - \frac{(j+\frac{1}{2})}{r}G_j + \frac{(E-W)}{\hbar c}F_j = 0 \tag{159.}$$

$$\frac{dF_j}{dr} + \frac{(j+\frac{1}{2})}{r}F_j - \frac{(E-W)}{\hbar c}G_j = 0 \tag{160.}$$

It is necessary to solve this pair of coupled equations, from which one can obtain a single second-order differential equation. It may easily be seen that the substitutions

$$x = kr \tag{161.}$$

$$w = \frac{W}{E} \tag{162.}$$

make the Eq. 159 and 160 dimensionless, in which case we obtain

$$\frac{dG_j}{dx} - \frac{(j+\frac{1}{2})}{x}G_j + (1-w)F_j = 0 \tag{163.}$$

$$\frac{dF_j}{dx} + \frac{(j+\frac{1}{2})}{x}F_j - (1-w)G_j = 0 \tag{164.}$$

In practice, w is generally a small quantity, though we shall not require w to be small in the following treatment.

It is well known [ref. (13), p. 78] that the long-range character (r^{-1}) of the Coulomb interaction distorts the waves far from the charge center into a form like Eq. 150 and 151, but containing an extra ln r term in the exponent of the exponential term. This additional radial dependence does not introduce any real difficulties into the problem, but it proves useful to illustrate first the phase-shift method with a simpler example not containing the additional radial term. Later we shall come back to the Coulomb case. With any non-Coulomb field, which falls to zero faster than r^{-1} outside a certain finite range, the wave function ϕ will have the asymptotic form

$$\phi_{incident} + \phi_{scattered} = \phi \cong \begin{pmatrix} 1 \\ 0 \end{pmatrix} e^{ix\cos\theta} + x^{-1}kf(\theta) \begin{bmatrix} 1 \\ \tan\dfrac{\theta}{2}\, e^{i\varphi} \end{bmatrix} e^{ix} \qquad 165.$$

which is Eq. 150 together with the substitution of Eq. 161. Now the differential scattering cross section employs Eq. 41, although we have now reduced the problem from four components to the two components of Eq. 165 by our previous elimination of the second spin state. As we have seen, this second state gives the same results as the spin state we are using. The incident beam is normalized to unity, according to the first term in Eq. 165 so that the cross section for the scattered wave is obtained from the two components of the second term and is

$$\frac{d\sigma}{d\Omega} = \frac{x^2}{k^2} \mid x^{-1}kf(\theta)\mid^2(1 + \tan^2\theta/2) = \sec^2\theta/2 \mid f(\theta)\mid^2 \qquad 166.$$

The usual method of finding $f(\theta)$ depends on a comparison of the wave function ϕ of Eq. 165 with the expansion of the incident plane wave into partial waves in a well-known manner (ref. 13, p. 22), thus

$$\phi_{incident} = \sum_{j-1/2=0}^{\infty} \left(\frac{\pi}{2x}\right)^{1/2} i^{j-1/2}\{J_j\chi_j^{(1)} + iJ_{j+1}\chi_j^{(2)}\} \qquad 167.$$

corresponding to the functions of Eq. 156 and 157. The J_j are the ordinary Bessel functions (114) and are related to the spherical Bessel functions (Eq. 100) through the relation

$$j_l(x) = \sqrt{\frac{\pi}{2x}}\, J_{l+1/2}(x) \qquad 168.$$

The expression for the incident wave is more commonly written as an expansion in terms of waves of a single parity instead of terms of mixed parity as in Eq. 167 . With some algebraic manipulations, the form of Eq. 167 may be shown to be equivalent to the more common expansion (ref. 13, p. 22).

The complete wave, $\phi_{incident}+\phi_{scattered}$, is also expanded into a series of eigenfunctions

$$\phi = \sum_{j-1/2=0}^{\infty} x^{-1} i^{j-1/2} e^{i\eta_j}[G_j\chi_j^{(1)} + iF_j\chi_j^{(2)}] \qquad 169.$$

and must be identical with ϕ of Eq. 165. Thus the expression in Eq. 167 is really a part of ϕ in Eq. 169. The $e^{i\eta_j}$ are introduced as arbitrary coefficients of expansion which are to be chosen to satisfy the particular conditions of the scattering problem. It will be seen that the η_j introduced here are the all-important phase shifts.

In Eq. 163 and 164, when $x \rightarrow \infty$, the asymptotic solutions for G and F are easily found to satisfy

$$\frac{d^2G_j}{dx^2} + G_j = 0; \qquad \frac{d^2F_j}{dx^2} + F_j = 0 \qquad 170.$$

since $w \to 0$ and the $1/x$ term approaches zero as $x \to \infty$. Consequently G_j and F_j are harmonic functions at ∞. Asymptotically, therefore,

$$G_j \to \sin\,(x - \tfrac{1}{2}(j - \tfrac{1}{2})\pi + K_j) \qquad 171.$$

and there is a similar equation for F_j. The phase K_j, which is a constant of integration, is written in the form of Eq. 171 so that G_j may be compared with the asymptotic behavior of Eq. 167, which is determined by (ref. 2, p. 868).

$$J_j(x) \to \left(\frac{2}{\pi x}\right)^{1/2} \sin\,(x - \tfrac{1}{2}(j - \tfrac{1}{2})\pi) \qquad 172.$$

By substitution of Eq. 171 into Eq. 169 and Eq. 172 into Eq. 167 and subsequent comparison, it is easily seen that

$$K_j \equiv \eta_j \qquad 173.$$

and thus the phases K_j are identical with the η_j originally introduced as arbitrary coefficients.

Now by equating Eq. 169 to Eq. 165 with the substitution for the incident wave equation 167 and by placing the coefficients of the e^{ikr} terms equal to each other, we obtain

$$f(\theta) = \frac{1}{2ik} \sum (e^{2i\eta_j} - 1)(j + \tfrac{1}{2})(P_{j-1/2} + P_{j+1/2}) \qquad 174.$$

$$= \frac{1}{2ik} \sum e^{2i\eta_j}(j + \tfrac{1}{2})(P_{j-1/2} + P_{j+1/2}) \qquad 175.$$

where the second part of the first parenthesis of the summation of Eq. 174 yields zero (96) except in the forward direction ($\theta = 0$), where we shall not use $f(\theta)$ anyway.

With $d\sigma/d\Omega$, given by Eq. 166 and the expression 175 just derived for $f(\theta)$, we are enabled to find the differential scattering cross section. However, now we see that it is necessary to find the series of values η_j. This is the main part and the most difficult part of the scattering problem and can only be done by solving Eq. 163 and 164 in a suitable manner, so that the solution for G_j joins on smoothly with the asymptotic value it must have in Eq. 171. However, G_j of Eq. 171 is the non-Coulombic solution for potentials w that vanish quickly enough with increasing r. Now the Coulomb functions do not vanish so quickly and therefore we must make a modification in the asymptotic behavior of G_j. In the Coulomb case [ref. (13), p. 78],

$$G_j(x) \to \sin\,[x + \gamma \ln 2x - \tfrac{1}{2}(j - \tfrac{1}{2})\pi + \eta_j] \qquad 176.$$

where

$$w = -\frac{Ze^2}{\hbar c}x^{-1} = -\gamma x^{-1} \qquad 177.$$

and where

$$\phi_{scatt} = x^{-1}kf(\theta)\begin{bmatrix} 1 \\ \tan\frac{\theta}{2}e^{i\varphi} \end{bmatrix} \exp i(x + \gamma \ln 2x) \qquad 178.$$

It may be shown, by a procedure like that used in the non-Coulomb case, that $f(\theta)$ is given once again exactly by the expression 175.

As we have stated, the difficult part of the problem is to integrate the differential equations 163 and 164 for the potential V provided by the nuclear-density distribution. This can be done in terms of well-known functions for the point-charge case, i.e., the pure Coulomb field. The solution for G in this case is a hypergeometric function [Ref. (13), p. 79]. For finite nuclear-density distributions, $\rho(x)$, the solutions are not expressible in simple form, except in the case of a shell distribution where the solutions are spherical Bessel functions (90). In any case, it is necessary to fit the regular solutions of the radial Eq. 163 and 164 inside the nucleus to the regular and irregular solutions of these equations outside the nucleus. Only the regular types of solutions arise in the pure Coulomb case because the solutions must not go to infinity at the origin. However, outside a finite nucleus, the behavior at $r=0$ is no longer of interest, and an independent set of irregular solutions does exist. Further, outside the nucleus the potential again becomes Coulombic. For the outside regions, therefore, the radial functions are a linear combination of regular and irregular point-charge or Coulomb functions and may be written

$$C_jG_j^+(x) + D_jG_j^-(x) \qquad 179.$$

and

$$C_jF_j^+(x) + D_jF_j^-(x) \qquad 180.$$

where the C_j and D_j are constants of integration. The + sign stands for a regular function and the − sign for an irregular one. Now the requirements of continuity of charge and current specify that the regular functions F_j and G_j inside the nucleus, corresponding to the solutions of Eq. 163 and 164 for the density ρ, must match the functions 179 and 180 at a radius outside the nucleus, where $\rho=0$. If we call this radius

$$x_0 = kr_0 \qquad 181.$$

the so-called "fitting-on radius," we must have

$$G_j(x_0) = C_jG_j^+(x_0) + D_jG_j^-(x_0) \qquad 182.$$

$$F_j(x_0) = C_jF_j^+(x_0) + D_jF_j^-(x_0) \qquad 183.$$

Putting in asymptotic forms of these functions, which must also satisfy the same relation, we have (see Eq. 176)

$$G_j = \sin\left[x + \gamma \ln 2x - \tfrac{1}{2}(j - \tfrac{1}{2})\pi + \eta_j\right] = C_j \sin\left[x + \gamma \ln 2x - \tfrac{1}{2}(j - \tfrac{1}{2})\pi + \eta_j^{c+}\right] + D_j \sin\left[x + \gamma \ln 2x - \tfrac{1}{2}(j - \tfrac{1}{2})\pi + \eta_j^{c-}\right] \qquad 184.$$

where η_j^{c+} stands for a pure Coulomb (point-charge) regular phase shift, etc. If we make the simplifications

$$\delta_j = \eta_j - \eta_j^{c+} \tag{185.}$$

$$\epsilon_j = \eta_j^{c-} - \eta_j^{c+} \tag{186.}$$

the trigonometric formula for the sum of two angles, when applied to Eq. 184, gives directly

$$\tan \delta_j = \frac{\sin \epsilon_j}{\dfrac{C_j}{D_j} + \cos \epsilon_j} \tag{187.}$$

and this simple formula was given by Elton (81) and Parzen (82). Now C_j/D_j is immediately obtained from Eq. 182 and 183

$$\frac{C_j}{D_j} = - \left\{ \frac{G_j^- - \left(\dfrac{G_j}{F_j}\right) F_j^-}{G_j^+ - \left(\dfrac{G_j}{F_j}\right) F_j^+} \right\}_{x=x_0} \tag{188.}$$

evaluated at $x = x_0$.

Thus, aside from the Coulomb values of G_j^-, G_j^+, F_j^-, F_j^+, which are all known, the ratio C_j/D_j depends simply on the value of $(G_j/F_j)_{x=x_0}$ for the charge distribution ρ. Finally, the relative phase shifts δ_j depend only on (C_j/D_j) and other known values of ϵ_j.

The actual values of the Coulomb phase shifts η_j^{c+} and ϵ_j are given by Mott & Massey [ref. (13), p. 79]

$$\exp 2i\eta_j^{c+} = \frac{\sigma_j - i\gamma}{j + \frac{1}{2}} \frac{\Gamma(\sigma_j - i\gamma)}{\Gamma(\sigma_j + i\gamma)} \exp \pi i (j + \tfrac{1}{2} - \sigma_j) \tag{189.}$$

and

$$\exp i\epsilon_j = \frac{1 - i \tan \pi(i + \frac{1}{2} - \rho_j) \coth \pi\gamma}{|1 - i \tan \pi(j + \frac{1}{2} - \rho_j) \coth \pi\gamma|} \exp - \pi i (j + \tfrac{1}{2} - \sigma_j) \tag{190.}$$

where

$$\sigma_j = [(j + \tfrac{1}{2})^2 - \gamma^2]^{1/2} \tag{191.}$$

The point-charge quantities and phase shifts needed above may be found in a report of Glassgold & Mack (115), but it is usually necessary to calculate these quite accurately in any practical case. Sample values of the phase shifts η_j^{c+}, ϵ_j, δ_j, are given in Yennie *et al.* (96) for gold. We have reproduced their values in our Table II. In this table, $\delta_j^{(1)}$ refers to a uniform charge distribution ($kR = 4.0$) and $\delta_j^{(2)}$ to a gaussian, $b = 2.12$ in Yennie's notation. It can be seen that the phase shifts increase slowly (numerically) as j increases.

The angular distributions, which are the ultimate objectives of the scattering problem, still need to be evaluated from Eq. 175, and this is a difficult problem because of the high accuracies needed. Yennie *et al.* (96) have

TABLE II

Phase Shifts for Gold

j	η_j^c	ϵ_j	$\delta_j^{(1)}$	$\delta_j^{(2)}$
1/2	0.40736	−1.17386	−0.85820	−0.71689
3/2	−0.23797	−0.54728	−0.27143	−0.18795
5/2	−0.53303	−0.36074	−0.07633	−0.04846
7/2	−0.72659	−0.26951	−0.01494	−0.01064
9/2	−0.87098	−0.21523	−0.00199	−0.00199
11/2	−0.98623	−0.17918	−0.00017	−0.00030
13/2	−1.08218	−0.15350	−0.00001	−0.00004
15/2	−1.16438	−0.13426	−0.00000	−0.00000
17/2	−1.23628	−0.11931	−0.00000	−0.00000

been most successful in developing a method of quickly summing the series for $f(\theta)$, Eq. 175. In older calculations the series converged very slowly, but Yennie *et al.* improved the evaluation of the sum considerably by introducing the method of their so-called "reduced" series. These series are formed by multiplying $f(\theta)$ by powers of $(1-\cos\theta)$. The reduced series converge rapidly and so $f(\theta)$ can be found quickly by dividing the reduced sum by the proper power of $(1-\cos\theta)$. This step was of great practical importance in finding exact values of the scattering cross section, particularly those due to the partial waves of large j value.

It should be pointed out that as j increases η_j and η_j^{c+} do not approach zero but approach closer and closer together. This may be seen very clearly in Figure 19 taken from a recent paper of Ravenhall & Yennie (116). Thus δ_j, which is the phase difference, must be known very accurately, especially for the scattering behavior at large scattering angles. Hence, although two charge distributions have very similar sets of η_j, they may yet correspond to quite different differential cross sections as a function of scattering angle.

This fact is shown clearly by Ravenhall & Yennie (116) in Figure 20; where the large-angle scattering cross section is shown for four different nuclear models shown in the inset. The phase shifts for all the models lie in a region around the lowest curve of Figure 19 and are indistinguishable on a plot of this size. Nevertheless the very slight differences in phase shifts between these models are responsible for the vast changes occurring in the summation of the Legendre series and in the corresponding cross sections of Figure 20. If the quantity δ_j, of Eq. 185, is plotted on semi-logarithmic paper, the differences between the models show up quite clearly. All δ_j curves and cross-section curves merge together at small values of q or at small angles where the nucleus appears effectively as a point.

From the above discussion we see that "model independence" cannot rest upon a similarity in phases η_j but must take into account their very slight differences for high j, and this in fact leads to the breakdown of "model

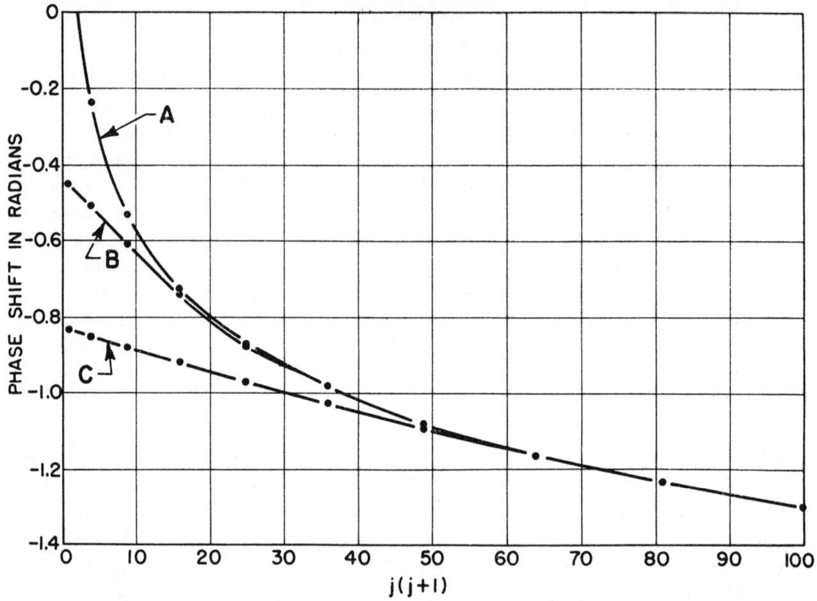

FIG. 19. Various phase shifts for gold are shown in this figure, drawn from the calculations of Ravenhall and Yennie (116). Curve A shows the regular Coulomb-phase shift. Curve B shows the phase shift, η_j, due to a uniform charge distribution in gold for which $kR=4.0$. Curve C shows η_j for a uniform model of gold at $kR=8$. Curve C is actually composed of four different curves which cannot be distinguished from each other on a plot of this size. The four curves are associated with (*a*) a uniform model of gold, (*b*) a Fermi 2-parameter best fit at 236 Mev in gold (see equation 192 below), (*c*) a Fermi 3-parameter model of gold at 236 Mev (see reference 101, Eq. 8), and (*d*) a shell distribution for which $kR=5.6$. The different charge distributions are shown in the inset of Fig. 20.

independence" at high energies. This point, established by Yennie & Ravenhall (116), does not appear to be adequately appreciated in recent literature.

We have now sketched the main method of Yennie *et al.*, and Elton, etc. in finding exact scattering patterns for high Z and high energies. No computational details will be discussed at this point, since the numerical methods employed have been very well described in the respective papers.

Various approximation methods have been discussed in the literature, but it is not certain at the moment that an approximate calculation involves less computation than the more exact methods. Furthermore it is probable that an approximation is less reliable than an exact calculation particularly when small differences are important.

It would be valuable to see exact calculations made for nuclear models of various shapes and sizes so that an interpolation between such models can be used to fit experimental cross sections for which suitable nuclear models

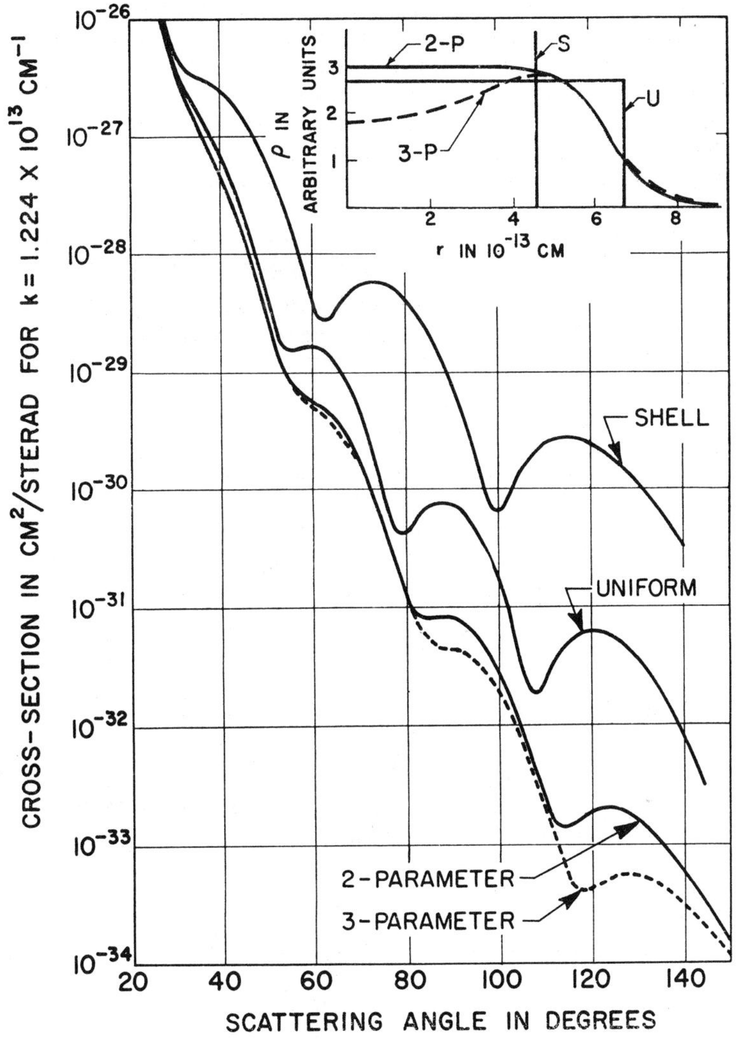

FIG. 20. The angular distributions in gold for the four different nuclear models shown in the inset. The electron energy is approximately 236 Mev. The corresponding phase shifts are given in (C) of Fig. 19. The curves of Fig. 19 and 20 demonstrate the breakdown of the idea of "model independence." This figure is taken from a forthcoming publication of Ravenhall & Yennie (116).

are not yet known. There are a few such models in the literature (96 to 101) but no systematic attempt in this direction has yet been made.

13. *Results for heavier nuclei.* Some of the principal results for heavier nuclei have already been described in reference 1, and we shall try to avoid repeating those except for brief mention of the more important features. Before discussing actual nuclear models, we shall show briefly the kind of results predicted by the phase-shift calculations.

Figure 21 shows the cross sections obtained by Yennie *et al.* (96) for

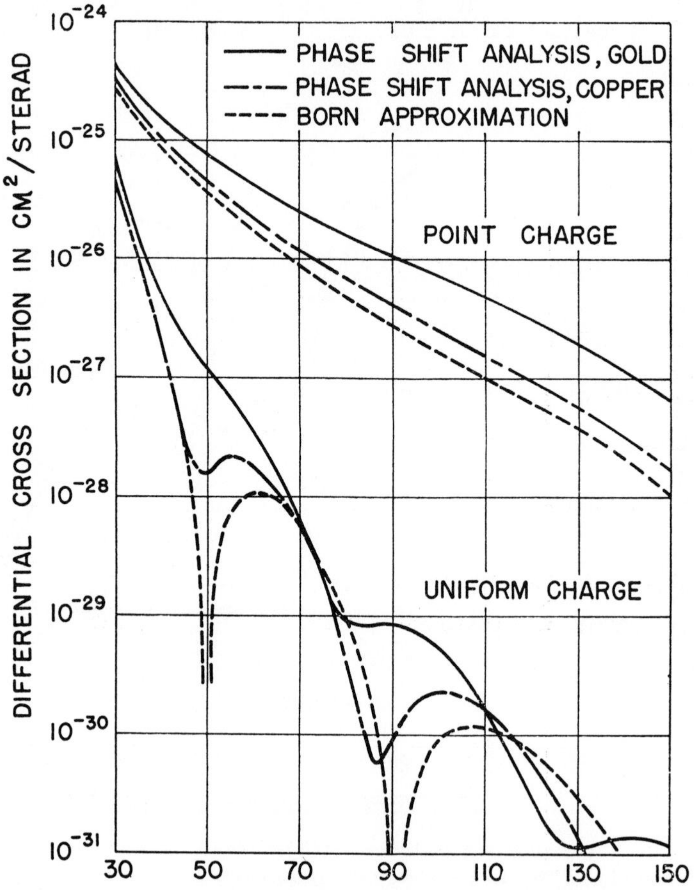

FIG. 21. This figure shows the results of exact phase-shift calculations for the point-charge and the uniform-charge models of gold at a value of $kR=5.4$ (approximately 155 Mev). The Fig. also shows similar curves for copper at about 230 Mev. Comparisons with the Born approximation are also given.

uniform charge distributions in copper and gold, as well as the point-charge cross sections given by the exact theory. Also shown for comparison are the Born-approximation results. The Born approximation is not accurate for copper and is particularly bad at the diffraction minima, as has been pointed out previously. Of particular interest is the manner in which the exact theory washes out the clear diffraction features of the Born approximation. Even so, the uniform charge distribution shows relatively prominent diffraction dips compared with smoother charge distributions.

Figure 22 shows the relative behavior of a gaussian-charge distribution given by exact calculation (96) and by the Born approximation both for

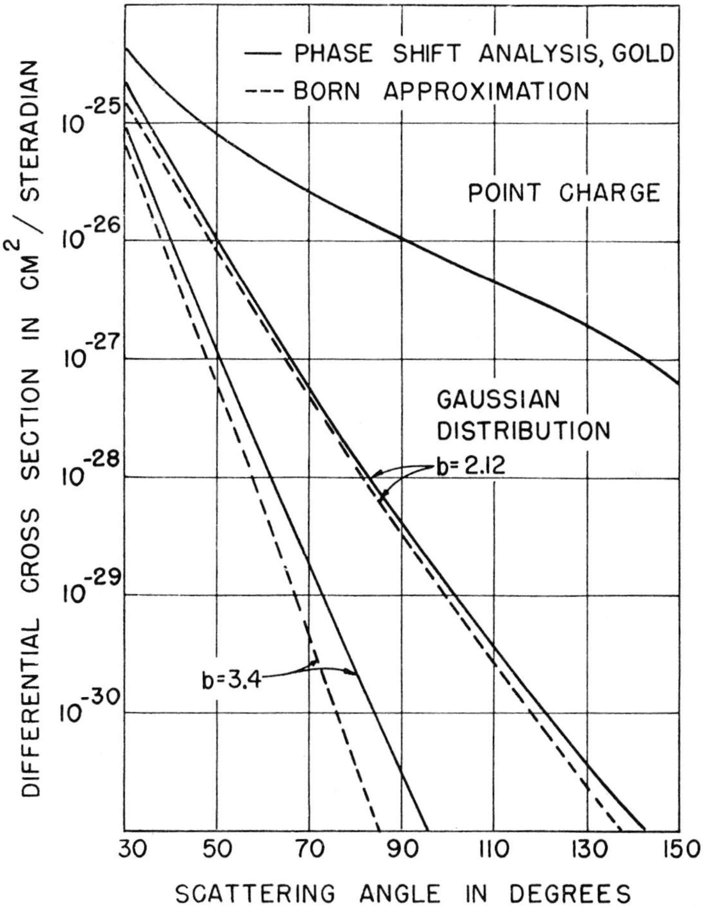

FIG. 22. Angular distributions in gold at an energy of about 155 Mev for two gaussian-charge distributions straddling the real distribution in gold. [The values of b are defined in ref. (96).] Born-approximation results are also indicated.

gold ($Z=79$). It is apparent that for low Z, say even copper ($Z=29$), the Born approximation would be excellent. This behavior appears to be true for relatively feature-less charge distributions. For those with sharp edges or "skin thicknesses," the approximations are not as good. In actuality the models that seem to fit the general trend of real nuclei fairly well are neither gaussian nor uniform and have been found by Hahn *et al.* (101) as shown in Figure 23. The accuracy obtained in these experiments does not make it

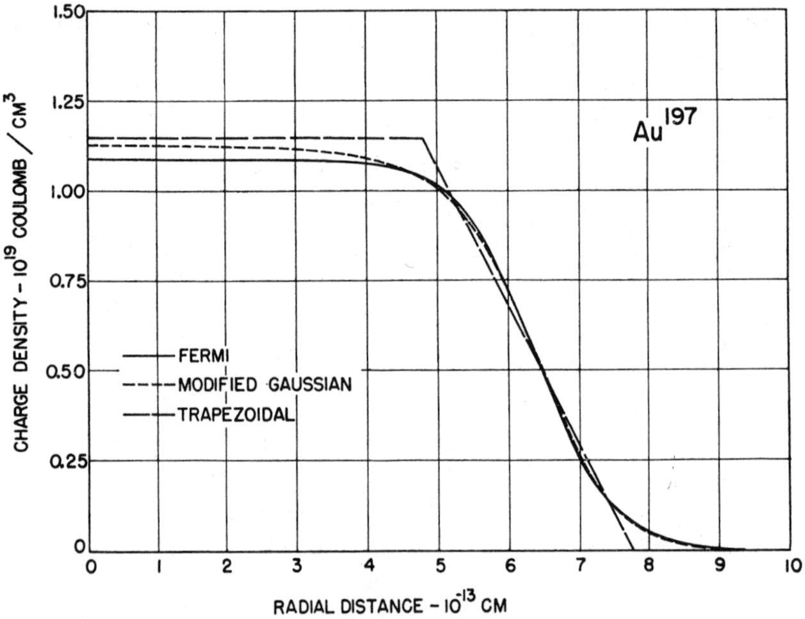

FIG. 23. The models which fit the experimental data for the medium and heavy nuclei (101). A typical set is shown for gold. Present accuracy in the experiments does not permit one to distinguish between the three types.

possible to tell the difference between these very close and alternative models. Newer experiments at higher energies now show signs of distinguishing between such models. However, even the older data definitely show that gaussian, exponential, uniform, etc. models are not like real nuclei and many possible nuclear models are definitely excluded by these experiments.

The types of models shown in Figure 23 appear to provide a fairly good characterization of the spherical nuclei investigated between $Z=20$ and $Z=83$. The charge densities of these nuclei are shown in Figure 24, where the "Fermi" model has been selected for general use from among the three types of Figure 23. The Fermi model has the analytic form

$$\rho(r) = \frac{\rho_1}{\exp\,[(r-c)/z_1] + 1} \qquad 192.$$

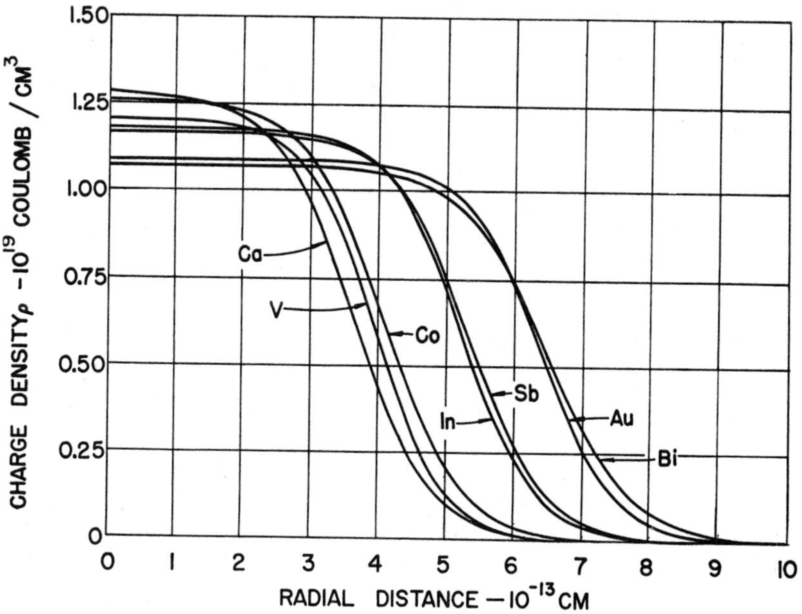

FIG. 24. The Fermi distribution for various nuclei (101). Note the tendency of the central charge density to diminish as A is increased.

and Figure 25 illustrates its shape and relevant parameters.

According to these ideas a model for the nuclei which have been investigated can be represented by a two-parameter family having a "half-density" radius of

$$c = 1.07A^{1/3} \times 10^{-13} \text{ cm.} \tag{193.}$$

and a skin thickness

$$t = 2.4 \times 10^{-13} \text{ cm.} = 4.4z_1 \tag{194.}$$

where t is measured between the 90 per cent and 10 per cent points, as shown in Figure 25. While this representation appears to give a satisfactory picture of most nuclei, newer experiments now in progress at 420 Mev are seeking finer details and possibly a third parameter to add to the two of Eq. 193 and 194. The Fermi type model, the trapezoidal model, and other similar models have the same values of the constants in Eq. 193 and 194 and are dealt with analytically by Hahn, Ravenhall & Hofstadter (101).

On the other hand, if the rules in Eq. 193 and 194 were to apply to still lighter nuclei such as Be^9, C^{12}, O^{16}, Mg^{24}, etc., the model would imply that these nuclei were "almost all surface." Experiments to test this point have been analyzed by various authors (36, 51, 52, 53). The model which follows the rules of Eq. 193 and 194, does not, of course, fit the light nuclei precisely, but the correspondence is surprisingly good as we shall see below.

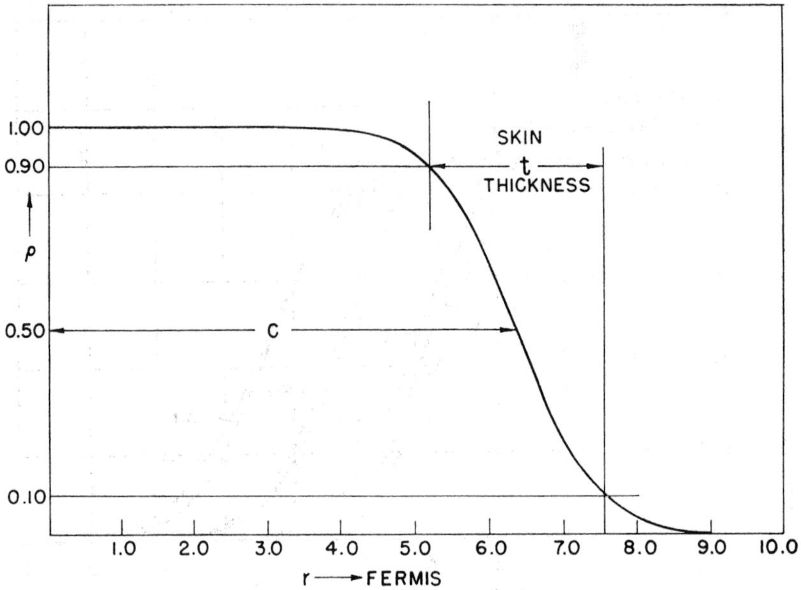

FIG. 25. Shape and parameters of the Fermi model as typified by the charge distribution in the gold nucleus.

Figure 3 shows the model ($\alpha = 4/3$) and dimensions which seems to fit C^{12} in a very satisfactory manner. The shape ($\alpha = 2$) fits O^{16} quite well, although the dimensions of length in the curve of Figure 3 are not appropriate to this nucleus. It can be seen that the "surface" forms a good part of these nuclei. For C^{12} and O^{16} the skin thicknesses are both approximately 1.90×10^{-13} cm. and represent about 73 to 83 per cent of the distance to the half-density points.

The nuclei Mg^{24}, Si^{28}, S^{32}, Sr^{88} have been investigated by Helm (36) who has analyzed the experimental data with the Born approximation using folded charge distributions. A uniform distribution, smeared at the edge by a gaussian, is called by Helm a gU charge distribution. A uniform distribution, smeared likewise by a second narrower uniform distribution, results in a uU charge distribution. These charge distributions are shown in Figure 26, and the values of c and t are listed below in Table IV. Also included in Figure 26 are representations of C^{12} and Ca^{40} according to these models. [The C^{12} and Ca^{40} charge distributions are observed to be in excellent agreement with those obtained in references (51), (52), and (101).] A correction factor, taking into account the change of dimensions arising from failure of the Born approximation (6 per cent for Sr), is included in the parameters of Figure 26. The above set of nuclei, with the exceptions of C^{12} and Ca^{40}, have not yet been analyzed by the exact phase-shift methods, but it is clear that the c and t values lies close to the values of Eq. 193 and 194.

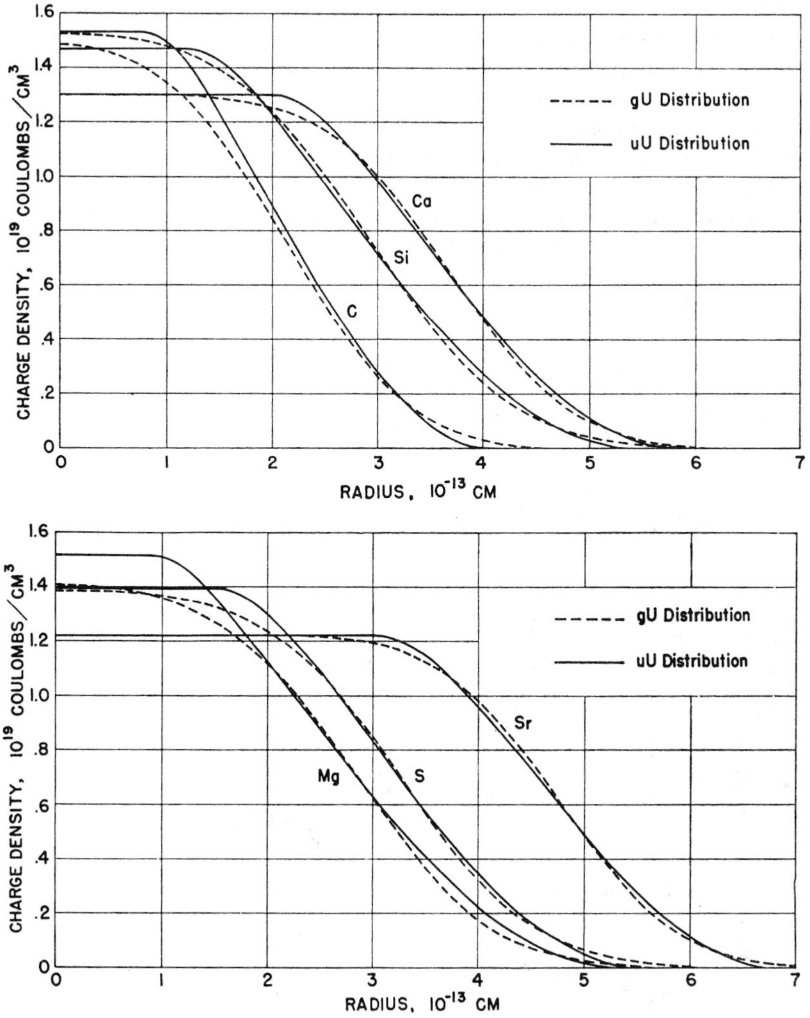

FIG. 26. Corrected Born-approximation deductions of the gU charge distribution in Mg^{24}, Si^{28}, S^{32}, and Sr^{88}, according to Helm (36). gU curves for C^{12}, and Ca^{40} are shown for comparison. The results for C^{12} and Ca^{40} on this model agree well with other more exact analyses of these distributions.

14. *Neighboring nuclei.* In this section we shall comment briefly on a new method of measuring small variations in the charge distributions of neighboring nuclei (117). It is desired to find out how the parameters c and t of Eq. 193 and 194 behave when the construction of a nucleus is varied slightly, e.g., as in proceeding from ${}_{28}Ni^{58}$ to ${}_{28}Ni^{60}$. In this case the number of neutrons is increased by two without any change in the number of protons.

The method is based on measuring ratios of elastic scattering from the two nuclei at the same angles. Experimentally, ratios of cross section can be found more accurately than individual cross sections. Furthermore, theory shows that the ratio of cross sections (R) depends only slightly on the exact analytical form of the charge distribution, so that changes in the parameters c and t may be found without knowing the precise type of nuclear model. Of course, the model employed in the calculation must be approximately of the right type for the nuclear pair under consideration. This is guaranteed by fitting the experimental angular distribution of either nucleus with a model

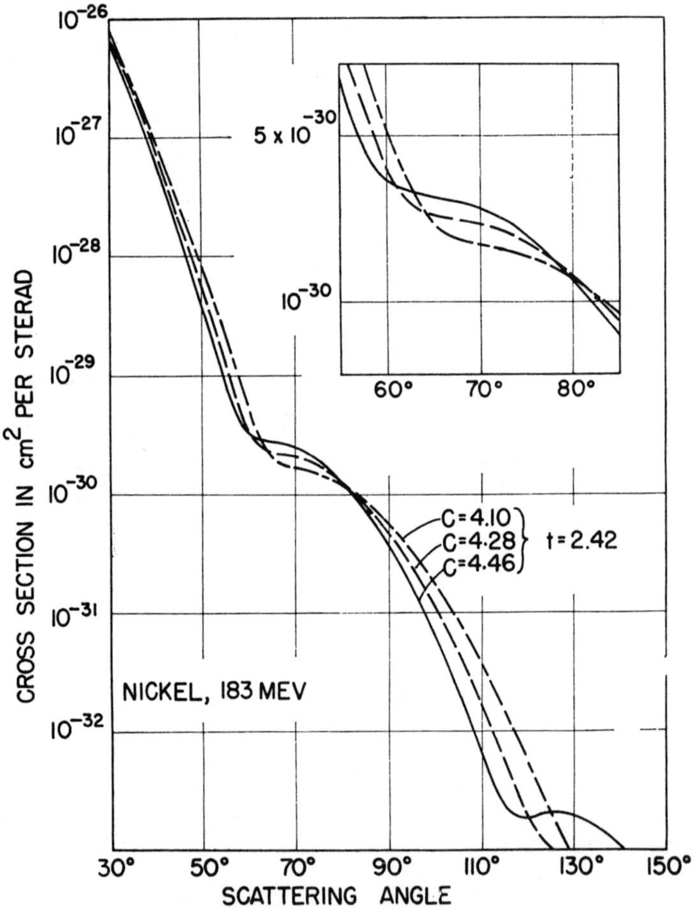

FIG. 27. The calculated behavior of the angular distribution in Ni at 183 Mev, when the c-value is varied from 4.10×10^{-13} cm. to 4.46×10^{-13} cm., and the skin thickness is left unchanged. The calculations are exact (117). The inset shows the crossover region in greater detail.

which gives by exact phase-shift methods the smallest least squares fitting errors. The Fermi model, Eq. 192, is satisfactory for this purpose and has been used in practice (117).

Figure 27 illustrates how the elastic cross section in nickel changes for the Fermi shape when the surface-thickness parameter, t, is unchanged but when the radius parameter c is varied by a small amount. The values of c which are used vary from 4.10×10^{-13} cm. to 4.46×10^{-13} cm. The inset in the

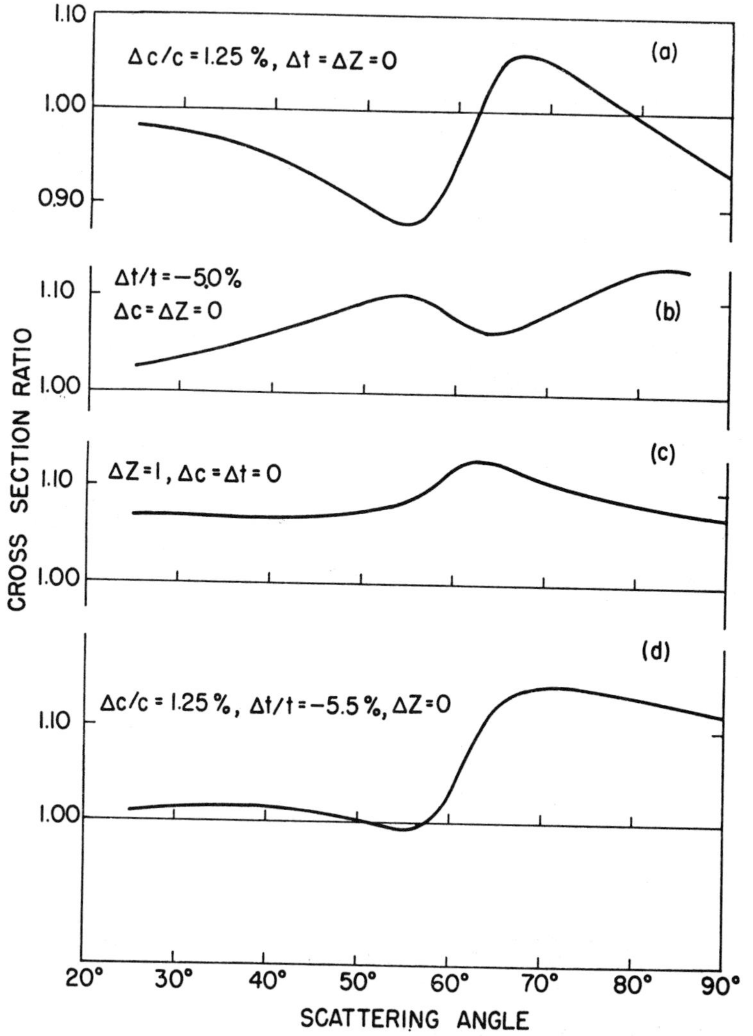

FIG. 28. The corresponding ratios of cross sections for the indicated changes in c, t, and Z. The ratios are calaculated for the Fermi model.

figure shows that there are two crossover regions near 63° and 80° in between which the ratio of cross sections undergoes wide variations. Immediately outside this region the curves also depart from each other rather strikingly. Figure 28 shows the ratio for some particular changes in c, t, and Z. It can be seen that certain characteristic trends are associated with the changes in Δc, Δt, and ΔZ. The absolute value of the ratio at small angles is

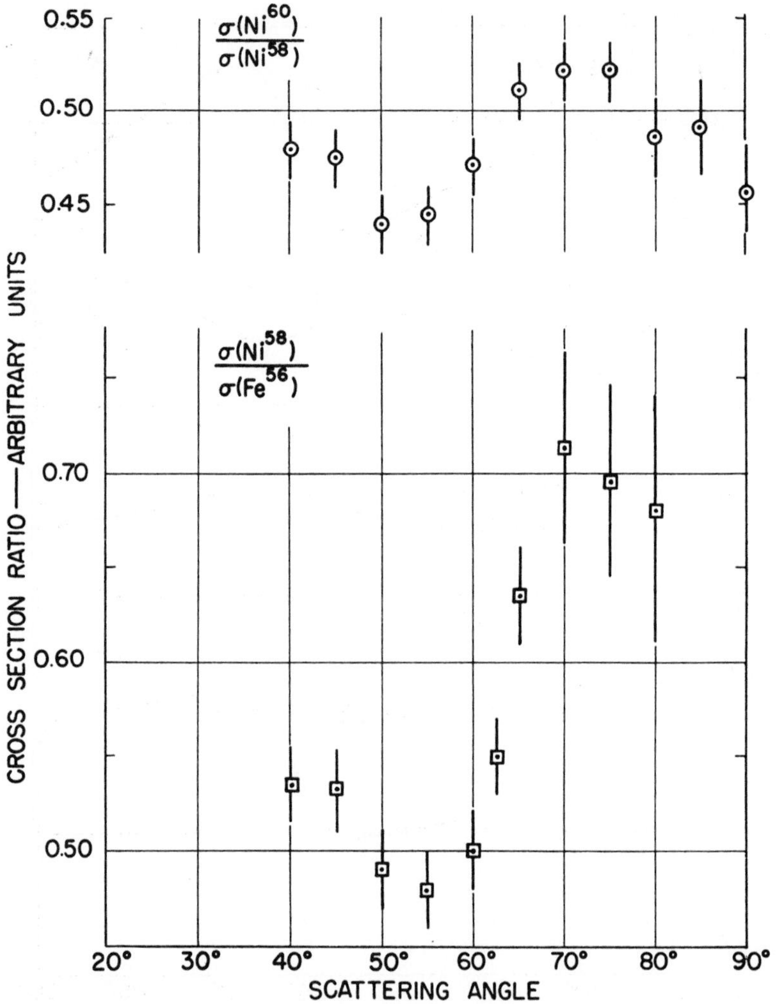

FIG. 29. The experimentally observed ratios in the pair of nickel nuclei (Ni^{60}, Ni^{58}) and in the combination (Ni^{58}, Fe^{56}). The ordinate is given in an arbitrary scale for the respective ratios.

also quite important. From curve (a) it appears that a change of $\Delta c/c$ by 1.25 per cent results in about a 20 per cent change of the cross-section ratio, and therefore the method can measure quite small differences in size. As curve (b) shows, the behavior of the ratio is also sensitive to small changes in t: a 5 per cent change in t is equivalent to a distance of about 1.3×10^{-14} cm.

The experimental cross sections at 183 Mev are illustrated for several isotopes in Figure 29 and show patterns similar to the curves of Figure 28. Unfortunately due to monitoring difficulties in the experiments the absolute value of the ratio was not obtained and this fact prevents complete identification of the changes taking place. For example, it is not possible to distinguish between curves (a) and (d) of Figure 28 within experimental error, since the absolute value of the ratio is unknown.

In spite of this temporary deficiency of the experimental data, it is possible to say that the charge distributions in the members of the pairs Ni^{58}, Ni^{60}, and Fe^{56}, Ni^{58} are different. Thus two extra neutrons in Ni^{60} affect the closed-shell proton structure in nickel. It is also possible to say that a change of the mass number introduces a change of c by a factor of approximately $[(A+2)/A]^{1/3}\cong1.01$ for a constant surface thickness t. However, it is not possible to exclude a 10 per cent change in t. Better data will rectify this situation.

Incidental information from this experiment yields the "best fit" for the Fermi model of the Ni^{58} isotope. The parameters of this fit are $c=4.28\times10^{-13}$ cm., $t=2.49\times10^{-13}$ cm., or $z^1=0.56\times10^{-13}$ cm.

15. *Assorted topics.* It is not possible to do justice in this article to many interesting subjects related to electron scattering. We may mention a few: inelastic scattering from discrete nuclear levels, polarization studies on non-spherical nuclei, positron scattering, correlation effects, radiative effects, electron scattering with meson production, etc. We have not been able to discuss such topics in detail in previous sections, and we shall not attempt to do so in this section. It seems worth while, however, to mention a few recent studies and to show where the problems in these fields lie. Perhaps these subjects may be treated at a later time in more detail.

(*a*) Inelastic level scattering. This interesting topic has been considered briefly (1) from an experimental standpoint. Theoretical papers dealing with level scattering have been written, for example, by Amaldi *et al.* (40, 118), Schiff (119), Sherman & Ravenhall (120), Ferrell & Vischer (55), Morpurgo (54), Tassie (59, 121), etc. The theoretical material is therefore well developed and it would be desirable to have complementary inelastic-electron scattering data from discrete nuclear levels.

We have briefly discussed electrodisintegration and the inelastic continuum in this article and elsewhere (1). It is interesting to see that Amaldi *et al.* (40) have indicated how the level scattering yields a behavior very suggestive of the inelastic continuum. The model chosen was the independent-particle type with an infinite harmonic-well potential. Amaldi's

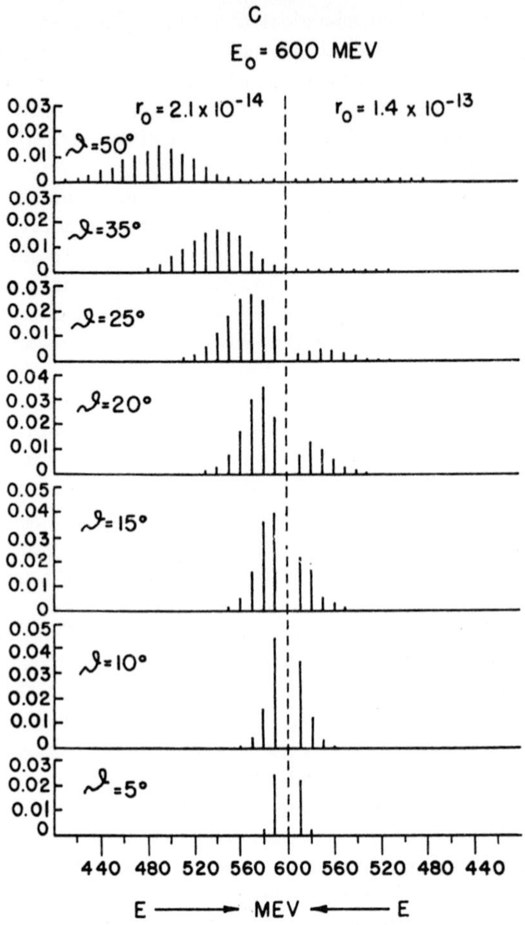

FIG. 30. Predictions of Amaldi *et al.* (40) for inelastic scattering at various angles in carbon at 600 Mev. The calculations are based on the Born approximation. r_0 in the figure refers to the proton size. The effects on the inelastic spectrum are shown to the left and right of center.

results are shown for carbon in Figure 30 for an incident energy of 600 Mev. As the angle of scattering is increased, the peak of the distribution of level scattering moves to lower energies in just the way the inelastic continuum behaves in helium or carbon (1).

Particular attempts at finding the quantum numbers of levels from observed transitions have been made (36, 51, 52, 54, 55, 119, 120, 121) and by Ravenhall (122). Not only do the data supply information about multipolarities of the transitions, but also the values of the transition matrix elements emerge rather directly from an interpretation of the experiments with the help of equations similar to (44).

In cases where the scattering from nuclear levels cannot be resolved from the elastic scattering, some information about the levels may still be obtained. An example of this occurs for Ta^{181}, where an analysis of experiments by Hahn *et al.* (101, 128) has been made by Downs *et al.* (126, 127) with a modified Born-approximation method. In this way it has been possible to estimate the distortion parameter in Ta^{181} which is found to be in good agreement with the spectroscopic and Coulomb-excitation values.

(*b*) Polarization studies. Interesting papers related to polarization phenomena have been written by Ferroni & Fubini (123), Newton (124), and Bernardini, Brovetto, & Ferroni (125). The last article contains references to other work in this field. Ferroni *et al.* (123) and Bernardini (125) carry out Born-approximation calculations for high-energy electrons scattered against polarized nuclei and consider Ta^{181} as a special case. The predicted azimuthal anisotropy in the cross section is shown to vary from 130 per cent to 50 per cent, depending on the nuclear model of Ta. While the Born approximation cannot be expected to be accurate for such a heavy nucleus, it is likely that the results are qualitatively correct. Therefore it appears desirable to attempt experiments of this type. Unfortunately the experiments are difficult mainly because, if a metallic target is to be used, the primary electron beam develops considerable heat in the target, and the required low temperature of the target cannot be maintained. Probably the Overhauser effect offers a reasonably practical method of obtaining the polarized target nuclei (125). The paper of Newton (124) considers double-electron scattering against lined-up magnetic moments of target nuclei, but these experiments presently appear to be difficult because of intensity reasons.

A simple use of a polarized target has been suggested by Downs *et al.* (127). They point out that the scattered waves from the spherically symmetric part of the charge distribution can interfere with those arising from the quadrupole distortion. The resulting diffraction structure, which will alter with the direction of polarization, should on analysis yield considerably more information about the radial charge distribution in these nuclei than has been obtainable hitherto.

Nonspherical nuclei may also be studied by direct-electron scattering experiments, without the necessity of employing polarization techniques (101, 126, 127, 128), but clearly polarization effects would add greatly to the amount of information that could be extracted from experiments on oriented nuclei.

(*c*) Positron scattering. In the first Born approximation, elastic scattering of positrons is identical with the corresponding scattering of electrons. The second Born approximation introduces relative differences in the cross sections of the order of $2\pi Z/137$ per cent, as may be seen from Eq. 135.

The calculations for point nuclei of higher atomic number have been evaluated by Massey (129), Feshbach (66), Yadav (130), Curr (68), Doggett & Spencer (77), and Parzen & Wainright (131). The experimental situation on point scattering of positrons has recently been summarized by Allen *et al.* (132) along with results of new experiments by this group at 9.8 Mev in xenon. Within the accuracy of the experiments, the recent results are in reasonable agreement with theory.

The difference between positron and electron scattering for point nuclei was shown by Massey to be due to a spin-orbit effect, and this effect acts to reduce the scattering cross section relative to that for electrons. Figure 31 shows the ratio of positron to electron cross sections calculated by Feshbach (66) for point nuclei for various angles as a function of the atomic number when $\beta = v/c \cong 1$.

Positron scattering from nuclei of finite size has been investigated by Elton & Parker (133). These authors used the exact phase-shift method up to energies of 20 to 30 Mev for the gold nucleus. For a model with a delta function at the surface (shell distribution) and the kR values used in the calculation, the presently accepted size of gold would imply an energy of 30.5 Mev. Although the shell distribution is not appropriate to a real gold nucleus, the typical effects of the finite size upon positron scattering may be observed in Table III, which is taken from the work of Elton & Parker (133).

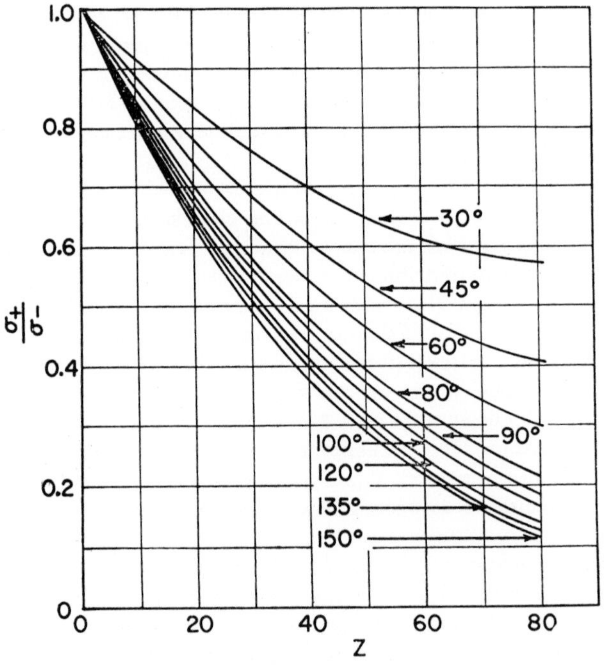

FIG. 31. The ratio of positron to electron-scattering cross sections calculated for point charges by Feshbach (66).

TABLE III

ELECTRON AND POSITRON CROSS SECTIONS FOR POINT GOLD NUCLEUS AND AN EXTENDED GOLD NUCLEUS

θ (deg.)		15	30	45	60	80	90	100	120	135	150
Electrons	k^2I_A	323	25.6	6.49	2.54	0.945	0.638	0.412	0.186	0.0897	0.0377
	k^2I_C	331	24.7	5.02	1.45	0.330	0.178	0.090	0.031	0.0123	0.0052
Positrons	k^2I_A	265	14.4	2.59	0.75	0.204	0.117	0.069	0.025	0.0110	0.0044
	k^2I_C	265	14.2	2.47	0.68	0.172	0.095	0.054	0.018	0.0075	0.0029

In the table quantities proportional to the differential cross sections for points are labeled k^2I_A and those for finite nuclei k^2I_C. It can be seen that the positron-point nucleus cross section is smaller than the electron-point nucleus value by rather considerable factors at the large angles (3 to 8), while the corresponding cross sections for a finite nucleus are less by factors only about 2. Thus the effect of the finite size is to increase the positron scattering in relation to that of the electrons. At higher energies the positron scattering will exceed that from electrons.

This behavior may be understood since the positron-nucleus Coulomb force is repulsive while the electron-nuclear force is attractive. Hence the electron waves, as measured by their probability amplitude, will tend to penetrate the nucleus to a greater extent than the positron waves, and the interference effects, which give rise to the form factors, are correspondingly greater for electrons than for positrons. Thus the cross sections for electrons are reduced greatly by the form factors while the positron form factors are not reduced so effectively.

New experimental information on positron scattering at high energies (50 to 170 Mev) has recently been made available by Miller & Robinson (134). In an ingenious experiment bremsstrahlung x-rays from a betratron were allowed to fall on a target foil. Electrons and positrons from the target were analyzed by a spectrometer magnet placed at various angles between 21° and 74° from the incident x-ray beam. By separating linear and quadratic yields from Pb targets of various thicknesses, the results could be analyzed in terms of (*a*) the scattering of electrons and positrons produced as pairs at zero degrees and (*b*) the direct large-angle pair production of electrons and positrons. For checking the experimental technique, previous electron-scattering results in the same energy range could be used. The results appear to confirm the predictions of Elton & Parker (133) and point to a new method of studying positron scattering by finite nuclei.

(*d*) Correlation effects in nuclear matter. This interesting subject has received considerable attention recently (9, 104, 105, 135, 136, 137, 138) and is related to the variations of local charge density in the neighborhood of a particular proton in a nucleus. The correlation effects are produced by the operation of the specifically nuclear and coulomb forces between nucleons and the intervention of the Pauli principle. In the first Born approximation, the correlations do not introduce any modifications in the elastic scattering of high-energy electrons (9, 135). In the same approximation, the sum over all possible inelastic transitions yields more information about correlations than a study of particular transitions to discrete nuclear levels (9, 135, 138). Schiff (138) has recently shown that the same behavior is obtained for all orders in the Born-approximation sum and is not merely a characteristic of the first and second Born approximations.

The qualitative way in which correlation effects may be expected to appear in experiment has been worked out by Smith (9) in the first-order Born approximation. As an extreme example he considers that heavy nuclei are built in the form of crystals with a regular lattice structure. The nucleons are permitted to be smeared about their regular lattice positions in a manner reminiscent of thermal motion, just as atoms in crystals are known to behave. Thus there are two parameters in the theory: one related to the side of the basic cell in the lattice and the second associated with the freedom or amplitude of motion about the occupation points.

The inelastic-scattering cross sections are summed by Smith (9) over an energy region ($\sim$15 to 30) Mev from the elastic-scattering peak and thus include essentially all the important transitions to the discrete levels. At the same time, the mean-energy change of the electron ($\sim$18 Mev) is still small compared with the energy of the incident or scattered electron ($\sim$200 Mev), and the value of q (momentum transfer of Eq. 11) may be assumed to be roughly constant at a given angle θ. The closure operation then permits Smith to evaluate the sum of the inelastic-scattering cross sections to the discrete levels and to evaluate an effective "form factor for summed inelastic scattering."

As is usual in such calculations, the "two-particle density" function is an important element in the analysis and is an example of the type of information which can be extracted from the experiments. The two-particle density characterizes the correlation in position of pairs of protons, while the single-particle density (Eq. 53) is the usual charge density $\rho(\boldsymbol{R})$ involved in elastic scattering. In theories of correlations effects, the two-particle density is a function integrated over all proton coordinates, except the two of a pair, and the single-particle density is integrated over all proton coordinates except one (9, 137).

With the crystal model of a Pb nucleus, Smith evaluates the inelastic form factor (F) referred to above, and finds that, at large q, F^2 has maxima and minima greater and less than unity. Thus there is a modulation of point-charge inelastic scattering with a factor greater and less than unity and it is this type of pattern that would be looked for if nuclei were really expected to have a crystalline structure. Of course, any other type of correlation or short range order would give a qualitatively similar modulation of the inelastic-scattering cross section. The sharpest interference patterns naturally result from the most definite or regular correlation effects (less equivalent "thermal" motion). In Smith's work the interference maxima or minima

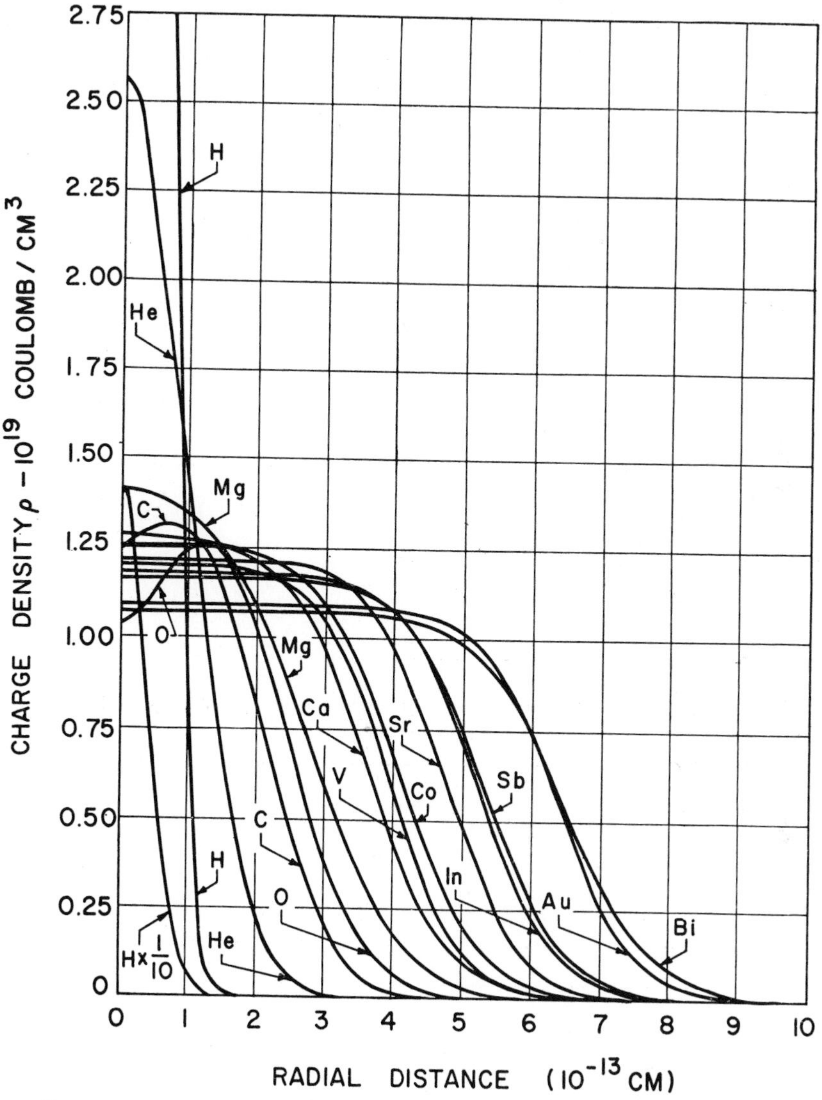

FIG. 32. This figure represents a summary of the charge distributions found for various nuclei by electron-scattering methods.

TABLE IV*

SUMMARY OF NUCLEAR SIZE PARAMETERS

Nucleus (1)	Type of charge distribution (2)	rms radius (3)	Radius of equivalent uniform model R_u (4)	$r_0=\frac{R_u}{A^{1/3}}$ (5)	Skin thickness t (6)	Half-density Radius c (7)	$r_1=\frac{c}{A^{1/3}}$ (8)	ρ_u† (9)	$A^{1/3}$ (10)	Ref. No. (11)
$_1H^1$	Gaussian	0.72	—	—	—	—	—	—	—	17, 18, 19
	Exponential	0.80 } 0.77 ± 0.10	1.00‡	1.00	—	—	—	0.239	1.00	
	Hollow exponential	0.78	—	—	—	—	—	—	—	
$_1D^2$	Deuteron wave-function plus proton	2.11 ± .05	2.73§	2.16	—	—	—	0.0116	1.26	33, 38
$_2He^4$	Gaussian	1.61	2.08	1.31	—	—	—	0.053	1.59	18
$_3Li^6$§§	Gaussian	2.37	—	—	—	—	—	—	—	
	Uniform	2.10 } 2.20(?)‖	2.84(?)#	1.56	—	—	—	0.03(?)	1.82	62
	Modified exponential	2.78	—	—	—	—	—	—	—	(see text)
	Harmonic-well $\alpha=1/3$	2.44	—	—	—	—	—	—	—	
$_3Li^7$	Approximately same as $_3Li^6$	2.20(?)	2.84(?)	1.49	—	—	—	0.03(?)	1.91	62 (see text)
$_4Be^9$	Harmonic-well $\alpha=2/3$	2.2 ± 0.2	2.84	1.37	—	—	—	0.04	2.08	60, 61, 62
$_6C^{12}$	Harmonic-well $\alpha=4/3$	2.37	3.04	1.33	1.9	2.3	1.00	0.051	2.29	10, 51, 52, 53
$_8O^{16}$	Harmonic-well $\alpha=2.0$	2.64	3.41	1.35	1.9	2.6	1.03	0.049	2.52	64

$_{12}Mg^{24}$	gU	2.98	3.84	1.33	2.6	2.93	0.99	0.051	2.89	36
$_{14}Si^{28}$	gU	3.04	3.92	1.29	2.8	2.95	0.97	0.056	3.04	36
$_{16}S^{32}$	gU	3.19	4.12	1.30	2.6	3.26	1.03	0.055	3.17	36
$_{20}Ca^{40}$	Fermi	3.52	4.54	1.32	2.5	3.64	1.06	0.052	3.42	101
$_{23}V^{51}$	Fermi	3.59	4.63	1.25	2.2	3.98	1.07	0.055	3.71	101
$_{27}Co^{59}$	Fermi	3.83	4.94	1.27	2.5	4.09	1.05	0.054**	3.90	101
$_{28}Ni^{58}$	Fermi	3.93	5.09	1.31	2.49	4.28	1.10	0.052	3.87	117
Sr^{88}	gU	4.14	5.34	1.20	2.3	4.80	1.08	0.060	4.45	36
$_{49}In^{115}$	Fermi	4.50	5.80	1.19	2.3	5.24	1.08	0.060	4.86	101
$_{51}Sb^{122}$	Fermi	4.63	5.97	1.20	2.5	5.32	1.07	0.058	4.96	101
$_{73}Ta^{181}$	Fermi plus quadrupole	5.50	~7.10††	~1.25	~2.8	~6.45	~1.14	0.049	5.66	126, 127, 128
$_{79}Au^{197}$	Fermi	5.32	6.87	1.180	2.32	6.38	1.096	0.0585	5.82	101
$_{82}Pb^{208}$	Hill‡‡ *et al.* (100) $n=10$; $s=0$	~5.42	7.0	1.18	~2.3	~6.5	~1.09	0.057	5.93	100
$_{83}Bi^{209}$	Fermi	5.52	7.13	1.20	2.7	6.47	1.09	0.0548	5.935	101

* All distances in the table are quoted in units of 10^{-13} cm.

† The units of ρ_u are proton charges per 10^{-39} cubic centimeter. ρ_u is derived from the expression $3Ze/4\pi R_u^3$ and R_u is given by Eq. 197.

‡ The magnetic distribution is similar to the charge distribution. The circumstance that $R=1.00$ is purely accidental.

§ This radius is different from that given elsewhere (ref. 1, Table VI), because the proton size is specifically included in this listing, whereas the R of Eq. 123 was quoted in the older reference. The charge distribution is given by the deuteron wave function modified by the folding-in of a finite proton's charge distribution.

‖ These values are at present uncertain.

\# These values are at present uncertain.

** A numerical error appeared in the corresponding item of Table VI of ref. 1.

†† The radial distances should be considered "effective" radii in view of quadrupole distortions.

‡‡ The model of Hill *et. al.* is similar to the Fermi model.

§§ Newer data at 420 Mev taken by G. Burleson and the author support the smaller size in the neighborhood of $a=2.1\times10^{-13}$ for the rms radius.

appear at large values of $x = qr_1$, where r_1 is a parameter which measures the lattice spacing. It is therefore necessary to go to high values of q to make the interference features experimentally observable. This is a reasonable result if one remembers that, in elastic scattering, diffraction features associated with small separations also require large q values.

Smith (9) also considers the effect of the Pauli principle on correlations by imagining the Z protons to be limited to a cubic box of side L. F^2 is found to increase from zero to unity in a gradual way when $x = qr_1$ varies from zero to ~ 3.0. r_1 in this case is the radius of a spherical volume containing one nucleon, thus

$$L^3 = \frac{4\pi}{3} A r_1^3 \qquad 195.$$

There is also a slight dependence of F^2 on R_{12}, where R_{12} is the upper limit for inter-particle distances in the nucleus. In the main, the effect of the Pauli principle is to repress inelastic scattering until q reaches a certain value where the recoil momentum given to the struck nucleon is large enough to eject it from the Fermi sea.

Unfortunately no experiments are available to test these ideas at present, although it is possible that the inelastic results in carbon (51, 52) might be analyzed in this connection. Considering the well-developed theoretical background for correlation effects in nuclear theory, as well as in atomic theory (139, 140, 141), it is to be hoped that electron-scattering experiments will be carried out soon to test the theory and to look for such effects in nuclei.

(*e*) Radiative effects. Very little experimental work on this topic has been carried out to date. For that reason we shall not discuss radiative effects in this article, and again particularly because the theory appears to be rather complex. It may be worth while to collect herewith some references to recent work in this field, e.g. (106 to 110, 142 to 145).

(*f*) Electron scattering with meson production. Figure 16 shows a low-energy scattering peak, labeled D, which results from electrons which have produced π-mesons of various kinds in deuterium (45). It can be seen that, apart from the intrinsic interest in this phenomenon, it is necessary to know the shape of the peak because of its possible contribution to the tail of the inelastic continuum at C in the figure. Even more so, as one goes to heavier nuclei, such as Li, Be, or C, the meson-producing scattered electrons grow in number (146) and the analogous peak D becomes comparable to peak C. A recent theoretical account of this process in electron-proton collisions has been given by Dalitz & Yennie (147). Related cross sections for production of mesons of definite energy and direction have been reported experimentally by Panofsky *et al.* (148).

16. *Summary of results.* A portion of the information presented in this paper can be summarized with the help of a graph and a table. Figure 32 shows a representation of the charge densities for typical nuclei investigated

by electron-scattering methods. Table IV presents the data pertaining to density distributions and the parameters appropriate to the various nuclei. Certain tendencies in the data stand out quite strikingly: (*a*) Our first observation is that the average-central charge density decreases as the nuclear charge is increased. The maximum-central density is reached in the proton. Next to the proton the alpha particle has the highest central density, and it is worth noticing that the charge density is extraordinarily high in this nucleus—roughly speaking about twice as high as in most heavier nuclei. (*b*) Except for extremely light nuclei such as He and Li, a reasonable representation of the charge density in all the remaining nuclei can be given by a two-parameter family of curves with half-density radius c and skin thickness t, corresponding to the constants of Eq. 193 and 194. "t" is thus a constant for all nuclei and it is as if the heavier nuclei could be manufactured from the light nuclei simply by stuffing nucleons in the central regions and pushing the constant skin outwards. Even lighter nuclei seem to subscribe to this plan. It is highly likely that, when additional parameters of the nuclear-charge distributions become known, variations from the prescription will be found, but it appears unlikely that the differences will be marked. (*c*) Associated with the description of c and t given above, the charge distributions of heavier nuclei are characterized by sizes smaller than those provided by older methods which depend on nuclear interactions rather than electromagnetic processes. Indeed it has not been necessary to refer to the "radius" of a nucleus in this paper, because it is apparent that the whole shape must be specified rather than a single parameter. It has been pointed out previously (1) that if one wishes to choose a single parameter representing nuclear "size," such as the "equivalent uniform-charge radius, R_u,"

$$R_u = r_0 A^{1/3} \qquad 196.$$

and where

$$a_u = \left(\frac{3}{5}\right)^{1/2} R_u \qquad 197.$$

is the root-mean-square radius, then it follows that

$$r_0 = \left(\frac{5}{3}\right) a_u A^{-1/3} \qquad 198.$$

is no longer a constant, as in older models, but is a variable. The value of r_0, consistent with electron-scattering data, ranges from about 1.18×10^{-13} cm. to 1.30 to 1.40×10^{-13} cm. for light nuclei. A recent redetermination of mirror-nuclei radii (149, 150) appears to be in excellent agreement with this conclusion. Only one size parameter, of course, is obtained in the mirror-nuclei method. Another recent investigation (151) which is in agreement with the electron-scattering data has been concerned with measurements of the diffraction and absorption cross sections of nuclei for negative pions of high kinetic energies (0.6–1.4 Bev). The data are found to be consistent with "radii" taken from electron-scattering results, provided one allows for a range of the pion-nuclear force of 1.0×10^{-13} cm. This is a reasonable value. Moreover, it is found that a uniform distribution of charge in nuclei is not consistent with the pion experiments, which is again in agreement with electron-scattering experiments (4). Finally, the size and shape found for the distribution of charge and magnetic moment in the proton and neutron appear to be difficult to understand with current field-theory, since the nucleon core appears unreasonably large. The apparent lack of charge independence in the mesonic clouds is also somewhat puzzling, though, of course, the neutron and proton are dissimilar in the values of their static moments. It is hoped that the forthcoming years will witness a clarification of the present "anomalies."

Acknowledgments

The author wishes to thank Drs. D. G. Ravenhall and D. R. Yennie for their kind and generous assistance in discussions of the theoretical material. He is also greatly indebted to Drs. U. Meyer-Berkhout and L. I. Schiff for their critical reading of the manuscript. For making available results in advance of publication, the author makes acknowledgment with thanks to: R. Blankenbecler, R. Cool, H. Ehrenberg, J. A. McIntyre, U. Meyer-Berkhout, R. C. Miller, D. G. Ravenhall, L. Rosenfeld, C. S. Robinson, L. I. Schiff, S. Sobottka, J. F. Streib, M. R. Yearian, and D. R. Yennie. For technical help with the manuscript, the author wishes to express his thanks to F. Adams, F. Bunker, J. E. Gill, R. Keith, E. McWhinney, E. Searby, and N. Vettini.

LITERATURE CITED

1. Hofstadter, R., *Revs. Modern Phys.*, **28**, 214 (1956)
2. Evans, R. D., *The Atomic Nucleus* (McGraw-Hill Book Co., Inc., New York, N. Y., 972 pp., 1955)
3. Born, M., *Z. Physik*, **38**, 803 (1926)
4. Heitler, W., *The Quantum Theory of Radiation*, 3rd ed., Chap. 4 (Oxford University Press, Oxford, England, 430 pp., 1954)
5. Schiff, L. I., *Quantum Mechanics*, 2nd ed. (McGraw-Hill Book Co., Inc., New York, N. Y., 417 pp., 1955)
6. Dalitz, R. H., *Proc. Roy. Soc. (London)*, **206A**, 509 (1951)
7. Heitler, W., *The Quantum Theory of Radiation*, 3rd ed., 214 (Oxford University Press, Oxford, England, 430 pp., 1954)
8. Schweber, S. S., Bethe, H. A., and de Hoffmann, F., *Mesons and Fields*, **1**, (Row, Peterson, and Co., Evanston, Ill., 449 pp., 1955)
9. Smith, J. H., *Phys. Rev.*, **95**, 271 (1954)
10. Sobottka, S., & Hofstadter, R. (To be published)
11. Møller, C., *Z. Physik*, **70**, 786 (1931)
12. Bethe, H. A., *Ann. Physik*, **5**, 325 (1930)
13. Mott, N. F., and Massey, H. S. W., *The Theory of Atomic Collisions*, 2nd ed., (Oxford University Press, Oxford, England, 388 pp., 1949)
14. Yennie, D. R., Lévy, M. M., and Ravenhall, D. G., *Revs. Modern Phys.*, **29**, 144 (1957)
15. Pauli, W., *Revs. Modern Phys.*, **13**, 203 (1941)
16. Rosenbluth, M. N., *Phys. Rev.*, **79**, 615 (1950)
17. Hofstadter, R., and McAllister, R. W., *Phys. Rev.*, **98**, 217 (1955)
18. McAllister, R. W., and Hofstadter, R., *Phys. Rev.*, **102**, 851 (1956)
19. Chambers, E. E., and Hofstadter, R., *Phys. Rev.*, **105**, 1454 (1956)
20. Foldy, L. L., *Phys. Rev.*, **87**, 688 (1952)
21. Salzman, G., *Phys. Rev.*, **99**, 973 (1955)
22. Clementel, E., and Villi, C., *Nuovo Cimento*, **10**, 1207 (1956)
23. Jankus, V. Z., *Phys. Rev.*, **102**, 1586 (1956)
24. Bethe, H. A., and Peierls, R., *Proc. Roy. Soc. (London)*, **148A**, 146 (1935)
25. Peters, B., and Richman, C., *Phys. Rev.*, **59**, 804 (1941)
26. Rose, M. E., *Phys. Rev.*, **73**, 282 (1948)
27. Thie, J. A., Mullin, C. J., and Guth, E., *Phys. Rev.*, **87**, 962 (1952)
28. Schiff, L. I., *Phys. Rev.*, **92**, 988 (1953)
29. Schiff, L. I., *Science*, **121**, 881 (1955)
30. Hofstadter, R., *Revs. Modern Phys.*, **28**, 214 (1956)
31. Jankus, V. Z., *Theoretical Aspects of Electron-Deuteron Scattering* (Doctoral Thesis, Stanford Univ., Stanford, Calif., 1956)
32. Blatt, J. M., and Weisskopf, V. F., *Theoretical Nuclear Physics* (John Wiley and Sons, Inc., New York, N. Y., 864 pp., 1952)
33. McIntyre, J. A., and Dhar, S., *Phys. Rev.*, **106**, 1074 (1957)
34. Smythe, W. R., "Recoil Protons from Meson Photoproduction in Hydrogen and Deuterium" (Doctoral Thesis, California Inst. of Technology, Pasadena, Calif., 1957)
35. Blankenbecler, R. (To be published)
36. Helm, R. H., *Phys. Rev.*, **104**, 1466, 1468, 1469 (1956)

37. Yennie, D. R., Lévy, M. M., and Ravenhall, D. G., *Revs. Modern Phys.*, **29,** 144, 146 (1957)
38. McIntyre, J. A., *Phys. Rev.*, **103,** 1464 (1956)
39. McIntyre, J. A., and Hofstadter, R., *Phys. Rev.*, **98,** 158 (1955)
40. Amaldi, E., Fidecaro, G., and Mariani, F., *Nuovo cimento,* **7,** 553 (1950)
41. Feshbach, H., *Symposium on Electron Physics* (National Bureau of Standards, Washington, D. C., Oct., 1951)
42. Hofstadter, R., *Revs. Modern Phys.*, **28,** 214 (1956)
43. Blankenbecler, R. (Private communication)
44. Drell, S. D., and Ruderman, M. A., *Phys. Rev.*, **106,** 561 (1957)
45. Yearian, M. R., and Hofstadter, R. (To be published)
46. McAllister, R. W., and Hofstadter, R., *Phys. Rev.*, **102,** 851 (1956)
47. Hofstadter, R., *Revs. Modern Phys.*, **28,** 214 (See Section Ve) (1956)
48. Rustgi, M. L., and Levinger, J. S., *Phys. Rev.*, **106,** 530 (1957)
49. Foldy, L. L. (To be published)
50. Levinger, J. S., and Bethe, H. A., *Phys. Rev.*, **78,** 115 (1950)
51. Fregeau, J. H., and Hofstadter, R., *Phys. Rev.*, **99,** 1503 (1955)
52. Fregeau, J. H., *Phys. Rev.*, **104,** 225 (1956)
53. Ravenhall, D. G. (Private communication)
54. Morpurgo, G., *Nuovo cimento,* **3,** 430 (1956)
55. Ferrell, R. A., and Visscher, W. M., *Phys. Rev.*, **104,** 475 (1956)
56. Tassie, L. J., *Australian J. Phys.*, **9,** 400 (1956)
57. Gatto, R., *Nuovo cimento,* **10,** 1559 (1953)
58. Feenberg, E., *Shell Theory of the Nucleus,* 20, 21 (Princeton University Press, Princeton, N. J., 211 pp., 1955)
59. Tassie, L. J., *Proc. Phys. Soc.* (*London*), **69A,** 205 (1956)
60. Hofstadter, R., Fechter, H. R., and McIntyre, J. A., *Phys. Rev.*, **92,** 978 (1953)
61. McIntyre, J. A., Hahn, B., and Hofstadter, R., *Phys. Rev.*, **94,** 1084 (1954)
62. Streib, J. F., *Phys. Rev.*, **100,** 1797 (1955)
63. Gatha, K. M., Patel, N. J., and Patel, R. F., *Proc. Phys. Soc.* (*London*), **67A,** 1111 (1954)
64. Ehrenberg, H., Meyer-Berkhout, U., and Hofstadter, R. (To be published)
65. Bartlett, J. H., and Watson, R. E., *Proc. Am. Acad. Arts Sci.*, **74,** 53 (1940)
66. Feshbach, H., *Phys. Rev.*, **88,** 295 (1952)
67. McKinley, W. A., Jr., and Feshbach, H., *Phys. Rev.*, **74,** 1759 (1948)
67a. Mott, N. F., *Proc. Roy. Soc.* (*London*), **124A,** 425 (1929); Mott, N. F., *Proc. Roy. Soc.* (*London*), **135A,** 429 (1932)
68. Curr, R. M., *Proc. Phys. Soc.* (*London*), **68A,** 156 (1956)
69. Yadav, H. N., *Proc. Phys. Soc.* (*London*), **68A,** 348 (1955)
70. Chapman, K. R., Matsukawa, E., Rose, P. H., and Stewardson, E. A., *Proc. Phys. Soc.* (*London*), **68A,** 928 (1955)
71. Brown, B., Matsukawa, E., and Stewardson, E. A., *Proc. Phys. Soc.* (*London*), **69A,** 496 (1956)
72. Bayard, R. T., and Yntema, J. L., *Phys. Rev.*, **97,** 372 (1955)
73. Damodaran, K. K., and Curr, R. M., *Proc. Phys. Soc.* (*London*), **69A,** 196 (1956)
74. Van de Graaff, R. J., Buechner, W. W., and Feshbach, H., *Phys. Rev.*, **69,** 452 (1946)
75. Buechner, W. W., Van de Graaff, R. J., Sperduto, A., Burrill, E. A., and Feshbach, H., *Phys. Rev.*, **72,** 678 (1947)

76. Urban, P., *Fortschr. Physik*, **III** (1) (1955)
77. Doggett, J. A., and Spencer, L. V., *Phys. Rev.*, **103**, 1597 (1956)
78. Sherman, N., *Phys. Rev.*, **103**, 1601 (1956)
79. Faxèn, H., and Holtsmark, J., *Z. Physik*, **45**, 307 (1927)
80. Rayleigh, Lord B., *Theory of Sound* (Dover Publications, New York, N. Y., 504 pp., 1945)
81. Elton, L. R. B., *Proc. Phys. Soc. (London)*, **63A**, 1115 (1950); *Phys. Rev.*, **79**, 412 (1950)
82. Parzen, G., *Phys. Rev.*, **80**, 355 (1950)
83. Guth, E., *Wien. Anz. Akad. Wiss.*, **24**, 299 (1934)
84. Lyman, E. M., Hanson, A. O., and Scott, M. B., *Phys. Rev.*, **79**, 228 (1950)
85. Acheson, L. K., Jr., *Phys. Rev.*, **82**, 488 (1951)
86. Feshbach, H., *Phys. Rev.*, **84**, 1206 (1951)
87. Elton, L. R. B., *Proc. Phys. Soc. (London)*, **66A**, 806 (1953)
88. Bitter, F., and Feshbach, H., *Phys. Rev.*, **92**, 837 (1953)
89. Bodmer, A. R., *Proc. Phys. Soc. (London)*, **66A**, 1041 (1953)
90. Glassgold, A. E., *Phys. Rev.*, **98**, 1360 (1955)
91. Rosenfeld, L., *Nuclear Physics*, **2**, 450 (1956)
92. Fowler, G. N., *Proc. Phys. Soc. (London)*, **68A**, 559 (1955)
93. Reignier, J., *Bull. Acad. Roy. Belg. Cl. Sc.*, **41**, 151 (1955)
94. Reignier, J., *Nuclear Physics*, **3**, 340 (1957)
95. Yennie, D. R., Wilson, R. N., and Ravenhall, D. G., *Phys. Rev.*, **92**, 1325 (1953)
96. Yennie, D. R., Ravenhall, D. G., and Wilson, R. N., *Phys. Rev.*, **95**, 500 (1954)
97. Brenner, S., Brown, G. E., and Elton, L. R. B., *Phil. Mag.* (7), **45**, 524 (1954)
98. Ravenhall, D. G., and Yennie, D. R., *Phys. Rev.*, **96**, 239 (1954)
99. Brown, G. E., and Elton, L. R. B., *Phil. Mag.*, (7), **46**, 154 (1955)
100. Ford, K. W., and Hill, D. L., *Ann. Rev. Nuclear Sci.*, **5**, 25 (1955)
101. Hahn, B., Ravenhall, D. G., and Hofstadter, R., *Phys. Rev.*, **101**, 1131 (1956)
102. Valk, H. S., *Nuovo cimento* (To be published)
103. Ravenhall, D. G. (Private communication)
104. Schiff, L. I., *Phys. Rev.*, **98**, 756 (1955)
105. Valk, H. S., and Malenka, B. J., *Phys. Rev.*, **104**, 800 (1956)
106. Schwinger, J., *Phys. Rev.*, **75**, 898 (1949)
107. Suura, H., *Phys. Rev.*, **99**, 1020 (1955)
108. Lomon, E. L., *Nuclear Physics*, **1**, 101 (1956)
109. McAllister, R. W., *Phys. Rev.*, **104**, 1494 (1956)
110. Tautfest, G. W., and Panofsky, W. K. H., *Phys. Rev.*, **105**, 1356 (1957)
111. Dirac, P. A. M., *Proc. Roy. Soc. (London)*, **117A**, 610 (1928); *The Principles of Quantum Mechanics*, Chap. 11, 256 (Oxford Univ. Press, Oxford, England, 311 pp., 1947)
112. Pauling, L., and Wilson, E. B., *Introduction to Quantum Mechanics* (McGraw-Hill Book Co., Inc., New York, N. Y., 468 pp., 1935)
113. Darwin, C. G., *Proc. Roy. Soc. (London)*, **118A**, 654 (1928)
114. Watson, G. N., *Theory of Bessel Functions* (Macmillan Co., New York, N. Y., 804 pp., 1948)
115. Glassgold, A. E., and Mack, E. W., *Mass. Inst. Technol. Research Lab. for Nuclear Sci. and Eng., Tech. Rept*, **65** (Aug. 31, 1954)
116. Ravenhall, D. G., and Yennie, D. R. (To be published)
117. Hahn, B., Hofstadter, R., and Ravenhall, D. G., *Phys. Rev.*, **105**, 1353 (1957)
118. Amaldi, E., Fidecaro, G., and Mariani, J., *Nuovo cimento*, **7**, 757 (1950)

119. Schiff, L. I., *Phys. Rev.*, **96**, 765 (1954); *Phys. Rev.*, **98**, 1281 (1955)
120. Sherman, B. F., and Ravenhall, D. G., *Phys. Rev.*, **103**, 949 (1956)
121. Tassie, L. J., *Australian J. Phys.*, **9**, 407 (1956)
122. Ravenhall, D. G. (Private communication)
123. Ferroni, S., and Fubini, S., *Nuovo cimento*, **1**, 263 (1955)
124. Newton, R. G., *Phys. Rev.*, **103**, 385 (1956)
125. Bernardini, M., Brovetto, P., and Ferroni, S., *Nuovo cimento*, **5**, 1292 (1957)
126. Downs, B. W., *A Study of Electric Quadrupole and Proton Correlation Effects in the Scattering of High-Energy Electrons by Heavy Nuclei* (Doctoral thesis, Stanford Univ., Stanford, Calif., 1955)
127. Downs, B. W., Ravenhall, D. G., and Yennie, D. R., *Phys. Rev.*, **98**, 277A (1955); Yennie, D. R., Ravenhall, D. G., and Downs, B. W., *Phys. Rev.*, **98**, 277A (1955); *Phys. Rev.*, **106**, 1285 (1957)
128. Hahn, B., and Hofstadter, R., *Phys. Rev.*, **98**, 278A (1955)
129. Massey, H. S. W., *Proc. Roy. Soc.* (*London*), **181A**, 14 (1942)
130. Yadav, H. N., *Proc. Phys. Soc.* (*London*), **65A**, 672 (1952)
131. Parzen, G., and Wainright, T., *Phys. Rev.*, **98**, 188 (1954)
132. Allen, K. R., Finlay, E. A., Lipsicas, M., Major, D., and Phillips, K., *Proc. Phys. Soc.* (*London*), **70**, 355 (1957)
133. Elton, L. R. B., and Parker, K., *Proc. Phys. Soc.* (*London*), **66**, 428 (1953)
134. Miller, R. C., and Robinson, C. S., *Ann. Phys.* (To be published)
135. Gatto, R., *Nuovo cimento*, **2**, 669 (1955)
136. Downs, B. W., *Phys. Rev.*, **101**, 820 (1956)
137. Lewis, R. R., *Phys. Rev.*, **102**, 544 (1956)
138. Schiff, L. I., *Nuovo cimento*, **5**, 1223 (1957)
139. Van Hove, L., *Phys. Rev.*, **95**, 249 (1954)
140. Waller, I., *Z. Physik*, **51**, 213 (1928)
141. Waller, I., and Hartree, D. R., *Proc. Roy. Soc.* (*London*), **124A**, 119 (1929)
142. Elton, L. R. B., and Robertson, H. H., *Proc. Phys. Soc.* (*London*), **65A**, 145 (1952)
143. Schiff, L. I., *Phys. Rev.*, **87**, 750 (1952)
144. Redhead, M. L. G., *Proc. Roy. Soc.* (*London*), **220A**, 219 (1953)
145. Biel, S. J., and Burhop, E. H. S., *Proc. Phys. Soc.* (*London*), **68A**, 165 (1955)
146. Bumiller, F., Ehrenberg, H., Hofstadter, R., and Meyer-Berkhout, U., *Proc. 7th Ann. Rochester Conf.* (1957)
147. Dalitz, R. H., and Yennie, D. R., *Phys. Rev.*, **105**, 1598 (1957)
148. Panofsky, W. K. H., Woodward, W. W., and Yodh, G. B., *Phys. Rev.*, **102**, 1392 (1956)
149. Kofoed-Hansen, O., *Nuclear Physics*, **2**, 441 (1956)
150. Cooper, L. N., *Nuovo cimento*, (Suppl. to Vol. IV), **3**, 1125 (1956)
151. Cronin, J. W., Cool, R., and Abashian, A. (To be published)

PAPER 43

Magnetic Form Factor of the Neutron*

M. R. Yearian and Robert Hofstadter
Department of Physics and High-Energy Physics Laboratory, Stanford University, Stanford, California
(Received December 2, 1957)

Electron scattering from the bound neutron and proton in the deuteron has been studied at various scattering angles between 75° and 135° for 500-Mev and 600-Mev electrons. A comparison of these scattering cross sections with those of the free proton permits a determination of the density distribution of the magnetic cloud around the neutron. By using theories developed by Jankus and Blankenbecler, the root-mean-square radius of the neutron is shown to lie between the limits 0.80×10^{-13} cm and 0.90×10^{-13} cm. The choice between these radii depends on whether the deuteron total cross sections or differential (peak) cross sections are compared with the protonic scattering cross section. Since presently available theory has not yet developed sufficiently to decide definitely between these possibilities, the root-mean-square size may be taken to be $(0.85\pm0.10)\times10^{-13}$ cm with small error. The neutron's magnetic cloud clearly does not have the small size obtained by measurement of its charge cloud from experiments on the neutron-electron interaction, and this anomaly challenges the present concepts of nucleon size.

I. INTRODUCTION

THIS paper is concerned with the internal magnetic structure of the neutron. Among many reasons why it is desirable to learn about this structure, we shall point to two aspects of the problem which are of current interest. The first concerns the intrinsically interesting problem of determining the neutron's internal electromagnetic features. These features are correlated with the details of the mesonic cloud in the neutron and with the question of whether there exists within it a dense core and "soft" outer cloud. Connected with this problem is the corresponding determination of the structure of the proton[1–3] and the question of charge independence. In most present theoretical discussions, it is usually assumed that the outer parts of the proton and neutron are identical except for the sign of the charge. This assumption is consistent with the nearly symmetrical anomalous magnetic moments of both particles. Thus it is of interest to see whether this supposition can really withstand a searching test afforded by electron-scattering methods.

A second reason for studying the neutron concerns the question of whether the deviations from point scattering, observed in the case of the proton,[1–3] are really structure effects or whether the deviations can be explained by a breakdown of electrodynamics.[4,5] In the latter case, all electromagnetic structures would appear to possess a similar limiting "size" at sufficiently small distances within which such breakdown has occurred. On the other hand, if differences in the "structures" of the neutron and proton can be detected, this observation would imply that not all of the structure or finite size effects can be ascribed to a breakdown of electrodynamics, although, of course, apparent finite size effects might still arise partially from such a breakdown. That the breakdown would be partial would appear to be unlikely, however.

For the above reasons, it appears that a direct comparison between the electron-scattering cross sections of the neutron and proton might resolve some of these questions. In the experiment to be described below, we have attempted to probe within the meson clouds of neutron and proton with electrons to examine the differences, if any, in the angular distributions of the corresponding scattered electrons. It is to be understood that we are dealing with the magnetic clouds in the two nucleons, as will appear more clearly below.

In order to make this direct comparison between neutron and proton, it is desirable to have a very large concentration of neutrons at rest in a small volume, like the protons in a corresponding gaseous target of hydrogen. Free neutrons are not available in sufficiently large numbers to form such a target. The next best solution is to use the neutron within the deuteron. The deuteron is, in fact, a very favorable nucleus for this purpose, since within it the neutron and proton are quite loosely bound. Although the nucleons are almost free, they are also in rapid motion, and this is a complication which must be taken into account. Thus the experiment we have carried out is based on incoherent scattering from the quasi-free neutron and proton of the deuteron, and the two nucleons involved have components of momentum along and opposite to the initial momentum of the incident electrons. The scattering can also be termed inelastic, since the deuteron is disintegrated in the process, the struck nucleon recoiling and shooting out of the deuteron.

The basic idea involved in the comparison has been described previously,[6] but it will be repeated here for

* The research reported here was supported jointly by the Office of Naval Research and the U. S. Atomic Energy Commission, and by the U. S. Air Force, through the Office of Scientific Research of the Air Research and Development Command.
1 R. Hofstadter and R. W. McAllister, Phys. Rev. **98**, 217 (1955).
2 R. W. McAllister and R. Hofstadter, Phys. Rev. **102**, 851 (1956).
3 E. E. Chambers and R. Hofstadter, Phys. Rev. **105**, 1454 (1956).
4 Yennie, Lévy, and Ravenhall, Revs. Modern Phys. **29**, 144 (1957).
5 R. Hofstadter, Revs. Modern Phys. **28**, 214 (1956).
6 See reference 5, Sec. VI.

reasons of convenience: for high momentum transfers and large scattering angles, say greater than 90°, the cross section for electron scattering from a nucleon's magnetic moment is much larger than the scattering from the specific charge of the nucleon, and the charge scattering may be neglected. Under such ideal conditions, the neutron should scatter electrons with a cross section which depends only on its magnetic moment, and, since the value of the latter is well established, a comparison with the proton can readily be made. In fact, the scattering from the proton has been studied in some detail,[1–3] so that the distribution of magnetic density is known, at least approximately. Now if the neutron and proton have similar structures, the electron-scattering cross section of the neutron ought to be approximately one half that of the proton. This figure is obtained from the ratio of squares of the corresponding magnetic moments, $(1.91)^2/(2.79)^2=0.45$, as follows from the Rosenbluth formula for magnetic scattering.[7] This implies that, for high momentum transfers and large angles, the cross-section ratio ought to be everywhere 0.45. On the other hand, if the neutron should have a point-structure, or a dense core, or smaller dimensions than the proton, the cross section ratio ought to exceed 0.45 by a detectable amount. Indeed, if the neutron is actually a point and the proton's size is given by the quoted experiments, namely, 0.77×10^{-13} cm, the cross-section ratio should be much larger than 0.45. In fact, the ratio should be 3.0 at 500 Mev and 135°. Such a large ratio can easily be measured and distinguished from 0.45. This was the basic motivation of the experiment.

As noted above, because the momentum transfer is high and because the deuteron's binding energy is low (2.223 Mev), the two nucleons may be considered to be free in first approximation. (This will call for further comment below.) However, as we have also pointed out, the nucleons are in motion in the deuteron. Hence we have a close analogy between our present problem and the scattering of x-rays from bound electrons in atoms when the binding energy is low. In atoms, such a process gives rise to the modified (Compton) line. The momentum distribution of the scattered electrons in the deuteron problem will appear correspondingly as a continuum with a maximum lying near the sharp scattering peak observed from a free proton. Figure 51, of reference 5, shows the type of incoherent scattering now under discussion. We may note also that the elastic scattering from the whole deuteron, i.e., the coherent scattering with respect to the two nucleons, is extremely small and not measurable under the conditions of large momentum transfer and large angles used in the present experiments.

By summing the area under the inelastic continuum of the deuteron, the cross section for the combined magnetic scattering of both the neutron and the proton can be found. An associated measurement of the area under the free proton peak provides the comparative datum. The difference between the area of the continuum and the free proton peak area yields the cross section of the neutron at a given angle. This procedure may be carried out for several different angles of scattering, and the magnetic form factor of the neutron can thus be determined. Corrections to this simple procedure will be discussed below. A second and important method relating to the peak height of the inelastic continuum will be discussed in Sec. V(b).

[7] M. N. Rosenbluth, Phys. Rev. **79**, 615 (1950).

II. THEORY

It may be stated at the beginning that a complete, relativistic treatment of incoherent electron scattering from the deuteron does not exist. However, certain good approximations have been worked out by Jankus[8] and by Blankenbecler.[9] Jankus developed a partially relativistic approximate result for the incoherent cross section at a given angle θ and incident energy E_0, as follows:

$$\left(\frac{d\sigma}{d\Omega}\right)_d^{\text{in}}=\left(\frac{e^2}{2E_0}\right)^2\frac{\cos^2(\theta/2)}{\sin^4(\theta/2)}\times\left(\frac{1}{1+(2E_0/Mc^2)\sin^2(\theta/2)}\right)\left\{(1-f_d^2)+\frac{\hbar^2q^2}{4M^2c^2}\left[2(\mu_p^2+\mu_n^2-3f_d^2)\tan^2(\theta/2)+\mu_p^2+\mu_n^2-3f_d^2\right]\right\},\quad(1)$$

$$|q|=\frac{(2p_0/\hbar)\sin(\theta/2)}{[1+(2E_0/Mc^2)\sin^2(\theta/2)]^{\frac{1}{2}}}=\frac{(2/\lambda\!\!\!^{-})\sin(\theta/2)}{[1+(2E_0/Mc^2)\sin^2(\theta/2)]^{\frac{1}{2}}},\quad(2)$$

where f_d is the deuteron's form factor, M, the mass of a nucleon, and the μ's refer to the magnetic moments of neutron and proton. Other symbols have their well-known meanings.[5] Equation (1) is valid[10] when the momentum transfer $q>\alpha$, where $1/\alpha$ is the usual size of the deuteron ($1/\alpha=4\times10^{-13}$ cm). Now, for large values of q, f_d is extremely small, and Eq. (1) becomes

$$\left(\frac{d\sigma}{d\Omega}\right)_d^{\text{in}}=\left(\frac{e^2}{2E_0}\right)^2\frac{\cos^2(\theta/2)}{\sin^4(\theta/2)}\times\left(\frac{1}{1+(2E_0/Mc^2)\sin^2(\theta/2)}\right)\left\{1+\frac{\hbar^2q^2}{4M^2c^2}\times\left[2(\mu_p^2+\mu_n^2)\tan^2(\theta/2)+\mu_p^2+\mu_n^2\right]\right\},\quad(3)$$

[8] V. Z. Jankus, Phys. Rev. **102**, 1586 (1956); also Ph.D. thesis, Stanford University, 1956 (unpublished).
[9] R. Blankenbecler, Bull. Am. Phys. Soc. Ser. II, **2**, 389 (1957).
[10] See reference 11, footnote 3, p. 266.

and this is essentially identical with the formulation

$$\sigma_d^{\text{in}}=\sigma_p+\sigma_n, \tag{4}$$

where σ_p and σ_n are new symbols standing for the differential cross sections of a point proton and a point neutron.

Now, if the proton and neutron have structures, our expectation might be that the same formula [Eq. (4)] would hold, except that each point cross section would have an appropriate (form factor)^2 multiplied into it. Blankenbecler[9] has examined this question, allowing for the presence of structure in the nucleons, as well as for an interaction in the final state. Moreover, he used a closure rule and has avoided making some of the approximations used by Jankus.[8] Without giving Blankenbecler's detailed result at this point, it may be stated that Eq. (4) still holds for the conditions used in this experiment, with the added modification of introducing form factors described above, except for a correction term of the order of a few percent. A discussion of Jankus' approximations and Blankenbecler's improvements will be found in Secs. 8 and 9 of a review article by Hofstadter.[11] We shall ignore the Blankenbecler correction in our first calculations, since it is small and presently within our experimental errors. Though small, the correction turns out to be most important in comparing the neutron size with the proton size. Hence we shall return to this important matter in Secs. IV and V. For the moment, ignoring the correction, we shall write

$$\sigma_n=\sigma_d-\sigma_p, \tag{5}$$

and this implies that a simple subtraction should provide the neutron's scattering cross section.

Expressions for σ_n and σ_p may be obtained from Rosenbluth's work.[7,11] We may further put $F_1\cong 0$ for the neutron,[4,5,11] because the static charge and second moment of the charge are both zero. We therefore write for the two cross sections:

$$\sigma_n=\sigma_{NS}F_{2n}^2\kappa_n^2\frac{\hbar^2q^2}{4M^2c^2}\{2\tan^2(\theta/2)+1\}, \tag{6}$$

where

$$\sigma_{NS}=\left(\frac{e^2}{2E_0}\right)^2\frac{\cos^2(\theta/2)}{\sin^4(\theta/2)}\left(\frac{1}{1+(2E_0/Mc^2)\sin^2(\theta/2)}\right),$$

$$\kappa_n=\mu_n;$$

and

$$\sigma_p=\sigma_{NS}F_p^2\left\{1+\frac{\hbar^2q^2}{4M^2c^2}[2(1+\kappa_p)^2\tan^2(\theta/2)+\kappa_p^2]\right\}, \tag{7}$$

where $1+\kappa_p=\mu_p$. The subscripts NS refer to a particle with no spin. The ratio $R=\sigma_n/\sigma_p$ then becomes

$$R=\frac{F_{2n}^2}{F_p^2}\times\frac{(\kappa_n^2\hbar^2q^2/4M^2c^2)[2\tan^2(\theta/2)+1]}{1+(\hbar^2q^2/4M^2c^2)[2(1+\kappa_p)^2\tan^2(\theta/2)+\kappa_p^2]}, \tag{8}$$

from which we may extract values of the quantity F_{2n}^2, since F_p^2 is known. The ratio R will be taken from the experimental data reported in this article. F_{2n}^2 may then be plotted as a function of angle, and it is the quantity of interest in this experiment: i.e., F_{2n} is the neutron's magnetic form factor.

It must be pointed out that mesonic exchange corrections may affect the above conclusions. For example, if an electron produces a virtual meson on one of the nucleons in the deuteron, and if it is reabsorbed by the second nucleon, an additional channel of interaction is possible, thus increasing the deuteron's inelastic cross section. We believe this effect is not a large one, but we shall return to this question later in Secs. IV and V.

III. EXPERIMENTAL RESULTS

The experimental results may be divided into four principal groups: (a) the earliest data taken with solid targets of light and heavy polyethylene (CH_2 and CD_2); (b) later data of the same sort taken with similar targets, but with more intense incident electron beams; (c) data taken with gas targets; (d) final data taken with liquid H_2 and D_2 targets.

(a) Eight independent sets of data were taken at an incident energy of 500 Mev and 135° with the polyethylene targets. The targets were matched so that they had the same numbers of protons and deuterons,

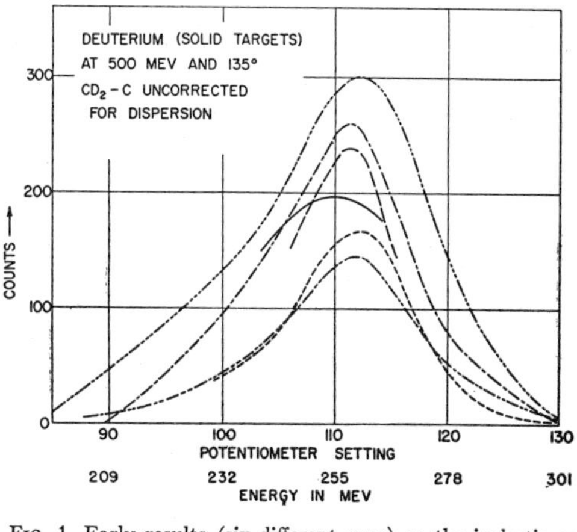

FIG. 1. Early results (six different runs) on the inelastic continuum in deuterium, obtained with solid targets of deuterated polyethylene. The abscissa is proportional to the energy of the scattered electron. The data were taken at 135° for an incident electron energy of 500 Mev.

[11] R. Hofstadter, *Annual Review of Nuclear Science* (Annual Reviews, Inc., Stanford, 1957), Vol. 7.

and this was checked with density measurements. For example, the data reported in Fig. 51, of reference 5, were taken with these targets. Figure 1 shows a summary of the final results obtained from some of these runs and indicates the wide spread in the heights and shapes of the inelastic continua in deuterium. The combination of statistical errors, the CH_2-C, CD_2-C differences, and a 15% nonreproducibility of the absolute results, led to the rather large spread in the data. Similar variable results were obtained with the sharper proton peaks.

Although we shall report improved data below, we have analyzed the solid target data as indicated in Table I. This table presents the ratio of the maximum height of the free proton peak to the height of the deuterium continuum at the maximum of the latter. The half-widths of the inelastic continua were always fairly constant and averaged about 44 Mev. Although the extreme spread in this ratio varies from 7.4 to 3.2, the remaining fluctuations about the mean, 4.8, are not great. The half-widths of the proton peaks averaged 3.8 Mev for the 1% slits used in these experiments. The approximate ratio (σ_d^{in}/σ_p) of areas can be found by assuming triangular shapes for the peaks, as follows:

$$1\times 44/(4.8\times 3.8)=2.4\pm 0.7.$$

Thus we may solve for σ_n, which is $(1.4\pm 0.7)\sigma_p$ for 500 Mev at 135°. A more careful estimate, using average curves and numerical integration of the areas including the tail of the proton peak, yields the result $\sigma_n=(1.1\pm 0.5)\sigma_p$ for 500 Mev and 135° and is about the same as the triangular mean value within the rather large error of the measurements. We shall return to the interpretation of these results later, although we may note in passing that the ratio appears to be larger than 0.45.

(b) The second set of experiments was also carried out with solid targets. These targets were cut from different sheets of CD_2 and CH_2. At the time, operating conditions of the linear accelerator produced very large beam currents; accordingly we used currents as high as 8×10^{10} electrons per pulse (60 pulses per second). To further increase the counting rate, we used targets twice as thick as those described in the previous paragraphs. Unfortunately, the validity of the results

TABLE I. Early experimental ratios of the maximum height of the free proton peak to the height of the deuterium continuum at the maximum of the latter, for solid targets at 500 Mev, 135°.

Run No.	Peak ratio
1	7.4
2	3.2
3	4.3
4	4.4
5	4.6
6	3.7, 4.9
7	5.2
Mean	4.8

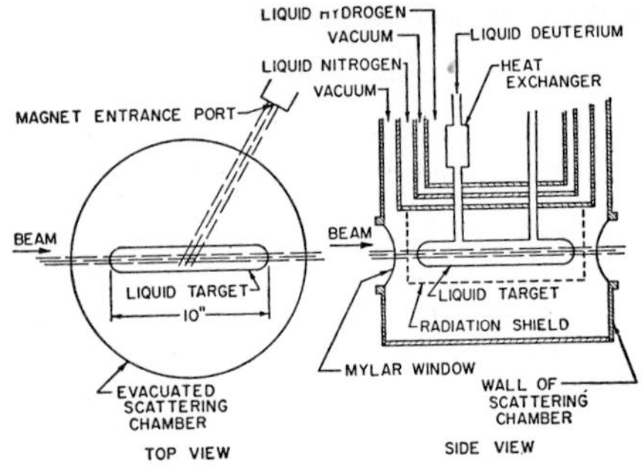

FIG. 2. Schematic diagram of the scattering arrangement and the liquid hydrogen and deuterium target.

obtained with these targets is highly questionable, since the beam currents were so intense that parts of the CD_2 targets were boiled away. This boiling occurred gradually over the period of several runs. Density measurements of samples taken at the conclusion of the runs indicated that, in the areas where the beam was concentrated most heavily, about half the deuterium atoms were missing. Now the CH_2 targets were in the beam for much less time than the CD_2 targets, because the former are used for comparison purposes and also because the counting rate in the peak is much higher. In view of the loss of deuterium, it is not surprising that the value of σ_n/σ_p at 135° fell from 1.1 to as low as 0.5 and even 0.3 for the runs during this phase of the experiment. We feel that the data from these runs are unreliable and hence these results will not be considered in the remainder of this paper. One of the curves, taken under these conditions, is shown in the *Proceedings of the Seventh Annual Rochester Conference.*[12]

(c) The advantages to be gained from using a target that has no carbon background are obvious. We therefore took one check run (at 500 Mev and 135°), using deuterium and hydrogen gases at 2000 psi as targets. The gas-target system used has been described in previous papers.[2,5] Since only one run with gas targets has been carried out and since the counting rates are necessarily lower than they are for solid targets, the statistics are not too good; however, the absence of the carbon background makes up for this. The value for σ_n/σ_p, obtained from this run, is 1.0 ± 0.3 at 500 Mev and 135°.

(d) The most reliable data were obtained with the liquid-deuterium and liquid-hydrogen targets. The data are more reliable because the difficulty with the carbon background is eliminated without loss of counting rate. In Fig. 2 we have shown the essential details of the liquid target in a schematic fashion. This target was designed by J. A. McIntyre. The diagrams are roughly to scale, and the walls are made of stainless steel of

[12] *Proceedings of the Seventh Annual Rochester Conference on High-Energy Nuclear Physics, 1957* (Interscience Publishers, Inc., New York, 1957).

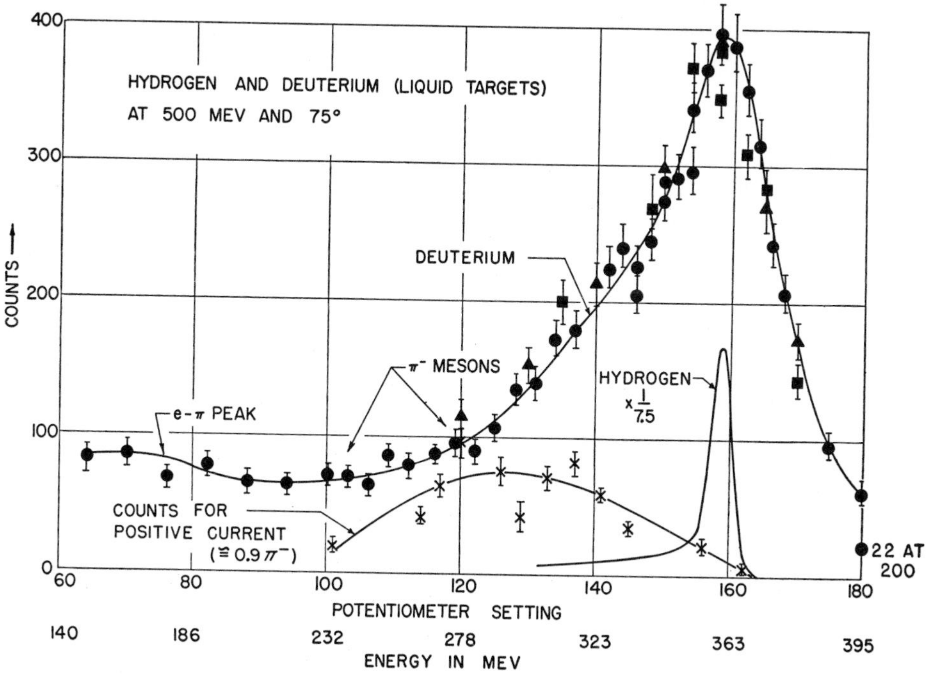

FIG. 3. The inelastic continuum at 500 Mev at a scattering angle of 75°. The large peak to the right corresponds to inelastic scattering from the moving neutron and proton in the deuteron. A negative pion contamination is indicated ("π^- mesons" in the figure). This contamination is eliminated by measurement of the positive pion yield, shown by crosses and a knowledge of the π^-/π^+ ratio. The peak, labeled "$e-\pi$," corresponds to electrons scattered after producing pions and consists also of a background of other low-energy electrons. The free proton peak is also shown. The solid circles, triangles, and squares refer to three runs. The deuteron curve should be multiplied by 0.87 to allow for the different densities of liquid deuterium and liquid hydrogen.

thickness 4 mils. In Figs. 3 and 4, we have shown two typical runs taken with the liquid target; the corrections indicated there, are discussed in the next section.

In all, ten runs have been taken with the liquid target, and the data are superior to the solid- and gas-target data. The remainder of this paper will be devoted almost entirely to the results from these liquid-target runs.

Before proceeding to a discussion of the various corrections applied to the data, we wish to report briefly our observations on the angular distribution of electrons scattered from free protons. In the original work on the structure of the proton at 500 Mev, Chambers and Hofstadter[3] report for the ratio of σ_p(500 Mev, 75°) to σ_p(500 Mev, 135°) a value of 10.0±1.0. Our observations with the liquid targets yield a value of about 13.0±1.0 for the same ratio. The geometry of the liquid targets is less favorable than that of the solid targets, since the former constitute quite broad sources of scattered electrons, and multiple-scattering losses become appreciable. To explain this discrepancy we have carried out experiments with a liquid target of hydrogen, placing a radiator in the path of the scattered electrons to simulate conditions in the actual target. We have shown that the above difference is due to multiple-scattering losses at the edges of the region seen by the spectrometer window. This type of loss does not occur with a source of small dimensions, such as a solid target of Chambers and Hofstadter. The multiple-scattering losses are larger at 135° than they are at 75°, because the scattered energy in the former case is 260 Mev, while it is 360 Mev for the latter scattering angle. The discrepancy has thus been explained satisfactorily and quantitatively, and the proton data for the liquid target can be corrected by using the more accurate values of Chambers and Hofstadter.[3] The discrepancy between liquid- and solid-target data does not affect our results on the neutron, which we shall report, since we always measure the *ratio* of the deuteron to proton cross sections and the discrepancy noted above cancels out. Any small residual error from this cause, not quite canceling out, would be well within our present experimental limits of error. This type of discrepancy may be of interest to future investigators who employ liquid targets and scattering geometry of the kinds used in this experiment.

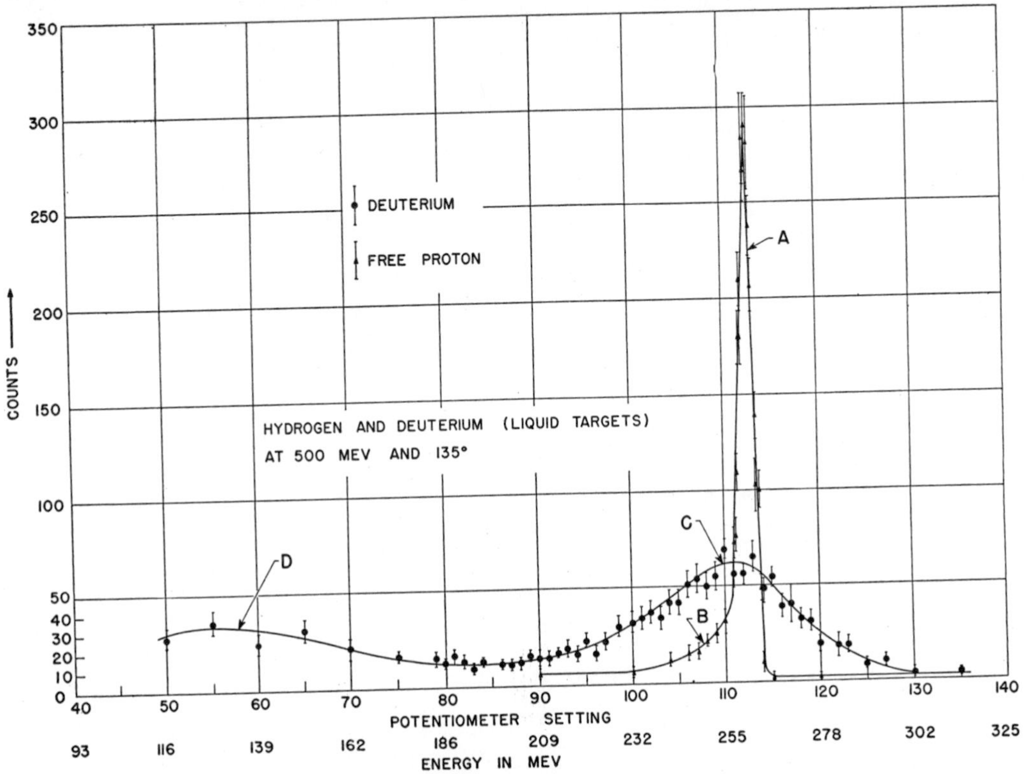

FIG. 4. A comparison of the inelastic scattering from the moving proton and neutron in the deuteron (C) and the elastic scattering of electrons from free protons (A). The data were observed at 500 Mev at a laboratory scattering angle of 135°. (D) represents the electron-pion peak and other low-energy electrons. The π^- contamination at 135° is negligible. The cross section for the neutron's magnetic scattering can be found from a comparison of the areas under the deuteron and proton peaks. The deuteron curve should be multiplied by 0.87 to allow for the different densities of liquid deuterium and liquid hydrogen.

IV. HANDLING OF THE DATA

Most early data were taken at 500 Mev and a scattering angle of 135°. With the liquid target, we have been able to take an angular distribution during a single run. At present we have investigated in detail one bombarding energy—namely, 500 Mev. We have studied the inelastic deuterium spectrum at five angles and the corresponding elastic proton spectrum at three angles at the same energy. It is not necessary to take the proton peak at all angles, since the proton's angular distribution is known.[3] We have also made one run at a higher energy, 600 Mev, and at scattering angle, 135°.

On inspection of the deuterium data, we discovered that the width of the inelastic deuterium peak at half-maximum is very nearly constant at different scattering angles. The width is approximately 44–48 Mev. This can be most easily seen by sliding the peaks (Fig. 5, taken at various angles) along the energy abscissa until the peak in question corresponds to the one at, say, 75°, and normalizing the ordinates to the same value at the maximum of the peak. It is then seen that the curves at all five angles nearly superimpose (Fig. 5) upon each other.

The similarity of the deuterium curves at different values of the momentum transfer can be of value in making the analysis of the data simpler. The simplification depends on the fact that we may now use a "standard" shape of the curve which can apply at any scattering angle. This is useful, because at different scattering angles different physical processes contribute to the background. For example, in addition to a direct pion yield coming through the spectrometer,[13,14] there is a contribution to the background from electrons that are scattered at the angle θ after having made a pion. The peak due to this process occurs at lower energies than the inelastic deuterium peak because of the energy required to produce a pion. In general, the cross section for inelastic deuteron scattering without pion production falls essentially to zero before the above process

[13] See reference 5, Sec. IV-c and Fig. 23.

[14] R. Hofstadter, *Proceedings of the CERN Symposium on High-Energy Accelerators and Pion Physics, Geneva, 1956* (European Organization of Nuclear Research, Geneva, 1956), Vol. 2, p. 75.

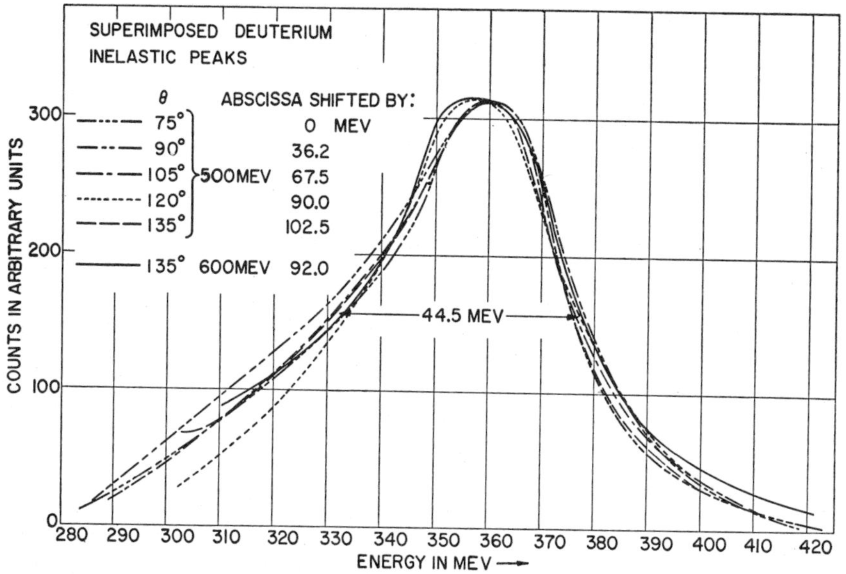

FIG. 5. The experimental spectra at five angles at 500 Mev and at 135° and 600 Mev. Within present experimental error, all curves are very similar and have equal half-widths approximating 45 Mev. Theory indicates that this behavior is to be expected. (See Fig. 7.)

becomes important, but at high values of q, say, at 135°, the two peaks begin to overlap. This can be seen in Figs. 3 and 4. (See also Fig. 12.) On the other hand, the direct negative pion background coming through the spectrometer magnet is important only at the *lower q* values. Thus, since the correct shape of the deuterium spectrum is known, both effects can be subtracted out, at least approximately.

These expectations have been confirmed at several scattering angles by examining the positive pion yield. Since the π^+/π^- ratio is known from the work of Sands *et al.*[15] and Watson *et al.*,[16] it is possible to find the negative pion yield from the measurement of the positive pion yield. The negative pion yield can then be subtracted from the inelastic spectrum. When this is done, good agreement is obtained between the resulting curve and the shape deduced from scattering angles where the pions do not contribute. The presence of the pions is indicated in Fig. 3.

We have had little hesitation in making these subtractions except in the vicinity of the extreme low-energy region of the spectrum, where the counting rates are low and the competing processes are most important. But, even in this region, the detailed shape of the curve can be found by another technique (see below).

In addition to the above subtractions, a standard instrumental correction is made. All curves must be corrected for the dispersion of the spectrometer. That is, since the width of the slits of the magnet is held fixed, the ordinates of the curves must be multiplied by a factor proportional to $1/E$.

A normalization has been made to allow for the different atomic densities of liquid deuterium and liquid hydrogen in the target.

Finally, a standard geometrical allowance has been made whenever cross sections, taken at different θ, have been compared because of varying target length in the beam. This amounts simply to multiplying the cross sections by $\sin\theta$.

In addition to the care involved in measuring the deuteron peak, considerable care is also required in handling the low-energy tail of the *proton* peak. The tail comes down rapidly at first, then falls to zero very slowly. Because the tail falls off so slowly, it comprises about 25% of the total area under the curve. Thus it is important to know the area under the tail as accurately as possible. If the tail were due entirely to bremsstrahlung, then it should be fairly simple to analyze. That is, we would expect it to decrease approximately as $1/(E-E_0')$, where E_0' is the energy at the peak. However, this seems not to be the case, presumably because of a small background. Since the counting rates are very low in the tail, the statistics are poor, and hence the tail is difficult to determine experimentally. There is undoubtedly some contribution from background effects such as wide-angle bremsstrahlung, pair-production, etc.

By using the radiative and straggling corrections,[5,17] we may estimate how much of the tail we are missing in measuring down to a certain energy from the peak. It is then not necessary to measure the tail at energies where the background is almost the whole effect we desire to know. If we cut off the measured curve (500

[15] Sands, Teasdale, and Walker, Phys. Rev. **95**, 592 (1954).
[16] Watson, Keck, Tollestrup, and Walker, Phys. Rev. **101**, 1159 (1956).
[17] J. Schwinger, Phys. Rev. **75**, 898 (1949).

Mev and 135°) at, say, 4.5% of the value at the peak, the part we are missing is calculated to be approximately 12.5% for the Schwinger correction and 12.5% for the radiative straggling in the target. Similar corrections can be applied to the inelastic deuteron peak. In this case, the curve can be measured rather well down to 33% of the peak, so that the amount missed is much smaller. In this case, we calculate the amount missed to be 8.0%. Corrections for other scattering angles are approximately the same.

We have extended the measurements in the proton tail as far as 50 Mev from the peak and have extrapolated this curve to zero counting rate. We have compared the area so obtained with the calculated missing part. In most cases the calculated values agree with the measured areas within 5%. Occasionally we have observed as much as a 10% difference. The calculated values are always less than the measured values, thus indicating a small background, probably due to wide-angle pairs, etc. We consider the proton peaks to be reasonably well measured.

In the case of the deuteron peak, we have approached the problem of the empirical shape of the peak in the following way: we shall think of the deuteron spectrum as consisting of the scattering from many little displaced proton (or neutron) peaks folded together, since the proton (or neutron) is moving in the deuteron. We have taken our most reliable proton curve (75°) and divided it into 20 small, similar proton curves; then we have folded the small peaks together again in an "empirical distribution," to see if we could reproduce the shape of the deuterium spectrum. Using this procedure, we have been successful in finding a distribution that will fit the entire curve except for the extreme low-energy end of the spectrum. Since this is exactly the place where we have experienced difficulties in subtracting out the background, we believe that our *folded* distribution

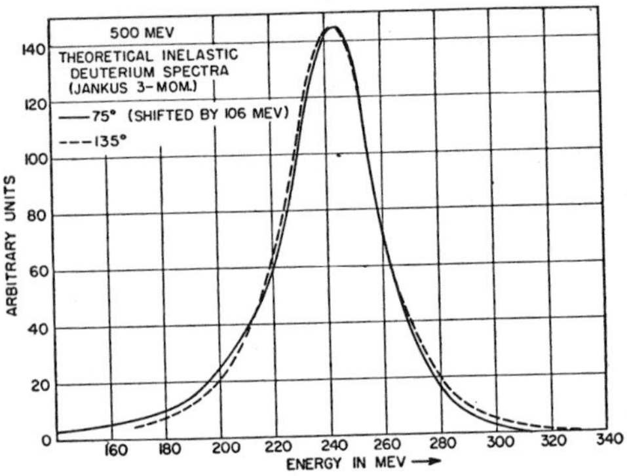

FIG. 7. This figure shows a comparison between the Jankus three-momentum, point-nucleon curves for 75° and 135° at 500 Mev. The two curves are very similar and have nearly equal half-widths.

gives us the exact shape of the lowest energy part of the actual deuteron curve. Upon comparing these results with the corresponding part of the experimental curve previously corrected for background, we find that the areas under the two curves are exactly the same. This procedure serves to convince us that (for instance) our method of subtracting mesons is substantially correct. Thus the shape of the *entire* spectrum (at any of the five angles) is known fairly well.

The above procedure was carried out and gave us an "empirical distribution" shape for the inelastic electron spectrum in the deuteron. We shall refer to this as the "unfolded" deuteron spectrum, since radiative effects have been removed (unfolded) by our calculations. This procedure resulted in a standard (for various scattering angles) deuteron spectrum yielded by our measurements.

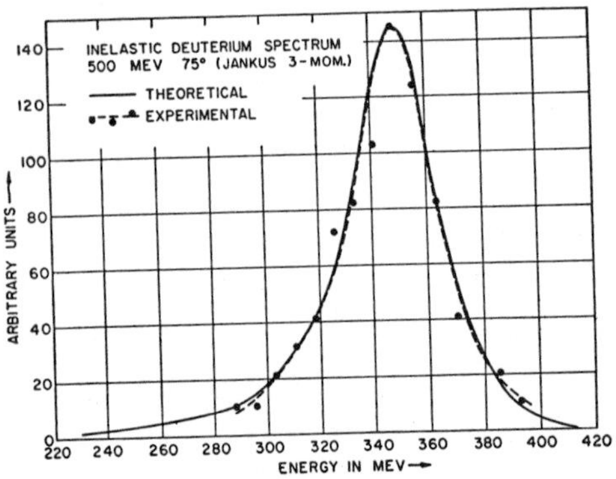

FIG. 6. The theoretical shape of the electrodisintegration spectrum at 75° and 500 Mev, according to the point-nucleon, three-momentum transfer, theory of Jankus. The experimental (unfolded) curve is also shown for comparison. The experimental curve is shifted to lower energy by 8 Mev to make the peak positions coincide.

The unfolded curve was prepared at a time before a comparison was made with theory. We shall now see that the result is in good agreement with theory. It is clear that because bremsstrahlung has been removed the unfolded spectrum is the shape to be compared with theory. Fortunately, a theory for the inelastic spectrum exists and has been given by Jankus.[8] It was worked out, of course, for a deuteron composed of point-nucleons.

The results of the Jankus[8] theory are given in his Eqs. (9), (10), and (11). For finite nucleons the same equations were also used (see below), but appropriate values of the nucleons' form factors were inserted in the proper places. We have computed the Jankus cross section at 75° and 135° at 500 Mev. Figures 6 and 7 show the spectra so obtained. It may be seen in Fig. 7 that, just as indicated by experiment, the shapes are very closely the same at these widely different angles. Furthermore, Fig. 6 shows the comparison between the unfolded curve, derived from our measurements at 75°, and the theoretical distribution of Jankus. The agreement is really very good. The width at half maximum

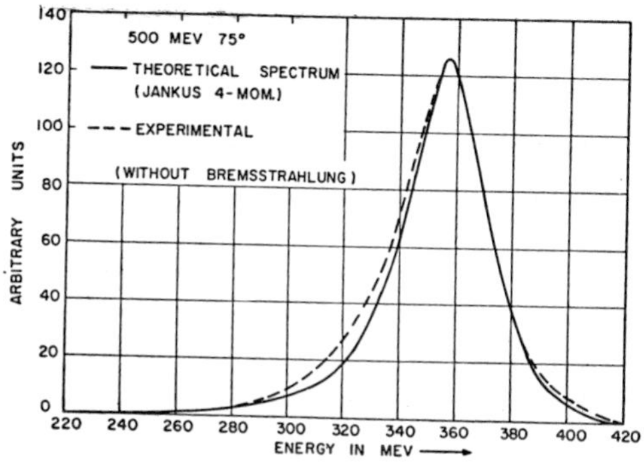

FIG. 8. The Jankus four-momentum, point-nucleon spectrum for 75° at 500 Mev in comparison with the experimental unfolded curve, i.e., the experimental spectrum with the effect of bremsstrahlung removed. The peak of the theoretical curve occurs at exactly the same energy as the peak of the experimental curve.

and shape are just as we have found experimentally. The good agreement between experiment and theory at all angles in the complicated matter of the shape of the inelastic spectrum convinces us that the Jankus theory is basically correct at the large momentum transfers even though it was designed for smaller values of q. The circumstances that the Jankus theory applies to point-nucleons, whereas the deuteron is really made of nucleons of finite size, is discussed in detail in Sec. V.

The shape of the inelastic spectrum, given in Figs. 6 and 7, thus is merely a reflection, or a transform of the momentum distribution within the deuteron. The influence of the final-state interaction has been considered by Jankus,[8] but, at the large momentum transfer considered in these experiments, its effect is very small.

A close inspection of the positions of the peaks in Figs. 6 and 7 shows that they are shifted in the direction of lower energies by 8 and 17 Mev with respect to the actual measured peak positions at 75° and 135°, respectively. Although these shifts are not large (~5%), they lie outside experimental error. We have therefore sought an explanation of these shifts.

It may be observed that Jankus' results do not reduce exactly to Rosenbluth's formulas at high energy, because Jankus uses the three-momentum transfer in his theory, whereas the Rosenbluth calculation employs the relativistically correct four-momentum transfer q_μ. [The three- and four-momentum magnitudes are called s and q, respectively, in reference 11, Eqs. (1) and (8).] By substituting the four-momentum transfer in Jankus' Eq. (10), as suggested in reference 11, the Jankus result will then reduce to the Rosenbluth formula, with almost negligible differences. The calculations involved in Jankus' Eq. (10) were also carried out with the four-momentum transfer q_μ instead of the space-momentum transfer. The results were gratifying since they yielded peaks in exactly the correct positions found by experiment. The curves are shown in Figs. 8 and 9. Although the positions of the peaks are now correct, the shapes of the curves are changed slightly compared with the three-momentum curves. At 75° the change is very small, but at 135° the four-momentum transfer curve becomes narrower by approximately 23%. Thus by changing to the four-momentum transfer, the kinematical fit is certainly improved, and the fit of the shape factor is made slightly poorer, but still quite good, considering how little is now known about the relativistic deuteron problem. It is to be noted that the 135° experimental curve is a little broader on the low-energy side than the Jankus curve with the four-momentum substitution.

We have also compared the area under Jankus' four-momentum curves, Figs. 8 and 9, with the more exact closure calculations of Blankenbecler.[9] The results for the integrated cross sections, without final-state interaction, may be expressed as follows:

$$\sigma_d^{\text{in}} = (1+\Delta)(\sigma_p+\sigma_n), \tag{9}$$

where σ_p and σ_n are given in Eqs. (6) and (7). For point nucleons in the Jankus theory, with four-momentum transfer, Δ is found to be $+0.02$ for 75° and -0.04 for 135°. On the other hand, Blankenbecler finds $\Delta=-0.006$ for 135° and 0.000 for 75° for point nucleons. This agreement is considered to be very satisfactory, since the corrections are so small.

Now the effect of the finite-size form factors and the interaction in the final state must be allowed for. These corrections are given for the total cross section by Blankenbecler as $\Delta=+0.03$ for 135° and $\Delta=+0.004$ for 75° with corresponding values in between these extreme angles. Thus we may use the corrected formula (9) instead of the simpler, but less exact, formula given in Eq. (4). We note, however, that no correction has been made for the meson exchange effects in the inelastic spectrum. These have been described at the end of Sec. 2 and were considered by Jankus[8] at lower q values, where they were found to be negligible. Drell and

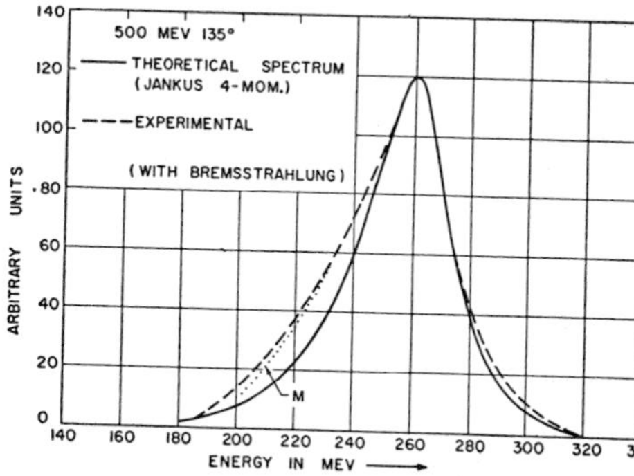

FIG. 9. The Jankus four-momentum, point-nucleon spectrum for 135° at 500 Mev in comparison with the experimental curve *with* bremsstrahlung included. The dotted curve, labeled M, indicates the experimental curve when corrected for the slight contribution of $(e-\pi)$ electrons. (See text and Fig. 12.)

Blankenbecler[18] are now working out a more accurate estimate of this correction, but, from the good agreement between our results and the Jankus theory, the resulting correction is expected to be small.

On carrying out the integration under the experimental deuteron inelastic and proton elastic peaks and applying the various corrections that we have described above, we have found the experimental σ_d^{in} and σ_p points shown in Fig. 10. These points are the ones found directly from the liquid target data. As we have seen, the liquid target points fall off a little too rapidly at the large angles because of the multiple scattering errors. For this reason we have labeled the ordinate in Fig. 10 "approximate differential cross section." As remarked before, the ratio $\sigma_d^{\text{in}}/\sigma_p$ is independent of such errors. Table II shows the measured values. Figure 11 now presents the σ_d^{in} and σ_p values when normalized to the Chambers-Hofstadter results for σ_p. The differences between Figs. 10 and 11 are seen to be slight.

Finally we wish to show in Fig. 12 the relation between the inelastic electron-pion peak and the tail of the ordinary deuteron electrodisintegration continuum. The electron-pion peak has been calculated[19] at 500 Mev and 135° from the results of the Dalitz-Yennie[20] theory with the proton form factor inserted from the results of Chambers and Hofstadter.[3] We have used the same form factor for the neutron and have folded the deuteron momentum spectrum into the electron-pion results. Since the deuteron spectrum is narrow compared to the electron-pion peak, the effect of the folding does not differ much from the original electron-pion peak. In any event, it can be seen that there is fortunately only a small effect (of the order of a few percent, in the worst case of 135°) of the electron-pion peak on the narrow deuteron peak we have investigated (135°), and that the effect at all other angles is smaller. The actual experimental overlapping is a little larger than calculated in the above way, and this is attributable to wide-angle pairs, Dalitz pairs, pairs from neutral pions, etc. The fortunate circumstance that the overlapping is small makes experiments of this type possible.

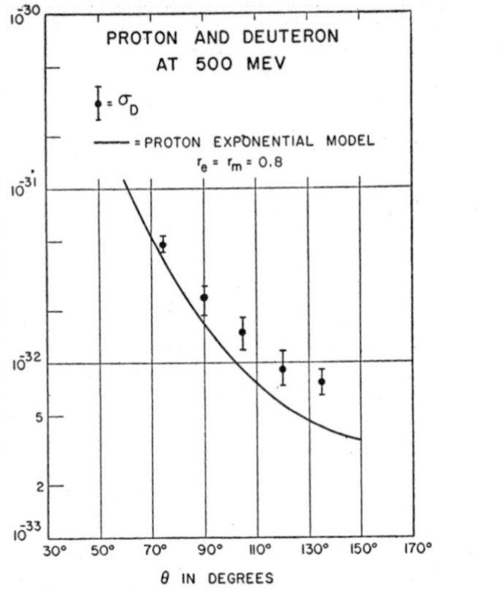

FIG. 11. This figure is similar to Fig. 10 except that the proton cross sections are corrected for multiple scattering and fit the earlier results of Chambers and Hofstadter.[3] Since the ratios are not affected by multiple scattering, the ratios σ_d/σ_p in Figs. 10 and 11 are identical, except that the density factor has been included here.

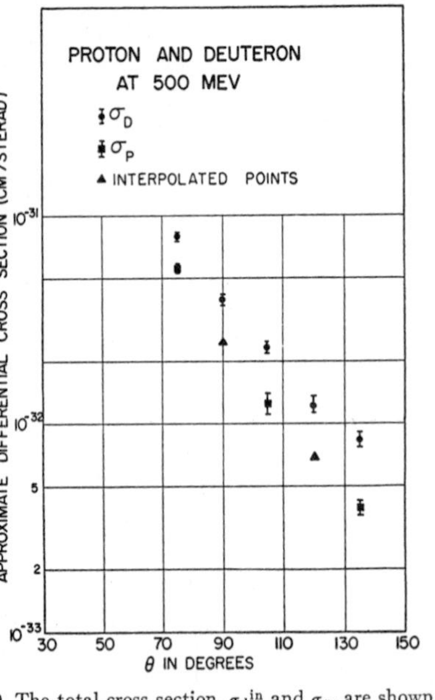

FIG. 10. The total cross section, σ_d^{in} and σ_p, are shown as obtained in this experiment. The triangles are interpolated. The cross sections are considered to be approximate on an absolute scale because multiple scattering corrections have not yet been applied. (See Fig. 11.) The deuteron cross sections should be multiplied by 0.87 to allow for the different densities of liquid deuterium and liquid hydrogen.

V. ANALYSIS OF THE DATA

(a) Total Cross Sections

Using the known theoretical treatment of the deuteron problem (Jankus, Blankenbecler), we shall express our results in the form of Eq. (9). If we use the calculated values of Δ due to Blankenbecler, we may solve for σ_n/σ_p as follows:

$$\frac{\sigma_n}{\sigma_p}=\frac{\sigma_d^{\text{in}}}{\sigma_p}\left(\frac{1}{1+\Delta}\right)-1, \tag{10}$$

[18] S. Drell and R. Blankenbecler (private communication).

[19] We wish to thank Professor R. H. Dalitz for making the calculations for the proton at our experimental conditions.

[20] R. H. Dalitz and D. R. Yennie, Phys. Rev. 105, 1598 (1957).

TABLE II. Cross-section ratios.

E (Mev)	θ	$\sigma_d^{\text{in}}/\sigma_p$	$(\sigma_n/\sigma_p)_{\Delta=0}$	$(\sigma_n/\sigma_p)_{\Delta\neq 0}$
500	75°	1.22±0.12	0.22±0.12	0.21±0.11
500	90°	1.40±0.24	0.40±0.24	0.39±0.23
500	105°	1.64±0.34	0.64±0.34	0.61±0.30
500	120°	1.57±0.36	0.57±0.36	0.53±0.34
500	135°	1.83±0.30	0.83±0.30	0.80±0.25
600	135°	1.55±0.30	0.55±0.30	...

and σ_d^{in} and σ_p are measured experimentally as shown in Fig. 11. As remarked before, the ratio $\sigma_d^{\text{in}}/\sigma_p$ in Eq. (10) is independent of the slight error introduced by the thick liquid target. The experimental values of $\sigma_d^{\text{in}}/\sigma_p$ are given in Table II, as well as values deduced for σ_n/σ_p from Eq. (10) with the appropriate values of Δ. The choice $\Delta=0$ is also made in the table and corresponds to a simple addition of the cross sections [Eq. (4)] without any corrections. Because of the small values of the Δ corrections, the $\Delta=0$ results for σ_n/σ_p are a good approximation to the final result obtained with better values of Δ, calculated by Blankenbecler.

Values of σ_n/σ_p from Table II may now be inserted in Eq. (8), and thus values of F_{2n}^2/F_p^2 may be found for the choices $\Delta=0$ and the Blankenbecler values of Δ. In Fig. 13 the choice $\Delta=0$ is taken and the values of F_{2n}^2 are computed as shown. In this figure the results are presented for F_{2n}^2 and F_p^2 when the proton form factors are modified slightly, as explained above, to fit the Chambers-Hofstadter data. Figure 13 also shows the values of F_{2n}^2 (open circles) when the Blankenbecler values of Δ are inserted. It may be seen that the changes introduced by $\Delta\neq 0$ are not large and within the present experimental errors. In both cases, ($\Delta=0$, $\Delta\neq 0$), the values of F_{2n}^2 lie: (a) on the average, a trifle above the proton form-factor curve, and (b) below the point charge values ($F^2=1.0$) by large amounts. We may conclude immediately, therefore, that (I) the neutron's magnetic radius is not zero or very small ($\sim 2\times 10^{-14}$ cm), i.e., the neutron is not a point. An equivalent phenomenological statement of this fact is that the neutron's form factor is not unity at the above values of q^2.

The exact root-mean-square size of the magnetic cloud in the neutron now becomes a matter of prime interest, since we should like to decide whether the cloud has the same dimensions as those of the proton. Phenomenologically speaking, we may state the question in this way: how closely similar are the form factors F_{2n}^2 and F_p^2? Both choices, $\Delta=0$, and the Blankenbecler Δ values, show that $F_{2n}^2\cong F_p^2$. However, the assumption implicit in this statement is that the mesonic exchange contributions to the deuteron electrodisintegration cross section are smaller than about 10%. Because of the good fit of the shapes of the inelastic continua with the Jankus theory (see below), we feel the mesonic effects are rather small. However, if the mesonic corrections prove to be as large as approximately 10% at all angles, it can easily be shown that the points in Fig. 13 will fall slightly below the proton curve, and the neutron and proton form factors will not be identical within the errors of this experiment. Thus we may state our second conclusion: (II) If mesonic corrections to deuteron electrodisintegration cross sections are less than approximately 10%, at the q values considered in this experiment, then the neutron's magnetic form factor does not differ from that of the proton, but if the mesonic corrections amount to approximately 10%, the neutron and proton have slightly different magnetic clouds.

If we continue to make the assumption that mesonic effects are small, we may make a determination of the rms size of the neutron. A curved line (exponential model) drawn through unity at $q^2=0$ and the experimental points of Fig. 13 may easily be analyzed to give an rms size of $(0.80\pm 0.10)\times 10^{-13}$ cm. Thus our third conclusion is as follows: (III) Subject to the assumption that mesonic effects are essentially small, the rms size of

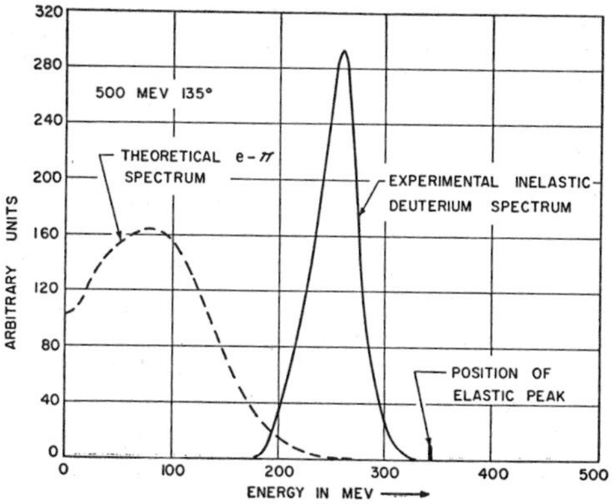

FIG. 12. This figure shows how little the electron-pion peak overlaps the deuteron inelastic continuum, under conditions of greatest overlap in these experiments. The electron-pion spectrum was calculated, using a theory of Dalitz and Yennie[19] and folding their results into the deuteron spectrum.

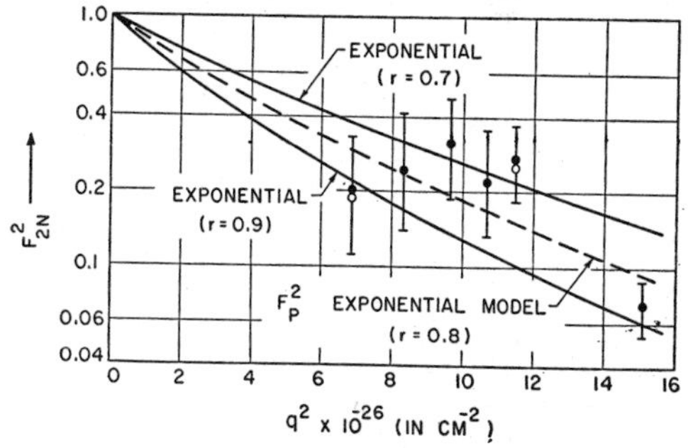

FIG. 13. The dashed line in this figure shows the proton (form factor)^2 curve, and the solid circles (with experimental limits) show the neutron results of this experiment assuming simple additivity [Eq. (4) or Eq. (10) with $\Delta=0$]. The open circles represent the same data when corrected by the more exact Blankenbecler closure calculations. The changes are slight.

the neutron's magnetic cloud is $(0.80\pm0.10)\times10^{-13}$ cm. It is not possible presently to distinguish a shape factor for the neutron's magnetic cloud, since e.g., within experimental error, both exponential or Gaussian density functions, for a radius of 0.80×10^{-13} cm, can be made to fit the experimental data.

(b) Differential Cross Sections

We shall now give some semi-independent evidence concerning the magnitude of the neutron's form factor. We may use the total cross-section results derived so far as a first approximation to the neutron's form factor, and now we shall consider a potentially more sensitive means of determining the form factor. It has been pointed out by Drell[21] that if the comparison between the neutron and the proton is carried out by employing the *peak* of the deuteron inelastic continuum and the proton's cross section, there is practically no influence on the results due to the previously troublesome mesonic exchange corrections. The reason for this is that in the center-of-mass system there is too little momentum transfer at the deuteron peak to excite the p-wave resonance in the pion-nucleon problem. Consequently, we can test and perhaps improve our previous results by comparing the *peak* of the deuteron continuum, rather than its area, with the value of the proton's total cross section.

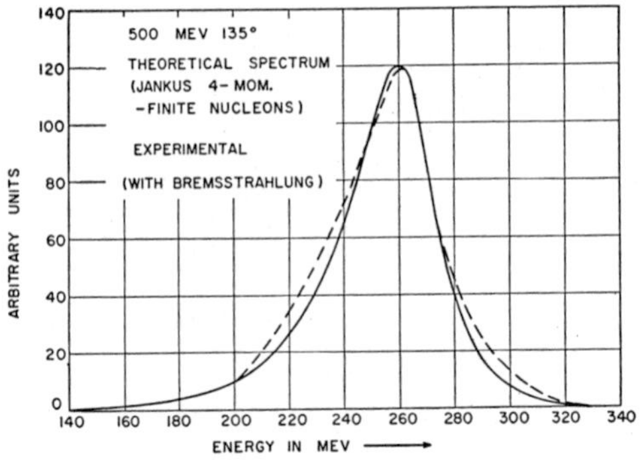

FIG. 14. This figure shows the Jankus four-momentum, finite-nucleon theory at 500 Mev and 135°. Also shown is the experimental spectrum. Bremsstrahlung has been folded into the Jankus theory so that the two curves may be compared directly. The Jankus curve has been adjusted so that its peak value agrees with the experimental curve to facilitate comparison of shape. The wider experimental curve may indicate evidence of small mesonic exchange corrections.

This test can readily be made by using the experimental curves such as those given in Figs. 3 and 4. The comparison with theory can be accomplished by employing the Jankus result [his Eqs. (9), (10), (11)] with the four-momentum inserted in the equation, in addition to the proton and neutron form factors. The proton form factors are taken from Chambers and Hofstadter[3] and the neutron form factors. We may try to use form factors for the neutron chosen to be equal to those of the proton. In this way, we obtain the new result shown in Fig. 14 at 135° and 500 Mev. The Jankus curve given in that figure represents the improved formulation in which the four-momentum and the form factors are employed and thus represents a deuteron built of finite nucleons. The effects of introducing the form factors are (a) to reduce the ordinate of the point-nucleon curves for the deuteron, as expected from simple considerations, and (b) to widen the theoretical spectrum, because the low-momentum transfers are associated with scattered electrons having energies lower than the peak, where the form factors are higher numerically. The broadening results in improving the agreement of the new curves with experiment, although the experimental curve at 135° is still slightly wider than indicated by theory. The residual width at 135° may represent the effect of mesonic exchange, and, if this is so, we shall have a new way of measuring this correction. In any case, we may compare the actual magnitude of the peak-ordinate of the experimental curve with the peak of the Jankus curve (form factors included). The result is gratifying, for the neutron radius required to give agreement with experiment lies between 0.80×10^{-13} cm and 0.90×10^{-13} cm and is closer to the latter value. For 135° the experimental peak value is 1.51×10^{-34} cm²/sterad Mev, while the theoretical results are 1.90×10^{-34} cm²/sterad Mev for 0.61×10^{-13} cm and 1.49×10^{-34} cm²/sterad Mev for 0.80×10^{-13} cm. The corresponding set of figures for 75° follows: the experimental cross section at the peak is 0.86×10^{-33} cm²/sterad Mev, while the theoretical results are 1.24×10^{-33} cm²/sterad Mev for 0.61×10^{-33} cm and 1.07×10^{-33} cm²/sterad Mev for 0.80×10^{-13} cm. The experimental value at 75° agrees almost exactly with 1.0×10^{-13} cm. At 75° the form-factor curve is similar in shape to the point-nucleon shape except, of course, for the ordinate, which is reduced by the appropriate amount. In view of experimental error, the results show that the peak-comparison-method also gives neutron form factors rather close to those of the proton. Further, the 600 Mev, 135° data are also consistent with size 0.8×10^{-13} cm.

Thus the two methods agree in finding that the neutron's form factors are quite close to those of the proton. The total cross section method favors a slightly smaller size (0.80×10^{-13} cm) and slightly larger form factors, while the method of differential cross sections favors a larger size (0.90×10^{-13} cm) and smaller form factors. We do not know exactly how to weigh these results at the present time. Historically, more effort was devoted to the total cross-section method, although future analyses will also concentrate on the peak-comparison method. If we weigh the two methods equally, the result is $(0.85\pm0.10)\times10^{-13}$ cm for the neutron's magnetic radius, which is equal to the proton's magnetic radius (0.80×10^{-13} cm) within

[21] S. Drell (private communication).

experimental error (0.10×10^{-13} cm). If the peak-cross-section method is weighed more heavily, the two nucleons have slightly different sizes.

Further work will be devoted to making a sensitive comparison of the neutron and proton by the differential cross-section method. We believe it will be possible, in this way, to test equality of form factors to within a few percent. In addition, the mesonic exchange effects may be investigated by the total cross-section method and by examining the shapes of the inelastic continua.

VI. CONCLUSIONS

We may now summarize the various conclusions which this experiment demonstrates:

(I) The neutron's magnetic cloud is not a point. This result is essentially independent of the various theories which apply to the electrodisintegration process.

(II) The neutron's magnetic form factor is similar to that of the proton. The possible difference between the two form factors is probably not larger than can be represented by the rms sizes of 0.90×10^{-13} cm (neutron) and 0.80×10^{-13} cm (proton).

(III) If mesonic exchange corrections to electrodisintegration are less than 5% or so, the smaller size (0.80) in (II) is suggested for the neutron. If mesonic exchange effects are of the order of 10%, the neutron and proton have slightly different magnetic structures. The results are obtained from the total cross-section method (see text).

(IV) A comparison between neutron and proton made by the differential cross-section method (see text) also indicates that the two nucleons have nearly identical magnetic form factors and identical sizes. By identical, we mean in this context the same to within 10%. This result is consistent with Conclusion III.

(V) The Jankus theory of electrodisintegration of the deuteron appears to be valid beyond the limits within which it was originally developed, provided one uses the four-momentum transfer in its formulas, rather than the three-momentum transfer. Substitution of form factors in the Jankus formulas gives results agreeing remarkably well with experiment. Possible small deviations from theory may be due to mesonic exchange effects.

(VI) Crudely speaking, the results of this experiment are consistent with charge independence. If the results are taken at face value, there is a small difference between the neutron and proton. However, the difference lies within experimental error.

(VII) The question of whether the finite dimensions of the proton[1–3] can be ascribed to real structural effects, or whether these dimensions indicate the limits below which quantum electrodynamics may break down, cannot at present be decided uniquely from this experiment. The fact that the Dirac form factor of the proton, the magnetic form factor of the proton, and the magnetic form factor of the neutron all have the same size is suggestive of a common origin, perhaps indicating some limitation of electrodynamics. On the other hand, the small difference that may exist between neutron and proton would suggest structural differences. A more accurate experiment is needed and this is one object of future studies of this type.

(VIII) It is possible that a charge form factor in the neutron could affect the values of F_{2n}^2, but, since the first and second moments of this distribution vanish, it is unlikely that the above results could be affected in an important manner. Because so little is known about the charge form factor of the neutron, it seems unprofitable to pursue this subject with our present data. On the other hand, Schiff[22] has considered this question from a phenomenological point of view.

(IX) In view of the uncertainty in deciding between the total cross-section and differential cross-section methods, the neutron's rms radius may be given as $(0.85\pm0.10)\times10^{-13}$ cm. This radius is consistent with all the conclusions within present experimental error.

ACKNOWLEDGMENTS

We wish to thank Dr. J. A. McIntyre for his help in designing the liquid target and for his assistance in the early stages of working with it. G. Burleson, P. Gram, S. Sobottka, and R. Taylor were also of great help in carrying out the experiment. Dr. F. Bumiller, Dr. H. Ehrenberg, and Dr. H. Kendall generously gave us their aid at various times, particularly with electronic equipment. On the theoretical side, Mr. R. Blankenbecler developed important formulas to interpret our data and we are very grateful to him. Professor S. Drell has pointed out several theoretical features of our problem, which proved to be of fundamental importance and we appreciate his friendly help and advice. We acknowledge with thanks the suggestions of Dr. B. Richter in connection with information on the π^-/π^+ ratio in deuterium. Finally, we wish to thank F. W. Bunker, B. R. Chambers, C. N. Davey, A. Marcum, E. Wright, and Mrs. E. McWhinney for technical assistance.

[22] L. I. Schiff, Bull. Am. Phys. Soc. Ser. II, 2, 389 (1957).

PAPER 44*

Incoherent Electron Scattering from the Nucleons in Beryllium and Carbon and the Magnetic Size of the Neutron*†

HANS F. EHRENBERG‡ AND ROBERT HOFSTADTER
Department of Physics and High-Energy Physics Laboratory, Stanford University, Stanford, California
(Received December 26, 1957)

The electron scattering at high momentum transfer has been measured from the nucleons in Be, in C, and from the free proton. The data yield the cross section of the average nucleon and of the neutron in relation to that of the proton. $\sigma_n/\sigma_p(\theta)$ is found to be 1.16±0.3 at 500 Mev and 135°; it decreases, as expected, for smaller angles and lower energies. If the assumption is made that meson-exchange effects and interactions in the final state are not important, the form factors obtained indicate an apparent root-mean-square radius of the neutron's magnetic-moment distribution of $(0.53\pm0.15)\times10^{-13}$ cm. It is possible that the apparent small size of the neutron in Be and C is due to the neglect of meson-exchange effects and interactions in the final state. The present result is smaller than a neutron size, given by Yearian and Hofstadter, who compared the cross sections of deuteron and proton and found equal sizes for neutron and proton. If one accepts the latter result, the present experiment can be used to yield a measure of the above neglected effects.

I. INTRODUCTION

ELECTRON scattering from free protons has been studied previously.[1–3] From the measured cross sections, the electric and magnetic structure of the proton have been determined.[1] It is now of interest to investigate the scattering cross section of the neutron. Since free neutrons are unavailable in sufficiently large densities, it is necessary to use neutrons bound in a light nucleus.

In elastic scattering (from which nuclear sizes may be determined) and in inelastic scattering, in which a nuclear level is excited, the electron is scattered coherently by the nucleus as a whole. In the incoherent scattering to be discussed in this paper, the incident electron is scattered primarily from a single nucleon which recoils and is emitted from the nucleus. Electrons scattered in this process appear in the energy spectrum near the free-proton peak which occurs, for not too small incident energies and scattering angles, at a distinctly smaller energy than the electrons scattered from the whole nucleus. Thus they may easily be distinguished from the latter. Owing to the internal motion of the nucleons, the incoherently scattered electrons have a wide energy distribution, reflecting the momentum distribution of the nucleons. The center of this wide peak is shifted to lower energies with respect to the free-proton peak by an amount corresponding in order of magnitude to the root-mean-square momentum of the various nucleons in the nucleus.

For further details, we may refer to a review article[4] on electron scattering (especially to its Secs. IIIb2, IIIc, and VI), where references to several preliminary measurements of incoherent scattering in deuterium, helium, and beryllium[5] are also reported. We may also call attention to a study of deuterium similar to ours.[6]

At high energies and large angles, that is, for large momentum transfers (q), the incoherent scattering is much larger than the combined elastic and inelastic level-scattering from the nucleus because the latter are greatly reduced by finite-size effects.[4] Furthermore, the scattering from individual protons and neutrons at high values of q is due almost exclusively to their magnetic moments, and the charge scattering from the protons contributes only a small amount. As pointed our previously,[4] the scattering from the neutron would be expected to be about half as large as that of the proton, if the neutron and proton have similar distributions of the density of their magnetic moments. This follows because the scattering is proportional to the square of the magnetic moment at large q values. On the other hand, a larger neutron cross section would imply either (1) that the magnetic cloud of the neutron is smaller than that of the proton, or (2) that in the special range of q values studied, because of an unknown complicated structure in the neutron, its form factor has variations leading to larger values than that of the proton. The latter type of behavior could occur if the density distribution goes through a value of zero at a distance at which the experiments have a high sensitivity.

It was the purpose of this work to study the incoherent electron scattering from beryllium in order to determine the cross section of the neutron. Some time

* The research reported here was supported jointly by the Office of Naval Research and the U. S. Atomic Energy Commission, and by the U. S. Air Force, through the Office of Scientific Research of the Air Research and Development Command.
† Presented at the Heidelberg Meeting of the German Physical Society, September, 1957 (unpublished).
‡ On leave of absence from Physikalisches Institut der Universität Bonn.
[1] R. Hofstadter and R. W. McAllister, Phys. Rev. **98**, 217 (1955).
[2] R. W. McAllister and R. Hofstadter, Phys. Rev. **102**, 851 (1956).
[3] E. E. Chambers and R. Hofstadter, Phys. Rev. **103**, 1454 (1956).
[4] R. Hofstadter, Revs. Modern Phys. **28**, 214 (1956).
[5] E. E. Chambers and R. Hofstadter (unpublished); see also reference 4 and *Proceedings of the Seventh Annual Rochester Conference on High-Energy Nuclear Physics, 1957* (Interscience Publishers, Inc., New York, 1957).
[6] M. R. Yearian and R. Hofstadter, Phys. Rev. **110**, 552 (1958) this issue.

* *See page 685 of this volume for corrections and addenda.*

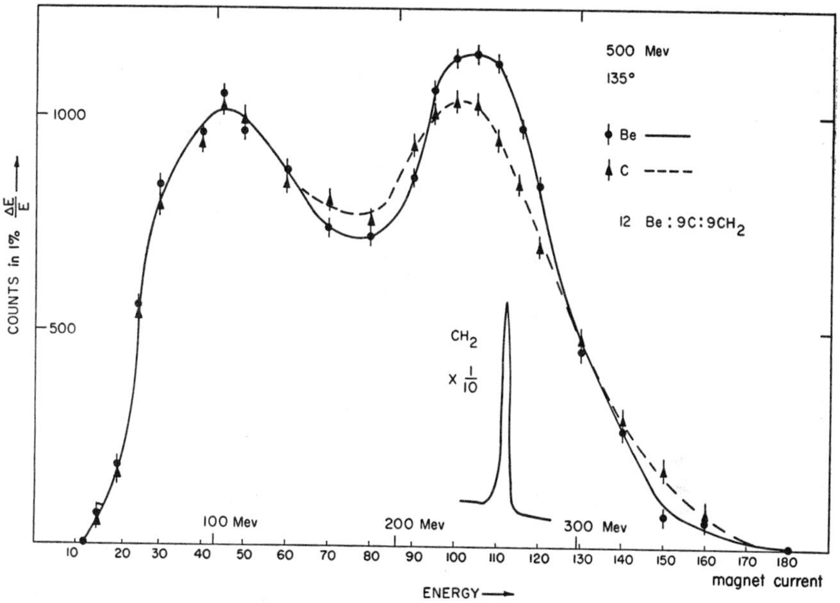

FIG. 1. Energy spectrum of the incoherently-scattered electrons of 500-Mev incident energy at 135° from the nucleons in Be and C. Both targets have equal numbers of nucleons per cm^2. The ordinate gives counts per 1.065×10^{24} nucleons/cm^2, per 3.75×10^{15} incident electrons (=600 microcoulombs), per solid angle 4.95×10^{-3} and per 1% energy interval. The second peak on the low-energy side is caused by electrons which have produced pions in their scattering process. The polyethylene peak is given in a scale corresponding to the same carbon content as in the carbon target.

ago, Chambers and Hofstadter[5] made a preliminary examination of that nucleus, which shows that the method is feasible with beryllium, where there is a well-known loosely-bound neutron. The cross section corresponding to this neutron might be expected to show up at the peak of the incoherent continuum. The idea was then to determine the scattering cross section of the neutron as the difference between the values for Be^9 and "Be^8." If the scattering is truly incoherent, "Be^8" can be considered to be $\frac{2}{3}$ of the C^{12} nucleus.

In the foregoing we have implicitly made the assumption that meson-exchange effects do not contribute appreciably to the area under the inelastic Be and C peaks. While real meson production is observed in the left-hand peak of Fig. 1, virtual meson production and meson exchange may add to the area under the right-hand peak. We will discuss this problem later (Sec. IV).

II. APPARATUS AND EXPERIMENTAL METHOD

This experiment has been performed with the Stanford linear accelerator as the source of electrons, by using the standard arrangement described in reference 4, Sec. IVb. The incident electron beam was analyzed magnetically so that the energy band was 1% wide. The electron current was measured by a large Faraday cup placed behind the target and integrated by a vibrating-reed electrometer with a feedback arrangement. Beam currents up to a maximum value of 4×10^{10} electrons per pulse ($=4\times10^{-7}$ amp) were used (60 pulses per second).

The targets of Be and C (graphite) were plates of equal weight/cm^2, namely, 683 mg/cm^2=408×10^{21} nucleons/cm^2. The comparison proton peak was measured in a polyethylene plate. A CsBr crystal was used as before to adjust the position and shape of the beam spot. The targets could easily be replaced by each other with the beam spot remaining fixed. In all cases the target angle was set at half the scattering angle.

The scattered electrons were analyzed by the 36-in. double-focusing magnetic spectrometer[3,4] and counted in a standard manner with a fluorocarbon Čerenkov counter (index of refraction=1.27). The energy acceptance slit was made 1% wide and the angular aperture was approximately 2° in the plane of the beam and 8° in the perpendicular plane. As has already been discussed in reference 4, the use of this Čerenkov counter, in connection with the discriminator setting high enough, eliminates meson counting, and a confirmation of this fact comes from the absence of counts when the spectrometer current is reversed. In the latter case, positive mesons would have been detected in approximately equal numbers compared to the negative mesons accompanying the scattered electrons.

In order to increase the accuracy of comparison, the data from Be and C were taken alternately at each spectrometer setting. In almost every run at least one free-proton peak from the polyethylene target was taken, and the carbon background could easily be subtracted by using the measured data in carbon. We made no special attempt to determine absolute values of the cross sections, since we related all our results to the proton cross section. The relative cross sections, obtained for the free proton at different angles and energies, are in good agreement with Chambers and Hofstadter.[3] The absolute value is somewhat less than that calculated in their work. The reason for this has

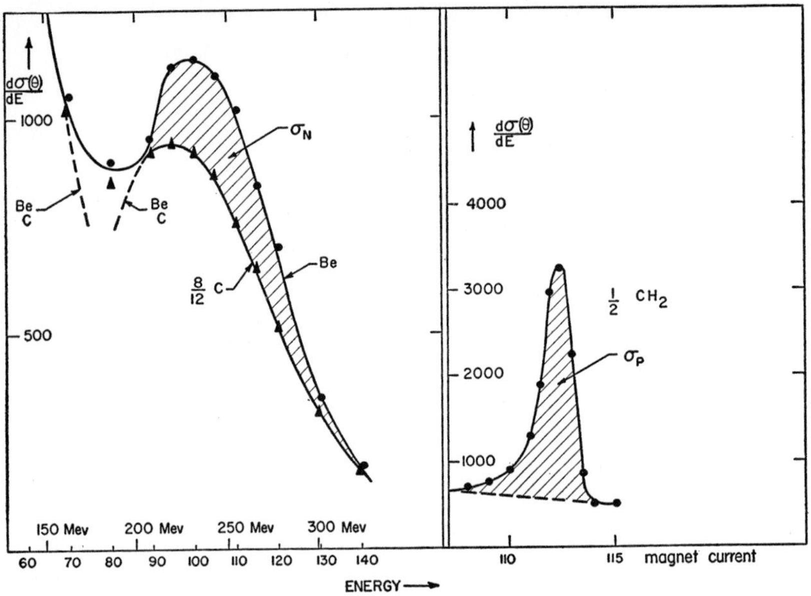

FIG. 2. Differential cross section for the Be nucleus, for 8/12 of the C nucleus, and for the free proton. The units of $d\sigma(\theta)/dE$ are 1.96 $\times 10^{-37}$ cm²/Mev sterad. The area between the Be and the C curve represents the cross section of one neutron in Be. σ_n/σ_p is found to be 1.16.

not been investigated, but is probably connected with the high bias setting of the discrimination mentioned above.

III. RESULTS

(a) 500 Mev, 135°

Figure 1 shows the energy distribution of the 500-Mev electrons scattered at 135°. These data form the main object of the experiment. The peak on the right represents the electrons scattered incoherently from the nucleons, while the peak to the left represents those electrons that have scattered while producing mesons and consequently have lower energy.[4]

The incoherent peak to the right is the one that will interest us in these experiments. This peak has been measured on several occasions with good statistics. The absolute counting rates were reproducible to within 6%, and the relative values between Be, C, and CH_2 agreed with each other to better than 2%.

In this figure we see clearly the shift of the maximum in relation to the free-proton peak. The shift is somewhat larger for C than for Be. Furthermore, one notices that the momentum distribution of the nucleons in C is slightly broader than in Be. These features are also observed in the measurements taken at smaller angles and lower energies.

The data in Fig. 1 were converted into counts per constant-energy interval by use of the spectrometer calibration and its dispersion characteristic. This correction is the familiar $1/E$ correction. In the curves thus corrected, the area under each peak (Be, C, p) represents the corresponding cross section, and from comparison of the areas we may obtain the cross section per nucleon (averaged over protons and neutrons) in Be and C, in relation to the cross section of the free proton. Unfortunately, there is superposed on the incoherent peak the tail of the meson-producing electron peak. Thus the left-hand side of the incoherent peak is not accurately known. Because of the spatial symmetry of the momentum distributions of the nucleons, half of the nucleons contribute to each half of the peak. We may take the area to the right of the center line and relate it to one-half of all nucleons in the target. The result obtained is $(\sigma_{\text{inel}})_{\text{Av}}=1.08\pm0.1$, in Be and $(\sigma_{\text{inel}})_{\text{Av}}=1.17\pm0.1$, in C.

The relative cross section for σ_p is taken to be 15.8% larger than the area shown in the right-hand side of Fig. 2. This correction accounts for the number of electrons not counted in the proton peak due to the radiative losses (Schwinger correction and straggling effects). The amount lost in the proton peak due to these causes is 25%, and the amount lost in the Be and C peaks is 8% in each case.

Since this determination of the area depends sensitively upon where one places the center line, we also took the area after shifting the center line far over to the right (actually to the position where the maximum appears when we omit the $1/E$ correction), and we obtained values of 0.82 and 0.96 for $(\sigma_{\text{inel}})_{\text{Av}}$ in Be and C, respectively. We believe that this is even less than a lowest possible limit, when we allow for quite a large distortion of the incoherent peak by the meson-production peak and for other effects, which might tend to falsify the true position of the center of the incoherent peak.

By relating the measured incoherent-scattering cross

sections of Be and C nuclei to the average nucleon, we have not made any special assumption about the particular nucleons in the nucleus. If we now make the assumption that the momentum transfer is high enough so that the nucleons may be treated as free and independent particles, we can interpret these results in terms of individual proton and neutron cross sections. This will be done in the discussion in the next section.

Under this assumption we can now make a second and independent evaluation of the data, which follows the procedure outlined in the introduction, and determine the cross section of the neutron in a differential method between Be and C. This means that we shall take the difference between Be and $\frac{2}{3}$ of C^{12}. Figure 2 shows this comparison between the experimental Be and C data after the spectrometer correction has been made and after the C data have been multiplied by 8/9. This factor corresponds to 8/12 in the number of atoms. The area between both curves gives the cross section of one neutron in Be. By comparison with the free-proton peak, we obtain

$$\sigma_n/\sigma_p = 1.16 \pm 0.1.$$

We may emphasize that this method is less affected by distortion from the meson-production peak than is the determination of the whole area for Be and C separately. Also the need for systematic corrections is greatly reduced.

Still another variation may be used as a third method, wherein we obtain the difference between the Be curve and the unreduced C curve (i.e., for equal numbers of nucleons) and calculate in this way

$$\sigma_n - \sigma_p = (0.00 \pm 0.1)\sigma_p; \quad \text{thus} \quad \sigma_n = (1.00 \pm 0.1)\sigma_p.$$

Each of the three methods described gives a somewhat different value for σ_n/σ_p because of the different ways in which the differences in shape and position between the Be and C curves influence the results. As a weighted average, we will take the value

$$\sigma_n/\sigma_p = 1.17 \pm 0.3 \text{ for 500 Mev and } 135°,$$

with a limit of error that we consider safe with respect to most kinds of possible systematic errors resulting from distortion by the meson-production peak and to the differences in the momentum distribution. The limits of errors also include the corrections which ought to be made for theoretical reasons (see below). The latter fortunately are not large, at high q values, and some of them tend to cancel each other.

The main effects of the corrections of the cross section are: (1) the center of the incoherent peak occurs at a lower energy than the free-proton peak, because the nucleon is bound and has a slightly lower "effective mass" in the kinematics of the scattering process, and (2) the moving nucleons with different momentum directions contribute differently to the total cross section, since energy and scattering angle in the center-of-mass system of each collision are different, depending upon the momentum of the nucleon.

Since *magnetic* scattering from point nucleons is nearly independent of energy and angle, and since the charge scattering is small for high q at large angles, the main part of the correction in each case comes from the change of the form factor with q. The q value for the center of the Be peak is 3% smaller than for the free proton; thus the form factor F^2 and the cross section are about 6% larger. Since in our calculations we used only the nucleons on the high-energy side of the center-of-peak, which is closer to the proton peak, we have already implicitly accounted for a large part of this correction. Regarding the effect of the moving nucleons, we may note that all nucleons on the right-hand side of the center line have a momentum component towards the electron. Therefore, their cross sections are slightly smaller than for nucleons at rest. In this sense our cross section is too small by a few percent. An accurate consideration of all these effects could be done by superposing the differential cross sections calculated for each moving nucleon in the corresponding center-of-momentum frame. Because of larger experimental uncertainties, it is not worth while to make those corrections in our data. For the differential Be$-\frac{2}{3}$C method, these corrections are even smaller, since the area corresponding to the single neutron is located at a position very close to the proton peak.

(b) Other Energies and Angles

As a check of the above-described work, we may employ a kind of counter-example which should be useful in understanding the results. At lower energies and smaller angles, the charge scattering becomes much larger than the magnetic scattering. Hence, at such values of q, the scattering cross section should be dominated by the scattering from the protons alone. Unfortunately, the test cannot be made uniquely, since, at the small q values, the incoherent scattering disappears because the different nucleons cannot be treated as independent. Moreover, there is the experimental difficulty that the elastic- and inelastic-level scattering peaks are also very large in comparison to the remaining small incoherent peak. However, it is possible to carry out some experiments in the intermediate region, where the magnetic scattering still contributes a fair amount, but less than at 500 Mev and 135°.

For example, in Fig. 3, we show curves for 400 Mev and 90°. The meson-production peak decreases quite noticeably as one goes to smaller angles. This is one favorable aspect of these experiments. The results of this, as well as of a set of later measurements under different conditions, are shown in Fig. 4. The evaluation of the data was made in the manner described for 500 Mev and 135°. The cross section of the average nucleon shows the expected decrease of the neutron's contribution as we go towards lower energies and smaller

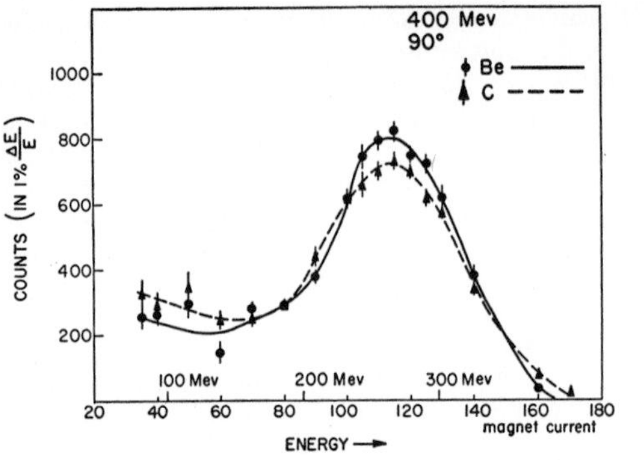

FIG. 3. Energy spectrum of the incoherent electron scattering at 400 Mev, 90°. Compared to Fig. 1, the decrease of the meson-production peak may be noticed.

angles, where it approaches the value given by the protons alone. The accuracy of the smaller-angle measurements is, in general, not good enough to make effective use of the differential Be$-\frac{4}{3}$C method, although in a few cases the agreement is satisfactory.

In the following discussion we shall tentatively make the assumption that meson-exchange effects add only very small amounts to the inelastic peaks. We shall later discuss what happens if this assumption is not made.

IV. DISCUSSION AND CONCLUSIONS

The cross section of the proton (mass M, Dirac moment 1, Pauli moment κ) and likewise of the neutron, for scattering of electrons of the incident energy E at the angle θ (in the laboratory frame), is given by Rosenbluth's[7] formula, which we may write here in the following form:

$$\sigma=\left(\frac{e^2}{Mc^2}\right)^2\frac{1}{[1+(2E/Mc^2)\sin^2(\theta/2)]^2}\left\{\frac{1}{[2\tan(\theta/2)]^2}\times\left[\left(\frac{2Mc}{\hbar q}\right)^2F_1^2+\kappa^2F_2^2\right]+\tfrac{1}{2}[F_1+\kappa F_2]^2\right\},$$

where

$$\hbar^2q^2=\frac{[2(E/c)\sin(\theta/2)]^2}{1+(2E/Mc^2)\sin^2(\theta/2)}$$

means the square of the momentum transfer of the electron in the scattering process. The form factors F_1 and F_2, both functions of q^2, take into account the finite size of both the Dirac and the Pauli magnetic-moment distributions. (As regards the exact meaning of F_1 and F_2 and their relation to the electric and magnetic density of the nucleon's structure, see Yennie, Lévy, and Ravenhall.[8])

In the static limit, i.e., for $q=0$, when proton and neutron can be considered as point particles, the form factors have the values $F_{1p}(0)=F_{2p}(0)=F_{2n}(0)=1$ and $F_{1n}(0)=0$. (Here and in the following equations the indices p and n refer to proton and neutron, respectively.) Thus the ratio of the cross sections for point proton and point neutron is

$$\left(\frac{\sigma_n}{\sigma_p}\right)_{\text{point}}=\frac{\kappa_n^2[1+\frac{1}{2}\cot^2(\theta/2)]}{\frac{1}{2}\cot^2(\theta/2)[(2Mc/\hbar q)^2+\kappa_p^2]+(1+\kappa_p)^2}=A(\theta,q).$$

For the interpretation of the experiments, we shall introduce, as usual, "total form factors," defined by $\sigma_{p,n}=(F_{p,n})^2\times(\sigma_{p,n})_{\text{point}}$ so that

$$\sigma_n/\sigma_p=(F_n^2/F_p^2)\times A(\theta,q).$$

From the measured cross section $\sigma_n/\sigma_p=1.17\pm0.3$, we may calculate $F_n^2/F_p^2=2.6\pm0.6$ at 500 Mev, 135°. Using the known proton form factor,[1–4] we obtain for the neutron

$$F_n^2=0.39\pm0.1 \quad \text{at} \quad q^2=11.5\times10^{26}\ \text{cm}^{-2}.$$

We may now turn back to Fig. 4, where the cross section of the average nucleon is plotted as a function of A. Under the assumption that the nucleons scatter

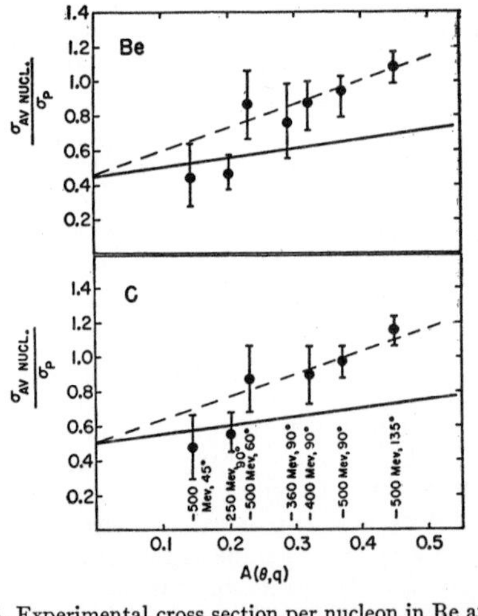

FIG. 4. Experimental cross section per nucleon in Be and in C, in units of the free-proton cross section for several experimental conditions. The data are arranged along an abscissa which is chosen for convenience and contains the experimental conditions θ and q in such a way that $A(\theta,q)$ is the ratio of σ_n/σ_p for point particles. The heavy lines indicate the cross section of the average nucleon as a function of A in the case that the neutron has the same magnetic form factor as the proton. (This coincides with the case of point particles and shows that, for $A=0$, the average nucleon cross section is 4/9 for Be and 6/12 for C.) The dotted lines through the experimental points correspond to a (form factor)² of the neutron = 2.4 (in Be) and 3.0 (in C) times that of the proton. The errors in this figure refer to the observational accuracy of the measurements.

---

[7] M. Rosenbluth, Phys. Rev. 79, 615 (1950).
[8] Yennie, Lévy, and Ravenhall, Revs. Modern Phys. 29, 144 (1957).

as independent particles, we obtain

$$\frac{\sigma_{\text{Av nucleon}}}{\sigma_p}=\frac{1}{9}\left(4+5\frac{F_n^2}{F_p^2}\times A\right)\text{ in Be}$$

$$=\frac{1}{12}\left(6+6\frac{F_n^2}{F_p^2}\times A\right)\text{ in C.}$$

The heavily-drawn straight line in each part of the figure refers to the case $F_n=F_p$. The experimental points at large A clearly fall above this line, thus indicating $F_n>F_p$. The slope of the dotted line corresponds to $F_n^2/F_p^2=2.4$ in Be and $=3.0$ in C. (The dotted lines do not, of course, imply that we believe that F_n/F_p is constant at all A values.)

The (form factors)^2 obtained for the neutron are shown in Fig. 5 as functions of q^2. The F_n for low q cannot be given with any accuracy, since the experiments at small A are very insensitive to the cross section of the neutron. However, the large values of the form factor are very persistent, and this may be some indication that the magnetic form factor at low q is in the neighborhood of unity or slightly higher, as might be given by a density distribution which changes sign as a function of radial distance. We may note that an analysis of the preliminary data of Chambers and Hofstadter[5] at 600 Mev and 135° gives a value of $\sigma_n/\sigma_p=1.0\pm0.3$.

The present data are certainly not sufficient to make a structural analysis of the neutron as has been made in the case of the proton.[1–4] There, $F_{1p}(q)$ and $F_{2p}(q)$ were evaluated separately from the experimental "total form factor" and turned out to be nearly identical. The root-mean-square radius was found to be 0.77×10^{-13} cm for each of the two distributions.

For the neutron not only is $F_{1n}(q=0)=0$ (zero total charge), but from the experiments on scattering of neutrons by atoms[9] it is known that the coefficient of q^2, in an expansion of $F_{1n}(q^2)$ in powers of q^2, is also close to zero. That makes it most probable that the "total form factor" F_n, obtained in our experiments, is the F_{2n} in the Rosenbluth formula and that we can thus place $F_{1n}\equiv0$. (A large coefficient of q^4 in F_{1n} would involve quite a complicated charge distribution in the neutron.)

With the above assumptions, we can state that the magnetic distribution in the neutron is apparently more confined than in the proton but not so confined as to be a point (see Fig. 5). For the rms radius of a bound neutron we obtain

$$\langle r_{2n}\rangle=(0.53\pm0.15)\times10^{-13}\text{ cm.}$$

This result is nearly independent of the special structural model chosen for transforming the form factor into $\langle r_{2n}\rangle$; as long as we assume that the distribution is monotonic. There appears to be little doubt that the bound neutron and proton are different in size or shape if the simple assumptions we have made, such as neglecting meson exchange, prove to be justified.

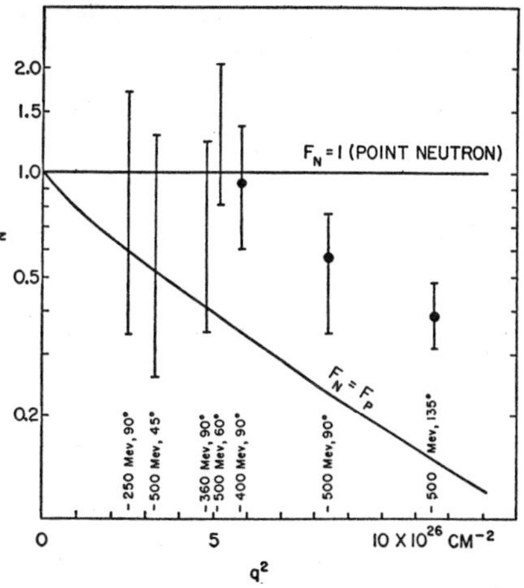

FIG. 5. Experimental (form factor)^2 of the neutron as a function of the square of the momentum transfer. At large q values, the form factor of the neutron is 2.6 times larger than that of the proton. The limits of error given include all possible systematic errors in the experiments. At low q values, the experiments are not able, for essential reasons, to yield information on the neutron cross section with any accuracy. The root-mean-square radius of the magnetic-moment distribution of the neutron is about $(0.53\pm0.15)\times10^{-13}$ cm, if the density distribution is monotonic.

However, since we have compared the cross sections of bound nucleons with that of the free proton, we are, of course, making the special assumption that the internal structures of neutron and proton are not affected by the fact that they are bound in a nucleus and thus are under the influence of the nuclear forces. Moreover, we have made the assumption that meson-exchange effects are unimportant. We may judge how well this assumption holds by the comparison of these results with those in the deuteron,[6] where the neutron and proton are under the influence of the strong nuclear force only a small fraction of the time and where the neutron size is essentially equal to that of a free proton.

It may thus be pointed out that the real use of experiments such as this one will probably be to tell what happens to the neutron when it is bound within a nucleus as compared with its free behavior. When related to the deuteron results, we may say that there are probably meson-exchange effects in Be and C and that these account for the apparently smaller neutron size.

ACKNOWLEDGMENTS

We wish to express our thanks to the operating crew of the Stanford linear accelerator and to all members

[9] See references 11 and 12 in reference 8.

of the electron-scattering group for their continued help in setting up the experiments, as well as for discussions on experimental and theoretical questions. We also wish to thank Dr. D. G. Ravenhall and Mr. R. Blankenbecler for valuable discussions. One of the authors (H. F. E.) is grateful to the Deutsche Forschungsgemeinschaft for the grant of a stipend which permitted him to stay at Stanford for one year.

Electromagnetic Structure of the Neutron*

L. I. Schiff

Stanford University, Stanford, California

RECENT experiments of McIntyre,[1] Hofstadter,[2] Panofsky,[3] and collaborators provide information on the structure of the neutron. It is known that the neutron has zero total charge, and from the magnitude of the low-energy electron-neutron interaction,[4] it is also known that the mean-square radius of the electric charge distribution of the neutron is very small or zero.[5,6] These properties are consistent with experimental results on the elastic scattering of high-energy electrons from deuterium.[1] In these experiments, the magnetic moments of proton and neutron play only a minor role, and the scattering can be interpreted in terms of a distribution of electric charge in the deuteron. This distribution is in good agreement with that obtained by assuming that the neutron contributes nothing, and that the finite size[7,8] of the proton is folded into the square of the deuteron wave function. The interpretation of the inelastic (break-up) scattering of high-energy electrons from deuterium,[2] on the other hand, involves mainly the magnetic moments and their distributions in space. The same is true of the experiments on the electron production of pions in hydrogen.[3]

The present paper is intended mainly to point out that experiments on the magnetic moment structure of the neutron involve its electric charge structure as well, since the latter determines the distribution of the normal magnetic moment as well as the electric charge. We assume forms for the electric charge and magnetic moment distributions of proton and neutron, and from these calculate quantities that are related to the experimental observations on elastic and inelastic electron-deuteron scattering. Corresponding calculations for the electron production of pions in hydrogen are somewhat more complicated, and have not been carried out.

The charge and moment distributions of the proton, as determined by electron scattering experiments,[8] can be chosen to have the same form (normalized to unit volume integral);

$$f_P(r) = (\alpha^3/8\pi)\exp(-\alpha r). \qquad (1)$$

Here, α is chosen to be 4.32 fermi^{-1}, so that the root-mean-square radius of f_P is 0.80 fermi (1 fermi$=10^{-13}$ cm). The corresponding form factor, or Fourier transform of Eq. (1), is

$$F_P(q) = \alpha^4/(\alpha^2+q^2)^2. \qquad (2)$$

We assume for the present that Eqs. (1) and (2) actually represent the proton, even though there is no theoretical basis for the exponential form of f_P. Another possible choice is considered briefly at the end of the paper.

In choosing a form for the neutron charge distribution, $f_N(r)$, we are guided by the theoretical suggestion[6,9] that for large r, the nucleon charge density is primarily an isotopic vector, so that f_N is roughly equal to $-f_P$. Then the assumed requirements that the total charge and the mean-square radius of the charge distribution be zero,

$$\int f_N(r)d\tau = 0, \quad \int r^2 f_N(r)d\tau = 0, \qquad (3)$$

imply that f_N has at least two zeros as a function of r. A simple and convenient form for f_N is

$$f_N(r) = -(\alpha^3/8\pi)\exp(-\alpha r) + (\beta^5/8\pi\alpha^2)\exp(-\beta r) - [(\beta/\alpha)^2 - 1]\delta(\mathbf{r}), \qquad (4)$$

where $\beta > \alpha$. Equation (4) has the desired properties: it is asymptotically equal to $-f_P$, and it satisfies Eqs. (3). The δ function need not be interpreted literally, but should merely be regarded as an analytically convenient description of a central negative charge density that has a radius somewhat smaller than $1/q$ for the largest q values of current interest. The form factor or Fourier transform of Eq. (4) is

$$F_N(q) = -\alpha^4/(\alpha^2+q^2)^2 + (\beta^6/\alpha^2)/(\beta^2+q^2)^2 + 1 - (\beta/\alpha)^2. \qquad (5)$$

The effect of a nonvanishing neutron charge density on the elastic electron-deuteron scattering is very simply calculated if we assume that the free nucleon charge densities are not distorted by the deuteron binding. Unfortunately, there appears at present to be no way in which to estimate the error associated with

* Supported in part by the U. S. Air Force through the Office of Scientific Research, Air Research and Development Command.

[1] J. A. McIntyre and S. Dhar, Phys. Rev. **106**, 1074 (1957).

[2] M. R. Yearian and R. Hofstadter, Phys. Rev. (to be published); references to earlier work are given in this paper. See also Bull. Am. Phys. Soc. Ser. II, **2**, 389 (1957).

[3] W. K. H. Panofsky and E. A. Allton, Phys. Rev. (to be published). See also Bull. Am. Phys. Soc. Ser. II, **2**, 391 (1957).

[4] Hughes, Harvey, Goldberg, and Stafne, Phys. Rev. **90**, 497 (1953); Melkonian, Rustad, and Havens, Bull. Am. Phys. Soc. Ser. II, **1**, 62 (1956).

[5] L. L. Foldy, Phys. Rev. **87**, 693 (1952).

[6] Yennie, Lévy, and Ravenhall, Revs. Modern Phys. **29**, 144 (1957).

[7] R. Hofstadter and R. W. McAllister, Phys. Rev. **98**, 217 (1955), **102**, 851 (1956); E. E. Chambers and R. Hofstadter, Phys. Rev. **103**, 1454 (1956).

[8] F. Bumiller and R. Hofstadter, Bull. Am. Phys. Soc. Ser. II, **2**, 390 (1957).

[9] Chew, Karplus, Gasiorowicz, and Zachariasen, Phys. Rev. (to be published).

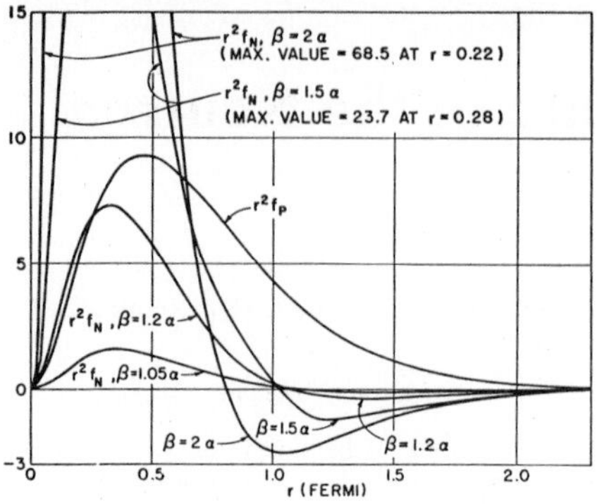

FIG. 1. Plots of $100r^2f_P$ and $100r^2f_N$ against r, where r is measured in fermis, and f_P and f_N are the proton and neutron charge densities given by Eqs. (1) and (4).

this assumption. Then the electric and normal magnetic contributions to the point-nucleon cross section are to be multiplied by $(F_P+F_N)^2$. For the experimental region, the uncorrected total magnetic contribution is always less than 12%,[1] and most of this arises from the normal magnetic moment of the proton, since the anomalous moments of neutron and proton always appear added together,[1,10] and hence nearly cancel. Thus to good approximation, we may ignore the anomalous moments and simply multiply the theoretical curves of McIntyre and Dhar, which allow for the finite size of the proton, by $(1+R)^2$, where

$$R(q)=F_N(q)/F_P(q). \tag{6}$$

Calculations have been performed for the neutron charge distributions shown in Fig. 1. Corresponding values of $(1+R)^2$, where R is given by Eqs. (2), (5), and (6), are plotted in Fig. 2. Comparison with Figs. 12 through 15 of reference 1 shows that $(1+R)^2$ cannot be less than about 0.8 for the largest value of q, which is about 2.9 fermi^{-1}. This implies that β must be somewhat less than 1.2α; according to Fig. 1, this is so small that in order for f_N to be approximately equal to $-f_P$, r must be so large (greater than 2 fermi) that both f_N and f_P are uninterestingly small. On the other hand, good agreement is obtained, as already noted by McIntyre and Dahr, by assuming that $f_N(r)=0$, which corresponds in our notation to $\beta=\alpha$ or $R(q)=0$.

The simplest interpretation of the inelastic (break-up) electron-deuteron scattering consists in putting

$$\sigma_D=\sigma_P+\sigma_N. \tag{7}$$

Here, σ_D is the area under the inelastic deuteron peak that corresponds to break up without meson production, and σ_P and σ_N are the elastic free proton and neutron cross sections, which may be calculated from the

[10] V. Z. Jankus, Phys. Rev. **102**, 1586 (1956).

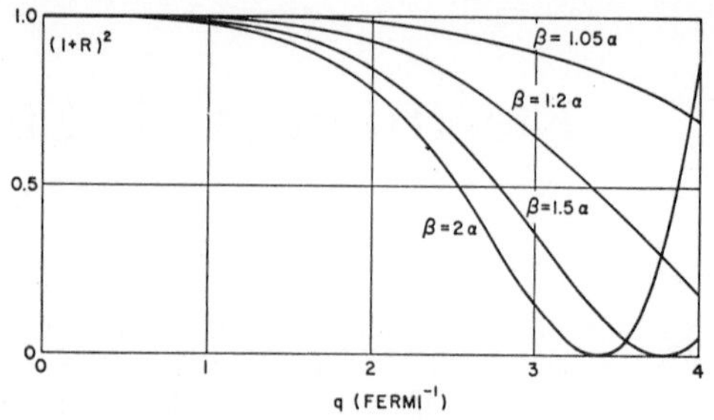

FIG. 2. Correction factors for elastic electron-deutron scattering that assume various neutron charge densities.

Rosenbluth formula,[11]

$$\begin{aligned}&\sigma=\sigma_0\{F_1^2+(q^2/4M^2)[2(F_1+\kappa F_2)^2\tan^2\tfrac{1}{2}\theta+(\kappa F_2)^2]\},\\&\sigma_0=e^4\cos^2\tfrac{1}{2}\theta/\{4E^2[1+(2E/M)\sin^2\tfrac{1}{2}\theta]\sin^4\tfrac{1}{2}\theta\},\\&q^2=4E^2\sin^2\tfrac{1}{2}\theta/[1+(2E/M)\sin^2\tfrac{1}{2}\theta].\end{aligned} \tag{8}$$

In Eqs. (8), σ is the free proton or neutron cross section in the laboratory system according as the charge and moment form factors F_1 and F_2, and the anomalous magnetic moment κ, refer to the proton or neutron; θ is the scattering angle, M the nucleon mass, q the magnitude of the four-momentum transfer, and units are chosen such that $\hbar=c=1$.

A detailed discussion of the validity of Eq. (7) has been given by Blankenbecler.[12] With the help of a sum-rule method, and taking kinematical but not meson-current effects into account, he finds that σ_D does not exceed $\sigma_P+\sigma_N$ by more than 10% for the experimental range of parameters. On the other hand, because of the increasing importance of virtual mesons as the scattered electron energy decreases below the inelastic peak and it becomes more nearly possible to create a real meson, Drell[13] has suggested that σ_D be related to the maximum value rather than the area of the inelastic peak. Hofstadter[14] has done this, making use of Jankus'[10] theory; he finds agreement within the experimental errors of about 15% between theory and experiment for $E=500$ Mev and θ between 75° and 135°, when he assumes that $f_N(r)=0$ and the neutron moment distribution is given by f_P.

The ratio σ_N/σ_P has been calculated from Eqs. (8), under the assumption that $F_1=F_2=F_P$ for the proton, and $F_1=F_N$ and $F_2=F_P$ for the neutron, where F_P and F_N are given by Eqs. (2) and (5). The results are plotted as the solid curves in Figs. 3 and 4 for the neutron charge distributions shown in Fig. 1. Since, as remarked in the last paragraph, Hofstadter finds agreement between theory and experiment at 500 Mev for $\beta=\alpha$ ($F_1=0$ and $F_2=F_P$ for the neutron), the solid curve so labelled provides the best present estimate for σ_N. It seems likely that deviations of σ_N from this curve by about

[11] M. N. Rosenbluth, Phys. Rev. **79**, 615 (1950).
[12] R. Blankenbecler, Phys. Rev. (to be published). See also Bull. Am. Phys. Soc. Ser. II, **2**, 389 (1957).
[13] S. D. Drell (private communication).
[14] Hofstadter, Bumiller, and Yearian, Revs. Modern Phys. **30**, 482 (1958), this issue.

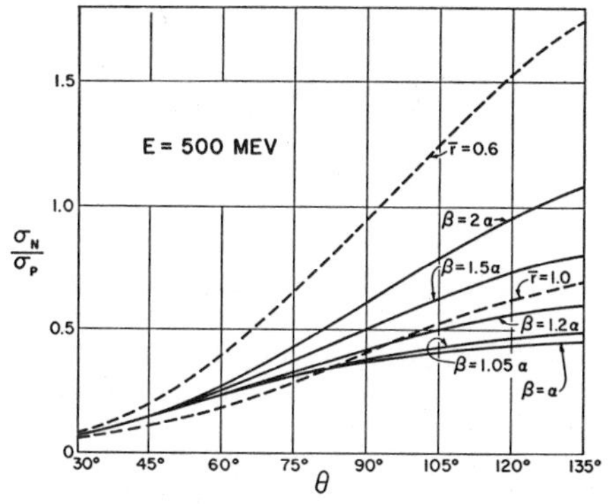

FIG. 3. Calculated ratio of free neutron to free proton cross section at 500 Mev. Solid curves are for the same neutron and proton magnetic moment distributions and various assumptions about the neutron charge density. Dashed curves are for a neutron charge density that is approximately equal and opposite to that of the proton for $r>1$ fermi, and a root-mean-square radius of the neutron anomalous magnetic moment given by the label $\bar{r}$.

40% are permitted by existing experiments and their interpretation.

It thus appears that both the elastic and inelastic electron-deuteron scattering results agree reasonably well with the assumption that the neutron has vanishing electric charge density, and the same magnetic moment distribution as the proton. The latter assumption is also in agreement with the theoretical indication[9] that the nucleon anomalous magnetic moment density is primarily an isotopic vector. However, a vanishing neutron charge density is in conflict with the idea underlying the choice of Eq. (4): that f_N should be

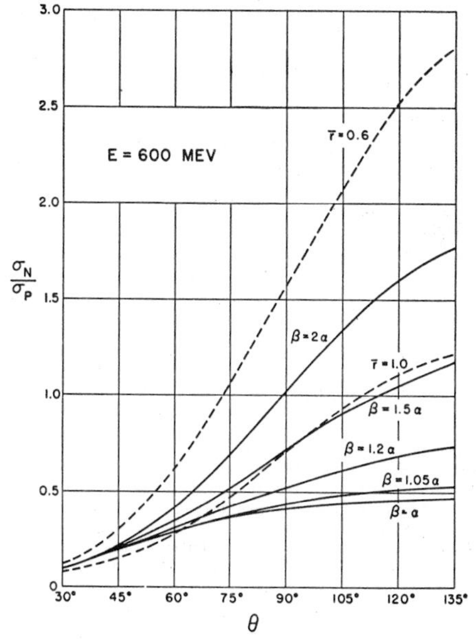

FIG. 4. Same as Fig. 3, for 600 Mev.

roughly equal to $-f_P$ for values of r that are fairly large, but not so large that f_N and f_P are uninterestingly small. Inspection of Fig. 1 shows that β must not be less than about 2α in order for f_N to have this property. While such a large value of β appears to be ruled out by the elastic electron-deuteron scattering results, it is possible (although unlikely) that it could be allowed either by distortion of the free nucleon charge densities in the deuteron bound state, or by unexpectedly large Fourier components of high momentum in the deuteron wave function that cancel off the decrease in $(1+R)^2$ as q increases. With this possibility in mind, σ_N/σ_P was calculated for $\beta=2\alpha$ and the neutron F_2 given by Eq. (2) with α replaced by a new parameter γ. The dashed curves in Figs. 3 and 4 correspond to choices of γ such that the root-mean-square radius of the neutron anomalous moment distribution is 0.6 or 1.0 fermi. As expected, the smaller radius greatly increases σ_N, while the larger radius decreases σ_N to such an extent that it would be difficult to distinguish experimentally from a neutron with a much smaller value of β and moment radius 0.8 fermi.

Essentially the same results are obtained if a different but equivalent form is chosen for f_P in place of Eq. (1),[14,15]

$$f_P'(r)=(\lambda\alpha^2/4\pi r)\exp(-\alpha r)-(\lambda-1)\delta(\mathbf{r}). \tag{9}$$

The Fourier transform of Eq. (9) is

$$F_P'(q)=[\alpha^2-(\lambda-1)q^2]/(\alpha^2+q^2). \tag{10}$$

If now we choose $\lambda=1.20$ and $\alpha=3.32$ fermi^{-1}, the root-mean-square radius of f_P' is 0.81 fermi; also F_P' of Eq. (10) agrees with F_P of Eq. (2) within 1% over the presently accessible experimental range of q from 0 to 4 fermi^{-1}, and so gives an equally good account of the experiments. With these values of the parameters, f_P' of Eq. (9) agrees with f_P of Eq. (1) within 10% for r between 1 and 2 fermi, which is the interesting range of r so far as a comparison of f_N with $-f_P'$ is concerned.

We conclude, then, that present indications favor a vanishing neutron charge density and an anomalous moment distribution like that of the proton. In order to have neutron and proton charge densities equal and opposite for r greater than about 1 fermi, it would be necessary to assume (1) either that there is considerable distortion of the free nucleon charge distributions in the deuteron, or that the deuteron wave function has hitherto unsuspectedly large Fourier components of high momentum, and (2) that the anomalous moment distribution of the neutron is substantially larger in spatial extent than that of the proton.

ACKNOWLEDGMENTS

The author takes pleasure in thanking Professor S. D. Drell, Professor R. Hofstadter, Professor W. K. H. Panofsky, and Mr. R. Blankenbecler, for helpful discussions and for access to as yet unpublished information.

[15] E. Clementel and C. Villi, Nuovo cimento 4, 1207 (1956).

PAPER 46

Electromagnetic Structure of the Proton and Neutron*

R. HOFSTADTER, F. BUMILLER, AND M. R. YEARIAN

Department of Physics and High-Energy Physics Laboratory, Stanford University, Stanford, California

I. INTRODUCTION

OVER the past few years high-energy electron-scattering measurements have demonstrated clearly the existence of deviations from point-nucleon scattering laws.[1] For the proton, represented by a point charge and a point magnetic moment, the scattering law is given by a formula due to Rosenbluth.[2] At large angles and high energies, deviations between the observed scattering and that given by the point Rosenbluth formula exceed a factor of ten. Recent work has shown that large deviations from point scattering also occur in the case of the neutron.[3–6] The results obtained in the proton and neutron investigations have been interpreted as evidence of the finite sizes of the nucleons.[1,7–9]

In the first part of this paper we try to summarize the results already established, as well as some of the most recent findings of the electron-scattering method. In the second part, we present a brief account of the significance of the observed deviations from point-nucleon scattering.

II. REVIEW OF EXPERIMENTAL FINDINGS

We take the point of view that the deviations from point scattering may be attributed entirely to finite structure effects in the nucleons. Although it is possible that some part of the deviations can be assigned to a breakdown of electrodynamics at small distances,[7–9] the phenomenological description of the results which we give is not influenced by a choice of either of these alternative explanations, and in many respects the two interpretations are presently indistinguishable. For convenience we adopt the language of finite size effects and return to this fundamental question later in the review.

By a "point" we mean any structure contained entirely within a sphere, whose radius is less than or equal to one nucleon Compton wavelength $= 2.1\times10^{-14}$ cm.

A. Proton

The first observations (Fig. 1) of a finite size of the proton were made by Hofstadter and McAllister.[7,10] Experimental points at the larger angles lie about a factor 1.6 below the theoretical Rosenbluth scattering law for a point proton. These results are not due to instrumental effects as was shown by examining the scattering at 100 Mev, at which energy the finite size effects were expected to play only a small role. At 100 Mev it was indeed found that the angular scattering distribution follows the Rosenbluth law quite satisfactorily,[10] as shown in Fig. 2.

In both Fig. 1 and Fig. 2 the Mott curve is exhibited.

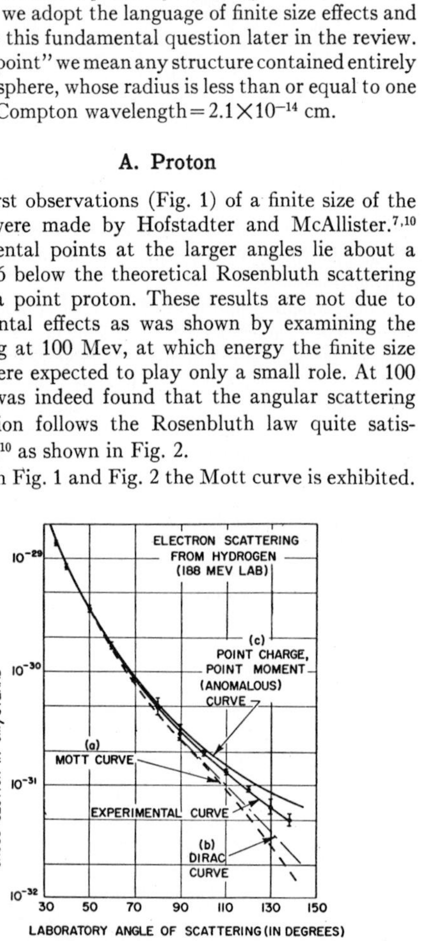

FIG. 1. The Mott curve corresponding to Eq. (1) is labeled (*a*). The Dirac curve (*b*) is given by the Rosenbluth formula, Eq. (2), with $\kappa=0$. Curve (*c*), the "Rosenbluth" curve, is obtained from Eq. (2) with $\kappa=1.79$ and takes into account the full effect of the proton's anomalous magnetic moment. If the proton could be represented by a point charge and a point magnetic moment, curve (*c*) would give the appropriate angular behavior. The experimental points lie below the curve (*c*) and therefore show that the proton has a spread-out structure.

* Supported jointly by the Office of Naval Research, U. S. Atomic Energy Commission, and U. S. Air Force, through the Office of Scientific Research of the Air Research and Development Command.

[1] R. Hofstadter, Ann. Rev. Nuclear Sci. **7**, 231 (1957). This article provides a recent review of electron scattering by nucleons and nuclei.

[2] M. N. Rosenbluth, Phys. Rev. **79**, 615 (1950).

[3] Blankenbecler, Hofstadter, and Yearian. This work was reported in a review article by R. Hofstadter, Revs. Modern Phys. **28**, 214 (1956).

[4] M. R. Yearian and R. Hofstadter, reference 1, pp. 267–271. (See also Proceedings of Seventh Annual Rochester Conference, 1957.)

[5] M. R. Yearian and R. Hofstadter, Bull. Am. Phys. Soc. Ser. II, **2**, 389 (1957).

[6] M. R. Yearian and R. Hofstadter, Phys. Rev. **110**, 552 (1958).

[7] R. Hofstadter and R. W. McAllister, Phys. Rev. **98**, 217 (1955).

[8] Yennie, Lévy, and Ravenhall, Revs. Modern Phys. **29**, 144 (1957).

[9] R. Hofstadter, Revs. Modern Phys. **28**, 214 (1956).

[10] R. W. McAllister and R. Hofstadter, Phys. Rev. **102**, 851 (1956).

The Mott distribution is given by the scattering law

$$\left(\frac{d\sigma}{d\Omega}\right)_{\text{Mott}}=\left(\frac{e^2}{2E_0}\right)^2\frac{\cos^2\theta/2}{\sin^4\theta/2}\times\frac{1}{1+(2E_0/Mc^2)\sin^2\theta/2}=\sigma_{NS}\qquad(1)$$

and is abbreviated by the symbol σ_{NS}. Thus, θ is the laboratory angle of scattering, and E_0 is the laboratory energy of the incident electron. M is the mass of the proton. Mott scattering is expected for a point proton with a charge $(+e)$ but without a magnetic moment. In the derivation of Eq. (1) the *electron* is assumed to have its usual charge and magnetic moment.[1] The presence of the proton's magnetic moment accounts for the additional scattering of a real proton over and above the Mott scattering for a point charge. The fact that the experimental curve (Fig. 1) lies between the Mott curve and the Rosenbluth point-charge, point-magnetic moment curve is taken as the evidence of finite structure in the proton. The ratio of the experimental scattering cross section to the Rosenbluth point-scattering cross section is called the square of the "form factor."[1,9]

The Rosenbluth point scattering curve is

$$\left(\frac{d\sigma}{d\Omega}\right)=\sigma_{NS}\left\{1+\frac{\hbar^2q^2}{4M^2c^2}[2(1+\kappa)^2\tan^2\theta/2+\kappa^2]\right\},\qquad(2)$$

where

$$q=\frac{2}{\lambda\!\!\!^{-}}\frac{\sin\theta/2}{[1+(2E_0/Mc^2)\sin^2\theta/2]^{\frac{1}{2}}}=\frac{2E_0}{\hbar c}\frac{\sin\theta/2}{[1+(2E_0/Mc^2)\sin^2\theta/2]^{\frac{1}{2}}}.\qquad(3)$$

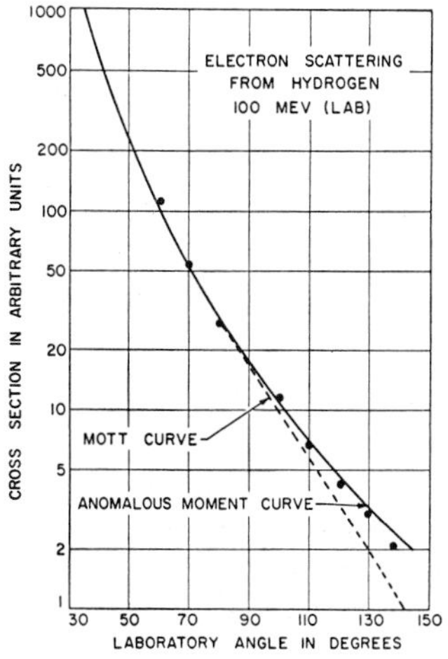

FIG. 2. At 100 Mev the effects of finite size are small and the experimental points, shown as black dots, lie very close to the point Rosenbluth curve, the upper of the two theoretical curves drawn in the figure.

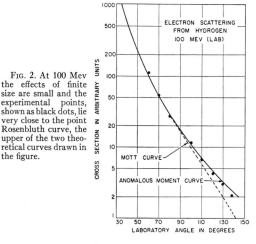

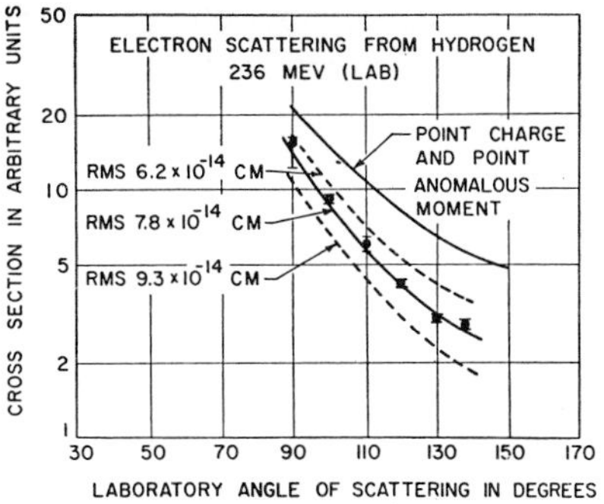

FIG. 3. Experimental points taken at an incident electron energy of 236 Mev are shown. The point-charge, point-moment curve is shown for comparison along with theoretical curves allowing for finite size effects. An rms of 0.78×10^{-13} cm gives good agreement with the experimental data. The best-fitting curve was chosen on the basis of relative cross sections rather than on absolute cross-section values. The choice 0.78×10^{-13} cm is in good agreement with the data in Figs. 1 and 2.

Here, $\kappa(=1.79)$ is associated with the Pauli or anomalous part of the proton's magnetic moment, and q is the so-called electron's (four-vector) energy-momentum-transfer.[1] Rosenbluth[2] and others[1,8,11] have shown that finite size effects or equivalently phenomenological form factors can be introduced into Eq. (2) as follows:

$$\left(\frac{d\sigma}{d\Omega}\right)=\sigma_{NS}\left\{F_1^2+\frac{\hbar^2q^2}{4M^2c^2}[2(F_1+\kappa F_2)^2\times\tan^2\theta/2+\kappa^2F_2^2]\right\}.\qquad(4)$$

F_1 and F_2 are the phenomenological form factors and are individually functions of the invariant momentum-transfer q. F_1 is associated with the Dirac charge and intrinsic magnetic moment of the proton and F_2 is associated with the Pauli part of the moment (κ). F_2 is usually associated with the mesonic cloud making up the outer parts of the proton's electromagnetic structure, and, in principle, can be obtained from a meson field theory. Early attempts to calculate the form factors F_1, F_2 were made by Rosenbluth[2] on the basis of a weak-coupling theory.

Further experiments on the proton were carried out by McAllister and Hofstadter[10] at an electron energy of 236 Mev. Their results are shown in Fig. 3. The figure indicates that an rms radius of the proton equal to $(0.78\pm0.20)\times10^{-13}$ cm provides a good fit with the experimental data. This "size" was in good agreement with the radius $(0.70\pm0.24)\times10^{-13}$ cm obtained in the 188-Mev experiment.[7]

The numerical results were arrived at by assuming that

$$F_1=F_2(\equiv F_P)\qquad(5)$$

[11] For important contributions to the development of Eq. (4), see reference 8 and the references therein.

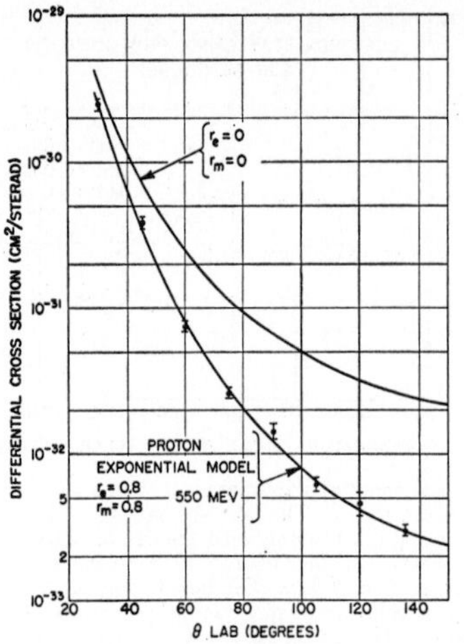

FIG. 4. The experimental electron-proton-scattering data of Chambers and Hofstadter[12] observed at an incident energy of 550 Mev. The Rosenbluth point-charge curve is shown above. Drawn through the experimental points is a theoretical curve with $F_1=F_2$ and a choice of an exponential model of the proton, Eq. (8), with appropriate choices of the rms radii. The best fit is obtained with $r_e=r_m=0.80\times10^{-13}$ cm.

as functions of q and effectively using the shape-independent approximation.

$$F=1-(q^2a^2/6)+\cdots, \tag{6}$$

where "a" is the rms radius of the charge or magnetic moment distribution. Equation (6) can be used where the higher terms in the expansion can be neglected, as in the case of the early data. F is related more generally to a density distribution through the Fourier transform[1,8,9]

$$F=\frac{4\pi}{q}\int_0^\infty \rho(\mathbf{r})\exp(i\mathbf{q}\cdot\mathbf{r})d^3\mathbf{r}, \tag{7}$$

which applies in the nonrelativistic limit in which $\rho(\mathbf{r})$ is the static density distribution and is a function of radius. When only small values of qa are involved, the expression (7) can be replaced by Eq. (6) and a size (rms radius) determined. In the experiments reported here, it is not practical to use Eq. (6), because many higher terms are involved in the expansion, i.e., it is possible to determine more than one parameter from the experiments. It would, of course, be desirable to determine "a" carefully in the shape-independent approximation, but since the deviations from point scattering are then small, the experiments require high accuracy and are difficult to perform.

The assumption, Eq. (5), that $F_1=F_2$ is an arbitrary one. However, the early experiments were in very good agreement with this assignment. Subsequent events have proved that $F_1=F_2$ in the current range of momentum transfers is a surprisingly good approximation. At large angles, where $\tan\theta/2\gtrsim1$, and at high energies, it becomes possible to distinguish magnetic moment scattering from charge scattering. Hence it becomes possible to find F_1 and F_2 separately.

Using a new magnetic spectrometer, Chambers and Hofstadter[12] carried out a detailed series of experiments on the proton extending to an energy of 550 Mev with scattering angles lying between 30° and 135° in the laboratory frame. These experiments showed at once very large deviations from point scattering. Typical data are reproduced in Fig. 4 and show the large reduction from point scattering (upper curve) due to finite size effects. Drawn through the experimental points is a

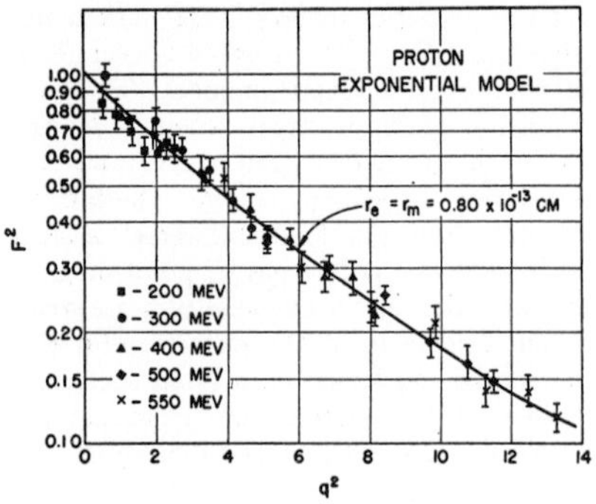

FIG. 5. $F_P{}^2(F_P=F_1=F_2)$ is plotted against q^2 in units of 10^{+26} cm^{-2}. The solid line represents the $F_P{}^2$ curve for an exponential model of a proton with $r_e=r_m=0.80\times10^{-13}$ cm. The experimental points are those of Chambers and Hofstadter.[12] The fitting procedure is described in the text.

theoretical curve calculated with Eq. (4) for $F_1=F_2=F_P$, where F_P corresponds by Eq. (7) to the transform of a charge density (and magnetic moment density) belonging to the exponential family

$$\rho=\rho_0\exp(-12^{\frac{1}{2}}r/a), \tag{8}$$

and thus F_P is

$$F_P(qa)=\frac{1}{[1+(q^2a^2/12)]^2}. \tag{9}$$

The fit is quite good. The agreement with experiment is excellent at all other energies as well. However, an equally good fit with experiment could be made with a Gaussian charge density (and Gaussian magnetic moment density) which leads also to a Gaussian form factor. Over the range of q values studied in these experiments, the exponential model, with rms radius 0.80×10^{-13} cm of the charge cloud (F_1), and rms radius 0.80×10^{-13} cm of the magnetic moment cloud, was indistinguishable from Gaussian density distributions, when a required change was made in the rms radii. For Gaussians the rms radii were very close to 0.70×10^{-13} cm. Figures 5 and 6 show the two corresponding graphs

[12] E. E. Chambers and R. Hofstadter, Phys. Rev. **103**, 1454 (1956).

of F^2 *versus* q^2 for the two models. The fitting procedure used in preparing Figs. 4–6 was based on the shape of the angular distributions and not on absolute values of the cross sections. Although absolute cross sections were obtained by Chambers and Hofstadter, they were not sufficiently accurate to distinguish between such models. Therefore, in fitting data at various energies, slight adjustments of the F^2 ratios were made by sliding the entire experimental distribution at a given energy up and down until the best match between theory and experiment was obtained. The just-discernible variations in F^2 between Figs. 5 and 6 represent the effects of such shifts. It also proved possible, with $F_1=F_2$, to find other one-parameter models which could fit the data. Such models are shown in Fig. 7, where $4\pi r^2\rho$ is plotted against radius. A model (Yukawa I) which does not fit is also shown. A uniform charge distribution cannot be made to fit the data.

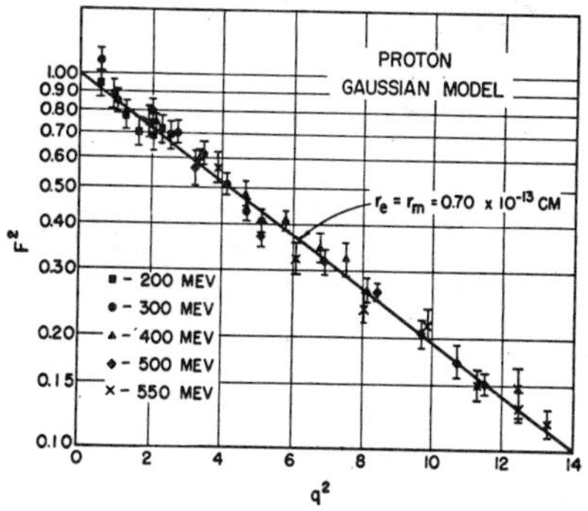

FIG. 6. This figure is similar to Fig. 5 except that a Gaussian model of the proton is employed to calculate F_P^2. On the basis of the data in Figs. 5 and 6, either the exponential or Gaussian model is satisfactory. Higher energies are needed to decide between these two models (see following).

When $F_1=F_2$, it is possible to plot a single curve showing F^2 at all energies. When $F_1 \neq F_2$ this is not possible, and a separate curve must be prepared for each energy. Figure 8, from Chambers and Hofstadter, shows an attempt to satisfy the experimental data with a model in which the F_1 corresponds to a point ($r_e=0$), and the F_2 is adjusted to give the best fit obtainable under these conditions with a Gaussian model ($r_m=1.0 \times 10^{-13}$ cm). No shifting of the theoretical curves will permit a fit with the data. Other simple models for F_2 with $r_e=0$ were also tried without success. It was concluded that a point charge and spread-out magnetic moment would not yield agreement with the experimental results. Small magnetic radii were also unsuitable, as shown by a typical choice reproduced in Fig. 9. Chambers[13] considered many combinations of different

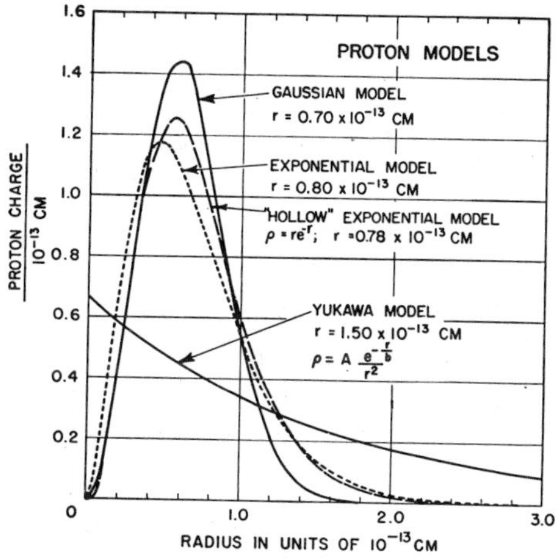

FIG. 7. This figure shows a plot of $4\pi r^2\rho$ *versus* radial distance from the center of the proton. Three models are shown (Gaussian, exponential, and hollow exponential) which fit the Chambers-Hofstadter experiments. $4\pi r^2\rho$ is a quantity proportional to the amount of charge in a shell at radius r. The Yukawa distribution, also shown in the figure, cannot be made to fit the data with any choice of radius. For these models, F_1 is taken equal to F_2.

choices for F_1 and F_2, i.e., $F_1 \neq F_2$, and concluded that within certain experimental errors no choice would fit the data as well as $F_1=F_2$, for the successful models discussed above (and reproduced in Fig. 7). In Fig. 7 values of $4\pi r^2\rho$ are plotted in preference to ρ itself, because the experiments are presently not sensitive to values of ρ at small radii. The plot in Fig. 7 de-emphasizes the density at small radii and is more useful.

The ratio, F_1/F_2, may be found independently of any model by comparing two cross sections at two different energies and two different angles, such that the momen-

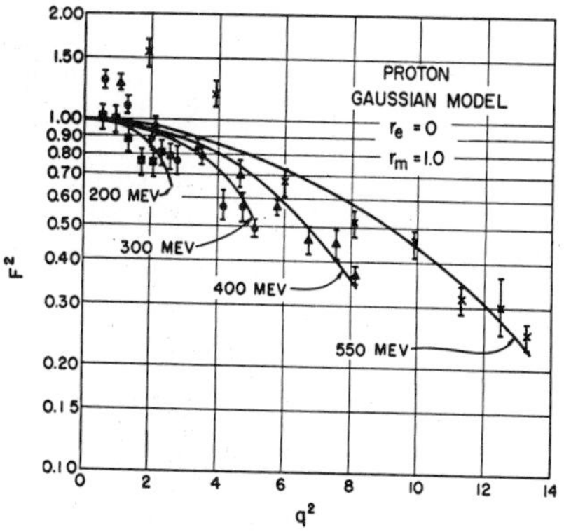

FIG. 8. This figure shows an attempt to fit the Chambers-Hofstadter results, at all the energies used in the experiments, with a Gaussian model such that $r_e=0$ and r_m is chosen to give the best agreement with experiment. $r_m=1.0 \times 10^{-13}$ cm for this case. The fit is not satisfactory and this model can be excluded. With $F_1 \neq F_2$, as in this case, separate theoretical curves are required for the various values of incident energy.

[13] E. E. Chambers, "Electron-proton scattering at electron energies up to 550 Mev," Ph.D. thesis, Stanford University (May, 1956).

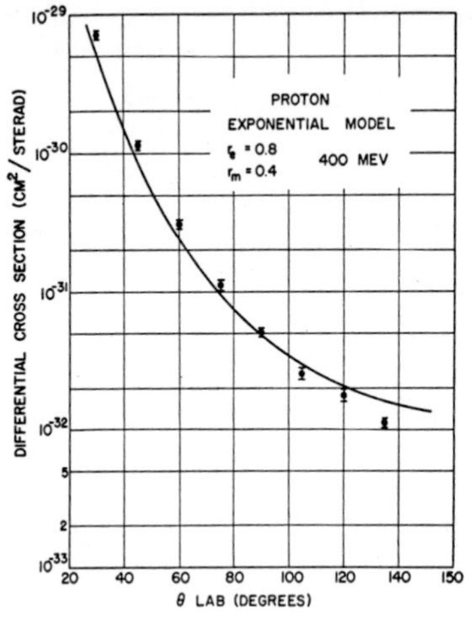

FIG. 9. A small magnetic radius of the proton cannot be made to satisfy the experimental data at 400 Mev. Similar results hold at other energies. The experimental points are those of Chambers and Hofstadter.[12]

tum transfer q is the same at both cross section determinations. At $q^2 \cong 4\times10^{26}$ cm^{-2}, a value of $F_1/F_2 = 1.1\pm0.2$ was found from the experiments.[12] At $q^2 = 9.33\times10^{26}$ cm^{-2}, $F_1/F_2 = 1.04\pm0.2$.[14]

Using the fact that magnetic moment scattering falls off more slowly at large angles than charge scattering, the large-angle, high-energy data may be analyzed to find $F_1+\kappa F_2$. Since $\kappa=1.79$, the data can yield F_2, if F_1 is known even approximately. Now, when F_2 becomes known approximately, e.g., by the method outlined above, the situation may be turned about by studying the small-angle data as a function of energy. At small angles the magnetic scattering is essentially zero, and hence F_1 may be investigated alone, that is, the scattering is practically purely charge scattering. Although F_2 enters into the cross-section calculations at small angles, the magnetic scattering (involving F_2) is small, so that even large errors in determining F_2 will not affect the results for F_1. Thus, by a series of successive steps first at small angles and then at large angles, F_1 and F_2 may be determined separately.

These procedures are demonstrated in Fig. 10, where

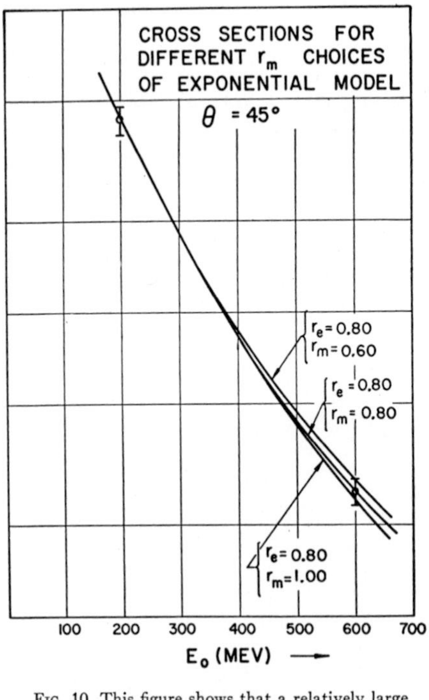

FIG. 10. This figure shows that a relatively large uncertainty in the value of F_2 (or in the choice of magnetic radius) has very little influence on the small-angle electron-proton cross sections as a function of energy. The experimental points represent the recent data of Bumiller and Hofstadter.[14]

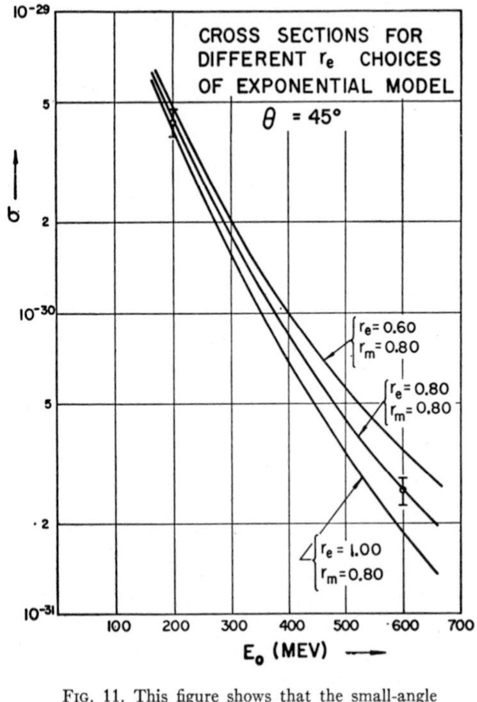

FIG. 11. This figure shows that the small-angle data (45°) are sensitive to the choice of F_1 (or the choice of electrical radius). Recent experimental data of Bumiller and Hofstadter,[14] shown in the figure, support the choice of $r_e = r_m = 0.80\times10^{-13}$ cm and an exponential model of the proton.

[14] F. Bumiller and R. Hofstadter (to be published).

the small influence on F_1 of a relatively large uncertainty in F_2 is shown. In this figure the magnetic rms radius is allowed to vary, for an exponential model, from $r_m=0.60\times10^{-13}$ cm to $r_m=1.0\times10^{-13}$ cm, while the cross section at 45° is shown as a function of E_0. The large changes in r_m barely produce an error as large as the experimental uncertainty. On the other hand, the recent 45° data,[14] shown in Figs. 10 and 11, show that, for an exponential model, the charge rms radius must be close to 0.80×10^{-13} cm. This result agrees very well with the earlier conclusions of Chambers and Hofstadter.

From this presentation it has become clear that one need not talk of models. It is sufficient to find F_1 and F_2 separately, as already indicated. We have used the model approach simply because it provides a convenient mnemonic device for calculating the F's under all conditions of scattering. If preferred the reader may use the Fourier transform [Eq. (9)] without ever thinking of the model. In this way, however, he loses sight of the spatial spreading of the density functions, which is especially of interest in connection with the charge densities of light nuclei, where the proton's spatial extent definitely contributes to the spreading of the nuclear charge throughout the nuclear volume and surface. While we may speak of a model, we wish it to be understood that we really mean that the Fourier transform of this model provides phenomenological form factors fitting the experimental data.

The value $r_e=0.80\times10^{-13}$ cm has been confirmed by McAllister,[15] who measured an absolute cross section for electrons of 189.6 Mev scattering from protons at 60° and found a value of $(1.20\pm0.07)\times10^{-30}$ cm²/sterad. In this shape-independent determination, McAllister found a radius of 0.75×10^{-13} cm consistent with the more accurate determination $(0.80\pm0.04)\times10^{-13}$ cm discussed above.[14]

An independent analysis of the elastic scattering of electrons by the deuteron has been carried out by McIntyre[16] and by McIntyre and Dhar.[17] In these experiments the magnetic effects are very small and the charge scattering appears essentially by itself. If it is assumed that the *neutron charge density* distribution does not influence the scattering of electrons by deuterons, which appears to be a very reasonable assumption from the experiments on the neutron-electron interaction,[18–23] the charge size of the proton is determined and is consistent with the rms size 0.80×10^{-13} cm. In fact, the experiment may be turned about[17] and used to determine the neutron-proton potential in the deuteron. At present, however, the deuteron elastic data are not sufficiently accurate to decide between various commonly used potentials.

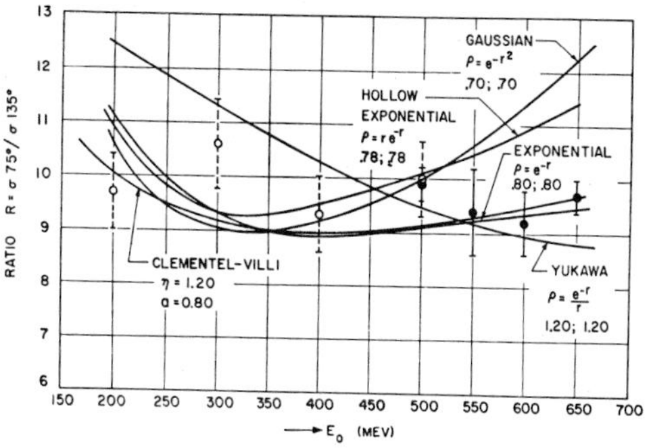

FIG. 12. The ratio of electron-proton cross sections at 75° and 135° is plotted as a function of incident energy. This type of measurement does not require a knowledge of absolute cross sections. The data of Bumiller and Hofstadter[14] are shown as solid circles while earlier data of Chambers and Hofstadter[12] are shown as hollow circles. The new data eliminate a Gaussian model with $r_e=r_m=0.70\times10^{-13}$ cm. The hollow exponential model ($r_e=r_m=0.78\times10^{-13}$ cm) is also excluded. The Yukawa model is excluded by this figure as well as other data (not shown in the figure). The exponential model with radii 0.80×10^{-13} cm still provides a satisfactory fit with all the experiments.

Recent extension of the proton data by Bumiller and Hofstadter[14] now makes it possible to distinguish between the various models proposed by Chambers and Hofstadter.[12] Figure 12 shows the behavior of the ratio R

$$R=\left(\frac{d\sigma}{d\Omega}\right)_{75°}\bigg/\left(\frac{d\sigma}{d\Omega}\right)_{135°} \qquad (10)$$

as a function of the incident energy for electron scattering from the proton. The experimental ratio is found to be almost constant and lies between 9.0 and 10.0 from 200 to 650 Mev. The dashed experimental points (hollow circles) show some of the Chambers-Hofstadter results and do not distinguish between the models (except for the Yukawa case, which provides a poor fit at small angles). The new data in Fig. 12 (solid points) now serve to distinguish between the various models and show that, for $F_1=F_2$, the exponential model with rms radii, $r_e=0.80\times10^{-13}$ cm and $r_m=0.80\times10^{-13}$ cm, fits the data very well. As explained above this should be understood to mean that Eq. (9) is to be used as the appropriate phenomenological form factor. Its square is given in Fig. 13 and extends to larger q^2 values than the older data.

A systematic attempt to study values of the total F^2 for $F_1\neq F_2$ and two different models is illustrated in Figs. 14 and 15. At 600 Mev and 45° the choices r_e, r_m, shown in the third column, are made for form factors of the type given by Eq. (9). The values of the total (form

[15] R. W. McAllister, Phys. Rev. **104**, 1494 (1956).
[16] J. A. McIntyre, Phys. Rev. **103**, 1464 (1956).
[17] J. A. McIntyre and S. Dhar, Phys. Rev. **106**, 1074 (1957).
[18] E. Fermi and L. Marshall, Phys. Rev. **72**, 1139 (1947); Hamermesh, Ringo, and Wattenberg, Phys. Rev. **85**, 483 (1952).
[19] Havens, Rainwater, and Rabi, Phys. Rev. **82**, 345 (1951).
[20] D. J. Hughes and M. T. Burgy, Phys. Rev. **81**, 498 (1951); Ringo, Hughes, and Burgy, Phys. Rev. **84**, 1160 (1951).
[21] Hughes, Harvey, Goldberg, and Stafne, Phys. Rev. **90**, 497 (1953); Melkonian, Rustad, and Havens, Bull. Am. Phys. Soc. Ser. II, **1**, 62 (1956).
[22] B. T. Feld, *Experimental Nuclear Physics*, edited by E. Segré (John Wiley and Sons, Inc., New York, 1953), Vol. II, p. 208. This article gives a summary of the experiments. See also Crouch, Krohn, and Ringo, Phys. Rev. **102**, 1321 (1956).
[23] See also reference 8 for a discussion of neutron size.

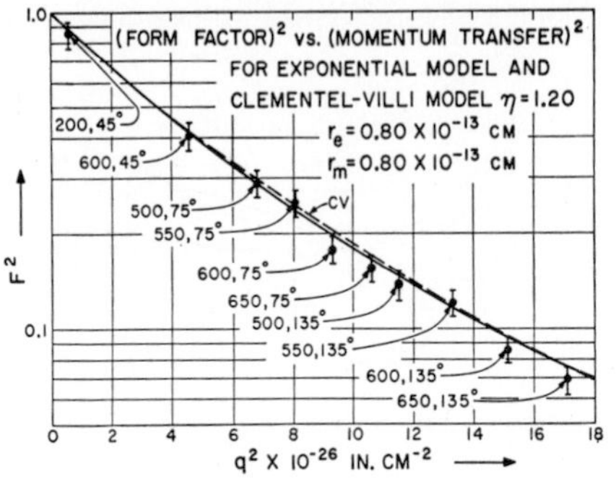

FIG. 13. The value of $F_P{}^2(F_1=F_2=F_P)$ is shown as ordinate in this figure and the abscissa is q^2 in appropriate units. This curve is similar to the one shown in Fig. 5 but is here extended to larger values of q^2 by the new experiments of Bumiller and Hofstadter.[14] Two equivalent choices of model are made: the exponential model and the Clementel-Villi model. The Clementel-Villi model is described in the text [Eqs. (11) to (13)]. The present experiments do not distinguish between these models.

factor)^2, i.e., the ratio of the calculated cross section to the point cross section, are shown in the fourth column. The absolute experimental value is shown in the fifth column in bold numerals with values permitted by experimental error in light numerals. The choices in the third column in bold numerals are permitted. The other choices are eliminated. Similar calculations are made for a Gaussian form factor, shown in the sixth column. The bars through the bold numerals mean that these possible choices have been eliminated, because such choices do not fit the experimental data at other angles and energies (see Fig. 15, 650 Mev, 135°). Thus no Gaussian will do.

In Fig. 15 a similar table shows that the Gaussian is unsatisfactory. The table also shows that only the form factor, corresponding to $r_e=0.80\times10^{-13}$ cm, $r_m=0.80\times10^{-13}$ cm for an exponential model, Eq. (9), is satisfactory, within, of course, the present experimental error.

Such studies do not preclude the possibility of finding other models which fit the data. In spite of the fact that

E_0 MEV	θ	r_e	r_m	TOTAL F^2 EXPONENTIAL	EXPERIMENTAL ± 10 %	GAUSSIAN
		0.6	0.6	.597		.570
		0.8	**0.6**	**.448**		~~**.408**~~
		1.0	0.6	.336		.208
		0.6	0.8	.562	.450	.530
600	45°	**0.8**	**0.8**	**.411**	**.410**	~~**.372**~~
		1.0	0.8	.302	.370	.243
		0.6	1.0	.534		.500
		0.8	**1.0**	**.386**		.340
		1.0	1.0	.276		.220

FIG. 14. The chart shows, by example, how different proton models may be distinguished between by the experimental data at 600 Mev and 45° (5th column). Descriptions of the method and the various columns in the figure are given in the text.

many models have been examined, it is still possible that one with a singularity at the origin will satisfy the experiments. It is probable, however, that this can occur only if the singularity contains a small fraction of the total charge. If the region about the singularity contains a large fraction of the protonic charge, we believe it unlikely that a model fitting the data could have been missed.

As an example of the above remarks, we consider a model having some theoretical justification. This model has been proposed by Clementel and Villi.[24] For this model (abbreviated C-V)

$$\rho(\mathbf{r})=\frac{\eta k^2}{4\pi r}\exp(-kr)-(\eta-1)\delta(\mathbf{r}), \qquad (11)$$

where $-(\eta-1)\delta(\mathbf{r})$ represents a negative singularity (a negative point charge) at the origin and $(\eta-1)$ determines the numerical fractional amount of proton charge placed in the singularity. The spread-out part of the C-V model is a Yukawa II distribution with η-total

E_0 MEV	θ	r_e	r_m	TOTAL F^2 EXPONENTIAL	EXPERIMENTAL ± 10 %	GAUSSIAN
		0.6	0.6	.194		.146
		0.8	0.6	.143		.096
		1.0	0.6	.116		~~**.072**~~
		0.6	0.8	.115	.080	~~**.071**~~
650	135°	**0.8**	**0.8**	**.076**	**.070**	.036
		1.0	0.8	.056	.060	.022
		0.6	1.0	~~**.076**~~		.040
		0.8	1.0	.045		.015
		1.0	1.0	.029		.006

FIG. 15. This figure is similar to Fig. 14 except that the experimental data refer to 650 Mev and 135°. An explanation of the table will be found in the text.

proton charges and has a low order positive singularity at the origin. The model provides a form factor

$$F(q)=\frac{1+\left(\dfrac{1-\eta}{k^2}\right)q^2}{1+q^2/k^2}, \qquad (12)$$

and the rms radius is found to be

$$a=(1/k)(6\eta)^{\frac{1}{2}}. \qquad (13)$$

As mentioned above, the C-V model may be considered a physical way of citing the form factor expression Eq. (12). Calculations with the C-V model (subject to $F_1=F_2$) show that an excellent fit with all the data, extending between 100 Mev and 650 Mev, is obtained with $\eta=1.2$ and $a=0.80\times10^{-13}$ cm. The theoretical C-V curve is shown in Fig. 13 as a dashed line. Thus a negative point charge with 20% of the value of the

[24] E. Clementel and C. Villi, Nuovo cimento 4, 1207 (1956).

proton charge can be placed at the center of the physical proton, and a positive spread-out charge amounting to 1.2 proton charges can be distributed around the negative point center as a Yukawa II cloud. The form factors, corresponding to this C-V distribution and to an exponential model with rms radius 0.80×10^{-13} cm are indistinguishable within experimental error, as far as a value of $q^2=17$, which is as far as the present experiments go. Since the C-V ($\eta=1.2$, $a=0.80\times10^{-13}$ cm) F's resemble closely the F's for an exponential model ($a=0.80\times10^{-13}$ cm), the F_1 may be chosen to belong to one model and an F_2 to the other. Within experimental error F_2 may also be selected from other closely fitting models, without prejudice.

It is not claimed that an actual proton resembles the C-V model, but this example demonstrates that *non-*

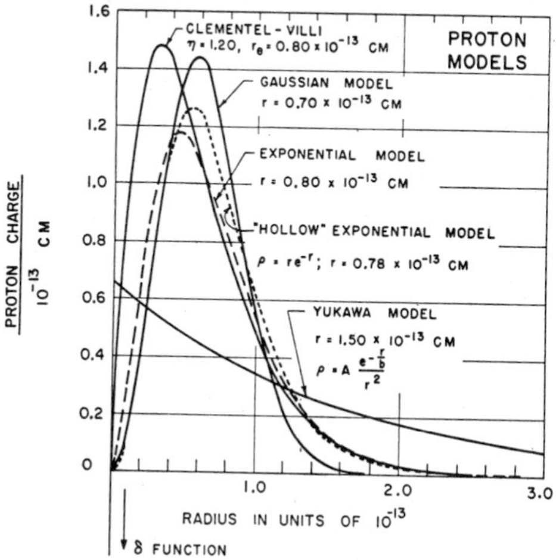

FIG. 16. A plot ($4\pi r^2\rho$) similar to Fig. 7 is shown. However, this figure shows also the Clementel-Villi model which fits the experimental data quite well (see Fig. 13). In the C-V model a negative δ function and a positive Yukawa II distribution are used and the density function is not monotonic. The C-V model fits best with $\eta=1.20$ and $a=0.80\times10^{-13}$ cm (see text).

monotonic density distributions can be made to represent the experimental data. In such cases the $4\pi r^2\rho$ distributions, similar to those shown in Fig. 7, will be nearly the same outside a certain small volume near the center of the proton. For example, Fig. 16 compares the C-V ($\eta=1.2$) and exponential models with $F_1=F_2$ and $r_e=r_m=0.80\times10^{-13}$ cm for each of the models. Outside a radius 0.4×10^{-13} cm, the C-V and exponential models have essentially the same $4\pi\rho r^2$ behavior. In Fig. 13 the C-V values of F^2 are plotted and are essentially indistinguishable from those of the exponential model. The significance of this example is that the present experiments probe the outside of the proton and are noncommittal about details in the central ($r\lesssim0.4\times10^{-13}$ cm) parts of that structure. However, it is unlikely that a monotonic type of singularity exists in the center of the proton containing more than a small fraction of the proton's charge.

This material describes the information accumulated up to the present concerning the proton's structure. The interpretation has been carried out using the Rosenbluth formula, Eq. (4), including the phenomenological form factors F_1 and F_2. Drell and Ruderman[25] and Drell and Fubini[26] have shown that the Rosenbluth representation, including F_1 and F_2, should be accurate within a few percent up to energies approaching 1.0 Bev, even at large angles.

B. Neutron

Experiments on the neutron[27] were motivated by a desire to see whether the small neutron size (essentially zero), found in experiments on the neutron-electron interaction,[18–23] implies as well a small rms radius of the magnetic moment cloud in the neutron. Early ideas[27] indicated that a study of the inelastic breakup of the deuteron by energetic electrons might provide an excellent way of probing the magnetic structure in the neutron. Thus a nucleon scattering electrons with high momentum-transfer (q) and at a large angle ($\tan\theta/2\gg1$), does so by virtue of its magnetic moment. That the "charge" scattering is small under these conditions is shown by the Rosenbluth equations (2) or (4). Hence proton scattering should not exhibit a much greater cross section than neutron scattering, if both nucleons possess approximately the same magnetic moment structure. The only reason that a proton should scatter with a greater cross section than a neutron is traceable, for the extreme conditions described in the foregoing, to the large numerical value of its magnetic moment ($\mu_P=2.79$ nm; $\mu_N=-1.91$ nm). Equation (4) for a proton and Eq. (14), for a free neutron, derived from Eq. (4)

$$\left(\frac{d\sigma}{d\Omega}\right)_N=\sigma_{NS}F_{2N}{}^2\kappa_N{}^2\frac{\hbar^2q^2}{4M^2c^2}[2\tan^2\theta/2+1], \quad (14)$$

by placing $eF_1{}^N\cong0$ (static charge and second moment for the neutron are both zero), show that the scattering cross section is proportional to the square of the nucleon's magnetic moment. In thus comparing the scattering by a free neutron and a free proton, the neutron-proton ratio would be approximately $(1.91)^2/(2.79)^2=0.45$, if the nucleons should have similar magnetic structures. If the neutron should have a point magnetic moment while the proton is spread out, the ratio at 500 Mev and 135° would be 3.0 instead of 0.45! This follows, because the proton's (form factor)^2 results in a reduction of the proton cross section to approximately 0.15 times the point cross section at 500 Mev and 135°. A deviation

[25] S. Drell and M. Ruderman, Phys. Rev. **106**, 561 (1957).
[26] S. Drell and S. Fubini (to be published).
[27] R. Hofstadter, Revs. Modern Phys. **28**, 214 (1956). See Sec. VI of this article for the early work on the neutron size by electron-scattering methods.

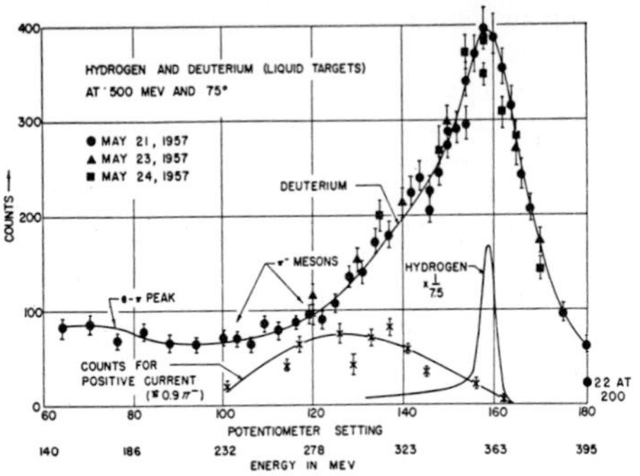

FIG. 17. The inelastic peak corresponding to scattering of 500 Mev electrons from deuterons at an angle of 75° in the laboratory system. Note the wide spread of scattered electron's energies compared with the sharp electron-proton peak near 360 Mev. The experimental data are those of Yearian and Hofstadter.[6] The deuteron curve should be multiplied by 0.87 to allow for the different densities of liquid deuterium and liquid hydrogen. The data are immediately seen to be incompatible with a neutron whose magnetic moment is a point.

from 0.45 as large as 3.0 can easily be detected. The goal of our neutron experiment is suggested to be the determination of which (if either) of the two above values corresponds to nature.

Unfortunately, free neutrons cannot be obtained in sufficient numbers to carry out electron-scattering experiments. The deuteron, however, offers an excellent vehicle for the test, since it is basically a weakly bound structure, having a low binding energy ($\epsilon=2.23$ Mev). Moreover, the conditions needed to make the simple ratio measurement, i.e., large momentum transfer, etc., are just those required to make the scattering from the neutron and proton in the deuteron essentially independent of the binding. The deuteron breakup (=incoherent scattering) at large q thus provides a fortunate possibility to study the neutron's magnetic structure.

It is possible that an extraordinarily large fourth moment in the neutron's *charge* distribution could contribute to the scattering cross section, but this seems extremely unlikely.

The fact that the nucleons are bound in the deuteron does imply that the incoherent scattering peak, observed at a given angle from the deuteron, will not have the sharp appearance characteristic of the proton peak.

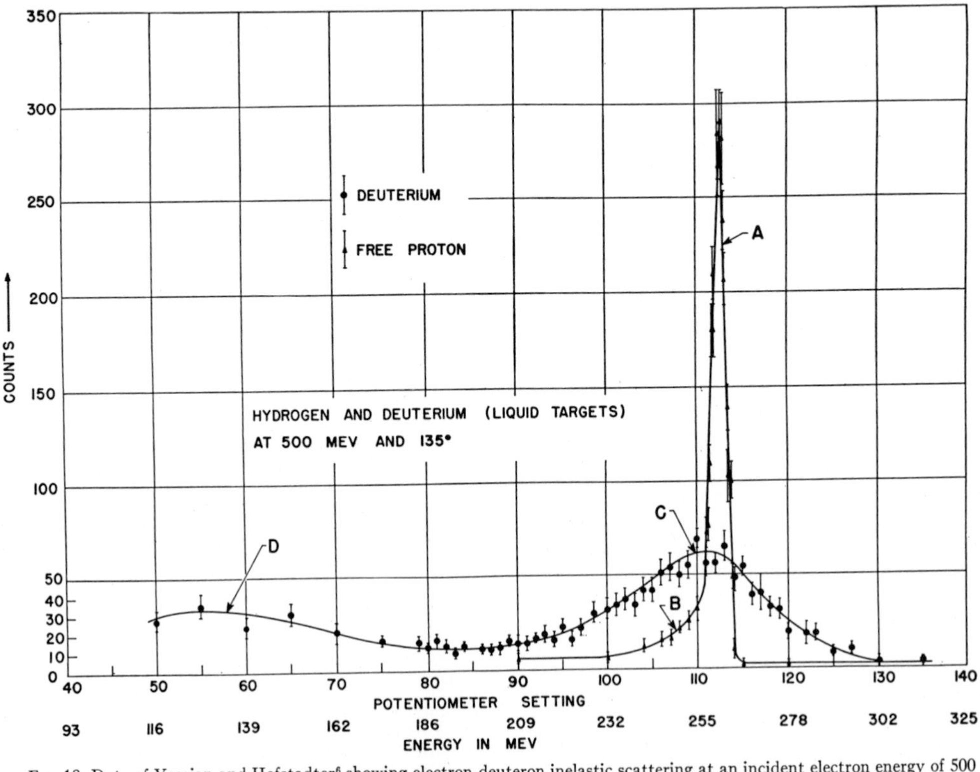

FIG. 18. Data of Yearian and Hofstadter[6] showing electron-deuteron inelastic scattering at an incident electron energy of 500 Mev and a scattering angle of 135°. The corresponding sharp proton peak is also shown. The deuteron curve should be multiplied by 0.87 as in Fig. 17. From such curves the neutron's electron-scattering cross section can be obtained. The neutron's cross section is too small to correspond to a point magnetic moment.

Instead, the deuteron peak will be spread out over a momentum (or for electrons, energy) range, given by the internal momentum distribution of the nucleons moving within the deuteron. Such an inelastic peak was observed early in the electron-scattering experiments.[28] Recent data[5,6,29] of the same kind are illustrated in Figs. 17, 18, and 19. They show that the areas under the deuteron peaks are too small to give a ratio $(d\sigma/d\Omega)_N/(d\sigma/d\Omega)_P=3.0$. Thus, the neutron's magnetic structure is not a point! In fact, the deuteron areas contain scattering due to the bound proton, and when this cross section is allowed for by subtraction, the residual neutron cross section is comparable with and smaller than that of the free proton.

In the present consideration we have been using implicitly the idea described in Eq. (15), where

$$\left(\frac{d\sigma}{d\Omega}\right)_D=\left(\frac{d\sigma}{d\Omega}\right)_P+\left(\frac{d\sigma}{d\Omega}\right)_N, \qquad (15)$$

and where $(d\sigma/d\Omega)_D$, $(d\sigma/d\Omega)_P$ are abbreviations for the integrated areas in Figs. 17, 18, and 19 under the deuteron and proton curves, respectively. The ordinates in these figures are differential cross sections with respect to angle and energy, thus $(d^2\sigma/d\Omega dE)_D$, $(d^2\sigma/d\Omega dE)_P$, etc. The neutron cross section of Eq. (15) can be obtained as a difference between the deuteron and proton cross sections (~areas in above figures). (In making the comparison, the deuteron curves should be multiplied by 0.87 to allow for the different densities of liquid deuterium and liquid hydrogen.) An equation such as (15) cannot be valid exactly, but Jankus[30] and Blankenbecler[31] have shown that it is remarkably good. Blankenbecler has used a closure rule to obtain this result. Jankus' results are described below.

The corrections needed to make an equation of type (15) valid appear to be of the order of a few percent. Although the corrections are small, they are important. Fortunately, it is not necessary to depend on knowing these corrections, because a second (and probably better) method for finding neutron size makes use of the *peak* of the deuteron curve instead of the area. Nevertheless, since the "area method" was used at first and since it provides a crude model-independent approximation to the correct answer, we describe briefly the consequences of comparing the deuteron area with the proton area.

Equation (15) may be replaced, in first approximation, by Eq. (16) where Δ represents the effect of the small corrections described above.

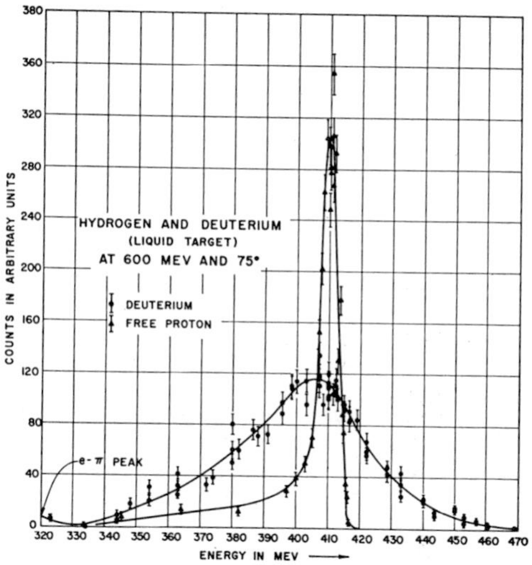

FIG. 19. The inelastic electron-deuteron scattering peak observed at the highest energy (600 Mev) at which such experiments have been carried out. The deuteron curve should be multiplied by 0.87 as in Fig. 17. The data are those of Yearian and Hofstadter[29] and were obtained at a scattering angle of 75° in the laboratory system. The comparison electron-proton peak is also shown in the figure. A point magnetic moment in the neutron would give a larger deuteron scattering peak.

$$\left(\frac{d\sigma}{d\Omega}\right)_D=(1+\Delta)\left\{\left(\frac{d\sigma}{d\Omega}\right)_P+\left(\frac{d\sigma}{d\Omega}\right)_N\right\}. \qquad (16)$$

The two terms in the final bracket of Eq. (16) are given by Eqs. (4) and (14), respectively. Thus, Δ will include kinematic effects resulting from motion of the nucleons and also the influence of variations in form factors of the finite nucleons over the momentum spread in the deuteron. Furthermore, Δ will include an effect corresponding to interaction of the two nucleons in the final state. These corrections have been discussed in detail by Blankenbecler[31] and also more briefly in references 1 and 6. However, the size of the correction Δ is indicated by the following examples: At 500 Mev and 75°, $\Delta\cong 0.004$ and at 500 Mev and 135°, $\Delta\cong 0.03$. Thus the corrections are very small.

One additional contribution to Δ, difficult to calculate, concerns a meson exchange effect, in which, for example, a meson created on one of the nucleons by the electron is reabsorbed by the second nucleon, after which the electron flies off. Such meson exchange effects may contribute to Δ an additional amount, of the order of 10%.[32] This correction is discussed in references 1 and 6. Some information may be found empirically about meson exchange effects, by comparing the low-energy side of the experimental deuteron peaks

[28] J. A. McIntrye and R. Hofstadter, Phys. Rev. **98**, 158 (1955).
[29] M. R. Yearian and R. Hofstadter, Bull. Am. Phys. Soc. Ser. II, **3**, 50 (1958).
[30] V. Z. Jankus, Phys. Rev. **102**, 1586 (1956).
[31] R. Blankenbecler, Bull. Am. Phys. Soc. Ser. II, **2**, 389 (1957). See also reference 1 of this article where Blankenbecler's work is reported.
[32] S. Drell and R. Blankenbecler (private communication).

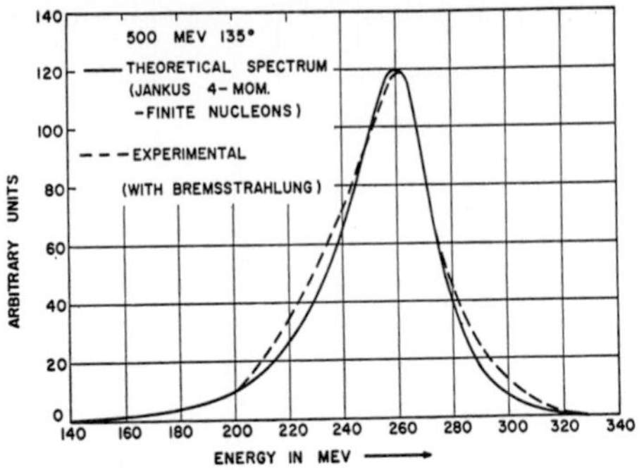

FIG. 20. The solid line is the result of a theoretical calculation, using the modified Jankus theory (see text), for the inelastic continuum corresponding to electron scattering from the deuteron at an angle of 135° at an incident electron energy of 500 Mev. The dashed line represents the experimental results. The theoretical curve takes account of bremsstrahlung, the effect of finite nucleon size, and substitution of four-momentum transfer for three-momentum transfer. The curves are normalized at the peaks.

with the shape of the curves predicted by the Jankus theory.[30] Such a comparison is made in Fig. 20 between an experimental and a Jankus theoretical curve. We now show how it is possible to compute the theoretical curves such as the one in Fig. 20. We then return to the area considerations and to the meson exchange effects.

In Fig. 20 the solid line is obtained from Eqs. (9) to (11) of Jankus' paper with suitable modifications: For point nucleons the Jankus formulas [Jankus, Eqs. (9) to (11)] may be used to provide inelastic continua such as the one shown in Fig. 21. Also shown are the corrections to the continuum due to the interaction in the final state. These final state corrections have been mentioned above. Jankus (point) curves, computed from his Eqs. (9) to (11) for the conditions under which the experiments have been performed, have several defects. (1) They do not include the effects of finite sizes of the nucleons. (2) They do not include effects of

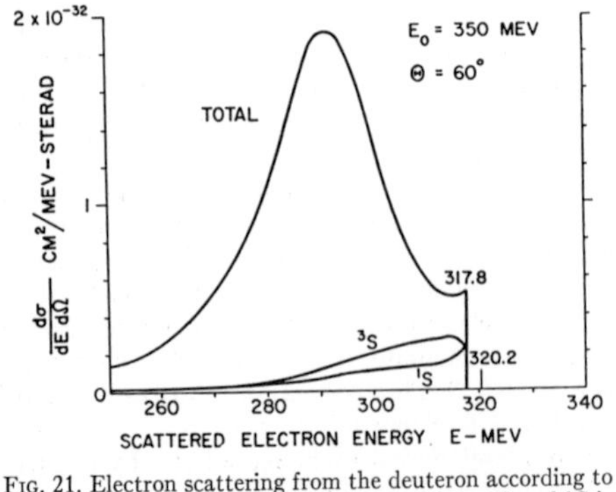

FIG. 21. Electron scattering from the deuteron according to the original Jankus[30] theory for point nucleons. The ^3S and ^1S interactions in the final state are shown below but are included in the upper curve.

bremsstrahlung, whereas the experiments do. (3) They do not reduce, at high energies, where binding can be neglected, to a sum of Rosenbluth formulas for the two nucleons.

Effect (3) was noticed immediately when the curves were compared with experiment. Each Jankus curve at a given angle showed a peak at an energy slightly different from the position of the experimental peak. At 500 Mev at 75° the Jankus peak appeared at an energy 2% below the experimental peak, and for 500 Mev at 135° the Jankus peak appeared at an energy about 5% below the experimental position. These shifts are not large, but are well outside experimental error (~1%) and indicate a systematic failure of the formulas. To make the Jankus formulas reduce to the Rosenbluth ones at high energy, it was necessary to replace the three-momentum transfer[1] (s) in Jankus' work with the four-momentum transfer (q). With this correction, all the peaks appeared in the correct experimental positions at all angles and energies. The ordinates of the Jankus

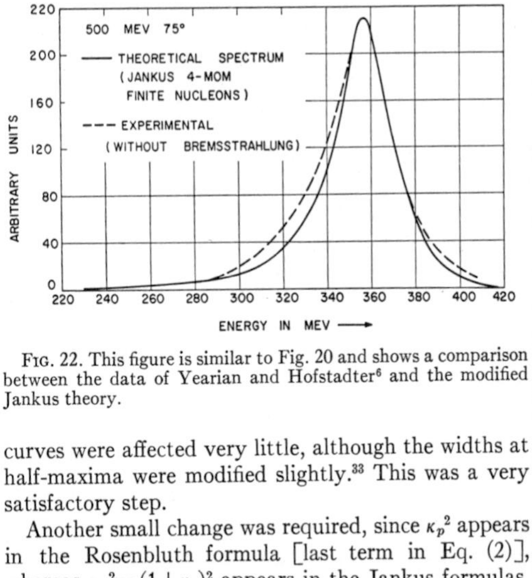

FIG. 22. This figure is similar to Fig. 20 and shows a comparison between the data of Yearian and Hofstadter[6] and the modified Jankus theory.

curves were affected very little, although the widths at half-maxima were modified slightly.[33] This was a very satisfactory step.

Another small change was required, since κ_p^2 appears in the Rosenbluth formula [last term in Eq. (2)], whereas $\mu_p^2=(1+\kappa_p)^2$ appears in the Jankus formulas. This is a very small term and its modification has little significance.

After the four-momentum was inserted into the Jankus formulas, it became quite easy to incorporate the effects of finite size, because the F^2 *vs* q^2 curves are known for the proton and could be inserted separately for the neutron. In the trials made so far, F_{2N} has been taken equal to F_{2P}. This now appears to be rather definite from additional evidence (peak method, see below). Thus Effects (3) and (1) were taken care of.

Effect (2) was taken into account by folding the shape of the observed proton peak, bremsstrahlung included, into the deuteron inelastic curves of Jankus,

[33] See reference 6 for details.

as modified above. This was a simple, although tedious, operation. Since the deuteron curve is already rather broad (~40 to 45 Mev width at half-maximum), the bremsstrahlung folding operation had little effect on the width.

In this way theoretical curves of the type shown in Fig. 20 were prepared for many angles at the energies 500 and 600 Mev. In all cases tested the experimental and theoretical curves were in unexpectedly good agreement (Figs. 20 and 22). The good agreement was unexpected since meson-exchange effects have not been included in the Jankus calculations. Furthermore, in the calculations performed at these high energies, the interaction in the final state was ignored. This was done without fear since the final state effects are governed by a form factor which rapidly reduces their values at high energy. In addition, experimental observations such as those shown in Fig. 23, at 600 Mev and 60°, demonstrate how small the final state interaction effect is under these conditions. When the deuteron elastic peak is allowed for, there is essentially nothing left for final state interaction. At large angles the final state effect is even smaller.

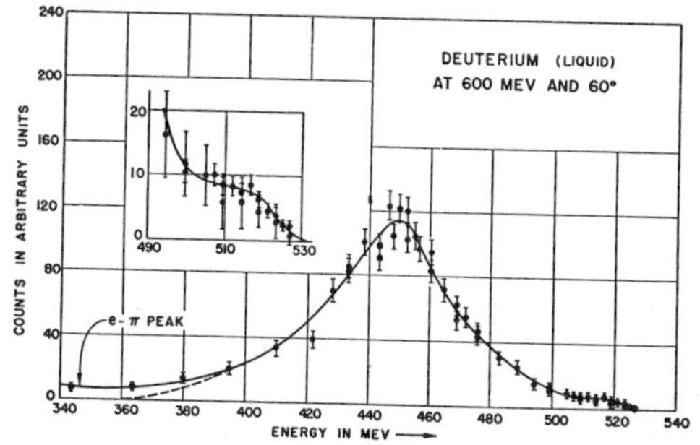

FIG. 23. The experimental inelastic continuum[29] for the deuteron at an energy of 600 Mev and 60°. In the inset and at the right extremum of the inelastic distribution there is a small plateau. This can be shown to be at the correct position and possesses the correct area to be given by the electron-deuteron *elastic* scattering peak. Thus there is very little that can be ascribed to the final-state interactions at this energy and angle.

Summarizing the above observations, we may say that a comparison between the modified Jankus theory (modified for four-momentum, finite size, bremsstrahlung) and experiment may now be expected to single out effects not included in the calculations, such as a possible meson exchange contribution to the inelastic scattering. The deviations between the experimental and theoretical curves of Fig. 20 and Fig. 22 may be thought of in this way. Differences in observed shape do not lie far outside the limits of experimental error, so that it can probably be said that experiment now gives evidence of rather small effects of meson exchange in inelastic scattering from the deuteron. Perhaps the deviations on the low-energy side of the inelastic curves of Figs. 20 and 22 are due to meson exchange and those on the right side to small interactions in the final state. Other possible causes of the deviations on both sides of the peak can be due to experimental errors, to inexactness in the Jankus three-momentum→four-momentum conversion, errors in the bremsstrahlung folding, imperfect knowledge of the neutron-form factor (this latter influences the shape only a trifle), etc. On the whole, the fact that the calculated curves agree as well as they do, over so broad a range of energies and angles, must be treated as strong evidence for the modified Jankus theory. Our extension of the Jankus theory appears to be valid beyond the range of energies for

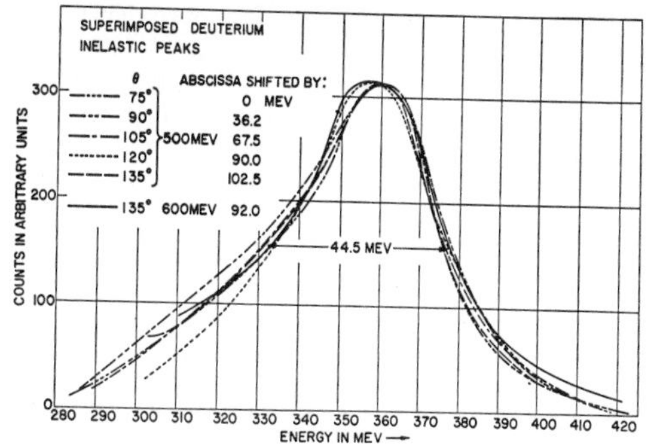

FIG. 24. When the electron-deuteron inelastic peaks are superimposed,[6] they all have approximately the same shape and width at half-maximum. The average width at half-maximum is approximately 45 Mev. This behavior is predicted by the modified Jankus theory and furnishes support for this theory.

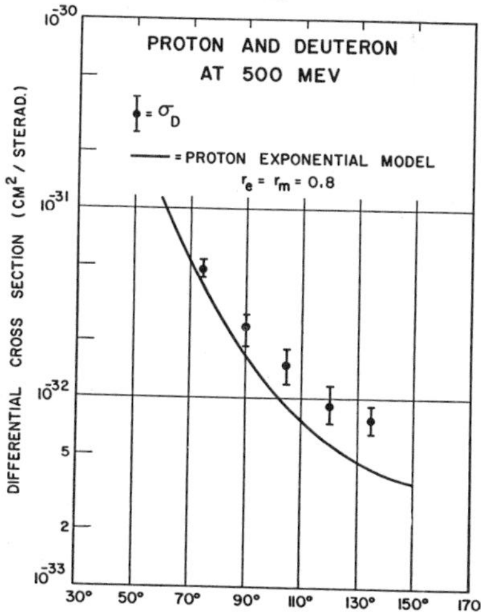

FIG. 25. The total cross sections under the deuteron inelastic continua are plotted as a function of scattering angle at 500 Mev. The comparison electron-proton curve is also shown at 500 Mev. From this curve the ratio R of Eq. (20) may be formed and values of F_{2N}^2 may be computed.

which the theory was originally developed. This is true at least approximately after making our modifications.

An additional check on the modified theory is related to the widths of the inelastic continua: Experiment shows that the widths at half-maxima of the deuteron inelastic peaks, observed at various angles and energies, are all essentially constant and approximate 45 Mev. This is shown in Fig. 24 and in Fig. 19. The approximate constancy of the width at half-maximum of the deuteron peaks is a feature of the Jankus theory and is thus further evidence that the modified theory is basically correct, even at such large values of momentum transfer. At very small angles the widths of the inelastic peaks are reduced, also as required by theory.

For the calculations reported here, the Jankus equations (9), (10), and (11) were replaced by

$$d^2\sigma_{in}=\frac{1}{4\pi}\frac{e^4}{p_0^2}\frac{\cos^2\theta/2}{\sin^4\theta/2}\left(\frac{2\alpha}{1-\alpha r_t}\right)\frac{1}{q^2k}O^2d\Omega_p dp, \quad (17)$$

where:

$$O^2=\left\{\frac{1}{Z^2-1}+\frac{1}{Z_1^2-1}-\frac{2}{Z_1-Z}[Q_0(Z)-Q_0(Z_1)]\right\}\left\{F_{1P}^2+\left[F_{1P}^2k^2+2\left(\frac{q}{2}\right)^2(F_{1P}+\kappa_P F_{2P})^2\right.\right.$$
$$\left.+2\left(\frac{q}{2}\right)^2\kappa_N^2F_{2N}^2\right]\tfrac{1}{2}[2\tan^2\theta/2+1-Z^2k^2]-\left.\left(\frac{q}{2}\right)^2(F_{1P}^2+2F_{1P}F_{2P}\kappa_P)\right\}$$
$$-\left\{\frac{Z}{Z^2-1}+\frac{Z_1}{Z_1^2-1}-\frac{Z_1+Z}{Z_1-Z}[Q_0(Z)-Q_0(Z_1)]\right\}2Zk^2F_{1P}^2-\left\{2+\frac{1}{Z^2-1}+\frac{1}{Z_1^2-1}-\frac{2ZZ_1}{Z_1-Z}[Q_0(Z)-Q_0(Z_1)]\right\}$$
$$\times\left\{\tfrac{1}{2}[2\tan^2\theta/2+1-Z^2k^2]-Z^2k^2\right\}k^2F_{1P}^2-\frac{(Z_1-Z)^2}{ZZ_1(Z_1+Z)}[Q_0(Z)+Q_0(Z_1)][-\tfrac{2}{3}(F_{1P}+\kappa_P F_{2P})\kappa_N F_{2N}]$$
$$\times\left(\frac{q}{2}\right)[2\tan^2\theta/2+1-Z^2k^2], \quad (18)$$

and where

$$\left.\begin{aligned} Z&=\frac{\Delta E}{qk}=\frac{\alpha^2+k^2+q^2/4}{qk}\\ Z_1&=\frac{\gamma^2+k^2+q^2/4}{qk}\\ Q_0(Z)&=\text{arc coth}Z=\tfrac{1}{2}\ln\left(\frac{Z+1}{Z-1}\right).\end{aligned}\right\} \quad (19)$$

Here, p_0 is the incoming electron momentum, and p is the outgoing (scattered) electron momentum. The vector **k** is the final momentum of the proton with respect to the center of mass of the recoiling deuteron.

TABLE I. Total cross sections for the deuteron at 500 and 600 Mev at various scattering angles.

θ	500 Mev $d\sigma_D/d\Omega$ (cm²/sterad)	θ	600 Mev $d\sigma_D/d\Omega$ (cm²/sterad)
45°	...	45°	$(2.84\pm0.29)\times10^{-31}$
60°	...	60°	$(7.63\pm0.77)\times10^{-32}$
75°	$(4.60\pm0.49)\times10^{-32}$	75°	$(3.31\pm0.34)\times10^{-32}$
90°	$(2.36\pm0.40)\times10^{-32}$	90°	$(1.08\pm0.19)\times10^{-32}$
105°	$(1.50\pm0.30)\times10^{-32}$	105°	$(9.58\pm2.40)\times10^{-33}$
120°	$(9.06\pm1.98)\times10^{-33}$	120°	$(4.79\pm1.15)\times10^{-33}$
135°	$(7.58\pm1.23)\times10^{-33}$	135°	$(3.09\pm0.60)\times10^{-33}$ and $(2.92\pm0.19)\times10^{-33}$

The ground-state wave function of the deuteron is the Hulthén wave function $e^{-\alpha r}-e^{-\gamma r}$, where α^2=binding energy and γ is fixed by the choice of the triplet effective range r_t.

We used the four-vector energy-momentum transfer for q; and for convenience, the formulas are expressed in dimensionless form, i.e., $\hbar=c=M=1$. The F's were put into the appropriate places demanded by the phenomenological theory[11] and by a proper reduction of the result to a sum of Rosenbluth formulas. No attempt was made to insert F_{1N}, because it is believed that this quantity lies very close to zero at all of the q values used in these experiments. The Jankus results, appearing in Eqs. (17) to (19) were obtained with a Hulthén potential, and it is not expected that the results will be sensitive to the neutron-proton potential[34] (<5%), although the small corrections corresponding to interaction in the final state may be affected by a choice of potential.

We return to the neutron size determination. To find a first approximation to the neutron size, we may now make a comparison between the deuteron areas under the peaks of Figs. 17, 18, and 19, and the areas under the corresponding proton curves. Typical data[6] taken at 500 Mev, 135°, are shown in Fig. 25 and in Table I along with the proton curve. The ratio R of cross

[34] V. Z. Jankus, "Theoretical aspects of electron-deuteron scattering," Ph.D. thesis, Stanford University (December, 1955).

sections, when $F_{1P}=F_{2P}=F_P$, is easily shown to be

$$R=\left(\frac{d\sigma}{d\Omega}\right)_N \Big/ \left(\frac{d\sigma}{d\Omega}\right)_P$$

$$=\frac{F_{2N}^2}{F_P^2}\times\frac{\frac{\kappa_N^2\hbar^2q^2}{4M^2c^2}[2\tan^2\theta/2+1]}{1+\frac{\hbar^2q^2}{4M^2c^2}[2(1+\kappa_P)^2\tan^2\theta/2+\kappa_P^2]}, \quad (20)$$

and F_{2N}^2 may be found from this equation, knowing F_P and R. It is desirable to use R in this method, since it is a directly measurable quantity. Using the data of Fig. 25 and more recent data at 600 Mev,[29] an F_{2N}^2 *vs* q^2 plot for the neutron may be prepared. Such values of F_{2N}^2 are shown in Fig. 26. The proton F^2 values are also shown in the figure. A (form factor)^2 curve for an exponential model with rms radius $r_m=0.80\times10^{-13}$ cm provides a fair fit to the neutron data. The errors are fairly large, but it is clear that the ratio of cross sections is far lower than the value 3.0 (for a point neutron). At the large q values, the ratio is possibly as high as 0.50. The two values, $r_m{}^N=0.8\times10^{-13}$ cm and ratio $=0.50$ are to be compared with the values $r_m{}^P=0.80\times10^{-13}$ cm and ratio $=0.45$, if the neutron and proton had exactly the same structures. Thus our first approximation to the neutron size shows that neutron and proton are very similar. If, e.g., a Gaussian distribution had been used for the neutron, the resulting size would have been a little smaller, but approximate equality of neutron and proton would still hold.

Fortunately, it is possible to improve on the accuracy of the comparison between the neutron and the proton. Drell[35] has pointed out that a determination of the *peak*

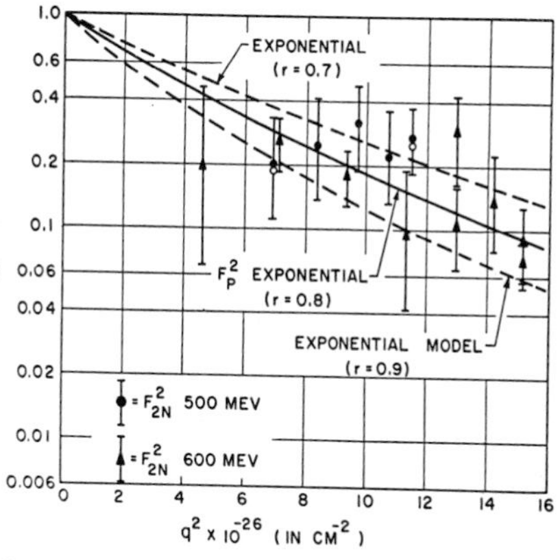

FIG. 26. This figure shows the value of F_{2N}^2 for the neutron plotted against q^2 for the data taken at 500 and 600 Mev. The dashed curves are theoretical curves given by the exponential model of the magnetic moment density of the neutron. The proton F_P^2 is shown as the solid line for comparison.

[35] S. Drell (private communication).

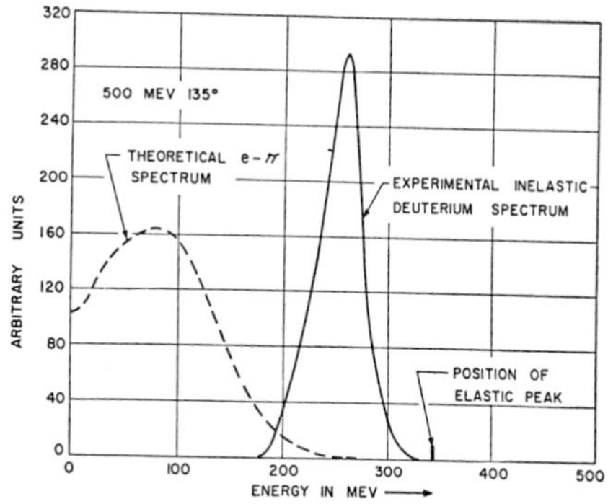

FIG. 27. This figure shows the small overlap between the electron-pion peak and the deuteron's inelastic continuum. The latter is the object of measurement in these studies. At other angles the overlap is smaller. The electron-pion spectrum was calculated from a theory of Dalitz and Yennie into which the deuteron momentum spread was folded.

ordinate of the deuteron inelastic continuum should give a more accurate means of finding the neutron's magnetic structure. This proposal would compare the experimental values of $(d^2\sigma/d\Omega dE)_D$ and the proton area $(d\sigma/d\Omega)$. Since the latter is known from past and recent proton work, the former can be determined by direct observation with considerable accuracy. Furthermore, and this is the main point, the various corrections needed in using the area method (contributants to Δ) are almost all zero at the position of the deuteron's inelastic peak. The interaction in the final state falls to zero in the neighborhood of the peak. The meson-exchange effects fall close to zero at this same position, because there is not enough energy in the center-of-mass system to excite the isobaric state of a nucleon ($\frac{3}{2}$–$\frac{3}{2}$ resonance). Experimentally speaking, the situation is quite favorable also because the deuteron peak and proton peak are always very close to each other, and in a ratio measurement many experimental errors must cancel out. The "contamination" of the deuteron peak by electrons, which have produced real pions, is also negligibly small at the position of the peak. This is shown[6] in the example of Fig. 27, where the theoretical electron-pion section is extremely small at the position of the deuteron peak. For (at least) all the above reasons, the "peak-comparison method" is to be preferred over the "area comparison" method. A possible cause of error in the peak method might exist if the deuteron ordinate at the peak depends on the neutron-proton potential. Recent estimates by Drell and Blankenbecler[36] and Schneider[37] make it seem unlikely that such a variation could exceed 5%. We, therefore, consider the peak method a more reliable index of the neutron's magnetic structure than the area method.

[36] S. Drell and R. Blankenbecler (private communication).
[37] W. Schneider (private communication).

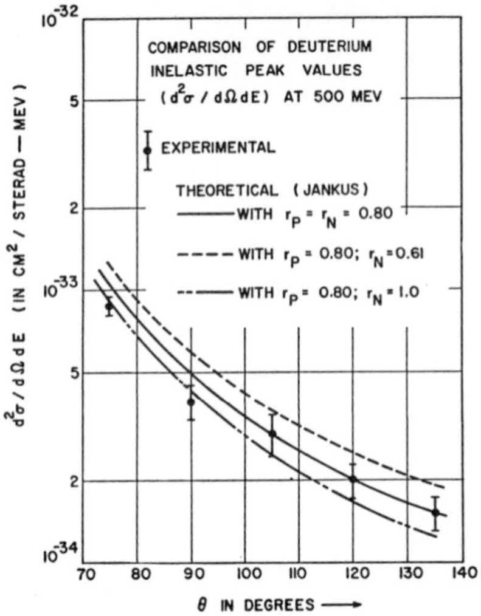

FIG. 28. The maximum values of the deuteron's inelastic cross section are plotted according to the differential cross-section method as a function of scattering angle. The data are those of Yearian and Hofstadter.[6] Theoretical curves have been prepared using the modified Jankus theory. Three such curves are shown. The dashed curves have been prepared for an exponential model of the neutron's magnetic moment density with the indicated rms radii. The solid line represents the same model with an rms radius of 0.80×10^{-13} cm. The proton radii were taken to be 0.80×10^{-13} cm for the exponential model. The experimental points fall slightly nearer the 0.80×10^{-13} curve.

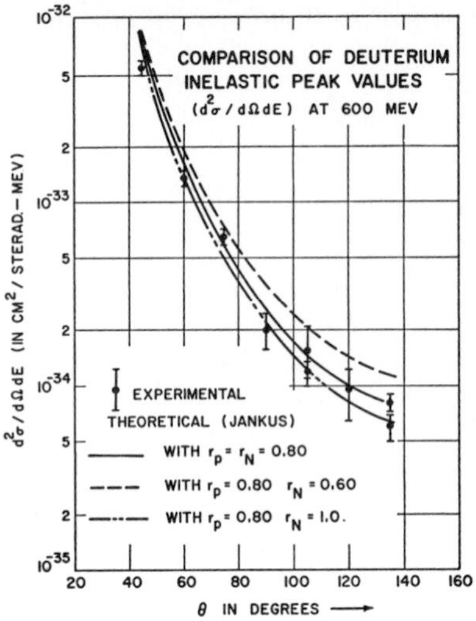

FIG. 29. This figure is similar to Fig. 28 except that the experimental data, due to Yearian and Hofstadter,[29] refer to 600 Mev. The theoretical curves are prepared with the modified Jankus theory for an exponential model of the neutron's magnetic moment density and various choices of rms radius shown in the figure. The proton radii are taken to be 0.80×10^{-13} cm. A neutron radius of 0.90×10^{-13} cm fits the experimental data fairly well.

When the experiments are carried out[6,29] at 500 Mev and at 600 Mev, the two sets of data in Figs. 28 and 29 and Table II are obtained. Various theoretical curves for an exponential model of a neutron with sizes 0.60, 0.61, 0.80, and 1.0×10^{-13} cm are also shown in these figures. The rms size 0.85×10^{-13} cm for an exponential model fits all the experiments fairly well. Calculations with other models of a neutron are in progress, but it seems clear that the rms size cannot differ very much from $r_m{}^N=0.80\times10^{-13}$ cm. Thus it appears the neutron and proton have magnetic sizes and structures that are the same within present experimental error! The error in the size determination is probably of the order of, or less than, 0.15×10^{-13} cm.

TABLE II. Differential (peak) cross sections for the deuteron at 500 and 600 Mev at various scattering angles.

500 Mev θ	$d^2\sigma_D/d\Omega dE$ (cm²/sterad Mev)	600 Mev θ	$d^2\sigma_D/d\Omega dE$ (cm²/sterad Mev)
45°	...	45°	$(5.30\pm0.52)\times10^{-33}$
60°	...	60°	$(1.32\pm0.13)\times10^{-33}$
75°	$(8.60\pm0.52)\times10^{-34}$	75°	$(6.35\pm0.65)\times10^{-34}$
90°	$(3.85\pm0.57)\times10^{-34}$	90°	$(1.96\pm0.44)\times10^{-34}$
105°	$(2.96\pm0.52)\times10^{-34}$	105°	$(1.54\pm0.52)\times10^{-34}$
120°	$(2.00\pm0.30)\times10^{-34}$	120°	$(9.38\pm2.78)\times10^{-35}$
135°	$(1.51\pm0.22)\times10^{-34}$	135°	$(8.0\ \pm0.70)\times10^{-35}$ and $(6.0\ \pm0.91)\times10^{-35}$

These results suggest that the area method may best be used to investigate the small effects of the various corrections we have mentioned in discussing that method.

The possibility that the neutron's charge cloud ($F_{1N}\neq0$) may have relatively large excursions as a function of radius has been considered by Schiff,[38] who uses the area method to evaluate the neutron form factors. He concludes that it is most likely that the neutron charge density is zero.

III. REMARKS ON THE SIGNIFICANCE OF THE RESULTS

This general problem has already been dealt with in an excellent article by Yennie *et al.*[8] summarizing the information as of a year and one-half ago. Since the innermost parts of the neutron and proton cannot be known at the present stage of our knowledge in physics, the correct experimental observations of structure can be taken as primary facts of nature. In this event, there are, of course, no anomalies. However, it is the aim of theory to attempt to fit the unknown into what is already known, and the proton and neutron structures are no exceptions to this aim. In the known (or rather, partially known) category of physical theory, we include the present body of meson field theory. Perhaps, with respect to this body of knowledge, an "anomaly" may be said to exist: That is, the *proton's* Dirac cloud

[38] L. I. Schiff, Revs. Modern Phys. **30**, 462 (1958), this issue.

(governed by F_1) appears to be very different from the neutron's corresponding cloud. This is a difficulty which has existed for some time in the interpretation of the neutron-electron experiments[18–22,39] on the basis of meson theory. The fact that the second radial moment of the charge distribution is almost exactly zero makes "it seem unlikely that any theory which describes only the pion charge cloud associated with the neutron, ignoring spatial distribution of the charge on the residual neutron core, will predict a vanishing r^2 moment," as Salzman has remarked.[40] The new experiments reported here do not enhance the nature of this difficulty, but, on the contrary, reinforce the view that the outer or pionic clouds of neutron and proton are basically similar, if one may judge these by the magnetic moment distributions. It is possible that small differences, not detectable in the present experiments, may yet exist in the outer (pionic) regions.

Perhaps there are also relatively large differences in the innermost parts of these two nucleons. Only experiments at higher energies (0.5 to 1.5 Bev) or more precise experiments at the present energies can furnish the answers to such problems.

Using the Chew-Low theory[41] and an upper cutoff momentum, Salzman[40] succeeded in showing that the electron-proton scattering data[7–10] at energies up to 236 Mev could be satisfactorily explained with a spread-out core distribution. The spread-out core is consistent with Salzman's earlier explanation of the anomalous neutron-electron results,[42] but the use of such a large core is not readily understandable in terms of the expected (smaller) dimensions associated with nucleons, antinucleons, or heavy mesons of various kinds. Attempts in this direction have been made by Sandri[43] and Tamm.[44]

Recently, dispersion-theoretic attacks have been made on the nucleon structure problem by a number of authors.[45–47] Chew *et al.* point out that[45] the magnetic moment "size" can be explained by the two-pion state, but that higher mass-configurations may be responsible for the charge "size." We do not know whether the assumptions involved in this treatment are equivalent to the large core hypothesis of Salzman, but it is apparent, once more, that to resolve the present problems, new data at higher energies, corresponding to the probing of smaller dimensions, are needed. Whether electrodynamics is valid in the realm of these same small dimensions is the dominant question. The presence of difficulties in our understanding of nucleon structure may be a forerunner of the troubles to be expected at very small distances when dealing with quantum electrodynamics[48,49] or with our concepts of space and time. It is also not clear why $F_1 \cong F_2$ as appears to be true in the case of the proton. This is another problem to be added to those already posed.

ACKNOWLEDGMENTS

We thank Mr. R. Blankenbecler for many stimulating discussions on the theory of electrodisintegration of the deuteron. We also thank Professor S. Drell for illuminating comments and helpful remarks on our work and, in particular, for his suggestion to emphasize the "peak" method of determining neutron size. Dr. W. Schneider and Dr. V. Z. Jankus have also aided us with their calculations on the deuteron. Conversations with Professor G. Chew, Professor M. Goldberger, Professor R. Karplus, and Professor F. Zachariasen have been helpful and encouraging. We also thank Professor L. I. Schiff for permitting us to examine his results before publication. We express appreciation to Mr. G. R. Burleson, Mr. C. N. Davey, Dr. H. W. Kendall, and Mr. G. Gilbert and the accelerator crew for their valuable assistance in obtaining the experimental data. We appreciate the constructive comments of Mr. S. Sobottka.

[39] R. Sachs and S. Treiman, Phys. Rev. **103**, 435 (1936).
[40] G. Salzman, Phys. Rev. **105**, 1076 (1957).
[41] G. F. Chew and F. E. Low, Phys. Rev. **101**, 1570 (1956); **101**, 1579 (1956).
[42] G. Salzman, Phys. Rev. **99**, 973 (1955).
[43] G. Sandri, Phys. Rev. **101**, 1616 (1956).
[44] I. Tamm, reported in footnote 38 of reference 8.
[45] Chew, Karplus, Gasiorowicz, and Zachariasen (to be published).
[46] J. Bernstein and M. L. Goldberger, Revs. Modern Phys. **30** 465 (1958), this issue.
[47] K. Tanaka (to be published).
[48] R. P. Feynman, Anais acad. brasil. cienc. **26**, (1954) (in English).
[49] S. Drell, Bull. Am. Phys. Soc. Ser. II, **2**, 376(T) (1957).

PAPER 47

Electromagnetic Structure of the Nucleon in Local-Field Theory*

GEOFFREY F. CHEW, ROBERT KARPLUS, STEPHEN GASIOROWICZ, AND FREDRIK ZACHARIASEN†
Department of Physics and Radiation Laboratory, University of California, Berkeley, California
(Received November 25, 1957)

In analogy to the dispersion-relation method for scattering, the description of nucleon electromagnetic structure by local-field theory is discussed in terms of mass-spectral representations for the form factors. The existence of such representations is made plausible although not proved, and it is shown that the spectral distribution functions are related to scattering amplitudes on the mass shell but sometimes in a nonphysical region. It is argued that the main contributor to the magnetic moment structure in the spectral distribution must be the two-pion state, and an attempt is made to evaluate this contribution in terms of the known behavior of pion-nucleon scattering. A semiquantitative calculation yields results in reasonable agreement with experiment.

It is emphasized that the large observed charge radius of the proton does not imply the dominance of the two-pion state in the charge structure. Thus it is not impossible that higher mass configurations supply the isotopic scalar charge needed to explain the small neutron-electron interaction.

I. INTRODUCTION

THEORETICAL calculations of the electromagnetic properties of the nucleon have been carried out for many years within the framework of local-field theory, but mainly by perturbation techniques[1] of dubious validity. Recently the use of dispersion relations in the problem of pion-nucleon scattering[2] and photopion production[3] has shown that local-field theory is capable of some quantitative correlation of physical phenomena even when the perturbation method fails. It is the purpose of this paper to attempt to apply the kind of relations that have successfully correlated experiments involving low-energy pions to the problem of the nucleon electromagnetic form factors. To the extent at least that the electromagnetic structure of the nucleon is determined by virtual pions of sub-Bev frequencies such a program should be enlightening, even though in the end local theories in the strict sense may be abandoned.

1.—There are at least three reasons for believing that the anomalous magnetic-moments structure of the nucleon is dominated by low-frequency virtual pions:

(*a*) The anomalous moment is almost entirely a vector in isotopic spin, i.e., the anomalous moments of neutron and proton are nearly equal in magnitude, with opposite signs. This situation prevails not only for the static moments but up to frequencies at which the moments have fallen to about $\frac{1}{3}$ of their static values.[4] It will be explained below that the π^+, π^- pair, the virtual configuration of lowest energy contributing to the nucleon electromagnetic structure, is a vector in isotopic spin space. It is of course possible for a combination of virtual effects other than pion pairs to produce an almost purely vector moment, but such a circumstance must be regarded as unlikely.

(*b*) The sign and the approximate magnitude of the anomalous moments are correctly given by the cutoff model of the Yukawa theory.[5] This model is normalized to the same low-frequency limits as the local theory, but neglects nucleon recoil as well as antinucleons and strange particles and excludes virtual pions of energy higher than about 1 Bev.

(*c*) The measured mean square radius of the magnetic-moment distribution[4] corresponds to the wavelength of a pion of about $\frac{1}{3}$ Bev.

In contrast to the anomalous magnetic moment, it is experimentally clear that the charge structure of the nucleon is *not* dominated by π^+, π^- pairs. The decisive fact here is the extremely small second radial moment of the neutron charge distribution as compared with that for the proton, which is at least ten times as large.[6] Thus the charge density is certainly not an isotopic vector.

2.—Before going into the details it is perhaps advisable to outline the approach to be used. It is well known that the linear interaction of nucleons with the electromagnetic field can be expressed in terms of four real scalar functions of q^2, the square of the energy-momentum-transfer four-vector.[6] We shall label these

* This work was supported in part by a grant from the National Science Foundation and done under the auspices of the U. S. Atomic Energy Commission.

† Now at Department of Physics, Stanford University, Stanford, California.

[1] References to most of the published perturbation calculations may be found in the paper by B. Fried, Phys. Rev. **88**, 1142 (1952), who gives the formulas for the neutron to lowest order in the pion-nucleon coupling constant. A numerical evaluation of the form factors is given by M. Rosenbluth, Phys. Rev. **79**, 615 (1950).

[2] References here may be found in the recent paper by Chew, Goldberger, Low, and Nambu, Phys. Rev. **106**, 1337 (1957).

[3] Chew, Goldberger, Low, and Nambu, Phys. Rev. **106**, 1345 (1957).

[4] E. E. Chambers and R. Hofstadter, Phys. Rev. **103**, 1454 (1956), and R. Hofstadter, in *Proceedings of the Seventh Annual Rochester Conference on High-Energy Nuclear Physics* (Interscience Publishers, Inc., New York, 1957).

[5] H. Miyazawa, Phys. Rev. **101**, 1564 (1955).

[6] For a recent review of experimental knowledge about the electromagnetic structure of the nucleon, see Lévy, Ravenhall, and Yennie, Revs. Modern Phys. **29**, 144 (1957). This article also discusses those theoretical features of the problem which follow from invariance considerations.

functions $G_1^S(q^2)$, $G_1^V(q^2)$, $G_2^S(q^2)$, $G_2^V(q^2)$, where the index 1 goes with the part of the interaction proportional to $\gamma_\mu A_\mu$ (the "charge") and the index 2 goes with the part of the interaction proportional to $\sigma_{\mu\nu}A_\mu q_\nu$ (the "magnetic moment").[6] The superscripts S and V refer to the isotopic character of the interaction, scalar or vector, the normalization being specified by the relations

$$G_1^S(0)+G_1^V(0)=e,\quad G_1^S(0)-G_1^V(0)=0, \quad (2.1)$$

$$G_2^S(0)+G_2^V(0)=\mu_p,\quad G_2^S(0)-G_2^V(0)=\mu_n, \quad (2.2)$$

where e is the proton charge and μ_p and μ_n the proton and neutron static anomalous magnetic moments, respectively. The conventional form factors[6] are given by the ratio of the appropriate $G(q^2)$ to the value at $q^2=0$. Thus in our notation the proton form factors are

$$F_{1,2}^P(q^2)=\frac{G_{1,2}^S(q^2)+G_{1,2}^V(q^2)}{G_{1,2}^S(0)+G_{1,2}^V(0)}.$$

Our approach is to be based on mass spectral representations of the type

$$G_1^S(q^2)=\frac{e}{2}-\frac{q^2}{\pi}\int_{(3m_\pi)^2}^\infty dm^2\frac{g_1^S(m^2)}{m^2(m^2+q^2)}, \quad (2.3)$$

$$G_1^V(q^2)=\frac{e}{2}-\frac{q^2}{\pi}\int_{(2m_\pi)^2}^\infty dm^2\frac{g_1^V(m^2)}{m^2(m^2+q^2)}, \quad (2.4)$$

$$G_2^S(q^2)=\frac{1}{\pi}\int_{(3m_\pi)^2}^\infty dm^2\frac{g_2^S(m^2)}{m^2+q^2}, \quad (2.5)$$

$$G_2^V(q^2)=\frac{1}{\pi}\int_{(2m_\pi)^2}^\infty dm_2\frac{g_2^V(m^2)}{m^2+q^2}, \quad (2.6)$$

which have been suggested by a number of authors.[7–9] The four real weight functions $g_{1,2}^{S,V}(m^2)$ may be nonzero for m equal to the mass of any system strongly coupled to the nucleon which at the same time can be created by the electromagnetic field. The lightest such isotopic vector system is the π^+, π^- pair, while the three-pion π^+, π^-, π^0 system is the lightest isotopic scalar; hence the thresholds at $(2m_\pi)^2$ and $(3m_\pi)^2$. It will be shown in Sec. III that, in general, systems of even numbers of pions contribute only to the isotopic vector charge and magnetic moment while odd numbers of pions give purely isotopic scalar contributions. Of a mass comparable to six pions is the K^+, K^- pair, and eventually of course one comes to the baryon pairs, starting with the nucleon-antinucleon system. From a practical standpoint one must hope that in the mass spectra the contributions from the simplest systems are the most important.

The derivation of the representations (2.3)–(2.6) to be given in Sec. II presupposes that $G_1(Z)/Z$ and $G_2(Z)$ approach zero for large Z. Actually, it may be inferred from the work of Lehmann, Symanzik, and Zimmermann[10] that $G_1(Z)$ approaches zero also. In that case one may write a relation of the form

$$G_1^{S,V}(q^2)=\frac{1}{\pi}\int dm^2\frac{g_1^{S,V}(m^2)}{m^2+q^2}, \quad (2.7)$$

with the restriction on $g_1^{S,V}$ implied by Eq. (2.1). The convergence, however, is achieved only because of electromagnetic damping, which sets in for extremely large $q^2\gtrsim M^2e^{137}$, while according to perturbation theory[1] the functions G_1 behave logarithmically for large q^2 in the range $M^2e^{137}\gg q^2\gg M^2$. It is possible that an exact solution of the pion-nucleon field theory would lead to functions G_1 which tend to zero even without electromagnetic damping. At present, however, we cannot feel at all confident of such a circumstance, so we prefer to use Eqs. (2.3) and (2.4) to avoid a large contribution from the uncertain regions. The anomalous magnetic-moment distribution, on the other hand, for reasons which are essentially dimensional, is definitely expected to approach zero for $q^2\gg M^2$ with or without electromagnetic damping. Thus for practical purposes we are confronted by a difference between the charge and magnetic moment distributions.

3.—Often it seems appropriate to discuss the nucleon electromagnetic structure in configuration-space language, and to that end one conventionally introduces three-dimensional Fourier transforms of the functions $G_{1,2}^{S,V}$:

$$\rho^{S,V}(r)=\frac{1}{(2\pi)^3}\int d\mathbf{p}\, e^{i\mathbf{p}\cdot\mathbf{r}}G_1^{S',V}(p^2), \quad (3.1)$$

$$\mathfrak{M}^{S,V}(r)=\frac{1}{(2\pi)^3}\int d\mathbf{p}\, e^{i\mathbf{p}\cdot\mathbf{r}}G_2^{S,V}(p^2). \quad (3.2)$$

Although the configuration-space functions ρ and $\mathfrak{M}$ have no precise physical meaning they correspond roughly to charge and anomalous magnetic-moment densities, respectively. Substituting Eqs. (2.5) and (2.6) into (3.2), we have

$$\mathfrak{M}^{S,V}(r)=\frac{1}{2\pi^2}\int dm^2\, g_2^{S,V}(m^2)\frac{e^{-mr}}{r}, \quad (3.3)$$

which shows that in the spectral decomposition of the magnetic moment the contribution of a particular mass value m has a "range" $\sim 1/m$. Thus the lightest masses that contribute to $g_2(m^2)$ give rise to the longest-range structure.

A quantity often used to characterize the size of the nucleon is the "mean square radius of the anomalous magnetic moment,"[6] that is (suppressing the super-

[7] Y. Nambu, Nuovo cimento 6, 1064 (1957).
[8] V. Glaser and B. Jaksic, Nuovo cimento 5, 1197 (1957).
[9] M. Gell-Mann (private communication).

[10] Lehmann, Symanzik, and Zimmermann, Nuovo cimento 2, 425 (1955).

scripts S and V),

$$\langle r_m{}^2\rangle_{Av}=\int d\mathbf{r}\, r^2\mathfrak{M}(r)\Big/\int d\mathbf{r}\,\mathfrak{M}(r), \tag{3.4}$$

which is easily shown to be related to the logarithmic derivative of $G_2(q^2)$ at $q^2=0$:

$$\tfrac{1}{6}\langle r_m{}^2\rangle_{Av}=-\frac{1}{G_2(0)}\left[\frac{dG_2(q^2)}{dq^2}\right]_{q^2=0}, \tag{3.5}$$

or

$$\tfrac{1}{6}\langle r_m{}^2\rangle_{Av}=\int dm^2\frac{g_2(m^2)}{m^4}\Big/\int dm^2\frac{g_2(m^2)}{m^2}. \tag{3.6}$$

Thus the mean square radius is related to some average mass in the weight function g_2/m^2,

$$\tfrac{1}{6}\langle r_m{}^2\rangle_{Av}=\langle m^{-2}\rangle_{Av}, \tag{3.7}$$

a notion which is useful if the spectral distribution is predominantly of one sign. Actual calculation, as will be seen in Sec. V, shows no tendency for g_2 to oscillate, although it has not been proved that a change of sign is impossible. Taking the measured root-mean-square radius of the anomalous (vector) nucleon magnetic moment,[4] one finds a corresponding average mass of $5m_\pi$, which, if divided between two particles, would give each an average total energy of 2.5 m_π. This low average energy suggests, as mentioned above, that virtual K particles and baryons play only a small role in the determination of the anomalous magnetic moment.

4.—Because of the uncertain behavior of $G_1(q^2)$ at infinity, there may not exist a useful connection between the second radial moment of the charge distribution and an average virtual mass. Going through the same manipulations as above but using Eqs. (2.3) and (2.4) rather than (2.5) and (2.6), one finds for the mean square radius of the (scalar or vector) charge the formulas

$$\tfrac{1}{6}\langle(r_\rho{}^2)\rangle_{Av}{}^S=\frac{2}{\pi e}\int_{(3m_\pi)^2}^{\infty}\frac{g_1{}^S(m^2)}{m^4}dm^2, \tag{4.1}$$

$$\tfrac{1}{6}\langle(r_\rho{}^2)\rangle_{Av}{}^V=\frac{2}{\pi e}\int_{(2m_\pi)^2}^{\infty}\frac{g_1{}^V(m^2)}{m^4}dm^2. \tag{4.2}$$

Often the statement is made that because the lowest-mass intermediate state the π^+, π^- pair, contributes to the vector charge but not to the scalar the latter should have a much smaller mean square radius than the former. Such reasoning, however, is tacitly based on the assumption that a formula of the type of (3.7) holds for the charge radius as well as for that of the magnetic moment. Formulas (4.1) and (4.2) in themselves imply nothing about either the relative or the absolute magnitudes of the second radial moments of the scalar and vector charge distributions.

The experimental fact that the scalar and vector second radial moments of the charge are almost equal means, of course, that configurations more complicated than the π^+, π^- pair are important. Why this should not also be true for the magnetic moment we must say at once we do not understand. It is, however, fortunate that at least part of the problem of the nucleon electromagnetic structure may be tractable.

5.—In our present state of knowledge an attempt at a specific evaluation of the weight functions $g_{1,2}{}^{S,V}(m^2)$ must be confined to the two-pion contribution, and even here we have not succeeded in formulating a reliable method of calculation. We shall show that the two-pion part of the weight function is proportional to the charge-exchange pion-nucleon scattering amplitude, but at a negative value for the square of the momentum transfer. An extension of the physical scattering amplitude is thus required, which we attempt to carry out by means of dispersion relations combined with Legendre polynomials. If integrals are cut off and an expansion is made in inverse powers of the nucleon mass the results of the static model[5] can be reproduced. Without a cutoff we are unable to make a definite calculation, but arguments will be given to support the belief that the local theory, properly evaluated, will be in agreement with the observations.

In Sec. II we discuss and to some extent justify the representations (2.2) to (2.6). Section III deals with general properties of the various intermediate-state contributions to the weight functions $g_{1,2}{}^{S,V}(m^2)$, and in Secs. IV and V we concentrate on the two-pion intermediate state. In Sec. VI our findings are summarized.

II. THE MASS-SPECTRAL REPRESENTATIONS

6.—Recently Bogoliubov, Medvedev, and Polivanov[11] and others[12] derived dispersion relations for meson-nucleon scattering from the causal nature of a local-field theory. In this section we shall show that the electromagnetic structure factor satisfies requirements that are analogous to the properties of the meson-nucleon scattering amplitude. We therefore infer that it has a spectral representation similar to the dispersion relation for the scattering amplitude. Our discussion closely follows that in reference 11.

We shall write the form factor for the emission of a virtual four-vector quantum with momentum $q_\mu (0\leq q^2)$,

$$\bar{u}(p's')F_\mu(p',q;p)u(p,s), \tag{6.1}$$

where the nucleon makes a transition from the state with momentum p, spin and isotopic spin s, to the state p', s'; u and $\bar{u}$ are the usual normalized spinors. The index s will be suppressed where no loss of clarity results. If the field operator $A_\mu(x)$ for the virtual electromagnetic field is introduced in addition to the

[11] Bogoliubov Medvedev, and Polivanov, Institute for Advanced Study Notes, Princeton, New Jersey, 1956 (unpublished).

[12] Bremermann, Oehme, and Taylor, Phys. Rev. **109**, 2178 (1958).

nucleon operators $\bar{\psi}(x)$ and $\psi(x)$, we can consider the function in Eq. (6.1) as an S-matrix element to which the reduction formulas[11] can be applied:

$$\bar{u}(p's')F_\mu(p',q;p)u(p,s)=(p's',q_\mu|S|ps)$$

$$=\frac{1}{(2\pi)^3}\int d^4x\,d^4y\,e^{-iqx}e^{ipy}\times\left(p's'\left|\frac{\delta^2 S}{\delta A_\mu(x)\delta\bar{\psi}(y)}S^\dagger\right|0\right)u(ps)$$

$$=-\frac{1}{(2\pi)^3}\int d^4x\,d^4y\,e^{-iqx}e^{ipy}\times(p's'|T(j_\mu(x)\bar{\eta}_\beta(y)|0)u(p,s),\quad(6.2)$$

plus a possible local contribution to the integrand when $x=y$. Here the currents are

$$j_\mu(x)=i\frac{\delta S}{\delta A_\mu(x)}S^\dagger,\quad \bar{\eta}_\beta(y)=i\frac{\delta S}{\delta\psi_\beta(y)}S^\dagger.\qquad(6.3)$$

In the final step of Eq. (6.2), the causality conditions have been used in the form

$$\delta j_\mu(x)/\delta\psi_\beta(y)=0,\quad x_0>y_0\quad\text{or}\quad(x-y^2)>0;$$
$$\delta\bar{\eta}_\beta(y)/\delta A_\mu(x)=0,\quad x_0<y_0\quad\text{or}\quad(x-y)^2>0.\quad(6.4)$$

We may now define the causal function $S^{(c)}$ and a set of related covariant functions,

$$(p'|T[j_\mu(x),\bar{\eta}_\beta(y)]|0)=-ie^{-\frac{1}{2}ip'(x+y)}S_{\mu\beta}{}^c(x-y);\quad(6.5a)$$

$$(p'|\delta j_\mu(x)/\delta\psi_\beta(y)|0)=-e^{-\frac{1}{2}ip'(x+y)}S_{\mu\beta}{}^{(\mathrm{adv})}(x-y);\quad(6.5b)$$

$$(p'|\delta\bar{\eta}_\beta(y)/\delta A_\mu(x)|0)=-e^{-\frac{1}{2}ip'(x+y)}S_{\mu\beta}{}^{(\mathrm{ret})}(x-y);\quad(6.5c)$$

$$(p'|j_\mu(x)\bar{\eta}_\beta(y)|0)=-ie^{-\frac{1}{2}ip'(x+y)}S_{\mu\beta}{}^{(-)}(x-y);\quad(6.5d)$$

$$(p'|\bar{\eta}_\beta(y)j_\mu(x)|0)=ie^{-\frac{1}{2}ip'(x+y)}S_{\mu\beta}{}^{(+)}(x-y).\quad(6.5e)$$

The translation invariance of the field equations assures that the functions $S^{(i)}$ defined in this way are functions only of the difference $x-y$. Two useful relations among these functions are

$$S_{\mu\beta}{}^{(c)}(x)=S_{\mu\beta}{}^{(\mathrm{adv})}(x)+S_{\mu\beta}{}^{(-)}(x)=S_{\mu\beta}{}^{(\mathrm{ret})}(x)-S_{\mu\beta}{}^{(+)}(x),\quad(6.6a)$$

and

$$S_{\mu\beta}{}^{(\mathrm{ret})}(x)=S_{\mu\beta}{}^{(\mathrm{adv})}(x)=S_{\mu\beta}{}^{(+)}(x)+S_{\mu\beta}{}^{(-)}(x).\quad(6.6b)$$

In terms of the Fourier transform $G^{(i)}(k)$,

$$S^{(i)}(x)=\frac{1}{(2\pi)^4}\int e^{ikx}G^{(i)}(k)d^4k,$$
$$G^{(i)}(k)=\int e^{-ikx}S^{(i)}(x)d^4x,\qquad(6.7)$$

the form-factor Eq. (6.2) is written

$$\bar{u}(p',s')F_\mu(p',q;p)u(p,s)=2\pi i\delta(p-q-p')G_{\mu\beta}{}^{(i)}(\tfrac{1}{2}p'+q)u(p,s).\quad(6.8)$$

The quantity of physical interest is this form factor considered as a function of positive q^2 when

$$p^2=p'^2=-M^2,\qquad(6.9)$$

where M is the nucleon mass.

Because of momentum conservation (or translation invariance) at least one momentum in addition to q_μ must be varied. The representation Eq. (6.2) we have constructed is most convenient when p' is held fixed, because then the dependence on momentum transfer is contained entirely in the exponential factor

$$e^{-iqx}e^{ipy}=e^{-i(q+\frac{1}{2}p')(x-y)}e^{-\frac{1}{2}ip'(x+y)},\qquad(6.10)$$

which has been used to obtain Eq. (6.8). We shall therefore use the rest system of the final nucleon with the following notation:

$$p_\mu'=(0,M),\qquad(6.11a)$$
$$q_\mu=(\lambda\mathbf{e},+\omega),\qquad(6.11b)$$
$$p_\mu=(-\lambda\mathbf{e},E=M+\omega).\qquad(6.11c)$$

The condition that p_μ be a nucleon momentum leaves ω the only variable (beside the trivial possibility of rotating $\mathbf{e}$), because λ is determined by Eqs. (6.9) and (6.11c) to be

$$\lambda=[(M+\omega)^2-M^2]^{\frac{1}{2}}.\qquad(6.12)$$

7.—In order to establish a dispersion relation we should now like to apply Cauchy's theorem to $G_{\mu\beta}{}^{(c)}(\frac{1}{2}p'+q)$ considered as a function of complex ω. The Fourier integral Eq. (6.7),

$$G_{\mu\beta}{}^{(c)}(\tfrac{1}{2}p'+q)=\int e^{-\frac{1}{2}ip'x}\exp[-i(\lambda\mathbf{e}\cdot\mathbf{x}-\omega x_0)]\times S_{\mu\beta}{}^{(c)}(x)d^4x,\quad(7.1)$$

unfortunately exists only on part of the real axis,

$$\mathrm{Im}\,\omega=0,\quad\mathrm{Re}\,\omega>0\quad\text{or}\quad\mathrm{Re}\,\omega<-2M,\quad(7.2)$$

where

$$|\mathrm{Im}\,\omega|\geq|\mathrm{Im}\,\lambda|.\qquad(7.3)$$

It is necessary to determine, therefore, whether there is an analytic function which is equal to the integral in Eq. (7.1) where that exists, and to locate its singularities if it can be found. In perturbation theory $S^{(c)}(x)$ and $G^{(c)}(k)$ can be exhibited explicitly as polynomials in the momentum components times simple functions of the invariant squares of the momenta, so that the analytic continuation can be carried out by inspection.[7]

We shall proceed by establishing a dispersion relation for nonphysical values of p^2,

$$p^2=-\tau,\quad\tau<0,\qquad(7.4)$$

so that Eq. (6.12) becomes

$$\lambda=[(M+\omega)^2-\tau]^{\frac{1}{2}}. \tag{7.5}$$

We then conjecture that the analytic continuations of the $G^{(i)}$ as a function of τ can be extended to

$$\tau\leq M^2, \tag{7.6}$$

for which they have the required values given by Eq. (7.1) and its obvious modifications.

The functions $G^{(\pm)}$ are the easiest to discuss. By introducing into Eqs. (6.5d) and (6.5e) a complete set of states labeled by the quantum number n, with the rest-energy M_n, and the energy-momentum vector $k_\mu(k^2=-M_n^2)$ we obtain

$$S_{\mu\beta}^{(+)}(x)=-\frac{i}{(2\pi)^3}\sum_n\int d^4k\; 2k_0\theta(k_0)\delta(k^2+M_n^2)$$
$$\times e^{ix(\frac{1}{2}p'-k)}\langle p'|\bar{\eta}_\beta(0)|n,k\rangle\langle n,k|j_\mu(0)|0\rangle, \tag{7.7a}$$

and

$$S_{\mu\beta}^{(-)}(x)=\frac{i}{(2\pi)^3}\sum_n\int d^4k\; 2k_0\theta(k_0)\delta(k^2+M_n^2)$$
$$\times e^{-ix(\frac{1}{2}p'-k)}\langle p'|j_\mu(0)|nk\rangle\langle nk|\bar{\eta}_\beta(0)|0\rangle. \tag{7.7b}$$

In view of Eq. (7.4), q^2 and the momentum λ are now given by

$$q^2=M^2+2M\omega-\tau,\quad \lambda=[(M+\omega)^2-\tau]^{\frac{1}{2}}, \tag{7.8}$$

whence follows

$$|\mathrm{Im}\,\omega|\geq|\mathrm{Im}\,\lambda|, \tag{7.9}$$

for all values of ω, real and complex. The Fourier transforms at the value $\frac{1}{2}p'+q$ can therefore be obtained as

$$G_{\mu\beta}^{(+)}(\tfrac{1}{2}p'+q)\equiv G_{\mu\beta}^{(+)}(\omega,\tau)$$
$$=2\pi i\sum_{n+}2\omega\theta(-\omega)\delta(q^2+M_{n+}^2)$$
$$\times\langle p'|\bar{\eta}_\beta(0)|n+,-q\rangle\langle n+,-q|j_\mu(0)|0\rangle \tag{7.10}$$

and

$$G_{\mu\beta}^{(-)}(\tfrac{1}{2}p'+q)=G_{\mu\beta}^{(-)}(\omega,\tau)$$
$$=2\pi i\sum_{n-}2E\theta(E)\delta(p^2+M_{n-}^2)$$
$$\times\langle p'|j_\mu(0)|n-,p\rangle\langle n-,p|\bar{\eta}_\beta(0)|0\rangle, \tag{7.11}$$

where we have introduced notation to indicate the functional dependence on ω,τ and to distinguish the sets of states $n\pm$ that contribute to $G^{(\pm)}$ respectively.

Since $j_\mu(0)$ is a vector operator, its matrix element $\langle n+,q|j_\mu(0)|0\rangle$ vanishes unless the state $n+$ contains at least two pseudoscalar mesons; hence the lowest-energy intermediate state has $M_{n+}=2m_\pi$ and the function $G^{(+)}(\omega,\tau)$ vanishes over a large part of the real axis,

$$G_{\mu\beta}^{+}(\omega,\tau)=0,\quad q^2>-4m_\pi^2$$
$$\text{or } \omega>\omega_0(\tau)=\frac{-M^2+\tau-4m_\pi^2}{2M}. \tag{7.12}$$

In particular, $G^{(+)}$ vanishes in the "physical" region $\omega\geq0$ where the quantum is really emitted $(E\geq M)$. Similarly, the matrix element $\langle n-,p|\bar{\eta}_\beta(0)|0\rangle$ vanishes unless the state $n-$ contains at least one nucleon and a meson, $M_n\geq(M+m_\pi)$, so that we have

$$G_{\mu\beta}^{(-)}(\omega,\tau)=0,\quad p^2\geq-(M+m_\pi)^2$$
$$\text{or } \tau<(M+m_\pi)^2. \tag{7.13}$$

Since the inequality is always satisfied in the region (7.6) in which we are interested, the function $G^{(-)}$ will not be considered further.

From Eq. (6.6) we may now infer the corresponding relations among the Fourier transforms,

$$G_{\mu\beta}^{(c)}(\omega,\tau)=G_{\mu\beta}^{(\mathrm{ret})}(\omega,\tau)$$
$$=G_{\mu\beta}^{(\mathrm{adv})}(\omega,\tau),\quad \omega>\omega_0(\tau), \tag{7.14}$$

and

$$G_{\mu\beta}^{(\mathrm{ret})}(\omega,\tau)-G_{\mu\beta}^{(\mathrm{adv})}(\omega,\tau)$$
$$=G_{\mu\beta}^{(+)}(\omega,\tau),\quad \omega<\omega_0(\tau). \tag{7.15}$$

8.—To construct the analytic continuation of the retarded and advanced functions we must exploit their space-time behavior, Eq. (6.4). To avoid the branch points at $\lambda=0$ in the integral representations Eq. (7.1), we shall treat the even and odd forms, i.e., the forms symmetrized and antisymmetrized in the sense of the vector $\mathbf{e}$,

$$^{(e,o)}G_{\mu\beta}^{(\mathrm{ret})}(\omega,\tau)=\int e^{-\frac{1}{2}ip'x}e^{i\omega x}$$
$$\times\left(\cos\lambda\mathbf{e}\cdot\mathbf{x},\ \frac{-i}{\lambda}\sin\lambda\mathbf{e}\cdot\mathbf{x}\right)S_{\mu\beta}^{(\mathrm{ret})}(x)d^4x, \tag{8.1}$$

which are even functions of λ. Because $S^{(\mathrm{ret})}(x)$ restricts the integration to the future light cone, these functions are analytic in the region

$$\mathrm{Im}\,\omega>|\mathrm{Im}\,\lambda|, \tag{8.2a}$$

or

$$\mathrm{Im}\,\omega>0, \tag{8.2b}$$

in view of Eq. (7.9). The functions

$$^{(e,o)}G_{\mu\beta}^{(\mathrm{adv})}(\omega,\tau)=\int e^{-\frac{1}{2}ip'x}e^{i\omega x_0}$$
$$\times\left(\cos\lambda\mathbf{e}\cdot\mathbf{x},\ \frac{-i}{\lambda}\sin\lambda\mathbf{e}\cdot\mathbf{x}\right)S_{\mu\beta}^{(\mathrm{adv})}(x)d^4x \tag{8.3}$$

are analytic in the region

$$\mathrm{Im}\,\omega<-|\mathrm{Im}\,\lambda| \tag{8.4a}$$

or

$$\text{Im}\,\omega<0 \quad (8.4b)$$

because the integration extends only over the past light cone.

Furthermore, Eq. (7.14) states that on part of the real axis

$$\omega>\omega_0(\tau) \quad (8.5)$$

the causal, advanced, and retarded functions are equal; they are, therefore, the same analytic function ${}^{(e,o)}\tilde{G}_{\mu\beta}(\omega,\tau)$, regular in the entire complex ω plane with a branch point at

$$\omega=\omega_0(\tau), \quad (8.6)$$

and a cut from there to infinity; we shall take the cut along the negative real axis. A retarded function is obtained by approaching the cut from the upper half plane and an advanced or causal function by approaching from the lower half plane.

Since the discontinuity in $\tilde{G}$ on the cut is known from Eq. (7 15), we can apply the Cauchy theorem to the function ${}^{(e)}\tilde{G}(\omega)/\omega$ if this function approaches zero for large values of ω. In accordance with the discussion in Sec. I, 2, we assume that this is the case, and that ${}^{(e)}\tilde{G}(\omega)$ may not approach zero The resulting dispersion relation or spectral representation is

$${}^{(e)}\tilde{G}_{\mu\beta}(\omega,\tau)=\frac{\omega}{2\pi i}\int_{\infty}^{\omega_0(\tau)}\frac{G_{\mu\beta}^{(+)}(\omega',\tau)}{\omega'(\omega'-\omega)}d\omega'+{}^{(e)}\tilde{G}_{\mu\beta}(0,\tau),\quad \omega>0. \quad (8.7)$$

It follows from covariance arguments that the function ${}^{(o)}\tilde{G}$ approaches zero for large values of ω if ${}^{(e)}\tilde{G}(\omega)/\omega$ does. The spectral representation for that function is therefore

$${}^{(o)}G_{\mu\beta}(\omega,\tau)=\frac{1}{2\pi i}\int_{-\infty}^{\omega_0(\tau)}\frac{{}^{(o)}G_{\mu\beta}^{(+)}(\omega,\tau)}{\omega'-\omega}d\omega',\quad \omega>0. \quad (8.8)$$

9.—We shall now assume that Eqs. (8.7) and (8.8) hold for

$$\tau=M^2. \quad (9.1)$$

The possibility of such an analytic continuation has been proved rigorously[12] only for the case in which the meson and nucleon masses satisfy the inequality

$$m_\pi>(\sqrt{2}-1)M.$$

We believe that this restriction is a result of the method used for the proof and that it will be removed when further progress is made in the study of this problem.

We may therefore write the spectral representations for the even and odd form factors ${}^{(e,o)}F$, which differ from the functions ${}^{(e,o)}\tilde{G}$ only by the constant final nucleon spinor. It is still more useful first to decompose the form factor into the four real scalar functions described in the introduction,

$$F_\mu(p',q;p)=i\gamma_\mu[G_1{}^S(q^2)+\tau_3G_1{}^V(q^2)]+\sigma_{\mu\nu}q_\nu[G_2{}^S(q^2)+\tau_3G_2{}^V(q^2)], \quad (9.2)$$

and to do the same for $G^{(+)}$,

$$G_{\mu b}{}^{(+)}(\omega,M^2)=-2i\bar{u}_\alpha(p',s)\{i\gamma u[g_1{}^S(-q^2)+\tau_3g_1{}^V(-q^2)]+\sigma_{\mu\nu}q_\nu[g_2{}^S(-q^2)+\tau_3g_2{}^V(-q^2)]\}. \quad (9.3)$$

It is clear that each of the functions $g_{1,2}{}^{S,V}$ is related to the analytic continuation of the corresponding $G_{1,2}{}^{S,V}$ in the same way as $G^{(+)}$ is related to $G^{(e)}$. Then the $g_{1,2}{}^{S,V}$ are real functions as a consequence of the Riemann-Schwarz "principle of reflection."

Each of the two functions $G_1{}^{S,V}$ has a spectral representation of the form Eq. (8.7), in which we may set [Eq. (7.8)]

$$\omega=q^2/2M,\quad \omega'=-m^2/2M, \quad (9.4)$$

to obtain Eqs. (2.3) and (2.4) The functions $q_\nu G_2{}^{S,V}$ satisfy a representation of the form (8.8), while $q_0G_2{}^{S,V}$ satisfy one of the form (8.7) with $[q_0G_2{}^{S,V}]_{q_0=0}=0$; both give the same result, which leads to Eq. (2.5) and (2.6) after the change of variables in Eq. (9.4).

III. GENERAL PROPERTIES OF INTERMEDIATE-STATE CONTRIBUTIONS

10.—Having obtained the spectral representation for the form factors, we now focus our attention on the four weight functions

$$g_{1,2}{}^{S,V}(m^2). \quad (10.1)$$

As already observed, these functions contain a sum of terms corresponding to the possible intermediate states in Formula (7.10); thus for each g,

$$g=g_{(2\pi)}+g_{(3\pi)}+\cdots+g_{(2K)}+\cdots+g_{(N\bar{N})}+\cdots \quad (10.2)$$

Each of these partial weight functions g_i vanishes for value of m^2 less than $(m_i)^2$, where m_i is the sum of the rest masses of the particles in the state i. As argued in the introduction, a particular g_i therefore contributes to the nucleon structure only within radii of the order of the Compton wavelength associated with the mass m_i. Thus it is appropriate to concentrate on the functions g_i corresponding to the low-mass intermediate states, in order to discuss the outer regions of the nucleon in configuration space.

According to (7.10) the weight functions g_i are proportional to the matrix element for a virtual photon of mass m to "decay" into the intermediate state in question. It follows that the total angular momentum of any possible intermediate state is one, while under either space inversion or charge conjugation the state must be odd. The total charge is of course zero. Furthermore the total isotopic spin I can be only zero or one, states with $I=0$ contributing to the isotopic scalar part of the nucleon electromagnetic structure and those with $I=1$ to the isotopic vector part.

To obtain a special selection rule for the least massive states, those containing only pions, one may consider the combined operation of charge conjugation and 180° rotation about the y axis in isotopic spin space. Under this operation a pion state is even or odd depending only on whether an even or an odd number of pions is present. Since the states of interest here are odd under charge conjugation, they will contain an even number of pions if the total isotopic spin is odd and an odd number of pions if I is even, i.e.,

$$g_{(n\pi)}{}^S=0, \quad \text{if } n \text{ is even,} \tag{10.3}$$

and

$$g_{(n\pi)}{}^V=0, \quad \text{if } n \text{ is odd.} \tag{10.4}$$

We thus have

$$\begin{aligned} g^S&=g_{(3\pi)}+g_{(5\pi)}+\cdots+g_{(2K)}{}^S+\cdots+g_{(N\bar{N})}{}^S+\cdots, \\ g^V&=g_{(2\pi)}+g_{(4\pi)}+\cdots+g_{(2K)}{}^V+\cdots \\ &\qquad +g_{(N\bar{N})}{}^V+\cdots. \end{aligned} \tag{10.5}$$

If the charge contribution from the three-pion intermediate state were of the same magnitude as that of the two-pion state, one might have an explanation for the difference in second radial moments between the proton and neutron charge distributions. There is no visible reason, of course, why the three-pion configuration should contribute substantially to the charge density and not at the same time to the magnetic moment. However, this same statement can be made in our current state of knowledge about any possible source of isotopic scalar charge, so that the three-pion state must be regarded as a possible candidate to supply the needed scalar charge. At the present time we know of no sensible way to estimate even the sign of the three pion contribution. On one side a closed nucleon loop is required to couple this system to the electromagnetic field and on the other side a nonphysical matrix element for the process $3\pi\rightarrow N+\bar{N}$ (or $\pi+N \rightarrow 2\pi+N$) is involved.

For intermediate states of mass greater than $2M$ the other factor in g_i, as given by (7.10), is the physical transition amplitude connecting the state i to a nucleon-antinucleon pair. According to calculations by Bernstein, Federbush, Goldberger, and Treiman,[13] the unitarity of the S matrix severely limits the size of contributions from such states, a circumstance that gives encouragement to a program of calculation which ignores the high mass region. In particular, the contribution from the nucleon-antinucleon intermediate state is given by the product of nucleon electromagnetic structure factors themselves, evaluated at $q^2=-m^2$, and nucleon-antinucleon elastic scattering amplitudes in the physical region. There seems no reason to think that this $(N\bar{N})$ contribution should be even remotely approximated by setting $G_2{}^{S,V}(-m^2)=0, G_1{}^{S,V}(-m^2)=\frac{1}{2}e$, and using the Born approximation for nucleon-antinucleon scattering, the procedure equivalent to the standard perturbation calculations.[1] This point is discussed further in Sec. VI.

[13] J. Bernstein and M. L. Goldberger, paper delivered at the 1957 Stanford Conference on Nuclear Sizes (unpublished).

IV. FORMULATION OF THE TWO-PION CONTRIBUTION

11.—The contribution to the nucleon electromagnetic structure from the two-meson intermediate state will be calculated in the next two sections. The reasons for concentrating on this part of the process are: (1) it is the only part for which at present anything like a calculation is feasible; (2) there is reason to hope, as explained in the introduction, that the two-meson contribution dominates the magnetic moment.

For an intermediate state consisting of mesons of four-momenta q_1 and q_2 with isotopic spin indices j and k, we have for the spectral distribution function, Eq. (7.10),

$$\begin{aligned} &\bar{u}(p')I_\mu{}^{(2\pi)}(p',p)u(p) \\ &=-\frac{1}{2i}[G_{\mu\beta}{}^{(+)}(\omega,M^2)\mu_\beta(p)]^{(2\pi)} \\ &=-\tfrac{1}{2}\pi\sum_{jk}\frac{1}{(2\pi)^3}\int d^3q_1d^3q_2\delta(q_1+q_2+q) \\ &\qquad\times\langle p|\bar{\eta}(0)|q_1jq_2k\rangle u(p)\langle q_1j,\,q_2k|j_\mu(0)|0\rangle. \end{aligned} \tag{11.1}$$

The second factor of the integrand, i.e., the matrix element describing the disappearance of the photon with the creation of a pion pair, may on the basis of invariance considerations be written

$$\begin{aligned} \langle q_1j,\,q_2k|j_\mu(0)|0\rangle&=\frac{-ie}{(4\omega_1\omega_2)^{\frac{1}{2}}}(q_1-q_2)_\mu \\ &\qquad\times(\delta_{j1}\delta_{k2}-\delta_{j2}\delta_{k1})F_\pi[(q_1+q_2)^2]. \end{aligned} \tag{11.2}$$

Here $F_\pi[(q_1+q_2)^2]$ is a form factor associated with the one-photon, two-meson vertex, normalized to unity for zero argument. This function for positive argument describes the electromagnetic structure of the pion in the same sense as the functions $G_{1,2}{}^{S,V}$ describe the nucleon, and in principle could be measured directly by electron-pion elastic scattering. In practice we shall be forced to set F_π equal to unity ("point pion" approximation) since there is at present no understanding, either experimental or theoretical, of the pion structure. However, this approximation may be postponed until the very end of the calculation, since $F_\pi(-m^2)$ appears simply as a multiplicative factor in the weight functions $g_{2\pi}(m^2)$.

The other factor in the integrand of Eq. (11.1) is related to the meson-nucleon scattering amplitude. Explicitly, if the amplitude for scattering a meson in the state q by a nucleon in the state p, leading to a meson

q' and a nucleon p', is denoted by $\langle p',q'|T|p,q\rangle$, then we have

$$\langle p'|\bar{\eta}(0)|q_1j,\, q_2k\rangle u(p)=\langle p_1',-q_2k|T|p,\, q_1j\rangle. \quad (11.3)$$

Of course, writing $-q_2$ for the final pion energy-momentum implies an extension of the scattering amplitude to a nonphysical region. This extension will occupy Sec. III, 14.

Using the notation introduced by Chew, Goldberger, Low, and Nambu,[14]

$$\langle p',-q_2k|T|p,\, q_1j\rangle$$
$$=\frac{1}{(4\omega_1\omega_2)^{\frac{1}{2}}}(\bar{u}(p')\{[-A^{(+)}(W^2,q^2)+i\gamma_\mu Q_\mu B^{(+)}(W^2,q^2)]\delta_{jk}+[-A^{(-)}(W^2,q^2)+i\gamma_\mu Q_\mu B^{(-)}(W^2,q^2)]\tfrac{1}{2}[\tau_k,\tau_j]\}u(p)), \quad (11.4)$$

where $-q=(q_1+q_2)$, $Q=\frac{1}{2}(q_1-q_2)$, $P=\frac{1}{2}(p+p')$, and $W^2=-(P+Q)^2$, we may carry out the isotopic-spin sum in Eq. (11.1) to obtain

$$I_\mu^{(2\pi)}(p',p)=-\frac{e}{4\pi^2}\tau_3\int d^4q_1d^4q_2\delta(q_1+q_2+q)\times\delta(q_1^2+m_\pi^2)\delta(q_2^2+m_\pi^2)\tfrac{1}{2}(q_1-q_2)_\mu\times[A^{(-)}(W^2,q^2)-i\gamma_\lambda Q_\lambda B^{(-)}(W^2,q^2)]F_\pi(q^2). \quad (11.5)$$

The three-dimensional integrals over q_1 and q_2 have been increased to four dimensions by adding the mass-shell delta functions. It can be seen that only positive frequencies contribute.

12.—It should be noted that in Eq. (11.5) only the charge-exchange scattering amplitudes occurs and that the contribution, as expected, is only to the isotopic vector part of the nucleon electromagnetic structure. Introducing q and Q in place of q_1 and q_2 and then performing the integration over d^4q, we obtain

$$I_\mu^{(2\pi)}(p',p)=-\frac{e}{4\pi^2}\tau_3\int d^4Q\,\delta[(\tfrac{1}{2}q+Q)^2+m_\pi^2]\times\delta[(\tfrac{1}{2}q-Q)^2+m_\pi^2]Q_\mu[A^{(-)}(W^2,q^2)-i\gamma_\lambda Q_\lambda B^{(-)}(W^2,q^2)]F_\pi(q^2). \quad (12.1)$$

The next task is to relate formula (12.1) to the scalar weight functions $g_{1,2(2\pi)}{}^V(m^2)$. Clearly we are to make the identification $m^2=-q^2$, and by standard invariance arguments we find

$$g_{1(2\pi)}{}^V(m^2)=[M\alpha(m^2)+\beta_1(m^2)+M^2\beta_2(m^2)]\frac{e}{4\pi^2}F_\pi(-m^2), \quad (12.2)$$

$$g_{2(2\pi)}{}^V(m^2)=[-\tfrac{1}{2}\alpha(m^2)-\tfrac{1}{2}M\beta_2(m^2)]\frac{e}{4\pi^2}F_\pi(-m^2), \quad (12.3)$$

where

$$\alpha(-q^2)=-\int d^4Q\delta(Q^2+\tfrac{1}{4}q^2+m_\pi^2)\delta(2q_\lambda Q_\lambda)\times(P_\nu Q_\nu/P^2)A^{(-)}(W^2,q^2), \quad (12.4)$$

$$\beta_1(-q^2)=\int d^4Q\delta(Q^2+\tfrac{1}{4}q^2+m_\pi^2)\delta(2q_\lambda Q_\lambda)\times\{[P^2Q^2-(PQ)^2]/2P^2\}B^{(-)}(W^2,q^2), \quad (12.5)$$

$$\beta_2(-q^2)=\int d^4Q\delta(Q^2+\tfrac{1}{4}q^2+m_\pi^2)\delta(2qQ)\times\{[P^2Q^2-3(PQ)^2]/2(P^2)^2\}B^{(-)}(W^2,q^2). \quad (12.6)$$

If we recall that

$$P^2=-M^2-\tfrac{1}{4}q^2, \quad (12.7)$$

then it is clear that these integrals indeed depend only on the single scalar q^2.

13.—In order to exploit these results, the pion-nucleon scattering amplitude is needed in a nonphysical region, in particular in a region where the square of the momentum transfer q^2 is negative. The variable $W^2=-(P+Q)^2$ also takes on nonphysical values, but the dispersion relations permit us to extend the scattering amplitude to values of W^2 anywhere in the complex plane. It is the technique of extension to negative q^2 that is our particular problem here.

Actually, for q^2 less than $-4M^2$, the matrix element we are concerned with can be identified with the physical amplitude for the process $\pi+\pi\rightarrow N+\bar{N}$. In the future this identification may turn out to be useful, but at the moment the only good theoretical approach we have to pion-nucleon matrix elements derives from the prominence of the $(\frac{3}{2},\frac{3}{2})$-state scattering resonance. Any calculation attempted now has to be based on pion-nucleon scattering rather than on pion-pion production of a nucleon pair. This conclusion is reinforced by the empirical fact, emphasized in the introduction, that the "average" value of m^2 in the magnetic-moment weight function $g_2{}^V(m^2)$ is less than M^2, so that we may hope not to have to be concerned with values of $(-q^2)=m^2$ that are greater than $4M^2$. If the high-virtual-mass region turns out to be crucial in understanding the nucleon magnetic moment, our motivation for concentrating on the two-pion contribution will be lost.

So long as one works with Feynman diagrams, i.e., with a perturbation evaluation of the pion-nucleon matrix element, there is no problem about continuing to negative values of q^2; the functional dependence is explicit. The whole point of the approach adopted here, however, is to avoid the perturbation method; and the most obvious alternative is the method already used with some success in the dispersion relations for non-forward scattering, where nonphysical values of q^2 also occur—that is, an extension by means of Legendre polynomials.

It is clear that a polynomial expansion cannot be

[14] Chew, Goldberger, Low, and Nambu, Phys. Rev. **106**, 1337 (1957).

valid for indefinitely high values of $|q^2|$. In fact, as pointed out by Symanzik, the possibility of meson-meson scattering implies that strictly speaking the expansion will not converge for $|q^2|>4m_\pi^2$, a condition which excludes our entire range of integration. However, there is reason to think that meson-meson scattering is weak and that for practical purposes the Legendre expansion may be used for $|q^2|<4M^2$. We shall make this optimistic assumption here, thereby allowing a crude calculation of $g_{2\pi}(m^2)$ in the low-mass region.

14.—Let us start with the conventional scattering dispersion relations in the form used by Chew, Goldberger, Low, and Nambu[14]:

$$A^{(-)}(W^2,q^2)=\frac{1}{\pi}\int_{(M+m_\pi)^2}^{\infty} dW'^2\,\mathrm{Im}\,A^{(-)}(W'^2,q^2)\times\left\{\frac{1}{W'^2+(P+Q)^2}-\frac{1}{W'^2+(P-Q)^2}\right\}. \quad (14.1)$$

$$B^{(-)}(W^2,q^2)=g_r^2\left[\frac{1}{M^2+(P+Q)^2}+\frac{1}{M^2+(P-Q)^2}\right]+\frac{1}{\pi}\int_{(M+m_\pi)^2}^{\infty} dW'^2\,\mathrm{Im}\,B^{(-)}(W'^2,q^2)\times\left\{\frac{1}{W'^2+(P+Q)^2}+\frac{1}{W'^2+(P-Q)^2}\right\}, \quad (14.2)$$

where g_r^2 is the rationalized and renormalized Yukawa coupling constant. As emphasized by these authors, the forms (14.1) and (14.2) correspond to the most optimistic assumption possible about the behavior of the amplitudes as W^2 approaches infinity. There is, however, some experimental evidence to support the optimistic assumption for charge-exchange scattering, the case with which we are dealing here.[15] We note for future reference that the Born approximation; i.e., neglect of $A^{(-)}$ and of the integral contribution to $B^{(-)}$ in the calculation of the weight functions Eqs. (12.2) to (12.6), is equivalent to including in the nucleon form factor only the lowest-order perturbation-theory contribution to the meson current effects.

The only place in Eqs. (14.1) and (14.2) where the dependence on q^2 is not explicit is in the imaginary parts of $A^{(-)}$ and $B^{(-)}$ in the dispersion integrals. It is here that the polynomial expansion is needed. According to Chew *et al.*,[14] these imaginary parts may be expressed in terms of partial-wave "total" charge-exchange cross sections $\sigma_{l\pm}^{(-)}$ for states with parity $(-1)^{l+1}$ and total angular momentum $l\pm\frac{1}{2}$,

$$\frac{1}{k}\,\mathrm{Im}\,(A^{(-)};B^{(-)})=\frac{(W+M;1)}{E+M}\sum_{l=0}^{\infty}\left[P_{l+1}'(x)\sigma_{l+}^{(-)}-P_{l-1}'(x)\sigma_{l-}^{(-)}\right]-\frac{(W-M;-1)}{E-M}\sum_{l=0}^{\infty}P_l'(x)\left[\sigma_{l-}^{(-)}-\sigma_{l+}^{(-)}\right]. \quad (14.3)$$

Here E is the nucleon energy and k the relative pion-nucleon momentum in the barycentric system, while $P_l'(x)$ are derivatives of Legendre polynomials of the cosine x of the scattering angle,

$$x=1-q^2/2k^2, \quad (14.4)$$

which exhibit the dependence on q^2.

Our intention, of course, is to use experimental information about the total cross sections for the first few partial waves in pion-nucleon scattering to effect an approximate evaluation of Eq. (14.3) and thus of Eqs. (15.1) and (14.2). Any single partial-wave contribution can then be extended to negative values of q^2. The difficulty, as explained above, is that the series in l does not converge for large $|q^2|$.

15.—In evaluating the quantities $\alpha(m^2)$, $\beta_1(m^2)$, and $\beta_2(m^3)$ as given by formulas (12.4) to (12.6), we may use the representations (14.1) and (14.2) to carry out the integration over Q, because they give the dependence on W and thus on Q. One obtains inverse trigonometric functions of a variable y,

$$y(W'^2,m^2)=\frac{2q_\pi q_n}{W'^2+q_\pi^2-q_n^2}, \quad (15.1)$$

where

$$q_\pi=(\tfrac{1}{4}m^2-m_\pi^2)^{\frac{1}{2}},\quad q_n=(M^2-\tfrac{1}{4}m^2)^{\frac{1}{2}}. \quad (15.2)$$

The functions are

$$I_\alpha(W'^2,+m^2)=\frac{\pi}{m}\left(\frac{q_\pi}{q_n^2}\right)\left[1-\frac{1}{y}\tan^{-1}y\right], \quad (15.3)$$

$$I_{\beta 1}(W'^2,+m^2)=\frac{\pi}{m}\frac{q_\pi^2}{2q_n}\left[\tan^{-1}y-\frac{1}{y}\left(1-\frac{1}{y}\tan^{-1}y\right)\right], \quad (15.4)$$

$$I_{\beta 2}(W'^2,+m^2)=\frac{-\pi}{m}\frac{q_\pi^2}{2q_n^3}\left[\tan^{-1}y-\frac{3}{y}\left(1-\frac{1}{y}\tan^{-1}y\right)\right], \quad (15.5)$$

[15] Goldberger, Miyazawa, and Oehme, Phys. Rev. 99, 986 (1955).

and the final formulas for the spectral functions are

$$g_1{}^V{}_{(2\pi)}(m^2)=\frac{e}{4\pi^2}F_\pi(-m^2)\bigg\{g_r{}^2[I_{\beta 1}(M^2,+m^2)+M^2I_{\beta 2}(M^2,+m^2)]+\frac{1}{\pi}\int_{(M+m_\pi)^2}^{\infty}dW'^2[M\,\mathrm{Im}\,A^{(-)}(W'^2,-m^2)$$
$$\times I_\alpha(W'^2,+m^2)+\mathrm{Im}\,B^{(-)}(W'^2,-m^2)(I_{\beta 1}(W'^2,+m^2)+M^2I_{\beta 2}(W'^2,+m^2))]\bigg\}, \quad (15.6)$$

$$g_2{}^V{}_{(2\pi)}(m^2)=\frac{e}{4\pi^2}F_\pi(-m^2)\bigg\{-\frac{M}{2}g_r{}^2I_{\beta 2}(M^2,+m^2)+\frac{1}{\pi}\int_{(M+m_\pi)^2}^{\infty}dW'^2[-\tfrac{1}{2}\,\mathrm{Im}\,A^{(-)}(W'^2,-m^2)I_\alpha(W'^2,+m^2)$$
$$-\tfrac{1}{2}M\,\mathrm{Im}\,B^{(-)}(W'^2,-m^2)I_{\beta 2}(W'^2,+m^2)]\bigg\}. \quad (15.7)$$

This is as far as one can carry the calculation without making approximations.

V. ATTEMPTED EVALUATION OF THE TWO-PION CONTRIBUTION

16.—Several different kinds of approximations may be distinguished. First one may take advantage of the dominance of the $(\frac{3}{2},\frac{3}{2})$ resonance in Eqs. (15.6) and (15.7) to treat $W'-M$ as small compared with M, this being the approach which has had considerable success in theoretical discussions of pion-nucleon scattering[14] and photopion production.[3] Of course for making practical use of the polynomial expansions it is also necessary that $m^2=-q^2$ be small—an unfortunate requirement, since for calculation of the electromagnetic form factors an integral over all values of m^2 is involved. Nevertheless, it may be of interest to see how the weight functions $g_{(2\pi)}(m^2)$ behave for small m^2; therefore we tentatively neglect all terms of order $1/M^2$ and assume $|q^2|$ sufficiently small that the polynomial expansions are well approximated by keeping only S and P waves. Formula (14.3) then becomes

$$\mathrm{Im}\,A^{(-)}(W'^2,q^2)\approx k'\left[\sigma_S{}^{(-)}+3\sigma_{P_{\frac{3}{2}}}{}^{(-)}\left(1-\frac{q^2}{2k'^2}\right)\right]-\frac{2M\omega'}{k'}[\sigma_{P_{\frac{1}{2}}}{}^{(-)}-\sigma_{P_{\frac{3}{2}}}{}^{(-)}], \quad (16.1)$$

$$\mathrm{Im}\,B^{(-)}(W'^2,q^2)\approx\frac{2M}{k'}[\sigma_{P_{\frac{1}{2}}}{}^{(-)}-\sigma_{P_{\frac{3}{2}}}{}^{(-)}], \quad (16.2)$$

where $\omega'=W'-M$.

Furthermore, in view of the uncertainties involved it seems legitimate to set all partial cross sections for pion-nucleon scattering, except that for the $(\frac{3}{2},\frac{3}{2})$ state, equal to zero and to approximate the latter by a delta function. From the effective-range approach[16] one may relate integrals over the $(\frac{3}{2},\frac{3}{2})$ resonance to the value of the coupling constant $g_r{}^2$, *viz.*,

$$\frac{1}{\pi}\frac{2M}{k'}\sigma_{P_{\frac{3}{2}}}{}^{(-)}\approx-\frac{4}{9}g_r{}^2\delta[W'^2-(M+\omega_r)^2], \quad (16.3)$$

[16] G. Chew and F. Low, Phys. Rev. **101**, 1570 (1956).

where ω_r is the resonance energy ($\omega_r\approx 2m_\pi$). In this way we approximately evaluate the integrals over dW'^2 in Eqs. (15.6) and (15.7) to find

$$g_{1(2\pi)}{}^V(m^2)\approx\frac{ef^2}{m_\pi{}^2}\left(\frac{2q_\pi}{m}\right)\bigg\{\left(\frac{m^2}{2}-m_\pi{}^2\right)-\frac{8}{9}\left(\omega_r{}^2+\frac{m^2}{2}-m_\pi{}^2\right)\left[1-\frac{\omega_r}{q_\pi}\tan^{-1}\left(\frac{q_\pi}{\omega_r}\right)\right]\bigg\}, \quad (16.4)$$

$$g_{2(2\pi)}{}^V(m^2)\approx\frac{ef^2}{m_\pi{}^2}\left(\frac{q_\pi{}^2}{m}\right)\times\left\{\frac{\pi}{2}+\frac{4}{9}\left[\frac{\omega_r{}^2+q_\pi{}^2}{q_\pi{}^2}\tan^{-1}\left(\frac{q_\pi}{\omega_r}\right)-\frac{\omega_r}{q_\pi}\right]\right\}, \quad (16.5)$$

where

$$f^2=\left(\frac{m_\pi}{2M}\right)^2\left(\frac{g_r{}^2}{4\pi}\right)\approx 0.08.$$

In Eqs. (16.4) and (16.5) only terms of lowest order in $1/M$ have been kept, in order to achieve simple formulas and to facilitate comparison with the cut off model. The first terms in the large brackets are due to the nucleon poles and are seen to be substantially larger than the contribution from the $(\frac{3}{2},\frac{3}{2})$ resonance.

The general form of these approximate (no-recoil, low-m^2) expressions is similar to results obtained by several authors using the cutoff model.[5,17] In that model one finds for the electromagnetic structure factor the lowest-order perturbation result plus relatively small corrections proportional to integrals over charge-exchange scattering cross sections. For the magnetic moment it is the spin-flip cross section that occurs, while for the charge it is the non-spin-flip, the same forms obtained here. If our expressions (16.4) and (16.5) are cut off at $m^2\sim(2M)^2$, numerical results close to those of the cutoff model emerge.[18]

[17] S. Treiman and R. Sachs, Phys. Rev. **103**, 435 (1956); G. Salzman, Phys. Rev. **105**, 1076 (1957).

[18] The algebraic forms of the structure factors so far derived from the cutoff model are more complicated than the spectral representations (2.4) and (2.6) even though the numerical content is approximately equivalent when the approximations (16.4) and (16.5) are employed.

Because of the approximations made, the results (16.4) and (16.5) have incorrect asymptotic behavior. Instead of vanishing at infinity, $g_{1(2\pi)}(m^2)/m^2$ approaches a constant while $g_{2(2\pi)}(m^2)$ increases as m. As explained already, it is not easy to remedy this defect because the polynomial expressions (14.3) and (14.4) are inappropriate for asymptotic considerations, and so long as the behavior at infinity is wrong we cannot calculate the electromagnetic structure factors without cutting off. For pion-nucleon scattering[14] and photopion production[3] it was possible, by use of the spectral-representation approach to local-field theory, to reproduce the essential results of the cutoff model once the position of the $(\frac{3}{2},\frac{3}{2})$ resonance was known. It was not necessary to introduce a cutoff explicitly. We have not been able to do the same here, and we infer that the cutoff model is correspondingly less reliable for describing the nucleon electromagnetic structure than it is for phenomena involving real pions of low energy.

17.—It is interesting to note, however, that in the low-m^2 region our results (16.4) and (16.5) are fairly well represented by making the Born approximation to the scattering amplitude, i.e., keeping only the rational term in Eq. (14.2) which comes from the single-nucleon intermediate state. For example, at the empirically determined "average" m^2 [see Eq. (3.7)] the contribution to the magnetic moment arising from the integral over the $(\frac{3}{2},\frac{3}{2})$ resonance is only 17%, according to Eq. (16.5). Once we recognize this simplifying fact, it is easily possible to evaluate the magnetic-moment form factor with no further approximations other than treating the π meson as a point charge. As stated earlier, the result is precisely equivalent to lowest-order perturbation theory.

It may seem remarkable that a perturbation result can be anywhere near the truth, since it is well known that the perturbation calculation of pion-nucleon scattering is grossly misleading. The main trouble for scattering, however, occurs for the non-charge-exchange amplitude, where the S-wave part is overestimated by an order of magnitude. The g^2 approximation to the charge-exchange amplitude, on the other hand, is not too bad at low energies even in the physical region and, in the nonphysical region required here, is relatively more accurate because one is closer to the pole at $W=M$ than to the $(\frac{3}{2},\frac{3}{2})$ resonance. In the immediate neighborhood of the pole, of course, the perturbation result is exact. The weight functions we obtain now without the neglect of nucleon recoil are

$$g_1^V(2\pi)\approx\frac{ef^2}{m_\pi^2}\left(\frac{2M^2q_\pi^2}{mq_n}\right)\left\{\frac{2}{y_0}\left(1-\frac{1}{y_0}\tan^{-1}y_0\right)\right.$$
$$\left.-\frac{m^2}{4q_n^2}\left[\tan^{-1}y_0-\frac{3}{y_0}\left(1-\frac{1}{y_0}\tan^{-1}y_0\right)\right]\right\},\quad(17.1)$$

and

$$g_2^V(2\pi)\approx\frac{ef^2}{m_\pi^2}\left(\frac{M^3q_\pi^2}{mq_n^3}\right)$$
$$\times\left\{\tan^{-1}y_0-\frac{3}{y_0}\left(1-\frac{1}{y_0}\tan^{-1}y_0\right)\right\},\quad(17.2)$$

where now

$$y_0=\frac{2q_\pi q_n}{\frac{1}{2}m^2-m_\pi^2}.\quad(17.3)$$

One is tempted to assume that the weight functions $g_{1,2}(m^2)$ are everywhere reasonably well represented by this approximation and proceed to an evaluation of the structure factors. The anomalous (vector) nucleon magnetic moment obtained from Eq. (17.1) is $1.5e/2M$, quite near the experimental value $1.84e/2M$, although the close agreement must be fortuitous because the mean square radius of the magnetic moment, similarly calculated, is only about half the experimental value. Nevertheless we may regard the perturbation result as giving a qualitative and perhaps a semiquantitative representation of $g_2(m^2)$.

Assuming the same to be true for $g_1(m^2)$, one may use Eq. (17.2) to estimate the mean square radius of the vector-charge cloud [Eq. (4.2)]. The result for $(r_\rho^{-2})^V$ is $0.24m_\pi^{-2}$, which agrees with the measured value[4,6] within the fairly large experimental uncertainties. It should be remarked that these results for the vector charge and magnetic-moment structure obtained from the local theory, using only the Born approximation to the meson-nucleon scattering amplitude, are not very different from those given by the cutoff model in the same approximation (both being in reasonable agreement with experiment). That is to say, the effect of nucleon recoil in the Born contribution introduces a natural "cutoff" in the neighborhood of $m^2=(2M)^2$. Presumably, if a correct method for handling the scattering corrections could be formulated, a natural cutoff would appear there also.

VI. SUMMARY AND DISCUSSION

18.—The reader may at this point feel that the authors have perpetrated a fraud, cloaking nothing more than old-fashioned perturbation theory in a vast cloud of words and equations. To refute this impression let us review what has been accomplished, starting with the problem of the magnetic-moment structure, which is much clearer than that of the charge.

We began with the observation that in the framework of the spectral representation the observed qualitative properties of the anomalous nucleon magnetic moment suggest that it is due principally to the two-pion intermediate state. We then attempted a calculation of this contribution and had to deal with the problem of extending the meson-nucleon scattering amplitude into the region of negative squared momentum transfer. However, it was found that for small values of $m^2=-q^2$

the main part of the weight function $g_{2(2\pi)}{}^V(m^2)$ was due to the nucleon pole in the pion-nucleon scattering amplitude, which depends only on the renormalized Yukawa coupling constant and which can be extended without difficulty. Thus it seems reasonable to ignore the scattering corrections and to use only the nucleon pole in order to gain a rough idea of the content of the local theory. When this is done, one finds a magnitude for the static anomalous moment and a "size" which are in semiquantitative agreement with the observations. Our conclusion from this result is that a correct calculation based on the local theory may very well yield complete agreement with experiment. The fact that the practical estimate finally carried out here is equivalent to a piece of lowest-order perturbation theory is irrelevant to the validity of this estimate.

It has of course not been shown that more complicated intermediate states fail to contribute appreciably to the magnetic moment. Here we are unable even to make an estimate until some understanding has been developed of the matrix elements coupling these states on one side to the electromagnetic field and on the other side to the nucleon.

The particular high-mass intermediate state that has discredited local-field theory in the magnetic moment problem is the $N\bar{N}$ system, whose contribution when evaluated by perturbation theory is of the same order of magnitude as that of the two-pion state and which contains a large incorrect isotopic scalar part. The reader may well ask why he should disbelieve perturbation theory for the $N\bar{N}$ state when he is asked to accept it for the 2π configuration. The situations in these two cases, however, are quite different, because in the former the relevant scattering matrix element $(N+\bar{N}\rightarrow N+\bar{N})$ is to be evaluated in the physical region and there is no reason to think it is even remotely approximated by the second-order Born approximation. This approximation is known to be totally misleading even for nucleon-nucleon scattering, and in the nucleon-antinucleon problem the influence of annihilation processes on elastic scattering is enormous. Furthermore the $N\bar{N}$ contribution to the magnetic moment involves the nucleon structure factors $G_{1,2}{}^{S,V}$, which we *know* are important but which are ignored in the perturbation calculation. The corresponding pion-structure factor F_π, which occurs in the 2π contribution, *may* be important but there is no evidence to this effect.

19.—The situation with regard to the charge structure of the nucleon is not nearly so clear, but we feel that in this case also one should not conclude that local-field theory is incapable of ever explaining the known facts. In particular the fairly large "charge radius" observed for the proton[4] does *not* imply that the two-pion state is the main contributor. It is quite possible that an isotopic scalar part, approximately equal in magnitude to the vector part, will be forthcoming from the 3π state to produce the required small charge radius for the neutron.

ACKNOWLEDGMENT

We should like to thank M. L. Goldberger for advance communication of the results obtained by his group.

PAPER 48*

Form Factor of the Photopion Matrix Element at Resonance*

W. K. H. PANOFSKY AND E. A. ALLTON
High-Energy Physics Laboratory, Stanford University, Stanford, California
(Received February 6, 1958)

The inelastic scattering of electrons in hydrogen leading to pion formation has been examined. Measurements were carried out in which a hydrogen target was bombarded by electrons of energy E_1 with secondary electrons of energy E_2 being detected by a magnetic analyzer at a fixed angle of 75°. The energies E_1 and E_2 were programed together such that the pions were produced at a constant energy near the peak of the pion-nucleon resonance in the $(\frac{3}{2},\frac{3}{2})$ state; at the same time the momentum transfer to the pion-nucleon system was varied. Special procedures were developed to eliminate contributions from competing processes. Approximately three fourths of the observed cross section corresponds to magnetic-dipole absorption of the incident virtual photon; the momentum transfer dependence can be interpreted in terms of a form factor of the difference between the magnetic moments of the neutron and proton. If the electron-scattering radii are assumed for the proton, then the data appear to require an rms radius of the magnetic moment of the neutron of about 1.1×10^{-13} cm, based on an exponential model; nucleon recoil corrections are still somewhat uncertain.

I. INTRODUCTION

A. General

IN a series of earlier papers[1–3] we have described our study of the direct production of π mesons in inelastic electron-proton collisions. In the previous experiments the π^+-meson yield from the reaction

$$e+p\rightarrow n+\pi^+ +e' \tag{1}$$

was measured and compared with the yield from the photopion process

$$\gamma+p\rightarrow n+\pi^+; \tag{2}$$

i.e., the yields of π^+ mesons from protons bombarded by real and virtual photons have been compared. The inelastic scattering reaction (1) and the photoproduction process (2) are nearly equivalent with the following basic difference: the interaction Hamiltonian of (2) is the product of the purely transverse photon vector potential with the current operator of the meson-nucleon current, while the corresponding Hamiltonian of (1) is the product of the Møller potential corresponding to the initial and final electron states times the meson-nucleon current. This general fact has the following consequences: (a) In the photoprocess the energy transfer to the nucleon-meson system is equal to the momentum transfer; in the electron process the energy transfer and the momentum transfer can be independently controlled by proper choice of the electron-scattering kinematics. (b) Longitudinal matrix elements can contribute to (1) but not to (2).

In our previous experiments[1–3] the quantitative significance of these effects was very difficult to establish. The reason for this problem is that the Møller potential favors electron-scattering processes where the final electron is directed in the forward direction; for

* Supported in part by the joint program of the Office of Naval Research, the U. S. Atomic Energy Commission, and the U. S. Air Force, Office of Scientific Research.

1 Panofsky, Newton, and Yodh, Phys. Rev. **98**, 751 (1955).
2 Panofsky, Woodward, and Yodh, Phys. Rev. **102**, 1392 (1956).
3 G. B. Yodh and W. K. H. Panofsky, Phys. Rev. **105**, 731 (1957).

* *See page 685 of this volume for corrections and addenda.*

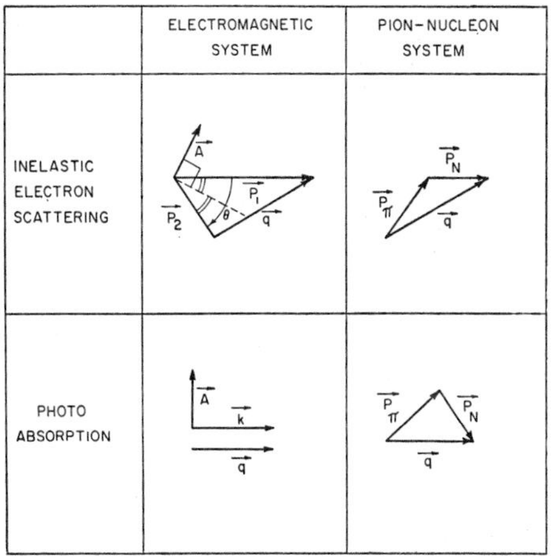

FIG. 1. Vector diagram showing the production of mesons by inelastic electron scattering and by photoproduction. Shown are the following quantities: meson momentum $\mathbf{p}_\pi$, nucleon recoil momentum $\mathbf{p}_N$, momentum transfer $\mathbf{q}$, the vector potential $\mathbf{A}$ for both processes, the initial and final momenta $\mathbf{p}_1$ and $\mathbf{p}_2$ in electron scattering, and the photon momentum $\mathbf{k}$ in photoproduction.

exact forward scattering the correspondence between processes (1) and (2) is exact (if the electron rest mass can be neglected), and therefore no information on the specific effects (a) and (b) results. Hence only the relatively small contribution from large-angle electron scattering carries any information beyond verification

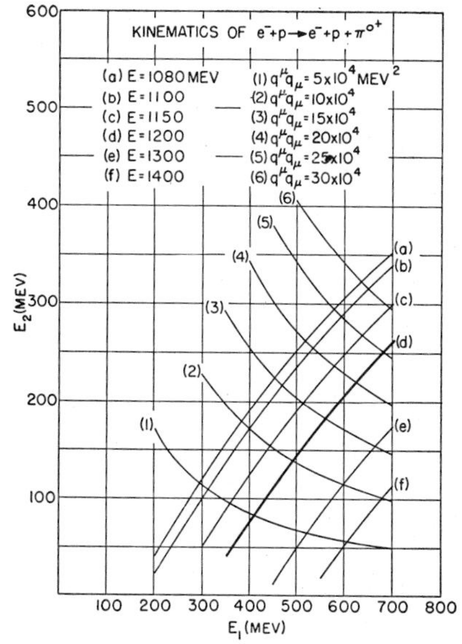

FIG. 2. Curves of constant c.m. energy E and constant invariant momentum transfer $q^\mu q_\mu$ as a function of initial and final electron energies E_1 and E_2.

of the purely electrodynamic assumptions. It became clear early in the previous work that it would be necessary to single out large-angle scattering events in order to investigate the property of the relevant matrix elements "off the energy shell," i.e., at momentum transfers exceeding the energy transfer.

The experiments described here are concerned with this problem. Inelastically scattered electrons are observed at a laboratory scattering angle of $\theta=75°$ under conditions of electron energies to correspond to pion production. The pions are not observed directly; a coincidence experiment observing both pions and electrons appears difficult.

B. Kinematics

In the experiment described here the initial electron energy (energy E_1, momentum $\mathbf{p}_1$) and the final electron energy and angle (energy E_2, momentum $\mathbf{p}_2$) are controlled. This fixes the momentum transfer

$$\mathbf{q}=\mathbf{p}_1-\mathbf{p}_2 \tag{3}$$

to the meson-nucleon system, as well as the total energy E of the meson-nucleon system in their center-of-mass frame which can be shown to be given by the relation

$$E^2=M^2-2E_1E_2(1-\cos\theta)+2(E_1-E_2)M, \tag{4}$$

where M is the nucleon mass and where the electron rest mass has been neglected. (We use units such that $\hbar=c=1$.) Equations (3) and (4) thus fix both the energy and momentum transfers; in the equivalent case of bombardment by a photon of energy k, we have simply

$$\mathbf{q}=\mathbf{k};\quad E^2=M^2+2kM. \tag{5}$$

Hence the kinematical conditions in inelastic electron scattering are identical to those in an experiment in which the sums of the total cross sections of π^+ and π^0 production were measured. Figure 1 shows the kinematical situation graphically; photoprocesses and electron processes are compared which yield the same value of E but operate under different conditions of momentum transfer.

The quantity describing the behavior of the matrix elements covariantly if the energy transfer E_1-E_2 and the momentum transfer $\mathbf{p}_1-\mathbf{p}_2$ differ, is the four-momentum transfer $q^\mu=(\mathbf{p}_1-\mathbf{p}_2, E_1-E_2)$; its magnitude is given by

$$\begin{aligned} q^\mu q_\mu &= 2(E_1E_2-p_1p_2\cos\theta-m^2) \\ &= M^2-E^2+2(E_1-E_2)M, \end{aligned} \tag{6}$$

where m is the electron rest mass; if m can be neglected, then

$$q^\mu q_\mu=2E_1E_2(1-\cos\theta). \tag{7}$$

Figure 2 describes the relations governing E and $q^\mu q_\mu$ as a function of E_1 and E_2 at a fixed electron angle $\theta=75°$. The curves in this figure have been computed using the approximate relation Eq. (7).

This experiment has been programmed such that we follow the line $E=1200$ Mev in Fig. 2, i.e., such that the energy of the fixed pion-nucleon system is constant; this energy is the same as that produced by a real photon of laboratory energy $k=298$ Mev, and is very near the maximum of the experimental pion photoproduction cross section.[4,5] The experimentally determined cross section $d^2\sigma/d\Omega dE_2$ thus traces the behavior of the photopion resonance matrix element away from the energy shell ($q^\mu q_\mu=0$).

Because of the finite value of the rest mass of the electron, the energy shell $q^\mu q_\mu=0$ cannot be quite reached; Fig. 3 shows the exact relation computed from Eq. (6) relating $q^\mu q_\mu$ to E_1 for E_1 for E held constant at 1200 Mev. It can be shown that the minimum value of $q^\mu q_\mu$ approached at a fixed electron scattering angle and energy E is given by

$$(q^\mu q_\mu)_{\min}=(m/M)[2(1-\cos\theta)]^{\frac{1}{2}}(E^2-M^2). \qquad (8)$$

If we neglect the electron rest mass, then in the limit of small secondary electron energy the observed inelastic differential cross section $d^2\sigma/d\Omega dE_2$ is directly related to the pion photoproduction cross section σ_k by purely kinematic and electrodynamic relations. From the analysis of Dalitz and Yennie,[6] we can derive the exact relation

$$\left.\frac{d^2\sigma}{d\Omega dp_2}\right|_{q^\mu q_\mu\to 0}=\frac{\alpha}{4\pi^2E_1}\frac{1}{(1-\cos\theta)}\sigma_k, \qquad (9)$$

where α is the fine structure constant. Hence the experimental photopion measurements[4,5] constitute a limiting point to which the measurements off the energy shell have to extrapolate, even though the limit $q^\mu q_\mu\to 0$ cannot strictly be reached physically.

Data have also been taken at fixed momentum transfer and variable E; these reproduce the behavior of the total cross section for photopion reactions.

The dominant term near the photopion resonance involves a magnetic-dipole absorption of the photon when a proton is changed into a neutron; the dominant pion-nucleon final state is then the $T=\frac{3}{2}$, $J=\frac{3}{2}$ state which will govern the relative yields of π^+ and π^0 mesons. The dominant matrix element thus comprises basically three factors: a factor containing kinematic terms, a factor proportional to the difference between the magnetic moments $\mu_p-\mu_n$ of proton and neutron, and the final-state interaction factor which is a function of the pion-nucleon phase shifts. Since we are programming the experiment to keep the energy of the pion-nucleon system constant, the last factor remains constant, and hence the principal unknown is the dependence of $\mu_p-\mu_n$ on the invariant momentum transfer given by

[4] Walker, Teasdale, Peterson, and Vette, Phys. Rev. **99**, 210 (1955).
[5] Tollestrup, Keck, and Worlock, Phys. Rev. **99**, 220 (1955).
[6] R. H. Dalitz and D. R. Yennie, Phys. Rev. **105**, 1598 (1957); hereafter referred to as "D-Y."

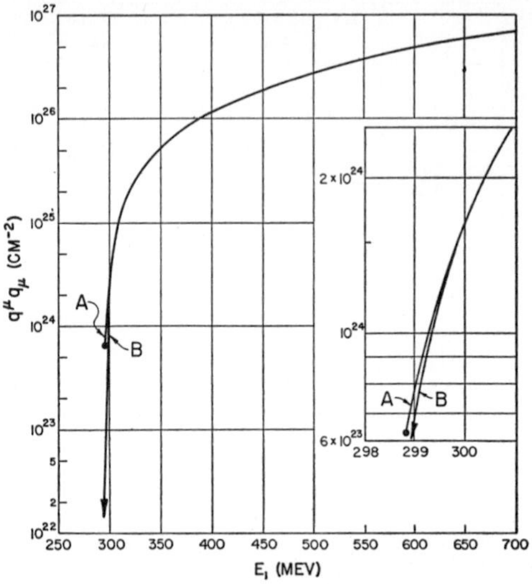

FIG. 3. The invariant momentum transfer $q^\mu q_\mu$ for electron scattering of electrons of finite rest mass m at a fixed scattering angle $\theta=75°$ for a fixed c.m. energy $E=1200$ Mev of the pion-nucleon system, plotted as a function of the initial energy E_1. Curve A is an exact calculation; Curve B is calculated for a zero-rest-mass electron; the insert shows the near-threshold behavior on a larger scale.

Eq. (6). It is in this sense that we interpret this experiment in terms of nucleon-moment form factors.

II. EXPERIMENTAL PROCEDURES

A. General Arrangement

Figure 4 shows a diagram of the experimental arrangement. A double-magnetic-analyzed[7] electron

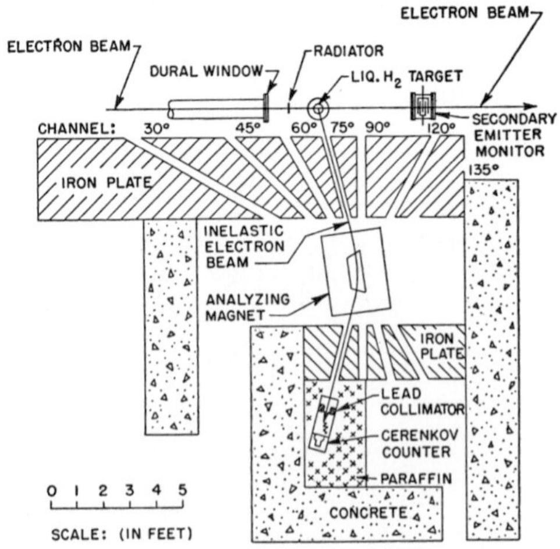

FIG. 4. General experimental arrangement.

[7] W. K. H. Panofsky and J. A. McIntyre, Rev. Sci. Instr. **25**, 287 (1954).

TABLE I. Electron-induced processes leading to degraded final electrons other than the processes of Eq. (10) to be studied. Column I lists those reactions in which the initial electron induces reactions in the liquid-hydrogen target leading to final electrons of lesser energy. Column II lists those reactions in which radiative degradation of the primary beam occurs in the material M preceding the target; the final electron is then produced in the target either by γ radiation or the degraded electron.

I. Processes induced by electrons of initial energy in target	II. Two-step processes involving radiation in material (M) preceding target, followed by reaction in target
(A) $e+p\rightarrow e'+p+\gamma$ [large-angle bremsstrahlung]	$e\rightarrow e'+\gamma(M)$ [radiative degradation in M] *followed by* $e'+p\rightarrow e'(\theta)+p$ [Coulomb scattering in target]
(B) $e+p\rightarrow e'+\pi^0+p$; $\pi^0\rightarrow 2\gamma\rightarrow e^-+e^+$ [by conversion or Dalitz pairs[a]]	$e\rightarrow e'+\gamma(M)$ [bremsstrahlung in M] *followed by* $\gamma+p\rightarrow\pi^0+p$; $\pi^0\rightarrow 2\gamma\rightarrow e^-+e^+$ [by conversion or Dalitz pairs[a]]
(C) $e+p\rightarrow e'+\pi^++\pi^-+p$; $\pi^-\rightarrow\mu^-\rightarrow e^-$	$e\rightarrow e'+\gamma(M)$ [bremsstrahlung in M] *followed by* $\gamma+p\rightarrow\pi^++\pi^-+p$; $\pi^-\rightarrow\mu^-\rightarrow e^-$
(D) $e+p\rightarrow e'+e^++e^-+p$ [triplet production]	$e\rightarrow e'+\gamma(M)$ [bremsstrahlung in M] *followed by* $\gamma+p\rightarrow p+e^++e^-$ [large-angle pair production]

[a] R. H. Dalitz, Proc. Phys. Soc. (London) **A64**, 667 (1951).

beam passes through a liquid-hydrogen target and is monitored by a secondary electron monitor.[8] Electrons scattered from the hydrogen are analyzed by a simple wedge magnet employing a 30° deflection. The electrons are detected by a Čerenkov counter containing a liquid of refractive index $n=1.27$.

The liquid-hydrogen target employs a separate liquid-hydrogen reservoir of 2-liter capacity, and a target cell in which hydrogen gas is condensed. The target cell consists of a cylindrical aluminum spinning of 3.5-in. diameter; the cell was spun from 0.020-in. material and was then electropolished to a thickness of 0.006 in. The reservoir loses about one liter in 24 hr in addition to beam energy loss and loss by incomplete ortho-parahydrogen conversion.

B. Competing Processes

Since we want to reduce the results in terms of the cross section of the processes

$$e+p\rightarrow p+\pi^0+e',\qquad e+p\rightarrow n+\pi^++e', \tag{10}$$

and since the pions are not observed, the question of other processes leading to electrons of reduced energy has to be considered quantitatively.

The possible competing processes are shown in Table I. These reactions have been divided into two classes. Class I contains those reactions in which the primary electron beam produces secondary competing electrons directly on the protons in the hydrogen target. Class II contains those reactions in which a radiative process in the material preceding the target occurs; either the degraded electron or the resultant γ ray produces a secondary electron (or a negative pion difficult to distinguish) in the target material. The various processes are tabulated as (A), (B), (C), (D), by their end products.

We shall now show that, to an excellent degree of approximation, we can eliminate the contribution from all reactions shown in Table I by studying the inelastic electron yield as a function of additional radiating material placed ahead of the target in the incident electron beam.

First let us consider processes I(A) (large-angle bremsstrahlung) and II(A) of Table I. The differential cross section for large-angle bremsstrahlung including all recoil effects can be obtained only as a result of a complex electrodynamic calculation. However, for this purpose the following procedure will suffice: In the limit of infinite nucleon mass the (Bethe-Heitler) cross section contains two separate terms: (a) a term which corresponds to radiation of the initial electron of energy E_1 of a photon essentially parallel to its direction, followed by Coulomb scattering of the resulting electron of energy E_2 through an angle θ; and (b) a term which corresponds to Coulomb scattering of the initial electron of energy E, through an angle θ, followed by emission of a photon essentially parallel to the direction of the final electron. Nucleon recoil, magnetic moment of the nucleon, and finite-size effects can then be introduced as corrections to each of these terms by correcting the relevant Coulomb scattering amplitudes. The integrals of the Bethe-Heitler formula for the two processes have been evaluated from a similar calculation by Schiff.[9] The approximate result is

$$\frac{d^2\sigma}{d\Omega dE_2}=\frac{r_0^2\alpha\mu^2}{4\pi}\left(1+\frac{E_2^2}{E_1^2}\right)\left(\frac{1}{E_1-E_2}\right)\frac{\cos^2(\theta/2)}{\sin^4(\theta/2)}\times\left[\frac{R(E_2)}{E_2^2}+\frac{R(E_1)}{E_1^2}\right]\ln\left(\frac{E_1}{\mu}\right). \tag{11}$$

[8] G. W. Tautfest and H. R. Fechter, Rev. Sci. Instr. **26**, 229 (1955).

[9] L. I. Schiff, Phys. Rev. **87**, 750 (1952).

As pointed out by Schiff,[9] the logarithmic factor is approximate; a more correct factor is $\{\ln[(2E_1/\mu)\times\sin(\theta/2)]-\frac{1}{2}\}$. Here r_0 is the classical electron radius; α is the fine structure constant; and μ is the electron rest energy. The factor $R(E)$ is the recoil and magnetic moment correction which has the form, according to Rosenbluth,[10]

$$R(E)=[1+(2E/M)\,\sin^2(\theta/2)]^{-1}$$
$$\times\left\{1+\frac{q^2}{4M^2}[2\mu_p{}^2\tan^2(\theta/2)+(\mu_p-1)^2]\right\}F^2(q). \quad (12)$$

Here μ_p is the magnetic moment of the proton in units of nuclear magnetons; $q=2E\sin(\theta/2)/[1+(2E/M)\times\sin^2(\theta/2)]^{\frac{1}{2}}$ is the c.m. momentum transfer in the scattering; and $F(q)$ is the electron-scattering form factor[11] to correct for the finite size of the proton.

Equation (11) is plotted in Fig. 5 for those parameters chosen in the basic experiment, namely that relation between E_2 and E_1 corresponding to an energy $E=1200$ Mev of the meson-nucleon system according to Eq. (4) if the scattering angle θ is 75°.

Note that Eq. (11) can be written in the simple form

$$\sigma_{\mathrm{I}}=\frac{d^2\sigma}{d\Omega dE_2}=\left[\frac{\alpha}{\pi}\left(1+\frac{E_2{}^2}{E_1{}^2}\right)\ln\left(\frac{E_1}{\mu}\right)\right]\frac{1}{E_1-E_2}$$
$$\times\left[\frac{d\sigma}{d\Omega}(E_1)+\frac{d\sigma}{d\Omega}(E_2)\right], \quad (13)$$

where $d\sigma(E)/d\Omega$ is simply the elastic electron-proton scattering cross section. The fact that (11) contains the elastic cross sections in factorable form implies that the electron in the intermediate state in the two diagrams governing the bremsstrahlung process is essentially real.

Now let us consider process II(A) of Table I (radiative degradation of the electron prior to scattering, followed by elastic scattering). Let the radiative degradation occur in t radiation lengths of material. The effective cross section due to this process is then given by

$$\sigma_{\mathrm{II}}=\frac{d^2\sigma}{d\Omega dE_2}=\frac{t'}{E_1-E_2}\cdot\frac{d\sigma}{d\Omega}(E_2), \quad (14)$$

where

$$t'=t[kN(k)]; \quad (15)$$

here $N(k)dk$ is the number of photons emitted per radiation length of radiator between energy k and $k+dk$. By the definition of radiation length, $kN(k)\approx 1$ or $t'\approx t$.

In Eq. (13),

$$\frac{d\sigma}{d\Omega}(E_1)\ll\frac{d\sigma}{d\Omega}(E_2). \quad (16)$$

[10] M. N. Rosenbluth, Phys. Rev. **79**, 615 (1950).
[11] E. E. Chambers and R. Hofstadter, Phys. Rev. **103**, 1454 (1956).

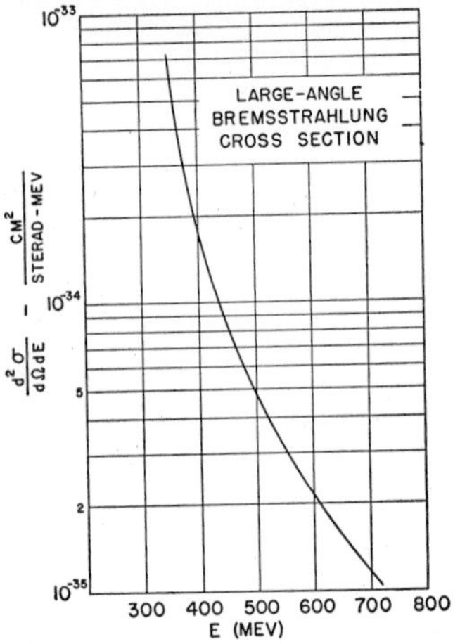

FIG. 5. Plot of the cross section for inelastic scattering of electrons of energy E_1 with the emission of bremsstrahlung leading to a final electron of energy E_2 at an angle of 75°. The cross section is plotted as a function of E_1 for that relation between E_1 and E_2 required by Eq. (6) for $E=1200$ Mev.

To a good approximation we can neglect $d\sigma(E_1)/d\Omega$; Eqs. (13) and (14) then have the same form; both processes are equivalent if we describe the large-angle bremsstrahlung by radiative degradation from an electron energy E_1 to an energy E_2, equivalent to that produced by a physical radiator of radiation length

$$N_B=(\alpha/\pi)[1+(E_2{}^2/E_1{}^2)]\ln(E_1/\mu), \quad (17)$$

followed by elastic scattering.

This analysis suggests the following procedure to eliminate the background due to both processes I(A) and II(A). Let us observe the count C^- under standard conditions where only a minimal amount of material of equivalent radiation length t_i' is in the beam. Then add a radiator of equivalent radiation length t_R' and observe the new increased count C_R^-. The corrected count C_C^- obtained by the simple proportionality

$$C_C^-=C^--(C_R^--C^-)[(N_B+t_i')/t_R'] \quad (18)$$

extrapolates the count to zero total (real plus effective) radiator thickness, and therefore will evidently not contain the contribution of either process I(A) or II(A); we have used the increase in count due to the radiator as a means of measuring the processes in question.

We shall now show that this same procedure serves to eliminate the contributions from the pion processes (B) and (C) of Table I, whether these are induced by real or virtual photons. As we have shown in our previous papers,[1-3] electron-induced pion production can be represented by an equivalent radiation length N_e; this is defined such that pion production by bremsstrahlung produced by electrons in a real radiator of radiation length N_e is equal to that produced by direct production by the electrons via virtual photons.

Theoretical values of N_e have been discussed extensively in D-Y. For purposes of these corrections the value of N_e for magnetic-dipole absorption given by

$$N_e=(\alpha/\pi)[1+(E_2^2/E_1^2)]\ln[2E_2E_1/\mu(E_1-E_2)] \quad (19)$$

is of sufficient accuracy. Computation shows that N_e given by Eq. (19) and N_B given by Eq. (17) are equal to within 10% over the range of variables of interest. Hence the extrapolation formula (18) also eliminates the contributions from all pions and pion decay products.

A similar argument applies qualitatively to the pair processes (D); however, these are two orders of magnitude lower in yield in comparison with (A), (B), and (C).

A sharp test of the validity of the extrapolation procedure represented by Eq. (18) is provided by observing positive secondary particles at rates C^+ and C_R^+, either without or with additional radiator. If the considerations above are valid, then the extrapolated count

$$C_C^+=C^+-(C_R^+-C^+)(N_e+t_j')/t_R' \quad (20)$$

should vanish within the statistical accuracy of the data. Our later discussion of the results shows that this is indeed so. This test is the more significant since the process $\gamma+p\rightarrow\pi^++n$ leads to an additional copious source of positrons beyond those originating from the processes tabulated in Table I.

There are thus two procedures for reducing the data of this experiment: *Procedure* I: Observe C^-, C_R^-, C^+, C_R^+, and calculate C_C^- by extrapolation using Eq. (18); check C_C^+ according to Eq. (20). *Procedure* II: Observe C^- and correct the data directly by the known cross sections (13) and (14); this procedure, since it clearly neglects processes (B)–(D) of Table I, gives an upper limit on the cross sections; owing to the lack of an extrapolation procedure the statistical accuracy is higher. Procedures I and II are expected to agree in the region of high secondary electron energies where the π^0 contributions are small; this is verified by the data.

C. Normalization of Data

The detection apparatus outlined in Sec. IIA does not permit the measurement of absolute cross sections. We thus chose to normalize the measurements against the well-established[11] cross section $d\sigma_e/d\Omega$ for elastic electron scattering. This normalization occurs in regions of electron energy where the form factors[11] are close to unity; hence no significant uncertainty exists in the values of the reference cross section.

The procedure adopted here in comparing the measured counts in the continuous inelastic spectrum corresponding to an inelastic cross section $d^2\sigma_i/d\Omega dE_2$ is designed to minimize errors depending on the performance of the analyzing spectrometer.

In the execution of the experiment we take two kinds of data: (1) inelastic counts $C_i(E_S,E_M)$ taken when the slit selector system of the primary analyzer is "set" at E_S and when the secondary-particle analyzer is "set" at E_M, and (2) elastic counts $C_e(E_S,E_M)$ taken under similar conditions but when E_S and E_M are near the values connected by the equation

$$E_2=f(E_1)=E_1[1+(E_1/M)(1-\cos\theta)]^{-1}, \quad (21)$$

describing the kinematics of elastic electron scattering. Let the number dN of primary electrons between energies E_1 and E_1+dE_1 passing through the primary analyzing system be given by

$$dN=\frac{N}{E_S}S\left(\frac{E_1-E_S}{E_S}\right)dE_1, \quad (22)$$

where N is the total number of electrons and S describes the incident electron spectrum.

Let the over-all detection efficiency of the analyzer at "setting" E_M be given by

$$\epsilon(E_2)=\eta(E_2)R\left(\frac{E_2-E_M}{E_M}\right), \quad (23)$$

where $\eta(E_2)$ is the efficiency of the final counter system. Analysis shows that C_i, $(d^2\sigma_i/d\Omega dE_2)$, C_e, and $(d\sigma_e/d\Omega)$, are related by

$$C_i(E_S,E_M)=N\int\int\frac{1}{E_S}S\left(\frac{E_1-E_S}{E_S}\right)\frac{d^2\sigma}{d\Omega dE_2} \times\eta(E_2)R\left(\frac{E_2-E_M}{E_M}\right)dE_1dE_2, \quad (24)$$

and

$$C_e(E_S,E_M)=N\int\frac{1}{E_S}S\left(\frac{E_1-E_S}{E_S}\right)\frac{d\sigma}{d\Omega} \times\eta(E_2)R\left(\frac{E_2-E_M}{E_M}\right)dE_1, \quad (25)$$

where, in (25), E_1 and E_2 are related by Eq. (21). If the primary spectrum S is narrow compared to the secondary resolution R, then it can be shown from (21), (24), and (25) that

$$\frac{d^2\sigma}{d\Omega dE_2}(E_S,E_M) =C_i(E_S,E_M)\bigg/\int\frac{C_e(E_S',E_M)}{d\sigma(E_S')/d\Omega}f'(E_S')dE_S'. \quad (26)$$

Hence in the actual execution of the experiment we take the count $C_i(E_S,E_M)$ and then vary E_S, the primary machine energy, near values demanded for elastic scattering into an energy E_M; $C_e(E_M,E_S)$ is then a typical "elastic curve" used for reference. Note that the configuration for the detection of the electrons E_2 remains the same during the observation of C_i and C_e; this method is thus totally independent of the behavior of the detecting system as to variation of efficiency with energy, slit scattering, radiative degradation after scattering, etc. In practice, it is not possible to carry out the integration,

$$I(E_M)=\int_0^L \frac{C_e(E_S',E_M)f'(E_S')}{d\sigma(E_S')/d\Omega}dE_S', \qquad (27)$$

in the denominator of (24) to arbitrarily large values of L; we have chosen $L=(5/4)E_S$ in our computation; this means that if the primary beam is radiation-straggled by an equivalent radiation length t_j', then a fraction

$$t_j' \ln\left(\frac{E_S}{L-E_S}\right)=1.39t_j' \qquad (28)$$

is lost to the integral. This amount can be added to Eq. (27) as a correction to a good degree of approximation. The loss of count due to radiation straggling of the scattered electrons is less important.

The normalization procedure outlined above makes absolute current measurements unnecessary. Nevertheless we have to assume that the readings of the secondary electron monitor[8] are sufficiently energy-independent. Tautfest and Fechter[8] carried out tests up to an electron energy of 300 Mev and found the energy variation of the response of a particular instrument to be less than 0.7% in the range 100 Mev$<E<$250 Mev. We have continued these tests up to an energy of 600 Mev by comparing the charge collected on the secondary-emission monitor with that collected on a large Faraday cup. This cup was designed by J. A. McIntyre to contain the entire shower produced by a 600-Mev electron with a charge loss of less than ½%; it has been used as a monitor by the electron-scattering group at this laboratory. Its performance as to small side effects (such as collection of secondary electrons from the entrance foil) has not as yet been evaluated. We found that in the range of energies 300 Mev$<E<$600 Mev the collection efficiency of the secondary-electron monitor relative to the Faraday cup increased linearly from 2.82 to 3.12%. This apparent increase of the sensitivity of the secondary-electron monitor may be due to a residual error in the Faraday cup. Applying this energy variation to our calculated cross sections, we find a correction of +11% to the point taken at $E_1=700$ Mev, and a correction of +9% to the point at $E_1=400$ Mev, with corresponding corrections for the intermediate points; the need for these corrections is dubious.

We have also examined the effect of placing a radiator in the beam on the efficiency of the monitor, and found the effect to be negligible.

D. Energy Calibration

The energy of the primary beam is defined by a collimator and slit system described previously.[7] These were calibrated by the floating-wire technique. Energy values above 100 Mev are believed accurate to better than 1%. The analyzer was calibrated by the floating-wire technique also. The consistency between the two calibrations was checked by the position of the "elastic peaks." Figure 6 shows values of E_2 chosen in this experiment as measured by the floating-wire technique and as inferred from the primary energy. Figure 6 also shows the kinematic relations between E_1, E_2, and E. It is clear from the consistency of the points that the value of E is not likely to deviate from the design value of 1200 Mev by more than ±10 Mev.

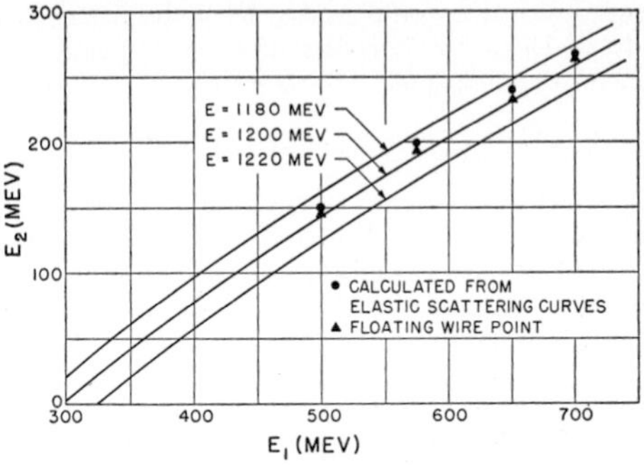

FIG. 6. Values of initial electron energy E_1 and final electron energy E_2 as actually used in this experiment to correspond to a c.m. energy $E=1200$ Mev. Values of E_2 plotted correspond to (a) the nominal setting of the magnetic analyzer as calibrated by the floating-wire method, and (b) the value computed from the peak of the elastic-scattering curves as calculated from the primary energy calibration and Eq. (21). Also shown are the kinematic relations between E_1 and E_2 for c.m. energies of E =1180, 1200, and 1220 Mev. This figure thus documents the consistency of the initial and final electron energy calibrations.

III. RESULTS

A. Tabulation of Data

Figure 7 shows a three-dimensional plot giving the values of $d^2\sigma/d\Omega dE_2$ measured as a function of the c.m. energy E and the invariant momentum transfer $q^\mu q_\mu$. Three classes of measurement are shown: (1) measurements taken at "resonance" at a constant value of $E=1200$ Mev; (2) measurements taken at a constant value of momentum transfer $[q^\mu q_\mu \cong 1.4\times10^5(\text{Mev}/c)^2]$ but variable energy; (3) a curve at $q^\mu q_\mu=0$, computed from experimental photoproduction data by means of Eq. (9). Our conclusions are based primarily on the first class of measurements. Figure 7 serves primarily to illustrate the relation of these measurements to the photoproduction data.

Tables II and III give a summary of our data. Included in these tables are the following entries: C^-, counts with negative analyzer, no additional radiator; C_R^-, counts with negative analyzer, an additional copper radiator of 0.476 g/cm², corresponding to a value of $t'=0.0336$ effective radiation length; C^+, counts with positive analyzer, no additional radiator;

TABLE II. Primary data. Shown are (1) the initial and final electron energies; (2) the c.m. energy E of the pion-nucleon system and the invariant momentum transfer; (3) the observed counts for analyzer magnet settings of either sign and with and without additional radiator; (4) the normalizing integral $I(E_M)$, and $I(E_M)_{corr}$ as corrected for radiation-tail cutoff and monitor calibration.

	E_1 (Mev)	E_2 (Mev)	E (Mev)	$q^\mu q_\mu$ (cm^{-2} $\times 10^{-26}$)	C^-	C_R^-	C^+	C_R^+	$I(E_M)$	$I(E_M)_{corr}$
					(counts/(2.0$\times 10^{14}$ electrons))				(counts$\times$Mev$\times 10^{35}$ / 2$\times 10^{14}$ electrons$\times$(cm^2/sterad))	
Constant E runs	700	262	1200	6.93	21.6±1.2	28.7±1.4	...	...	2.02	1.85
	650	235	1200	5.75	26.9±1.0	33.0±1.0	6.67±0.53	16.6±0.8	1.76	1.61
	575	192	1200	4.13	39.1±1.3	47.4±1.4	11.0 ±0.70	21.4±0.9	1.62	1.50
	500	145	1200	2.75	47.9±0.9	70.4±1.1	12.8 ±0.8	25.3±1.2	1.17	1.09
	400	78	1200	1.13	73.8±2.7	128 ±3.1	31.7 ±2.0	67.5±2.6	0.647	0.617
Constant momentum-transfer runs	440	215	1080	3.46	27.3±1.4	46.1±1.8	...	...	2.09	1.97
	488	193	1135	3.46	30.2±1.7	45.1±2.1	...	...	1.70	1.60
	650	144	1300	3.46	34.6±1.3	62.0±1.8	...	...	1.17	1.06
	700	133	1340	3.46	32.9±1.3	59.0±1.7	...	...	(1.17)	1.04

C_R^+, counts with positive analyzer, additional radiator as given above; $I(E_M)$, the integral of Eq. (27); σ^-, σ_R^-, σ^+, σ_R^+, the counts C^-, C_R^-, C^+, and C_R^+ normalized by $I(E_M)$ and corrected for (a) counts lost by radiation [Eq. (28)] and (b) energy sensitivity of the monitor; σ_C^-, and σ_C^+, the cross sections corresponding to the desired process by eliminating the contribution of the processes of Table I by means of Eqs. (18) and (20); and $(\sigma^-)_{max}$, the "upper-limit" cross section obtained by subtracting the calculated contributions σ_{I} and σ_{II} from large-angle bremsstrahlung and Coulomb scattering of degraded electrons, Eqs. (13) and (14), from σ^-.

We can draw the following conclusions by inspection of this table: (a) The values of σ_C^+ vanish within statistics; the sum of all the corrected cross sections σ_C^+ calculated from Eq. (20) is $(0.028\pm0.064)\times10^{-34}$ cm^2/Mev-sterad. (b) For the larger values of E_1 and E_2 the upper-limit cross sections $(\sigma^-)_{max}$ are only slightly above the extrapolated cross sections σ_e^-; at lower values the difference widens; this is due to the neglect of the π^0 contribution in calculating the "upper limit" cross section $(\sigma^-)_{max}$.

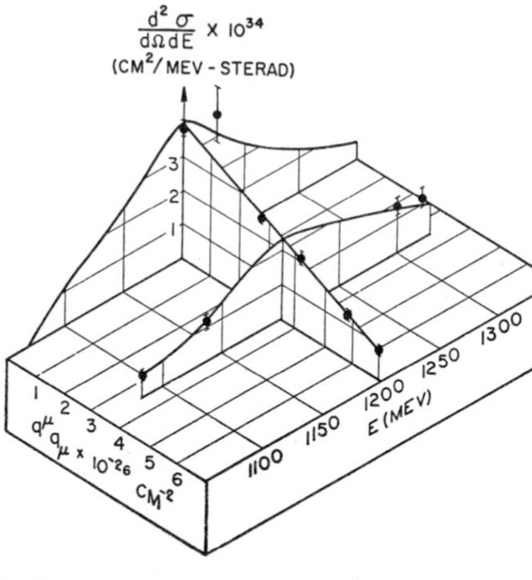

FIG. 7. Three-dimensional isometric plot of the experimental data. Plotted are the measured cross sections $d^2\sigma/d\Omega dE_2$ *vs* the c.m. energy E and the invariant momentum transfer $q^\mu q_\mu$. The points in the $q^\mu q_\mu=0$ plane are computed from experimental photoproduction data.

B. Comparison with Pion Photoproduction Data

The results for σ_C^- have been plotted on the three-dimensional (isometric) representation Fig. 7. The values of σ_C^- and σ_{max}^- for $E=1200$ Mev are also shown in Fig. 8 plotted against the values of the invariant momentum transfer, Eq. (7). Plotted on both figures are the values for $q^\mu q_\mu\to0$ as computed from photoproduction data. The photoproduction values adopted are $\sigma_{\pi^0}=2.50\times10^{-28}$ cm^2 at $k=298$ Mev ($E=1200$ Mev); $\sigma_{\pi^+}=2.06\times10^{-28}$ cm^2 at $k=298$ Mev ($E=1200$ Mev). Hence, from Eq. (9),

$$\lim_{q^\mu q_\mu\to0}\left(\frac{d^2\sigma}{d\Omega dE_2}\right)=(3.81\pm0.30)\times10^{-34}\text{ cm}^2\text{ sterad}^{-1}\text{ Mev}^{-1}. \quad (29)$$

We have found it somewhat difficult to assign a probable error to this figure. The values quoted are means of the measurements made at the California Institute of Technology[4,5]; it is well-known[12] that the analysis of photoproduction data by dispersion theory[13,14] gives an excellent fit[15] to π^0-production cross sections, but that the fit for π^+ production is less satisfactory. If the same coupling constant is used for the S- and P-wave terms, then the π^+ cross section at resonance exceeds the experimental value if the coupling constant is chosen in accordance with the π^0 results.

The "quartic analysis" of Moravcsik[16] does not add

[12] See the report by E. L. Goldwasser, *Proceedings of the Seventh Annual Rochester Conference on High-Energy Nuclear Physics* (Interscience Publishers, Inc., New York, 1957), pp. II-50 ff.
[13] Chew, Goldberger, Low, and Nambu, Phys. Rev. **106**, 1345 (1957), and earlier papers cited there.
[14] A. A. Saganov and B. M. Stepanov, Doklady Akad. Nauk S.S.S.R. **110**, 3 (1956).
[15] L. J. Koester and F. E. Mills, Phys. Rev. **105**, 1900 (1957).
[16] M. J. Moravcsik, Phys. Rev. **107**, 600 (1957). We are indebted to Dr. Moravcsik for helpful correspondence concerning the uncertainties of his data-fitting procedures.

TABLE III. The observed cross sections. The cross sections corresponding to the various counts of Table II are shown. Given also are the cross sections extrapolated to zero-radiator thickness by Eqs. (18) and (20) for negative and positive settings; the column σ_C^- thus represents the final cross sections. The last columns give the theoretical [Eq. (13)] large-angle bremsstrahlung cross sections and the upper-limit cross sections $(\sigma^-)_{\max}$ calculated by subtracting the large-angle bremsstrahlung cross sections and the Coulomb scattering from degraded-electrons from the uncorrected cross sections σ^-.

	E Mev	$q^\mu q_\mu$ (cm^{-2} $\times10^{-26}$)	σ^-	σ_R^-	σ^+	σ_R^+	σ_C^-	σ_C^+	σ_B	$(\sigma^-)_{\max}$
			[cm²/(sterad-Mev)]×10³⁴				[cm²/(sterad-Mev)]×10³⁴		[cm²/(sterad-Mev)] ×10³⁴	
Constant E runs	1200	6.93	1.17±0.06	1.55±0.08	...	...	0.82±0.13	...	0.197	0.97±0.06
	1200	5.75	1.67±0.07	2.05±0.07	0.413±0.03	1.03±0.05	1.33±0.14	−0.165±0.08	0.270	1.40±0.07
	1200	4.13	2.61±0.09	3.16±0.09	0.728±0.05	1.43±0.06	2.10±0.19	0.09 ±0.11	0.458	2.15±0.09
	1200	2.75	4.40±0.08	6.47±0.10	1.17 ±0.07	2.32±0.11	2.57±0.16	0.19 ±0.48	0.875	3.52±0.08
	1200	1.13	11.9 ±0.4	20.8 ±0.5	5.06 ±0.3	10.8 ±0.4	4.8 ±0.8	0.38 ±0.56	2.22	9.2 ±0.4
Constant momentum-transfer runs	1080	3.46	1.39±0.07	2.34±0.09	...	...	0.61±0.15	...	...	...
	1135	3.46	1.89±0.11	2.81±0.13	...	...	1.17±0.24	...	...	...
	1300	3.46	3.26±0.12	5.85±0.17	...	...	1.35±0.25	...	...	...
	1340	3.46	3.16±0.13	5.68±0.16	...	...	1.16±0.27	...	...	...

substantially to the accuracy of computation of the total cross section over the earlier two-coefficient fits used by the original experimenters.[4,5] The values adopted above thus ignore the theoretical incompleteness of the fit of the data to photoproduction data. We are thus considering the point as given in Eq. (29) as being an *experimental* point contributed by the California Institute of Technology work[4,5] to our data.

IV. ANALYSIS OF FORM FACTORS

The matrix elements for pion photoproduction contain the following primary terms: (a) magnetic-dipole

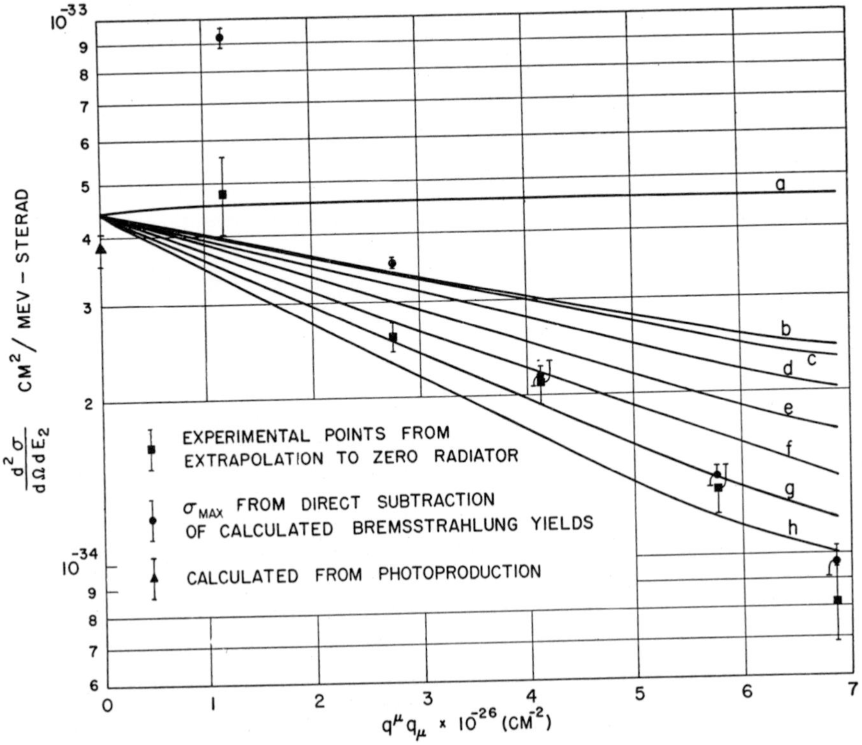

FIG. 8. Experimental data obtained at constant c.m. energy E=1200 Mev plotted against the invariant momentum transfer. Shown are both the extrapolated cross sections σ_e^- and upper-limit cross sections $(\sigma^-)_{\max}$. These measurements are compared with the following theoretical curves: (a) point interaction; (b) a_p=electric and magnetic proton radius=0.8×10⁻¹³ cm, a_n=magnetic neutron radius=0; (c) a_p=0.8×10⁻¹³ cm, a_n=0.2×10⁻¹³ cm; (d) a_p=0.8×10⁻¹³ cm, a_n=0.4×10⁻¹³ cm; (e) a_p=0.8×10⁻¹³ cm, a_n=0.6×10⁻¹³ cm; (f) a_p=0.8×10⁻¹³ cm, a_n=0.8×10⁻¹³ cm; (g) a_p=0.8×10⁻¹³ cm, a_n=1.0×10⁻¹³ cm; (h) a_p=0.8×10⁻¹³ cm, a_n=1.2×10⁻¹³ cm. Radii are rms values based on an exponential model.

absorption leading to the final "resonant" $(\frac{3}{2},\frac{3}{2})$ state of the nucleon-meson system; (b) electric-dipole absorption leading to a final S state of the pion-nucleon system; (c) the "direct interaction" term of the photon with the virtual meson cloud surrounding the nucleus calculated in Born approximation. Neutral-pion production is concerned with the first term (a) only; assuming charge independence, term (a) contributes half as much to positive-pion production as to neutral-pion production. Since at the c.m. energy $E=1200$ Mev used here the neutral and charged cross sections are approximately equal, we conclude that roughly three fourths of the measurements reported here come from the "resonant" term (a); "off the energy shell" the relative contribution of the (a) term becomes still larger.

The primary interpretation of this work will thus be in terms of the nuclear form factor associated with term (a), which is the form factor associated with $\mu_p-\mu_n$. This interpretation is singularly insensitive to a particular choice of constants of a specific theoretical fit since the form factors depend only on the relative cross sections as a function of momentum transfer; constants have to be chosen to agree with experiment on the energy shell; as long as the magnetic-dipole term is dominant, the details of handling the other terms are unimportant.

In the more detailed analysis we have followed the dispersion theoretical analysis of photoproduction by Chew *et al.*[13] extended to the electron-pion process by Fubini, Nambu, and Wataghin.[17] Unfortunately, their analysis is not complete with respect to the inclusion of kinematic nucleon recoil terms; some of the quantitative conclusions can thus be improved as soon as further calculations have been completed.

It was shown by FNW that the electric-dipole absorption term (b) involves the electric form factor (F_1 in the notation of Hofstadter[18] and collaborators); the appropriate factor here involves the difference between the electric form factors of the proton and neutron. Since the neutron's charge and its second moment vanish (as concluded from the low-energy electron-neutron interaction), we have used simply the F_1 factor appropriate to the proton in computing the electric-dipole term, thus assuming the electric form factor of the neutron to vanish even for large momentum transfers. For the reasons enumerated above, we are not sensitive to this assumption; however, further work of this nature, in which the kinematic relations are programmed to emphasize the electric-dipole term, should have important bearing on this question.

The analysis of FNW contains several small terms other than the large contributions (a), (b), and (c), discussed above. These contain the appropriate electric or magnetic form factors linearly or quadratically, depending on whether the terms are interference terms or not. These form factors have been included in the computation treating the magnetic radius of the neutron as a variable, letting the electric radius of the neutron vanish, and taking the electric and magnetic radius of the proton as 0.8×10^{-13} cm rms.

Figure 8 shows our experimental data [both the extrapolated cross section σ_C^- and the upper-limit cross section $(\sigma^-)_{\max}$ of Table II] plotted on a logarithmic scale against the invariant momentum transfer, $q^\mu q_\mu$ (λ^2 in the notation of FNW). The various terms from FNW have been computed by C. Lindner with the collaboration of S. Gartenhaus; the authors are greatly indebted to them for their contributions. The same renormalized coupling constant ($f_r^2=0.090$) was used for all terms in the matrix elements; this gives a reasonable fit to the magnitudes of the neutral-pion cross sections, while the experimental charged-pion cross section is somewhat low; as discussed above, the conclusions are insensitive to the choice of this number. Using the computed terms, we have plotted a number of theoretical curves showing the dependence of the cross sections on various nucleon structure parameters. The following curves are shown: Curve (a), all form factors unity, i.e., all nucleons are points. Curves (b)–(h), the form factor of the electric-dipole term equal to the electric form factor F_1 of the electron-proton scattering results[11,18] has been used as discussed above. The magnetic moment of the proton has been multiplied by the appropriate magnetic form factor F_2; the magnetic moment of the neutron has been multiplied by a set of form factors corresponding to various radial parameters. We have computed the form factors using an exponential radial distribution whose Fourier transform is $[1+(q^\mu q_\mu a^2/12)]^{-2}$, where a is the rms radius. We have used $a_p=0.8\times10^{-13}$ cm for both the electric and magnetic form factors of the proton, in accordance with the electron-scattering results. Unfortunately, the accuracy for small values of the momentum transfers is poor (and is very difficult to improve); hence we are unable to analyze the results in terms of an rms radius without assuming a specific form of distribution. We have used here the exponential model in order to permit comparison with the parameters obtained from elastic electron scattering on the proton and quasi-elastic scattering on the deuteron.[19]

By inspection of Fig. 8 we see that a best fit is obtained for values of a_n between 1.0×10^{-13} and 1.1×10^{-13} cm for the rms neutron magnetic radius, based on the exponential model. The experimental values permit little latitude toward smaller values since the upper-limit cross section $(\sigma^-)_{\max}$ agrees with the extrapolated value at large momentum transfers.

---

[17] Fubini, Nambu, and Wataghin, Phys. Rev. (to be published); hereafter called "FNW." Dr. Fubini acquanted us with this work in the summer of 1957, and Professor Nambu discussed some of the problems associated with the nucleon recoil contributions in December, 1957.

[18] R. Hofstadter, Revs. Modern Phys. 28, 214 (1956).

[19] M. R. Yearian and R. Hofstadter, Phys. Rev. (to be published).

The principal remaining uncertainty relates to the treatment of nucleon recoil terms in the off-the-energy-shell behavior of the magnetic-dipole absorption matrix element. We have been assured[20] that such recoil terms are not fundamentally ambiguous and are subject to calculation. Until such calculations have been performed, we would consider a value of the rms magnetic radius of the neutron as low as 0.8×10^{-13} cm to be compatible with the data.

We should like to add that the experimental method described here has much more general validity beyond the limited range of electron variables explored. In particular, a more complete mapping of the surface of Fig. 7 is being planned. If higher energy electron beams are available, the electromagnetic production mechanism of particles other than the pion can be studied by similar methods.

ACKNOWLEDGMENTS

We are pleased to acknowledge the valuable collaboration of many members of this laboratory in connection with this experiment. A. Grubman and E. A. Wright gave necessary assistance with the liquid-hydrogen target; J. Pope developed the difficult electropolishing technique to produce a liquid-hydrogen cell of well-defined geometry, thin wall thickness, and capable of withstanding intense electron bombardment. The experiment imposed severe requirements on the operation of the accelerator, including reliable operation at 700 Mev; these demands were met by the accelerator operating group under the direction of R. G. Gilbert. We gratefully acknowledge the collaboration of G. B. Yodh in the early planning of the experiment, and the assistance of R. Alvarez, F. Bulos, K. Brown, L. Becker, F. Bumiller, and A. Lazarus during data-taking runs.

Our theoretical understanding of this problem was substantially improved by discussions with Dr. Yennie, Dr. Fubini, Dr. Nambu, and Dr. Gartenhaus; in addition, we gratefully acknowledge the specific contributions of Dr. Gartenhaus and of C. Lindner. We are also grateful to Professor R. Hofstadter and to M. Yearian for keeping us informed on the progress of their work on quasi-elastic electron scattering on the deuteron and its interpretation in terms of the magnetic form factor of the neutron. We also thank Dr. Burton Richter for his help in handling the spectrometer resolution problem.

[20] Y. Nambu (private communication).

PAPER 49

Electron-Deuteron Scattering by the Impulse Approximation*

A. Goldberg†
Stanford University, Stanford, California
(Received June 19, 1958)

The cross section for inelastic scattering of high-energy electrons by deuterons is calculated using the impulse approximation. The results agree with those of Jankus. The cross sections are given for several neutron charge and moment distributions. The peak cross sections are simply related to the free-nucleon cross sections with this approximation.

I

RECENT high-energy electron-deuteron scattering experiments by Hofstadter and Yearian[1] have yielded information about the neutron's electromagnetic structure. In these experiments, the electrons are scattered inelastically, disintegrating the deuteron, and the energy spectrum of the outgoing electrons is measured. The results show an inelastic peak of about 26- to 45-Mev width, centered slightly below the energy of elastic scattering from a free nucleon. The objective of this paper is to relate the peak cross sections or the area under these curves to the sum of the free proton and neutron cross sections. Since the proton cross section has been measured independently, the neutron cross section can then be determined.

Jankus[2] has calculated these cross sections by considering the Møller potential acting on the nuclear charge and current. At small momentum transfers, where the nucleons can be treated nonrelativistically, his results can be fitted to the experimental data. However, for large values of q^2, Jankus' curves show the peak at too low an energy. Blankenbecler[3] has suggested that the corrections to Jankus' results can be estimated by replacing the three-momentum transfer by the corresponding four-vector. With this modification, Hofstadter and Yearian have been able to fit the peak cross sections to their data within experimental limits.

Although Jankus' model breaks up the nuclear charge and current into separate proton and neutron terms, the electrons interact with the deuteron as a whole. Hence he obtains interference effects between the proton and the neutron. At large bombarding energies, with the electron wavelength much shorter than the separation between nucleons, the interference is expected to be small. To test the importance of these interference effects, we have used the impulse approximation to calculate the inelastic scattering cross section as a function of outgoing electron energy.

In this approximation, the nucleons are free particles, with a distribution of momenta due to the deuteron binding. The electron interacts separately with the neutron or the proton as a moving free particle. As a result, the interacting nucleon is given a large outgoing momentum, while the other is unaffected. The scattering from the two nucleons is then incoherent, and one may add the cross section for each process. This must then be averaged over the initial nucleon momenta to give the total differential cross section.

II

If we consider scattering by a free proton of initial momentum $\mathbf{p}_p$, the transition rate for the electron from the state of momentum $\mathbf{k}$ to momentum $\mathbf{k}'$ (energy k

* This research was supported in part by the U. S. Air Force through the Air Force Office of Scientific Research.

† Holder of a National Science Foundation Fellowship for the years 1955–56, 1956–57, and 1957–58.

[1] M. R. Yearian and R. Hofstadter, Phys. Rev. **110**, 552 (1958).
[2] V. Jankus, Phys. Rev. **102**, 1586 (1956).
[3] R. Blankenbecler, Phys. Rev. **111**, 1684 (1958).

and k') is

$$Wd^3k' = \frac{\langle|K|^2\rangle_{Av}}{(2\pi)^2}\delta(E_p+k-E_p'-k')\frac{m}{k'}\frac{M}{E_p'}d^3k'.$$

E_p and E_p' are the initial and final proton energies,

$$E_p=(M^2+\mathbf{p}_p^2)^{\frac{1}{2}},\quad E_p'=(M^2+(\mathbf{p}_p+\mathbf{q})^2)^{\frac{1}{2}}.$$

$\langle|K|^2\rangle_{Av}$ is the square of the transition matrix element, which has been summed and averaged over initial and final spin states, and also summed over final proton momenta, to give

$$\langle|K|^2\rangle_{Av}=\frac{(2\pi)^2}{m^2M^2}e^4\frac{1}{q^4}\Big\{F_{1p}^2[M^2q^2+2(k\cdot p_p)^2+2(k'\cdot p_p)^2]$$

$$-\frac{q^2}{2M^2}(\kappa_pF_{2p})^2\left[(k\cdot p_p)^2+(k'\cdot p_p)^2-\frac{M^2q^2}{2}+q\cdot p_p\frac{q^2}{2}\right]$$

$$+q^4F_{1p}\kappa_pF_{2p}\Big\}.$$

$k\cdot p_p$ and $k'\cdot p_p$ are the invariant four-products,

$$k\cdot p_p=kE_p-\mathbf{k}\cdot\mathbf{p}_p,\quad k'\cdot p_p=k'E_p-\mathbf{k}'\cdot\mathbf{p}_p.$$

F_{1p} and F_{2p} are the proton electric and magnetic form factors, and are functions only of the invariant q^2.

This must now be averaged over the initial proton momentum states. Since the neutron and proton masses are equal, the relative and center-of-mass momenta of the deuteron are

$$\mathbf{p}=\tfrac{1}{2}(\mathbf{p}_1-\mathbf{p}_n),\quad \mathbf{P}=\mathbf{p}_p+\mathbf{p}_n.$$

Taking the deuteron at rest, $P=0$, $p_p=-p_n=p$. Hence the probability of finding the proton with momentum p_p is $|\phi(\mathbf{p})|^2$ where $\phi(\mathbf{p})$ is the deuteron wave function in momentum space,

$$\phi(\mathbf{p})=\frac{1}{(2\pi)^{\frac{3}{2}}}\int d^3r\, e^{-i\mathbf{p}\cdot\mathbf{r}}\psi(\mathbf{r}),$$

where $\mathbf{r}$ is the relative coordinate. $\phi(\mathbf{p})$ is normalized to unit volume, while in the matrix element the plane wave states are normalized to volume $(2\pi)^3E/M$. The initial density of states is then $|\phi(\mathbf{p})|^2(M/E)d^3p$.

Assuming a spherically symmetric wave function, and doing the angular integrals over d^3p, we find that the cross section for electrons scattering into solid angle $d\Omega$ and energy interval dk' is

$$\frac{d^2\sigma}{d\Omega dk'}=e^4\frac{k'}{k}\frac{(I_1+I_2)}{q^4},$$

$$I_1=\frac{2\pi}{|\mathbf{q}|}\frac{q^2}{4}\left\{4M^2F_{1p}^2+q^2\left(1+\frac{q^2}{2M^2}\right)\right.$$

$$\left.\times(K_pF_{2p})^2+4q^2F_{1p}\kappa_pF_{2p}\right\}\mathcal{I}_3,\quad (1)$$

$$I_2=\frac{2\pi}{|\mathbf{q}|}\left\{F_{1p}^2-\frac{q^2}{4M^2}(\kappa_pF_{2p})^2\right\}\{T_1\mathcal{I}_1+T_2\mathcal{I}_2+T_3\mathcal{I}_3\}.$$

The quantities T_1, T_2, and T_3 are given by

$$T_1=\frac{2\mathbf{q}^2-q^2}{\mathbf{q}^2}(k^2+k'^2)-\frac{4q_0}{\mathbf{q}^2}[k\mathbf{k}\cdot\mathbf{q}+k'\boldsymbol{\kappa}'\cdot\mathbf{q}]$$
$$+\frac{2q_0^2+q^2}{\mathbf{q}^4}[(\mathbf{k}\cdot\mathbf{q})^2+(\mathbf{k}'\cdot\mathbf{q})^2],$$

$$T_2=-q_0\frac{q^2}{\mathbf{q}^2}(k^2+k'^2)-\frac{2q^2}{\mathbf{q}^2}[k\mathbf{k}\cdot\mathbf{q}+k'\mathbf{k}'\cdot\mathbf{q}]$$
$$+\frac{3q_0q^2}{\mathbf{q}^4}[(\mathbf{k}\cdot\mathbf{q})^2+(\mathbf{k}'\cdot\mathbf{q})^2],$$

$$T_3=-\frac{(M^2\mathbf{q}^2+\frac{1}{4}q^4)}{\mathbf{q}^2}(k^2+k'^2)+\frac{(M^2\mathbf{q}^2+\frac{3}{4}q^4)}{\mathbf{q}^4}$$
$$\times[(\mathbf{k}\cdot\mathbf{q})^2+(\mathbf{k}'\cdot\mathbf{q})^2].$$

$\mathcal{I}_1$, $\mathcal{I}_2$, and $\mathcal{I}_3$ are integrals over the deuteron wave function,

$$\mathcal{I}_1=\int_{-\frac{1}{2}q_0+\frac{1}{2}[\mathbf{q}^2(1-4M^2/q^2)]^{\frac{1}{2}}}^{\infty}E^2|\phi(p)|^2dE,$$

$$\mathcal{I}_2=\int_{-\frac{1}{2}q_0+\frac{1}{2}[\mathbf{q}^2(1-4M^2/q^2)]^{\frac{1}{2}}}^{\infty}E|\phi(p)|^2dE,$$

$$\mathcal{I}_3=\int_{-\frac{1}{2}q_0+\frac{1}{2}[\mathbf{q}^2(1-4M^2/q^2)]^{\frac{1}{2}}}^{\infty}|\phi(p)|^2dE.$$

Equation (1) gives the cross section for scattering by the proton only. Since the neutron differs only in its form factors, it gives an identical term and the total cross section is the sum of these two. Hence in I_1 and I_2, F_{1p}^2, $F_{1p}K_pF_{2p}$, and $(K_pF_{2p})^2$ are replaced by

$$F_1^2=F_{1p}^2+F_{1n}^2,$$
$$F_1KF_2=F_{1p}K_pF_{2p}+F_{1n}K_nF_{2n},$$
$$(KF_2)^2=(K_pF_{2p})^2+(K_nF_{2n})^2.$$

Equation (1) then gives the total cross section for scattering by the deuteron.

It can be shown that the lower limit for the integrals $\mathcal{I}_1$, $\mathcal{I}_2$, and $\mathcal{I}_3$ is greater than or equal to M. Hence the peak cross section occurs when these integrals extend over their maximum range, from M to ∞. In this case, one has

$$k'=k/[1+2(k/M)\sin^2(\tfrac{1}{2}\theta)],$$

that is, the peak energy should occur at the energy of elastic scattering by a free nucleon. Experimentally, the peak is about 2 Mev below this, probably due to the deuteron binding energy. To account for this, we must note that the energy available to the nucleon after the collision is decreased by the deuteron binding energy ϵ. The energy of the peak is then approximately

$$k'=\frac{k}{1+(2k/M)\sin^2\frac{1}{2}\theta}-\frac{k}{M}\frac{\epsilon}{1+(2k/M)\sin^2\frac{1}{2}\theta}.$$

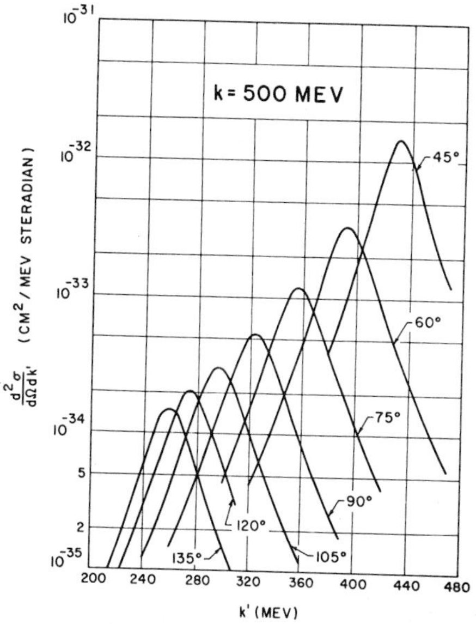

FIG. 1. Each curve is the cross section for 500-Mev electrons at the angle shown *vs* outgoing energy.

This is roughly equivalent to considering the mass of the nucleon to be decreased by some average potential.[4] For the purposes of computation, we have taken the nucleons to be in an attractive well of average depth 20 Mev. The major effect of this is to shift the curve down to the right peak energy. The peak heights are raised by approximately 5%.

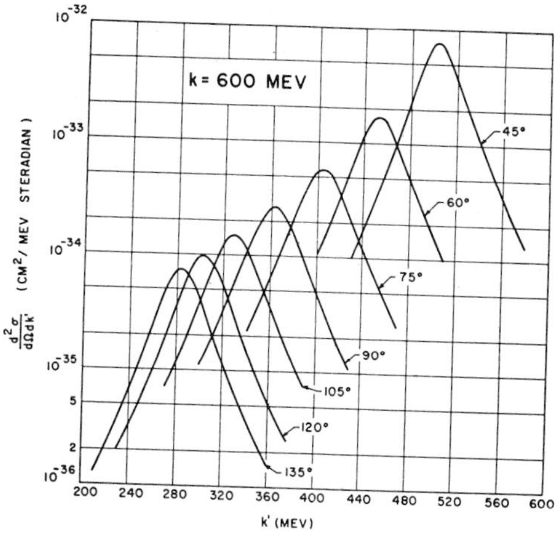

FIG. 2. Each curve is the cross section for 600-Mev electrons at the angle shown *vs* outgoing energy.

[4] R. Blankenbecler; the theoretical consequences of this are discussed in a paper to be published shortly.

III

The proton form factors are known from electron-proton scattering[5] to be[6]

$$F_{1p}=F_{2p}=\alpha^4/(\alpha^2-q^2)^2, \quad \alpha=4.32 \text{ fermi}^{-1}$$
$$(1 \text{ fermi}=10^{-13} \text{ cm}).$$

This corresponds to a charge distribution of mean square radius 0.80 fermi. The neutron electric form factor must satisfy the requirement that the total charge and mean square radius be zero.[7] Elastic electron-deuteron scattering data[8] are consistent with zero neutron charge distribution, i.e., $F_{1n}=0$. Hofstadter and Yearian also fit their data to Jankus' model with $F_{1n}=0$, finding the magnetic form factor equal to that of the proton. With these choices, we have computed

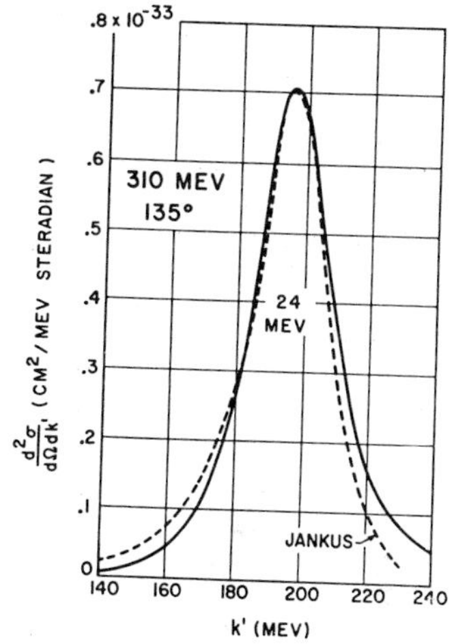

FIG. 3. Cross section at 310-Mev incident energy and scattering angle of 135° *vs* outgoing energies. (The dashed-line curve is that based on Jankus' model.)

the inelastic cross sections at electron energies of 500 and 600 Mev from 45° to 135° scattering angle. We have used the same deuteron wave function as Jankus, the Hulthén wave function

$$\psi(r)=\left[\frac{\gamma_1\gamma_2(\gamma_1+\gamma_2)}{2\pi(\gamma_1-\gamma_2)^2}\right]^{\frac{1}{2}}\left(\frac{e^{-\gamma_1 r}-e^{-\gamma_2 r}}{r}\right),$$

$$\phi(p)=\left[\frac{\gamma_1\gamma_2(\gamma_1+\gamma_2)}{\pi^2(\gamma_1-\gamma_2)^2}\right]^{\frac{1}{2}}\left\{\frac{1}{p^2+\gamma_1^2}-\frac{1}{p^2+\gamma_2^2}\right\},$$

$$\gamma_1=2.316\times10^{12} \text{ cm}^{-1}=46.03 \text{ Mev}, \quad \gamma_2=6.21\gamma_1.$$

The results are shown in Figs. 1 and 2. Each curve gives the outgoing electron energy spectrum for given

[5] E. E. Chambers and R. Hofstadter, Phys. Rev. **103**, 1454 (1956).
[6] In this metric q^2 is negative.
[7] L. Foldy, Phys. Rev. **87**, 693 (1952).
[8] J. McIntyre and S. Dhar, Phys. Rev. **106**, 1074 (1957).

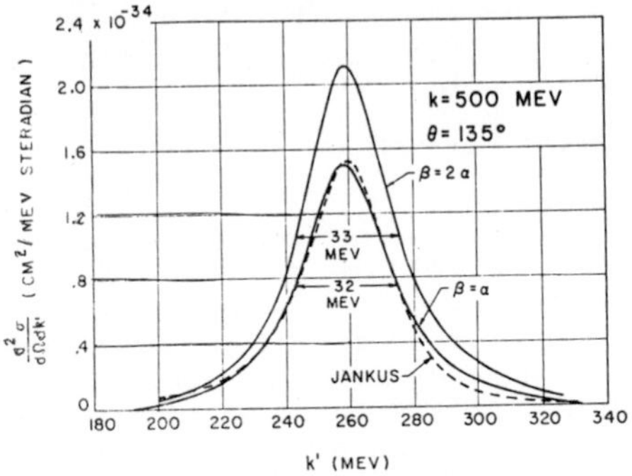

FIG. 4. Cross section at 500 Mev incident energy and scattering angle of 135° *vs* outgoing energies. (The dashed-line curve is that based on Jankus' model.) The $\beta=2\alpha$ curve shows the effect of Schiff's form factor (see below) over the whole spectrum.

incident energy and scattering angle. In Figs. 3, 4 and 5, several curves are compared with those of Jankus.[9] The agreement is typical of all the results. At large angles greater than 75°, the peak heights agree within 2%. At smaller angles, where the impulse approximation is expected to break down, they disagree by about 5%. The half-widths seem to agree throughout. The largest discrepancies are on the wings of the curves. At small energy transfer (the high sides of the curves), Jankus' cross sections go to zero more rapidly, while at large energy transfer, they extend to a longer tail. The choice of zero neutronelectric form factor is, however, not required by the experiments. To give a charge distribution to the neutron, Schiff[10] has suggested the form factor

$$F_{1n}=-\frac{\alpha^4}{(\alpha^2-q^2)^2}+\frac{\beta^6/\alpha^2}{(\beta^2-q^2)^2}+1-\frac{\beta^2}{\alpha^2}.$$

This gives both zero charge and zero mean square radius. With $\beta=\alpha$, $F_{1n}=0$ while with $\beta=2\alpha$, F_{1n} corresponds to a charge density at large distances similar to that of the proton (although opposite in sign). To test the effect of this, we have also computed the in-

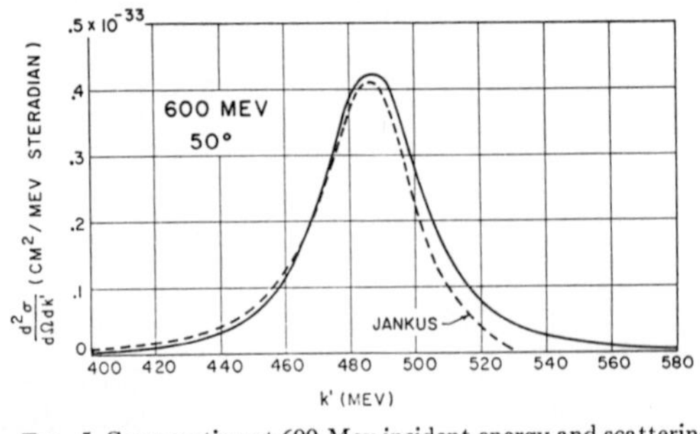

FIG. 5. Cross section at 600-Mev incident energy and scattering angle of 50° *vs* outgoing energies. (The dashed-line curve is that based on Jankus' model.)

[9] R. Herman (to be published).

[10] L. I. Schiff, Revs. Modern Phys. **30**, 462 (1958).

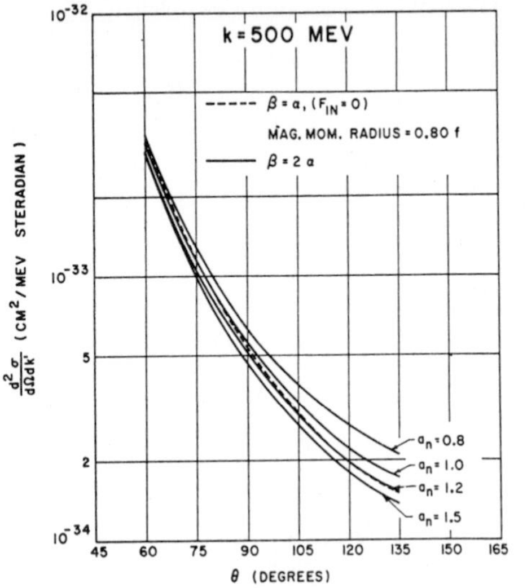

FIG. 6. Peak cross section *vs* scattering angles at 500-Mev incident energy. (The dashed-line curve is for $F_{1n}=0$, $F_{2n}=F_{1p}$. The solid-line curves are for $\beta=2\alpha$, with various neutron moment radii a_n.)

elastic cross sections with this F_{1n}, using $\beta=2\alpha$. The magnetic form factor F_{1n} is of the same form as above. However, several moment radii, $a_n=0.80$, 1.00, 1.20, and 1.50 fermi, were used. The peak cross sections are plotted *versus* scattering angle in Figs. 6 and 7. At

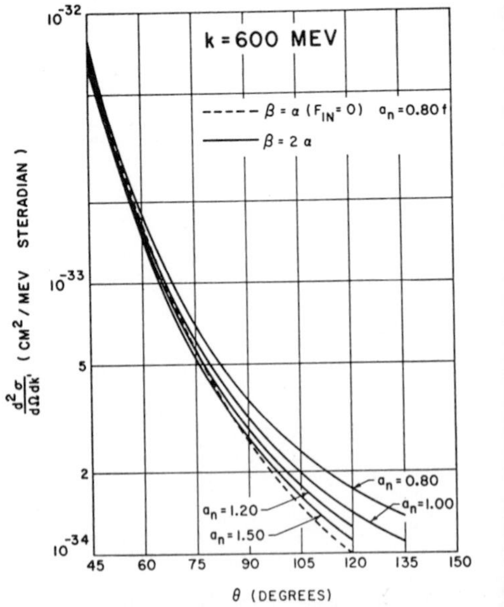

FIG. 7. Peak cross sections *vs* scattering angles at 600-Mev incident energy. (The dashed-line curve is for $F_{1n}=0$, $F_{2n}=F_{1p}$. The solid-line curves are for $\beta=2\alpha$, with various neutron moment radii a_n.)

small angles there is little effect ($\sim$5% variations). At large angles, F_{1n} increases the cross sections considerably, and as is seen in the 600-Mev curve, a_n would have to be unreasonably large to bring the curves down.

Since the impulse approximation and Jankus' cross sections agree over the major parts of the curves, the interference effects, as expected, are small.

We may also note that with this approximation, the peak cross sections may be simply related to the free proton and neutron cross sections, σ_p and σ_n. At the peak the integrals $\mathcal{I}_1$, $\mathcal{I}_2$, and $\mathcal{I}_3$ become expectation values over the deuteron,

$$\mathcal{I}_1=(1/4\pi)\langle E/P\rangle,\ \mathcal{I}_2=(1/4\pi)\langle 1/P\rangle,\ \mathcal{I}_3=(1/4\pi)\langle 1/EP\rangle;$$

E is the total energy, including the nucleon rest energy. Therefore replacing E by M should introduce only a small error. For the Hulthén wave function above, this error is about 1% for both $\mathcal{I}_1$ and $\mathcal{I}_3$. Taking $E=M$, the peak cross section becomes

$$\frac{d^2\sigma}{d\Omega dk'}=\tfrac{1}{2}M\langle 1/P\rangle\frac{1}{|\mathbf{q}|}\frac{k}{k'}(\sigma_p+\sigma_n).$$

σ_p and σ_n are given by the Rosenbluth formula,[11]

$$\sigma_p=\frac{e^4\cos^2(\frac{1}{2}\theta)}{4k^2\sin^4(\frac{1}{2}\theta)[1+2(k/M)\sin^2(\frac{1}{2}\theta)]}\times\left\{F_{1p}^2-\frac{q^2}{4M^2}\{2[F_{1p}+(K_pF_{2p})^2]\times\tan^2(\tfrac{1}{2}\theta)+(K_pF_{2p})^2\}\right\}.$$

The only deuteron dependence here is as a constant multiplicative factor $\langle 1/P\rangle$. At the energies and angles plotted above, this agrees with the complete expression to within 3%.

ACKNOWLEDGMENTS

We wish to thank Professor L. I. Schiff for suggesting this calculation and for helpful discussions. Also we are grateful to Professor R. Hofstadter, Dr. R. Blankenbecler, Dr. M. R. Yearian, S. E. Sobottka, and L. N. Hand for several discussions. Lastly, we are indebted to Dr. R. Herman for allowing us to use his computations of Jankus' cross sections.

[11] M. N. Rosenbluth, Phys. Rev. 79, 615 (1950).

PAPER 50

Electromagnetic Structure of the Nucleon*†

P. FEDERBUSH,‡ M. L. GOLDBERGER, AND S. B. TREIMAN
Palmer Physical Laboratory, Princeton University, Princeton, New Jersey

(Received June 6, 1958)

The electromagnetic structure of the nucleon is studied by using dispersion relation techniques. Contributions to the magnetic moments and mean square radii from the two-pion intermediate state are studied exhaustively. It is shown that the electromagnetic structure of the meson itself may play an important role here; this structure is also discussed. The two-pion state seems to account reasonably for the isotopic vector magnetic moment and magnetization mean square radius, but the charge-density radius appears to be much smaller than the currently accepted experimental value. As regards the isotopic scalar properties of the nucleon, we have studied the contributions from intermediate states with two K mesons and nucleon-antinucleon pairs (more generally baryon pairs). The K-meson state is treated by perturbation theory and found to have a small effect. By use of an argument based on the unitarity of the S matrix, it is shown that the pair contributions must be small. Certain general properties of the three-pion state, believed to be the most important contributor to isotopic scalar quantities, are discussed; but we are unable to make any quantitative statements.

I. INTRODUCTION

QUANTITATIVE experiments on the scattering of electrons by protons and deuterons, carried out by Hofstadter and his collaborators,[1] have provided considerable information on the electromagnetic structure of the nucleon. There have been many theoretical attempts to treat this problem in a semiquantitative way.[2] We mention in particular the recent investigations based on cutoff meson theory,[3] and the relativistic generalizations discussed by Okubo[4] and Tanaka.[5] In the latter approach one attempts to relate the contributions from meson and nucleon currents to the electromagnetic vertex function in terms of scattering amplitudes for pion-nucleon and nucleon-nucleon scattering. Unfortunately, these amplitudes are required for particles "off the mass shell" (i.e., $p^2 \neq -m^2$), and the connection with the true physical amplitudes is not known. The precise nature of the approximations which are made (where a definite extrapolation procedure is adopted) is very difficult to assess.

An approach essentially identical in spirit to ours but somewhat less ambitious in scope has been made by Chew, Karplus, Gasiorowicz, and Zachariasen.[6] They have applied dispersion relation methods to the problem and have shown that certain aspects of nucleon structure can be understood from this viewpoint. Since our methods are so similar we shall not describe the work of Chew *et al.* further at this point but shall refer to it at the appropriate places below. A summary of our general procedure and a statement of some of the results have been given in a recent paper.[7] Before entering into detailed calculations, we shall first state the theoretical problem more precisely and give some of the experimental results.

The quantity of most direct theoretical interest is the matrix element of the current density operator j_μ taken between one-nucleon states. This matrix element is related to the vertex operator Γ_μ according to

$$\langle p'|j_\mu|p\rangle = i(m^2/p_0'p_0)^{\frac{1}{2}} q^2 \Delta_{Fc}(q^2)\bar{u}(p')\Gamma_\mu(p',p)u(p), \quad (1.1)$$

where $q^2=(p'-p)^2$ is the invariant momentum transfer and Δ_{Fc} is the exact Feynman photon propagation function. The Dirac spinors are normalized according to $\bar{u}(p)u(p)=\pm 1$, for positive- and negative-energy spinors, respectively. To lowest order in the electric charge, $q^2\Delta_{Fc}(q^2)=1$; note that a breakdown of electrodynamics (i.e., a real modification of Δ_{Fc}) would multiply into the structure proper as expressed by $\bar{u}(p')\Gamma_\mu(p',p)u(p)$.

It is both conventional and convenient to express (1.1) in terms of certain scalar functions of q^2. Two equivalent forms which we shall use are

$$\begin{aligned}\langle p'|j_\mu|p\rangle &= (m^2/p_0'p_0)^{\frac{1}{2}}\bar{u}(p') \\ &\quad\times[F_1(q^2)i\gamma_\mu - F_2(q^2)i\sigma_{\mu\nu}(p'-p)_\nu]u(p) \quad (1.2)\\ &= (m^2/p_0'p_0)^{\frac{1}{2}}\bar{u}(p') \\ &\quad\times[G_1(q^2)i\gamma_\mu - G_2(q^2)(p'+p)_\mu]u(p) \quad (1.3)\end{aligned}$$

where $G_1=F_1+2mF_2$ and $G_2=F_2$. That the above structure is the most general one follows from Lorentz and gauge invariance. The function F (G) may be further subdivided into isotopic scalar and vector components according to

$$\begin{aligned}F_1&=F_1{}^S+\tau_3F_1{}^V,\\ F_2&=F_2{}^S+\tau_3F_2{}^V,\end{aligned} \quad (1.4)$$

* Work supported in part by the Air Force Office of Scientific Research, Air Research and Development Command.
† This paper is based partially on a thesis submitted by one of the authors (P.F.) to Princeton University in partial fulfillment of the requirements for the Ph.D. degree.
‡ National Science Foundation Predoctoral Fellow. Now at Massachusetts Institute of Technology.

1 R. Hofstadter, Revs. Modern Phys. (to be published).
2 For earlier references, see B. D. Fried, Phys. Rev. **88**, 1142 (1952).
3 H. Miyazawa, Phys. Rev. **101**, 1564 (1956), R. Sachs and S. Treiman, Phys. Rev. **103**, 435 (1956), and G. Salzman, Phys. Rev. **105**, 1076 (1957).
4 S. Okubo, Nuovo cimento **6**, 542 (1957).
5 K. Tanaka, Phys. Rev. **109**, 578 (1958).
6 Chew, Karplus, Gasiorowicz, and Zachariasen, Phys. Rev. **110**, 265 (1958), hereafter referred to as C.
7 J. Bernstein and M. L. Goldberger, Revs. Modern Phys. (to be published).

so that the problem is characterized by four scalar functions. One generally refers to F_1 as the charge density form factor and to F_2 as the magnetization density form factor. The things which are surely known about them are their values at zero momentum transfer:

$$F_1{}^S(0)=F_1{}^V(0)=e/2,$$
$$F_2{}^S(0)=(\mu_p+\mu_n)/2, \quad (1.5)$$
$$F_2{}^V(0)=(\mu_p-\mu_n)/2,$$

where e is the proton charge and μ_p and μ_n are the static anomalous magnetic moments of proton and neutron, respectively.

Other experimental knowledge concerning the form factors is rather less certain. If one thinks of the form factors as Fourier transforms of spatial distributions, than $F'(0)$, the derivative evaluated at $q^2=0$, is related to the mean square radius of the spatial distribution. Except for the neutron charge radius, one defines

$$\langle r^2\rangle/6=-F'(0)/F(0). \quad (1.6)$$

Experiments on electron-proton scattering at small q^2 are now being carried out and one will soon have an unambiguous measurement of $\langle r_1{}^2\rangle$ for the proton (this is defined according to (1.6) with $F_1{}^p=F_1{}^S+F_1{}^V$). Preliminary results[1] indicate that $0.18/\mu^2<\langle(r_1{}^2)\rangle<0.32/\mu^2$, where $1/\mu$ is the meson Compton wavelength. The corresponding quantity for the magnetization density is not easy to measure directly since the scattering at small q^2 is dominated by F_1. If one extrapolates with simple functions from the large momentum transfer data, one finds that $\langle r_2{}^2\rangle$ for the proton is in the neighborhood of $0.32/\mu^2$. Needless to say, this is an uncertain and conceivably misleading procedure. Experiments on high-energy electron-deuteron scattering indicate that F_2 for the neutron (at least for the large values of q^2 at which the experiments are carried out) is about the same as for the proton.

The mean square radius for the neutron charge density distribution, conventionally defined as

$$\langle(r_1{}^2)_n\rangle/6=-F_1{}'^n(0)/e, \quad (1.7)$$

with $F_1{}^n=F_1{}^S-F_1{}^V$, is the quantity measured in low-energy electron-neutron scattering. One finds experimentally a very small upper limit on $\langle(r_1{}^2)_n\rangle$, much below the proton value.[8] This constitutes one of the most puzzling features of the whole problem of nucleon structure. We shall define the isotopic scalar and vector radii according to

$$\langle(r_1{}^2)_p\rangle=\tfrac{1}{2}[\langle(r_1{}^2)_S\rangle+\langle(r_1{}^2)_V\rangle], \quad (1.8)$$
$$\langle(r_1{}^2)_n\rangle=\tfrac{1}{2}[\langle(r_1{}^2)_S\rangle-\langle(r_1{}^2)_V\rangle]. \quad (1.9)$$

The smallness of the neutron charge radius implies $\langle(r_1{}^2)_S\rangle\approx\langle(r_1{}^2)_V\rangle$. The mystery is compounded in that, although the scalar charge radius is unexpectedly large, the scalar magnetic moment is small: $\mu_S=(\mu_p+\mu_n)/2\approx-0.06(e/2m)$, as contrasted with $\mu^V=(\mu_p-\mu_n)/2\approx1.8(e/2m)$. While it is not impossible to imagine charge-current distributions with such dual capabilities, they are certainly not very pleasant or simple.

The present discussion of the electromagnetic structure problem is based on dispersion relation techniques. By this we mean that the form factors are represented by expressions such as

$$F_1{}^S(q^2)=\frac{e}{2}\frac{q}{\pi}\int_{(3\mu)^2}^{\infty}d\sigma^2\frac{\rho_1{}^S(\sigma^2)}{\sigma^2(\sigma^2+q^2-i\epsilon)}, \quad (1.10)$$

$$F_2{}^V(q^2)=\frac{1}{\pi}\int_{(2\mu)^2}^{\infty}d\sigma^2\frac{\rho_2{}^V(\sigma^2)}{\sigma^2+q^2-i\epsilon}, \quad (1.11)$$

where the slight difference in structure and in limits of integration will be explained later. The variable σ^2 represents the square of the mass of the various intermediate states through which the photon-nucleon interaction is effected. The task of the theory is to compute the weight functions ρ which express the contribution of these states.

In Sec. II we discuss the structure of the dispersion relations in detail and describe how the weight functions are to be calculated and what the most important intermediate states are expected to be. In Sec. III the two- and three-pion intermediate states' contributions are treated, as well as the question of the electromagnetic structure of the pion to which one is naturally led. Also discussed in Sec. III is the contribution from intermediate K-meson pairs. The role of nucleon-antinucleon pairs is taken up in Sec. IV. It is shown here—and this is one of the principal results of the present work—that an upper limit on the contribution of such states to the moments and mean square radii can be set by use of the unitarity condition on nucleon-antinucleon scattering. The pairs, in our formulation, can enter in only two angular momentum states and the amplitudes for scattering in these channels are limited in the familiar geometrical way.

Our over-all results concerning nucleon electromagnetic structure can be summarized in the following way. (1) In C it was argued that the isotropic vector moment and radii probably receive their main contributions from intermediate two-pion states and that these contributions can be adequately calculated in perturbation theory. What we find is that the perturbation-theoretic expressions seriously violate unitarity, so that "rescattering" corrections must be significant. We discuss this rescattering but are unable to compute it in any trustworthy way. It is an open question, then, whether or not the isotopic vector properties of the nucleon can be adequately accounted for by the two-pion state. In any case, the apparent agreement between experiment and perturbation theory must be regarded as fortuitous. (2) As for the mystery of the

[8] Hughes, Harvey, Goldberg, and Stafne, Phys. Rev. **90**, 947 (1953).

large isotropic scalar charge radius, our chief result is a negative one. It has often been conjectured that intermediate nucleon-pair states might account for this effect. Our unitarity arguments seem quite reliably to rule this out. The same arguments rule out the possibility of significant contributions from hyperon pairs. We have likewise investigated, this time in perturbation theory, the contributions from intermediate K-meson pairs; it does not seem likely that such states contribute appreciably to the isotopic scalar moment and radii. A theoretically interesting but numerically inaccurate ladder approximation for the pair state is discussed in Appendix A. Among the remaining states of simple configuration, a possible candidate is still the three-pion state. We discuss the general structure of the contributions from this state, but we are completely unable to make any quantitative estimates.

What we achieve here, then, is not a quantitative understanding of the isotopic scalar properties of the nucleon but rather a moderate sharpening of the mystery.

A theoretical process which is very similar to electron-nucleon scattering is scattering of a nucleon by an external mesonic field. Although such fields are rather rare in nature, the process occurs as an intermediate stage in many real reactions. What we are discussing is, of course, the matrix element of the mesonic vertex operator $\Gamma_5(p',p)$, or more exactly, the matrix element of the meson current operator defined as $(\mu^2-\Box)\phi_i=J_i$. The precise connection between the two is

$$\begin{aligned}\langle p'|J_i|p\rangle &= -i(m^2/p_0p_0')^{\frac{1}{2}}(\mu^2+q^2)\Delta_{F_c}\\ &\quad\times(q^2)\bar{u}(p')\Gamma_5(p',p)u(p) \qquad (1.12)\\ &= -i(m^2/p_0p_0')^{\frac{1}{2}}g\bar{u}(p')\tau_i\gamma_5u(p)K(q^2),\end{aligned}$$

where if K is normalized such that $K(-\mu^2)=1$, g is the renormalized Lepore-Watson coupling constant,[9] and Δ_{F_c} is the complete meson propagation function. The quantity $K(q^2)$ satisfies an equation analogous to (1.10) and under certain simplifying assumptions may be calculated quite accurately. These matters are taken up in Appendix B and comparison is made with an early attempt of Edwards[10] to calculate a related quantity. Our result has been used in a discussion of $\pi-\mu$ decay to which the reader is referred for a more heuristic discussion of $K(q^2)$.[11]

Before proceeding to the detailed calculations we would like to say a word about the general theoretical status of the dispersion relations upon which our whole treatment is based. There does not as yet exist a derivation as general and rigorous as the ones which have been given for pion-nucleon scattering. In fact, the only complete derivation that has been given for the electromagnetic or mesonic nucleon vertex function is based on perturbation theory. It is our feeling, however, that the result is correct more generally and we proceed on this basis. In one case, the electromagnetic structure of the meson, a general derivation may be given quite easily. At the appropriate point we will sketch it; for the bulk of the paper we will not concern ourselves with derivations but rather with applications.

II. STRUCTURE OF THE DISPERSION RELATIONS

In this section we shall analyze the general structure of the dispersion relations which we shall encounter. We begin with the electromagnetic nucleon vertex; more precisely we consider a quantity I_μ defined by

$$\begin{aligned}I_\mu &\equiv (p_0p_0'/m^2)^{\frac{1}{2}}\langle p'|j_\mu|p\rangle\\ &= \bar{u}(p')[F_1i\gamma_\mu - F_2i\sigma_{\mu\nu}(p'-p)_\nu]u(p). \qquad (2.1)\end{aligned}$$

We express this in the standard way as[12]

$$I_\mu=\left(\frac{p_0}{m}\right)^{\frac{1}{2}} i\int d^4x\, e^{-ip'\cdot x}\bar{u}(p')\langle 0|(f(x)j_\mu(0))_+|p\rangle, \qquad (2.2)$$

where $f(x)$ is defined as

$$[\gamma_\mu\partial/\partial x_\mu+m]\psi(x)=f(x), \qquad (2.3)$$

and ψ is the nucleon field operator. In writing Eq. (2.2) we have dropped a term which would in general contribute a constant [or at most a polynomial in $(p'-p)^2$] to F_1. The possible existence of such terms will be taken into account when the precise dispersion relations for the F's are given.

We next remark that in place of the time-ordered product we may write

$$\begin{aligned}I_\mu=\left(\frac{p_0}{m}\right)^{\frac{1}{2}} i\int d^4x\, e^{-ip'\cdot x}\bar{u}(p')\\ \times\langle 0|[j_\mu(0),f(x)]\theta(-x)|p\rangle, \qquad (2.4)\end{aligned}$$

where $\theta(-x)$ is zero for $x_0>0$ and unity for $x_0<0$. It would now be the task of a good derivation to show that the coefficient of $\bar{u}(p')$, considered, say, as a function of p_0' in a coordinate system where $\mathbf{p}=0$, has certain definite analyticity properties. For example, since the integrand in (2.4) vanishes for space-like x_μ (the causality condition states that the commutator vanishes in this circumstance), and also for $x_0>0$, we would be led to expect that our function is analytic in the lower half of the p_0' plane. If this were so, it would then be easy to show that the function may be continued into the upper half plane. The remaining problem would be to state the location of the singularities. According to Nambu's perturbation-theory argument (and also, according to one's physical intuition!) one would find

[9] J. Lepore and K. M. Watson, Phys. Rev. **76**, 1157 (1949).
[10] S. F. Edwards, Phys. Rev. **90**, 284 (1953).
[11] M. L. Goldberger and S. B. Treiman, Phys. Rev. **110**, 1178 (1958).
[12] Lehmann, Symanzik, and Zimmermann, Nuovo cimento **1**, 205 (1955).

that there is a branch line from $-\infty$ to $m-2\mu^2/m$ for the isotopic vector form factors, $m-9\mu^2/2m$ for the isotopic scalar.[13] In terms of the invariant variable $q^2=(p'-p)^2$, the branch line in the q^2 plane runs from $-\infty$ to $-(2\mu)^2$ [or $-(3\mu)^2$].

Assuming these things, we can immediately write down the dispersion relations for the form factors, except for the usual uncertainty about the behavior of the functions at infinity. We shall take the dispersion relations to be as follows:

$$F_1{}^S(q^2)=\frac{e}{2}\frac{q^2}{\pi}\int_{(3\mu)^2}^{\infty}d\sigma^2\frac{\mathrm{Im}F_1{}^S(-\sigma^2)}{\sigma^2(\sigma^2+q^2-i\epsilon)}, \quad (2.5a)$$

$$F_1{}^V(q^2)=\frac{e}{2}\frac{q^2}{\pi}\int_{(2\mu)^2}^{\infty}d\sigma^2\frac{\mathrm{Im}F_2{}^V(-\sigma^2)}{\sigma^2(\sigma^2+q^2-i\epsilon)}, \quad (2.5b)$$

$$F_2{}^S(q^2)=\frac{1}{\pi}\int_{(3\mu)^2}^{\infty}d\sigma^2\frac{\mathrm{Im}F_2{}^S(-\sigma^2)}{\sigma^2+q^2-i\epsilon}, \quad (2.5c)$$

$$F_2{}^V(q^2)=\frac{1}{\pi}\int_{(2\mu)^2}^{\infty}d\sigma^2\frac{\mathrm{Im}F_2{}^V(-\sigma^2)}{\sigma^2+q^2-i\epsilon}. \quad (2.5d)$$

The assumed analyticity properties enable us to relate I_μ to the matrix element of j_μ between the vacuum and a state containing a nucleon-antinucleon pair. Since this will be useful for us in our later work, let us note the precise relationship. For an "in" state,

$$J_\mu=\left(\frac{p_0\bar{p}_0}{m^2}\right)^{\frac{1}{2}}\langle 0|j_\mu|\bar{p},p;\mathrm{in}\rangle$$

$$=-i\left(\frac{p_0}{m}\right)^{\frac{1}{2}}\int d^4x\exp(i\bar{p}\cdot x)\bar{v}(\bar{p})\langle 0|(f(x)j_\mu(0))_+|p\rangle$$

$$=-i\left(\frac{p_0}{m}\right)^{\frac{1}{2}}\int d^4x\exp(i\bar{p}\cdot x)\bar{v}(\bar{p})$$

$$\times\langle 0|[j_\mu(0),f(x)]\theta(-x)|p\rangle, \quad (2.6)$$

where $v(\bar{p})$ is the spinor which satisfies $(i\gamma\cdot\bar{p}-m)v(\bar{p})=0$. We are led to the association, assuming that the continuation can be made,

$$J_\mu=-\bar{v}(\bar{p})\{F_1[(p+\bar{p})^2]i\gamma_\mu$$
$$+F_2[(p+\bar{p})^2]i\sigma_{\mu\nu}(p+\bar{p})_\nu\}u(p). \quad (2.7)$$

We are using the phase convention, to which we must consistently adhere, that $|\bar{p}p\rangle=a_{\bar{p}}{}^\dagger|p\rangle$, where $a_{\bar{p}}{}^\dagger$ is the ("in" field) antiparticle creation operator. For an "out" state, which we write as $|\bar{p}p,\mathrm{out}\rangle$, we replace the above form factors by their complex conjugates, which amounts to changing the sign of ϵ in (2.5 a-d). Thus the variable q^2 approaches the real axis from below for $|\bar{p}p,\mathrm{in}\rangle$ and from above for $|\bar{p}p,\mathrm{out}\rangle$.

In order to calculate the imaginary parts of the form factors we write out the absorptive part of I_μ or J_μ. This is the part which arises from the first term in $\theta(-x)=\frac{1}{2}-\frac{1}{2}(x_0/|x_0|)$. We write this absorptive part as $iA_\mu{}^I$ or $iA_\mu{}^J$. Introducing a sum over a complete set of states $|s\rangle$ and carrying out the integrations over x, we find

$$A_\mu{}^I=\pi(p_0/m)^{\frac{1}{2}}\sum_s\bar{u}(p')$$
$$\times\langle 0|j_\mu|s\rangle\langle s|f|p\rangle\delta(p_s+p'-p)$$
$$=\bar{u}(p')\{\mathrm{Im}F_1(q^2)i\gamma_\mu$$
$$-\mathrm{Im}F_2(q^2)i\sigma_{\mu\nu}(p'-p)_\nu\}u(p); \quad (2.8)$$

$$A_\mu{}^J=-\pi(p_0/m)^{\frac{1}{2}}\sum_s\bar{v}(\bar{p})$$
$$\times\langle 0|j_\mu|s\rangle\langle s|f|p\rangle\delta(p_s-\bar{p}-p)$$
$$=-\bar{v}(\bar{p})\{\mathrm{Im}F_1(\Delta^2)i\gamma_\mu$$
$$+\mathrm{Im}F_2(\Delta^2)i\sigma_{\mu\nu}(p+\bar{p})_\nu\}u(p); \quad (2.9)$$

with $\Delta^2=(p+\bar{p})^2$. In these expressions the δ-function is to be regarded as a Kronecker δ-function insofar as the spatial components of the momenta are concerned (we are using box normalization). That $\mathrm{Im}F_1$ and $\mathrm{Im}F_2$ are indeed the imaginary parts of F_1 and F_2 may be demonstrated using invariance under inversion of motion. In order to make the reality manifest at all stages of approximation, we shall write the sum over states as half the sum over "in" and "out" states, although for brevity we will not explicitly indicate this.

In writing Eq. (2.8) we have, of course, assumed that the spatial integrations may be carried out without difficulty. Actually one encounters formally rising exponentials if $-p_s{}^2<(2m)^2$. Nevertheless, the instruction from perturbation theory is to evaluate the integrals as indicated. Stated more elegantly, one may write p' as $p'=([p_0'^2-\xi]^{\frac{1}{2}}\hat{n}, ip_0')$, in the system where $\mathbf{p}=0$. Here $\hat{n}$ is a fixed unit vector and ξ is some negative parameter. Then there is no trouble carrying out the integrals. Now assume that the continuation of ξ to the physical value, m^2, may be carried out.

We turn to the question of what states enter the sums in $A_\mu{}^I$ and $A_\mu{}^J$. Since the operator f lowers the nucleon number by unity, $|s\rangle$ must have nucleon number zero. Furthermore it must have zero strangeness and zero total charge. Thus it may consist of pions, even numbers of K mesons, nucleon-antinucleon pairs or more generally baryon pairs of zero strangeness, etc. The least massive of these states would be a one-pion state, but $\langle 0|j_\mu|\pi_0\rangle$ is zero because of charge conjugation invariance: $j_\mu\to -j_\mu$, $|\pi_0\rangle\to|\pi_0\rangle$. Next we encounter a two-pion state. It is easy to show that only the isotopic vector part of j_μ contributes to $\langle 0|j_\mu|2\pi\rangle$.

The case of n pions may be just as easily discussed as far as isotopic spin is concerned. We introduce the operator $G=\mathfrak{C}\exp(i\pi I_2)$ where $\mathfrak{C}$ is the operation of charge conjugation and $\exp(i\pi I_2)$ generates a rotation of π about 2 axis in isotopic spin space. (I_2 is the 2-

[13] Y. Nambu, Nuovo cimento 6, 1064 (1957) and to be published.

component of the rotation operator in that space.) Then if we write $j_\mu = S_\mu + V_\mu$ where S_μ is an isotopic scalar and V_μ the third component of an isotopic vector, we have $Gj_\mu G^{-1} = -S_\mu + V_\mu$. Furthermore, G induces a sign change in all three components of the meson field, so that $G|n\pi\rangle = (-1)^n|n\pi\rangle$. It follows then that the isotopic scalar contributes for states involving an odd number of pions whereas the isotopic vector part of j_μ involves states with an even number. The lower limits in Eqs. (2.5a), (2.5d) reflect these remarks.

Intermediate states consisting of two K particles (K and $\bar{K}$), of course, contribute to both isotopic scalar and isotopic vector form factors. Continuing in this way our enumeration of contributing intermediate states, we ultimately encounter nucleon-antinucleon states, more generally baryon-pair states. It is interesting to note that from the dispersion standpoint it is quite natural when discussing low momentum transfer (small q^2) to expect the two-pion state to enter on a quite different footing from the nucleon-antinucleon state. This is to be contrasted with the perturbation approach, where in lowest order they would be treated together as a unit.

There are a few more general remarks which should be made before we go on to detailed calculations. Since we know the general structure of the various matrix elements we shall encounter, we may use any convenient coordinate system in which to effect the evaluation of $A_\mu{}^I$ and $A_\mu{}^J$. For most purposes $A_\mu{}^J$ is the more convenient quantity and we shall discuss it in a system where the pair p, $\bar{p}$ is at rest: $\mathbf{p}+\bar{\mathbf{p}}=0$. It follows from gauge invariance that $(p+\bar{p})_\mu J_\mu = 0$, so that $J_4 = 0$ in our system. Evidently, then, the states $|s\rangle$ reached in $\langle 0|\mathbf{j}|s\rangle$ must have angular momentum unity and odd parity. For the two-pion state this means we have only a p state and similarly for the $2K$ state. With three pions we have many more possibilities. We must have a π^+, π^-, π^0 configuration and calling the π^+-π^- relative angular momentum l, and the π^0 angular momentum L, we have $l = L = 1, 3, 5, \cdots$. For the nucleon-antinucleon state, only the $^3S_1$ and $^3D_1$ configurations are relevant.

The significance of these remarks is as follows: for the two-pion state, aside from $\langle 0|j_\mu|\pi_1\pi_2\rangle$, we have to do with the matrix element $\bar{v}(\bar{p})\langle\pi_1\pi_2|f|p\rangle$, with the condition $p+\bar{p}=\pi_1+\pi_2$. This is proportional to the amplitude for pair annihilation into two pions which are restricted to be in a p state. Unfortunately, $-(p+\bar{p})^2$ begins in our dispersion integrals at $(2\mu)^2$, and hence this is a slightly unphysical process. We shall describe in the next section a method to evaluate this approximately. When $-(p+\bar{p})^2 > 4m^2$, of course, it becomes a physical amplitude and as such can receive contributions only from $^3S_1$ and $^3D_1$ states whose intensities are limited geometrically by $\pi/[-\frac{1}{4}(p+\bar{p})^2 - m^2]$. This is used to estimate an upper limit to the contributions of the two-pion state for very high values of $\sigma^2(>4m^2)$ in Eqs. (2.5b, d). Evidently the various three-pion amplitudes may be estimated in a similar way once $-(p+\bar{p})^2 > 4m^2$.

For the nucleon-antinucleon intermediate state we encounter, besides $\langle 0|j_\mu|N\bar{N}\rangle$, the factor $\bar{v}(\bar{p})\langle N\bar{N}|f|p\rangle$, with the restriction $N+\bar{N}=p+\bar{p}$. This is directly proportional to the *physical* amplitude for nucleon-antinucleon scattering. Our angular momentum considerations tell us that we need only the amplitudes for $^3S_1 \to {}^3S_1$, $^3S_1 - {}^3D_1$, and $^3D_1 \to {}^3D_1$ ($^3D_1 \to {}^3S_1$ is the same as $^3S_1 \to {}^3D_1$). These are again geometrically limited and this enables us to put an upper limit on the contribution of the pair intermediate state.

We note in passing that in the case of the meson-nucleon vertex $\langle p'|J_i|p\rangle$, we would discuss $\langle 0|J_i|\bar{p}p\rangle$, which again may be treated in the rest system $\mathbf{p}+\bar{\mathbf{p}}=0$. Since J_i is a pseudoscalar, the state $|\bar{p}p\rangle$ must be $^1S_0$. Similarly all of the intermediate states in the expression for the absorptive part similar to that for $A_\mu{}^J$ must have angular momentum zero and odd parity. The first few relevant states are those with 3, 5, $\cdots$ pions, 4, 6, $\cdots$ K particles, $N\bar{N}$, etc.

III. CONTRIBUTIONS FROM MESON STATES

A. Two-Pion State

We begin our detailed discussion by considering the least massive of the states described in Sec. II, namely that consisting of two pions. Although the contributions from this state have been analyzed by Chew *et al.*,[6] for completeness we shall repeat some of their work. In addition we shall take into account certain effects which they did not consider.

In lowest order perturbation theory the contribution from the two-meson state may be described as follows: the nucleon emits a virtual meson which interacts as a point particle with the electromagnetic field and is then reabsorbed by the nucleon. This term may be separated in a gauge-invariant way from its natural partner in perturbation theory, namely, the term in which the nucleon, after emitting a virtual meson, interacts with the electromagnetic field. The two obvious modifications of the perturbation treatment of the meson current contribution which are suggested by our dispersion approach are that the structure of the meson's electromagnetic interaction be taken into account and that the emission and reabsorption of the virtual meson be treated more accurately. Expressed in the terms of (2.9), what we encounter with the two-pion intermediate state are the matrix elements $\langle 0|j_\mu|\pi\pi\rangle$ and $\langle\pi\pi|f|p\rangle$. The former is determined by the electromagnetic structure of the meson; the latter is proportional to the matrix element which describes nucleon pair annihilation into two mesons.

The predictions of perturbation theory, calculated directly by Feynman techniques or by our dispersion formulas given below, are as follows:

$$G_2{}^V(0)=\frac{e}{2m}\left(\frac{g^2}{4\pi}\right)\left(\frac{1}{2\pi}\right)\left[(1-2\eta)-\eta(2-\eta)\ln\eta\right.$$
$$\left.-\left(\frac{\eta}{1-\eta/4}\right)^{\frac{1}{2}}(2-4\eta+\eta^2)\cos^{-1}(\eta^{\frac{1}{2}}/2)\right],\quad(3.1)$$

$$G_2{}'^V(0)=\frac{e}{2m}\left(\frac{g^2}{4\pi}\right)\left(\frac{1}{8\pi m^2}\right)\left[\frac{4\eta^2-(62/3)\eta+20}{\eta-4}\right.$$
$$+[-2\eta^2+(16/3)\eta-2]\ln\eta-\frac{2\cos^{-1}(\eta^{\frac{1}{2}}/2)}{(4\eta-\eta^2)^{\frac{1}{2}}}$$
$$\left.\times\left(\frac{-2\eta^5+(52/3)\eta^4-46\eta^3+36\eta^2-(8/3)\eta}{\eta^2-4\eta}\right)\right],\quad(3.2)$$

$$G_1{}'^V(0)=e\left(\frac{g^2}{4\pi}\right)\left(\frac{1}{16\pi m^2}\right)\left[\left(-\frac{10}{3}+\frac{4}{3}\eta\right)\right.$$
$$+\left(-\frac{2}{3}\eta^2+\frac{8}{3}\eta-2\right)\ln\eta-2\frac{(-\frac{2}{3}\eta^3+4\eta^2-6\eta+\frac{4}{3})}{(4\eta-\eta^2)^{\frac{1}{2}}}$$
$$\left.\times\cos^{-1}\left(\frac{\eta^{\frac{1}{2}}}{2}\right)\right],\quad(3.3)$$

where $\eta=(\mu/m)^2=0.022$. The derivatives in (3.2) and (3.3) are taken with respect to the squared momentum transfer $q^2=(p'-p)^2$. Using $g^2/4\pi=15$, we find the following numerical results:

$$G_2{}^V(0)=\frac{\mu_p-\mu_n}{2}=1.67\left(\frac{e}{2m}\right);$$
$$G_2{}'^V(0)=-\frac{1.48}{m^2}\left(\frac{e}{2m}\right);\quad G_1{}'^V(0)=-\frac{2.36}{m^2}e;\quad(3.4)$$
$$\langle(r_1{}^2)_V\rangle=-\frac{12}{e}[G_1{}'^V(0)-2mG_2{}'^V(0)]=\frac{0.24}{\mu^2};$$
$$\langle(r_2{}^2)_V\rangle=-6\frac{G_2{}'^V(0)}{G_2{}^V(0)}=\frac{0.12}{\mu^2}.$$

We see that the predicted vector magnetic moment agrees well with the experimental value $1.86(e/2m)$. If we assume that $\langle(r_1{}^2)_V\rangle\approx\langle(r_1{}^2)_S\rangle$ as would be indicated from the neutron-electron interaction experiments, we would have for the proton $\langle(r_1{}^2)_p\rangle=0.24/\mu^2$, which agrees quite well with the experimental results which put this quantity in the range $0.18/\mu^2$ to $0.32/\mu^2$. Neglecting the isotopic scalar contribution to the magnetization radius, we have $\langle(r_2{}^2)_p\rangle\approx0.12/\mu^2$, which seems rather small, although as we have commented $\langle(r_2{}^2)_p\rangle$ is not directly measured experimentally.

We turn now to the dispersion relation treatment. For convenience we record again Eq. (2.9), writing in explicitly the two-pion state now under discussion (recall that we eventually take half the sum over "in" and "out" states):

$$A_\mu{}^J(2\pi)=-\pi\left(\frac{p_0}{m}\right)^{\frac{1}{2}}\sum_{ij}\frac{d^3qd^3k}{(2\pi)^3}\bar{v}(\bar{p})\langle0|j_\mu|q_ik_j\rangle$$
$$\times\langle q_ik_j|f|p\rangle\delta(q+k-p-\bar{p}),\quad(3.5)$$

where the indices i and j are isotopic labels. From gauge invariance and isotopic spin requirements it follows that the first matrix element in (3.5) may be written

$$(4k_0q_0)^{\frac{1}{2}}\langle0|j_\mu|q_ik_j\text{ out}\rangle$$
$$=i(e/\sqrt{2})\epsilon_{3ij}(q-k)_\mu M^*[(q+k)^2],\quad(3.6)$$

where $M^*(0)=1$. (The reason for writing M^* is that it will be our convention to define the various form factors of our theory in terms of the "natural" order for the states; i.e., initial states are "in", final states are "out.") The form factor M will be studied later by dispersion relation methods; for the moment we need only the structure of (3.6). The important thing to notice here is that in the rest frame of the pion pair ($\mathbf{q}+\mathbf{k}=0$), we deal only with states of total angular momentum unity; also in this frame we see that gauge invariance, $(q+k)_\mu\langle0|j_\mu|q_ik_j\rangle=0$, implies $\langle0|j_4|q_ik_j\rangle=0$.

Consider next the matrix element $\bar{v}(\bar{p})\langle q_ik_j\text{ out}|f|p\rangle$, where $q+k=p+\bar{p}$. This matrix element describes nucleon pair annihilation into two pions; however, it is required for unphysical values of the total energy of the system. This may be seen by noting the consequences of the δ-function in (3.5). In the rest frame of the meson pair we have the energy condition $4(\mu^2+|\mathbf{q}|^2)=-(p+\bar{p})^2$, where $\mathbf{q}$ is the pion momentum. One sees that in Eq. (2.5) the dispersion variable $-(p+\bar{p})^2$ can be as small as $4\mu^2$ (corresponding to $\mathbf{q}=0$). Once this variable exceeds $4m^2$ we are, of course, in the physical region.

It is easy to see that the matrix element in question may be written

$$\sqrt{2}(4k_0q_0p_0/m)^{\frac{1}{2}}\bar{v}(\bar{p})\langle q_ik_j\text{ out}|f|p\rangle$$
$$=\bar{v}(\bar{p})\{A_{ij}-i\gamma\cdot[\tfrac{1}{2}(q-k)]B_{ij}\}u(p),\quad(3.7)$$

where

$$(A_{ij},B_{ij})=(A_1,B_1)\delta_{ij}+(A_2,B_2)\tfrac{1}{2}[\tau_i,\tau_j];\quad(3.8)$$

and the A's and B's are to be regarded as functions of $\Delta^2=(q+k)^2$ and $\nu=-(p-\bar{p})\cdot(q-k)/4m$. Evidently only the charge exchange amplitudes A_2 and B_2 contribute in (3.5). Inserting (3.6)–(3.8) into (3.5), we now have

$$A_\mu{}^J(2\pi)=\frac{\pi e}{4}\int\frac{d^3qd^3k}{(2\pi)^3q_0k_0}(q-k)_\mu\delta(q+k-p-\bar{p})\bar{v}(\bar{p})$$
$$\times\{\mathrm{Re}(M^*A_2)-i\gamma\cdot[\tfrac{1}{2}(q-k)]\,\mathrm{Re}(M^*B_2)\}\tau_3u(p),$$
$$(3.9)$$

where we have carried out the isotopic spin summations and taken the symmetrized sum over "in" and "out" states.

We now reduce (3.9) further by going over to the variables ν and Δ^2. Separating out the contributions to $\mathrm{Im}F_1$ and $\mathrm{Im}F_2$ we find

$$\mathrm{Im}F_1{}^V(\Delta^2)=\frac{e}{16\pi}(-\Delta^2)^{-\frac{1}{2}}\,\mathrm{Re}M^*(\Delta^2)\int_{-PQ/m}^{PQ/m}d\nu\times\left[\frac{2m^3}{P^3}\nu A_2(\nu,\Delta^2)-\frac{mQ^3}{PQ}\left\{\frac{m^2}{P^2}\left(\frac{3m^2\nu^2}{P^2Q^2}-1\right)-\left(1-\frac{m^2\nu^2}{P^2Q^2}\right)\right\}B_2(\nu,\Delta^2)\right]\theta(-\Delta^2-4\mu^2), \quad (3.10)$$

$$\mathrm{Im}F_2{}^V(\Delta^2)=\frac{e}{32\pi}(-\Delta^2)^{-\frac{1}{2}}\,\mathrm{Re}M^*(\Delta^2)\int_{-PQ/m}^{PQ/m}d\nu\times\left[\frac{m^2Q^3}{P^3Q}\left(\frac{3m^2\nu^2}{P^2Q^2}-1\right)B_2(\nu,\Delta^2)-\frac{2m^2\nu}{P^3}A_2(\nu,\Delta^2)\right]\theta(-\Delta^2-4\mu^2), \quad (3.11)$$

where

$$P=(\tfrac{1}{4}\Delta^2-m^2)^{\frac{1}{2}};\quad Q=(-\tfrac{1}{4}\Delta^2-m^2)^{\frac{1}{2}};$$

and one is instructed to take the real part of everything to the right of Re.

B. Formulation in Terms of Pion-Nucleon Scattering

To proceed further we must know how the amplitudes A_2 and B_2 depend on the variables ν and Δ^2. As already mentioned, they can be regarded as amplitudes for nucleon pair annihilation into two pions; but we require the continuation of these amplitudes into an unphysical region. We can also regard A_2 and B_2 as continuations of pion-nucleon scattering amplitudes[14]; as in C, this is the approach which we shall follow here. The possibility of making this continuation is based on the observation that $\langle q_ik_j\,\mathrm{out}|f|p\rangle\sim\langle q_i|f|-k_jp\,\mathrm{in}\rangle$, from which it follows that the variable ν may be identified with the analogous quantity defined in the scattering problem; and our variable $\Delta^2=(q+k)^2$ is identical with the momentum transfer variable in the scattering problem. The precise relation is as follows: If the scattering process $l+p\rightarrow q+p'$ is described by the matrix element

$$(4l_0q_0p_0/m)^{\frac{1}{2}}\bar{u}(p')\langle q_i|f|l_jp\,\mathrm{in}\rangle=\bar{u}(p')F(p',q_i;p,l_j)u(p), \quad (3.12)$$

[14] For a discussion of pion-nucleon scattering in terms of dispersion relations, see Chew, Goldberger, Low, and Nambu, Phys. Rev. **106**, 1337 (1957).

then our matrix element can be written

$$\sqrt{2}(4k_0q_0p_0/m)^{\frac{1}{2}}\bar{v}(\bar{p})\langle q_ik_j\,\mathrm{out}|f|p\rangle=\bar{v}(\bar{p})F(-\bar{p},q_i;p,-k_j)u(p). \quad (3.13)$$

What we can now do, then, is write down the pion-nucleon dispersion relations for A_2 and B_2:

$$A_2(\nu,\Delta^2)=\frac{1}{\pi}\int_{\mu-\Delta^2/4m}^{\infty}d\nu'\,\mathrm{Im}A_2(\nu',\Delta^2)\times\left\{\frac{1}{\nu'-\nu-i\epsilon}-\frac{1}{\nu'+\nu-i\epsilon}\right\}; \quad (3.14)$$

$$B_2(\nu,\Delta^2)=\frac{g^2}{2m}\left[\frac{1}{\nu-(\mu^2/2m)-(\Delta^2/4m)}-\frac{1}{\nu+(\mu^2/2m)+(\Delta^2/4m)}\right]+\frac{1}{\pi}\int_{\mu-\Delta^2/4m}^{\infty}d\nu'\,\mathrm{Im}B(\nu',\Delta^2)\times\left\{\frac{1}{\nu'-\nu-i\epsilon}+\frac{1}{\nu'+\nu-i\epsilon}\right\}, \quad (3.15)$$

It should be emphasized that in the present problem we are concerned with values of Δ^2 which are negative, a situation not envisaged in the usual derivations of the pion-nucleon dispersion relations. We have, however, verified up to fourth order in perturbation theory that the extension to $\Delta^2=-4m^2$ which we ultimately require (see below) is legitimate and we conjecture that this is a general result.

Even with all this formal manipulation we are still faced with the problem of determining how $\mathrm{Im}A_2$ and $\mathrm{Im}B_2$ depend on their arguments ν and Δ^2 over the range which concerns us. Physical pion-nucleon scattering is characterized by positive Δ^2 and $\nu>(m^2+\Delta^2/4)^{\frac{1}{2}}(\mu^2+\Delta^2/4)^{\frac{1}{2}}/m$. However, in our problem, as already said, Δ^2 is always negative. The only way known at present to deal with this situation is to continue $\mathrm{Im}A_2$ and $\mathrm{Im}B_2$ from the physical region by means of a Legendre polynomial expansion. The legitimacy of such a procedure is not assured. It has been established by Lehmann[15] that one may in fact use this method for Δ^2 up to about $32\mu^2/3$. What the precise situation is for our negative Δ^2 we do not know; but it is our feeling, and this is the point of view adopted in C, that one might get at least qualitative indications by using a finite number of Legendre polynomials. We shall return to this formulation below. For the moment, we shall make a digression and discuss the limitations imposed by the requirement of unitarity.

C. The Unitarity Condition

Once the dispersion variable $-\Delta^2$ exceeds $(2m)^2$, the matrix element $\bar{v}(\bar{p})\langle q_ik_j\,\mathrm{out}|f|p\rangle$ describes physical nucleon pair annihilation into two pions. Here an entirely different approach is possible. We have already

[15] H. Lehmann (to be published).

noted that the matrix element $\langle 0|j_\mu|q_ik_j\rangle$ selects only two-pion states with angular momentum unity. It is evident, then, that for the pair-annihilation matrix element we are concerned only with pairs which are in $^3S_1$ and $^3D_1$ states of isotopic spin unity. The magnitudes of the contributions from each of these channels is limited in the usual way by unitarity and we can therefore set an upper limit on the contributions from the two-pion state for the region $-\Delta^2>(2m)^2$. Of course, the whole contribution of the two-pion state could be formulated *ab initio* from the annihilation standpoint, but the use of unitarity is limited to the physical region.

Let us return to (3.5) and evaluate $A_\mu{}^J(2\pi)$ in the rest frame of the nucleon pair, where, as we have noted, $A_4{}^J=0$. We now reduce all Dirac spinors to Pauli 2-component spinors, χ, in this reference frame. Thus, from (2.9) we have

$$\mathbf{J}=\frac{p_0}{m}\langle 0|\mathbf{j}|p\bar{p}\rangle=-\frac{p_0}{m}\chi_{\bar{p}}{}^*\left[\left\{\frac{2p_0+m}{3p_0}F_1+\frac{2m+p_0}{3m}2mF_2\right\}\boldsymbol{\sigma}+\left\{\frac{p_0-m}{3m}2mF_2-\frac{p_0-m}{3p_0}F_1\right\}\{3\boldsymbol{\sigma}\cdot\hat{p}\hat{p}-\boldsymbol{\sigma}\}\right]\chi_p, \quad (3.16)$$

where $\hat{p}=\mathbf{p}/p$. The structure of (3.16) makes it evident that only $^3S_1$ and $^3D_1$ pair states are involved in this problem.

To evaluate the absorptive part $\mathbf{A}^J(2\pi)$ we could now express the angular momentum decomposition of $\bar{v}(\bar{p})\langle q_ik_j|f|p\rangle$ in terms of the amplitudes A_2 and B_2 introduced earlier. But it is more convenient to simply express this matrix element directly in terms of Pauli spinors and effect the calculation in the rest frame of the nucleon pair. We therefore write

$$\bar{v}(\bar{p})\langle q_ik_j|f|p\rangle=-\pi(\tfrac{3}{2}mq_0|\mathbf{q}|^3|\mathbf{p}|)^{\frac{1}{2}}\chi_{\bar{p}}{}^*\tfrac{1}{2}[\tau_i,\tau_j]\times\{\sqrt{2}\beta_S\boldsymbol{\sigma}\cdot\mathbf{q}-\beta_D[3\boldsymbol{\sigma}\cdot\hat{p}\hat{p}\cdot\mathbf{q}-\boldsymbol{\sigma}\cdot\mathbf{q}]\}\chi_p, \quad (3.17)$$

where the kinematic factors have been so chosen that β_S and β_D are just the S-matrix elements for production of a p-wave pion pair by a nucleon pair in the $^3S_1$ and $^3D_1$ states, respectively. The amplitudes β_S and β_D are to be regarded as functions of $p_0=(-\Delta^2/4)^{\frac{1}{2}}$. For physical processes $(-\Delta^2>4m^2)$ we can apply the unitarity condition, which tells us that $|\beta_S|, |\beta_D|\leqslant 1$.

Finally, we evaluate (3.6) in the rest frame of the pions, insert this along with (3.17) into (3.5), evaluate $\mathbf{A}^J(2\pi)$ and thus find the two-pion contribution to $\mathrm{Im}F_1{}^V$ and $\mathrm{Im}F_2{}^V$. We find

$$\mathrm{Im}F_1{}^V(\Delta^2)=e\left(\frac{3|\mathbf{q}|^3}{16|\mathbf{p}|p_0{}^2}\right)^{\frac{1}{2}}\mathrm{Re}M^*\times\left[\frac{p_0}{p_0+m}\left(\frac{\sqrt{2}\beta_S+\beta_D}{3}\right)+\frac{mp_0}{|\mathbf{p}|^2}\beta_D\right], \quad (3.18)$$

$$\mathrm{Im}F_2{}^V(\Delta^2)=\frac{e}{2}\left(\frac{3|\mathbf{q}|^3}{16|\mathbf{p}|p_0{}^2}\right)^{\frac{1}{2}}\mathrm{Re}M^*\times\left[\left(\frac{1}{p_0+m}\right)\left(\frac{\sqrt{2}\beta_S+\beta_D}{3}\right)-\frac{p_0}{|\mathbf{p}|^2}\beta_D\right]. \quad (3.19)$$

We imagine that all quantities are expressed as functions of $\Delta^2=(p+\bar{p})^2$.

In Eqs. (3.10) and (3.11) on the one hand, and (3.18) and (3.19) on the other, we have two alternate formulations of the problem of computing the contributions to $\mathrm{Im}F_1$ and $\mathrm{Im}F_2$ from the two-pion intermediate state. With either formulation, the final computation of the two-pion contribution to the real parts of the form factors is to be effected by use of the dispersion relations (2.5), where the integration variable Δ^2 ranges from $-(2\mu)^2$ to $-\infty$. In the formulation represented by (3.18) and (3.19), the amplitudes β_S and β_D are restricted by unitarity to absolute value less than or equal to unity, provided $-\Delta^2>4m^2$. For $-\Delta^2<4m^2$, β_S and β_D are continuations of the $^3S_1$ and $^3D_1$ annihilation amplitudes and here the unitarity restriction does not apply

D. Quantitative Estimates

Before a complete discussion of the two-pion contribution can be given, it is necessary to make a study of the pion electromagnetic form factor $M(\Delta^2)$. This is a major undertaking in its own right; and in order not to mix up too many effects at one time, we prefer to put this off until later. Here we shall adopt the customary approximation of setting $M(\Delta^2)=1$, which is tantamount to treating the pion as structureless. As we shall later see, this may be a drastic approximation.

It has been argued in C that the effect of the rescattering terms in (3.14) and (3.15) is not significant in the nucleon structure problem; that is, one can set $A_2=0$ and for B_2 retain only the Born term, i.e., neglect the integral in (3.15). If this approximation is adopted, the dispersion relations (2.5) yield precisely the results of lowest order perturbation theory, already discussed in subsection A. What we shall show here is that this approximation, while it yields fair agreement with experiment, is quite unjustified in principle, at least as regards the magnetic moment and charge density radius; i.e., the agreement with experiment must be looked upon as fortuitous.

The point is that in the dispersion integrals (2.5) (where $\sigma^2=-\Delta^2$ is the dispersion variable) the region of integration $\sigma^2>4m^2$ contributes far too much to the charge radius and magnetic moment if one adopts the Born approximation; i.e., unitarity is badly violated. One finds, for example, that the calculated magnetic moment, $1.67(e/2m)$, receives a contribution of $0.8(e/2m)$ from this region of integration. That this is too large one sees by computing the annihilation amplitudes β_S and β_D in perturbation theory. For

$-\Delta^2>4m^2$, the resulting expressions exceed the unitarity limit $|\beta_S|$, $|\beta_D|\leqslant 1$ by factors of three or four over the important range of integration in (2.5). We can obtain an upper limit on the contributions in (2.5) coming from the range $\sigma^2>4m^2$ by setting the amplitudes β_S and β_D at their maximum values in (3.18) and (3.19). For the magnetic moment we find that the maximum contribution from the region $\sigma^2>4m^2$ is only $0.2(e/2m)$; and this is probably far larger than the true contribution. Even if we were to adopt this upper limit and add to it the perturbation theory result for $\sigma^2<4m^2$, we would find for the moment the value $(0.87+0.2)(e/2m)=1.1(e/2m)$. This is to be compared with the experimental value $1.85(e/2m)$. The agreement is no longer so impressive. Moreover, in view of the fact that perturbation theory is so badly in error for $\sigma^2>4m^2$, there is no compelling reason to trust it for $\sigma^2<4m^2$. In connection with the magnetization density radius, the violation of unitarity is less significant numerically, since this quantity does not receive much contribution from the range $\sigma^2>4m^2$, even in perturbation theory.

We are faced with at least three possibilities: (1) The rescattering corrections below $4m^2$ are quite important, just as they must be above $4m^2$; and if they were treated correctly one would find that indeed most of the vector magnetic moment comes from the low σ^2 part of the two-pion configuration. (2) The meson vertex function $\langle 0|j_\mu|\pi\pi\rangle$ must be treated properly before one can get agreement with experiment. (3) The two-pion state alone cannot account for the low momentum transfer properties of nucleon electromagnetic structure and one must look to more massive configurations for unexpectedly large contributions. We shall discuss these possibilities in turn.

Let us first attempt an estimate of the rescattering corrections. We base this treatment on the formulas (3.10), (3.11), (3.14), and (3.15) developed above. As in C, the Δ^2 dependence of $\mathrm{Im}A_2$ and $\mathrm{Im}B_2$ is obtained from a Legendre polynomial expansion, in which we include only the contribution from the (3,3) amplitudes in pion-nucleon scattering. However, we make no nonrelativistic approximation. The relevant formulas are as follows:

$$\frac{A_2(\nu',-\sigma^2)}{4\pi}=3\frac{W'+m}{E'+m}f_3^{(-)}\left(1+\frac{\sigma^2}{2k'^2}\right)+\frac{W'-m}{E'-m}f_3^{(-)}, \quad (3.20)$$

$$\frac{B_2(\nu',-\sigma^2)}{4\pi}=\frac{3}{E'+m}f_3^{(-)}\left(1+\frac{\sigma^2}{2k'^2}\right)-\frac{1}{E'-m}f_3^{(-)}; \quad (3.21)$$

where k' and E' are, respectively, the momentum and energy of the nucleon in the center-of-mass system (and are to be regarded as functions of ν' and $\sigma^2=-\Delta^2$); and

$$W'^2=[(\mu^2+k'^2)^{\frac{1}{2}}+(m^2+k'^2)^{\frac{1}{2}}]^2 =m^2+\mu^2+2m(\nu'-\sigma^2/4m). \quad (3.22)$$

The amplitude $f_3^{(-)}$ is related to the pion nucleon scattering amplitudes in the $J=\frac{3}{2}$, $I=\frac{1}{2}$ and $J=\frac{3}{2}$, $I=\frac{3}{2}$ states according to

$$f_3^{(-)}=\tfrac{1}{3}[f(\tfrac{3}{2},\tfrac{1}{2})-f(\tfrac{3}{2},\tfrac{3}{2})]. \quad (3.23)$$

For the dependence of $f_3^{(-)}$ on W', the total center-of-mass energy, we make essentially the same approximation as in C, namely,

$$\frac{2m}{\pi k'}\frac{4\pi\,\mathrm{Im}f_3^{(-)}}{k'}=-\frac{4}{9}g^2\left(1+\frac{w_r}{m}\right)\delta[W'^2-(m+w_r)^2], \quad (3.24)$$

where w_r is the energy of the (3,3) resonance ($w_r\approx 2\mu$). We now use these expressions to compute $\mathrm{Im}F_2$ and substitute the result in (2.5). For the magnetic moment the integration interval $(2\mu)^2<\sigma^2<(2m)^2$ is found to contribute the value $(0.87+1.03)(e/2m)=(1.90)(e/2m)$. The first term, 0.87, is the Born contribution, whereas the second represents the rescattering. In all probability the latter contribution is overestimated since our Legendre polynomial continuation procedure may be diverging badly for the large negative momentum transfers ($\Delta^2\sim -4m^2$) of importance here. It is perhaps reassuring that the sign and approximate size of the rescattering contributions restore the fairly good agreement with experiment that had previously been obtained (unjustifiably) with perturbation theory. Notice that the Legendre polynomial continuation was not, and could not be, extended to all $\sigma^2>4m^2$: if this were done, the dispersion integrals would diverge badly.

Our feeling is that the two-pion state may well largely account for the vector magnetic moment, in which we concur with C. What we do not agree with is that the quantitative estimate can be meaningfully based on perturbation theory. In C, the assertion that the rescattering corrections are small (~17%) was based on an unwarranted ($1/m$) expansion and an imprecise integration. Our conclusion is that one must effectively disregard the contribution to the dispersion integral from masses greater than $2m$ and for smaller masses must take careful account of rescattering. The rescattering effect is so large, however, that we do not have much confidence in the procedure we used, but the results obtained suggest that a careful treatment might lead to good agreement with experiment. One must, of course, also expect some contributions to the moment from more massive intermediate states.

Thus far our discussion has been confined largely to the magnetic moment. The magnetization density radius is not greatly effected by the rescattering. Taking into account only the region $4\mu^2<\sigma^2<4m^2$, we find that $\langle r_2^2\rangle$ increases from $0.12/\mu^2$, the perturbation value, to $0.16/\mu^2$. It should be noted that in calculating $\langle r_2^2\rangle$ we normalize in each case with respect to the theoretical magnetic moment. The charge density radius, however, changes drastically, going from $0.24/\mu^2$ to $0.033/\mu^2$, in apparently strong disagreement with experiment. The complete numerical situation will be summarized after we have discussed the question of the meson's electromagnetic structure.

E. Meson Electromagnetic Form Factor

The last point which must be discussed in connection with the two-pion state concerns the meson form factor $M(\Delta^2)$, which until now we have set equal to unity in our numerical estimates. We now study this quantity with dispersion relation methods.

Consider the quantity M_μ defined [see Eq. (3.6)] by

$$M_\mu(q_ik_j)=(4q_0k_0)^{\frac{1}{2}}\langle 0|j_\mu|q_ik_j\text{ in}\rangle =i(e/\sqrt{2})\epsilon_{3ij}(q-k)_\mu M[(q+k)^2], \quad (3.25)$$

where, as we recall, the factors are chosen so that $M(0)=1$. As remarked earlier, only the isotopic vector part of j_μ contributes here. In the standard way we find

$$M_\mu=iq_0^{\frac{1}{2}}\int d^4x\, e^{ik\cdot x}(\mu^2-\Box_x) \times\langle 0|(j_\mu(0)\phi_j(x))_+|q^i\rangle. \quad (3.26)$$

When the indicated operations are carried out, there appear terms coming from equal-time commutators; on invariance grounds and from the assumed locality of the theory, such terms must have the form $(q-k)_\mu$ times polynomials in $(q+k)^2$. We shall assume that in fact only a constant times $(q-k)_\mu$ appears; and this constant will later be fixed, through use of a subtracted dispersion relation, to guarantee the condition $M(0)=1$. We therefore drop these terms for the moment and write simply

$$M_\mu=iq_0^{\frac{1}{2}}\int d^4x\, e^{ik\cdot x}\langle 0|(J_j(x),j_\mu(x))_+|q^i\rangle. \quad (3.27)$$

We obtain a final form for M_μ by writing $(j_\mu(0)J_j(x))_+ =[j_\mu(0),J_j(x)]\theta(-x_0)+J_j(x)j_\mu(0)$ and noting that the last term makes no contribution for $k_0>\mu$. Thus

$$M_\mu=iq_0^{\frac{1}{2}}\int d^4x\, e^{ik\cdot x}\langle 0|[j_\mu(0),J_j(x)]\theta(-x_0)|q_i\rangle. \quad (3.28)$$

Now it follows from the dynamical independence of the vector potential and the meson field that $[j_\mu(0),J_j(x)]$ vanishes for space-like x. Thus M_μ is the Fourier transform of a function which vanishes everywhere except in the past light cone. This suggests that it should be possible to derive a dispersion relation for M_μ, or, more properly, for the scalar function $M[(q+k)^2]$. Note that we can isolate the latter in an obvious way to obtain

$$[-4\mu^2-(q+k)^2]M[(q+k)^2] =iq_0^{\frac{1}{2}}\sum_{i,j}\int d^4x\, e^{ik\cdot x}(q-k)_\mu\epsilon_{3ij} \times\langle 0|[j_\mu(0),J_j(x)]\theta(-x_0)|q_i\rangle. \quad (3.29)$$

Finally, the factor $(q-k)_\mu$ can be replaced by a spatial derivative of the matrix element, since by gauge invariance $q_\mu M_\mu=-k_\mu M_\mu$. We shall not discuss the details but merely content ourselves with the remark that the derivation of the dispersion relations can be carried out by the method of Oehme.[16] The masses are such that where one is required to integrate the absorptive part of the amplitude over an unphysical region ($|k_0|<\mu$), that part conveniently vanishes. One now readily establishes that the quantity $[-4\mu^2-(k+q)^2]M$, regarded as a function of k_0 in the rest frame of q, is analytic in the k_0 plane cut from μ to infinity. Assuming that M has no pole at $-(q+k)^2=4\mu^2$, we can write the once-subtracted dispersion relation

$$M[(q+k)^2]=1-\frac{(q+k)^2}{\pi}\times\int_{4\mu^2}^{\infty}d\xi'\frac{\text{Im}M(-\xi')}{\xi'[\xi'+(q+k)^2-i\epsilon]}. \quad (3.30)$$

To determine ImM, we write down the absorptive part, A_μ, of (3.28):

$$A_\mu=\pi q_0^{\frac{1}{2}}\sum\nolimits_s\langle 0|j_\mu|s\rangle\langle s|J_j|q_i\rangle\delta(p_s-k-q). \quad (3.31)$$

As usual we have introduced a sum over a complete set of states; and in order to preserve the proper reality conditions at each stage of approximation we understand this to be one-half the sum over "in" and "out" states. The least massive state which can contribute is the two-pion state. Generally, states consisting only of pions must contain an even number of them. States with a pair of K mesons may contribute, as can the nucleon-pair state, etc. Suppose we limit our attention to the two-pion and the nucleon-pair intermediate states. Then in (3.31) we encounter $\langle 0|j_\mu|\pi\pi\rangle$, which leads us back to our amplitude M_μ, and $\langle 0|j_\mu|N\bar{N}\rangle$, which is the nucleon electromagnetic vertex function, aside from trivial factors. We thus generate a set of coupled integral equations which relate the meson and nucleon electromagnetic form factors.

Fortunately, it can be shown that the nucleon-pair state probably makes a very small contribution to $M[(q+k)^2]$, at least for $-(q+k)^2\lesssim 4m^2$. This follows from a unitarity argument of the sort we have employed

[16] R. Oehme, Nuovo cimento **10**, 1316 (1956).

previously. Thus, the nucleon-pair state contribution to A_μ is given by

$$A_\mu(\text{pair})=\pi q_0^{\frac{1}{2}}\sum_{\text{spins}}\int\frac{d^3Nd^3\bar{N}}{(2\pi)^3}\langle 0|j_\mu|N\bar{N}\rangle \times\langle N\bar{N}|J_j|q_i\rangle\delta(N+\bar{N}-q-k). \quad (3.32)$$

It is obvious that only the vector part of j_μ contributes here. The matrix element $\langle N\bar{N}|J_j|q_i\rangle$ describes the production of a nucleon pair in the collision of two pions; and one sees from the δ-function that we require this matrix element only in the physical region. Further, one sees by going into the rest system of the pair that only ${}^3S_1$ and ${}^3D_1$ pair states are involved here. Let us carry out the operations implied in (3.32) in this system.

The structure of $\langle 0|j_\mu|N\bar{N}\rangle$ in this system has already been given, in (3.16). For the matrix element $\langle N\bar{N}|J_j|q_i\rangle$ we write, in Pauli spinor notation,

$$\langle N\bar{N}\,\text{out}|J_j|q_i\rangle=-\left(\frac{m^2}{q_0N_0\bar{N}_0}\right)^{\frac{1}{2}}\chi_N{}^+\tfrac{1}{2}[\tau_i,\tau_j]\{B_S\boldsymbol{\sigma}\cdot(\mathbf{q}-\mathbf{k}) -B_D[3\boldsymbol{\sigma}\cdot\hat{N}\hat{N}\cdot(\mathbf{q}-\mathbf{k})-\boldsymbol{\sigma}\cdot(\mathbf{q}-\mathbf{k})]\}\chi_{\bar{N}}, \quad (3.33)$$

where B_S and B_D are related to the ${}^3S_1$ and ${}^3D_1$ amplitudes, respectively, and are functions of N_0. Carrying out the integrations in (3.32), we find

$$(\text{Im}M)_{\text{pair}}=+\frac{\sqrt{2}}{\pi}\left(\frac{|\mathbf{N}|N_0}{2}\right) \times\text{Re}\left\{\tfrac{2}{3}(B_S+B_D)(F_1{}^*+2mF_2{}^*)+\tfrac{1}{3}(B_S-2B_D) \times\left(\frac{m}{N_0}F_1{}^*+\frac{N_0}{m}2mF_2{}^*\right)\right\}\theta(-\xi-4m^2); \quad (3.34)$$

where, in terms of the invariant variable $\xi=(N+\bar{N}^2)$ $=(k+q)^2$ we have

$$|\mathbf{N}|=(-\tfrac{1}{4}\xi-m^2)^{\frac{1}{2}},\quad N_0=(-\tfrac{1}{4}\xi)^{\frac{1}{2}}. \quad (3.35)$$

The unitarity limits on the amplitudes B_S and B_D are obtained by computing the total pair production cross section from (3.33) and demanding that this cross section be no larger than what is allowed by unitarity for pion-pion collisions in the $J=1$, $I=1$ state. We find

$$\frac{2|\mathbf{k}||\mathbf{N}|}{\pi}[|B_S|^2+2|B_D|^2]\leqslant\frac{3\pi}{|\mathbf{k}|^2}, \quad (3.36)$$

where $|N|$ is given by (3.35). In order to obtain a rough upper limit on ImM, we set the nucleon form factors in (3.34) equal to their static values: $F_1=e/2$; $F_2=(\mu_p-\mu_n)/2$. We further allow $|B_S|$ and $|B_D|$ to take on separately the maximum values permitted by (3.36), choosing algebraic signs to maximize ImM. Substituting ImM into the dispersion relation (3.30) and looking at the leading terms in an expansion in $(q+k)^2$, we find

$$M((q+k)^2)=1-\frac{1}{3m^2}(q+k)^2+\cdots. \quad (3.37)$$

This result corresponds to a mean square radius of $2/m^2$ for the meson form factor; but our whole procedure has been such as to probably grossly overestimate this quantity. In any case, this estimated upper limit coming from the pair state is, as we shall see, probably small compared to the contribution from the two-pion intermediate state. Before turning to the latter, it is perhaps worth noting that if we had used perturbation theory to compute the matrix element $\langle N\bar{N}|J_j|q_i\rangle$ we would have found for the mean square radius the result $\langle r^2\rangle=0.7/\mu^2$, which is about 16 times as large as the above result. Again, this is attributable to the fact that perturbation theory badly violates unitarity. Since the nucleon-pair state seems to make such a small contribution to the meson form factor, we shall ignore it from now on and retain only the two-pion state.

We have already noted that the two-pion state generates an integral equation for the form factor $M((q+k)^2)$. It is possible to discuss the structure of this in quite general terms and we shall begin in this way. Setting $\xi=(q+k)^2$, let us introduce a phase angle $\varphi(-\xi)$ according to

$$\text{Im}M(\xi)=\tan\varphi(-\xi)\,\text{Re}M(\xi)\theta(-\xi-4\mu^2), \quad (3.38)$$

where the step function appears because the lowest mass configuration which contributes to (3.31) is the two-pion state. Of course, (3.38) determines φ only to within an additive multiple of π. It is physically reasonable, however, to suppose that $\tan\varphi(-4\mu^2)=0$, and we shall make the convention that $\varphi(-4\mu^2)=0$. In place of (3.30) we can now write

$$M(\xi)=1-\frac{\xi}{\pi}\int_{4\mu^2}^{\infty}d\xi'\frac{\tan\varphi(\xi')\,\text{Re}M(-\xi')}{\xi'(\xi'+\xi-i\epsilon)}. \quad (3.39)$$

We now regard the function $\varphi(\xi)$ as a known quantity. Then Eq. (3.39) may be interpreted as an integral equation for $M(\xi)$, the general solution to which is easily given. The information about M which may be read from (3.39) is the following: (1) The function $M(\xi)$ can be extended to a function analytic in the ξ plane cut from $-\infty$ to $-4\mu^2$. (2) Just below the cut the real and imaginary parts are related according to (3.38). (3) M has the value unity at $\xi=0$. Evidently we seek a solution such that $\tan\varphi(\xi)\,\text{Re}M(-\xi)/\xi$ approaches zero since otherwise the equation as it stands is meaningless.

The mapping problem posed by Eq. (3.39) is a

standard one and the general solution is[17]

$$M(\xi)=P(\xi)\exp\left\{-\frac{\xi}{\pi}\int_{4\mu^2}^{\infty}d\xi'\frac{\varphi(\xi')}{\xi'(\xi'+\xi-i\epsilon)}\right\}, \quad (3.40)$$

where $P(\xi)$ is as yet an arbitrary polynomial. As a matter of fact the more general problem where the 1 in (3.39) is replaced by a function of ξ may also be easily solved but we shall not go into the question here. The only restrictions which we may impose upon the polynomial $P(\xi)$ are that $P(0)=1$ and the degree must be no higher than would permit the existence of the integral in (3.39). This leaves, of course, a great deal of arbitrariness, in general, depending on the asymptotic form of $\varphi(\xi)$. It may also happen that $\varphi(\xi)$ is such that there is no solution to Eq. (3.39) even with $P(\xi)=1$; this would mean that the equation as it stands is meaningless and further subtractions (which would introduce new constants into the theory) would be required. We shall not consider this possibility further but assume in fact that solutions do exist and see to what extent they may be uniquely specified.

The existence of a multiplicity of solutions to dispersion equations like (3.39) is an old story, and the problem cannot be disposed of without supplying more information from the outside. One simple way to get rid of $P(\xi)$ is to assert that M has no zeros in the finite plane. There is no physical basis for such an assumption. What is equivalent to this, however, is the requirement that the solution (3.40) be chosen such as to agree with the *iteration* solution of (3.39). Thus we imagine that φ has a parameter of smallness associated with it and insist that the power series expansion of (3.40) agree with the series generated by the iteration solution of (3.39). This evidently leads to $P(\xi)=\text{const}=1$ and we take finally as our solution

$$M(\xi)=\exp\left\{-\frac{\xi}{\pi}\int_{4\mu^2}^{\infty}d\xi'\frac{\varphi(\xi')}{\xi'(\xi'+\xi-i\epsilon)}\right\}. \quad (3.41)$$

We shall discuss below, through an analysis of the two-pion contribution to (3.31), the physical meaning of $\varphi(\xi)$—at least for small ξ. For large ξ we have no simple physical interpretation of φ and have no feeling about its asymptotic behavior, which is, of course, crucial for the asymptotic value of M. It may be possible to prove by the method of Lehmann, Symanzik, and Zimmermann[18] that $M(\xi)$ in fact approaches zero at infinity and we shall assume that this is true. [A sufficient condition for this to happen is $\varphi(\xi)\to$ constant$=\varphi_0>0$; in this case $M(\xi)\to|\xi|^{-\varphi_0/\pi}$]. If $M(\xi)$ does approach zero at infinity, then since we require it in our dispersion integrals for only moderate ξ values, the precise asymptotic form of φ will not play an important role. In the model to be discussed below, φ is probably given quite reasonably in the interval $4\mu^2<\xi<30\mu^2$ and what happens beyond that is for our purposes not important.

In a related problem which we have discussed elsewhere by use of reaction matrix techniques,[11] it has been shown that in a situation of the sort under discussion we can express φ in the form

$$\tan\varphi=\frac{\text{Re}(e^{i\delta}\sin\delta)}{1-\text{Im}(e^{i\delta}\sin\delta)}, \quad (3.42)$$

where in the present problem δ is to be identified with the (complex) phase shift for pion-pion scattering in the state of angular momentum unity, isotopic spin unity $(J=1, I=1)$. To see how this comes about in dispersion theory, and to obtain some idea of the range of ξ for which it has validity, let us turn to the calculation of the absorptive part A_μ of (3.31). For values of ξ sufficiently small so that the main contributions come from the two-pion state, we have

$$A_\mu=\pi q_0^{\frac{1}{2}}\sum_{r,s}\int\frac{d^3p\,d^3l}{(2\pi)^3}\langle 0|j_\mu|p_rl_s\rangle \times\langle p_rl_s|J_j|q_i\rangle\delta(p+l-q-k), \quad (3.43)$$

where r and s are isotopic labels and p and l are the four-momenta of the intermediate pions. The first factor is just the vertex we are studying and is expressed in terms of the form factor M by (3.35), in the case of two-pion "in" states; for "out" states, one replaces M by M^*. Recall that half the sum of "in" and "out" states is implied in (3.43). The second factor in (3.43) is proportional to the scattering amplitude for pion-pion scattering and it is clear that we are always in the physical region. Obviously $A_0=0$ in the rest frame of the pions; and since j transforms like a vector it is evident that only two-pion $J=1$ states contribute. It is also evident that only the isotopic-spin-one states are relevant here. The matrix element is then completely characterized by the complex phase shift δ for pion-pion scattering in the $J=1$, $I=1$ state. The precise relation is as follows:

$$\langle p_rl_s\,\text{out}|J_j|q_i\rangle=(8p_0l_0q_0)^{-\frac{1}{2}}\frac{4\pi}{\sqrt{2}}\frac{(-\xi)^{\frac{1}{2}}}{(-\frac{1}{4}\xi-\mu^2)^{\frac{3}{2}}} \times 3e^{i\delta}\sin\delta\left(\frac{\delta_{ri}\delta_{sj}-\delta_{rj}\delta_{si}}{2}\right)(p-l)\cdot(q-k), \quad (3.44)$$

where $\xi=(q+k)^2$ and δ is to be regarded as a function of ξ through its dependence on the center-of-mass wave number $(-\frac{1}{4}\xi-\mu^2)^{\frac{1}{2}}$. For an "in" state the right-hand side of (3.44) would be replaced by its complex conjugate.

We now have all the elements required for the evaluation of (3.43), and hence of the two-pion contribution

[17] N. I. Muskhelishvili, *Singular Integral Equations* (P. Boordhoff N. V., Groningen, Holland, 1953).

[18] Lehmann, Symanzik, and Zimmermann, Nuovo cimento 2, 425 (1955).

to ImM. We find the result

$$\mathrm{Im}M(\xi)=\mathrm{Re}(M^* e^{i\delta}\sin\delta)\theta(-\xi-4\mu^2), \tag{3.45}$$

hence

$$\mathrm{Im}M(\xi)=\frac{\mathrm{Re}(e^{i\delta}\sin\delta)}{1-\mathrm{Im}(e^{i\delta}\sin\delta)}\mathrm{Re}M\theta(-\xi-4\mu^2). \tag{3.46}$$

This is precisely the result stated in (3.42). The argument given in reference 11 makes it plausible, as we also see here, to retain a complex value of δ even though we have dropped states other than the two-pion state. The point is that other states could be relatively unimportant in contributing to ImM, at least for small ξ, even if they play an important role in pion-pion scattering when inelastic processes compete with the scattering. Of course, δ is real below the threshold for inelastic processes.

Needless to say, we have no experimental—or theoretical—information on the pion-pion scattering phase shift. However, since the scattering presumably takes place through virtual baryon pairs it is reasonable to assume that the "range" of the interaction is small. Consequently we propose to represent the energy dependence of the phase shift by a scattering length approximation; namely, with k the center-of-mass wave number, we take

$$\tan\delta(-\xi)=k^3a^3=(-\tfrac{1}{4}\xi-\mu^2)^{\frac{3}{2}}a^3, \tag{3.47}$$

where a is the scattering length, expected to be of order m^{-1}. Of course, the representation of (3.47) makes no sense for large k, when inelastic processes can seriously compete with scattering and cause δ to become complex. But as already said, we are only concerned with the behavior of the form factor M for not too large ξ insofar as we restrict our attention to the low momentum-transfer structure of the nucleon.

Because in our model the phase shift δ is taken real, we see from (3.42) that the phase φ is just identical with δ. We can now evaluate (3.41). Setting $\alpha=\mu a$ and $y=\xi/4\mu^2$, we find

$$\mathrm{Re}M(y)=M(y)=\frac{1+\alpha+\alpha^2}{1+\alpha}\left(\frac{\alpha^2(y+1)-1}{[\alpha^2(y+1)]^{\frac{3}{2}}-1}\right),$$
$$-1<y<\infty, \tag{3.48a}$$

$$\mathrm{Re}M(y)=\frac{1+\alpha+\alpha^2}{1+\alpha}\left(\frac{\alpha^2(-y-1)+1}{[\alpha^2(-y-1)]^3+1}\right),$$
$$y<-1, \tag{3.48b}$$

$$\mathrm{Im}M(y)=\frac{1+\alpha+\alpha^2}{1+\alpha}[\alpha^2(-y-1)]^{\frac{3}{2}}$$
$$\times\left(\frac{\alpha^2(-y-1)+1}{[\alpha^2(-y-1)]^3+1}\right),\quad y<-1. \tag{3.48c}$$

We see that for large positive y, $M(y)\sim y^{-\frac{1}{2}}$; for large negative y, $\mathrm{Re}M(y)\sim(-y)^{-2}$, $\mathrm{Im}M(y)\sim(-y)^{-\frac{1}{2}}$.

For the mean square charge radius of the meson we find the result

$$\langle r^2\rangle=\frac{3}{4\mu^2}\alpha^2\left(\frac{\alpha^3+\alpha^2-\alpha+2}{(\alpha+1)(\alpha^4+\alpha^2+1)}\right). \tag{3.49}$$

There is no need to emphasize that this quantity is not at present accessible to direct measurement. For illustration, we plot in Fig. 1 the function Re$M(y)$ for the case $a=2/m$, hence $\alpha\approx0.3$. For this choice, $\langle r^2\rangle=0.08/\mu^2$, which is twice as large as the upper bound on the contribution from the nucleon-pair state.

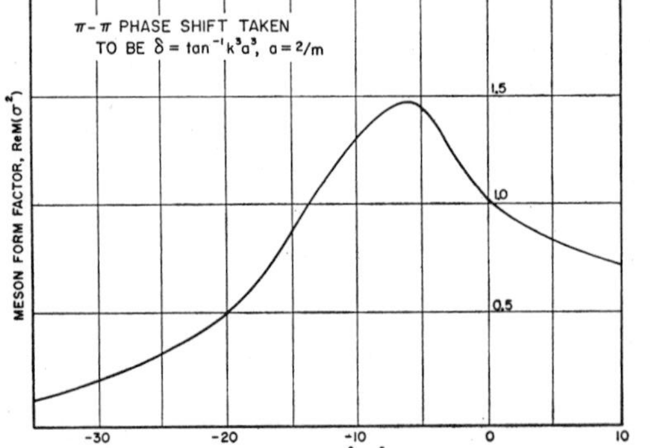

FIG. 1. Real part of the pion form factor; the pion-pion scattering phase shift is taken to be $\delta=\tan^{-1}(k^3a^3)$, where k is the wave number in the center-of-mass system and a is the scattering length chosen to be $2/m$.

F. Quantitative Summary

Although our evaluation of the meson form factor M has no validity for large ξ, it is clear that if M really does vanish asymptotically then the convergence properties of the dispersion integrals for the isotopic vector nucleon form factors would be greatly improved. This raises the more general question as to whether it is really necessary to use a subtracted dispersion relation for the isotopic vector form factor $F_1{}^V$, as we have done. If it is assumed that no subtraction need be made, one in effect assumes that he can compute the charge $2F_1{}^V(0)$. This point has been discussed by Chew,[19] who carries out the computation by determining $\mathrm{Im}F_1{}^V(-\sigma^2)$ in perturbation theory and cutting off the dispersion integral at $4m^2$. In this way he finds $2F_1{}^V(0)=1.28e$. Taking into account rescattering we find $2F_1{}^V(0)\approx0$. It may be that the rescattering estimates are unreliable, or that higher mass configurations play an important role. The matter evidently cannot easily be decided. We prefer in the absence of trustworthy calculations to adopt a subtracted dispersion relation.

We now return to the main question, which is to introduce the structure of the meson into the problem

[19] G. F. Chew (to be published).

of nucleon structure. We carry out the evaluation of the nucleon isotopic vector form factors using (3.48) together with (3.10) and (3.11). The rescattering corrections are treated as before. In the dispersion integrals we drop contributions from (mass)^2 values larger than $4m^2$, since we have already seen from unitarity arguments alone that such contributions are small. For illustration we again take the pion-pion scattering length to be $a=2/m$. In Table I we exhibit the whole numerical situation for the contributions from the two-pion state. Qualitatively, the situation can be summarized in the following way: the isotopic vector magnetic moment and magnetization density radius seem to be reasonably well accounted for in terms of the two-pion state contributions. The charge density radius on the other hand turns out to be far too small relative to the experimental value. It may be that this quantity is peculiarly sensitive to our rescattering correction approximation; or what is equally likely (assuming the experiments are correct!) higher configurations are playing an unexpectedly important role. It is amusing to note that if the charge density radius is computed under the assumption that we have no subtraction in the dispersion relation for $F_1{}^V$ [and hence is given by $-6F_1{}^{V\prime}(0)/F_1{}^V(0)$ instead of $-12F_1{}^{V\prime}(0)/e$] we would get a very large value, since $F_1{}^V(0)\simeq 0$ according to our estimates.

G. Three-Pion State

The least massive state which contributes to the isotopic scalar properties of nucleons is the three-pion state; and one would expect this state to be the most important one in determining the isotopic scalar magnetic moment and mean square radii. Unfortunately, we are unable to make any even crude quantitative estimates of the effects from the three-pion state. Even a perturbation calculation (lowest order $\sim eg^6$ is prohibitive.

What we shall do, therefore, is merely carry out an analysis which separates off purely kinematic effects and exposes the basic structure of the problem. From (2.9) we see that what is involved here is the product $\langle 0|j_\mu|3\pi\rangle\langle 3\pi|f|p\rangle$. In the rest frame of the nucleon pair

TABLE I. Summary of the two-pion contributions to the isotopic vector magnetic moment μ_V, magnetization density mean square radius $\langle (r_2{}^2)_V\rangle$, and charge density mean square radius $\langle (r_1{}^2)_V\rangle$. In the first column the quantities in parentheses denote the limits of integration in the appropriate dispersion integrals.

	μ_V	$\langle (r_2{}^2)_V\rangle$	$\langle (r_1{}^2)_V\rangle$
Pert. theory ($4\mu^2\to\infty$)	$1.67\ e/2m$	$0.12/\mu^2$	$0.24/\mu^2$
Pert. theory ($4\mu^2\to 4m^2$)	$0.87\ e/2m$	$0.22/\mu^2$	$0.19/\mu^2$
Pert. theory+pion form factor ($4\mu^2\to 4m^2$)	$0.77\ e/2m$	$0.28/\mu^2$	$0.20/\mu^2$
Pert. theory+rescattering ($4\mu^2\to 4m^2$)	$1.90\ e/2m$	$0.16/\mu^2$	$0.03/\mu^2$
Pert. theory+rescattering +pion form factor ($4\mu^2\to 4m^2$)	$1.39\ e/2m$	$0.23/\mu^2$	$0.07/\mu^2$

(which is, of course, also the rest frame of the three-pion system), the first matrix element describes the process of a virtual photon producing three pions in a state of total angular momentum unity. The second matrix element describes the process of pair annihilation into three mesons. One sees that only the $^3S_1$ and $^3D_1$ pair states are involved here. From charge-conjugation invariance it follows that the three pions must have different charges (i.e., $|3\pi\rangle=|\pi^+\pi^-\pi^0\rangle$). This, together with gauge invariance, $(p^++p^-+p^0)_\mu\langle 0|j_\mu|p^+p^-p^0\rangle=0$, leads to the structure of the matrix element, which must transform like a pseudovector, given by

$$\langle 0|j_\mu|p^+p^-p^0\ \text{out}\rangle = -i(8w_+w_-w_0)^{-\frac{1}{2}}\epsilon_{\mu\nu\lambda\sigma}p_\nu{}^+p_\lambda{}^-p_\sigma{}^0H^*, \quad (3.50)$$

where H is a scalar function of the momenta and the pion energies have been denoted by w.

In the rest system of the three pions let us denote by $\mathbf{k}$ the relative momentum of π^+ and π^- and by $\mathbf{q}$ the momentum of π^0. Let $2E$ denote the total center-of-mass energy, so that E is the energy of either member of the nucleon pair. Then in the rest frame $-i\epsilon_{\mu\nu\lambda\sigma}p_\nu{}^+p_\lambda{}^-p_\sigma{}^0$ reduces to $2E(\mathbf{k}\times\mathbf{q})_\mu$, $\mu=1, 2, 3$ ($\mu=4$ does not contribute). In terms of the well-known Dalitz description,[20] in which the relative angular momentum of (π^+,π^-) is denoted by l and that of π^0 relative to the center of mass of (π^+,π^-) denoted by L, we have $l=L=$odd integer. In the rest frame we then have

$$\langle 0|\mathbf{j}|p^+p^-p^0\ \text{out}\rangle = 2E(\mathbf{k}\times\mathbf{q})(8w_+w_-w_0)^{-\frac{1}{2}}H^*(k^2,q^2,\lambda^2), \quad (3.51)$$

where

$$\lambda^2=\mathbf{k}\cdot\mathbf{q}/|\mathbf{k}|\,|\mathbf{q}|.$$

The other matrix element which we require is that describing pair annihilation into three pions. Retaining only the contributions from pairs in the $^3S_1$ and $^3D_1$ states, we have in the center-of-mass system

$$\bar{v}(\bar{p})\langle p^+p^-p^0\ \text{out}|f|p\rangle = -(m/E)^{\frac{1}{2}}(8w_+w_-w_0)^{-\frac{1}{2}}\pi_{\bar{p}}{}^*\{\alpha\boldsymbol{\sigma}\cdot\mathbf{k}\times\mathbf{q} - (\beta/\sqrt{2})[3\boldsymbol{\sigma}\cdot\hat{p}\hat{p}\cdot(\mathbf{k}\times\mathbf{q})-\sigma(\mathbf{k}\times\mathbf{q})]\}\chi_p, \quad (3.52)$$

where α and β are, respectively, amplitudes for three-pion production by nucleon pairs in the $^3S_1$ and $^3D_1$ states. They of course depend on the variables k^2, q^2, λ^2.

The expressions (3.51) and (3.52) are now to be inserted into (2.9). Some of the integrations can be carried out explicitly and one finds for the contribution from the three-pion state, in the rest system,

$$\mathbf{A}^J(3\pi)=+\frac{4E}{3(2\pi)^3}\int_0^{q(E)}q^2dq\int_{\kappa(q,E)}^{K(q,E)}k^2dk\left(\frac{1-\lambda^2}{\lambda^2}\right)\times\left(\frac{2E-(\mu^2+k^2)^{\frac{1}{2}}}{(\mu^2+k^2)^{\frac{1}{2}}}\right)\chi_{\bar{p}}{}^*\Big\{\boldsymbol{\sigma}\ \mathrm{Re}(H^*\alpha) + (3\boldsymbol{\sigma}\cdot\hat{p}\hat{p}-\boldsymbol{\sigma})\frac{1}{\sqrt{2}}\mathrm{Re}(H^*\beta)\Big\}\chi_p; \quad (3.53)$$

[20] R. H. Dalitz, Phys. Rev. 94, 1046 (1954).

where

$$q(E)=[(E-\tfrac{1}{2}\mu)^2-\mu^2]^{\frac{1}{2}},$$

$$K(q,E)=\left[\frac{(3\mu^2+4q^2-4E^2)^2}{16E^2}-\mu^2\right]^{\frac{1}{2}},$$

$$\lambda^2=\frac{1}{k^2q^2}\left\{\left(\mu^2+q^2+\frac{k^2}{4}\right)^2-\frac{1}{4}\left[[2E-(\mu^2+k^2)^{\frac{1}{2}}]^2-2\left(\mu^2+q^2+\frac{k^2}{4}\right)\right]^2\right\}, \quad (3.54)$$

and $\kappa(q,E)$ is the value of k which corresponds to $\lambda=1$ if such exists; otherwise $\kappa=0$. Finally, for the imaginary parts of the isotopic scalar form factors we obtain the results

$$\mathrm{Im}F_1{}^S[(p+\bar{p})^2]=-\frac{4m}{3(2\pi)^3}\int_0^{q(E)}q^2dq\times\int_{\kappa(q,E)}^{K(q,E)}k^2dk\left(\frac{1-\lambda^2}{\lambda^2}\right)\left(\frac{2E-(\mu^2+k^2)^{\frac{1}{2}}}{(\mu^2+k^2)^{\frac{1}{2}}}\right)\times\mathrm{Re}\left\{\frac{E}{E+m}H^*\left(\alpha+\frac{1}{\sqrt{2}}\beta\right)+\frac{3mE}{E^2-m^2}\frac{1}{\sqrt{2}}H^*\beta\right\}; \quad (3.55)$$

$$\mathrm{Im}F_2{}^S[(p+\bar{p})^2]=-\frac{4m}{3(2\pi)^3}\int_0^{q(E)}q^2dq\int_{\kappa(q,E)}^{K(q,E)}k^2dk\times\left(\frac{1-\lambda^2}{\lambda^2}\right)\left(\frac{2E-(\mu^2+k^2)^{\frac{1}{2}}}{(\mu^2+k^2)^{\frac{1}{2}}}\right)\mathrm{Re}\left\{\frac{H^*}{2(E+m)}\left(\alpha+\frac{1}{\sqrt{2}}\beta\right)-\frac{3E}{2(E^2-m^2)}\frac{1}{\sqrt{2}}H^*\beta\right\}; \quad (3.56)$$

and $E^2=-\frac{1}{4}(p+\bar{p})^2$. We have not written it in, but each of the above expressions should be multiplied by the step function $\theta[-(p+\bar{p})^2-(3\mu)^2]$.

It is scarcely necessary to remark that one cannot obtain any quantitative impressions from these results. There are sufficiently many unknown functions here so that one could easily arrange it to produce a large isotopic scalar charge radius and at the same time a very small magnetic moment. It is unfortunately the case that the three-pion state, which is perhaps the most significant contributor to the mysterious isotopic scalar properties of the nucleon, cannot be treated quantitatively without prohibitive labor. We remark again that even a perturbation calculation would be very worthwhile.

H. K Meson-Pair State Contributions

It was suggested some time ago by Sandri[21] that the electromagnetic structure of the nucleon would be influenced by the interaction between nucleons and strange particles. In particular he considered the coupling of K mesons to nucleons on the basis of a cutoff model and found rather sizable effects. More recently, relativistic perturbation theory calculations have been carried out along these lines.[22] For reasons to be discussed in Sec. IV in connection with nucleon pair intermediate states we feel that such calculations are meaningless. What might be more reasonable [depending on the size of K-nucleon-hyperon coupling constants] is to treat the contribution of the K-meson current to nucleon structure by perturbation theory and neglect that coming from the intermediate hyperon current. In view of the fact that $g_K{}^2<g_\pi{}^2$, the use of perturbation theory may be more reliable in the present instance than it was for the pion current.

The algebra of the $|2K\rangle$ contribution is essentially the same as that for the $|2\pi\rangle$ state; the only difference is that the mass of the intermediate hyperon, a Λ or a Σ, is different from that of the nucleon. There is, of course, also the question of the parity of the K meson relative to baryons. We have done the calculation for both cases. For the proton, there are two diagrams, corresponding to $p\rightarrow(\Sigma_0,\Lambda_0)+K_+\rightarrow p$; whereas for the neutron we have only $n\rightarrow\Sigma^-+K_+\rightarrow n$ in lowest order. The couplings are taken in the form given by Gell-Mann.[23]

Using for convenience the same mass for Σ and Λ, chosen intermediate between the two actual masses, we obtain the numerical results shown in Table II. If, as has been suggested by Schwinger,[24] $g_\Lambda{}^2=g_\Sigma{}^2$, we have only isotopic scalar contributions. It is impossible, however, for any value of $g_s{}^2$ or choice of parity to obtain both a large charge mean square radius and a small anomalous moment. For example, if $g_s{}^2\sim1$ and the K meson is pseudoscalar, the moment is of reasonable size (but wrong sign) but the charge radius is negligibly small. If the K meson is scalar and $g_s{}^2\sim15$, the charge radius is reasonable ($\sim0.2/\mu^2$) but the moment is absurd ($\sim2.4e/2m$).

We conclude that K mesons very likely do not play any important role in nucleon electromagnetic structure, unless the coupling constants turn out to be so large that, here as in the pion case, rescattering corrections to perturbation theory are very important.

TABLE II. Contribution of K-meson current to nucleon structure. To obtain the isotopic scalar and vector contributions, in the above table set $g^2=g_S{}^2=(3g_\Sigma{}^2+g_\Lambda{}^2)/16$ or $g^2=g_V{}^2=(g_\Lambda{}^2-g_\Sigma{}^2)/16$, respectively.

	Pseudoscalar coupling	Scalar coupling
$F_2(0)$	$g^2(0.0573)e/2m$	$-g^2(0.16)e/2m$
$F_2'(0)$	$-g^2(0.0074)e/2m^3$	$g^2(0.030)e/2m^3$
$F_1'(0)$	$-g^2(0.0101)e/m^3$	$-g^2(0.0475)e/m^3$

[21] G. Sandri, Phys. Rev. **101**, 1616 (1956).

[22] Y. Nogami, Nuovo cimento **4**, 985 (1957).
[23] M. Gell-Mann, Phys. Rev. **106**, 1296 (1957).
[24] J. Schwinger, Phys. Rev. **104**, 1164 (1956).

IV. ROLE OF NUCLEON-ANTINUCLEON PAIRS

The last topic we shall treat is the role of intermediate nucleon-antinucleon pair states in the electromagnetic structure problem. In lowest order perturbation theory such states appear simultaneously and on essentially an equal footing with the two-pion state. It has long been recognized that in perturbation theory the pairs make an unreasonably large contribution to the anomalous moment; there have been frequent speculations that a more accurate treatment would correct this situation.

The results of lowest order perturbation theory, calculated either directly by Feynman methods or from the dispersion formula (4.2) [into which one inserts the lowest order amplitudes], are as follows:

$$\tfrac{2}{3}F_2{}^S(0)=-2F_2{}^V(0)=-\frac{e}{2m}\left(\frac{g^2}{4\pi}\right)\frac{1}{4\pi}\times\left[(1+2\eta)+\eta(1-\eta)\ln\eta+\frac{\eta^{\frac{1}{2}}(1-3\eta)}{(1-\eta/4)^{\frac{1}{2}}}\cos^{-1}\left(\frac{\eta^{\frac{1}{2}}}{2}\right)\right]=-1.13e/2m;$$

$$\tfrac{2}{3}F_2{}'^S(0)=-2F_2{}'^V(0)=-\frac{e}{2m}\cdot\left(\frac{1}{m^2}\right)\left(\frac{g^2}{4\pi}\right)\frac{1}{8\pi}\times\left[\frac{2\eta^2-(19/3)\eta-\frac{4}{3}}{4-\eta}+(\eta^2-\tfrac{2}{3}\eta)\ln\eta+\left(20-\frac{40}{3}\eta+2\eta^2\right)\left(\frac{\eta}{4-\eta}\right)^{\frac{1}{2}}\cos^{-1}\left(\frac{\eta^{\frac{1}{2}}}{2}\right)\right]=0.181e/2m^3;$$

$$\tfrac{2}{3}G_1{}'^S(0)=-2G_1{}'^V(0)=-\frac{e}{m^2}\left(\frac{g^2}{4\pi}\right)\frac{1}{16\pi}\times\left[\frac{4-5\eta+2\eta^2}{3(4-\eta)}+\frac{\eta^2}{3}\ln\eta+\left(\frac{\eta}{4-\eta}\right)^{\frac{1}{2}}(4-4\eta+\tfrac{2}{3}\eta^2)\cos^{-1}\left(\frac{\eta^{\frac{1}{2}}}{2}\right)\right]=-0.1e/m^3. \quad (4.1)$$

The anomalous moment is seen to be quite large, whereas the contributions to the mean square radii are seen to be negligible.

The dispersion-theoretic treatment of the pair state proceeds from Eq. (2.9) where the state $|s\rangle$ is taken as $|n\bar{n}\rangle$. We have

$$A_\mu{}^J(N\bar{N})=-\pi\left(\frac{p_0}{m}\right)^{\frac{1}{2}}\sum_{\text{spins}}\int\frac{d^3n\,d^3\bar{n}}{(2\pi)^3}\bar{v}(\bar{p})\times\langle 0|j_\mu|n\bar{n}\rangle\langle n\bar{n}|f|p\rangle\delta(n+\bar{n}-p-\bar{p}), \quad (4.2)$$

where, as usual, we take half the sum of "in" and "out" pair states. As we have described in Sec. II, $\bar{v}(\bar{p})\langle n\bar{n}|f|p\rangle$ is proportional to the amplitude for nucleon-antinucleon scattering. The first factor, $\langle 0|j_\mu|n\bar{n}\rangle$, is the very quantity we are studying; just as in the case of the pion vertex (see Sec. III), we are generating an integral equation. In Appendix A we discuss the solution of this equation for the isotopic scalar quantities, $F_1{}^S$ and $F_2{}^S$, when the nucleon-antinucleon amplitude is treated in lowest order perturbation theory. This is a sort of ladder approximation similar to a treatment given by Edwards. We find that although this represents a great improvement over perturbation theory it is probably not a very accurate approximation.

The evaluation of (4.2) is most conveniently carried out in the rest frame of $|n\bar{n}\rangle$. As we have discussed several times before, one need then consider only ${}^3S_1$ and ${}^3D_1$ intermediate pair states, and only the nucleon-antinucleon amplitudes leading to these final states are required. A certain amount of caution must be exercised in expressing the scattering amplitudes in terms of two-component spinors since we have been using negative-energy four-component spinors, $v(\bar{p})$, in our discussion instead of true antiparticle quantities. In particular, for a matrix element in Pauli spin space such as $\langle\bar{n}|Q|\bar{p}\rangle$ we must for consistency write $\chi_{\bar{p}}{}^*\sigma^{(2)}Q^T\sigma^{(2)}\chi_{\bar{n}}$ where the χ's are the usual two-component spinors. This has the effect of changing the signs of all quantities linear in $\boldsymbol{\sigma}$ since $\sigma^{(2)}\boldsymbol{\sigma}^T\sigma^{(2)}=-\boldsymbol{\sigma}$.

We write then for the relevant part of the nucleon-antinucleon scattering amplitude, in the rest system $\mathbf{p}+\bar{\mathbf{p}}=\mathbf{n}+\bar{\mathbf{n}}=0$,

$$\bar{v}(\bar{p})\langle n\bar{n},\text{out}|f|p\rangle=-\frac{4\pi p_0}{m^2|\mathbf{p}|}\left(\frac{m}{p_0}\right)^{\frac{1}{2}}\left[\beta_S\frac{3+\boldsymbol{\sigma}_1\cdot(-\boldsymbol{\sigma}_2)}{4}+\frac{\beta_{SD}}{8^{\frac{1}{2}}}\left\{\frac{3\boldsymbol{\sigma}_1\cdot\mathbf{n}(-\boldsymbol{\sigma}_2\cdot\mathbf{n})}{|\mathbf{n}|^2}-\boldsymbol{\sigma}_1\cdot(-\boldsymbol{\sigma}_2)+\frac{3\boldsymbol{\sigma}_1\cdot\mathbf{p}(-\boldsymbol{\sigma}_2\cdot\mathbf{p})}{|\mathbf{p}|^2}-\boldsymbol{\sigma}_1\cdot(-\boldsymbol{\sigma}_2)\right\}+\frac{\beta_D}{8}\left\{\left[\frac{3\boldsymbol{\sigma}_1\cdot\mathbf{n}(-\boldsymbol{\sigma}_2\cdot\mathbf{n})}{|\mathbf{n}|^2}-\boldsymbol{\sigma}_1\cdot(-\boldsymbol{\sigma}_2)\right]\times\left[\frac{3\boldsymbol{\sigma}_1\cdot\mathbf{p}(-\boldsymbol{\sigma}_2\cdot\mathbf{p})}{|\mathbf{p}|^2}-\boldsymbol{\sigma}_1\cdot(-\boldsymbol{\sigma}_2)\right]\right\}^T\right], \quad (4.3)$$

where

$$\boldsymbol{\sigma}_1=\chi_n{}^*\boldsymbol{\sigma}\chi_p,\quad \boldsymbol{\sigma}_2=\chi_{\bar{p}}{}^*\boldsymbol{\sigma}\chi_{\bar{n}},\quad 1=\chi_n{}^*\chi_p\chi_{\bar{p}}{}^*\chi_{\bar{n}}. \quad (4.4)$$

The over-all minus sign in (4.3) as well as the factor $4\pi p_0/m^2|\mathbf{p}|$ are inserted so that the β's have the familiar scattering-matrix significance. For example, $\beta_S=[\exp 2i\delta_s-1]/2i$ with δ_s the complex phase shift describing $S-S$ scattering. The unitarity restriction states that $|\beta_S|\leqslant 1$, $|\beta_{SD}|\leqslant 1/2$, $|\beta_D|\leqslant 1$. The minus sign that appears with $\boldsymbol{\sigma}_2$ in the various projection operators has been explained above; the superscript T on the last curly brace in (4.3) means that the $\boldsymbol{\sigma}_2$ operators are to be written in the order opposite to their appearance. The expression is then reduced to a linear function of $\boldsymbol{\sigma}_1$ and $\boldsymbol{\sigma}_2$ and the result interpreted according to (4.4). For $\langle 0|j_\mu|n\bar{n}\rangle$ we use the form given in Eq. (3.16).

The evaluation of (4.2) with these expressions is elementary. Still in the rest system, $\mathbf{p}+\bar{\mathbf{p}}=0$, we have

$$\frac{m}{p_0}\mathbf{A}^J(N\bar{N})=-\chi_p^*\boldsymbol{\sigma}\chi_p\,\mathrm{Re}\left[\beta_S\left(A^*+\frac{B^*}{3}\right)+\frac{\beta_{SD}}{\sqrt{2}}\left(A^*-\frac{B^*}{3}\right)-\frac{\beta_D}{3}B^*\right]-\chi_{\bar{p}}^*\frac{(\boldsymbol{\sigma}\cdot\mathbf{p})\mathbf{p}}{|\mathbf{p}|^2}\chi_p\times\mathrm{Re}\left[-\frac{3\beta_{SD}}{\sqrt{2}}\left(A^*+\frac{B^*}{3}\right)+\beta_D B^*\right],\quad(4.5)$$

where

$$A=F_1+2mF_2,$$

$$B=\left[\frac{2mF_2}{mp_0}-\frac{F_1+2mF_2}{p_0(p_0+m)}\right]|\mathbf{p}|^2.\quad(4.6)$$

Comparison of (4.5) with (2.9) yields for the pair state contribution to $\mathrm{Im}F_1$ and $\mathrm{Im}F_2$ the results

$$\mathrm{Im}F_1=\frac{p_0}{p_0+m}C-\frac{mp_0}{|\mathbf{p}|^2}D,$$
$$\mathrm{Im}F_2=\frac{1}{2(p_0+m)}C+\frac{p_0}{2|\mathbf{p}|^2}D,\quad(4.7)$$

where

$$C=\mathrm{Re}\left[\beta_S\left(A^*+\frac{B^*}{3}\right)+\frac{\beta_{SD}}{\sqrt{2}}\left(A^*-\frac{B^*}{3}\right)-\frac{\beta_D}{3}B^*\right],\quad(4.8)$$

$$D=\mathrm{Re}\left[-3\frac{\beta_{SD}}{\sqrt{2}}\left(A^*+\frac{B^*}{3}\right)+\beta_D B^*\right].$$

For substitution into the dispersion relations we must imagine all quantities to be expressed in terms of the invariant variable $-(p+\bar{p})^2$ according to $p_0^2=-\frac{1}{4}(p+\bar{p})^2$, $|\mathbf{p}|^2=-\frac{1}{4}(p+\bar{p})^2-m^2$.

We have not kept track of the isotopic spin labels in the above equations, but these are easily inserted now. The scattering amplitudes are expressed in terms of isotopic scalar and vector parts (i.e., $I=0, I=1$) according to

$$\beta_S=\tfrac{1}{4}(3-\boldsymbol{\tau}_1\cdot\boldsymbol{\tau}_2)\beta_S{}^V+\tfrac{1}{4}(1+\boldsymbol{\tau}_1\cdot\boldsymbol{\tau}_2)\beta_S{}^S,\quad(4.9)$$

and similarly for β_{SD} and β_D. [The unusual signs in the projection operators have the same origin as those appearing with $\boldsymbol{\sigma}_2$ in (4.3).] The sum over intermediate isotopic spin states in (4.2) leads to

$$(j_\mu{}^S+\tau_3 j_\mu{}^V)(\tfrac{3}{4}\beta_S{}^V+\tfrac{1}{4}\beta_S{}^S)+\tau_i(j_\mu{}^S+\tau_3 j_\mu{}^V)\tau_i(\tfrac{1}{4}\beta_S{}^S-\tfrac{1}{4}\beta_S{}^V)=\beta_S{}^S j_\mu{}^S+\beta_S{}^V\tau_3 j_\mu{}^V.\quad(4.10)$$

Thus the isotopic vector and scalar parts of $\mathrm{Im}F_1$ and $\mathrm{Im}F_2$ are obtained by taking the corresponding isotopic amplitudes β in Eqs. (4.6–4.9).

We confine our attention to the isotopic scalar quantities since these are not coupled to the two-pion contributions discussed earlier. Substitution of Eq. (4.7) into the dispersion relations (2.5) leads one to a very complicated system of two coupled integral equations. This system may be reduced to a single Fredholm equation about whose solution little can be said without very much effort. Rather than attempt this, we have made only rough estimates of the contributions to the magnetic moment and charge radius.

The following rather drastic assumptions will be made: (a) Only the amplitude β_S will be retained; inclusion of β_{SD} and β_D should not modify the results appreciably. We assume that β_S has the maximum value allowed by unitarity, independent of energy. One would in fact expect it to be much smaller since there is an appreciable annihilation probability. (b) In computing $\mathrm{Im}F_1{}^S$ and $\mathrm{Im}F_2{}^S$ from (4.6) we shall replace F_1 and F_2 (which occur in A and B) on the right-hand side equal to their zero momentum transfer values, namely $F_1{}^S(0)=e/2$, $F_2{}^S(0)\approx 0$. Furthermore we neglect B in comparison with A. With these approximations, only the real part of β_S enters and this is set equal to one-half. Substituting into the dispersion integrals (2.5), we find for the pair state contributions

$$|F_1'^S(0)|\leqslant\frac{1}{\pi}\int_{4m^2}^{\infty}d\xi\,\xi^{-2}\frac{p_0}{p_0+m}\times\frac{1}{2}\times\frac{e}{2}=\frac{e}{8\pi m^2}(1-\ln 2)=\frac{0.012e}{m^2},$$
$$|F_2{}^S(0)|\leqslant\frac{1}{\pi}\int_{4m^2}^{\infty}d\xi\,\xi^{-1}\frac{1}{2(p_0+m)}\times\frac{1}{2}\times\frac{e}{2}=\frac{\ln 2}{2\pi}\times\frac{e}{2m}=0.11\frac{e}{2m},\quad(4.11)$$

where $p_0^2=\xi/4$ in these integrals. We conclude from these estimates that the pair plays a numerically unimportant role in nucleon structure, at least for small momentum transfers.

There are a few points in connection with the above calculations which should be discussed further. In particular the replacement of the F's on the right-hand side of (4.6) by their static values requires comment. First let us assume that there are states less massive than the nucleon-pair state (e.g., three pions) which contribute appreciably to isotopic scalar quantities. By analogy with the behavior of the pion vertex $\langle 0|j_\mu|\pi\pi\rangle$ treated in Sec. III, we would expect the $F_1(-\xi)$ and $F_2(-\xi)$ in (4.6) to rise from their static values and then fairly soon after the threshold of the important masses (say $\xi\sim 9\mu^2$) decreases strongly; their value at $\xi=4m^2$, which is the lower limit for the nucleon pair contribution, should be much less than the static value, so that our rough procedure of using the static values should be a gross overestimate. If, on the other hand, the nucleon-pair state itself is the first significant source of isotopic scalar, the fact that the $F(-4m^2)$ might be significantly larger than the $F(0)$ might cause some concern over the validity of our estimate. We have studied this question in some detail and, using various models for the F's discussed in another connection,[11] have found that in spite of the fact that $F(-4m^2)>F(0)$ (as much as seven times larger in one example) and that, for $\xi>4m^2$, $F(-\xi)$ rises further before falling, there are no appreciable modifications of our estimates. The point is that the width of the peak in $F(-\xi)$, described as ξ increases, is very small and that much of the large ξ contributions to the values given in (4.11) are lost by the fact that $F(-\xi)$ approaches zero quite rapidly in all of the models treated. (The higher the maximum the more rapid is the decrease for large ξ.)

We have further studied certain special models of nucleon-antinucleon scattering for which the coupled integral equations described above could be exactly solved. For example, if one sets $\beta_D=0$ and $\beta_{SD}/\sqrt{2}=\beta_S$ and forms $G_1=F_1+2mF_2$, the integral equations for G_1 and F_2 decouple. The solutions are too complicated to exhibit although they are readily obtained. Rough evaluations of these based on reasonable assumptions for β_S, such as used in reference 11 lead to contributions which lie within the estimates given in (4.11). The perturbation example treated in Appendix A is characterized by the relations $(\beta_S-\beta_D)=\beta_{SD}/\sqrt{2}$ and $\beta_D=\beta_S/2$. The latter condition is very pathological, of course; in addition, the numerical value given to β_S in that Appendix violates unitarity by about a factor of six. If the value of the quantity ρ appearing there were approximately reduced to correct this violation, we would again find values for $F_1{}^{S\prime}(0)$ and $F_2{}^S(0)$ within the range of (4.11).

Our conclusion is then that the structure of the integral equations obtained by substituting (4.6) in (2.5) is such that the nucleon-pair intermediate state is quite unimportant and that a quantitative limit on the contribution of this state to $F_1{}'^S(0)$ and $F_2{}^S(0)$ is provided by the simple iteration scheme leading to Eq. (4.11).

V. CONCLUDING REMARKS

We have made quantitative estimates of all of the low-mass configurations which would be intuitively expected to dominate the low-momentum-transfer characteristics of nucleon structure. The theoretical understanding we have obtained is disappointingly small. Let us summarize the results of our investigation.

First, with regard to isotopic vector quantities, we had expected the two-pion intermediate state to provide the bulk of the contributions. This is probably true but it is not easy to say how true, since there is no way at present to make a believable calculation. It had been argued in C that, in fact, perturbation theory could be relied upon for a quantitative estimate. We have shown, however, by a rigorous argument based on unitarity, that once the mass σ of the two-pion intermediate state exceeds $2m$, the perturbation theory must be wrong. The rescattering corrections, together with the very likely appearance of a pion form factor, must reduce the contribution of the region $\sigma>2m$ to a very minor one. Now we cannot conclude from our argument that because perturbation theory is bad for $\sigma>2m$ it is necessarily bad in the unphysical region $\sigma<2m$ to which our unitarity argument does not apply. It seems very unreasonable however, to expect that the rescattering effects are suddenly unimportant for $\sigma<2m$.

The practical implication of these remarks is the following: The perturbation-theoretic value for the vector magnetic moment is $1.67e/2m$ which is quite close to the experimental value, $1.86e/2m$. Unfortunately, half of the value 1.67 comes from the region $\sigma>2m$ and must be almost totally discarded. We have evaluated the rescattering corrections using the method proposed in C, which involves a probably unwarranted analytic continuation of pion-nucleon scattering amplitudes; it is, however, the only known way of making an estimate. Aside from the questionable continuation procedure, we make no approximations beyond the familiar one of including only the (3,3) pion-nucleon scattering amplitude. We find then an additional contribution to the magnetic moment of about the right order of magnitude, namely about $1.03e/2m$, which together with the $0.87e/2m$ from perturbation theory makes for impressive agreement with experiment. Inclusion of the form factor for pions given in Fig. 1 reduces the total answer to $1.4e/2m$ which, considering that the $|2\pi\rangle$ state is one of an infinite number, would be quite satisfactory. The rescattering correction is, however, uncomfortably large (it must be judged independent of the pion form factor) and we have little confidence in it. It is not impossible that in fact even the sign of the correction is wrong, in which case the role of more massive states would become unpleasantly important. The quantitative situation for the magnetic moment is thus uncertain.

The mean square radius of the magnetization density

is also affected by the rescattering corrections to perturbation theory and by the pion structure. Lowest order perturbation theory yields $\langle(r_2^2)_V\rangle=0.12/\mu^2$, a surprisingly small value, pointing again to the importance of large σ values in the dispersion integral. Inclusion of rescattering and the pion form factor causes this number to increase to $0.23/\mu^2$, a rather more reasonable value. The correspondingly experimental quantity is not directly obtainable. To the extent that the isotopic scalar contribution to the proton or neutron radius is negligible [which will be the case unless $\langle(r_2^2)_S\rangle\sim 20\langle(r_2^2)_V\rangle$], one may hope to find $\langle(r_2^2)_V\rangle$ from the electron-proton scattering experiments. Unfortunately, the magnetization density plays a minor role in the scattering until the momentum transfers are so large that the form factor F_2^P can no longer be characterized by a mean square radius alone. Extensive curve fitting in the large-momentum-transfer region has led Hofstadter and his collaborators to a value $\langle(r_2^2)_p\rangle=0.32/\mu^2$; in view of the way this number has been deduced it cannot be regarded as being in conflict with our theoretical number. *Unless one knows the actual functional form of the magnetization form factor, no amount of curve fitting at large momentum transfers can yield a meaningful value for the initial slope.*

The situation with respect to the charge density mean square radius is much more distressing. The prediction of lowest order perturbation theory is that $\langle(r_1^2)_V\rangle=0.24/\mu^2$; if we accept the empirical fact that for a neutron $\langle(r_1^2)_n\rangle\approx 0$ [which implies $\langle(r_1^2)_V\rangle=\langle(r_1^2)_S\rangle$] this leads to $\langle(r_1^2)_p\rangle=0.24/\mu^2$. The proton charge radius is in principle subject to direct measurement with electron scattering experiments at very low momentum transfer. What are needed are accurate absolute cross-section measurements in a region where the cross section is varying rapidly for uninteresting (i.e., ordinary Coulomb scattering) reasons and one is looking for small superimposed variations. The current interpretation of these difficult measurements by Hofstadter leads to a mean square charge radius of the proton of $0.32/\mu^2$. If this is, in fact, true, the theory may be in a very difficult position. The same rescattering effects which were helpful in connection with the magnetic moment have a devastating effect here. In the first place, the perturbation contribution from the region $\sigma>2m$ must be discarded; this amounts to about one-fourth of the above-mentioned value $0.24/\mu^2$. Secondly, the rescattering and pion form factor corrections in the region $\sigma<2m$ reduce the value further to $0.07/\mu^2$. Thus if the two-pion state is assumed to be the principal contributor to the isotopic vector charge radius, we appear to have a sharp disagreement with experiment. If we accept the small value of the neutron charge radius, we cannot rely on the isotopic scalar contribution to raise $0.07/\mu^2$ to $0.32/\mu^2$. It is obviously of crucial importance to obtain an accurate determination of the proton charge radius.

One may, of course, argue that the charge density form factor receives contributions from very high mass values and that we should not be too distressed by our inability to get a large radius from the two-pion configuration. It was, in fact, a certain fear of these high masses which led to our original forms for the dispersion relation for F_1^S, F_1^V. One argument supporting the importance of high mass values may be found by evaluating the integral over $\mathrm{Im}F_1^V(-\sigma^2)/\sigma^2$, which, if it exists, should equal $e/2$. Using our approximate rescattering and pion form factor we find instead approximately 0. As we have stated previously, we have very little confidence in our method of calculating the rescattering effects; it is not out of the question that the charge radius shows an extraordinary sensitivity to the pion-nucleon continuation method not shared by the magnetization density and that the large effects noted could be easily upset by changing the numbers slightly. Our inability to carry out a reliable calculation of the rescattering makes it difficult to draw any sharp conclusions.

In order to try to get some feeling for the possible contributions of higher mass configurations, we have studied several particular ones. The most important (in that it is the least massive) isotopic scalar contribution should come from the three-pion state. We were unable to even estimate this. The configuration of two K mesons was treated in perturbation theory; barring incredible accidents it is hard to see how this state can be of much importance. The nucleon-antinucleon pair states which have long played a rather enigmatic role in the nucleon structure problem have also been shown to make very small contributions to the moments and radii. Which, if any, of the high-mass states (i.e., $>2\pi$, 3π) are important we cannot say.

Of all of the quantities we have attempted to calculate, only the vector magnetic moment and magnetization density mean square radius appear to be reasonable. If our estimate of the two-pion state is reliable, we are unable to explain a proton charge radius any larger than about one-fifth the presently alleged value without an appeal to high-mass (and needless to say incalculable) configurations. If we somehow got a large vector charge radius we would still face the old dilemma of finding a sufficiently large isotopic scalar charge radius to explain the difference between neutron and proton. As has been emphasized by Yennie,[25] one then must also insure that this prolific source of charge radius should not yield too large a scalar magnetic moment.

In conclusion, there remain at least the following four alternatives: (1) The experiments are wrong and the proton charge radius is very small (this would obviously be the nicest solution for theoreticians). (2) The two-pion state is grossly mistreated in our theory so that one gets a large vector charge radius, and necessary isotopic scalar quantities ultimately appear,

[25] D. Yennie (private communication).

presumably from the three-pion state. (3) States of uncomputable complexity are important. (4) Our whole dispersion approach is wrong. The last possibility would be catastrophic.

ACKNOWLEDGMENTS

It is a pleasure to acknowledge several useful conversations with Professor F. J. Dyson, Professor J. R. Oppenheimer, Dr. R. Oehme, and Dr. J. G. Taylor. In particular we are indebted to Professor Dyson for his help in solving the class of integral equations which have arisen in this work. We should like also to thank Professor G. F. Chew for advance communications concerning the results obtained by his group.

APPENDIX A. LADDER APPROXIMATION TO THE NUCLEON PAIR CONTRIBUTIONS TO THE ELECTROMAGNETIC STRUCTURE

We noted in Sec. IV that if the nucleon-antinucleon scattering encountered there were treated in perturbation theory, one would obtain a kind of ladder approximation to the vertex operator. An approach similar in spirit was made some time ago by Edwards.[10] His techniques were quite different and his results rather more ambiguous.

We proceed from Eq. (4.2) for the absorptive part of $A_\mu^J(N\bar{N})$ which for convenience we reproduce here:

$$A_\mu^J(N\bar{N})=-\pi\left(\frac{p_0}{m}\right)^{\frac{1}{2}}\sum\int\frac{d^3n\,d^3\bar{n}}{(2\pi)^3}\bar{v}(\bar{p})\times\langle 0|j_\mu|n\bar{n}\rangle\langle n\bar{n}|f|p\rangle\delta(n+\bar{n}-p-\bar{p}).\quad\text{(A.1)}$$

The second matrix element is to be calculated in lowest order perturbation theory (with $f=-ig\gamma_5\tau_j\phi_j\psi+\delta m\psi$); we find

$$\left(\frac{n_0\bar{n}_0p_0}{m^3}\right)^{\frac{1}{2}}\bar{v}(\bar{p})\langle n\bar{n},\,\text{out}|f|p\rangle=-g^2\frac{\bar{v}(\bar{p})\tau_j\gamma_5v(\bar{n})\bar{u}(n)\gamma_5\tau_ju(p)}{(n-p)^2+\mu^2-i\epsilon}+g^2\frac{\bar{u}(n)\tau_j\gamma_5\bar{v}(\bar{n})v(\bar{p})\tau_j\gamma_5u(p)}{(n+\bar{n})^2+\mu^2-i\epsilon}.\quad\text{(A.2)}$$

It is convenient to use $\langle 0|j_\mu|n\bar{n}\rangle$ in the following form (Eq. 1.3):

$$(n_0\bar{n}_0/m^2)^{\frac{1}{2}}\langle 0|j_\mu|n\bar{n},\,\text{out}\rangle=-\bar{v}(\bar{n})\{G_1^*[(n+\bar{n})^2]i\gamma_\mu+G_2^*[(n+\bar{n})^2](\bar{n}-n)_\mu\}u(n).\quad\text{(A.3)}$$

When (A.3) and (A.4) are substituted into (A.1) and the spin sums carried out, the second term in (A.2) does not contribute. We find, in fact,

$$A_\mu^J(N\bar{N})=-\frac{\pi g^2}{4(2\pi)^3}\int\frac{d^3n\,d^3\bar{n}}{n_0\bar{n}_0}\frac{\delta(n+\bar{n}-p-\bar{p})}{(n-p)^2+\mu^2}\bar{v}(\bar{p})\tau_j\gamma_5\times(-i\gamma\cdot\bar{n}-m)[i\gamma_\mu\,\text{Re}G_1+(\bar{n}-n)_\mu\,\text{Re}G_2]\times(-i\gamma\cdot n+m)\tau_j\gamma_5u(p).\quad\text{(A.4)}$$

We have, as usual, taken half the sum over "in" and "out" states and this accounts for the appearance of $\text{Re}G_1$, $\text{Re}G_2$. In the present approximation, the nucleon-antinucleon amplitude is real. [Compare (4.3) and the discussion following (4.4).] Recalling that the G's have the structure $G^S+\tau_3G^V$, we see that the effect of the τ_j's in (4.4) is to convert G into $\tilde{G}=3G^S-\tau_3G^V$. Finally we rewrite (A.4) in the form

$$A_\mu^J(N\bar{N})=\frac{-\pi g^2}{(2\pi)^3}\int d^4n\int d^4\bar{n}\int d^4k\,\frac{\bar{v}(\bar{p})i\gamma\cdot k[i\gamma_\mu\,\text{Re}\tilde{G}_1-(\bar{n}-n)_\mu\,\text{Re}\tilde{G}_2]i\gamma\cdot ku(p)}{k^2+\mu^2}\times\delta((p-k)^2+m^2)\delta((k+\bar{p})^2+m^2)\delta(n-p+k)\delta(\bar{n}-k-\bar{p})\quad\text{(A.5)}$$

$$=-\frac{\pi}{2}\frac{g^2}{(2\pi)^3}\int d^4k\,\bar{v}(\bar{p})i\gamma\cdot k\frac{[i\gamma_\mu\,\text{Re}\tilde{G}_1+(p-\bar{p}-2k)_\mu\,\text{Re}\tilde{G}_2]i\gamma\cdot ku(p)}{k^2+\mu^2}\times\delta(k\cdot\Delta)\delta(k^2-P\cdot k),\quad\text{(A.6)}$$

where we have introduced $\Delta=p+\bar{p}$, $P=p-\bar{p}$; note that $P^2=-4m^2-\Delta^2$.

The integrations in (A.6) are most easily carried out in the rest system of $p+\bar{p}$, namely $\Delta=0$. Comparison with the standard form (A.3) yields

$$\text{Im}G_1(\Delta^2)=\frac{g^2}{4\pi}\frac{\theta(-4m^2-\Delta^2)}{8P^3(-\Delta^2)^{\frac{1}{2}}}\left\{P^4-2\mu^2P^2+2\mu^4\ln\frac{P^2+\mu^2}{\mu^2}\right\}\text{Re}\tilde{G}_1(\Delta^2),\quad\text{(A.7)}$$

$$\text{Im}G_2(\Delta^2)=\frac{g^2}{4\pi}\frac{\theta(-4m^2-\Delta^2)}{2P(-\Delta^2)^{\frac{1}{2}}}\left[m\left\{-\frac{1}{2}+\frac{3\mu^2}{P^2}-\left(\frac{3\mu^4}{P^4}+\frac{\mu^2}{P^2}\right)\ln\frac{P^2+\mu^2}{\mu^2}\right\}\text{Re}\tilde{G}_1(\Delta^2)+\left\{\mu^2-\left(\frac{\mu^2}{2}+\frac{\mu^4}{P_2}\right)\ln\frac{P^2+\mu^2}{\mu^2}\right\}\text{Re}\tilde{G}_2(\Delta^2)\right].\quad\text{(A.8)}$$

We shall be particularly interested in the scalar part of these equations. So long as states with 3, 5, $\cdots$ pions are neglected, the only source of isotopic scalar contributions is the pair state under discussion and the equations are entirely uncoupled from the two-pion state. Although it is not at all necessary, for simplicity we shall set the pion mass equal to zero. Experience with perturbation theory shows that this does not cause appreciable error. In this limit we have

$$\mathrm{Im}G_1{}^S(\Delta^2)=\frac{3}{8}\left(\frac{g^2}{4\pi}\right)\left(\frac{-4m^2-\Delta^2}{-\Delta^2}\right)^{\frac{1}{2}}\theta(-4m^2-\Delta^2)\times\mathrm{Re}G_1{}^S(\Delta^2), \quad (A.9)$$

$$\mathrm{Im}G_2{}^S(\Delta^2)=-\frac{3}{4}\left(\frac{g^2}{4\pi}\right)\frac{M\theta(-4m^2-\Delta^2)}{[(-\Delta^2-4m^2)(-\Delta^2)]^{\frac{1}{2}}}\times\mathrm{Re}G_1{}^S(\Delta^2) \quad (A.10)$$

$$=-2m\frac{\mathrm{Im}G_1{}^S(\Delta^2)}{(-\Delta^2-4m^2)}. \quad (A.11)$$

The mathematical problem posed by the condition (A.9) together with the dispersion relation

$$G_1{}^S(\Delta^2)=G_1{}^S(0)-\frac{\Delta^2}{\pi}\int_{4m^2}^{\infty}d\sigma^2\frac{\mathrm{Im}G_1{}^S(-\sigma^2)}{\sigma^2(\sigma^2+\Delta^2-i\epsilon)}, \quad (A.12)$$

is exactly the same as the one met earlier in connection with Eqs. (3.39) and (3.41), and the solution which agrees with perturbation theory in the limit of $g^2\rightarrow 0$ is

$$G_1{}^S(\Delta^2)=G_1{}^S(0)\exp\left\{-\frac{\Delta^2}{\pi}\int_{4m^2}^{\infty}d\sigma^2\frac{1}{\sigma^2(\sigma^2+\Delta^2-i\epsilon)}\times\tan^{-1}\left[\frac{3g^2}{32\pi}\left(\frac{\sigma^2-4m^2}{\sigma^2}\right)^{\frac{1}{2}}\right]\right\}. \quad (A.13)$$

The solution for $G_2{}^S(\Delta^2)$ is obtained immediately by substituting (A.11) into the dispersion relation for $G_2{}^S$:

$$G_2{}^S(\Delta^2)=\frac{1}{\pi}\int_{4m^2}^{\infty}d\sigma^2\frac{\mathrm{Im}G_2{}^S(-\sigma^2)}{\sigma^2+\Delta^2}$$

$$=-\frac{2m}{\pi}\int_{4m^2}^{\infty}d\sigma^2\frac{\mathrm{Im}G_1{}^S(-\sigma^2)}{(\sigma^2-4m^2)(\sigma^2+\Delta^2)}. \quad (A.14)$$

Making a partial-fraction decomposition, we find immediately

$$G_2{}^S(\Delta^2)=\frac{2m}{\Delta^2+4m^2}[G_1{}^S(\Delta^2)-G_1{}^S(-4m^2)]. \quad (A.15)$$

It is worth noting some of the easily obtained properties of these solutions. Recalling that by definition $G_2(0)$ is the scalar anomalous moment, μ_s, and that $G_1{}^S(0)=\frac{1}{2}e+2m\mu_s$, we find from (A.15)

$$\mu_s=\frac{1}{2}\left(\frac{1-\rho}{\rho}\right)\frac{e}{2m}, \quad (A.16)$$

where

$$\rho=\frac{G_1{}^S(-4m^2)}{G_1{}^S(0)}=\exp\left\{\frac{2}{\pi}\int_0^{3g^2/32\pi}dy\frac{\tan^{-1}y}{y}\right\}, \quad (A.17)$$

$$\simeq\exp\left[\frac{2}{\pi}\left(\frac{\pi}{2}\ln\lambda+\frac{1}{\lambda}-\frac{1}{3^2\lambda^3}+\frac{1}{5^2\lambda^5}-\cdots\right)\right], \quad (A.18)$$

and $\lambda=3g^2/32\pi\approx 5.6$. For this value of λ, $\rho=6.28$, and $\mu_s\simeq -0.42e/2m$. This value is about three times larger than the upper limit given in Eq. (4.11), a first indication of the inadequacy of our ladder approximation. The derivatives of $G_1{}^S$ and $G_2{}^S$ at $\Delta^2=0$ are also easily found:

$$G_1{}^{S\prime}(0)=-\frac{G_1{}^S(0)}{4\pi m^2}\left(\frac{\lambda^2+1}{\lambda^2}\tan^{-1}\lambda-\frac{1}{\lambda}\right),$$

$$\approx-\frac{e}{16m^2\rho}\left(1-\frac{2}{\pi\lambda}+\lambda^{-2}-\cdots\right) \quad (A.19)$$

$$=-0.010\frac{e}{m^2}.$$

$$G_2{}^{S\prime}(0)=-\frac{1}{4m^2}\mu_s+\frac{1}{2m}G_1{}^{S\prime}(0)=+\frac{0.095}{m^2}\frac{e}{2m},$$

$$F_1{}^{S\prime}(0)=G_1{}^{S\prime}-2mG_2{}^{S\prime}=\frac{1}{2m}\mu_s=-\frac{0.105e}{m^2}. \quad (A.20)$$

This value of $F_1{}^{S\prime}(0)$ is about nine times larger than the upper limit given in (4.11), again showing the poorness of the approximation.

In spite of the fact that the ladder model is not very good in any absolute sense, it does represent a considerable improvement over perturbation theory: The magnetic moment is reduced by a factor of about four, $G_1{}^{S\prime}(0)$ by about fifteen, and $G_2{}^{S\prime}(0)$ by about three. The asymptotic forms ($\Delta^2\rightarrow+\infty$) of (A.13) and (A.15) are quite different from perturbation theory for which $G_1\rightarrow\ln\Delta^2$ and $G_2\rightarrow\ln\Delta^2/\Delta^2$. In the present treatment we have

$$G_1{}^S(\Delta^2)\rightarrow G_1{}^S(0)\left(\frac{\Delta^2}{4m^2}\right)^{-(1/\pi)\,\mathrm{arc\,tan}\lambda}=G_1{}^S(0)\left(\frac{\Delta^2}{4m^2}\right)^{-0.44},$$

$$G_2{}^S(\Delta^2)\rightarrow-\frac{2m}{\Delta^2}G_1{}^S(-4m^2)=-\frac{2m\rho G_1{}^S(0)}{\Delta^2}\simeq\frac{-G_1{}^S(0)}{2m}6.28\left(\frac{4m^2}{\Delta^2}\right). \quad (A.21)$$

The general form of our solution is similar to that found by Edwards[10] who studied certain aspects of the same problem. The two approaches are not directly comparable; he typically obtained asymptotic behaviors like $(\Delta^2)^{-\lambda/\pi}$ so that the results coincide for small λ. The solutions (A.13) and (A.15) cannot be expanded in powers of λ unless $\lambda<1$ which is not satisfied experimentally.

APPENDIX B. MESON-NUCLEON VERTEX

The meson nucleon vertex which describes the scattering of a nucleon by an external meson field occurs in a variety of problems such as π-μ decay and π^0 decay. The mathematical treatment of it follows so closely what has been developed in this paper that we felt it worthwhile to include the discussion here.

The quantity of interest, I, is defined according to Eq. (1.12) as

$$\begin{aligned} I&=(p_0'p_0/m^2)^{\frac{1}{2}}\langle p'|J_i|p\rangle \\ &=-i[\mu^2+(p-p')^2]\Delta_{Fc}[(p-p')^2]\bar{u}(p')\Gamma_5(p',p)u(p) \\ &=-ig\bar{u}(p')\tau_i\gamma_5u(p)K((p-p')^2), \qquad \text{(B.1)}\end{aligned}$$

where we imagine that $K(-\mu^2)=1$; the renormalized meson propagation function Δ_{Fc} is normalized so that the product of the first two factors in (B.1) is unity in the limit $(p-p')^2\rightarrow\mu^2$. Evidently we have to do with one scalar function, $K(\Delta^2)$, whose structure we must study.

As in the corresponding electromagnetic vertex, it is rather more convenient to study a quantity J defined by

$$\begin{aligned} J&=(\bar{p}_0p_0/m^2)^{\frac{1}{2}}\langle 0|J_i|\bar{p}p,\text{ in}\rangle \\ &=ig\bar{v}(\bar{p})\tau_i\gamma_5u(p)K((p+\bar{p})^2); \qquad \text{(B.2)}\end{aligned}$$

the analyticity assumption we customarily make enable us to relate the scalar functions involved in I and J in the simple fashion indicated. Making the standard reduction, dropping an equal-time commutator as usual, we have

$$\begin{aligned} J=-i\left(\frac{p_0}{m}\right)^{\frac{1}{2}}\int d^4x\,\bar{v}(\bar{p}) \\ \times\langle 0|[J_i(0),f(x)]\theta(-x_0)|p\rangle\exp(i\bar{p}\cdot x). \qquad \text{(B.3)}\end{aligned}$$

The absorptive part, A_J, is given by

$$\begin{aligned} A_J=-\pi(p_0/m)^{\frac{1}{2}}\textstyle\sum_s\bar{v}(\bar{p})\langle 0|J_i|s\rangle \\ \times\langle s|f|p\rangle\delta(p_s-p-\bar{p}). \qquad \text{(B.4)}\end{aligned}$$

The least massive intermediate state is that consisting of three pions, the neglect of which by this time scarcely needs comment. The first state to be considered is that involving a nucleon-antinucleon pair, and, as always, we take half the sum over "in" and "out" states.

We shall first treat this problem in the same way we did in Appendix A, namely by describing the matrix element $\langle N\bar{N}|f|p\rangle$ in lowest order perturbation theory. In fact, we use Eq. (A.2) for the matrix element. Substituting (A.2) and (B.2) into (B.4) (with $|s\rangle$ taken as $|\bar{N}N\rangle$) and carrying out the indicated operations, just as in (A.6), we find by comparison with (B.2)

$$\begin{aligned} \text{Im}K(\Delta^2)=\frac{g^2}{16\pi}\frac{\theta(-\Delta^2-4m^2)}{\sqrt{-\Delta^2}} \\ \times\left[P-\frac{\mu^2}{P}\ln\frac{P^2+\mu^2}{\mu^2}-\frac{4\Delta^2P}{\Delta^2+\mu^2}\right]\text{Re}K(\Delta^2), \qquad \text{(B.5)}\end{aligned}$$

where $P^2=-\Delta^2-4m^2$. The first two terms in (B.5) come from the first term in (A.2) whereas the last comes from the second term. We have purposely separated these contributions, since the first two terms in (B.5) comprise what may be called the proper vertex part $\bar{v}(\bar{p})\Gamma_5(\bar{p},p)u(p)$, while the second comes from a nucleon bubble in a meson propagation function and represents the deviation of $(\Delta^2+\mu^2)\Delta_{Fc}(\Delta^2)$ from unity. As we'll see in a moment, keeping or dropping the modified propagation function has a very profound effect.

For simplicity we set the pion mass equal to zero. Then if we drop the last term in (B.5), we will have to do with the proper vertex part; and this quantity, which we shall call $\Gamma(\Delta^2)$, is directly comparable with the ladder approximation to G_1 in Appendix A. For Γ, we have then

$$\begin{aligned} \text{Im}\Gamma(\Delta^2)=\frac{g^2}{16\pi}\left(\frac{-\Delta^2-4m^2}{-\Delta^2}\right)^{\frac{1}{2}} \\ \times\text{Re}\Gamma(\Delta^2)\theta(-\Delta^2-4m^2). \qquad \text{(B.6)}\end{aligned}$$

The structure of (B.6) is exactly that of (A.9); since the dispersion relation in this case is taken to be

$$\Gamma(\Delta^2)=1-\frac{\Delta^2+\mu^2}{\pi}\int_{4m^2}^{\infty}d\sigma^2\frac{\text{Im}\Gamma(-\sigma^2)}{(\sigma^2-\mu^2)(\sigma^2+\Delta^2-i\epsilon)}, \qquad \text{(B.7)}$$

the solution of the integral equation is

$$\begin{aligned} \Gamma(\Delta^2)=\exp\Bigg\{\frac{-(\Delta^2+\mu^2)}{\pi}\int_{4m^2}^{\infty}d\sigma^2\frac{1}{(\sigma^2-\mu^2)(\sigma^2+\Delta^2-i\epsilon)} \\ \times\tan^{-1}\left[\frac{g^2}{16\pi}\left(\frac{\sigma^2-4m^2}{\sigma^2}\right)^{\frac{1}{2}}\right]\Bigg\}, \qquad \text{(B.8)}\end{aligned}$$

and it has been chosen to agree with perturbation theory in the limit of small g^2. The asymptotic form of $\Gamma(\Delta^2)$ is easily seen to be

$$\Gamma(\Delta^2)\rightarrow(4m^2/\Delta^2)^{(1/\pi)\arctan(g^2/16\pi)}. \qquad \text{(B.9)}$$

If we keep both the proper vertex part and the propagation function modification, i.e., the whole of

(B.5), with $\mu^2=0$ we have

$$\operatorname{Im}K(\Delta^2)=-\frac{3g^2}{16\pi}\left(\frac{-\Delta^2-4m^2}{-\Delta^2}\right)^{\frac{1}{2}}\times\operatorname{Re}K(\Delta^2)\theta(-\Delta^2-4m^2), \quad \text{(B.10)}$$

and the solution corresponding to (B.8) is evidently

$$K(\Delta^2)=\exp\left\{\frac{\Delta^2+\mu^2}{\pi}\int_{4m^2}^{\infty}d\sigma^2\frac{1}{(\sigma^2-\mu^2)(\sigma^2+\Delta^2-i\epsilon)}\times\left[\tan^{-1}\left(\frac{3g^2}{16\pi}\right)\right]\left(\frac{\sigma^2-4m^2}{\sigma^2}\right)^{\frac{1}{2}}\right\}. \quad \text{(B.11)}$$

The asymptotic form of $K(\Delta^2)$ is easily seen to be

$$K(\Delta^2)\rightarrow(\Delta^2/m^2)^{(1/\pi)\arctan(3g^2/16\pi)}. \quad \text{(B.12)}$$

Thus we see that $\Gamma(\Delta^2)$ approaches zero for large Δ^2 whereas $K(\Delta^2)$ increases indefinitely in the present approximation.

This behavior does not contradict any general principles. Making reasonable assumptions about the propagation function Δ_{F_c} it has been shown by Lehmann *et al.*,[18] quite generally, that $\Gamma(\Delta^2)\rightarrow 0$ as $\Delta^2\rightarrow\infty$. On the other hand $[\Delta^2+\mu^2]\Delta_{F_c}((\Delta^2+\mu^2))$ in the limit of large Δ^2 approaches the renormalization constant $1/Z_3$ which is generally believed to be infinite, so that having K increase is not necessarily unreasonable. It is amusing to combine (B.11) and (B.8) to give a formula for Δ_{F_c} which sums nucleon bubbles with various numbers of ladders going across the bubbles. We find

$$\Delta_{F_c}(\Delta^2)=\frac{1}{\Delta^2+\mu^2}\exp\left\{\left(\frac{\Delta^2+\mu^2}{\pi}\right)\times\int_{4m^2}^{\infty}d\sigma^2\frac{1}{(\sigma^2-\mu^2)(\sigma^2+\Delta^2-i\epsilon)}\times\left[\left(\frac{\sigma^2-4m^2}{\sigma^2}\right)^{\frac{1}{2}}\tan^{-1}\left(\frac{3g^2}{16\pi}\right)+\left(\frac{\sigma^2-4m^2}{\sigma^2}\right)^{\frac{1}{2}}\tan^{-1}\left(\frac{g^2}{16\pi}\right)\right]\right\} \quad \text{(B.13)}$$

$$\rightarrow\frac{1}{\Delta^2}\times\left(\frac{\Delta^2}{4m^2}\right)^{\kappa}, \quad \text{(B.14)}$$

where

$$\kappa=\frac{1}{\pi}\left[\tan^{-1}\left(\frac{3g^2}{16\pi}\right)+\tan^{-1}\left(\frac{g^2}{16\pi}\right)\right]\simeq 1-\frac{16}{3\pi}\left(\frac{4\pi}{g^2}\right)+\cdots. \quad \text{(B.15)}$$

Thus $\Delta_{F_c}\rightarrow 0$ rather slowly for large g^2 in this approximation. The results of our ladder approximation to $\Gamma(\Delta^2)$ are quite similar to those of Edwards.[10]

We turn finally to a more accurate treatment of the problem. Instead of using lowest order perturbation theory to describe the nucleon-antinucleon scattering amplitude $\bar{v}(\bar{p})\langle N\bar{N}|f|p\rangle$, we shall characterize it by a complex phase shift. The crucial observation which makes this possible is that the matrix element $\langle 0|J_i|N\bar{N}\rangle$ is different from zero only if the nucleon-antinucleon pair are (in their rest system) in a state of angular momentum zero, odd parity, and isotopic spin unity. There is only one such state, namely ${}^1S_0{}^3$ where the superscript 3 designates the isotopic triplet. We write now, in the rest frame of the pair,

$$J=(p_0/m)ig\chi_{\bar{p}}{}^*\tau_i\chi_pK((p+\bar{p})^2), \quad \text{(B.16)}$$

$$\bar{v}(\bar{p})\langle N\bar{N}|f|p\rangle=-\frac{4\pi n_0}{m^2n}\times\left(\frac{m^3}{n_0{}^3}\right)^{\frac{1}{2}}\frac{3\chi_{\bar{p}}{}^*\chi_{\bar{n}}\chi_n{}^*\chi_p-\chi_{\bar{p}}{}^*\boldsymbol{\tau}\chi_{\bar{n}}\cdot\chi_n{}^*\boldsymbol{\tau}\chi_p}{4}\beta_0, \quad \text{(B.17)}$$

where here

$$\beta_0=\sin\delta\exp(i\delta), \quad \text{(B.18)}$$

and δ is the complex phase shift for the ${}^1S_0{}^3$ nucleon-antinucleon state and is a function of wave number, $[-\frac{1}{4}(p+\bar{p})^2-m^2]^{\frac{1}{2}}$.

The calculation is now trivial and follows what should by now be well established patterns. Substituting (B.16) and (B.17) into (B.4), we find by referring to (B.16)

$$\operatorname{Im}K(\Delta^2)=\operatorname{Re}(K^*\beta_0), \quad \text{(B.19)}$$

from which we obtain

$$\operatorname{Im}K(\Delta^2)=\frac{\operatorname{Re}\beta_0}{1-\operatorname{Im}\beta_0}\operatorname{Re}K(\Delta^2). \quad \text{(B.20)}$$

This is of the standard form discussed in Sec. III in connection with the pion vertex. The phase angle φ defined there has exactly the same form in this case,

$$\tan\varphi(-\Delta^2)=\operatorname{Re}\beta_0/(1-\operatorname{Im}\beta_0). \quad \text{(B.21)}$$

If we fix φ by the requirement of $\varphi=0$ at zero wave-number $(-\frac{1}{4}\Delta^2=m^2)$ and further assume that K has no zero, we have

$$K(\Delta^2)=\exp\left[-\frac{(\Delta^2+\mu^2)}{\pi}\times\int_{4m^2}^{\infty}d\sigma^2\frac{\varphi(\sigma^2)}{(\sigma^2-\mu^2)(\sigma^2+\Delta^2-i\epsilon)}\right] \quad \text{(B.22)}$$

in accordance with our normalization convention.

The asymptotic form of K depends on what happens to φ for large σ^2. If $\varphi \to 0$ at infinity, $K(\Delta^2) \to 1$; if φ approaches a positive constant, $K \to 0$. Within the framework of our model as expressed by (B.21), if there is any absorption whatsoever, φ is less than $\pi/2$. This may be seen by writing $\delta_0 = \xi + i\eta$ and noting that

$$\tan\varphi = \frac{e^{-2\eta}\sin 2\xi}{1+e^{-2\eta}\cos 2\xi}. \tag{B.23}$$

It may be argued that since in (B.4) we dropped reference to all states other than that involving a pair, we have no right to contemplate complex δ_0's, for it is just those states which lead to the complexity of the phase. It is our feeling, however, that there is sense to our procedure, since what we require for the validity of the approximation made is confined specifically to (B.4): The other terms may be small because of $\langle 0|J_i|s\rangle$ being small irrespective of the structure of the other factor. This point is also discussed in reference 11 where in addition the structure of K is examined for some simple models.

PAPER 51

NUCLEON STRUCTURE — Theoretical I

S.D. DRELL, Rapporteur

Stanford University, Stanford (Cal.)

Theoretical approximations and assumptions in obtaining nucleon form factors from the data

A) **e (lectron) + p (proton) → e + p** **for proton structure**

B) **e + d (euteron) → e′ + p + n (eutron)** **for neutron structure**

C) **e + d → e + d** **for neutron structure**

D) $\mathbf{e + p \to e' + \left\{ \begin{array}{l} n + \pi^+ \\ p + \pi^0 \end{array} \right.}$ **for neutron structure**

The form factors are defined as follows by the electromagnetic vertex operator between real physical nucleon states :

for the proton

$$G_1{}^P(q^2)\,\gamma_\mu + i\,G_2{}^P(q^2)\,\sigma_{\mu\nu}\,q^\nu,$$

for the neutron (1)

$$G_1{}^N(q^2)\,\gamma_\mu + i\,G_2{}^N(q^2)\,\sigma_{\mu\nu}\,q^\nu.$$

$q^2 = -q_\mu q^\mu$ is the square of the four momentum transfer which will be given here in units of

$$10^{13}\ \text{cm}^{-1} = (1\ \text{fermi})^{-1} \simeq 200\ \text{MeV}.$$

We use units of $\hbar = c = 1$.

For theoretical analysis it is more convenient to consider the isotopic scalar and vector form factors defined by

$$G_{1,2}{}^P = G_{1,2}{}^S + G_{1,2}{}^V\ ;\ G_{1,2}{}^N = G_{1,2}{}^S - G_{1,2}{}^V$$

with

$$G_1{}^S(0) = G_1{}^V(0) = \tfrac{1}{2}e\,;$$

$$G_2{}^V(0) = 1.85\left(\frac{e}{2M}\right) = 1.85\mu_B = \tfrac{1}{2}(K_P - K_N)\mu_B\,;$$

$$G_2{}^S(0) = -0.06\mu_B = \tfrac{1}{2}(K_P + K_N)\mu_B\,.$$

I A. Here there is no problem. Elastic scattering of electrons from protons gives $G_1{}^P(q^2)$ and $G_2{}^P(q^2)$ directly so long as it is adequate to treat their electromagnetic interaction in lowest order perturbation theory, i.e. with one quantum exchange. Polarizability corrections involving the exchange of two photons have been shown to be small [1,2] in the range of present experiments, so that the measurements can be analysed using the Rosenbluth [3] formula

$$\frac{d\sigma}{d\Omega} = \frac{\alpha^2}{4E_0^2}\,\frac{\cos^2\frac{\Theta}{2}}{\sin^4\frac{\Theta}{2}}\,\frac{1}{1 + 2\frac{E_0}{M}\sin^2\frac{\Theta}{2}}\left\{F_1{}^2(q^2) + \frac{-q_\mu q^\mu}{4M^2}\left(2\,[F_1 + K F_2]^2\tan^2\frac{\Theta}{2} + K^2 F_2{}^2\right)\right\}, \quad (2)$$

where

$$G_1 \equiv e\,F_1\,, \qquad G_2 \equiv \mu_B\,F_2\,,$$

$$-q_\mu q^\mu = \frac{(2E_0\sin\frac{\Theta}{2})^2}{1 + 2\frac{E_0}{M}\sin^2\frac{\Theta}{2}},$$

plus the Schwinger [4] radiative correction. Assuming validity of the present quantum-electrodynamic field theory of the electron, one learns the invariant (normalized) functions $F_1{}^P(q^2)$ and $F_2{}^P(q^2)$ directly. Evidently measurements at different E_0 and Θ, but fixed q^2, provide separate information on $F_1{}^P$ and $F_2{}^P$. It is found [5] that $F_1{}^P / F_2{}^P \simeq 1.0 \pm 0.2$, up to momentum transfers $\sim 3\,f^{-1}$.

I B. Inelastic electron scattering from the deuteron,

$$e + d \to e' + n + p,$$

leads to three final particles and thus to a continuous energy spectrum of scattered electrons at a given angle. For such an experiment to probe nucleon size there must be large momentum transfers. Since the deuteron form factor is very small for such large values of q, in first approximation one can neglect the interference between scattering amplitudes from the neutron and the proton and express the cross-section as a sum of single particle cross-sections. A simple approximate sum rule gives the area under the inelastic curve—that is, the cross-section for all electrons emerging in a given solid angle $d\Omega_e$ according to process (I B)—as the sum of free particle cross-sections,

$$\int dk_e \left(\frac{d^2\sigma_D}{dk_e d\Omega_e}\right) = \frac{d\sigma_P}{d\Omega_e} + \frac{d\sigma_N}{d\Omega_e}. \quad (3)$$

There are corrections to this sum rule but we remark first that the contribution of the neutron in (3) is appreciable only for large scattering angles and high incident energies such that the magnetic scattering dominates in (2). This is because the neutron is neutral and, in addition, as first shown by Foldy [6] (*), the second moment of its charge distribution is very small. In fact not until

$$q \equiv \sqrt{-q_\mu q^\mu} > 2.5 f^{-1},$$

corresponding to scattering of 600 MeV incident electrons through 60° or 500 MeV electrons through 75°, does scattering from the neutron contribute as much as 30% as that from the proton. Hence under conditions for which (3) provides information on neutron structure, what is being measured is $(F_1^N + K_N F_2^N)^2$.

In principle, if not yet in practice (**), measurements at different E_0 and Θ but the same q values give separate information on F_1^N and F_2^N as in the proton case.

In anticipation of more precise experimental numbers we inquire into corrections to approximate sum rule (3).

These have been discussed by Blankenbecler [8] and may be summarized briefly as follows, in terms of a correction factor Δ:

Kinematic corrections contributing to Δ:

(*a*) Knowledge of the free particle cross-sections over a finite energy range is required by the width of the momentum distribution in the deuteron.

(*b*) Bound nucleons do not satisfy the free particle energy-momentum relation so that terms in the current operator which are proportional to $(E^2 - |\mathbf{p}|^2 - m^2)$ may contribute.

Mesonic corrections contributing to Δ:

(*a*) Additional currents exist in the deuteron due to exchange of charged mesons.

(*b*) The nucleon electromagnetic vertex may be " warped" by meson exchange with the other nucleon.

(*c*) Effects of meson exchange between outgoing nucleons are not completely summarizable by a static interaction potential.

Blankenbecler has evaluated the kinematic corrections. For a physical picture of this effect consider two free nucleons moving back-to-back in arbitrary directions with a mean relative speed $\langle v^2 \rangle = \frac{1}{M}\langle T \rangle$. Evidently an electron scattering from them is scattering from a neutron or proton in a band of relative energies about the laboratory energy and there are corrections to Eq. (3) resulting from the curvature of the cross-section with energy (as well as angle, which must be properly transformed in relating relative and laboratory co-ordinates). Numerical values for this correction have been given by Blankenbecler who considered a Breit deuteron with instantaneous interaction potential. The current operator then reduces to the sum of free nucleon current operators and effects included are final state interactions, correct relativistic kinematics and phase-space factors. His results take the form

$$\int dk_e \frac{d_2\sigma^D}{dk_e d\Omega_e} = \left(1 + \delta \frac{\langle T \rangle}{M}\right) \left\{\frac{d\sigma_P}{d\Omega_e} + \frac{d\sigma_N}{d\Omega_e}\right\}.$$

where both δ and average ground state kinetic energy $\langle T \rangle$ depend on the deuteron model. For 500 MeV incident electrons scattering through 135°, $\Delta = +4\text{-}5\%$ for $\langle T \rangle = 30$ MeV; it decreases for smaller scattering angles.

On dimensional grounds one expects kinematical correction (*b*) to be $\sim \frac{\langle V \rangle}{M}$ which may again contribute terms of the order of a few per cent. Without a knowledge of the bound current operator nothing more can be said.

One can discuss the mesonic corrections only in relation to their observed role in deuteron photodisintegration since there exists no successful theory of these effects from first principles. We do this as follows. At high energies, the cross-section for $\gamma + d \rightarrow n + p$ is proportional to the Fourier transform of the deuteron wave function at the corresponding large momentum transfer. Both the simple one-body currents and the meson exchange currents contributing here are weighted by approximately the same two-body correlation function which falls off rapidly for large q. Fig. 1 indicates the importance of meson exchange effects which give rise to a resonance when the two outgoing nucleons have a relative kinetic energy corresponding to resonant exchange of a meson. Taking into account centre of mass motion and folding with the deuteron form factor has the effect of displacing this resonance from a relative kinetic energy of 320 MeV to 250 MeV. On the other hand, electrodisintegration frees the energy from the momentum transfer by the virtual photon and can occur strictly as a one-nucleon process. At the peak of the inelastic electron spectrum the second nucleon is an idle spectator and the one-body currents contribute in proportion to the zero momentum amplitude of the deuteron

(*) References to the original papers are contained in this very informative paper.

(**) Yearian and Hofstadter [7] quote experimental errors of $\sim 20\%$ for the sum rule (3) so that $\frac{d\sigma^N}{d\Omega}$ is not presently known to better than 50% and it is not yet possible to provide a severe limitation on the ratio $(F_1{}^N/F_2{}^N)$. As a numerical example the observations at 600 MeV, 90° and at 500 MeV, 135°, corresponding to $q = 3.4 f^{-1}$, can be fit by assuming $F_2{}^N = F_2{}^P$ and with $0 \geqslant F_{1N} \geqslant -0.7\, F_1{}^P$. A negative value for F_{1N} corresponds to the intuitive notion of negative charge extending beyond a positive core. We return to this question in part I C.

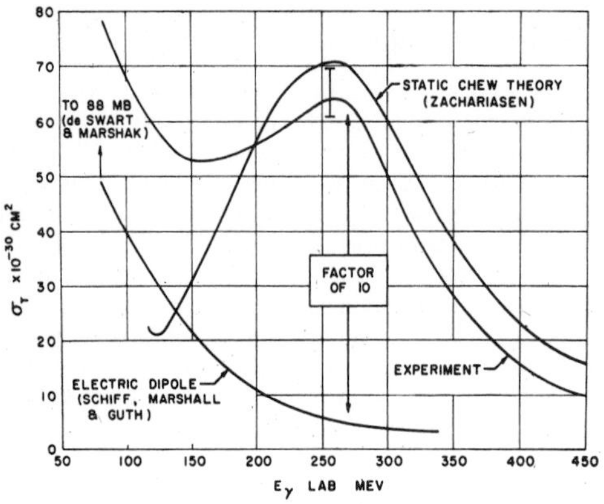

Fig. 1. *Comparison between theories and experiment for deuteron photo-disintegration.*

form factor, whereas the meson exchange effects are inhibited by a deuteron form factor at a momentum transfer of the order of the meson resonance. A rough calculation of this effect based on the observed photodisintegration resonance leads to a 10% increase in the total cross-section for 600 MeV electrons scattered through 135°. This increase is less important for scattering at lower energies and through smaller angles. It comes from the large energy loss collisions (*) corresponding to the left side of the curve in Fig. 2 and falls to a negligible value at the peak.

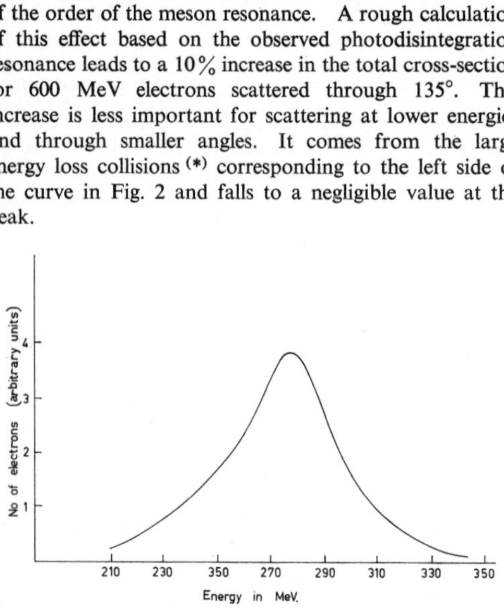

Fig. 2. *Spectrum of inelastically scattered electrons from deuterium as a function of energy of the scattered electron for an incident electron energy of* 600 *MeV and a scattering angle of* 135°.

This result suggests that it is possible to avoid the meson corrections in (3) by turning to an analysis of the peak of the inelastic spectrum as a measure of neutron structure. The primary uncertainty here is the zero momentum amplitude of the deuteron wave function, the difference between a Hulthén and Rustgi [9] (**) repulsive-core wave function being $< 5\%$. A. Goldberg [10] has made an impulse approximation calculation of the inelastic spectrum and peak height, in particular, which takes into account the correct relativistic kinematics. As in the sum rule discussion, the peak analysis measures $(F_1^N + K_N F_2^N)^2$ with an uncertainty of 50% with present experimental errors. Recent work of Marshak and collaborators on the important role played by final state potential interactions in photodisintegration contributes only small corrections in this analysis, since it is the low and not the high momentum components which are important here.

I C. Elastic electron-deuteron scattering measures the isotopic scalar part of the charge form factor $(F_1^S)^2 = (F_1^N + F_1^P)^2$, since the nucleons scatter coherently in an elastic process. Also the isoscalar part of the anomalous moments is very small, Eq. (1), and contributes negligibly here. McIntyre and Dhar [11] have made measurements of the elastic cross-section up to $q = 2.8 f^{-1}$ and therefore have probed beyond the second moment [6] of F_1^N.

Schiff [12] has shown that any deviation of the neutron from a point with $F_1^N(q^2) \equiv 0$ appreciably depresses the cross-section in the range $2 < q \sim 3 f^{-1}$ if this deviation is in accord with our intuitive notions and corresponds to a negative charge at large distances from the centre surrounding a net positive charge (*). He finds that only $-0.03e$ at a distance of the meson Compton wavelength reduces the cross-section by 30% at $q = 3 f^{-1}$, and that $-0.10e$ reduces it by more than 60% and below the stated experimental errors.

However theoretical attempts to make a quantitative determination of the neutron's charge distribution on the basis of this process again run into difficulties of the relativistic two-nucleon problem. Blankenbecler [8] has studied relativistic corrections to the usual description of a deuteron as two statically bound Pauli nucleons by considering a simplified but calculationally feasible model of two bosons, one of which is charged, which satisfy a Bethe - Salpeter equation. For a separable potential model with correct scattering length and effective range [13] he found a 25-30% reduction in the cross-section at $q = 3 f^{-1}$ below its value calculated using a Schrödinger equation. This reduction appears to be due in part to relativistic corrections to the current operator and in part to Lorentz contraction of the recoiling deuteron's wave function as seen in the laboratory system, which has the effect of reducing wave function overlap in the scattering matrix

(*) The " resonance " between the outgoing nucleons occurs $\sim$ 100 MeV below the peak and with a half width $\sim$ 70 MeV.

(**) This corresponds to a potential which is repulsive and $\alpha \frac{1}{r^2}$ for $r < 0.38$ Fermi.

(***) The form factor is, of course, constructed to have zero or very small second moment.

element [14] (*). Perhaps this result may be best stated in a way which relates it to the sensitivity of the cross-section to the nuclear forces. A relativistic calculation whose static limit corresponds to a Hulthén deuteron gives a scattering curve close to that calculated for a non-relativistic deuteron with hard-core interaction. Such effects along with contributions from the D-state in a physical deuteron play an important role because the cross-section is small and depends on the high Fourier components of the deuteron distribution.

Finally we remark that elastic scattering at small q-values measures the proton charge radius but only in the combination $\langle r^2_D \rangle + \langle r^2_{1P} \rangle$, and so is not a sensitive way of determining $\langle r^2_{1P} \rangle$.

I D. The process

$$e + p \rightarrow e' + \begin{cases} p + \pi^0 \\ n + \pi^+ \end{cases}$$

probes the electromagnetic structure of the neutron and is free of the complications of the two-nucleon problem. This was first realized by Fubini, Nambu, and Wataghin [15] who have given a dispersion theory analysis of this cross-section, and may be understood as follows. We write the matrix element for the process in Fig. 3 as

$$T_{k\,q} = e\,A_\mu(q) \langle P_2 k \,|\, j^\mu(q) \,|\, P_1 \rangle$$

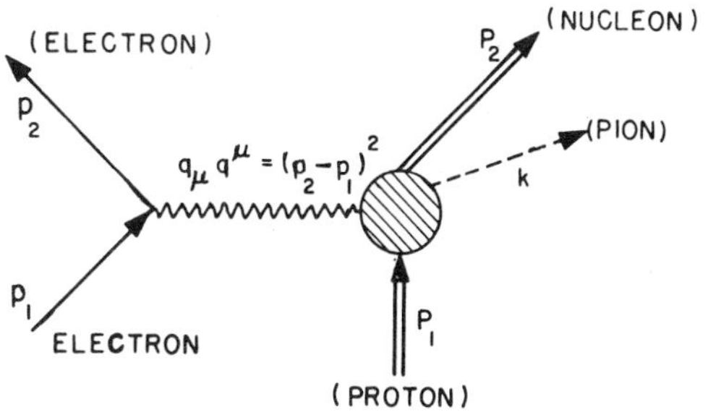

$$\underset{k \rightarrow q}{T} = e A^\mu_{\text{Møller}} (q) \langle P_2 k \,|\, j_\mu \,|\, P_1 \rangle$$

$\langle P_2 k \,|\, j_\mu \,|\, P_1 \rangle$ is photo-meson production matrix element for «photon» momentum $q_\mu q^\mu < 0$.

Fig. 3. *The matrix element for electron-production of mesons.*

where $\langle P_2 k \,|\, j^\mu(q) \,|\, P_1 \rangle$ is the photo-meson production matrix element for a " photon " of four-momentum q_μ. Subjecting it to a dispersion analysis, the inhomogeneous terms correspond to Fig. 4 and differ from those for photoproduction by the presence of electromagnetic form factors $F_{1,2}(q^2)$ for the nucleon. There

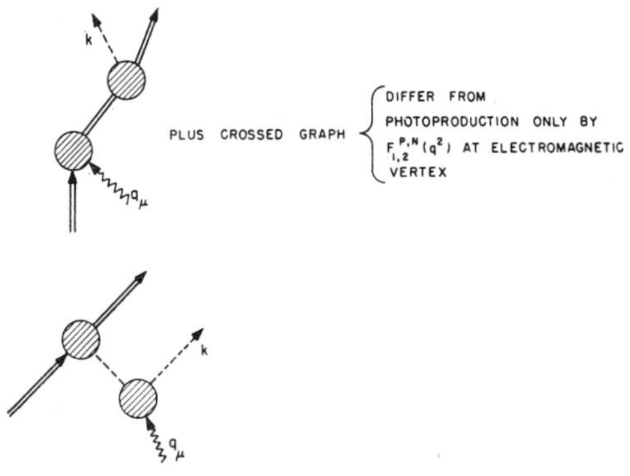

Fig. 4. *The inhomogeneous terms in dispersion relations for electron production of mesons.*

is also a meson electromagnetic form factor in the meson current term but we set it to unity since this term is of secondary importance in the present Panofsky [16] experiments. The theoretical problem is in principle, if not in fact, clear and well defined.

Experimentally [16] one measures $F_{1,2}(q^2)$ by programming runs for fixed relative pion-nucleon momentum, riding down the ledge of Fig. 5 near threshold to measure s-wave π^+ production via the Kroll - Ruderman term, and hence [15] $(F_1^P - F_1^N)^2 = (F_1^V)^2$, or riding down the peak to determine primarily the magnetic form factors. We note that

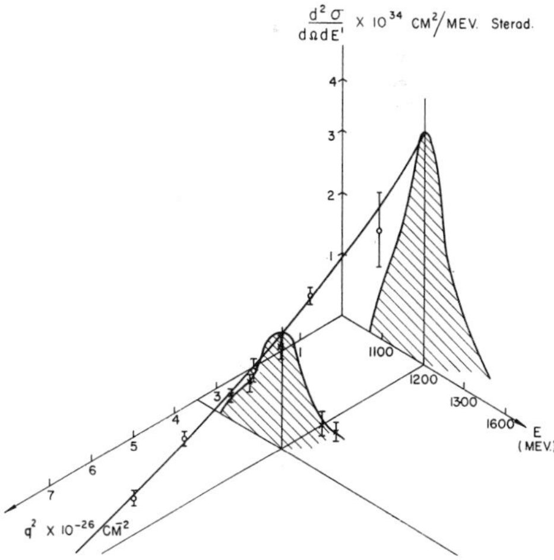

Fig. 5. *Cross-section for electron production of mesons as a function of momentum transfer $q_\mu q^\mu$ and of the relative pion-nucleon energy E. The shaded curve at $q_\mu q^\mu = 0$ is theoretically computed for photo-meson production. The curve and experimental points are taken from Panofsky's report (p. 16).*

(*) No increase of the type found by Bernstein was found in this special model.

it is the isovector part of the moment form factor, $[F_1{}^V + (K^P - K^N)F_2{}^V]$, which dominates at resonance in contrast with the inelastic deuteron cross-section in which the neutron and proton contribute incoherently.

The theoretical difficulties centre about the problem of obtaining accurate solutions to the dispersion relations for the conditions of large momentum transfer q^2 and low energy of the final pion-nucleon system in its centre of mass, so that it is dominated by the 3,3-resonance. The large momentum transfer makes the static approximation, which was the reference point for the photo-meson analysis [17], a much poorer approximation here. Fubini, Nambu and Wataghin have formulated the dispersion relations covariantly taking only the 3,3-resonance into account in the absorptive amplitudes. Work on their solutions [18] is now in progress. The solutions which exist at present calculate the imaginary parts of the $e-\pi$ amplitudes in the static approximation. The imaginary parts are then inserted into the relativistic dispersion relations to obtain real parts, i.e. only the resonant amplitudes in a multipole expansion have imaginary parts and these imaginary parts generate real amplitudes for all multipoles. The recoil effects are important because, for $q \sim 3f^{-1}$, there is a relative velocity of $v/c \sim 1/2$ between the natural system of dispersion relations $(\mathbf{P}_1 + \mathbf{P}_2 = 0)$ and the centre of mass system $(\mathbf{P}_1 + \mathbf{q} = 0)$ in which the phase of the amplitudes for each (J, L) and isospin I is given by $e^{i\delta}{}_{JIL}$, with δ_{JIL}, the corresponding pion-nucleon scattering phase-shift [15]. The recoil effects are found to play a more important role in generating new multipoles than in modifying the resonant ones.

It is difficult to define the quantitative accuracy of this present treatment but in view of the fact that the photoproduction analysis is in error $\sim 20\%$ at the π^+ maximum, and in view of other difficulties and uncertainties involving the crossing terms and the role of longitudinal quanta, it is impossible to claim better than $\sim 30\%$ [18] (*).

In resumé to Part I, both theory and experiment have a long way to go before anything definitive can be said about the neutron beyond the fact that its moment is not a point but is similar to the protons, and that its charge has zero $(< 0.1f)$ root mean square radius. The proton is in good shape, and in particular so is the isovector part of the moment form factor $F_2{}^V$ for $q \leqslant 2.8 f^{-1}$ since the isoscalar part of the anomalous moment is very small,

$$G_2^S(0) \,/\, G_2^V(0) \simeq 3\%, \text{ and } F_2^V \text{ is still} \geqslant \tfrac{1}{2}.$$

LIST OF REFERENCES — see p. 33.

(*) Lindner and Gartenhaus [19] have been analysing the accuracy of this problem.

NUCLEON STRUCTURE — Theoretical II

S. D. DRELL, Rapporteur

Stanford University, Stanford (Cal.)

Theoretical attempts to interpret form factors

Prior to 1955 and the original work of Hofstadter, Chambers, and McAllister [21, 22], theory was presented with the problem of explaining the magnetic moments and the electron-neutron result [5] that the root mean square charge radius

$$\langle r^2_{1N} \rangle = 6 \frac{d}{d(q^2)} F_1^N(q^2) \Big|_{q^2=0} < (0.1f)^2 .$$

In this it has not succeeded. Now it is presented with the richer body of information on the variation of F_1 and F_2 over a considerable range of values of q^2.

Let us find what appears to be the simplest challenge for theory in the available data on $F_{1,2}$ and analyse to what extent theory succeeds in meeting it. I shall be primarily concerned with recent dispersion theoretic attacks on the nucleon structure problem [20, 23] which make use of a spectral representation for the form factors $F_1^{S,V}$ and $F_2^{S,V}$.

The point I shall develop is the following: the value and structure of the isovector part of the magnetic moment, $G_2^V(q^2)$, appear to present the most modest challenge to the theory and the theory does poorly in attempting to explain it.

First recall the status of previous attempts.

II A. Relativistic perturbation theory failed badly—its most flagrant disagreement being the prediction of a large isotopic scalar moment, $G_2^S(0) = -1.7\mu_B$, for $f^2 = 0.080$. This difficulty comes from a large isoscalar contribution by the nucleon current, i.e. from the second of the two perturbation diagrams, Fig. 6 (*b*). We note that the meson current contributes only to the isovector part, its second order contribution, Fig. 6 (*a*), being $+1.6\mu_B$. This result is increased by less than 10% when fourth order contributions are included [24] (*).

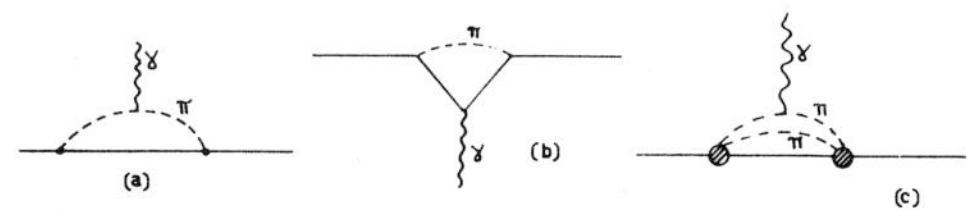

Fig. 6. *Graphs representing the electromagnetic structure of the nucleon in the static model: a) meson current. b) nucleon current, c) meson nucleon rescattering correction to the meson current.*

II B. The static theory in the original Chew cut-off version and subsequently in the more satisfying form of Chew and Low appears to do quite well in providing a qualitative basis for understanding both the size and structure of $G_2^V(q^2)$, but is ambiguous in its treatment of the Dirac moment and of the electron-neutron interaction. It takes into account the meson current, Fig. 6 (*a*), with the core cut-off replacing recoil of the nucleon, and goes beyond perturbation theory by taking into account meson rescattering in the resonant 3,3-state, corresponding to Fig. 6 (*c*). The current is then entirely an isovector. Miyazawa and Fubini [25] have obtained reasonable values in this way for the moment

$$G_2^V(0) = \begin{cases} 1.36 + 0.36 = 1.72 & \text{for } K = 5\, m_\pi \\ 1.80 + 0.50 = 2.30 & \text{for } K = 6\, m_\pi , \end{cases}$$

where the first numbers are the perturbation values and the second ones are the rescattering contributions for the two indicated choices of a cut-off for the momentum integrals. We remark that the perturbation values depend linearly on the cut-off. The mean square radius of the moment distribution depends on derivatives of the cut-off function; a reasonable value of $0.56f^2$ emerges [23] for a gaussian cut-off with $K \approx 5\, m_\pi$. In view of their strong cut-off sensitivity, the significance of this agreement is debatable. The charge distribution is even more sensitive to the cut-off, the total charge in the meson cloud depending quadratically on the cut-off. Salzman [26] and Zachariasen [27] have shown that $\sim 0.5\, e$ is in the meson charge cloud with a mean square radius of $\sim 0.42 f^2$, for a cut-off of $\sim 5\, m_\pi$, and that resonant rescattering corrections are -20%. This result indicates that the nucleon core, which one would like to forget in the analysis of the isovector moment, must be spread out to a very large distance in order to cancel the neutron's r.m.s. charge radius. In

(*) On the other hand the fourth order contribution from the nucleon current greatly alters the second order results of $-1.7\mu_B$ and $+0.57\mu_B$ to ~ 0 and $+4.4\mu_B$ for the isoscalar and isovector parts, respectively.

fact the distinction between core and meson cloud becomes unclear. I would like to make here two pessimistic remarks about the validity of the results of the static model as applied to the nucleon structure problem:

1) Suura [28] has shown that recoil corrections to the static meson charge cloud distribution reduce its radius by a factor of two.

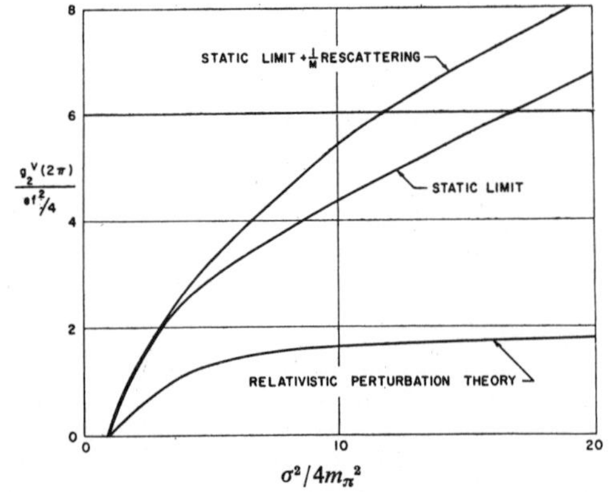

Fig. 7. *The spectral weight function of the magnetic moment in the static model and in the relativistic theory.*

2) The momentum distribution of intermediate mesons in the calculation of $G_2^V(q^2)$ is indicated in Fig. 7, as a function of the mass of the intermediate state $\sigma^2 = 4(k_\pi^2 + m_\pi^2)$. These distribution functions are weighted by $1/\sigma^2$ for the value of the moment, by $(1/\sigma^2)^2$ for the r.m.s. size, and so forth. Comparison of the curves calculated with relativistic perturbation theory, and with the static model, with and without resonant rescattering, shows that recoil effects are very important, and in fact surprisingly large. It should be recalled, perhaps, that previous successes of the static model have applied to processes dominated by a resonance which is not the case here.

II C. We turn then to a relativistic dispersion analysis of the vertex function and attempt to avoid both the critical cut-off dependence of the static theory and the weak coupling approximation of perturbation theory. Our discussion is based on the following spectral representations

$$G_1^{s,v}(q^2) = \frac{e}{2} + \frac{q^2}{\pi} \int_{4m^2_\pi}^{\infty} \frac{d\sigma^2}{\sigma^2(\sigma^2 - q^2 - i\varepsilon)} \operatorname{Im} G_1^{s,v}(\sigma)^2$$

$$G_2^{s,v}(q^2) = \frac{1}{\pi} \int_{4m^2_\pi}^{\infty} \frac{d\sigma^2}{\sigma^2 - q^2 - i\varepsilon} \operatorname{Im} G_2^{s,v}(\sigma^2)\ . \qquad (4)$$

We do not discuss here the possibility of making a rigorous proof of these representations. They have been derived on the basis of perturbation theory [29, 30, 31] and, in particular, Nambu has shown that a spectral representation is valid to all finite orders of perturbation theory. Since the nucleon does not dissociate into a system of lighter mass, there are no difficulties in the perturbation derivation of these relations. Three comments are of interest here concerning (4):

1) A subtracted form is used for G_1 because we ask of the theory only that it account for the anomalous moments and not the charge e. In this we follow perturbation theory which indicates $G_2(\sigma^2) \sim \frac{m^2}{\sigma^2} \ln \sigma^2/m^2 \rightarrow 0$ as $\sigma^2 \rightarrow \infty$ whereas $G_1(\sigma^2) \sim \ln \sigma^2/m^2$. By adopting this form we do not rule out the possibility that G_1 vanishes as $\sigma^2 \rightarrow \infty$, we just take a less controversial approach. We return to this debatable point at the end.

2) The spectral weight functions, or absorptive amplitudes, Im $G(\sigma^2)$, are related to the matrix elements for processes in which the photon produces particles of total mass σ, which particles are annihilated forming a nucleon-antinucleon pair. They are expressed as a sum over all possible states which can be produced by a photon, the threshold for each state being the rest mass of the particles produced. This sum over states replaces the perturbation expansion and has several interesting regularities which may be exploited. As indicated in Fig. 8, charge independence of the meson-nucleon interaction and invariance of the theory under charge conjugation imply that states with an even number of pions contribute only to G^V whereas states with an odd number of pions contribute only to G^S. The threshold for contributions to G^V is thus $4m_\pi^2$ and to G^S, $9m_\pi^2$, and one might naturally anticipate the two-meson state to be important for the low q and large distance behaviour of G^V. The nucleon-antinucleon state contributes to both G^V and G^S with a very high threshold of $4M^2$. The $K\bar{K}$ state also contributes to both G^V and G^S, its threshold being $4M_K^2$.

$$\operatorname{Im} F(\sigma^2) = \Sigma\, a_n(\sigma^2)$$

$$\operatorname{Im} F^S = a_{3\pi} + a_{5\pi} + \cdots + a^S_{K\bar{K}} + \cdots + a^S_{\eta\bar{\eta}} + \cdots$$

$$\operatorname{Im} F^V = a_{2\pi} + a_{4\pi} + \cdots + a^V_{K\bar{K}} + \cdots + a^V_{\eta\bar{\eta}} + \cdots$$

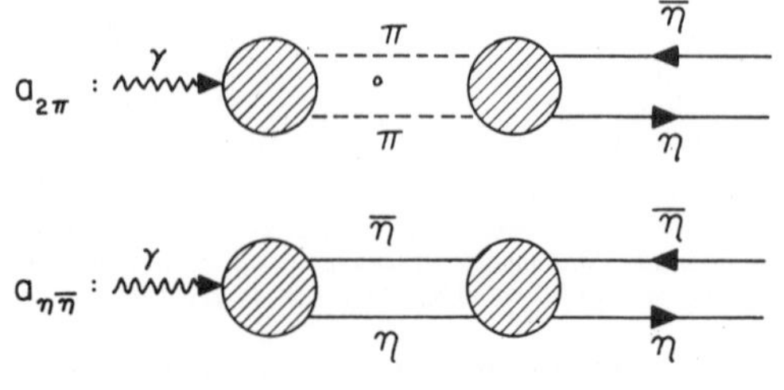

Fig. 8. *States contributing to the spectral functions.*

3) One can calculate $G(q^2)$ from the spectral representations and for $q^2 < 0$, corresponding to a scattering experiment, compare directly the theoretical and experimental values. Except in the case of the electron-neutron interaction, experiment determines $G(q^2)$ over a large range of q^2, but must necessarily rely upon model dependent extrapolations to determine the r.m.s. radius — i.e. the slope of $G(q^2)$ at $q^2 = 0$. It is neither desirable nor necessary to compare theoretically calculated and experimentally extrapolated radius values when the form factors can be directly compared and should be reliable up to the meson resonance at $q^2 \sim 8f^{-2}$.

With these three points in mind we study first the isovector moment form factor G_2^V. Our earlier discussion has provided a number of reasons why G_2^V should be the first object of study:

1) G_2^V appeared to be in the best quantitative shape in the earlier perturbation calculations with the meson current and in the static theory considerations.

2) It is in the best quantitative shape experimentally.

3) G_2^V is large in value and spatial extension, which leads one to believe that there are no delicate cancellations and that contributions to it are dominated by low momentum states, such as the two-meson state, which can be calculated. The isoscalar moment requires study of the three-pion-state which is very difficult to compute and is experimentally of unknown structure since it is weighted so lightly ($G_2^S(0) / G_2^V(0) = 0.06 / 1.85$).

4) As formulated here the moment structure is a richer problem than the charge structure because we require that theory account for both its magnitude and extension, whereas the value of the charge e is assumed and the problem of calculating it is legislated away. We thus ask of the theory both that it put the correct area under the dispersion integral and that it weight the area correctly.

Following Federbush, Goldberger, and Treiman [20] (*), we attack the evaluation of the weight function Im $G_2(q^2)$ with successively increasing degrees of elaborateness and complexity.

At first we limit ourselves to contributions from the two-pion intermediate state for which we can write schematically

$$\mathrm{Im}\,[G_2^V(\sigma^2)]_{2\pi} = \mathrm{Re}[e\, F_\pi(\sigma^2) \langle \pi\pi | N\bar{N} \rangle] . \qquad (5)$$

Step I: The pion form factor is set equal to unity and the amplitude for $\pi + \pi \rightarrow N + \bar{N}$ is set equal to the Born approximation. This then is just relativistic perturbation theory for the meson current only and gives a moment of 1.6 μ_B but a weight function much too concentrated at high momenta. This is usually stated by quoting a calculated value of $\langle r^2 \rangle_2^V = 0.24\ f^2$ as compared with the experimental value of $0.64\ f^2$. The form of $F_2^V(q^2)$ is given in Fig. 9 and evidently there is too large a contribution to Im $G_2^V(\sigma^2)$ from large values of σ^2.

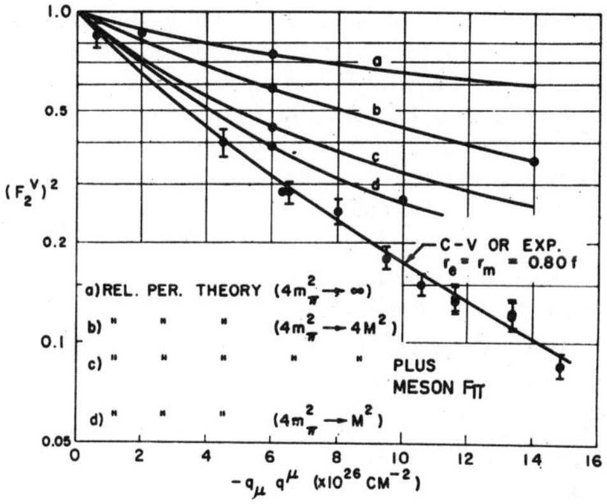

Curve	Moment	$\langle r^2 \rangle / (0.8\,f)^2$
a	$1.6\mu_B$	0.36
b	$0.87\mu_B$	0.69
c	$0.77\mu_B$	0.86
d	$0.4\mu_B$	~ 1

Fig. 9. *Comparison of the experimental values of F_2^V with different theoretical approximations.*

Step II: FGT have pointed out that it is possible to put an upper bound on the contributions to the absorptive amplitude from high momenta by appealing to physical unitarity limitations. The physical threshold for the process pion plus pion annihilating to form a nucleon-antinucleon pair is $\sigma^2 = 4M^2$, or an energy of $2M$ in the centre of mass system. Whereas there is no upper bound which can be constructed for $\langle \pi\pi | N\bar{N} \rangle$ in the non-physical region $4m_\pi^2 \leqslant \sigma^2 < 4M^2$, this amplitude can be limited by unitarity in the physical region. This is because only two reaction channels contribute and the amplitudes for them achieve their maximum value when $|\sin\delta\, e^{i\delta}| \rightarrow 1$. That there are only two channels may be understood as follows. In the centre of mass system only the two-pion state with $l = 1$ connects to the photon and so the $N\bar{N}$ pair can be produced only in $^3S_1$- and $^3D_1$-states with unit isospin. In this way, again setting $F_\pi = 1$, FGT find that the maximum possible contribution to μ_π^V from $\sigma^2 > 4M^2$ is 0.2 μ_B.

What does this tell in the light of Step I: breaking up the integrand in the relativistic perturbation calculation, one finds that a contribution of $0.73\mu_B$ was obtained there from the region $\sigma^2 > 4M^2$. Evidently it was very bad to use the perturbation amplitude above $4M^2$ since, at most, a small contribution can come from that region. So, guided by this unitarity argument, we can choose as Step II

(*) In the following the abbreviation FGT is used.

to cut off the weight function Im $G_2^V(\sigma^2)$ above $4M^2$. We obtain thereby $\mu_2^V = 0.87\ \mu_B$, or one-half of the observed moment, and evidently, a larger structure, with $\langle r^2 \rangle_2^V$ increasing to $0.44\ f^2$ or 70% of the observed value (*). However, as is seen from curve *b* of Fig. 9, the structure is still too concentrated and even with this cut-off too large a fraction of Im $G_2^V(\sigma^2)$ is coming from high values of σ^2. In fact one can run the cut-off down to M^2 before achieving a reasonable structure (Fig. 9, curve *d*) but the moment value is then only $0.4\ \mu_B$. The problem shapes up here as one of increasing the contribution to the spectral function from low momenta.

Since we have seen that perturbation theory is very bad above $4M^2$, perhaps rescattering corrections to the Born approximation for $\langle \pi\pi | N\bar{N} \rangle$ are important also below $4M^2$. Study of these is:

Step III: The problem here is how to continue the pion-nucleon amplitude into the non-physical region. The σ^2 dependence of the perturbation amplitude is *explicit* and its continuation presents no problem.

However to go beyond a perturbation treatment of the pion-nucleon interaction, one subjects $\langle \pi\pi | N\bar{N} \rangle$ to a dispersion analysis, entirely in the non-physical region for pion-nucleon scattering. The rescattering terms, i.e. the corrections to the Born approximation result, are extended into the non-physical region by means of the Legendre polynominals which are used to express their angular dependence. Taking only rescattering in the resonant 3,3-state into account as in the static theory and for simplicity approximating the 3,3-resonance to a sharp peak, one obtains a large increase in the weight function just below the cut-off at $4M^2$. This serves to add $1\mu_B$ to the moment but to reduce $\langle r^2 \rangle_2^V$ to one-half of its experimental value. The reliability of this result as a guide to the rescattering corrections is doubtful, as FGT themselves emphasize. This procedure more than doubles the moment contribution from $\sigma^2 < 4M^2$ with the large part of the enhancement coming from high momenta so that $\langle r^2 \rangle_2^V$ is reduced. Above the threshold $4M^2$ the unitary argument leads to a large reduction in the weight function. Also the validity of the Legendre expansion for such large values of σ^2 is open to question, since it diverges for $\sigma^2 \to \infty$. Finally, both the relativistic perturbation theory and the static theory give much smaller rescattering contributions to the meson current contribution. The fourth order contribution in relativistic perturbation theory as calculated by Nakabayasi, Sato, and Akiba [24] increased the perturbation result by only 9%. Miyazawa [25] calculated a rescattering increase of $\sim 30\%$ in the static theory. By making a $1/M$ expansion of the weight function in their dispersion analysis of the rescattering correction, Chew, Karplus, Gasiorowicz, and Zachariasen [23] reproduced the static theory result with a 17% resonant rescattering correction. Perhaps it is reasonable to expect the Born approximation to $\langle \pi\pi / N\bar{N} \rangle$ to be a fair approximation in this calculation because the large nucleon-antinucleon pair term, i.e. the ϕ^2 term of the Dyson-Foldy-Tani transformed Hamiltonian plays no role in the calculation of G_2^V and also one is in the non-physical region far from the resonance.

In résumé of our rescattering discussion, the large moment increase is not above mathematical doubts which FGT have indeed emphasized themselves. Moreover, it is not satisfying physically because the main contribution comes from high momenta and therefore gives too tight a structure, reducing $\langle r^2 \rangle_2^V$ to $0.32\ f^2$, or one-half the observed value, from the result of $0.44\ f^2$ in Step II.

Step IV: We here analyse contributions to the spectral weight function from additional intermediate states as considered by FGT. Since we are concerned with the isovector form factor, there is no contribution from the three-pion state and we must turn to 4π, $K\bar{K}$, $N\bar{N}$, etc., states. Nothing can be said about the four-pion contribution, and little more about the $K\bar{K}$ state except that in perturbation theory it appears to be unimportant and, in fact, the K meson current contributes zero to G_2^V if one adopts Schwinger's symmetric form of coupling K mesons to Λ's and Σ's, viz. $g^2_{K\Lambda} = g^2_{K\Sigma}$.

Turning to the $N\bar{N}$ state we have schematically,

$$\text{Im}\,[G_2^V(\sigma^2)]_{N\bar{N}} = \text{Re}[G_1^V(\sigma^2) \langle N\bar{N} | N\bar{N} \rangle_{12} + G_2^V(\sigma^2) \langle N\bar{N} | N\bar{N} \rangle_{22}]. \quad (6)$$

Here the scattering amplitude $\langle N\bar{N} | N\bar{N} \rangle$ is in the physical region, since the threshold is $(2M)^2$, and can be limited over the entire range of integration by unitarity arguments. As in the earlier discussion a $N\bar{N}$ pair must be in the $3S_1$- or $3D_1$- state to connect with a photon. The difference in kinematical factors between this and the two-pion state discussed in Step II prevents one from putting an upper bound on the contribution to the isovector moment on the basis of unitarity arguments alone as was done there. One can, however, put such a bound on the radius upon setting $G_1^V(\sigma^2) = e/2 = G_1^V(0)$ and $G_2^V(\sigma^2) = 1.85\ \mu_B = G_2^V(0)$ in Eq. (6), obtaining (*) from Eqs. (4) and (6)

$$\langle r^2{}_{N\bar{N}} \rangle_2^V < \frac{1}{\pi M^2} = 0.013\ f^2.$$

(*) This increase in mean square radius by a factor of two is primarily the result of the fact that the value of the moment is cut in half by removal of the high momentum contributions. Thus $\langle r^2 \rangle_2^V \equiv \frac{6}{G_2^V(0)} \left[\frac{d}{dq^2} G_2^V(q^2) \right]_{q^2=0}$ and the numerator is relatively insensitive to the cut-off whereas the calculated moment is sensitive to high momenta.

(**) This assumes also that $(G_2^V(0)_{2\pi} + (G_2^V(0))_{N\bar{N}} \geqslant \mu_B$ and that there is no strong cancellation between the moment contributions from these states.

Therefore, whereas it is impossible to limit the moment contribution of the $N\bar{N}$-state, the radius contribution corresponding to it is very small and a large contribution to the moment from the $N\bar{N}$-state will make the problem of its spatial extension more accute. We mention here that in perturbation theory, the contribution of the $N\bar{N}$-state to the isovector moment is $+0.57\ \mu_B$ but that the $N\bar{N}$ scattering amplitude in the Born approximation leads to a cross-section larger than the observed ≈ 50 millibarns. Also the unitarity argument is a gross overestimate of $\langle N\bar{N}|N\bar{N}\rangle$ at high energies since it ignores the annihilation channels. The rescattering corrections to the physical amplitude of $N\bar{N}$ scattering are evidently important and appreciably decrease the weight function.

It is at this point that one sees most clearly the difference between the dispersion theoretical and the perturbation approaches. By appealing to a high threshold of two nucleon masses and by relating the spectral amplitude to the physical process of nucleon-antinucleon scattering, the dispersion approach suggests a strong depression in the contribution from the nucleon currents relative to their prominent role in perturbation calculations. An analysis of even higher mass states such as $N\bar{N}\pi$ has not yet been made.

Step V: We return to the two-pion state and consider the influence of meson structure $F_\pi(\sigma^2)$ in the weight function, Eq. (5). In the absence of any knowledge of meson electromagnetic structure one can only make theoretical guesses and then check how sensitive the predicted results are to these guesses. FGT have calculated F_π using a dispersion relation, keeping only the two-pion intermediate state (Fig. 10).

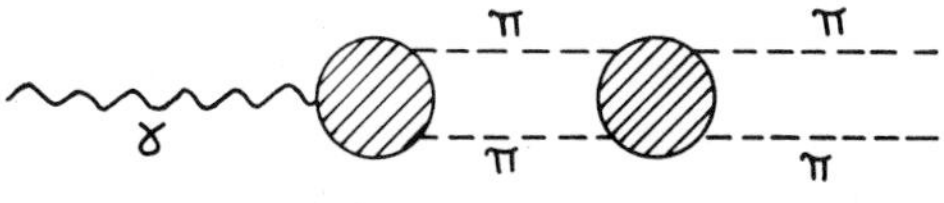

Fig. 10. *Representation of the pion form factor due to pion-pion interaction.*

The weighting function

$$\mathrm{Re}\,[F_\pi(\sigma^2)\,\langle\pi\pi\,|\,\pi\pi\rangle]$$

contains the π–π scattering amplitude in the physical region, $\sigma^2 > 4m_\pi^2$. The resulting integral equation for $F_\pi(\sigma^2)$ can be solved with various assumptions on this experimentally unknown physical amplitude. FGT make a scattering length approximation for the π–π scattering, choosing $\tan\delta = k^3a^3$. This corresponds to p-wave scattering, with a scattering length which is expected to be $\sim 1/M - 1/2M$, corresponding to the " range " of an intermediate nucleon pair state. In fact, with the choice $a = 1/M$, the pion form factor has little effect on the previous results (*) since the Re $F_\pi(\sigma^2)$ stays close to unity over the range of the dispersion integral, Fig. 11, and Im $F_\pi(\sigma^2)$ stays small. The Re $F_\pi(\sigma^2)$ is of primary concern here since it multiplies the real Born approximation amplitude in the weight function, Eq. (5). For a somewhat larger choice $a = 2/M$, the phase-shift $\delta \to \pi/2$ over a large part of the range of the dispersion integral, $\sigma^2/4m_{\pi^2} \gtrsim 10$, corresponding to a π–π scattering resonance which enhances the absorptive amplitude for $\gamma \to 2\pi$ at the expense of Re $F_\pi(\sigma^2)$ as shown in Fig. 11. This is an interesting result by FGT because it suggests that pion structure might lead to an enhancement of low momentum contributions to the weight function which is needed if a large spatial extension of the moment is to be achieved. The present choice however depresses the magnitude of the moment further so that although it leads to a mean square radius of 0.56 f^2 when used with the perturbation weight function of Step II, the resulting moment is only $0.77\mu_B$. $F_2{}^V(q^2)$ in this approximation is shown in Fig. 9, curve c and is still seen to weight the high momentum states somewhat too heavily.

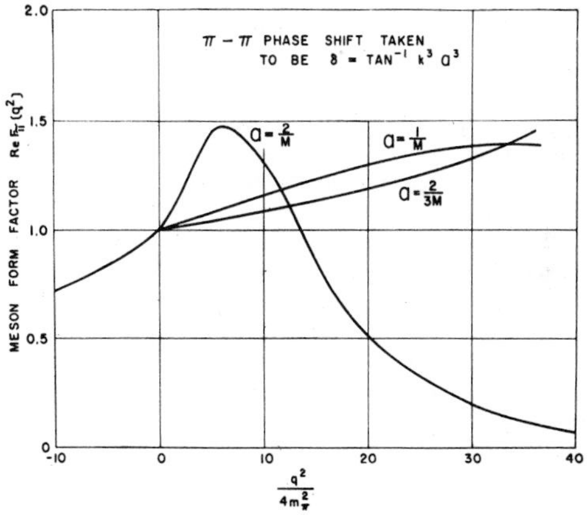

Fig. 11. *The form factor of the pion for different choices of the pion-pion phase shift.*

It is of great interest to give further study to the " size " of the pion and its role in nucleon structure. The contribution to F_π of a $N\bar{N}$ intermediate state can be neglected only if the pion emerges with a large mean square radius [23] (**) and for momenta where $F_\pi(q^2)$ has not yet fallen to small values as in Fig. 11. Also π–π scattering models with resonances but no bound states, so that

(*) Incorporating this in the perturbation calculation of Step II with $4m_\pi^2 < \sigma^2 < 4M^2$, one increases the moment to $0.9\mu_B$ and decreases the mean square radius by $\sim 10\%$ to 0.40 f².

(**) For scattering length $a = 2/m$, $\langle r^2\rangle_\pi = 0.16 f^2$, whereas for $a = 1/m$, $\langle r^2\rangle_\pi = 0.054 f^2$, which is less than unitarity bound on the $N\bar{N}$ contribution.

δ goes trough $\pi/2$ at least twice, will lead to different forms of F_π for which $\mathrm{Re}F_\pi(q^2)$ approaches a finite constant for large q^2, but oscillates through zero in the resonance region.

We can certainly not rule out the possibility of a pion-pion interaction, or equivalently of pion size, which will help both the magnitude and spatial extension of the nucleon moment. At this point, however, the theory is still in difficulty attempting to make both μ_2^V and $F_2^V(q^2)$ compatible with observation. Even if the very large rescattering corrections of FGT are included together with the meson form factor, using the scattering length $a = 2/m$, the root mean square radius is significantly too small, $0.46 f^2$, while the moment value is reasonable, $1.39\mu_B$.

The question to be answered then is whether or not this is a fundamental difficulty of the theory or just a calculational one, and if it is a calculational one, is the approach with mass spectral representations adequate to the task of a full quantitative study of higher states, of rescattering corrections, and of pion structure.

Turning to the situation with regard to the charge structure the results are even less satisfactory. By using the subtracted form of the representations (4) we ask of the theory only that it account for the structure of $F_1^V(q^2)$, and this it fails to do by a wide margin, predicting $\langle r^2\rangle_1^V < 0.4 f^2$ by Steps II or V and $\langle r^2\rangle_1^V < 0.14 f^2$ when the large rescattering corrections of Step III are included.

For the isoscalar form factors we must look to the three-pion state, the evaluation of which requires knowledge of the meson production amplitude in the non-physical region. To explain the small neutron charge size, we must require of it that it cancel the isovector form factor for low q-values. If one appeals to a simple physical model of the charge distribution which attributes to it an $\langle r^2\rangle_1^V \simeq 0.64 f^2$, then one is led to the problem of requiring the three-pion state to play a prominent role in charge but negligible role in moment structure. Unitarity arguments again limit the $N\bar{N}$ state to a negligible radius contribution.

Perhaps we should be more modest in our demands on the theory, and since the moment μ_2^V was observed in steps I and II to weight the high momenta heavily, give up at this stage the hope of calculating it. Turning then to a subtracted dispersion relation and introducing $\mu_2^V = 1.85\,\mu_B$ as a parameter in the theory we find mean Square radii differing in each case from the values of our earlier discussion by the ratio of the calculated to the observed moment. Since in each case $(\mu_2^V)_{\text{calc.}}/1.85\mu_B < 1$, the radius disagreement becomes more acute.

Finally we remark on the possibility of calculating the charge e by using the non-substracted form of dispersion relation in Eq. (1) for the charge form factor as well as the moment form factor. Chew [32] has raised this question and calculated $G_1^V(0) = 0.64\,e$ using the non-subtracted form of dispersion relations with the spectral weighting function of relativistic perturbation theory, with cut-off at $\sigma^2 = 4M^2$ (this is Step II). On the other hand the rescattering calculation of FGT (Step III) leads to $G_1^V(0) \approx 0$ showing the extreme sensitivity of this calculation to the high momentum region and, consequently, also to the higher states which are neglected.

However, in principle, a very interesting question can be raised here. What are the consequences of the assumption that all physical amplitudes satisfy dispersion relations which require no subtraction in their construction. This " no subtraction " philosophy leads to an infinite set of coupled homogeneous integral equations for these amplitudes, which may or may not have solutions for any, none, or some values of the coupling constants.

With the motivation of exploring this point of view, Zachariasen [33] and I have studied the quantum electrodynamics (QED) vertex. We selected the electromagnetic form factors of an electron because there is only one coupling in pure QED; at low energies perturbation theory leads to experimentally valid solutions; and a simple type of dispersion relation is obtained since there are only three external lines at a vertex.

In evaluating the absorptive amplitude we keep only the lowest order state in $\frac{e^2}{4\pi} = \alpha$, i.e. the electron-positron pair state which leads to two coupled homogeneous integral equations which we write symbolically as

$$G_{1,2}(q^2) = \int \frac{\mathrm{Re}\{G_{1,2}(\sigma^2)\langle e\bar{e}|e\bar{e}\rangle\}}{\sigma^2 - q^2 - i\varepsilon}\, d\sigma^2 . \tag{7}$$

Since these equations are homogeneous in $G_{1,2}$ only the ratio $G_2(0)/G_1(0)$ and the structure of the form factors are determined. These are equations of the type discussed recently by Omnès [34] and have a solution in agreement with perturbation theory for small q^2 as follows :

$$G_2(0) = \frac{\alpha}{2\pi}\,; \qquad \langle r^2\rangle_2 = \left(\frac{1}{m_e}\right)^2,$$

$$G_2(q^2) \propto \left(\frac{m^2}{q^2}\right) \ln \frac{q^2}{m^2} \qquad \text{for} \qquad q^2 \to \infty,$$

$$\langle r^2\rangle_1 = -\left(\frac{1}{m_e}\right)^2 \frac{\alpha}{\pi}\left(\frac{33}{20} - 2\,C\right)$$

$$G_1(q^2) \propto \left(\frac{q^2}{m^2}\right)^{\frac{\alpha}{\pi}\left(\frac{13}{12} - C\right)} \qquad \text{for} \qquad q^2 \to \infty,$$

where $C = 0.577$ and by definition, $G_1(0) = e$. The asymptotic behaviour of the charge form factor is different from the perturbation result of $\ln q^2/m^2$, but violates the " no subtraction " philosophy. The negative value of the mean square charge radius is analogous to the result for boson propagators.

The conservative conclusion to be inferred from this result is that neglect of all but the $e\bar{e}$ state is inadequate. In fact, it is an indefensible approximation because all values of q^2 contribute in (7) whereas $e\bar{e}$ is the leading order state only for processes with $\ln q^2/m^2 < 137$. It is for values $q^2/m^2 \sim e^{137}$, corresponding to energies above which Landau argues that QED processes must be damped out, that $G_1(q^2)$ begins to deviate from unity.

It is hoped that further work along these lines will shed light on the question of whether the " no subtraction " philosophy and the condition $G_1(q^2) \to 0$ as $q^2 \to \infty$, lead to equations which are identities in e, or whether these requirements lead to equations $e = f(e)$ with solutions for particular e values only.

Of more immediate experimental concern, we look forward to experimental information on electron-electron scattering and on large angle pair production to test QED at small distances where " small " means $\sim$ nucleon Compton wavelength.

LIST OF REFERENCES

1. Drell, S. D. and Ruderman, M. A. Phys. Rev., *106*, p. 561, 1957.
2. Drell, S. D. and Fubini, S. (to be published)
3. Rosenbluth, M. N. Phys. Rev., *79*, p. 615, 1950.
4. Schwinger, J. Phys. Rev., *76*, p. 790, 1949.
5. Bumiller, F. and Hofstadter, R. (private communication)
6. Foldy, L. L. Rev. mod. Phys., *30*, p. 471, 1958.
7. Yearian, M. R. and Hofstadter, R. Phys. Rev., *110*, p. 552, 1958, to be followed by another article also to be published in Phys. Rev.
8. Blankenbecler, R. Stanford University, Physics Dept., Doctoral Dissertation 1958. (to be published in Phys. Rev.)
9. Rustgi, M. L. Rev. Mex. Fis., *6*, p. 135, 1957.
10. Goldberg, A. (to be published)
11. McIntyre, J. A. and Dhar, S. Phys. Rev., *106*, p. 1074, 1957.
12. Schiff, L. I. Rev. mod. Phys., *30*, p. 462, 1958.
13. Yamaguchi, Y. Phys. Rev., *95*, p. 1628, 1954.
14. Bernstein, J. Phys. Rev., *104*, p. 249, 1956.
15. Fubini, S., Nambu, Y. and Wataghin, V. (to be published in Phys. Rev.)
16. Panofsky, W. K. H. and Allton, E. A. Phys. Rev., *110*, p. 1155, 1958.
17. Chew, G. F., Goldberger, M. L., Low, F. E. and Nambu, Y. Phys. Rev., *106*, p. 1345, 1957.
18. Nambu, Y. (private communication)
19. Lindner, C. and Gartenhaus, S. (private communication)
20. Federbush, P., Goldberger, M. L. and Treiman, S. B. (to be published)
21. Hofstadter, R. and McAllister, R. W. Phys. Rev., *98*, p. 217, 1955.
22. Chambers, E. E. and Hofstadter, R. Phys. Rev., *103*, p. 1454, 1956.
23. Chew, G. F., Karplus, R., Gasiorowicz, S. and Zachariasen, F. Phys. Rev., *110*, p. 265, 1958.
24. Nakabayasi, K., Sato, I. and Akiba, T. Progr. theor. Phys., *12*, p. 250, 1954.
25. Miyazawa, H. Phys. Rev. *101*, p. 1564, 1956.
    Fubini, S. Nuov. Cim., *3*, p. 1425, 1956.
26. Salzman, G. Phys. Rev., *105*, p. 1076, 1957.
27. Zachariasen, F. Phys. Rev., *102*, p. 295, 1956.
28. Suura, H. Phys. Rev., *108*, p. 470, 1957.
29. Nambu, Y. (to be published)
30. Oehme, R. (to be published)
31. Karplus, R., Sommerfield, C. M. and Wichmann, E. H. (to be published)
32. Chew, G. F. (unpublished)
33. Drell, S. D. and Zachariasen, F. (to be published)
34. Omnès, R. Nuov. Cim., *8*, p. 316, 1958.

PAPER 52

High-Energy Electron Scattering and the Charge Distribution of Carbon-12 and Oxygen-16*

HANS F. EHRENBERG,† ROBERT HOFSTADTER, ULRICH MEYER-BERKHOUT,‡ D. G. RAVENHALL,§ AND STANLEY E. SOBOTTKA
Department of Physics and W. W. Hansen Laboratories of Physics, Stanford University, Stanford, California
(Received August 20, 1958)

The scattering of high-energy electrons from C^{12}, reported previously, has been extended to 420 Mev. The elastic and inelastic scattering from the first excited level at 4.43 Mev has been studied between 33° and 70°. The new data are in good agreement with what one would expect from the earlier measurements on C^{12} performed at 187 Mev. Additional measurements of the elastic O^{16}-scattering cross sections of 240-, 360-, and 420-Mev electrons as functions of the scattering angle furnish information on the size and shape of the O^{16} nucleus. Pronounced diffraction minima in the angular distributions were observed for C^{12} and O^{16}. The experimental results are compared with the predictions of a theoretical phase-shift analysis derived for the harmonic-well independent-particle model of the nucleus. Preliminary best fits confirm the shell-model predictions for the charge density distribution of these p-shell nuclei. The preliminary analysis of the data shows that the length parameter of the well is 1.66×10^{-13} cm for C^{12}, and 1.76×10^{-13} cm for O^{16}, thus indicating a slight variation of the curvature of the harmonic well as the p shell is filled in.

I. INTRODUCTION

IN two previous papers by Fregeau and Hofstadter[1] and by Fregeau,[2] the scattering of 187-Mev electrons from C^{12} at angles up to 135° was reported. This work has been extended to electron energies of 420 Mev. In addition, the elastic scattering of 240-, 360-, and 420-Mev electrons from the O^{16} nucleus has been investigated in considerable detail. The purpose of the present paper is to present these new experimental results, which were obtained as part of a program to study the charge density distribution of the nuclei of the first p shell, i.e., those lying between lithium and oxygen. The analysis, while only preliminary and incomplete, has concentrated on a comparison with theoretical predictions of the nuclear shell model. The 187-Mev experiments on carbon indicated[3,4] that the assumption of a parabolic potential well for the shell model gives better agreement than either the (infinite) square or linear potentials. Accepting this result, we have examined in rather more detail the first-mentioned model, which we find in remarkably good agreement with the 420-Mev experiments.[5] Various modifications of this model necessary for comparison with these more extensive experiments are noted. Also included are investigations of two phenomenological charge distributions used in previous work, which do not give such good agreement with the experiments.

The present work is part of a program to study systematically the nuclei in the $1p$ shell. The two nuclei here examined have characteristics which make them particularly well suited for a detailed investigation. Since the first excited levels lie 4.43 (6.06) Mev above the ground state for C^{12} (O^{16}), it is much easier to resolve the elastic-scattering peak from inelastic scattering events than for most other nuclei. Even a slight lack of resolution could have an appreciable effect on the angular distribution of the elastically scattered electrons especially at those scattering angles where the inelastic scattering is greater than the elastic scattering, i.e., at large angles or in the neighborhood of a diffraction dip in the elastic scattering angular distribution. Although in principle any resolution down to 0.1% can be achieved with our present equipment, high resolution inevitably means low beam currents. The beam current available, however, largely determines the minimum cross section which is still measurable within reasonable efforts. This means that those nuclei are best suited for a detailed investigation whose first excited states are highest. A survey of some other $1p$-shell nuclei like Li^6, Be^9, B^{11}, and N^{14}, however, is being carried out at present and the results will be published later.

II. APPARATUS AND PROCEDURE

These experiments have been performed with the Stanford linear accelerator as a source of electrons. The scattering apparatus used in this work has already been described in several earlier papers.[6] The beam was analyzed magnetically so that the energy band was 0.35% wide for the measurements at 420 and 360 Mev and 0.60% at 240 Mev. The electron current was measured by a large Faraday cup placed behind the

* The research reported here was supported in part by the joint program of the Office of Naval Research, the U. S. Atomic Energy Commission, and the U. S. Air Force, Office of Scientific Research.

† Now at the University of Bonn, Bonn, Germany.
‡ Now at the University of Heidelberg, Heidelberg, Germany.
§ Now at the University of Illinois, Urbana, Illinois.

[1] J. H. Fregeau and R. Hofstadter, Phys. Rev. **99**, 1503 (1955).
[2] J. H. Fregeau, Phys. Rev. **104**, 225 (1956).
[3] See especially Sec. III B of reference 2.
[4] A comparison of the results for parabolic and square potentials has also been given by L. J. Tassie, Australian J. Phys. **9**, 400 (1956); also Proc. Phys. Soc. (London) **69A**, 205 (1956).
[5] A preliminary account of these results was given at the Stanford Conference on Nuclear Sizes; see D. G. Ravenhall, Revs. Modern Phys. **30**, 430 (1958). The numerical values given in that paper are, however, too small.
[6] E. E. Chambers and R. Hofstadter, Phys. Rev. **103**, 1454 (1956).

target and was integrated by an Applied Physics Corporation Model 31 vibrating reed electrometer. Beam currents up to a maximum value of 2.5×10^{10} electrons per pulse (2.5×10^{-7} amp) were used (60 pulses per second), but were always kept low enough to avoid any appreciable loss of counts due to pileup. The energy slit of the 36-in. double-focusing magnetic spectrometer was set to 0.35% for most of the measurements which corresponds to an over-all resolution of about 0.5% for a point beam spot. At 240 Mev the detector slit was set at 0.60%, thus limiting the over-all resolution to about $\sqrt{2}\times0.60=0.85\%$. The angular aperture was approximately $\pm0.83°$ in the horizontal scattering plane and $\pm2.3°$ in the vertical plane. The over-all angular resolution, however, depends not only on the finite acceptance angle of the analyzing magnet but in addition on the size of the beam spot and on the multiple scattering of the electrons in the target. It is estimated that the over-all angular resolution in our experiments was about $\pm1.2°$. The electrons were detected and counted in the standard manner with a liquid $C_8F_{16}O$ ($n=1.276$) Čerenkov counter.

Carbon target (graphite) plates of 0.150 in. thickness and occasionally of twice this thickness were used. The absolute value of the C^{12} elastic-scattering cross section at 420 Mev and 40°, as well as the absolute value of the cross section for inelastic scattering from the 4.43-Mev 2^+ level, were determined by comparison of the corresponding yields of scattered electrons with the yield of electrons scattered elastically from free protons in a polyethylene target. The free proton cross section was taken from Rosenbluth's formula and was computed assuming a proton with an exponential charge distribution of rms radius 0.8×10^{-13} cm. In order to derive the cross-section ratios from the measured areas under the elastic and inelastic C^{12} peaks and the free-proton peak, the $1/E$ dispersion correction allowing for the constant relative momentum acceptance of the spectrometer has to be applied. If $Y(E)$ is the yield of scattered electrons as function of the energy setting of the spectrometer, then $\int[Y(E)/E]dE$ integrated over the peak can in good approximation be set equal to $\{(1/E)(dE/di)\}_{E'}\int Y(i)di$, since the peak is rather narrow, where now the yield $Y(i)$ is expressed as function of the current setting i of the spectrometer and where

$$E'=E_0/[1+(2E_0/Mc^2)\sin^2(\theta/2)].$$

In addition the bremsstrahlung straggling correction and the Schwinger-Suura radiative correction must be applied for the free-proton as well as to the C^{12} peak, since the low-energy tails of the peak were cut off at unequal values of $\Delta E/E$.

For the measurements on O^{16}, a water target was used. The target was disk-shaped, 2.50 in. in diameter and 0.300 in. thick. Occasionally targets of 0.200 or 0.400 in. thickness were used. The end windows, sealed with O-rings onto the aluminum target frame, consisted of 0.001-in. Dural foil. For a 0.300-in. thick water target, this means an $Al^{27}:O^{16}$ atomic ratio of about 1:83, which, although small, gives rise to a background from Al-scattering which proved to be not always negligible. The electron-scattering cross sections of O^{16} and Al^{27} are of the same order of magnitude at most of the scattering angles and energies investigated. In order to correct for the undesirable Al background, an identical, but empty, dummy target was bombarded each time after an elastic O^{16} peak was taken under otherwise unchanged conditions. Subtraction of the Al background determined in this way then could be made. Even around the scattering angle at which the O^{16} diffraction dip occurs, the counts originating from Al scattering amounted only to a few percent of the total number of counts. The absolute O^{16} cross sections were measured just as described for C^{12}. The use of a water target offers the advantage of an exactly known proton-O^{16} ratio. In addition a water target has, as compared to a gas target filled with oxygen to a pressure of 2000 psi, the advantage of a 4.6 times higher O^{16} concentration per cubic centimeter, although this could be counteracted by using a gas target chamber of considerable length along the direction of the beam, especially if cooled down to liquid nitrogen temperature. During the numerous runs which were devoted to the measurements on O^{16}, a gas target of conventional design was once also tried. With the target chamber filled with oxygen up to a pressure of 2000 psi, it was found, however, that the width of the elastic O^{16} scattering peak at half maximum was appreciably wider than that observed with the water target under otherwise unchanged conditions, causing a non-negligible loss in energy resolution. It is believed that this broadening can be ascribed to geometrical effects. Both for this reason and those mentioned above, the gas target was abandoned.

Whereas the water target was always held at an angle of 30° with respect to the direction of the incident beam, measured counterclockwise, the carbon target was rotated in such a way that at each scattering angle the normal to the target bisected the scattering angle. Thus, in the case of the C^{12} measurements, a correction was made for the change in effective target thickness with varying scattering angle.

For O^{16} only the elastic scattering was investigated, since the four lowest excited levels lying between 6.06 and 6.12 Mev could not be resolved from each other with our present apparatus. Angular distributions were measured for elastically scattered electrons of 420, 360, and 240 Mev. In the case of C^{12}, the inelastic scattering from the first excited level at 4.43 Mev was studied to some extent in addition to the elastic scattering at 420 Mev. The measurements were performed in the standard manner. Runs from different nights were always normalized to each other by measuring a standard peak. It turned out that the angular distributions derived from the areas under the peaks agreed very well with those derived from peak heights. The over-all accuracy of the relative cross sections obtained in these experiments is believed to be about ±10% except for the measurements at the very largest momentum transfers where the cross sections are of order of magnitude 10^{-33} cm²/steradian and smaller. Reproducibility often was better and errors due to counting statistics were often smaller, but even so an error of ±10% is given, allowing for drifts in various parts of the experimental equipment, etc. Besides those already mentioned, no corrections were found to be important enough to be applied to the experimental data.

III. THEORY

The assumptions made in the analysis of the present experiments are essentially the same as have been made in all of the earlier work. Both carbon and oxygen have zero spin, so that the use of spherically symmetric charge distributions is rigorously justified. The neglect of any possible energy dependence of these distributions rests on the demonstrations of Schiff and others[7] that the dispersion contribution to the scattering is inappreciable, and the good agreement obtained at different energies supports this assumption.

Although the dimensionless parameter $\gamma = Ze^2/\hbar c$ is small for these nuclei, the angular regions examined experimentally cover the first diffraction minimum, where the first Born approximation cannot give accurate results, since it predicts zero cross section there. The numerical results have therefore all been obtained by means of a partial-wave analysis, details of which have been given previously.[8] As will be seen, however, the Born approximation gives quite accurate information about other features of the cross section, and particularly the *position* of the diffraction minimum. It is necessary to allow for nuclear recoil, but it is only a small effect: the maximum value of v/c, v being the velocity of the nucleus in the center-of-mass system, is only 3.4%. The only dynamic effect of recoil on the scattering (as distinct from changes in kinematics) which it is possible to calculate without a relativistic theory of the nucleus is caused by the exchange of *transverse* photons between the electron and the moving nucleus. It is easy to show that for a spin-zero nucleus, this interaction gives zero contribution to the scattering in Born approximation. The inclusion of dynamic recoil effects in a partial-wave calculation of the scattering has been made by Foldy, Ford, Hill, Hill, and Wills.[9] They use the Breit interaction to describe the exchange of transverse photons, and relate their results to scattering by a spin-zero nucleus by neglecting terms depending on the nuclear spin. To the extent that this is the same effect as that we mention, their conclusions are in agreement with the observation we make above, since they find that in carbon at 420 Mev the result of including this interaction is to change the radial parameter in the charge distribution by only 0.7%. Because we were not able to include such effects in our phase-shift calculations, the only allowance we have made for a recoil has been in the angular scale, for which we have assumed that the partial-wave analysis describes most accurately the scattering in the center-of-mass system. (The correction is very small, of order one percent.) Our analysis is therefore somewhat inaccurate in the comparison of absolute differential cross sections. The uncertainties involved are only a few percent, however, and are not important compared with the experimental uncertainties in this quantity.

As in the analysis of experiments on other nuclei,[10] the procedure is necessarily that of trial and error. Charge distributions of various functional forms with variable parameters are inserted into the calculation, and by comparison of the resulting differential cross section with experiment the correct values for the parameters can be determined.

Of great interest for these nuclei, which are in a region where the nuclear shell model has had considerable success in predicting level structure, etc., is an examination of the electron scattering cross section in the light of this model.[2,4,11] If for simplicity it is assumed that the ground states of these nuclei can be adequately described by the lowest shell-model configuration, $(1s)^4(1p)^{2Z-4}$, then energy level structure, etc., involves specification of, firstly, the shape of the common central potential well; secondly, the strength of the spin-orbit coupling; and thirdly the type, shape, and strength of the residual two-nucleon interaction. Comparison with experiment then allows a determination of some of the functions and parameters involved.[12] The relation of these quantities to those of a real nucleus, obtained by using the observed *n-p* interaction and making a self-consistent field analysis of the Brueckner-Bethe type, is a problem of such complexity that little is known of it at this time. One can imagine that such a calculation would yield an equivalent central potential which would be fairly smooth, resembling more a parabolic (harmonic oscillator) well than a square well. The results of shell-model calculation do in fact seem to favor the former shape of a harmonic well.

Electron scattering provides an independent check on some of the shell-model assumptions; in this simple

[7] L. I. Schiff, Nuovo cimento **5**, 1223 (1957). This paper also lists and discusses the earlier work on this problem.

[8] Yennie, Ravenhall, and Wilson, Phys. Rev. **95**, 500 (1954).

[9] Foldy, Ford, Hill, Hill, and Wills (to be published). We thank those authors for a prepublication copy of their work.

[10] Hahn, Ravenhall, and Hofstadter, Phys. Rev. **105**, 1353 (1957).

[11] Comparisons with the shell model using a parabllic well have been made by G. Morpurgo, Nuovo cimento **3**, 430 (1956); R. A. Ferrell and W. M. Visscher, Phys. Rev. **104**, 475 (1956); and M. K. Pal and S. Mukherjee, Phys. Rev. **106**, 811 (1957).

[12] See, e.g., D. Kurath, Phys. Rev. **101**, 216 (1956); **106**, 975 (1957).

case (lowest configuration only) the elastic scattering depends only on the shape of the central well, and not on any of the other features of the model. (This is true to the extent that "dispersion scattering" is neglected.) A program of interest would thus be to start not from assumed charge distribution, but from assumed shell-model well shapes, and to calculate the dependence of electron scattering cross sections on the adjustable parameters inserted in them. In the earlier experiments on carbon at 187 Mev,[3] where it was permissible to use the Born approximation to calculate the scattering, this was done for three simple one-parameter well shapes, namely the infinite square well, the infinite parabolic well, and the infinite linear well. Comparison with the experiment clearly favored the harmonic well, with a length parameter $a=1.64\times10^{-13}$ cm.

Because of the computational complexity that would be involved in starting the partial-wave analysis of the scattering from the shell-model potential, we have not carried out a general program of this kind in the analysis of the experiments at the higher energies. We have considered only the infinite parabolic well $V\propto r^2$, where the function which determines the scattering $\rho_{\text{c.m.}}$, has the very simple analytic form

$$\rho_{\text{c.m.}}(r)=\sum_P\int d^3r_1\cdots d^3r_A\,\psi_{\text{g.s.}}^*(r_1\cdots r_A)\times\delta(r-r_p)\psi_{\text{g.s.}}(r_1\cdots r_A)$$
$$=\rho(0)[1+\alpha r^2/a^2]\exp(-r^2/a^2),\qquad(1)$$

where $\alpha\equiv(Z-2)/3$ is proportional to the number of protons in the $1p$ shell.[2,4,11] Our avoidance of the term "charge distribution" for this quantity, and an understanding of its subscript, are explained by the observation that the protons in the nucleus themselves have a finite charge distribution (presumably close to that measured for free protons). Thus since $\rho_{\text{c.m.}}$ describes the distribution in space of the centers of mass of the protons, the charge distribution is[13,5]

$$\rho(r)=\int d^3r'\,\rho_{\text{c.m.}}(r')\rho_{\text{proton}}(|r-r'|).\qquad(2)$$

Because the radius of the proton is considerably smaller than that of the nuclei we are considering (0.76×10^{-13} cm compared with $\sim3\times10^{-13}$ cm) the form chosen for ρ_{proton} is not important. For convenience we choose it to be Gaussian, so that the folding integral can be performed analytically, giving us for $\rho(r)$ the same expression as (1), except that in the exponent a^2 is replaced by $a^2+a_p^2$, where $a_p^2=\frac{2}{3}\langle r^2\rangle_{\text{proton}}$.

Another effect which must be allowed for in obtaining a charge distribution from even this simple version of the shell model is that the nuclear wave functions given by the model are not translationally invariant, i.e., because the shell model has a fixed origin (the origin of the central potential) the system described does not have a center of mass which is fixed in space. The effect this has on $\rho(r)$ for the parabolic-well case has been investigated by Schwartz[14] and by Tassie and Barker.[15] The main modification (of order $1/A$) is to insert into the exponent of (1) a factor $(1-1/A)$. There are terms of order $1/A^2$, but for carbon and oxygen they are not important, and we have omitted them. This effect acts independently of the finite proton size.

[13] Yennie, Lévy, and Ravenhall, Revs. Modern Phys. **29**, 144 (1957).

IV. RESULTS

The shapes examined were the parabolic-well shell-model distribution

$$\rho(r)=\rho(0)[1+\alpha r^2/a_{\text{c.m.}}^2]\exp[-r^2/a_{\text{charge}}^2],\qquad(\text{A})$$

where $a_{\text{charge}}^2=(1-1/A)a_{\text{c.m.}}^2+a_{\text{proton}}^2$; and the two phenomenological shapes

$$\rho(r)=\rho_0/\{1+\exp[(r^2-c^2)/Z^2]\},\qquad(\text{B})$$

and

$$\rho(r)=\rho_0[1+r/b+\beta r^2/b^2]e^{-r/b}.\qquad(\text{C})$$

Shape (B) was used in the analysis of the results for gold, and (C) by Fregeau for carbon at 187 Mev.[2]

The striking feature of the cross sections for both elements is the deep, narrow diffraction minimum. The observed depth is somewhat decreased because of finite experimental resolution. That the cross section should have this behavior is predicted by the Born approximation. The form factor $F(q)$, defined by

$$F(q)=\int d^3r\,\rho(r)\exp(i\mathbf{q}\cdot\mathbf{r}),$$

has for shape (A) the simple analytic form

$$F_A(q)=\left[1-\frac{\alpha}{2(2+3\alpha)}q^2a^2_{\text{c.m.}}\right]\exp(-\tfrac{1}{4}q^2a^2_{\text{charge}}),$$

which has one zero. The angular position of this zero turns out to be a surprisingly close guide to the minimum in the cross section, although the actual shape of $d\sigma/d\Omega$ must be obtained by the partial-wave analysis. In each of the shapes examined, the fitting of the angular position of this dip provides an accurate determination of one of the parameters, mainly the parameter which adjusts the radial size. We have confined our attention to two-parameter shapes, and the best value of the other parameter is then selected by comparing the shape of the cross section away from the dip. Mainly because of time limitation we have not made a least-squares analysis. The extent to which alteration of the parameter spoils the fit with experi-

[14] C. Schwartz (private communication). We thank Dr. Schwartz for an informative discussion of this point.

[15] L. J. Tassie and F. C. Barker, Phys. Rev. **111**, 940 (1958). We thank these authors for a prepublication copy of their work.

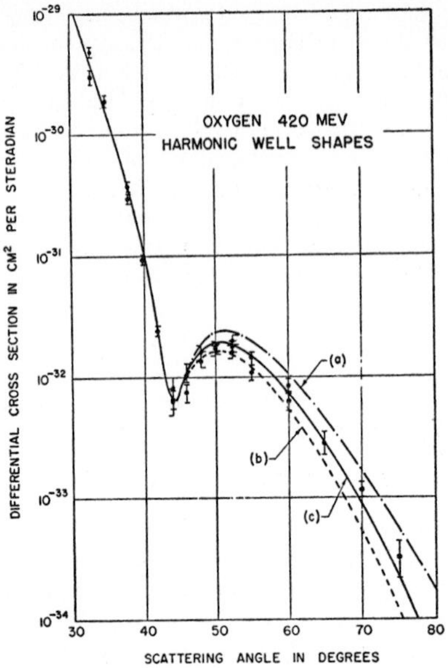

(A)

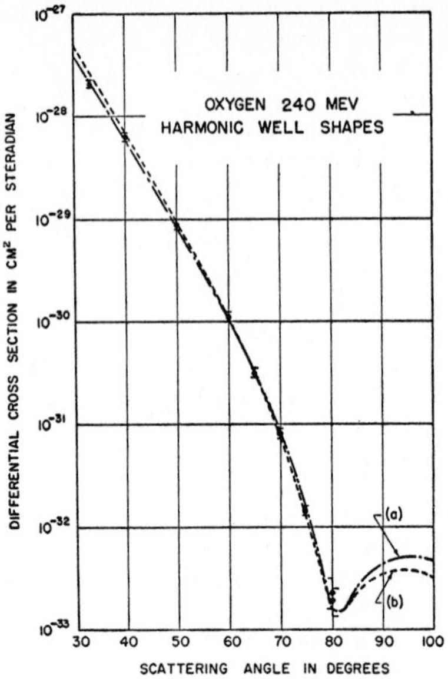

(C)

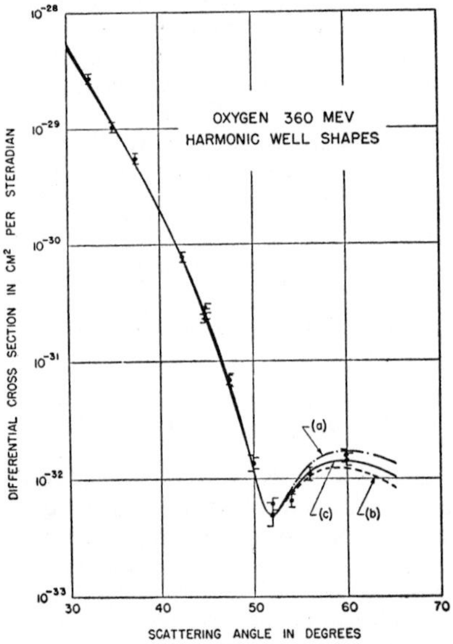

(B)

FIG. 1. (A) Elastic scattering of 420-Mev electrons by O^{16}. The curves are the calculated scattering predicted by the shell model with a parabolic well, as described in the text. Curve (a) has no corrections, curve (b) has been corrected for finite proton size, and curve (c) includes this effect and also allowance for center-of-mass motion in the shell model. Curves (a) and (b) have been scaled vertically so as to be coincident with curve (c) at the smaller angles. The values of the parameters for each model are given in Table I. (B) Same as Fig. 1(A) except for $E_0=360$ Mev. (C) Same as Fig. 1(A) except for $E_0=240$ Mev.

ment is determined graphically. Previous experience with other nuclei suggests that with such pronounced diffraction structure a least-squares fit will do little more than confirm the results obtained by graphical fitting.

The comparison of cross sections for the shell-model distribution (A) with the oxygen experiments are shown in Fig. 1. This model contains only one parameter, $a_{c.m.}$, and fixing the position of the diffraction dip determines it. The excellent agreement over the whole angular range of the 420-Mev experiments [Fig. 1(A)] is a very significant endorsement of this model. The differences between the three versions of the model show up in a pronounced way only beyond the diffraction minimum. Consequently the comparison with the 360- and 240-Mev experiments [Fig. 1(B) and 1(C)], which contain little information in that region, can give not nearly so much information about the charge distribution. The complete agreement at these lower energies is, however, experimental verification that any energy-dependent contributions to the scattering are inappreciable.

The sensitivity of the agreement with experiment to the radial parameter a is demonstrated in Fig. 2. The three cross sections shown there are all for the complete version of the shell model, including finite proton size and the center-of-mass effect. It is from this comparison that we tentatively propose an error on a of $\pm 0.02\times 10^{-13}$ cm in the case of O^{16}, although the error on the C^{12} value may be a little larger.

The central potential of the shell model is not actually an infinite well, and it is necessary to find out if the flattening of the well at some large distance, so as to reproduce qualitatively the finite binding, affects the

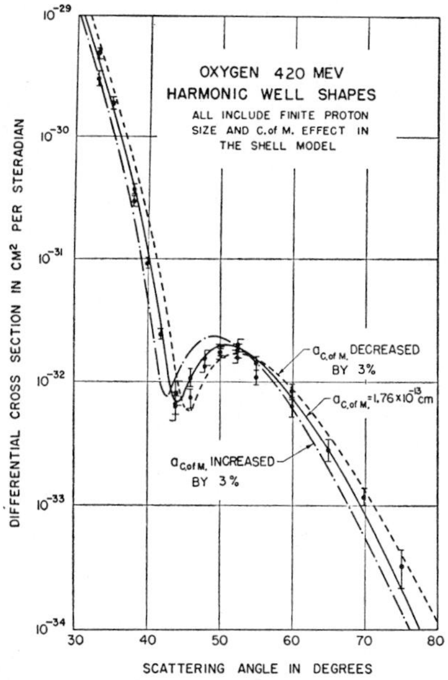

FIG. 2. Elastic scattering of 420-Mev electrons by O^{16}. The curves are all obtained using the complete version of the shell model, corresponding to curve (c) of Fig. 1(A), and show the effect of varying the radial parameter $a_{c.m.}$ by $\pm 0.05\times 10^{-13}$ cm.

agreement with experiment. To do such a calculation would have involved numerical integration of greater complexity than time allowed, so we investigated this point in an approximate way, by fitting the distribution $\rho_A(r)$ smoothly onto a decreasing exponential charge distribution at a certain radius r_0. The results for two values of r_0, corresponding to $1p$ shell binding energies of 10 Mev and 5 Mev, are shown in Fig. 3. In oxygen even the last proton has a binding energy of $\sim$12 Mev. It is thus clear from Fig. 3 that the finite binding will have very little effect on the cross section in the angular regions of present interest, although it can change the cross section significantly at larger q values.

The comparison with the carbon experiments is illustrated in Fig. 4. Because the cross section beyond

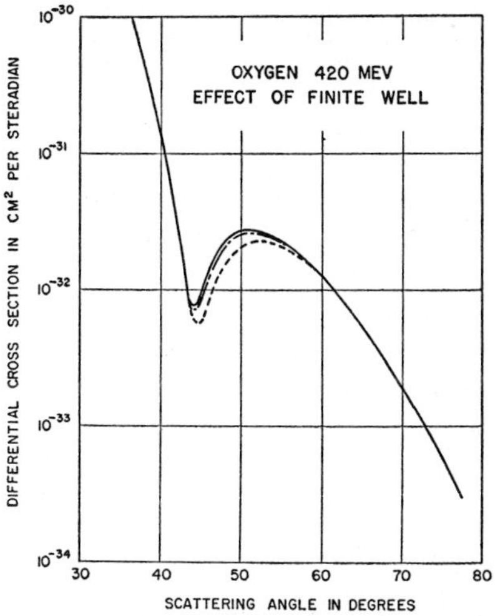

FIG. 3. Theoretical cross sections for O^{16} at 420 Mev. The full curve is curve (c) of Fig. 1(A), and the broken and dashed curves are cross sections obtained by flattening the parabolic well of the shell model at energies 10 Mev and 5 Mev above the $1p$ level, respectively.

the minimum is almost a factor ten smaller than in oxygen, the experimental information is sparser, and the discrimination among the three versions of the

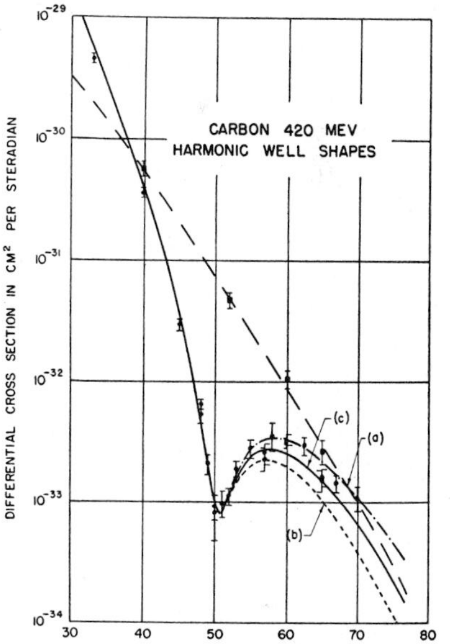

FIG. 4. Elastic and inelastic scattering of 420-Mev electrons by C^{12}. The elastic scattering cross sections are calculated under the same conditions as those for O^{16}, given in the caption to Fig. 1. The inelastic scattering is that arising from excitation of the 4.43-Mev level in C^{12}. The dashed curve is semitheoretical, as is explained in the text. The circles represent the elastic scattering data whereas the squares represent scattering from the 4.4-Mev first excited level.

TABLE I. Values of the parameters obtained from comparison with the 420-Mev experiments of the shell-model charge distribution assuming a parabolic well. The quantities $a_{c.m.}$, a_{charge}, and α occur in the definition below Eq. (A) of Sec. IV. The lengths are in units of 10^{-13} cm. Shape (a) contains no corrections, (b) includes the finite proton size (for a Gaussian proton shape with rms radius 0.76×10^{-13} cm), and (c) contains both this and the effect of center-of-mass motion in the shell model. The parameters α' and a' relate to the charge distribution (1) if regarded as a phenomenological fit to the experiments. The rms radius is obtained from the formula[a] $\langle r^2\rangle^{\frac{1}{2}}=[3(2+5\alpha')/2(2+3\alpha')]^{\frac{1}{2}}a'$.

Nucleus	Shape	$a_{c.m.}$	a_{charge}	α	a'	α'	$(\langle r^2\rangle^{\frac{1}{2}})_{charge}$
O^{16}	(a)	1.76	1.76	2	1.76	2	2.64
	(b)	1.76	1.87	2	1.87	1.34	2.75
	(c)	1.76	1.82	2	1.82	1.60	2.70
C^{12}	(a)	1.65	1.65	$\frac{4}{3}$	1.65	$\frac{4}{3}$	2.42
	(b)	1.66	1.77	$\frac{4}{3}$	1.77	0.94	2.58
	(c)	1.66	1.71	$\frac{4}{3}$	1.71	1.12	2.50

[a] Useful formulas concerning form factors of other simple charge distributions, and expressions for rms radii, are given in R. Hofstadter, Revs. Modern Phys. **28**, 214 (1956).

shell model is not so clear. There is good agreement with the most complete version (the middle curve in Fig. 4), and this shape gives satisfactory agreement with the 187-Mev experiments of Fregeau.[2] The numerical values of $a_{c.mc}$ and a_{charge} are presented in Table I, and the charge distributions for O^{16} and C^{12} are plotted in Fig. 5.

These results can also be regarded as the fit to experiment of a general two-parameter charge distribution of of the form (1), with parameters α' and a' to be determined. The values of these parameters are included in Table I. One observes that among the three curves, whose common property is the position of the diffraction minimum, the rms radius varies quite appreciably. This is not surprising, since it is a derived quantity not measured directly in these experiments.

Because of some uncertainties in the effect of recoil which were mentioned in Sec. III, and because experimentally the absolute values of the cross section cannot be obtained so precisely as the relative values from one angle to another, the comparison between theory and experiment on this point is not so fine, although it is

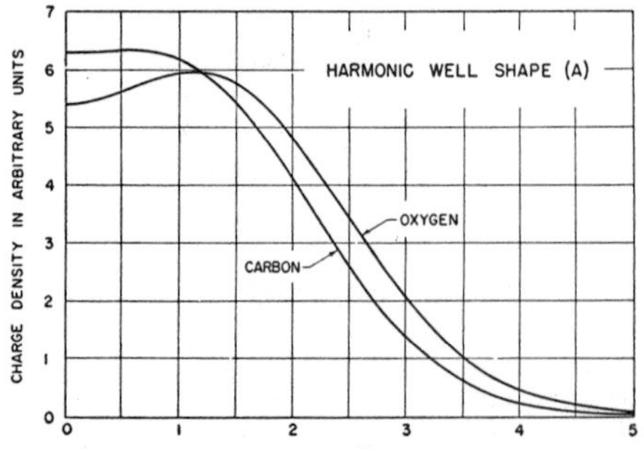

FIG. 5. Charge distributions for O^{16} and C^{12}, as given by the complete version of the shell model with parabolic well, and corresponding curves (c) of Figs. 1 and 4.

still very satisfactory. In Figs. 1(A), (B), and (C), and Fig. 4 the ordinate scale refers to the complete version of the shell model (the other two curves have been shifted vertically). The vertical shift of the whole set of experimental points necessary to obtain an absolute fit was never larger than compatible with the limits of error ascribed to the absolute cross-section measurements. The results of the absolute cross-section measurements, performed as described earlier for both nuclei at one angle at each energy, are listed in Table II.

The experimental results for the inelastic scattering corresponding to the excitation of the 4.43-Mev level in carbon are also plotted in Fig. 4. Since this level is known to be 2+, the transition is $E(2)$. A result of the analysis of the 187-Mev experiments[3,11] was that the single-particle shell model, with parabolic well, gives good agreement as regards the angular variation of this cross section, but that the absolute magnitude predicted is too low for all modes of coupling. Since a completely collective nuclear model, on the other hand, overestimates the absolute magnitude by a considerable factor,[16] it is reasonable that a small admixture of collective motion can yield the correct value. The dashed curve drawn through the experimental points

TABLE II. Values of the measured absolute cross sections.

Nucleus	Energy Mev	Angle Degrees	$d\sigma/d\Omega$ cm²/steradian
O^{16}	420	40	$(1.0\pm0.25)\times10^{-31}$
	360	55	$(0.9\pm0.4)\times10^{-32}$
	240	60	$(1.1\pm0.5)\times10^{-30}$
C^{12}	420	40	$(3.8\pm1.0)\times10^{-31}$

is therefore semitheoretical, in that its angular variation is that predicted by the shell model, with the same parabolic well as has been used for the elastic scattering. In absolute magnitude, however, it is about 40% lower than one would expect from the 187-Mev results.[17] It is significant that even for these large recoil momenta there is still good agreement with this very simple theory, for the inelastic as well as for the elastic scattering.

The comparison of shapes (B) and (C) with the 420-Mev experiments in oxygen are illustrated in Figs. 6 and 7, respectively. Fixing the position of the diffraction minimum determines a relation between the two parameters in each shape, and a selection of shapes are given. Shape (B) can be made to agree with experiment at all but the largest angles, but shape (C) cannot be made to agree at all. In addition, the absolute cross section for Model (C) is definitely too small. From the plot of charge distributions shown in Fig. 8 we see that in fact shape (C) has about zero central charge density,

[16] See e.g., Ferrell and Visscher, reference 11.

[17] The calculation even with these restrictions is still approximate, in that we have used the Born approximation with suitably modified wave number to calculate the *ratio* of inelastic to elastic scattering, and have then multiplied this ratio by the elastic cross section calculated using the partial-wave analysis.

so that its inability to agree with experiment is perhaps not surprising. This conclusion was earlier drawn by Fregeau, from the analysis of the 187-Mev results on carbon.[2] Because of the very limited extent of our analysis with arbitrary shapes we cannot draw any general conclusions. It is difficult to see how any shape could give better agreement than (A), the shell-model distribution, but our calculations are not extensive enough to say how far we can deviate from it before there is marked disagreement.

V. CONCLUSION AND DISCUSSION

A comparison has been made between new experiments on C^{12} and O^{16} at energies up to 420 Mev and

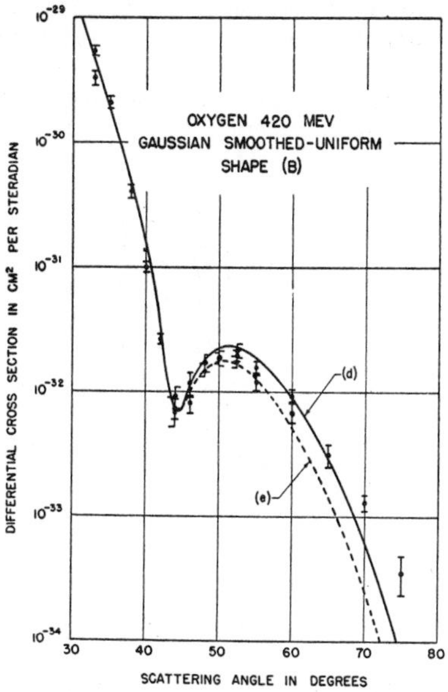

FIG. 6. Elastic scattering by O^{16} at 420 Mev. The curves are calculated using shape (*B*), with parameters (d) $c=2.17$, $Z=1.89$, and (e) $c=2.39$, $Z=1.72$, all in units of 10^{-13} cm. Curve (d) has been scaled vertically so as to coincide with (e) at the smaller angles.

the theoretical predictions of the nuclear shell model, assuming a parabolic central well. After corrections have been made for the finite proton size and the center-of-mass effect, we find for the length parameter $a_{c.m.}$ associated with the parabolic well

$$a_{\text{carbon}}=1.66\times10^{-13}\text{ cm},\quad a_{\text{oxygen}}=1.76\times10^{-13}\text{ cm}.$$

The error in a_{oxygen} is of order $\pm0.02\times10^{-13}$ cm, and in a_{carbon} somewhat larger. The rms radii of the charge distributions are

$$\langle r^2\rangle_{\text{carbon}}^{\frac{1}{2}}=2.50\times10^{13}\text{ cm},\quad \langle r^2\rangle_{\text{oxygen}}^{\frac{1}{2}}=2.70\times10^{-13}\text{ cm}.$$

The results obtained without the above corrections are in very good agreement with the earlier value $a_{\text{carbon}}=1.64\times10^{-13}$ cm of Fregeau.[2] The fact that the rms

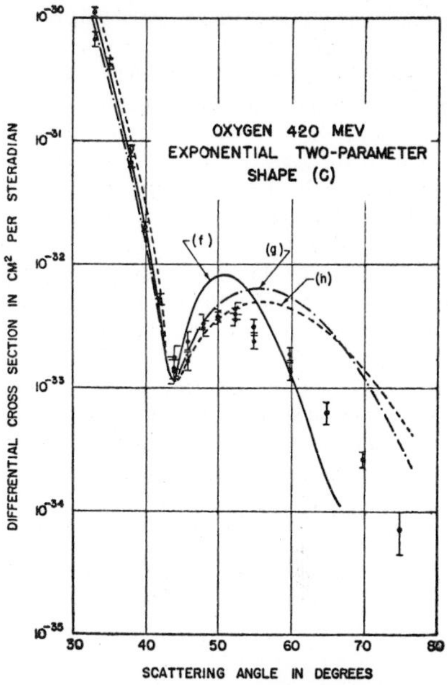

FIG. 7. Elastic scattering by O^{16} at 420 Mev. The curves are calculated using shape (*C*), with parameters (f) $b=0.664$, $\beta=4.7$, (g) $b=0.674$, $\beta=7.5$, and (h) $b=0.645$, $\beta=16.3$. The length parameters b are in 10^{-13} cm. Curves (f) and (g) have been scaled vertically so as to agree with (h) at the diffraction minimum. In order to make a shape fit possible it was necessary to shift the experimental point considerably, as can be noticed from Table II.

radius is somewhat larger than his value is a consequence of the finite proton size: for a folded distribution such as (2),

$$\langle r^2\rangle_{\text{charge}}=\langle r^2\rangle_{\text{matter}}+\langle r^2\rangle_{\text{proton}},$$

and $\langle r^2\rangle_{\text{matter}}$ is, roughly speaking, fixed by the position of the diffraction minimum. The center-of-mass effect tends to change it in the other direction, but it is not such a large effect.

Another source of information on the well size in the

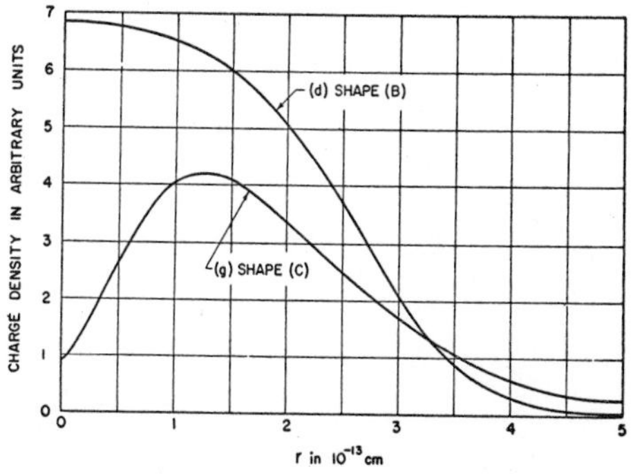

FIG. 8. Charge distributions in O^{16}, examples of shapes (B) and (C). That labeled (d) corresponds to curve (d) of Fig. 6, and that labeled (g) corresponds to curve (g) of Fig. 7.

shell model is the Coulomb energy of mirror nuclei. A calculation of this quantity for the mirror nuclei $F^{17}-O^{17}$ and $O^{15}-N^{15}$, including exchange effects, was made by Jancovici[18] some time ago. He compared the apparent Coulomb radius $\langle 1/r\rangle^{-1}$ with the rms radius $\langle r^2\rangle^{\frac{1}{2}}$ and found that in the case of the parabolic well the ratio $\langle 1/r\rangle^{-1}/\langle r^2\rangle^{\frac{1}{2}}$ was 1.29 and 1.16, respectively, for the two pairs of nuclei. The ratio is, of course, independent of a. If we use for $\langle 1/r\rangle$ the experimental Coulomb energies,[15] and for $\langle r^2\rangle$ our result for O^{16}, the ratios are experimentally 1.26 and 1.16. The agreement is a very satisfactory check on these two independent measurements of nuclear size.

Experiments are under way on other $1p$ shell nuclei,[19,20] to investigate in detail the changes occurring as one goes through the shell. The analysis of the elastic scattering will be somewhat more involved, however, since because of the looser binding we may expect nuclei like Li to have more prominent exponential tails to their charge distributions.

[18] B. A. Jancovici, Phys. Rev. **95**, 389 (1954).

[19] G. R. Burleson and R. Hofstadter, Phys. Rev. **112**, 1282 (1958).

[20] U. Meyer-Berkhout (to be published).

ACKNOWLEDGMENTS

We wish to express our thanks to the members of the operating crew of the Stanford linear accelerator for operation of the machine. The phase-shift analyses used in this work were performed by the computer Univac of the California Radiation Laboratory at Livermore. We thank the authorities of this laboratory, particularly Dr. S. Fernbach, for the use of this computer, and Mrs. Mary G. Shepherd and Mr. Charles Emmert for their help in its operation. One of the authors (H.F.E.) is grateful to the "Deutsche Forschungsgemeinschaft" for the grant of a stipend which permitted him to stay at Stanford for one year. Another of us (U.M.-B.) would like to express his thanks to the same organization for financial support during the time this work was performed.

PAPER 53

EFFECT OF A PION-PION SCATTERING RESONANCE ON NUCLEON STRUCTURE*

William R. Frazer and Jose R. Fulco†
Lawrence Radiation Laboratory, University of California, Berkeley, California
(Received March 25, 1959)

The electromagnetic properties of the nucleon have recently been studied by the dispersion-relation method.[1,2] Although qualitatively successful in accounting for the isotopic vector properties of the nucleon, these treatments proved incapable of explaining simultaneously the value of the magnetic moment and the radii of the charge and moment distributions.[3] The purpose of this Letter is to show that the inclusion of a strong pion-pion interaction could explain these aspects of nucleon structure.

Let us first consider the general formulation and solution of the dispersion relations. In the notation of reference 1, we write the following representations for the form factors[4]:

$$G_i^V(s) = \frac{1}{\pi}\int_{(2m_\pi)^2}^{\infty} \frac{g_i^V(s')\,ds'}{s'-s}, \tag{1}$$

$$G_i^S(s) = \frac{1}{\pi}\int_{(3m_\pi)^2}^{\infty} \frac{g_i^S(s')\,ds'}{s'-s}, \quad i = 1 \text{ or } 2, \tag{2}$$

where $s = (p'-p)^2 = (p_0'-p_0)^2 - (\vec{p}\,'-\vec{p})^2$, the square of the energy-momentum transfer four-vector. The weight functions $g_i(s)$ are related to a sum over all virtual intermediate states that can be reached from a photon and lead to a nucleon-antinucleon pair. For the isotopic vector functions $g_i^V(s)$, invariance considerations show that the least massive state is the two-pion state. We shall assume, as in previous treatments,[1,2] that the two-pion contribution dominates in the dispersion integrals. On the other hand, the least massive state contributing to $g_i^S(s)$ is the three-pion state. We have nothing to say here about this contribution and shall limit ourselves to the isotopic vector properties.

In the approximation stated above, $g_1^V(s)$ and $g_2^V(s)$ are proportional to the pion form factor multiplied by the appropriate projection of the amplitude for the process $\langle N\bar{N}|\pi\pi\rangle$ in the state $J=1$, $I=1$. Using the Mandelstam representation,[5] we are able to study the analytic properties of these projections, which we label $J_i(s)$. It can be shown that in the complex s-plane these functions are analytic except for branch cuts on the real axis for $s \leq 4m_\pi^2[1-(m_\pi^2/4M^2)]$ and $s \geq (2m_\pi)^2$. The right-hand branch cut, which was not considered in previous treatments, corresponds to π-π scattering. We shall show that it has an important effect on nucleon structure.

We can then write the dispersion relation

$$J_i(s) = \frac{1}{\pi}\int_{-\infty}^{a} \frac{\mathrm{Im}J_i(s')\,ds'}{s'-s-i\epsilon} + \frac{1}{\pi}\int_{(2m_\pi)^2}^{\infty} \frac{\mathrm{Im}J_i(s')\,ds'}{s'-s-i\epsilon}, \qquad (3)$$

where $a \equiv 4m_\pi^2(1-m_\pi^2/4M^2)$. Application of the unitarity condition shows that in the region $(2m_\pi)^2 \leq s \leq (4m_\pi)^2$, the phase of $J_i(s)$ is equal to the π-π scattering phase shift δ in the $J=1$, $I=1$ state. Considering only the two-pion intermediate state, we shall use this phase relation over the entire range of the right-hand integral in Eq. (3).

Because the left-hand integral is related to the pion-nucleon scattering amplitude, we shall consider it to be a known function. Equation (3) is then an integral equation, whose general solution has been found by Omnes.[6] In our case, his solution can be modified into the more tractable form

$$J_i(s) = e^{u(s)}\frac{1}{\pi}\int_{-\infty}^{a} \frac{ds'\,\mathrm{Im}J_i(s')}{s'-s-i\epsilon}\,e^{-u(s')}, \qquad (4)$$

where

$$u(s) = \frac{1}{\pi}\int_{(2m_\pi)^2}^{\infty} \frac{\delta(s')\,ds'}{s'-s-i\epsilon}. \qquad (5)$$

It can easily be seen that Eq. (4) reproduces the content of the integral equation (3); namely, $J_i(s)$ has the proper singularities, has the phase of π-π scattering on the right-hand cut, and has the correct imaginary part on the left-hand cut. If the integral defining $u(s)$ fails to converge, one can use the subtracted form

$$u_0(s) = \frac{s}{\pi}\int_{(2m_\pi)^2}^{\infty} \frac{\delta(s')\,ds'}{s'(s'-s-i\epsilon)}. \qquad (6)$$

We now require an expression for the pion form factor, $F_\pi(s)$, which satisfies the dispersion relation:

$$F_\pi(s) = 1 + \frac{s}{\pi}\int_{(2m_\pi)^2}^{\infty} ds'\,\frac{\mathrm{Im}F_\pi(s')}{s'(s'-s-i\epsilon)}. \qquad (7)$$

Unitarity allows us to conclude that the phase of $F_\pi(s)$ is the π-π scattering phase shift in the $J=1$, $I=1$ state,[7] and again we shall use this condition over the entire range of integration. In this case Eq. (4) degenerates into the solution

$$F_\pi(s) = e^{u_0(s)}. \qquad (8)$$

Combining Eqs. (4) and (8), we find

$$g_i^V(s) = |F_\pi(s)|^2\,\frac{1}{\pi}\int_{-\infty}^{a} \frac{ds'\,\mathrm{Im}J_i(s')}{(s'-s-i\epsilon)F_\pi(s)}. \qquad (9)$$

Equation (9) reveals the important fact that, because of the phase conditions imposed by unitarity, it is the absolute value of the pion electromagnetic form factor which appears in the weight functions $g_i^V(s)$. Thus the well-known condition that $g_i(s)$ be real is satisfied.

Using Eqs. (9) and (1), let us now investigate the effect of π-π scattering on the nucleon structure. It has been shown by Drell[3] that in order to obtain agreement with the nucleon magnetic moment and radii, an enhancement of $g_i^V(s)$ by a factor of the order of five is required for $s < M^2$. From Eq. (9) it is apparent that a suitable peak in the pion form factor would produce this enhancement. We shall now show that a π-π resonance would result in such a peak.

An investigation of π-π scattering now in progress by Chew and Mandelstam has shown that the singularities of the partial-wave amplitude in the $J=1$, $I=1$ state are confined to branch cuts along the real axis in the range $s \leq 0$, $4m_\pi^2 \leq s$.[8] In the physical region, the effect of the left-hand singularities can be estimated by replacing the branch cut by a pole of appropriate position and residue. This approximation seems reasonable because for nucleon-nucleon scattering it leads to well-known effective-range formulas. Making this approximation, one finds the following solution for the $J=1$ state, for $\nu > 0$:

$$f_{\pi\pi}(s) = \left(\frac{\nu+1}{\nu^3}\right)^{1/2} e^{i\delta}\sin\delta = \frac{\Gamma}{\nu_r - \nu[1-\Gamma\alpha(\nu)] - i\Gamma[\nu^3/(\nu+1)]^{1/2}}, \quad (10)$$

where

$$\nu = \tfrac{1}{4}s - m_\pi^2,$$

$$\alpha(\nu) = (2/\pi)[\nu/(\nu+1)]^{1/2} \ln[\nu^{1/2} + (\nu+1)^{1/2}].$$

A suitably continued form holds for $\nu < 0$. The constants Γ and ν_r are determined by the position and residue of the pole. By examination of the structure of the π-π equations, Chew and Mandelstam have found that the sign of the residue must be positive, corresponding to an attractive force and raising the possibility of a resonance. Further theoretical information about the equivalent pole must await numerical solution of the very complicated π-π equations. We shall now show, however, that if the constants ν_r and Γ are properly chosen, agreement with the nucleon-structure data may be achieved.

A properly normalized solution for $F_\pi(s)$ is

$$F_\pi(s) = f_{\pi\pi}(s)(s+s_0)/[s_0 f_{\pi\pi}(0)], \quad (11)$$

where s_0 is the position of the equivalent pole. The justification of this solution is, again, that it has the correct singularities and phase. Equation (11) clearly shows that a resonance in $f_{\pi\pi}$ will be reflected in the form factor F_π. The ob-

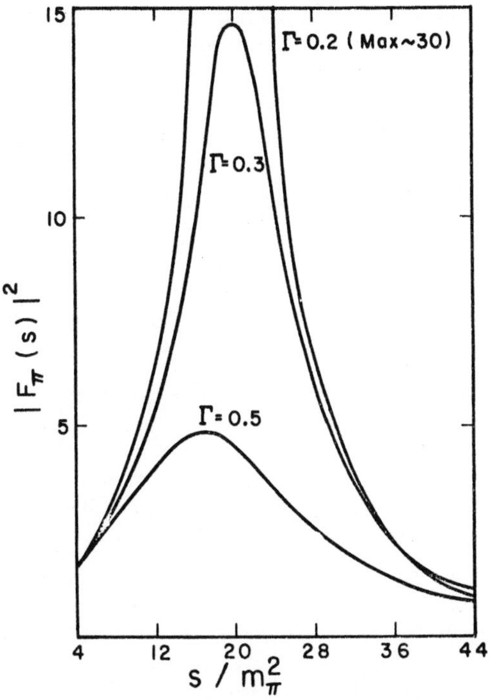

FIG. 1. The square of the magnitude of the pion form factor for $s \geq 4\mu^2$, for three values of the width Γ.

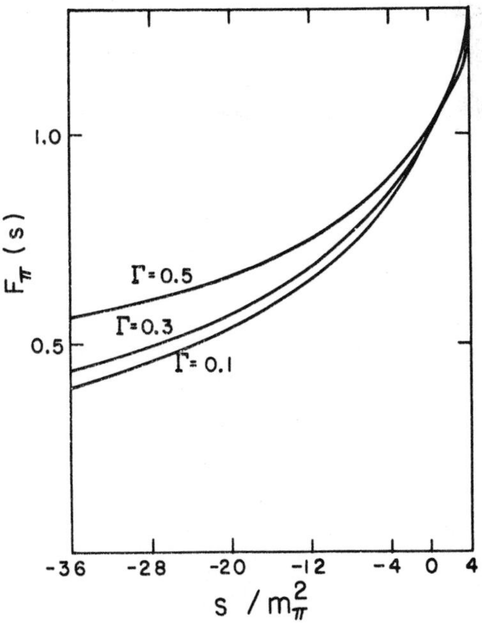

FIG. 2. The pion form factor in its physical region, for three values of the width Γ.

367

served values of the charge and magnetic-moment radii indicate that this resonance should occur at $\nu_\gamma \sim 3.5 m_\pi^2$ (square of the pion momentum in the π-π barycentric system). In Fig. 1 the function $|F_\pi(s)|^2$ is plotted for this value of ν_γ and several values of the width Γ. In Fig. 2 the pion form factor is plotted for $s < a$. Since it is less than one over most of this region, its appearance in the denominator of the integral of Eq. (9) will produce an additional enhancement.

In conclusion, our Eq. (9) for the weight functions together with the approximation given in Eq. (10) for the pion-pion scattering amplitude suggests that a π-π resonance of suitable position and width could lead to agreement between dispersion theory and many aspects of nucleon electromagnetic structure. Detailed calculations are in progress.

We are indebted to Professor Geoffrey F. Chew for his advice throughout this work, and for advance communication of some of the results on pion-pion scattering. We also acknowledge the help of James S. Ball and Peter Cziffra in obtaining Eq. (4).

---

*This work was done under the auspices of the U. S. Atomic Energy Commission.

†Visitor from the Argentine Army.

[1]Chew, Karplus, Gasiorowicz, and Zachariasen, Phys. Rev. 110, 265 (1958).

[2]Federbush, Goldberger, and Treiman, Phys. Rev. 112, 642 (1958).

[3]S. D. Drell, 1958 Annual International Conference on High-Energy Physics at CERN, edited by B. Ferretti (CERN, Geneva, 1958).

[4]If the integral in Eq. (1) fails to converge, one can use the usual subtracted form, as discussed in reference 1.

[5]S. Mandelstam, Phys. Rev. 112, 1344 (1958).

[6]R. Omnes, Nuovo cimento 8, 316 (1958).

[7]See, for example, Appendix II of Fubini, Nambu, and Wataghin, Phys. Rev. 111, 329 (1958).

[8]G. F. Chew, Lawrence Radiation Laboratory (private communication, 1959).

PAPER 54

Experimental Determination of the Nonmagnetic Neutron-Electron Interaction*

E. Melkonian, B. M. Rustad, and W. W. Havens, Jr.
Columbia University, New York, New York, and Brookhaven National Laboratory, Upton, New York
(Received January 21, 1959)

A precise set of measurements of the variation of the transmission of liquid bismuth with energy in the range 0.1 ev to 10 ev has been made. After correction for neutron capture, Doppler effect and liquid diffraction, a value of $V_0=-4.34\pm0.14$ kev is obtained as the depth of the potential well having a radius equal to the classical electron radius. This gives -0.26 ± 0.14 kev as the strength of the intrinsic neutron-electron interaction after subtraction of the Foldy term.

INTRODUCTION

The strength of the nonmagnetic neutron-electron interaction has been the subject of numerous experimental and theoretical investigations. The measurements to date have yielded an attractive interaction of the order of 4000 electron volts expressed as the effective potential acting over a sphere having a radius equal to the classical electron radius. Foldy[1] has pointed out that a spin and velocity independent interaction of 4080 electron volts is expected purely on the basis that the neutron possesses an anomalous magnetic moment. The difference between this value and the observed interaction strength is denoted by the term intrinsic neutron-electron interaction and is expected to arise if the neutron virtually dissociates part of the time into two oppositely charged particles, as is postulated by current meson theories concerning nuclear structure.[2] All measurements to date indicate that the intrinsic neutron-electron interaction is small or zero to within the experimental error of a few hundred electron volts. Calculations of the expected value of the intrinsic neutron-electron interaction based on current meson theoretical ideas of the structure of the neutron indicate a much larger value for this interaction. Thus the magnitude of the intrinsic neutron-electron interaction provides a stringent test for any meson theory, and the accurate experimental determination of this quantity is of prime importance.

The cross section for the nonmagnetic neutron-electron interaction is about 10^6 smaller than ordinary neutron-nucleon interactions and cannot be detected directly by current methods. The three methods which have been successfully used have taken advantage of the considerably larger interference term between the scattering of neutrons by the nucleus and by the electrons of the same atom. The first results were given by Havens, Rabi, and Rainwater,[3,4] who measured the energy dependence of the total cross section of liquid lead and liquid bismuth and interpreted their results in terms of the variation of the interference term as the neutron wavelength is changed. Fermi and Marshall[2] and later Hamermesh *et al.*[5] observed the angular dependence of the scattering of neutrons from krypton and xenon. The latest reported results were by Hughes *et al.*,[6] who measured the total reflection of neutrons from the interface between bismuth and liquid oxygen. An account of these measurements, as well as a detailed treatment of the theory involved, are given in an excellent review paper by Foldy.[7]

The measurements of Havens, Rabi, and Rainwater were made with the neutron velocity spectrometer system in conjunction with the Columbia 36-inch cyclotron where, because of low intensities, it was difficult to obtain sufficient statistical accuracy. By the use of the same method and the much higher neutron fluxes available with a neutron crystal spectrometer at a nuclear reactor, results with much higher statistical accuracy were expected. This paper presents the results of such a set of measurements on liquid bismuth. A preliminary account of this work has been reported previously.[8]

METHOD

For an isolated atom, the scattering amplitude is given by

$$a=a_N+Za_{ne}f,$$

where $a_N\equiv$nuclear scattering amplitude, $a_{ne}\equiv$nonmagnetic neutron-electron scattering amplitude, Z =atomic number, and $f\equiv$electronic form factor. Integration of a^2 over all directions gives the total scattering cross section in the center-of-mass system.

$$\sigma=\sigma_N+2Z(\sigma_N\sigma_{ne})^{\frac{1}{2}}\bar{f}+Z^2\sigma_{ne}\langle f^2\rangle_{\text{Av}}.$$

The last term gives a negligible contribution within the limits of error of these measurements and will henceforth be omitted. The method of measuring σ_{ne} consists, then, of measuring the cross section at several neutron energies and determining the coefficient of $\bar{f}$, which is assumed to be a known function of energy. Before the

* This work partially supported by the U. S. Atomic Energy Commission.
[1] L. L. Foldy, Phys. Rev. **87**, 693 (1952).
[2] E. Fermi and L. Marshall, Phys. Rev. **72**, 1139 (1947).
[3] Havens, Rabi, and Rainwater, Phys. Rev. **72**, 634 (1947).
[4] Havens, Rabi, and Rainwater, Phys. Rev. **82**, 345 (1951).
[5] Hamermesh, Ringo, and Wattenberg, Phys. Rev. **85**, 483 (1952).
[6] Hughes, Harvey, Goldberg, and Stafne, Phys. Rev. **90**, 497 (1953).
[7] L. L. Foldy, Revs. Modern Phys. **30**, 471 (1958).
[8] Melkonian, Rustad, and Havens, Bull. Am. Phys. Soc. Ser. II, 1, 62 (1956).

latter can be done, however, corrections must be made for neutron capture by the nucleus, the effect of thermal motion, and the effect of liquid diffraction. Each of these effects will be discussed subsequently.

Since the interference term is only a small percentage of the main nuclear term, cross section measurements to better than 0.1% must be made in order to obtain significant results. The choice of material for investigation must also be made carefully since most materials exhibit large variations of cross section with energy from other effects, and these mask the effect to be measured. Liquid bismuth was chosen for these measurements because (a) it has a small and adequately well-known capture cross section, (b) it does not have the crystal diffraction effects exhibited by most solids, (c) it has negligible spin incoherence, (d) it has a high atomic number, giving a relatively large effect, (e) its large atomic weight reduces the amount of Doppler correction and hence minimizes possible uncertainties arising from this correction, (f) it is monoisotopic, and (g) it is readily available. The only other available material which appears suitable for this type of investigation is gaseous argon at high pressure. Although argon is superior to liquid bismuth in many respects, it has not been used because the desired effect is smaller and its appreciable capture cross section is not sufficiently well-known. However, recent work[9] on the Columbia University crystal spectrometer at the Brookhaven National Laboratory reactor, extending its range to 11 A, may make it possible to determine the capture cross section with adequate accuracy.

EXPERIMENTAL EQUIPMENT

The Spectrometer

The Columbia University neutron crystal spectrometer in conjunction with the BNL reactor was used as a source of monochromatic neutrons for these measurements. This spectrometer is similar to other single crystal spectrometers which are used for high precision neutron spectroscopy.[10] A sodium chloride crystal (200 planes) was used as a neutron monochromator. A proportional counter filled with $B^{10}F_3$ was used for neutron detection. The main requirement of this determination is accurate measurement of transmission. Therefore, the various factors concerned were extensively studied:

(a) The knowledge of the neutron energy and the lack of perfect resolution contributed a negligible amount to the uncertainty of the final results of this experiment since the observed transmission of liquid bismuth varied very slowly with neutron energy.

(b) The contamination of the diffracted neutron beam with higher order neutrons was determined by

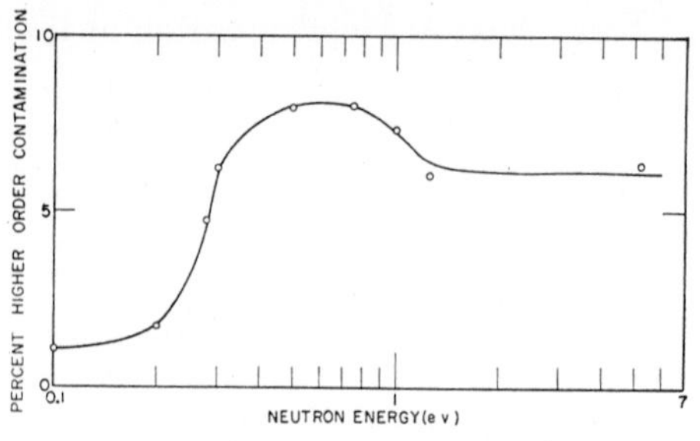

FIG. 1. Higher order contamination in reflection from the pile neutron beam incident on the 200 plane NaCl crystal monochromator of the neutron crystal spectrometer.

measuring the transmission of various thicknesses of cadmium in the region below 1 ev. A few measurements were made at energies above 1 ev by observing the counting rate at resonance through thick samples of indium, gold, and silver. These results, which were used for correcting the data for higher order contamination, are shown in Fig. 1. It is apparent that uncertainties in the amount of contamination are unimportant because of the slow variation of the transmission with energy.

(c) It was observed for this system, as for an earlier one,[11] that the counting rate produced by the BF^3 detection system was not strictly proportional to the intensity of neutrons reaching the BF^3 counter. The counting rate loss was determined from measurements of the transmission of a standard piece of solid bismuth taken at the full intensity of the spectrometer and at an intensity reduced to about one-third by a bismuth filter placed in the neutron beam. Repeated measurements over the course of three years indicated that the counting rate loss corresponded to a dead time, calculated in the usual way, of 3.0 ± 0.3 microseconds and did not change appreciably. At the maximum intensity of the spectrometer, this correction can amount to 3% for a transmission of about one-quarter. Although the counting losses were approximately proportional to the neutron intensity, as for true dead time, possible variations from this behavior were not determined with high precision. Instead, the neutron intensity was always reduced by suitable filters to a value such that the dead time correction was less than 0.2% and, therefore, the uncertainty in this correction negligible.

(d) Corrections for background were determined at frequent intervals during each transmission measurement by rotating the crystal one or two degrees off the diffraction peak and subtracting these results from measurements made with the crystal on peak.

The Liquid Bismuth Cell

A diagram of the sample holder used to contain the liquid bismuth for these measurements is shown in

[9] Gould, Taylor, and Havens, Phys. Rev. **100**, 1248A (1955).
[10] See, for example, Sailor, Foote, Landon, and Wood, Rev. Sci. Instr. **27**, 26 (1956).
[11] E. Melkonian, Phys. Rev. **76**, 1744 (1949).

Fig. 2. The neutron beam passes through the compartment in contact with a platinum resistance thermometer. A mixture of He with 2% H_2 is used to move the liquid bismuth out of this compartment for a "sample out" measurement or into this compartment for a "sample in" measurement. Earlier measurements, which used He without the H_2, resulted in oxidation of the liquid bismuth from the small contamination of O_2 in the He. Those portions of the cell which come into contact with liquid bismuth were fabricated of low carbon steel, which is one of the best structural materials for containing molten bismuth from the point of view of corrosion resistance. The vacuum jacket and radiation shields help to maintain the sample at a uniform temperature by reducing heat losses to a minimum. A temperature regulating device, which uses a platinum resistance thermometer as a sensing element, maintains the cell at a temperature within $\frac{1}{2}$°C of the required temperature, a range which produces negligible change in transmission. The bismuth sample was supplied by American Smelting and Refining Company and was claimed to be of purity better than 99.99%. It received special handling throughout to avoid contamination with material having high capture cross sections.

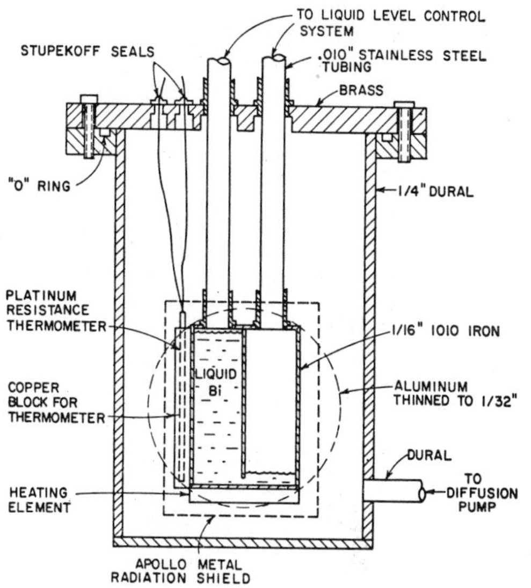

FIG. 2. Diagram of liquid bismuth cell. Stupekoff seals in the brass plate are used for the electrical connections.

RESULTS

Ten separate determinations on two samples of liquid bismuth were made over the course of about two years. Each determination consisted of a series of transmission measurements at three or four widely spaced values of the neutron energy. To eliminate possible variations of the sample in the time taken for one series of runs, all of the data at a particular energy were not taken at once but rather broken up into five to ten determinations interspersed with measurements at the other energies. Each transmission measurement consisted of many cycles following the pattern, open—sample—sample—open, in order to minimize reactor drifts. Background data in the same pattern were taken periodically. Data were computed on the 409.2 *R* Remington-Rand computer at Brookhaven National Laboratory. After a preliminary calculation using all of the data from one run at a particular energy, those cycles were rejected whose deviations from the mean exceeded 2.5 times the standard deviation. The number of cycles rejected in this manner, without determining the cause of the high deviation, was about the number expected from statistical considerations. The remaining cycles were used to compute the final average transmission for that particular run. The distributions of cycle by cycle transmissions of each set of data were found to be acceptable on the basis of Pearson's chi-squared test. The standard spectrometer corrections for dead time and order contamination were then made and cross sections computed on the basis of g/cm² of sample obtained from the density of liquid Bi and the cell dimensions. The results, after corrections to be described, are listed in Table I. There is some decrease of calculated cross section with time. This is attributed to an effective decrease of the sample thickness resulting from a buildup of deposits on the walls of the chamber. This uncertainty in sample thickness makes calculation of absolute cross sections unreliable. However, the measurement of the magnitude of the neutron-electron interaction depends primarily upon the variation of the cross section with energy, and the procedure of taking data described above eliminates the effect of a long term change of sample thickness. The results were ultimately normalized to a free bismuth atom cross section of 9.29 barns.[12]

CORRECTIONS

There are three major corrections to be made on the cross section data in order to interpret them in terms of neutron-electron interaction. These corrections are (a) neutron capture, (b) Doppler effect, and (c) liquid diffraction. Correction implies subtraction of these effects from the observed cross section values to give the results which would have been obtained had these effects not been present.

Neutron Capture

A correction for radiative neutron capture was made on the basis of 32 millibarns[12] at kT and a $1/v$ behavior, i.e., $\sigma_c = 0.0178\ \lambda$ barns, where λ is the neutron wave-

[12] *Neutron Cross Sections*, compiled by D. J. Hughes and R. B. Schwartz, Brookhaven National Laboratory Report BNL-325, (Superintendent of Documents, U. S. Government Printing Office, Washington, D. C., 1958), second edition.

TABLE I. The cross section data for liquid bismuth corrected for neutron capture, Doppler effect and liquid diffraction, and the derived values of the neutron-electron interaction for each run.

Sample No.	Temp. °C	$E=0.1$ ev	$E=0.28$ ev	$E=1.0$ ev	$E=4.0$ ev	$E=10.0$ ev	σ_0 (barns)	$-b$ (barns)	V (kev)	V_0 (kev)[a]
#1	300°	9.1542±0.0043		9.2302±0.0116		9.2853±0.0164	9.2904±0.0133	0.2861±0.0303	4.41±0.47	4.41±0.47
#1	500°	9.1420±0.0050	9.2304±0.0116	9.2285±0.0082			9.2973±0.0133	0.3182±0.0325	4.91±0.50	4.91±0.50
#1	500°	9.1705±0.0038	9.2134±0.0033	9.2457±0.0041			9.2967±0.0068	0.2604±0.0192	4.02±0.30	4.02±0.30
#1	500°	9.1627±0.0046	9.2046±0.0067	9.2406±0.0062			9.2915±0.0100	0.2687±0.0263	4.15±0.41	4.15±0.41
#1	500°	9.1601±0.0038	9.1934±0.0041	9.2348±0.0039			9.2798±0.0067	0.2568±0.0187	3.96±0.29	3.96±0.29
#2	300°	9.1197±0.0029	9.1659±0.0034	9.2099±0.0031	9.2430±0.0050		9.2643±0.0040	0.3147±0.0119	4.86±0.18	4.87±0.18
#2	300°	9.0806±0.0042	9.1260±0.0034	9.1674±0.0034	9.1852±0.0094		9.2202±0.0055	0.2893±0.0169	4.46±0.26	4.49±0.26
#2	300°	9.0758±0.0042	9.1263±0.0031	9.1553±0.0031	9.1886±0.0094		9.2085±0.0051	0.2667±0.0162	4.12±0.25	4.16±0.25
#2	300°	9.0837±0.0034	9.1274±0.0036	9.1611±0.0031	9.2081±0.0109		9.2148±0.0050	0.2735±0.0148	4.22±0.23	4.25±0.23
#2	300°	9.0512±0.0038	9.0938±0.0034	9.1283±0.0047	9.1405±0.0076		9.1724±0.0060	0.2479±0.0170	3.83±0.26	3.88±0.26

[a] Normalized to $\sigma_0=9.29$.

length in A. A sample of the same bismuth used for these measurements was investigated by Langsdorf on a pile oscillator[13] and found to have the capture cross section for bismuth listed to within the accuracy stated, which has a standard deviation of 6%.

After these measurements were completed, the capture cross section of the sample used was measured by another method, since no pile oscillators were in operation, to see whether it was still the same, that is, to see whether material having high neutron capture had been dissolved by the liquid bismuth, since this could produce an appreciable error in the deduced value of the neutron-electron interaction. In order to perform this measurement, the liquid bismuth samples used were allowed to solidify and were then machined into the form of a good transmission sample. Measurements were made in the neighborhood of 10 A, which is much larger than the wavelength of the Bragg break. At this energy the large coherent cross section has vanished, and only a residual incoherent temperature dependent cross section and the capture cross section remain. Similar measurements were made on a portion of the original bismuth sample which had been set aside and had not gone through the melting process for this experiment. The results of these measurements are listed in Table II. Data read from the "$T=300°$K" curve in BNL 325[12] are included for comparison. It is evident that there has been no significant change in the capture characteristics of the liquid bismuth sample used during the course of the measurements.

Doppler Effect

In the region of high atomic mass and not too low neutron energy, the Doppler effect on an otherwise constant cross section is fairly small and is given by[14]

$$\frac{\delta\sigma}{\sigma_0}=1+\frac{kT}{2\mu E_0},$$

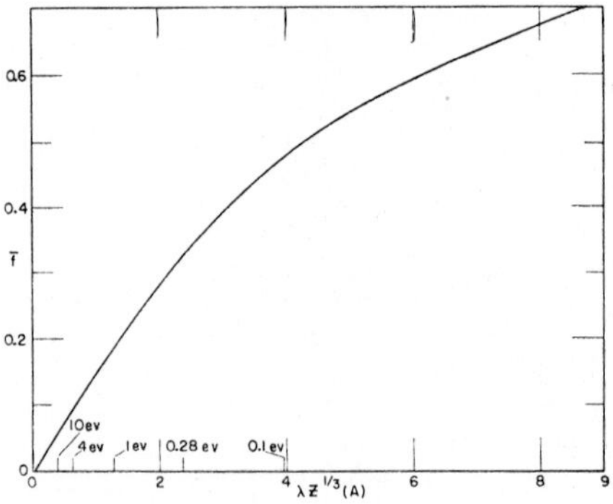

FIG. 3. Electronic form factor as a function of $\lambda Z^{\frac{1}{3}}$. Values of $\lambda Z^{\frac{1}{3}}$ corresponding to this experiment are indicated.

[13] A. S. Langsdorf (private communication).

[14] G. Placzek, Phys. Rev. **86**, 377 (1952).

TABLE II. The data for the determination of the capture cross section of the bismuth sample before and after the measurements compared with the standard sample which was not used in the measurements and the standard values from BNL 325.

	λ (A)	E (10^{-3} ev)	σ_{stand} (barns)	$\sigma_{sample\ 1}$ (barns)	$\Delta\sigma_1=\sigma_{stand}-\sigma_{sample\ 1}$ (barns)	$\Delta\sigma_1/\lambda$ (barns/A)	$\sigma_{sample\ 2}$ (barns)	$\Delta\sigma_2=\sigma_{stand}-\sigma_{sample\ 2}$ (barns)	$\Delta\sigma_2/\lambda$ (barns/A)	σ BNL 325 (barns)
	8.75	1.08	0.657±0.025	0.640±0.024	−0.017±0.035	−0.0019±0.0040				0.65
	10.0	0.82	0.557±0.025	0.588±0.022	+0.031±0.033	+0.0031±0.0033	0.555±0.020	0.002±0.032	0.0002±0.0032	0.57
	11.5	0.62	0.610±0.025	0.574±0.024	−0.036±0.035	−0.0031±0.0030				0.56
Average						−0.0007±0.0019			0.0002±0.0032	

so that for $\sigma_0=9.29$ b,

$$\delta\sigma=0.0134\,\lambda^2 \quad \text{at} \quad 300°\text{C}$$
$$=0.0181\,\lambda^2 \quad \text{at} \quad 500°\text{C}.$$

Liquid Diffraction

Even though liquid bismuth does not exhibit the diffraction effects shown by crystalline materials, there is a small variation of cross section with energy acused by the diffraction of neutrons arising from the fact that each bismuth atom is surrounded by other bismuth atoms at approximately the same distance so that some regularity exists in the liquid. This effect has been examined in great detail by Placzek *et al.*,[15] who give the following formulas for the relative change in cross section arising from the effect of liquid diffraction:

$$\delta\sigma/\sigma_0=-(\lambda_0^2\rho^{\frac{2}{3}}/8\pi)I,$$

where λ_0=neutron wavelength (cm), ρ=number of particles/unit volume, $I<3$, ~3 for close packing of particles. The quantity I depends on the liquid structure of the sample. The calculations for many reasonable forms of distribution of atoms indicate that I must be about 2.85. For mercury, Placzek *et al.*[15] analyzed the data of Hendus and found $I=2.82$. It was expected that I would be slightly smaller for bismuth than for mercury; therefore, for bismuth I was taken as 2.80. Using $I=2.80$, the liquid diffraction term becomes

$$\delta\sigma=-0.0976\,\lambda^2 \quad \text{at} \quad 300°\text{C}$$
$$-0.0959\,\lambda^2 \quad \text{at} \quad 500°\text{C}.$$

The question of the effect of interference between the nucleus of one atom and the electrons of another has been raised by Weiss.[16] It was studied in detail by Placzek[17] and was shown to have an insignificant effect on this experiment.

Table III gives the details of these corrections for one case to illustrate their magnitudes. Table I gives the value of the cross section of bismuth at the various energies after corrections for all effects mentioned above.

INTERPRETATION OF RESULTS

An inspection of Table I shows that there is a very definite decrease in the cross section of bismuth with increasing wavelength in each run. To interpret this variation in terms of the strength of neutron-electron interaction, the variation of the average electronic form factor with energy must be known. The average electronic form factor, $\bar{f}$, was computed on the basis of both the Fermi-Thomas model of the atom and the Hartree functions. In the 0.1-1 A region of neutron wavelengths, which is of interest here, both calculations give essentially the same results. Figure 3 shows the dependence of $\bar{f}$, computed from the Fermi-Thomas model, upon the wavelength. For each energy or wavelength at which neutron transmission measurements were made, a value of $\bar{f}$ was determined from an expanded version of Figure 3. The corrected cross section of the bismuth atom is then expected to be a linear function of $\bar{f}$. Figure 4 shows the plot of $\bar{\sigma}$ *vs* $\bar{f}$ for Sample 2. A straight line fits the observed points fairly well, lending confidence to the validity of the corrections made. However, calculations were carried out separately on each of the ten runs and averaged only at the end for the final result. Table I gives a list of the slope and intersections for the ten runs made. The slope b is related to the well depth by

$$b=2Z(\sigma_N\sigma_{ne})^{\frac{1}{2}},$$

TABLE III. Sample calculation for the data on liquid bismuth at 300°C showing the corrections for capture, Doppler effect and liquid diffraction on data.

λ (A)	E (ev)	$\bar{f}$	σ (barns)	$\delta\sigma$ (barns)	Correction: Capture	Correction: Doppler	Correction: Liquid diffraction	Sum of corrections	$\sigma_{corrected}$ (barns)
0.906	0.10	0.477	9.0307	±0.0034	−0.0161	−0.0110	+0.0801	+0.0530	9.0837
0.542	0.28	0.330	9.1122	±0.0036	−0.0096	−0.0039	+0.0287	+0.0152	9.1274
0.286	1.00	0.186	9.1593	±0.0031	−0.0051	−0.0011	+0.0080	+0.0018	9.1611
0.143	4.00	0.086	9.2089	±0.0109	−0.0025	−0.0003	+0.0020	−0.0008	9.2081

[15] Placzek, Nijboer, and Van Hove, Phys. Rev. **82**, 392 (1951).
[16] R. Weiss (private communication).
[17] G. Placzek (private communication).

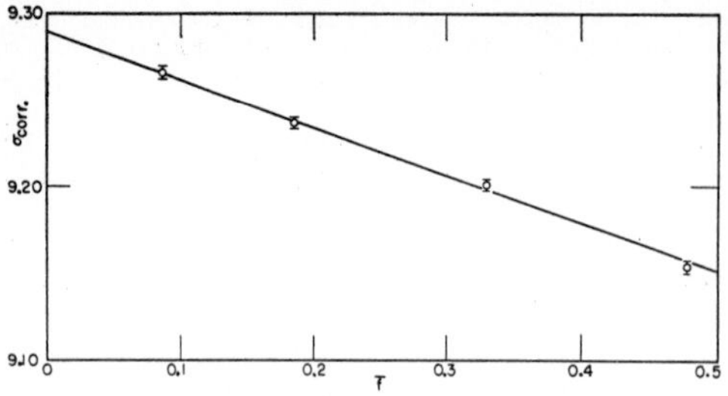

FIG. 4. σ_{corr} vs $\hat{f}$ for Sample 2 averaged over the five runs after individual normalization to $\sigma_0 = 9.29$.

TABLE IV. The results of the experiments on the different samples, at two different temperatures, and the average of all runs.

	$\overline{V}_0$ (kev)	$\Delta V = V_{\text{Foldy}} - \overline{V}_0$ (kev)
Sample 1 (300° and 500°)	4.16±0.16	−0.26±0.19
Sample 2 (300° and 500°)	4.42±0.10	
300° (Sample 1 and Sample 2)	4.42±0.10	−0.29±0.20
500° (Sample 1 and Sample 2)	4.13±0.17	
All 10 runs	4.34±0.09[a]	−0.26±0.14

[a] Standard deviation, based upon spread of values about the mean, is ±0.12.

where $\sigma_{ne} = 4\pi[\frac{2}{3}(M/\hbar^2)a^3V]^2$ and M = neutron mass, V = depth of potential well, $a = e^2/mc^2 = 2.82 \times 10^{-13}$ cm = classical electron radius giving $b = 6.48 \times 10^{-5} V$, when b is in barns and V is the depth of potential well in ev.

The values of V as computed are listed in Table I. Since only approximate values of the sample thickness were used in calculating the cross sections, the intercepts do not give the true free atom bismuth cross section V_0 is obtained from V by multiplying by the ratio $9.29/\sigma_0$. These values are also included in Table I.

Table IV gives averages for several groups of measurements taken on the same sample and also gives the results for two different temperatures of liquid bismuth as well as the final average for all runs. The differences between the groupings are only slightly outside of the standard deviations and will be assumed to have no significance.

The average result from all ten runs is $V_0 = -4.34 \pm 0.09$ kev, when the error is based on counting statistics only. The standard deviation based upon the spread of values about the mean is ±0.12. We will adopt this value as the error arising from the transmission measurements. The only additional significant source of error appears to be the uncertainty of I in the correction for the effect of liquid diffraction. The maximum possible value for I is 3.00, so we take ±0.20 as a reasonable estimate of the outside limit of uncertainty. Division by 2.5 gives ±0.08 as an estimate of the standard deviation on I, giving an uncertainty of ±0.08 on V. The uncertainties in the corrections for capture and the Doppler effect are small compared with the uncertainty in the liquid diffraction correction. The variation of a_n with energy due to the higher energy resonances has also been determined over the energy interval of interest and found to be negligible. Combining errors then gives $V_0 = -4.34 \pm 0.14$ kev as the final value. This value is consistent with results obtained from all the other measurements[7] but has a much smaller uncertainty. The difference between this and the Foldy term (−4.08) is −0.26±0.14 kev as the intrinsic neutron-electron interaction. Although this is attractive, as expected, and larger than the uncertainty, it is still not accurate enough to indicate a definite nonzero intrinsic interaction. Averages of these results with those of Hughes et al.[6] (−3.86±0.37 kev) and Hamermesh et al.[5] (−3.90±0.81 kev) gives $V_0 = -4.27 \pm 0.13$ kev and an intrinsic interaction of −0.19±0.13 kev.

In view of the difficulty of obtaining significantly better statistical accuracy by this method, and the inherent uncertainty of the correction for liquid diffraction, it is probably not worthwhile at this time to perform any further measurements on liquid bismuth.

ACKNOWLEDGMENTS

It is a pleasure to acknowledge the assistance of T. H. Kruse in the design and construction of the liquid bismuth cell, E. S. Troubetzkoy in the calculation of the form factor, R. Graeser in the taking of the data, and A. S. Langsdorf in making the capture cross section measurements on the bismuth sample used. Thanks are also due to S. A. Clough, G. J. Safford, C. E. Engelke, J. Liebowitz, I. Schroeder, and S. M. Puri for assistance in the calculations. We wish to thank the Watson Scientific Computing Laboratories of Columbia University and the computer group at Brookhaven National Laboratory for the use of their electronic computing facilities.

We are greatly indebted to Dr. George Placzek for many invaluable discussions about the liquid interference effects. His work on liquid interference effects before his recent death contributed invaluably to the interpretation of this experiment.

PAPER 55

Charge Distributions of Nuclei of the 1*p* Shell*†

ULRICH MEYER-BERKHOUT‡

High-Energy Physics Laboratory, Stanford University, Stanford, California

AND

KENNETH W. FORD§ AND ALEX E. S. GREEN||

University of California, Los Alamos Scientific Laboratory, Los Alamos, New Mexico

New data have been obtained at energies of 160 to 420 Mev for the scattering of electrons by Be^9, B^{10}, B^{11}, N^{14}, and O^{16}. A detailed analysis of these elastic scattering data and of other available data for p-shell nuclei is carried through, using various methods and a wide variety of assumed functional forms of the nuclear charge distribution. It is possible to fix rather accurately the spherically symmetric part of the charge distributions of Li^6, C^{12}, N^{14}, and O^{16}, and with less accuracy, those of Be^9 and B^{11}. Central densities are uncertain in all cases. Quadrupole scattering appears to be important in N^{14}, in B^{11}, and possibly in Be^9, and a crude estimate of the quadrupole moment of N^{14} is inferred from the data. The quadrupole scattering depends sensitively on the source of the quadrupole moment, as well as on its value. Regularities within the p-shell are discussed, and connection made with the properties of heavier nuclei. Be^9 and all heavier nuclei have a common value of peak particle density corresponding to a mean particle spacing of $(1.13 \pm 0.01) \times 10^{-13}$ cm. Only Li^6 fails to reach this density of saturated nuclear matter.

* The part of this work carried out at Stanford was supported by the joint program of the Office of Naval Research and the U. S. Atomic Energy Commission, and by the U. S. Air Force, through the Office of Scientific Research of the Air Research and Development Command.

† The part of this work carried out at Los Alamos was supported by the U. S. Atomic Energy Commission.

‡ Present address: Erstes Physikalisches Institut der Universität, Heidelberg, Germany.

§ Present address: Physics Department, Brandeis University, Waltham 54, Massachusetts. A part of this work was carried out at Brandeis with the support of the National Science Foundation.

|| Present address: Physics Section, Convair, San Diego, California.

PAPER 56

Experimental Evidence for the Pion-Pion Interaction at 1 GeV.

I. Derado

CERN - Geneva

(ricevuto il 1° Febbraio 1960)

The experimental results so far obtained on the production of single charged pions in $\pi+p$ collisions can be explained quantitatively if one assumes that the process proceeds predominantly via the $(\frac{3}{2}, \frac{3}{2})$ isobar. This predominance results from the existence of the pure $T=\frac{3}{2}$ $(\pi^- n)$ state among the outgoing particles in this process. However, the production of neutral pions is not satisfactorily explained by this assumption (1).

For the production of a neutral pion the pure $T=\frac{3}{2}$ state does not exist, and it is reasonable to expect important contributions from other possible interactions (for example $\pi\pi$). For this reason it should be easier to measure the effects of $\pi\pi$ interaction in the production of neutral pions. From this point of view the recent paper by Bonsignori and Selleri (BS) (2) is particularly interesting. They make theoretical predictions concerning π production on the assumption of a $\pi\pi$ interaction. Thus, in a pion-nucleon collision, the incident pion is able to produce a second pion from the virtual meson cloud.

Assuming that the production process is that shown in the accompanying Feynman diagram:

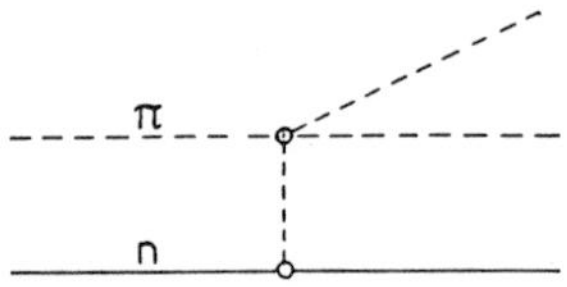

new line.

they are able to predict the existence of a low energy peak in the spectrum of the protons in the laboratory system for the reaction:

$$\pi^- + p \rightarrow \pi^- + \pi^0 + p\ .$$

We have worked out this spectrum for π^--mesons of 1 GeV on the basis of these assumptions and also on the basis of the statistical model. (N.B. - For the Lindenbaum-Sternheimer model (3) one obtains almost the same curve as for the statistical model if one assumes that the isobar is emitted isotropically in the c.m.s. of the colliding particles.) These theoretical curves are now com-

(1) I. Derado and N. Schmitz: to be published in *Phys. Rev.*

(2) F. Bonsignori and F. Selleri: *Nuovo Cimento*, **15**, 465 (1960).

(3) S. J. Lindembaum and R. M. Sternheimer: *Phys. Rev.*, **109**, 1723 (1958).

pared with the experimental results already published (now with improved statistics) (4).

The histogram in Fig. 1 represents our experimental measurements with the statistical errors. Curve A represents the predictions of the statistical model and curve B those of the (BS) model.

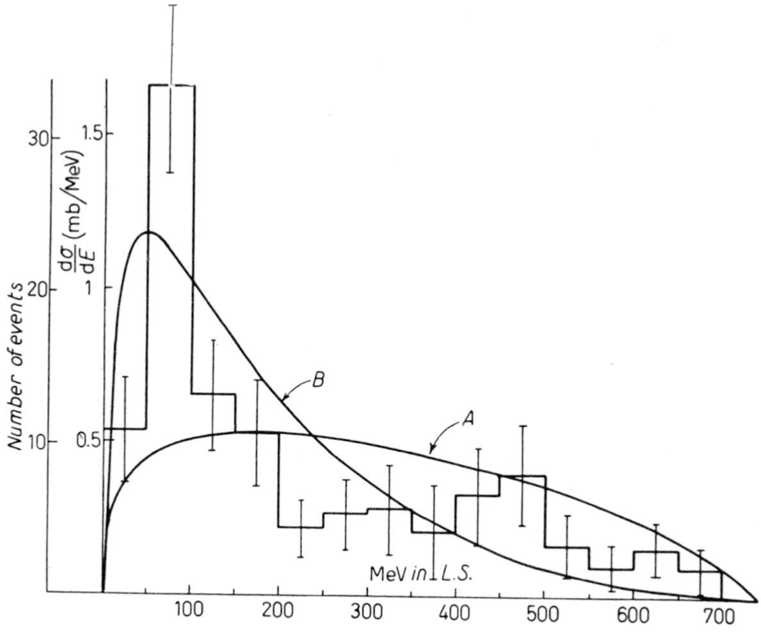

Fig. 1.

The peak at 50 MeV can thus be interpreted as the effect of a $\pi\pi$ interaction. It is evident that curve B is in much better agreement with experiment than curve A.

By normalizing curve B to the area of the histogram, the mean value of the $\pi^- + \pi^0$ scattering cross-section is estimated to be

$$\bar{\sigma} \simeq 30 \text{ mb} .$$

It must, however, be realized that this gives only the order of magnitude of the pion-pion cross-section.

If a $\pi\pi$ resonant state ($\pi\!\!\pi$) exists we would expect the reaction to proceed thus:

$$\pi^- + p \to p + \pi\!\!\pi \to p + \pi^- + \pi^0 ,$$

so that one would expect to find a strong peak in the spectrum of recoil protons in the c.m.s. If we take into

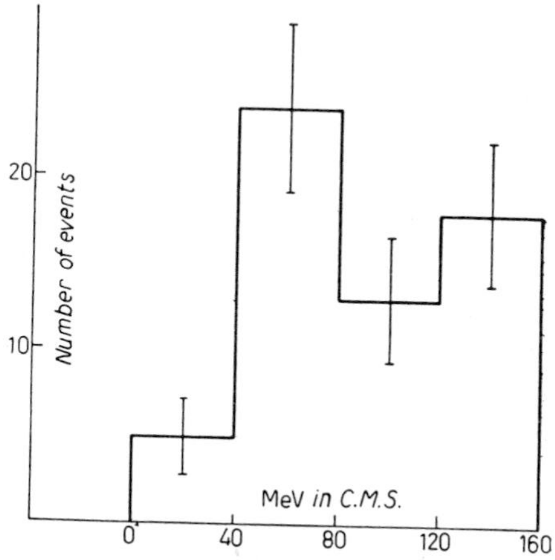

Fig. 2.

(4) I. DERADO, G. LÜTJENS and N. SCHMITZ: *Annal. der Phys.*, **4**, 103 (1959).

account only these protons in the neighbourhood of the maximum in Fig. 1, the effect of the resonance, if it exists, should be all the more apparent. Thus, the histogram shown in Fig. 2 represents the c.m.s. energy distribution of the protons occurring in the interval $(0 \div 190)$ MeV in Fig. 1. This result suggests that the maximum may occur in the neighbourhood of 60 MeV in the c.m.s. If one assumes this maximum to be real, then one can calculate the energy of the resonant $\pi\pi$ state:

$$m_{\pi\pi} = 4.7 m_\pi ,$$

where m_π is the pion mass.

From this results it appears that the $\pi\pi$ interaction is important in the production process. By a combination of $(\frac{3}{2}, \frac{3}{2})$ isobar and the assumption of a $\pi\pi$ interaction it is perhaps possible to explain the present experimental results on π production. The present experimental results suggest that the $\pi\pi$ interaction becomes increasingly important above 1 GeV.

* * *

We are grateful to Dr. Y. GOLDSCHMIDT-CLERMONT and Dr. SELLERI for numerous valuable discussions. We are also indebted to Dr. D. W. POWELL and Dr. R. VAN DE WALLE for their helpful interest in this paper.

PAPER 57

Neutron Form Factors from High-Energy Inelastic Electron-Deuteron Scattering*

S. SOBOTTKA†
Department of Physics and High-Energy Physics Laboratory, Stanford University, Stanford, California
(Received November 30, 1959)

The inelastic electron-deuteron scattering cross section has been measured for incident electron energies between 300 Mev and 650 Mev and for final electron energies primarily at the maxima of the inelastic continua. The data were interpreted in terms of neutron form factors by employing the impulse approximation calculations of Goldberg. The results indicate that F_{2n}^2 is nearly equal to the proton form factor F_p^2 for $2.65<q^2<15.1$ (fermi)$^{-2}$ but may be 20% or 30% higher than F_p^2 for the lowest of these q values. Uncertainties, primarily in the theory, make it impossible to determine whether the difference is real. The results also indicate that $-2.5<F_{1n}/F_{2n}<0.5$ for $5.1<q^2<12.8$ f^{-2}.

I. INTRODUCTION

It is possible to learn about the electromagnetic properties of the neutron by scattering high-energy electrons from deuterium and by detecting those electrons which have scattered after breaking up the deuteron into free nucleons. In this experiment, attention was directed to the peak of inelastic continuua measured as a function of final electron energy, for incident energies between 300 and 650 Mev. In addition, a few measurements were made of the cross section for essentially all final electron energies corresponding to deuteron breakup, in order to compare the shape of the cross-section curve with the theory of Jankus[1] for low values of the four-momentum transfer q.

Yearian and Hofstadter[2] have previously measured the cross section for deuteron breakup for incident electron energies of 500 and 600 Mev. The cross sections, integrated over final electron energies, were interpreted in terms of the theories of Jankus[1] (with modifications described in reference 2) and of Blankenbecler.[3] The cross sections for final electron energies at the maximum were interpreted in terms of the modified Jankus theory.[2] In the analysis, the above authors assumed $F_{1n}^2=0$ and determined F_{2n}^2. They found that F_{2n}^2 was about the same as F_p^2, the proton form factor[4] squared, and that an exponential density distribution with a rms radius of 0.76 ± 0.1 fermi led to a form factor which agreed with their data.

In the present work the data are considerably improved and the analysis was done with the aid of the impulse approximation calculations of Goldberg.[5] Initially, F_{1n} was assumed to equal zero in order to find F_{2n}^2. Upper limits were also placed on F_{1n}/F_{2n} by making measurements at both large and small angles with the incident energy adjusted to give the same value of q.

II. THEORY

Goldberg[5] used the impulse approximation to calculate the cross section, thus assuming it to be the sum of the cross sections for two free nucleons with a momentum distribution derived from a ^3S deuteron ground-state wave function. The nucleons were also assumed to be unbound in the final state. Since then, Goldberg has extended the calculation to include the ^3D state as well.[6] The values of $d^2\sigma/d\Omega dE'$, where E' is the final electron energy, for E' taken at the maximum of the inelastic continuua were within 6% of those predicted by the modified Jankus theory. Goldberg's expression for the cross section included the integrals

$$I_1=\int_b^\infty \epsilon^2 F_u^2(p)d\epsilon,$$

$$I_2=\int_b^\infty \epsilon F_u^2(p)d\epsilon,$$

and

$$I_3=\int_b^\infty F_u^2(p)d\epsilon,$$

where p is the relative momentum of the nucleons in the deuteron, ϵ is the relativistic energy corresponding to p,

$$b=\hbar c\left\{\frac{-q_0}{2}+\frac{1}{2}\left[\mathbf{q}^2\left(1-\frac{4M^2c^2}{\hbar^2q^2}\right)\right]^{\frac{1}{2}}\right\},$$

q_0 is the time-like part of q, $\mathbf{q}$ is the vector spatial part, M is the nucleon mass,

$$F_u=\left(\frac{2}{\pi}\right)^{\frac{1}{2}}\int_0^\infty u(r)j_0(pr)rdr,$$

$u(r)$ is the radial S-state deuteron wave function with

* Supported by the joint program of the Office of Naval Research, the Atomic Energy Commission, and the Air Force Office of Scientific Research.

† Now at Boeing Scientific Research Laboratories, Boeing Aircraft Company, Seattle, Washington.

[1] V. Z. Jankus, Phys. Rev. **102**, 1586 (1956).
[2] M. R. Yearian and R. Hofstadter, Phys. Rev. **110**, 552 (1958); **111**, 934 (1958).
[3] R. Blankenbecler, Phys. Rev. **111**, 1684 (1958).
[4] See R. Hofstadter, F. Bumiller, and M. R. Yearian, Revs. Modern Phys. **30**, 482 (1958), for a review of the experiments on the proton.
[5] A. Goldberg, Phys. Rev. **112**, 618 (1958).
[6] A. Goldberg (private communication).

normalization such that

$$4\pi\int_0^\infty u^2(r)dr=1,$$

and j_0 is the zeroth order spherical Bessel function. When the deuteron D state is included, the sole changes are to replace the integrals above with

$$I_1=\int_b^\infty \epsilon^2[F_u^2(p)+(1/\sqrt{8})F_u(p)F_w(p)+(9/32)F_w^2(p)]d\epsilon,$$

$$I_2=\int_b^\infty \epsilon[F_u^2+(1/\sqrt{8})F_uF_w+(9/32)F_w^2]d\epsilon,$$

$$I_3=\int_b^\infty [F_u^2+(1/\sqrt{8})F_uF_w+(9/32)F_w^2]d\epsilon,$$

where

$$F_w(p)=\left(\frac{2}{\pi}\right)^{\frac{1}{2}}\int_0^\infty w(r)j_2(pr)rdr,$$

and where w is the radial D-state deuteron wave function and the normalization is now such that

$$4\pi\int_0^\infty [u^2(r)+w^2(r)]dr=1.$$

Goldberg has also shown that the peak cross section is proportional, within about 3%, to the sum of the Rosenbluth[7] cross sections for electron scattering from a free neutron and a free proton. He also showed that the deuteron dependence in the peak cross section was primarily multiplicative and independent of incident electron energy and other such parameters.

Goldberg's complete expression for the cross section was used by the present author to calculate the peak cross sections on an IBM 650 computer for three different wave functions:

(a) The Hulthén[8] S-state wave function,
(b) The Rustgi[9] S-state wave function,
(c) Analytic approximations to the Gartenhaus[10] S- and D-state wave functions. The S-state approximation of case (c) was one constructed by Moravcsik,[11] while the D-state approximation was constructed by the present author and designed to simplify the calculation of F_w. The ratios of the peak heights with these three wave functions were 1.00:1.02:0.98, respectively. The terms in I_1, I_2, I_3 involving w produced negligible contributions to the peak height in case (c).

A calculation was also made of the complete spectrum at 500 Mev, 60°, for the Gartenhaus wave functions and compared to that for the Hulthén wave function. The result is shown in Fig. 1. Also shown is the result of a calculation including all but the first term in each of I_1, I_2, I_3, using the Gartenhaus wave functions in order to show the D-state contributions.

The uncertainty in the peak cross sections is thus about 2% due to the uncertainty in the deuteron wave function. In the present analysis, the Hulthén wave function was used.

Other uncertainties in the theoretical peak cross section result from the neglected final-state interaction, neutron-proton interference terms, and meson-exchange contributions. Durand[12] has estimated that at 500 Mev, 75°, there may be a 5 or 10% contribution from the first and 1 or 2% from the third. For no final-state interaction, the interference terms are less than 1% as calculated from a semirelativistic expression for the cross section given by Durand, although these terms will probably be larger with a final state interaction.

The conclusion is that if Durand's calculations are taken seriously the theoretical peak cross section (at 500 Mev, 75°) is in doubt by 5 or 10%, and since the peak section is proportional to the sum of the elastic neutron and proton cross sections, it will be seen that the error in the experimental neutron cross sections of this work may be from 3 to 6 times as large.

III. EXPERIMENTAL APPARATUS AND PROCEDURE

The apparatus was largely that used in previous electron-scattering experiments.[13] The peak-height data were taken with a liquid target having a radiation length only about $\frac{2}{3}$ of that previously used,[2] so the radiation corrections are smaller. Over-all energy resolution figures for these data were about $2\frac{1}{2}$%, necessitating resolution corrections to the deuteron data but rendering the elastic hydrogen normalizing data reasonably insensitive to instrumental fluctuations.

Absolute cross sections were made possible by measuring the elastic proton cross section at each incident electron energy and scattering angle and normalizing with the calculated proton cross section using the exponential model of radius 0.8 f shown to be valid by Chambers and Hofstadter and by Hofstadter, Bumiller, and Yearian.[4] Instrumental errors were minimized by measuring both the deuteron and proton data during the same runs. The statistical accuracy of the deuteron data was usually between 2 and 3%, although a low counting rate and large π^- backgrounds at a couple of the points produced larger uncertainties. The relative accuracy of the proton data was judged to

[7] M. N. Rosenbluth, Phys. Rev. **79**, 615 (1950).
[8] The Hulthén wave function was that used by Jankus. See reference 1.
[9] M. L. Rustgi, Rev. mex. fis. **6**, 135 (1957).
[10] S. Gartenhaus, Phys. Rev. **100**, 900 (1955).
[11] M. J. Moravcsik (unpublished). However, see M. J. Moravcsik, Nuclear Phys. **7**, 113 (1958), for similar approximations.
[12] L. Durand, III, Phys. Rev. **115**, 1020 (1959).
[13] R. Hofstadter, Revs. Modern Phys. **28**, 214 (1956).

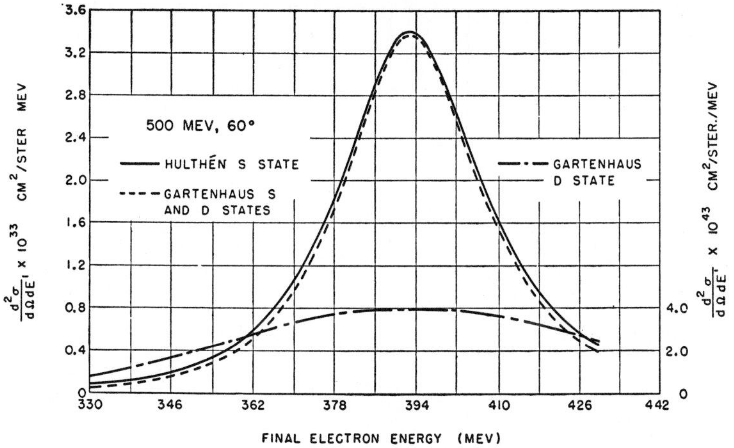

FIG. 1. Impulse approximation calculations of the cross section at 500 Mev, 60°, using Hulthén and Gartenhaus wave functions (left-hand ordinate axis). The D-state contribution for the Gartenhaus wave function is also plotted (right-hand ordinate axis).

be about 3% although the standard deviations calculated from the number of counts were between 1 and 2%. The proton data were useful only for normalizing purposes since no attempt was made to maintain counting efficiencies independent of incident energy and scattering angle.

IV. CORRECTIONS TO THE DATA

The radiation corrections were calculated using the following energy spectrum for electrons which radiated before and after scattering from a nucleon:

$$v(E_0,E_4,E')dE' = \frac{(1+\frac{3}{4}s)}{\Gamma(y+y'+1)}\left(\frac{E_0}{E_0'}\right)^{y} E_0'^{-y}E_4^{-y'} \times (E_4-E')^{y+y'-1}\left\{y\left[\frac{1}{2}+\frac{1}{2}\left(\frac{E_3}{E_0}\right)^2\right]\sigma(E_3) + y'\left[\frac{1}{2}+\frac{1}{2}\left(\frac{E'}{E_4}\right)^2\right]\sigma(E_0)\right\}dE', \quad (1)$$

where E_0 is the initial electron energy and E_0' is the corresponding final energy for elastic scattering, E_3 is the initial energy corresponding to an elastic peak at $E_0'-(E_4-E')$, E' is the final electron energy, $s=(2\alpha/\pi)[\ln(\hbar q/mc)-\frac{1}{2}]$ where m is the electron mass, $y=bx+s$ where $b=1/0.739T$ and T is one radiation thickness of the target medium, x is the target thickness in cm before scattering, $y'=bx'+s$ where x' is the target thickness after scattering. The origin of Eq. (1) is given in the Appendix. It combines the probabilities for radiation in the target medium before and after scattering with the probability for radiating at the time of scattering. The latter results from the Schwinger correction[14] and wide-angle bremsstrahlung formula.[15]

[14] J. Schwinger, Phys. Rev. **75**, 899 (1949). See also, D. R. Yennie and H. Suura, Phys. Rev. **105**, 1378 (1957).

[15] W. K. H. Panofsky and E. A. Allton, Phys. Rev. **110**, 1155 (1958). These authors used integrals evaluated in L. I. Schiff, Phys. Rev. **87**, 750 (1952).

Equation (1) is precise in the limit of small energy losses and is accurate to about 10% for energy losses of half of the incident energy. The elastic proton peaks were measured only for energies down to $0.95E_0'$ and the remaining cross section was calculated by letting $E_4=E_0'$ in Eq. (1) and integrating for E' between E_0' and $0.95E_0'$. The radiation corrections to the deuteron peak-height data were calculated by a method equivalent to evaluating the integral

$$v_{\text{in}}(E_0,E')dE' = dE'\int_{E'}^{E_0}\left(\frac{d^2\sigma}{d\Omega dE_4}\right)v(E_0,E_4,E')dE_4, \quad (2)$$

where E' is equal to the energy at the cross-section maximum and $v_{\text{in}}(E_0,E')$ is the observed cross section (neglecting other than radiative corrections). Equation (1) was also used to calculate the magnitude of the radiative tail of the elastic deuteron peak at the inelastic maximum; this tail was found to be negligible. The radiation corrections to the complete deuteron spectra were calculated by using a numerical procedure which yielded $d^2\sigma/d\Omega dE_4$ of Eq. (2) for any E_4 in the spectrum. The correction applied to the peak-height data was the ratio of the correction for the deuteron peak to that of the proton peak. This ratio varied between 1.035 at 350 Mev, 60°, and 0.980 at 300 Mev, 135°. Individually, the proton peak- and deuteron peak-height corrections were between 15 and 20%.

A negative meson background was observed and was calculated by multiplying the measured π^+ counting rate by the π^-/π^+ cross-section ratio,[16,17] and then was subtracted from the data. Energy resolution corrections varied between 1.3% at 500 Mev, 135°, and 5.9% at

[16] M. Sands, J. G. Teasdale, and R. L. Walker, Phys. Rev. **95**, 592 (1954). See also K. M. Watson, J. C. Keck, A. V. Tollestrup, and R. L. Walker, Phys. Rev. **101**, 1159 (1956).

[17] G. Neugebauer, W. D. Wales, and R. L. Walker, Phys. Rev. Letters **2**, 429 (1959).

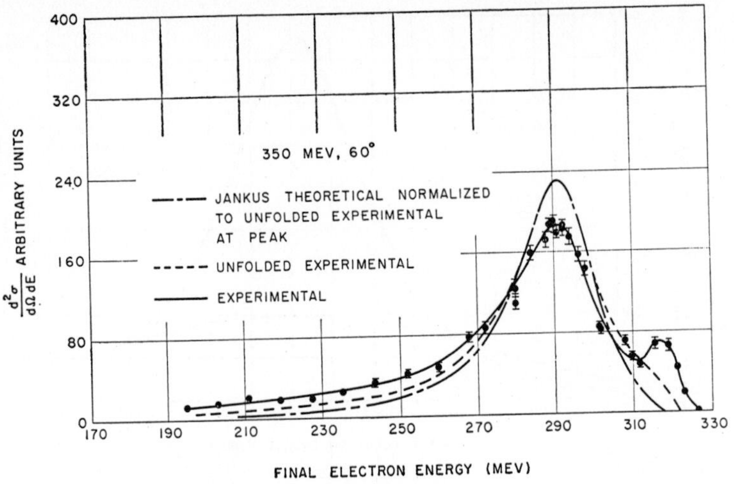

FIG. 2. Experimental cross section at 350 Mev, 60°, compared to the modified Jankus theoretical curve. The "Unfolded Experimental" is the radiation-corrected experimental curve. The Jankus theoretical curve is normalized to the latter at the maximum. These two curves do not include the elastic peak at the right on the experimental curve.

500 Mev, 60°, and were applied to the peak-height data. Angular resolution corrections were unnecessary because calculations showed that they cancelled with negligible error in the ratio of deuteron to proton cross section. Counting rate corrections to account for the fact that the counting apparatus could record no more than one count per incident beam pulse were applied and were always less than 6%. The larger corrections occurred at smaller angles. The usual correction was applied accounting for the fact that the spectrometer dispersion is a function of the energy. The difference between the atomic densities of the deuterium and the hydrogen was taken into account in normalizing the data. The proton contamination of the deuterium was found to be between 0.4 and 0.5% by mass spectrographic analysis and because of this a 1% correction was made to the peak-height data. A correction of up to 5% was applied to the complete spectrum at 600 Mev, 55° to correct for the variation in effective solid angle of the spectrometer at the large values of magnetic field where a certain amount of saturation occurs.

The total uncertainty in the peak cross section resulting from the uncertainty of the corrections is probably no more than 2%.

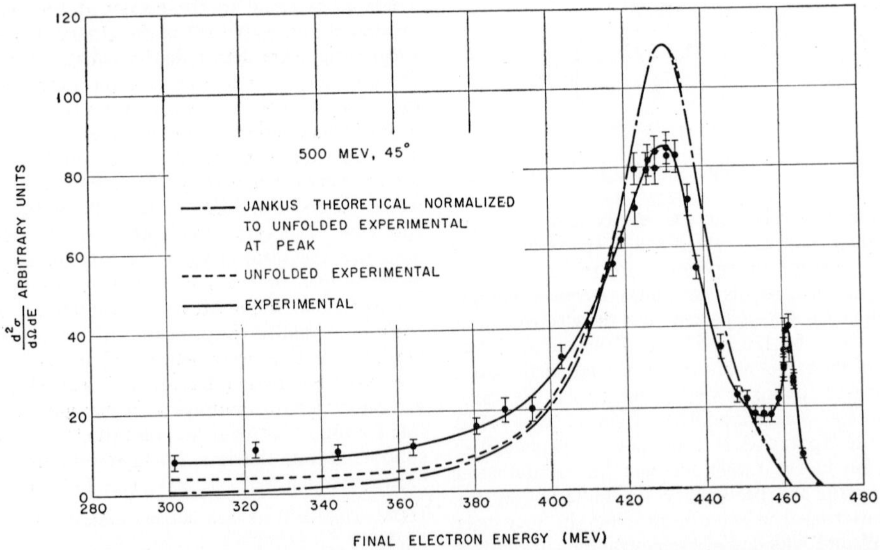

FIG. 3. Experimental cross section at 500 Mev, 45°, compared to the modified Jankus theoretical curve. The "Unfolded Experimental" is the radiation-corrected experimental curve. The Jankus theoretical curve is normalized to the latter at the maximum. These two curves do not include the elastic peak at the right on the experimental curve.

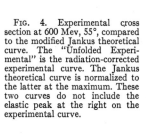

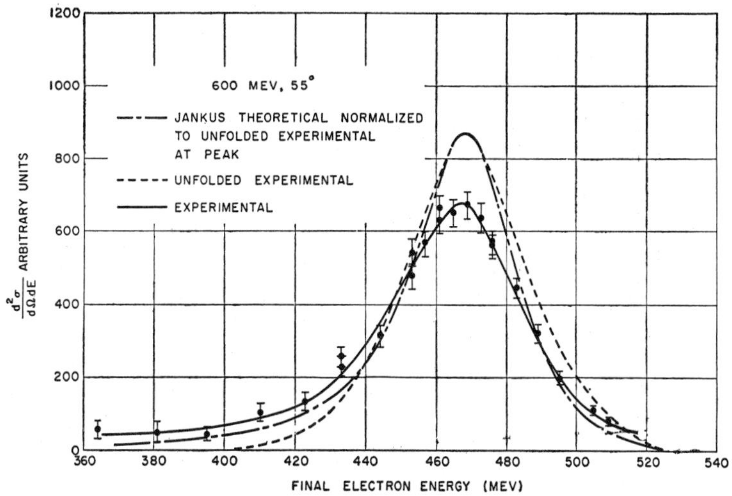

FIG. 4. Experimental cross section at 600 Mev, 55°, compared to the modified Jankus theoretical curve. The "Unfolded Experimental" is the radiation-corrected experimental curve. The Jankus theoretical curve is normalized to the latter at the maximum. These two curves do not include the elastic peak at the right on the experimental curve.

The radiative corrections produced larger errors in the complete spectra than in the peak-height results because of errors in the numerical method and errors in Eq. (1) for large radiative energy losses. The corrections are accurate to about 2 or 3% for points near the maxima and on the high-energy sides of the maxima. For points at lower energies, the accuracy becomes increasingly poor. Points with counting rates higher than 20% of the maxima have errors less than about 10% but the errors may be as large as 50% in the low-energy tails. No absolute cross sections were deduced from such data. The complete curves are used only to compare their spectral shapes with those predicted by the Jankus theory.

V. EXPERIMENTAL DATA AND ANALYSIS

Figures 2, 3, and 4 show three inelastic spectra, two of which are at lower q values than those reached by Yearian and Hofstadter. The 350 Mev, 60°, curve was measured with the new target, while the other two were measured with the old target. These data have somewhat larger statistical errors than the peak-height data. The curve at 600 Mev, 55°, has about the same half-width as all those measured by Yearian and Hofstadter. The experimental curves were drawn by eye through the data points, which had received all corrections except the radiative correction. A rough subtraction of the elastic data was then made and the radiative corrections applied to the remainder, resulting in the unfolded experimental curves. These curves are rather inaccurate in the region of the elastic peak because of the low resolution and the crudeness of the subtraction. The theoretical curves were calculated on an IBM 707 computer by R. Herman from the modified Jankus theory.[2] The theoretical and unfolded experimental curves are normalized together at the peak in order to facilitate comparison of the spectrum shapes. It is seen that, for the low q values, the agreement is reasonably good. As q increases, however, the experimental curves become wider than the theoretical ones so that the unfolded curve at 600 Mev, 55°, is about 5 Mev wider than the theoretical. Some of the discrepancy in width would be removed if comparison had been made with the impulse approximation calculations.[5] Also, inclusion of the final-state interaction would widen the curves somewhat although the effect is expected to diminish as q increases.

The experimental full widths at half maximum are seen to vary from about 28 Mev at 350 Mev, 60°, to about 44 Mev at 600 Mev, 55°, while the unfolded experimental widths vary from about 25 Mev to 39 Mev.

TABLE I. Experimental values of the deuteron cross section at the maxima of the inelastic continua. The uncertainties given are statistical.

Energy (Mev)	Angle (degrees)	$(d^2\sigma/d\Omega dE)_{\max}\times 10^{34}$ (cm²/sr Mev)	Uncertainty (%)
300	105	17.5	4.2
300	135	8.32	4.4
350	60	121	3.9
350	135	5.16	3.6
425	135	2.85	3.9
450	135	2.21	4.2
500	60	35.8	3.8
500	60	36.0	3.7
500	135	1.45	3.8
550	75	8.66	5.2
550	135	1.16	4.3
550	135	1.02	5.1
600	60	17.9	4.2
600	60	17.7	3.7
600	75	5.82	4.0
600	75	5.81	3.9
600	90	2.89	4.3
600	135	0.770	4.9
650	90	2.00	6.1

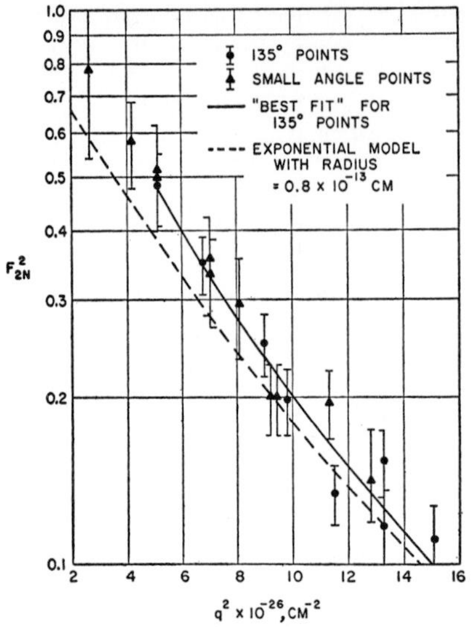

FIG. 5. F_{2n}^2 assuming $F_{1n}=0$. The triangles refer to the small angle points, and the circles refer to the 135° points. The dotted line represents F_p^2 and the solid line is a line drawn by eye through the 135° points for interpolation purposes.

The results of the peak-height measurements are given in Table I. The uncertainties quoted are statistical. An additional uncertainty is introduced by the 10% possible error in the calculated proton cross section[4] used to normalize the data. It is believed that all other uncertainties associated with this experiment do not total more than about 3%.

The data were first analyzed assuming $F_{1n}=0$ and the results are shown in Fig. 5 and Table II. We see that F_{2n}^2 is about equal to F_p^2 for the large q values but appears to be 25 or 35% larger than F_p^2 at the low q values. It is impossible at this time to tell whether this difference is real for several reasons. An increase of about 6 or 8% in the theoretical cross section at low q values would remove the difference. The calculations done to date by Durand[12] and by Jankus[1] indicated that the corrections due to final state interaction would decrease the cross section, and if this is actually the case, the difference between F_{2n}^2 and F_p^2 would become even greater. However, the calculations probably are too rough to preclude an increase in the cross section due to final state interaction.

TABLE II. Experimental values of the neutron magnetic form factor squared. The uncertainties are statistical.

Energy (Mev)	Angle (degrees)	$q^2\times10^{-26}$ (cm^{-2})	F_{2n}^2	Uncertainty (%)
300	105	4.15	0.580	15
300	135	5.11	0.479	13
350	60	2.65	0.782	26
350	135	6.56	0.348	10
425	135	8.92	0.250	12
450	135	9.76	0.198	13
500	60	5.08	0.498	17
500	60	5.08	0.516	17
500	135	11.48	0.134	12
550	75	8.04	0.295	18
550	135	13.26	0.153	14
550	135	13.26	0.117	16
600	60	7.02	0.351	16
600	60	7.02	0.329	14
600	75	9.31	0.199	14
600	75	9.31	0.199	13
600	90	11.30	0.196	15
600	135	15.09	0.111	16
650	90	12.84	0.147	19

Another uncertainty results from the unknown magnitude of F_{1n}. However, the limits placed on F_{1n} by the elastic scattering experiments of McIntyre et al.[18] and by the neutron-electron interaction experiments[19] show that this error is only about 2% in F_{2n}^2 at $q^2=3$ f^{-2}, 4% at $q^2=5$ f^{-2} and 9% at $q^2=8$ f^{-2}.

Also, the uncertainty in the calculated value of the proton cross section produces an equal uncertainty in the measured values of F_{2n}^2. Thus there are several possible sources of error in F_{2n}^2, the primary one corresponding to a theoretical uncertainty. The aggregate error could be large enough to remove the difference between F_{2n}^2 and F_p^2.

As Fig. 5 indicates, data were taken at both small angles (60°, 75°, and 90°) and at a large angle (135°). From the values of F_{2n}^2 deduced from a small angle point and a large angle point at the same value of q it is possible to determine F_{1n}/F_{2n} for that value of q. Since Goldberg has shown that the peak cross section is nearly proportional to the sum of the free neutron and proton cross sections, this value of F_{1n}/F_{2n} can be found simply by using the Rosenbluth formula and the values of F_{2n}^2 in Fig. 5. If $Y=F_{1n}/F_{2n}$ and R is the ratio of F_{2n}^2 for the small angle θ_s to that for the large angle θ_L, then

$$R=\frac{\{Y^2+(\hbar^2q^2/4M^2c^2)[2(Y+K_n)^2\tan^2(\theta_s/2)+K_n^2]\}[2\tan^2(\theta_L/2)+1]}{\{Y^2+(\hbar^2q^2/4M^2c^2)[2(Y+K_n)^2\tan^2(\theta_L/2)+K_n^2]\}[2\tan^2(\theta_s/2)+1]}, \quad (3)$$

where M is the nucleon mass and K_n is the neutron magnetic moment in nuclear magnetons. F_{2n}^2 for θ_L was interpolated *via* the solid line connecting the 135° points in Fig. 5. Figure 6 shows the values of Y resulting from solving Eq. (3) for Y. The values of Y at the theoretical minimum of R were chosen when the experimental values of R led to an imaginary Y.

The sensitivity of this experiment to F_{1n}/F_{2n} is low and any limits to be set on F_{1n}/F_{2n} are rather large.

[18] J. A. McIntyre and R. Hofstadter, Phys. Rev. **98**, 158 (1956); J. A. McIntyre, Phys. Rev. **103**, 1464 (1956); J. A. McIntyre and S. Dhar, Phys. Rev. **106**, 1074 (1957); and J. A. McIntyre and G. R. Burleson, Phys. Rev. **112**, 1155 (1958).

[19] For a summary of the theoretical aspects and experimental results, see L. I. Foldy, Revs. Modern Phys. **30**, 471 (1958).

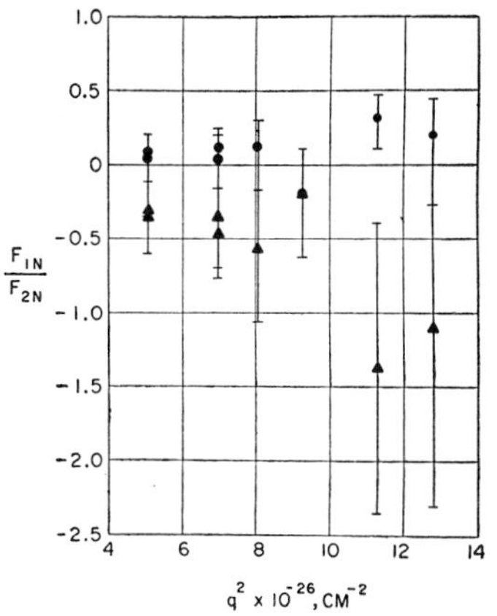

FIG. 6. F_{1n}/F_{2n} calculated from Eq. (3). There is a triangle and a circle for each small angle data point.

However, the values of q at which it is possible to make measurements are larger than those of the more sensitive elastic scattering experiments of McIntyre et al.[18] The points of Fig. 6 would not be shifted significantly by a change in the theoretical cross section which was of the order of 5% or less and which was independent of energy and angle or was primarily a function of q alone. Also, the validity of the assumption that the contributions from F_{1n} and F_{2n} to the deuteron peak height have the Rosenbluth angular dependence with negligible error was checked by substituting the measured values of F_{1n}/F_{2n} back into the complete expression given by Goldberg for the peak cross section and the original data was reproduced.

VI. CONCLUSIONS

The conclusions to be drawn from the peak-height data are the following:

(a) There is an apparent small difference between F_{2n}^2 and F_p^2 although the difference could be removed if various errors, primarily theoretical, were near their presumed limits.

If the difference is real, the implication is that the apparent nucleon size is not a manifestation of the breakdown of quantum electrodynamics at these distances.

(b) The measured values of F_{1n}/F_{2n} indicate that for $q^2<12.8$ f^{-2}, F_{1n}/F_{2n} lies between limits of $+0.5$ and -2.5.

VII. ACKNOWLEDGMENTS

I wish to thank Professor R. Hofstadter for suggesting this experiment and for much inspiration during its course. I am grateful to Dr. R. Herman and the Research Staff of General Motors Corporation for the computations of the Jankus theory. My gratitude is also extended to A. Goldberg for the use of some of his results prior to publication and for his continuing interest; to A. Pittenger for aid in the computer programming; and to the electron scattering group and the crew of the Mark III linear accelerator for their assistance during this experiment.

APPENDIX

The Bethe-Heitler formula[20] for the bremsstrahlung cross section leads to the probability that a high-energy electron will lose a fractional energy λ due to emission of a photon while passing through a low-Z medium of thickness dx cm:

$$w_x(\lambda)d\lambda \cong b\lambda^{-1}(1-\lambda+\tfrac{3}{4}\lambda^2)d\lambda dx,$$

where b is a constant depending only on the medium. For a small but finite thickness x, this expression must be modified to give

$$w_x(\lambda)d\lambda = [\lambda^{bx-1}/\Gamma(bx+1)](bx)(1-\lambda+\tfrac{3}{4}\lambda^2)d\lambda. \quad \text{(A1)}$$

Terms of order $(bx\lambda)$ and $(bx\lambda)^2$ have been neglected in this expression, which is deduced by an argument similar to one given by Heitler.[21]

The probability that an electron will lose a fractional energy λ due to photon emission at the time of scattering is calculated, for the case of small λ, from the Schwinger correction[14] to be (in a form analogous to (A_1))

$$w_s(\lambda)d\lambda \cong (1+\tfrac{3}{4}s)/\Gamma(s+1)s\lambda^{s-1}d\lambda. \quad \text{(A2)}$$

This expression must be applied twice, for photon emission corresponding to electron energies both before and after scattering. For large λ, an expression for the probability of wide angle bremsstrahlung must be used,[15] i.e.,

$$w_s(\lambda)d\lambda = s\lambda^{-1}(1-\lambda+\tfrac{1}{2}\lambda^2)d\lambda. \quad \text{(A3)}$$

Equations (A2) and (A3) can be incorporated into one as follows:

$$w_s(\lambda)d\lambda = [(1+\tfrac{3}{4}s)/\Gamma(s+1)]\lambda^{s-1}s(1-\lambda+\tfrac{1}{2}\lambda^2)d\lambda. \quad \text{(A4)}$$

For small λ, this reduces to Eq. (A2) and is equal to Eq. (A3) within a few percent for large λ.

The net probability for a fractional energy loss λ due to radiation both in the target medium and at the time of scattering is then

$$w_{xs}(\lambda)d\lambda = d\lambda\int_0^\lambda w_x(\lambda_1)w_s\left(\frac{\lambda-\lambda_1}{1-\lambda_1}\right)\frac{d\lambda_1}{1-\lambda_1}$$
$$= [(1+\tfrac{3}{4}s)/\Gamma(bx+s+1)]\lambda^{bx+s-1} \times (bx+s)(1-\lambda+\tfrac{1}{2}\lambda^2)d\lambda,$$

where, for simplicity, we have let the coefficient of λ^2 in the parentheses of Eq. (A1) be equal to that in Eq. (A4), with negligible error for the conditions of

[20] W. Heitler, *The Quantum Theory of Radiation* (Oxford University Press, New York, 1954), 3rd ed., p. 249. The contribution from the atomic electrons has approximately the same functional form so this is included in the constant b. See H. A. Bethe and J. Ashkin, *Experimental Nuclear Physics*, edited by E. Segrè (John Wiley & Sons, Inc., New York, 1953), Vol. I, p. 263.

[21] W. Heitler, reference 20, p. 378.

this experiment. Terms similar to those neglected in Eq. (A1) have also been neglected here.

If we let $w_{xs}(\lambda)d\lambda = w(E_1,E_2)dE_2$, corresponding to an electron energy E_1 before radiation and E_2 after radiation, then the probability that an electron of initial energy E_0 will have an energy E' after radiating, scattering, and again radiating will be

$$v(E_0,E')dE' = dE' \int_{E'}^{E_0} \int_{E'}^{E_0} w(E_0,E_1) \times\sigma(E_1,E_2)w'(E_2,E')dE_1dE_2, \quad \text{(A5)}$$

where $\sigma(E_1,E_2)$ is the theoretical scattering cross section for electrons of initial energy E_1 and final energy E_2 and w and w' are the probabilities for radiation before and after scattering, respectively.

For an elastic cross section, $\sigma(E_1,E_2)$ is a delta function and the integrals of Eq. (A5) can be evaluated approximately to yield Eq. (1) of the text if E_4 in that equation is replaced by E_0'. Again, terms of the same order as those neglected in Eq. (A1) were neglected in Eq. (1), in addition to terms depending on $(E_0 - E_3)$ but which were considerably smaller than those that were retained.

If $\sigma(E_1,E_2)$, as a theoretical inelastic cross section, is considered to be a series of many delta functions (elastic cross sections), Eq. (2) of the text results, where the summation has been replaced by the integral sign of that expression. In deducing Eq. (2), it was assumed that the shape of $\sigma(E_1,E_2)$ as a function of E_2 with fixed E_1 does not change with E_1. This assumption gives adequate accuracy for this work.

PAPER 58*

*THE NUCLEON-NUCLEON SPIN-ORBIT POTENTIAL**

BY GREGORY BREIT

YALE UNIVERSITY

Communicated March 21, 1960

Introduction.—Bryan[1] has recently reported an improved fit to *p-p* scattering data employing a modification of the Signell-Marshak[2] potential in which the spin-orbit force is represented by a short-range potential, the effective part of which is located mainly on the outer edge of the repulsive core, somewhat as in the potential of Gammel and Thaler.[3] The fact that Bryan's fits to data have many features in common with a more extensive purely phenomenological phase-parameter analysis at Yale[4] gives increased confidence in the probable physical significance of the potential used by him. The general relationship of Bryan's central and tensor potentials to those derived by Gartenhaus[5] on the Chew–Low[6] extended source theory would further increase this confidence if there were an explanation of the spin-orbit potential.

A possibility of accounting for the general features of the $\mathbf{L} \cdot \mathbf{S}$ potential which apparently has not received attention in recent literature is that of a vector meson field. The short-range character of the potential calls for a sufficiently large meson mass. The various searches for new particles have not shown the existence of such a meson capable of strong interactions with nucleons. If it exists, it is more likely, therefore, that it is neutral rather than charged, although a sufficiently high mass could also decrease the chances of its detection even if the meson were charged. A neutral vector meson field is, however, the simplest possibility. The particles of such a field would be, in a sense, heavy photons. It has been known for some time[7] that the sign of the V_{LS} for such a field has the same relationship to its central potential as for the electromagnetic field. In order to reproduce the phenomenologically-indicated sign, it will be speculatively supposed that all nucleons carry the same heavy photon-producing charge. In the case of nucleons this charge could be taken to be a constant multiple of the baryon charge. This hypothesis accounts for the repulsion at short distances between nucleons. For the "extended source" pion-produced potential a short-range repulsion is already present in triplet-even states, but for triplet-odd states it gives an attractive potential which has customarily been modified by the phenomenological introduction of a repulsive core. Similarly, a repulsive core is helpful for the singlet-odd states even though the Gartenhaus calculation gives in this case a strongly attractive potential at short distances. The neutral heavy meson field gives a repulsive core in all states and the details of the Gartenhaus or any other pion-theoretical calculation have, on the present view, only secondary importance, since the core-producing field may be expected to modify the part of the interaction caused by pion exchange. The modification would be weak for large internucleon distances r in agreement with empirical evidence regarding the validity of the one pion exchange potential at large r. Since the nucleons do not penetrate the core appreciably and since the large meson mass makes the core potential drop off rapidly, the most effective part of V_{LS} is just outside the core. It is striking that Bryan's improved fit gave a shorter range for V_{LS} than that of the previous phenomenologi-

See page 686 of this volume for corrections and addenda.

cal potentials. The possible origin of the nucleon-nucleon V_{LS} which has been suggested[8] does not give as steep a dependence of V_{LS} on r as Bryan's and is not likely to be more than contributory to the whole V_{LS}. As has been previously emphasized,[8] both the previously derived V_{LS} and the then attempted explanation of the core were too qualitative and did not pretend to take into account phenomena of virtual nucleon-antinucleon pair formation. On the hypothesis considered now the calculations would, furthermore, need serious modification. It appears simplest, therefore, to use the heavy meson in order to account for V_{LS} as well as the core.

Approximate Magnitudes.—In terms of the first of the references in footnote 7 the interaction potential $-J$ including the spin-orbit correction which arises from considerations of invariance to order v^2/c^2 form the combination

$$-J - \frac{3}{2}\frac{\hbar^2}{M^2c^2}\frac{dJ}{rdr}(\mathbf{L}\cdot\mathbf{S}) \tag{1}$$

for any J arising from a field with the same transformation properties as the vector field. The applicability of this form has been verified for the present purpose by the procedure of the third reference in footnote 7 for the case of special interest, viz.

$$J = -(q^2/r)e^{-\kappa r}. \tag{2}$$

Here q has the dimensions of electric charge in electrostatic units. For simplicity it is taken to have the same value for p-p, p-n, and n-n interactions. Two fits to Bryan's $V_{LS} = -12\,x^{-8}e^{-2x}$, $x = m_\pi c\,r/\hbar$ by the above formulae have been made at $x = 0.6$ with adjustment to produce a fit in $0.6 < x < 1$. In the first $\kappa = 9\,m_\pi c/\hbar$, $q^2\kappa = 4.15 \times 10^5$ Mev; in the second $\kappa = 12\,m_\pi c/\hbar$, $q^2\kappa = 2.85 \times 10^5$ Mev. The first gives a somewhat too gradual fall of V_{LS} in $0.6 < x < 1$; the second gives, on the whole, a somewhat too steep decrease but is reasonably good in reproducing the slope of log V_{LS} at $x = 0.6$. Present evidence would thus appear to indicate the mass of the vector meson to be $m_{hp} \cong 11\,m_\pi$. Here the suffix hp stands for heavy photon. Since Bryan's fits are not as good as those that have been obtained at Yale[4] by means of a gradient search employing most nucleon-nucleon scattering data, it may be expected that the V_{LS} will undergo changes in further fitting with attendant changes in m_{hp}.

For the first fit the values of the repulsive core potential $-J$ at $x = 0.5, 0.6, 0.8, 1.0$ are, respectively, 1026, 348, 43, 5.7 Mev. This core potential appears to be more than sufficiently strong. The pion potential would have to be assumed to be sufficiently strong to counter-balance the vector field in some of the region $0.6 < x < 1.0$. There appears to be no *a priori* objection to such strong pion effects, the convergence of the pion potential calculation being poor. For the second fit the core potential has values 148, 29.5, 2.0, 0.15 Mev at $x = 0.5, 0.6, 0.8, 1.0$, respectively. The core potential produces, in this case, minor effects for $x > 0.6$ but increases sufficiently steeply as x decreases below $x = 0.6$ to reproduce the main features of the phenomenological core. It is supposed that the $1/r^3$ singularity present in the OPEP is either cancelled by the as yet unknown terms of the pion potential beyond those in g^4 or else are made non-singular by nucleon structure effects [9–11] which may be expected to smear out the location of the pion source and thus to reduce the effect of the singularity. Since the hypothetical vector meson field interacts with the nucleon field, one would expect some smearing out of the pion source function and hence a rounding off of the $1/r^3$ and $1/r^2$ potentials at small r. The large magnitude of the core potential at $x \cong 0.5$ is thus not expected to be offset by singularities at $x = 0$ of the pion-produced potential.

The proposed view regarding the core and V_{LS} appears to fit the general features of the interpretation of antinucleon-nucleon scattering by Ball and Chew[12] and the phenomenological considerations of Koba and Takeda.[13] In the work of Chew and Ball the nucleon-nucleon ($\mathfrak{N}$–$\mathfrak{N}$) core is converted into a nucleon-antinucleon ($\mathfrak{N}$–$\bar{\mathfrak{N}}$) sink within which the particles annihilate each other. This process is held responsible for the introduction of the ingoing wave boundary condition at the core radius. The vector meson field speculated on here is supposedly produced by a baryon type charge. The antinucleon constitutes a deficiency of this charge and hence the $\bar{\mathfrak{N}}$–$\mathfrak{N}$ short-range interaction may be expected to be strongly attractive. The two particles may therefore be expected to come together so as to annihilate each other. In the attractive core region some annihilations with emission of heavy photons may be expected, the simultaneous emission of two heavy mesons being expected by analogy with electromagnetic theory. A possible objection is that some of the pion-producing annihilations may be replaced by heavy vector mesons producing annihilations, while the cross section measurements[14] are concerned with the detection of pion production. The pion production has, however, an advantage in the competition on account of the direct coupling of positive to negative energy states caused by the γ_5 term in the pseudoscalar coupling and the effectiveness of heavy vector meson production is reduced by the $e^{-\kappa r}$ factor at all but the shortest $\mathfrak{N}$–$\bar{\mathfrak{N}}$ distances. The effectiveness of pion annihilation in the competition appears reasonable in the outer region of the core. If most antinucleons are annihilated in that region, it is not important whether the heavy photon process is dominant in the innermost region or not. The heavy vector mesons are, furthermore, not necessarily elementary particles. Their disintegration with pion emission is conceivable. If the mass of the heavy meson is as high as the second of the above-mentioned fits to Bryan's V_{LS} suggests, the simultaneous production of two heavy mesons would require an energy excess in the center of mass system of $2 \times 12 \times 270\ m_ec^2 - 2Mc^2 \cong 1{,}420$ Mev corresponding to roughly 3.9 Bev of incident energy in the laboratory system. The mass of the particle being in doubt, it is therefore not clear that there would have been enough energy in the experiments to make the simultaneous emission of two heavy vector mesons energetically possible. The maximum antiproton incident energy in the experiments quoted was 1.07 Bev.

Discussion.—In the calculations of Ball and Chew[12] the same V_{LS} is used for the $\mathfrak{N}$–$\bar{\mathfrak{N}}$ interaction as for $\mathfrak{N}$–$\mathfrak{N}$. On the view proposed here one would expect these interactions to differ by a sign. This circumstance does not appear to matter seriously in the existing comparison with experimental values of the total cross section because the weighted mean value of $(\mathbf{L} \cdot \mathbf{S})$ over all sublevels is zero. Ball and Chew used the Signell–Marshak V_{LS} which has a longer range than either Gammell–Thaler's or Bryan's and which does not reproduce polarization data especially well. The details of agreement with experiment obtained by Ball and Chew cannot be taken literally, therefore, and the reversal of the sign of V_{LS} for the $\bar{\mathfrak{N}}$–$\mathfrak{N}$ case does not appear unreasonable.

On the view proposed there is less reason to doubt the validity of static nucleon-nucleon potentials than heretofore. The phenomenologic core has been a way of getting around the supposedly very complicated conditions at small r. The adjustment of core radii to fit data on $\mathfrak{N}$–$\mathfrak{N}$ scattering had at best a symbolic meaning, the direct effect of the core in $\mathfrak{N}$–$\mathfrak{N}$ scattering theory being that of making the radial functions have nodes at the core radius. On the pion theory of nuclear forces it has been doubtful, however, that the infinitely large repulsive potential inside the core radius should be given a literal significance, it being possible to produce a node of the wave function by an attractive potential or to regard the existence of the node as a manifestation or indirect consequence of the many-body character of the problem inside the core radius. On the heavy vector meson hypothesis, however, the core has a rather literal meaning. The only region within which there is then serious doubt regarding the validity of the static potential picture is that between the region of applicability of the one pion exchange potential[15] ($x > \sim 1$) and the core. Although here also the static picture may be inadequate, it would be expected, perhaps, to be more directly applicable than inside the core. Perhaps this is one of the reasons for the good agreement[16] of calculations on the photodisintegration of the deuteron employing static potentials with experiment. It may also be connected with the success of the Brueckner method of calculating properties of nuclear matter as carried out by Gammel and Brueckner.[17] In view of changes made in the potentials obtained from fits to scattering data, the latter evidence is not conclusive and the treatment of photodisintegration data also has not been carried out with potentials representing scattering data accurately. Higher electromagnetic multipoles may also contribute to the process. Therefore, these indications must be regarded as purely qualitative.

On the viewpoint that the whole potential is essentially static, a difficulty arises in connection with the binding energy of the triton H^3. It has recently been shown by Derrick and Blatt[18] that the Gammel-Thaler potential does not give a bound state of this nucleus. As the authors remark, the reason for this failure of the Gammel–Thaler potential is the relative weakness of the central triplet even potential (${}^3V_c{}^+$) in comparison with the tensor potential for the same state (${}^3V_T{}^+$). According to Figure 3 of Signell and Marshak's paper,[2] the employment of the Gartenhaus potential in place of that of Gammel and Thaler does not appear obviously hopeful since ${}^3V_c{}^+$ is even smaller for the Gartenhaus potential. As long as one dealt with a core within which the two-body treatment of $\mathfrak{N}$–$\mathfrak{N}$ scattering could be seriously questioned, the discrepancy with H^3 could be regarded as a manifestation of the inadequacy of the two-body picture inside the core radius. With the heavy vector meson core, however, the nucleon density inside the core is small and the effect of the core may be expected to be described rather well by a large repulsive potential, so that the discrepancy has to be taken more seriously.

It is not clear, however, that there is a discrepancy between the requirements of $\mathfrak{N}$–$\mathfrak{N}$ scattering data and that of the binding energy of H^3. The reasons for this belief are as follows. (*a*) The Gammel–Thaler potential does not reproduce scattering data especially well. It represents data on polarization better than those on cross sections and from this viewpoint there is no binding reason for considering either its ${}^3V_c{}^+$ or ${}^3V_T{}^+$ to be especially accurate. (*b*) Even with the heavy meson core some velocity dependence of the potential for $x < 1$ may be expected; this is corroborated by the qualitative features of ref. 8 which may still be expected to to apply. Arguments regarding phenomenological indications of velocity dependence have been given by Gammel and Thaler[19] and other theoretical arguments previously by Breit and Yovits.[19] (c) A fit similar to Bryan's has not been made to n-p data. It is not clear that a reasonable fit cannot be made with a potential having a larger $|^3V_c^+|$ and somewhat subordinated V_T^+. (d) A covariant calculation has recently been made for the g^4 term V_4 of the nucleon-nucleon potential by S. N. Gupta.[20] According to this, the $(^3V^+)_4$ potential is much deeper than the potential used by Gammel and Thaler while the $(^1V^+)_4$ agrees very well with that of Bryan's $^1V_c^+$. This agreement cannot be interpreted as indicating that the V_4 potential is adequate because V_4 is much too deep for Bryan's $^3V_c^-$ and especially because $|V_4| \gg |V_2|$ in $x_c < x < 1$ so that higher powers of g may be expected to make appreciable contributions. Nevertheless, Gupta's calculation shows that the pion interaction cannot be claimed to give a small $|^3V_c^+|$. (e) It is conceivable that charged heavy vector mesons participate in the interaction, that the effective core radius is thereby affected, and that the influence of $^3V_c^+$ is increased. (f) Even with the neutral vector meson the possibility of "tensor coupling" of the meson which has been under discussion in the theory of Møller and Rosenfeld[21] can give differences in interaction potentials which contribute both to the spin-spin interaction and to V_T. These interactions would affect the region close to the core and on account of their short range would differ qualitatively from those of the older meson theories of nuclear forces. The existence of the "tensor"-type interaction with the baryon charge might perhaps be doubted if the vector meson is an elementary particle. But if it is composite, it would not be unnatural and appears hard to exclude. In summary, the binding energy of the triton involves several unknown questions and does not appear to provide an objection to the heavy vector meson hypothesis.

It is not clear that the proposed heavy vector meson has a connection with the heavy vector meson proposed by Feynman and Gell-Mann and by Sudershan and Marshak[22] for the divergenceless current form of weak interactions theory. Since the vector meson field of very large mass is supposed to give an interaction of the proton-neutron current with itself, and since this is supposed to be "weak," the two types of heavy mesons may have only a remote relationship because the interaction used here is decidedly strong. One could still try to have the heavy vector meson postulated in this note participate in beta decay in the manner of Møller and Rosenfeld. This would leave, however, the μ decay in a different category and the universality of weak interaction coupling would be unexplained. The connection, if any, appears to be indirect.

The theory of pion-nucleon interactions experiences difficulty in accounting for the electron-neutron interaction[10] and the form factors required by electron-proton and electron-deuteron scattering experiments.[9, 11] It has proved difficult to give a reasonable charge distribution to the neutron which reconciles the theoretical requirement at large r, which arises in its supposed isovector character, with the simple phenomenologic suggestion that the neutron charge density is nearly zero while the neutron's magnetic moment form factor is the same as the proton's and also the same as that of the proton's charge distribution. The interaction with the heavy vector meson does not appear to bring in new difficulties and even appears to help in explaining this situation. If it were the only interaction present, it would smear all nucleon electromagnetic densities by the same amounts in space. Since the "undressed" neutron has no charge, the empirically suggested picture is reproduced. The situation is, of course, complicated by the pion-nucleon interaction. Perhaps the facts should be interpreted in the sense that the heavy photon interaction is the more important of the two for nucleon structure theory.

The neutral vector version of the hypothesis correlates the large nucleon mass with the interaction with the heavy photon and the small electron mass with the interaction with the light photon. In wave field theory, the self mass on renormalization becomes the experimental mass as a consequence of the procedural conventions and the connection of the Fermion mass with properties of the Boson-field particles is lost. Nevertheless, it appears natural to have the heavier Bosons associated with the larger self-mass, whose origin is perhaps to be found partly in the energy of the virtual Bosons even though renormalization techniques imply no direct connection.

The question of the comparison of effectiveness of the vector meson field in different states has been left open throughout most of the discussion. So far as nucleon structure is concerned, the most natural variant of the theory is one in which the field acts completely symmetrically for protons and neutrons. Charge independence of nuclear forces also requires this assumption. It may be noted that according to the last reference in footnote 4 concerned with phenomenological phase shift analysis, there are indications of the correctness of charge independence not only for the one pion exchange part of the interaction but also for the part arising from smaller distances in agreement with the first indications which were based on the $^1S_0$ state. There is at present no conclusive evidence regarding the equality of spin-orbit forces or of repulsive core potentials for different values of the total isotopic spin τ. The evidence regarding the spin-orbit potential is clearer for $\tau = 1$. On the other hand, the Gammel-Thaler fits are based on a ratio of 7300/5000 of the $\tau = 1$ to the $\tau = 0$ spin-orbit potential. This number may not be regarded as final, especially in view of imperfections of fits to n-p data. There is, at present, no clear objection to supposing that this ratio will become unity with improved fits. A repulsive core has to be added to the singlet-odd Gartenhaus potential and on this basis there is again qualitative agreement with the simplest variant of the hypothesis, viz., isotopic spin independence of the interaction. On the other hand, there is no clear evidence for postulating such independence and even the possibility of participation of different meson fields comes under consideration. Further work on the interpretation of n-p scattering data and improvements in the data are desirable in this connection.

In advocating repulsive core potentials in order to preserve charge independence of nuclear forces, Jastrow[23] has mentioned the possibility that the core may be connected with the action of a heavy meson with unspecified transformation properties. At the time, however, the evidence regarding spin-orbit interactions was not clear and the repulsive core was regarded as a substitute for the proposal of Case and Pais who intended to preserve charge independence by invoking spin-orbit forces. There was no apparent reason at the time for correlating the spin-orbit potential with the core. The heavy meson proposal thus became submerged in pion-theoretic explanations of the core.

More recently S. N. Gupta[24] proposed an explanation of $\mathbf{L} \cdot \mathbf{S}$ forces in terms of the hypothesized ρ_0 meson which has a supposed mass of roughly 2 m_π. The resulting V_{LS} agrees well with that of Signell and Marshak and of Signell, Zinn, and Marshak and is associated with an additional central attractive potential. Since the short range Gammel–Thaler and Bryan V_{LS} gives better fits to scattering data, the Signell, Zinn, and Marshak V_{LS} does not appear promising and the repulsion in the core remains unrelated to the spin-orbit potential. The correlation of the repulsion in the core with spin-orbit interaction appears, therefore, to point to the vector meson as the explanation. The possibilities of the vector meson in relating the repulsive core with the spin-orbit interaction has been entertained by the writer for some years and has been discussed with colleagues at Yale and elsewhere. The empirical evidence which has accumulated lately makes the hypothesis especially attractive and publication appears therefore desirable.

Summary.—Empirical evidence for considering the repulsive core of nucleon-nucleon interactions and the spin-orbit interaction as originating in a vector field coupling is discussed. It is shown that the large mass of the mesons which appears to fit present scattering experiments should have been an obstacle in their direct detection. Antinucleon-nucleon scattering falls in naturally with the explanation. Related phenomena such as the photodisintegration of the deuteron, the binding energy of the trition, and electromagnetic nucleon form factors are found not to contain direct contradictions with the hypothesis and even to support it to a degree.

* This research was supported by the U. S. Atomic Energy Commission under Contract AT (30-1)-1807 and by the Office of Ordnance Research, U. S. Army.

[1] Bryan, R. A., *Bull. Amer. Phys. Soc.*, **5**, 35 (1960), Paper IA 10. The writer is indebted to Mr. Bryan for a private discussion of his results and a preprint of a note prepared by him.

[2] Signell, P. S., and R. E. Marshak, *Phys. Rev.*, **109**, 1229 (1958); Signell, P. S., R. Zinn, and R. E. Marshak, *Phys. Rev. Letters*, **1**, 416 (1958).

[3] Gammel, J. L., and R. M. Thaler, *Phys. Rev.*, **107**, 291, 1337 (1957).

[4] Breit, G., *International Conference on Nuclear Forces and the Few Nucleon Problem*, University College, London, July, 1959. This report was based on work done in collaboration with M. H. Hull, Jr., K. D. Pyatt, Jr., C. R. Fischer, K. Lassila, and T. Degges; Hull, M. H., Jr., G. Breit, K. Lassila, K. D. Pyatt, Jr., and H. Ruppel, "Nucleon-Nucleon Phase Parameters at Energies from 9–340 Mev," paper to be read at the Washington Meeting of the American Physical Society, April, 1960; Breit, G., M. H. Hull, Jr., K. Lassila, and K. D. Pyatt, Jr., *Phys. Rev. Letters*, **4**, 79 (1960).

[5] Gartenhaus, S., *Phys. Rev.*, **107**, 291 (1957).

Chew, G. F., *Phys. Rev.*, **94**, 1748 (1954); **94**, 1755 (1954); **95**, 1669 (1954); Low, F. E., *Phys. Rev.*, **97**, 1392 (1955); Chew, G. F., and F. E. Low, *Phys. Rev.*, **101**, 1570 (1956), and **101**, 1579 (1956); *cf.* also Wick, G. C., *Revs. Modern Phys.*, **27**, 339 (1955).

[7] Breit, G., *Phys. Rev.*, **51**, 248 (1937); **51**, 778 (1937); **53**, 153 (1938).

[8] *Ibid.*, **111**, 652 (1958).

[9] Hofstadter, R., F. Bumiller, and M. R. Yearian, *Revs. Modern Phys.*, **30**, 482 (1958).

[10] Foldy, L. L., *Revs. Modern Phys.*, **30**, 471 (1958).

[11] Schiff, L. I., *Revs. Modern Phys.*, **30**, 462 (1958).

[12] Ball, J., and G. F. Chew, *Phys. Rev.*, **109**, 1395 (1958).

[13] Koba, Z., and G. Takeda, *Prog. Theoret. Phys.* (Kyoto), **19**, 269 (1958).

[14] Elioff, T., L. Agnew, O. Chamberlain, H. Steiner, C. Wiegand, and T. Ypsilantis, *Phys. Rev. Letters*, **3**, 285 (1959).

[15] Breit, G., and M. H. Hull, Jr., *Nuclear Physics*, **15**, 216 (1960).

[16] Czyz, W., and J. Sąwicki, *Phys. Rev.*, **110**, 900 (1958); de Swart, J. J., and R. E. Marshak, *Phys. Rev.*, **111**, 272 (1958); Nicholson, A. F., and G. E. Brown, *Bull. Amer. Phys. Soc., Ser.*

II, **3**, 172 (1958); *Proc. Phys. Soc.* (*London*), **73**, 221 (1959). Zernik, W., M. L. Rustgi, and G. Breit, *Phys. Rev.*, **114**, 1358 (1959), also report read on extension of above work by G. Breit at the International Conference on Nuclear Forces and the Few Nucleon Problem, University College, London, July, 1959.

[17] Brueckner, K. A., and J. L. Gammel, *Phys. Rev.*, **109**, 1023 (1958).

[18] Blatt, J. M., report at London International Conference on Nuclear Forces and Few Nucleon Problems, University College, London, July, 1959 (to be published). Derrick, G. H., and J. M. Blatt, *Nuclear Physics*, **8**, 310 (1958), and preprint on further work by the same authors.

[19] Gammel, J. L., and R. M. Thaler, *Annual Reviews of Nuclear Science* (to be published). Cf. Breit, G., and M. C. Yovits, *Phys. Rev.*, **81**, 416 (1951).

[20] Gupta, S. N., "Pion Theory of Nuclear Forces with Nucleon Recoil," *Phys. Rev.* (to be published). The author is grateful to Professor Gupta for an advance copy of this paper and a discussion of its contents.

[21] Møller, C., and L. Rosenfeld, *Proc. Roy. Danish Acad.*, **17**, 8, 1 (1940); Rosenfeld, L., *Nuclear Forces* (Amsterdam: North Holland Publishing Company; New York: Interscience Publishers, Inc., 1949), vol. 2.

[22] Feynman, R. P., and M. Gell-Mann, *Phys. Rev.*, **109**, 193 (1958); Sudershan, E. C. G., and R. E. Marshak, *Phys. Rev.*, **109**, 1860 (1958).

[23] Jastrow, R., *Phys. Rev.*, **79**, 389 (1950).

[24] Gupta, S. N., *Phys. Rev. Letters*, **2**, 124 (1959).

form

$$\alpha^{(+)}(s', t) = \frac{1}{\pi}\int\limits_{L(s')}^{\infty} \frac{u^{(+)}(s', t')}{t'-t}\,\mathrm{d}t' + \frac{1}{\pi}\int\limits_{-\infty}^{M(s')} \frac{v^{(+)}(s', t')}{t'-t}\,\mathrm{d}t'.$$

Fourth order perturbation theoiy ([9]) indicates that both α_{el}^{+} and α_{inel}^{+} satisfy this representation with

$$M(s') < -4\,M\mu\,,$$

$$L(s') \geqslant 4\mu^2 \qquad \text{for} \qquad \alpha_{\text{inel}}^{(+)}\,,$$

$$L(s') \geqslant 16\,\mu^2 \qquad \text{for} \qquad \alpha_{\text{el}}^{(+)}\,.$$

We will take this to be so.

Let us write eq. (3.1) as

$$\text{(3.2)} \qquad A^{(+)}(s, t) = \frac{1}{\pi}\int\limits_{(m+\mu)^2}^{\infty} \mathrm{d}s'\,\alpha_{\text{el}}^{(+)}(s', t)\left\{\frac{1}{s'-s} + \frac{1}{s'-\bar{s}}\right\} + \frac{1}{\pi}\int\limits_{(m+2\mu)^2}^{\infty} \mathrm{d}s'\,\alpha_{\text{inel}}^{(+)}\left\{\frac{1}{s'-s} + \frac{1}{s'-\bar{s}}\right\}.$$

In the first integral of (3.2) the nearest cut in the t variable begins at $t = 16\,\mu^2$. For this reason we shall assume the validity of keeping for the integral only the first few terms of a power series expansion in t. For the second integral in (3.2), however, the nearest cut in t begins a $4\mu^2$ whereas. the cuts in s and $\bar{s}$ now begin at the inelastic threshold $(m+2\mu)^2$. Accordingly, we shall expand this integral in power series in s and $\bar{s}$ (preserving crossing symmetry), keeping again only the first few terms. Thus the second integral of (3.2) is of the form

$$\text{(3.3)} \qquad \frac{1}{\pi}\int\limits_{4\mu^2}^{\infty} \mathrm{d}t'\,\frac{a^{(+)}(t', s, \bar{s})}{t'-t} + \frac{1}{\pi}\int\limits_{(m+2\mu)^2}^{\infty} \mathrm{d}s' \int\limits_{-\infty}^{M(s')} \mathrm{d}t'\,\frac{v_{\text{inel}}(s', t')}{(t'-t)}\left\{\frac{1}{s'-s} + \frac{1}{s'-\bar{s}}\right\},$$

where

$$\text{(3.4)} \qquad a^{(+)}(t', s, \bar{s}) = \frac{1}{\pi}\int\limits_{(m+2\mu)^2}^{\infty} \mathrm{d}s'\,u_{\text{inel}}^{(+)}(s', t')\left\{\frac{1}{s'-s} + \frac{1}{s'-\bar{s}}\right\}.$$

The second term in (3.3) should have only a weak dependence on all three variables since the cuts are all distant. We shall replace terms of this form by real constants.

([9]) S. MANDELSTAM: *Phys. Rev.*, **115**, 1752 (1959).

In this manner we obtain a representation of $A^{(+)}$:

$$(3.5a)\qquad A^{(+)}(s,t)=\frac{1}{\pi}\int\limits_{(m+\mu)^2}^{\infty}\alpha_{\text{el}}^{(+)}(s',t)\left\{\frac{1}{s'-s}+\frac{1}{s'-\bar{s}}\right\}\mathrm{d}t'+\frac{1}{\pi}\int\limits_{4\mu^2}^{\infty}\frac{a^{(+)}(t',s,\bar{s})}{t'-t}\,\mathrm{d}t'+C_A^{(+)}\,,$$

where $\alpha^{(+)}(s',t)$ is a real polynomial of low degree in t and $a^{(+)}(t',s,\bar{s})$ is a sum of a real polynomial of low degree in s and an identical polynomial in $\bar{s}$.

$A^{(-)}$ has a similar representation except that from crossing symmetry it must be odd under interchange of s and $\bar{s}$, so that the arbitrary constant must be zero in this case. Thus

$$(3.5b)\qquad A^{(-)}(s,t)=\frac{1}{\pi}\int\limits_{(m+\mu)^2}^{\infty}\mathrm{d}s'\,\alpha_{\text{el}}^{(-)}(s',t)\left\{\frac{1}{s'-s}-\frac{1}{s'-\bar{s}}\right\}+\frac{1}{\pi}\int\limits_{4\mu^2}^{\infty}\frac{a^{(-)}(t',s,\bar{s})}{t'-t}\,\mathrm{d}t'\,.$$

Representations of identical form (satisfying the symmetry properties of eq. (2.8)) hold for $B^{(+)}$ and $B^{(-)}$ except that to these must be added the single nucleon pole term, *i.e.*

$$B^{(\pm)}=g_r^2\left(\frac{1}{M^2-s}\mp\frac{1}{M^2-\bar{s}}\right)+\text{terms similar to (3.5)}\,.$$

Since the weight functions $a^{(+)}$, etc., are real we can make the association

$$(3.6)\qquad \operatorname{Im}A^{(+)}(s,t)=\alpha_{\text{el}}^{(+)}(s,t)$$

at least for s and t in the physical region of channel I.

From (2.9) and (2.11) Im $A^{(+)}(s,t)$ in this region is expandable as a sum over partial wave pion nucleon scattering amplitudes. We will take this sum to be saturated by the $P_{\frac{3}{2},\frac{3}{2}}$ resonance which we take from experiment. From (3.6) this gives that $\alpha^{(+)}(s,t)$ is a first order polynomial in t, the behaviour of which as a function of s is given by the $P_{\frac{3}{2},\frac{3}{2}}$ partial wave amplitude. As t is not necessarily a physical momentum transfer corresponding to the energy s' in the region of integration of (3.5) an analytic continuation in t of Im $A(s,t)$ from the physical region of its arguments is implied.

It is clear that the first terms in eq. (3.5*a* and *b*), and in the corresponding equations for $B^{(\pm)}$, are identical with the representation used by CHEW, LOW, GOLDBERGER and NAMBU (6) since both in their work and in the present one the integrals are saturated with the (3, 3) resonance. The difference lies in the addition, here, of a strongly t-dependent term representing the contribution of inelastic pion-nucleon scattering.

The weight function $a^{(+)}(t, s, \bar{s})$ is equal to $\text{Im}\, A^{(+)}(t, s, \bar{s})$ in the region $t > 4\mu^2$ for small value of s and $\bar{s}$. $t > 4\mu^2$ corresponds to the energy region of pion-pion scattering although for $t \lesssim 4M^2$, t is below the threshold for $\mathcal{N}\bar{\mathcal{N}}$ production. What must be fed in here is the imaginary part of the $\pi + \pi \rightarrow \mathcal{N} + \bar{\mathcal{N}}$ production amplitude analytically continued to the relevant values of s, $\bar{s}$ and t.

The integral equations for this production amplitude can be derived directly from our representation (3.5) by means of analyticity arguments similar to those of FRAZER and FULCO (7). We shall use the amplitude $f_{\pm}^{(\pm)J}(t)$ as defined in (2.14).

The analytic properties for $A_J^{(\pm)}$ and $B_J^{(\pm)}$ may be deduced from (2.16) and (3.5). For $A_J^{(\pm)}(t)$ for example, one finds a right-hand cut starting at $t = +4\mu^2$ and extending to $t = +\infty$ due to the second term in (3.5) and a left-hand cut from $-\infty$ to 0 arising from the vanishing of the denominators in the first term. The same is true of $B_J^{(\pm)}$ except that the left-hand cut will extend from $-\infty$ to $a = 4\mu^2(1 - (\mu^2/4M^2))$ because of the presence of the pole terms. From eq. (2.15) this leads to the following dispersion relations for $f_{\pm}^J$, identical with those of FRAZER and FULCO:

$$f_{\pm}^J(t) = \frac{1}{\pi}\int_{-\infty}^{a} \frac{\text{Im}\, f_{\pm}^J(t')\, dt'}{t' - t - i\varepsilon} + \frac{1}{\pi}\int_{4\mu^2}^{\infty} \frac{\text{Im}\, f_{\pm}^J(t')\, dt'}{t' - t - i\varepsilon}, \tag{3.7}$$

where $\text{Im}\, f_{\pm}^{(\pm)J}(t)$ on the left hand cut is given in terms of the pion nucleon $P_{\frac{3}{2},\frac{3}{2}}$ resonance parameters and the single nucleon pole term as given by eq. (5.7) and (5.8) of Ref. (7).

It can be seen from a theorem by FUBINI, NAMBU and WATAGHIN (10) that below the threshold for inelastic processes the phase of the production amplitudes $f_{\pm}^{(\pm)J}$ are equal to the phase shift of the two colliding particles, *i.e.* the π-π scattering phase shift. As there are at present no experimental data on pion-pion scattering we shall make the currently favoured assumption of a resonance in the $J = 1$, $T = 1$ state.

Returning to eq. (3.5), we can then replace $a^{(\pm)}(t', s, \bar{s})$ by its expansion in terms of $\text{Im}\, f_{\pm}^{(\pm)J}(t')$ using eq. (2.16). Keeping only the $J = 1$, $T = 1$ terms in the sums and noting that $A^{(+)}$ and $B^{(+)}$ are unaffected by a $T = 1$ pion-pion

(10) S. FUBINI, Y. NAMBU and V. WATAGHIN: *Phys. Rev.*, **111**, 329 (1958).

resonance, we get the following representations for the four invariant amplitudes

$$(3.8)\quad \begin{cases} A^{(+)} = \dfrac{1}{\pi}\displaystyle\int_{(m+\mu)^2}^{\infty} \alpha_{\text{el}}^{(+)}(s', t)\left\{\frac{1}{s'-s} + \frac{1}{s'-\bar{s}}\right\} ds' + C_A^{(+)}, \\[2ex] A^{(-)} = \dfrac{1}{\pi}\displaystyle\int_{(m+\mu)^2}^{\infty} \alpha_{\text{el}}^{(-)}(s', t)\, ds' \left\{\frac{1}{s'-s} - \frac{1}{s'-\bar{s}}\right\} + (s-\bar{s})\frac{1}{\pi}\int_{4\mu^2}^{\infty} \frac{\varrho(t')}{t'-t} dt', \\[2ex] B^{(+)} = g_r^2\left(\dfrac{1}{M^2-s} - \dfrac{1}{M^2-\bar{s}}\right) + \dfrac{1}{\pi}\displaystyle\int_{(m+\mu)^2}^{\infty} \beta_{\text{el}}^{(+)}(s, t)\left\{\frac{1}{s'-s} - \frac{1}{s'-\bar{s}}\right\} ds', \\[2ex] B^{(-)} = g_r^2\left(\dfrac{1}{M^2-s} + \dfrac{1}{M^2-\bar{s}}\right) + \dfrac{1}{\pi}\displaystyle\int_{(m+\mu)^2}^{\infty} \beta_{\text{el}}^{(-)}(s', t)\left\{\frac{1}{s'-s} + \frac{1}{s'-\bar{s}}\right\} ds' + \\[2ex] \qquad\qquad + \dfrac{1}{\pi}\displaystyle\int_{4\mu^2}^{\infty} \frac{\sigma(t')}{t'-t} dt' + C_B^{(-)}, \end{cases}$$

where

$$\varrho(t') = \frac{3\pi}{p'^2}\left(\frac{M}{\sqrt{2}} \operatorname{Im} f_-^{(-)1}(t) - \operatorname{Im} f_+^{(-)1}(t)\right),$$

$$\sigma(t') = \frac{12\pi}{\sqrt{2}} \operatorname{Im} f_-^{(-)1}(t').$$

In the absence of a solution to the Chew-Mandelstam π-π scattering equations ([11]) we shall adopt a resonance form that satisfies the requirements of unitarity, correct low energy behaviour and the existence of a cut from $t = 4\mu^2$ to ∞. Such a form is

$$(3.9)\qquad f_{\pi\pi} = \frac{\exp[i\delta_{\pi\pi}]\sin\delta_{\pi\pi}}{q^3} = \frac{\gamma}{t_r - t - i\gamma q^3}. \qquad (J = T = 1).$$

If this were a correct solution to the Chew-Mandelstam equations, γ would be a function of t. For $f_{\pi\pi}$ to be a resonance, however, γ would have to be a slowly varying function of t, at least in the resonance region; we shall take it to be a real constant (*).

([11]) G. F. CHEW and S. MANDELSTAM: UCRL 8728.

(*) Taking γ to be a constant introduces a spurious pole in $f_{\pi\pi}(t)$. However, for a sharp resonance this pole will have a small residue and be distant from the region of interest.

One can now directly write down an expression for $f_{\pm}^{(-)1}(t)$ that satisfies the analyticity requirements of (3.9) and has the desired phase in the region $4\mu^2 \leqslant t \leqslant 16\mu^2$. A solution, equivalent to that of OMNÈS ([12]), having all the required properties is

$$f_{\pm}^{(-)1}(t) = f_{\pi\pi}(t) \int_{-\infty}^{a} \frac{\operatorname{Im} f_{\pm}^{(-)1}(t')}{f_{\pi\pi}(t')\,(t'-t-i\varepsilon)}\, dt' , \tag{3.10}$$

into which we must now substitute the expressions given by eq. (5.7) and (5.8) of Ref. ([7]) for $\operatorname{Im} f_{\pm}^{(-)1}(t')$. If we attempt, however, to evaluate these integrals keeping only the contributions from the nucleon pole term and the (3.3) resonance we find that the integrals do not converge, essentially due to the fact that we are using a power series expansion in t' for $\operatorname{Im} f_{\pm}^{(-)1}(t')$ over a region where the expansion no longer converges. FRAZER and FULCO have attempted to estimate the integrals appearing in (3.10) by introducing a cut-off. Our procedure is to replace them by constants representing their value at $t = t_r$, this approximation being based on the assumption that the structure of $f_{\pm}^{(-)1}(t)$ in the region of interest $4\mu^2 < t < \infty$ is dominated by a strongly peaked π-π resonance.

Let us write therefore

$$f_{\pm}^{(-)1} = \frac{N_{\pm}}{t_r - t - i\gamma q^3} . \tag{3.11}$$

In the following section we shall show how one may estimate these constants by comparison with nucleon electromagnetic structure data.

4. – The electromagnetic structure of the nucleon.

It has been pointed out by FRAZER and FULCO ([3,4]) that both the magnitude of the isotopic vector part of the anomalous magnetic moment of the nucleon and the radii of the charge and magnetic moment distributions can be adequately explained if the pion-pion interaction is assumed to have a resonance in the $J=1$, $T=1$ state. Earlier attempts by dispersion relation techniques to explain these properties, neglecting the pion-pion interaction, were unable to account for them all simultaneously.

We shall use the notation of FEDERBUSH, GOLDBERGER and TREIMAN ([13]). They consider the nucleon current density operator j_μ taken between single

([12]) R. OMNÈS: *Nuovo Cimento*, **8**, 316 (1958).

([13]) P. FEDERBUSH, M. L. GOLDBERGER and S. B. TREIMAN: *Phys. Rev.*, **112**, 642 (1958).

nucleon states. From Lorentz and gauge invariance this can be expressed in terms of two scalar functions

$$\langle p'|j_\mu|p\rangle = \left(\frac{M^2}{p'_0 p_0}\right)^{\frac{1}{2}} \bar{u}(p')[F_1(t)i\gamma_\mu - F_2(t)i\sigma_{\mu\nu}(p'-p)^\nu]u(p)\,,$$

where $u(p)$ and $u(p')$ are the Dirac spinors for the initial and final nucleons and $t = -(p-p')^2$.

The functions F_1 and F_2 may be subdivided into isotopic scalar and vector parts

$$F_1 = F_1^S + \tau_3 F_1^V\,, \tag{4.1}$$

$$F_2 = F_2^S + \tau_3 F_2^V\,. \tag{4.2}$$

We consider here only the isotopic vector parts F_1^V and F_2^V as these are the easiest to handle by dispersion relation techniques. For $t = 0$ they satisfy the relations

$$F_1^V(0) = \frac{e}{2}\,, \tag{4.3}$$

$$F_2^V(0) = \frac{\mu_p - \mu_n}{2} = \frac{ge}{2m}\,, \tag{4.4}$$

μ_n and μ_p are the anomalous magnetic moments of the neutron and proton respectively (experimentally g, the gyromagnetic ratio $= 1.83$) e is the electron-charge. The functions $F_1^V(t)$ and $F_2^V(t)$ are taken to satisfy the dispersion relations:

$$F_1^V(t) = \frac{e}{2} + \frac{t}{\pi}\int_{4\mu^2}^{\infty} \frac{\operatorname{Im} F_1^V(t')\,dt'}{t'(t'-t)}\,, \tag{4.5}$$

$$F_2^V(t) = \frac{ge}{2m} + \frac{t}{\pi}\int_{4\mu^2}^{\infty} \frac{\operatorname{Im} F_2^V(t')\,dt'}{t'(t'-t)}\,. \tag{4.6}$$

Subtractions have been performed in order to ensure better convergence of the integrals. The reader is referred to the paper by FEDERBUSH, GOLDBERGER and TREIMAN ([13]) for a discussion of these equations and for an evaluation of the two pion contribution to $\operatorname{Im} F_1^V(t')$ and $\operatorname{Im} F_2^V(t')$ in terms of the pion electromagnetic form factors and the $\pi + \pi \to \mathcal{N} + \overline{\mathcal{N}}$ production amplitudes.

They obtain expressions for this contribution which can be written in terms of the $\pi+\pi \to \mathcal{N}+\overline{\mathcal{N}}$ JACOB and WICK ([14]) amplitudes as ([4])

$$\text{Im}\, F_i^V(t) = -\frac{eF_\pi^*(t)q^3}{2E}\,\Gamma_i(t)\,, \tag{4.7}$$

where

$$\Gamma_2(t) = \frac{1}{2p^2}\left\{\frac{M}{\sqrt{2}}\,f_-^{(-)1}(t) - f_+^{(-)1}(t)\right\},$$

$$\Gamma_1(t) = \frac{M}{p^2}\left\{-\frac{E^2}{M\sqrt{2}}\,f_-^{(-)1}(t) + f_+^{(-)1}(t)\right\},$$

$F_\pi(t)$ is the pion electromagnetic form factor. By arguments similar to those used in the derivation of the integral representations for the nucleon electromagnetic form factors it can be shown that $F_\pi(t)$ satisfies the integral representation ([3])

$$F_\pi(t) = 1 + \frac{t}{\pi}\int_{4\mu^2}^{\infty}\frac{\text{d}t'\,\text{Im}\,F_\pi(t')}{t'(t'-t)}\,. \tag{4.8}$$

Also, by the Fubini, Nambu, Wataghin theorem ([10]) $F_\pi(t)$ has the same phase as the π-π scattering amplitude in the $J=1$, $T=1$ state below the inelastic threshold $t=16\mu^2$. The problem of the construction of $F_\pi(t)$ is analogous to that of $f_\pm^{(\pm)1}(t)$ except that the former has no left hand cut. A solution arrived at in the same manner, equivalent to the Omnès solution ([12]), is

$$F_\pi(t) = \frac{t_r+\gamma}{t_r - t - i\gamma q^3}\,. \tag{4.9}$$

Using this expression and eq. (4.7) we obtain,

$$\text{Im}\, F_2^V(t) = -\frac{e}{2E}\,q^3\,\frac{t_r+\gamma}{(t_r-t)^2+\gamma^2q^6}\,\frac{1}{2p^2}\left(\frac{M}{\sqrt{2}}\,N_- - N_+\right), \tag{4.10}$$

$$\text{Im}\, F_1^V(t) = -\frac{e}{2E}\,q^3\,\frac{t_r+\gamma}{(t_r-t)^2+\gamma^2q^6}\,\frac{M}{p^2}\left(-\frac{E^2}{M\sqrt{2}}\,N_- + N_+\right). \tag{4.11}$$

If we now make the assumption that the resonance is narrow, we can replace

$$\frac{q^3\gamma}{(t_r-t)+\gamma^2q^6} \quad \text{by} \quad \pi\,\delta(t_r-t)\,,$$

([14]) M. JACOB and G. C. WICK: *Ann. Phys.*, **7**, 404 (1959).

and obtain by substitution into (4.5) and (4.6)

$$F_1^V(t) = \frac{e}{2}\left(1 - \frac{at}{t_r - t}\right), \tag{4.12}$$

$$F_2^V(t) = \frac{ge}{2m}\left(1 - \frac{bt}{t_r - t}\right). \tag{4.13}$$

The two constants a and b are

$$a = \frac{C_1}{E_r\gamma}\,\frac{t_r + \gamma}{t_r},$$

$$b = \frac{M}{g}\,\frac{C_2}{E_r\gamma}\,\frac{t_r + \gamma}{t_r},$$

$$C_2 = \frac{1}{2p_r^2}\left(\frac{M}{\sqrt{2}}N_- - N_+\right),$$

$$C_1 = \frac{M}{p_r^2}\left(-\frac{E_r^2}{\sqrt{2}M}N_- + N_+\right),$$

p_r and E_r are p and E evaluated at $t = t_r$.

The form factors $F_1^V(t)$ and $F_2^V(t)$ have been investigated experimentally by high energy electron scattering from protons and deuterons ([15]). It appears from this experimental data that it is consistent to assume that

$$\frac{2}{e}F_1^V(t) = \frac{2m}{ge}F_2^V(t) = \frac{1}{\mu_p}F_2^p(t) = \frac{1}{\mu_n}F_2^N(t) = \frac{1}{e}F_1^p(t), \qquad \text{for } 0 > t > -25\mu^2,$$

where $F_2^p(t)$ is the magnetic moment form factor of the proton.

Taking this to be so, the equality of $(2/e)F_1^V(t)$ and $(2m/ge)F_2^V(t)$ gives the relation

$$\frac{C_2}{C_1} = \frac{g}{m}. \tag{4.14}$$

In order to fit the form of $F_2^p(t)$, we note that our form factors (4.12) and (4.13) have the same form as those predicted by the Clementel and Villi model ([16]) for the proton charge and magnetic moment distributions. This model is known to give a good fit to the experimental data with values of the

---

([15]) R. Hofstadter: High Energy Physics Laboratory, Stanford University, Cal., HEPL 176.

([16]) E. Clementel and C. Villi: *Nuovo Cimento*, **4**, 1207 (1958).

parameters $a = b = 1.2$ [17]

$$t_r = 22.4\,\mu^2 \tag{4.15}$$

and

$$\frac{C_1}{\Gamma} = -\frac{1.2E_r}{q_r^3} = -\frac{.286}{\mu^2}, \qquad \Gamma = \gamma q_r^3, \tag{4.16}$$

corresponding to an r.m.s. charge radius of the proton and radius of the proton and neutron magnetic moment distribution of $.8\cdot10^{-13}$ cm.

5. – Projection of partial wave amplitudes.

In order to compare the theoretical and experimental phase shifts we need to evaluate expressions for the $f_{l\pm}$ defined in eq. (2.12). This is done by using the relation (2.13) into which we must substitute the expressions for f_1 and f_2 from (2.9) and use the approximate A's and B's evaluated in Section **3**. In what follows we shall restrict ourselves to the calculation of S, P and $\boldsymbol{D}$ waves only. Applying these operations to a) the pole terms and b) the integrals involving $1/(s'-s)$ and $1/(s'-\bar{s})$ and keeping only the contribution from the (3, 3) state in the absorptive part of f_1 and f_2, we obtain, in the static limit, expressions identical to those written down by CHEW, GOLDBERGER, LOW and NAMBU [6]. These are reproduced here.

$$f_S = \begin{bmatrix} f_S\,(T=\frac{1}{2}) \\ f_S\,(T=\frac{3}{2}) \end{bmatrix} = -2\lambda^+ + \begin{pmatrix} 2 \\ -1 \end{pmatrix}\frac{\omega}{M}\lambda^-, \tag{5.1}$$

where

$$\left\{\begin{aligned} \lambda^+ &= \frac{g^2}{2M} - \frac{4M}{3\pi}\int_1^\infty \frac{\mathrm{d}\omega'}{q'^2}\left(1+\frac{2\omega'}{M}\right)\operatorname{Im} f_{33}(\omega')\,, \\ \lambda^- &= \frac{g^2}{2M} - \frac{4M}{3\pi}\int_1^\infty \frac{\mathrm{d}\omega'}{q'^2}\operatorname{Im} f_{33}(\omega')\,, \end{aligned}\right. \tag{5.2}$$

$$\left\{\begin{aligned} f_{11} &= -\frac{8}{3}\frac{f^2q^2}{\omega} + \frac{16}{9}\frac{q^2}{\pi}\int_1^\infty \frac{\mathrm{d}\omega'}{q'^2}\frac{\operatorname{Im} f_{33}(\omega')}{\omega'+\omega}, \\ f_{13} &= f_{31} = \tfrac{1}{4} f_{11}\,, \\ f_{33} &= \frac{4}{3}\frac{f^2q^2}{\omega} + \frac{q^2}{\pi}\int_1^\infty \frac{\mathrm{d}\omega'}{q'^2}\operatorname{Im} f_{33}\left(\frac{1}{\omega'-\omega}\right). \end{aligned}\right. \tag{5.3}$$

([17]) R. HOFSTADTER, F. BUMILLER and M. R. YEARIAN: *Rev. Mod. Phys.*, **30**, 482 (1958).

With the assumption of a narrow $P_{\frac{3}{2},\frac{3}{2}}$ resonance these expressions become

$$(5.4)\quad \begin{cases} f_{11} = -\dfrac{8}{3}\dfrac{f^2q^2}{\omega}\dfrac{1}{1+\omega/\omega_r}, \\ f_{13} \simeq f_{31} \simeq \frac{1}{4} f_{11}, \end{cases}$$

where ω_r is the centre of mass pion energy corresponding to the resonant (3.3) state. For D-waves

$$(5.5)\quad \begin{cases} \delta_{D^{1/2}_{3/2}} = -\lambda_D\left[1+\dfrac{112}{9}\left(\dfrac{\omega}{\omega+\omega_r}\right)^2\right], \\ \delta_{D^{3/2}_{3/2}} = \lambda_D\left[2-\dfrac{28}{9}\left(\dfrac{\omega}{\omega+\omega_r}\right)^2\right], \\ \delta_{D^{1/2}_{5/2}} = \lambda_D\left[4-\dfrac{32}{9}\left(\dfrac{\omega}{\omega+\omega_r}\right)^2\right], \\ \delta_{D^{3/2}_{5/2}} = -\lambda_D\left[8+\dfrac{8}{9}\left(\dfrac{\omega}{\omega+\omega_r}\right)^2\right], \end{cases}$$

with

$$\lambda_D = \frac{1}{15}\frac{f^2}{M}\frac{q^5}{\omega^2}.$$

We must now evaluate the contribution to f_s of the terms in f_1 and f_2, representing the effect of the π-π interaction. These terms are given by (2.9), (3.8) and (3.11), and under the assumption of a narrow π-π resonance, are given in the static limit by

$$(5.6)\quad \begin{cases} [f_1^{(\pi\pi)}] = \begin{bmatrix} f_1^{(\pi\pi)}(T=\frac{1}{2}) \\ f_1^{(\pi\pi)}(T=\frac{3}{2}) \end{bmatrix} = \begin{pmatrix} 2 \\ -1 \end{pmatrix}\dfrac{M}{W}\dfrac{2}{t_r-t}\left(\dfrac{3}{2}q^2\cos\theta C_2-\dfrac{3}{2}\omega C_1\right), \\ [f_2^{(\pi\pi)}] = \begin{pmatrix} 2 \\ -1 \end{pmatrix}\dfrac{M}{W}\dfrac{-2}{t_r-t}\dfrac{3}{2}q^2\left(C_2+\dfrac{C_1}{2M}\right). \end{cases}$$

Here the superscript $(\pi\pi)$ denotes the contribution from the terms of (3.13) with denominator $t'-t$. The factor $\begin{pmatrix} 2 \\ -1 \end{pmatrix}$ comes from having kept the contribution of the $T=1$ pion-pion scattering state only.

From eq. (2.13),

$$f_s = \frac{1}{2}\int_{-1}^{1}(f_1+f_2\cos\theta)\,\mathrm{d}\cos\theta\,,$$

we find that the terms in C_2 do not contribute in the static limit and we get

$$(5.7)\qquad [f_s^{(\pi\pi)}] = -\frac{3}{2}\frac{M}{W}\begin{pmatrix} 2 \\ -1 \end{pmatrix}\frac{\omega}{t_r}\, C_1\, F_0\left(\frac{2q^2}{t_r}\right),$$

where

$$F_\alpha\left(\frac{2q^2}{t_r}\right) = \int_{-1}^{1} \frac{\mathrm{d}c\, c^\alpha}{1 + (2q^2/t_r)(1-c)}\,. \qquad c = \cos\theta.$$

This result is quite general in the sense that for all higher values of l the terms in C_2 do not contribute in the static limit to the non-spin flip amplitude. Indeed, the non spin flip amplitude for scattering in an l state is

$$(5.8)\qquad [(l+1)f_{l+} + lf_{l-}]P_l$$

and one may easily verify, using (2.13), that

$$(5.9)\qquad (l+1)f_{l+} + lf_{l-} = \frac{2l+1}{2}\int_{-1}^{1}\mathrm{d}c(f_1 + f_2 c)P_l\,,$$

from which the result follows immediately. The spin flip amplitude

$$(5.10)\qquad (f_{l-} - f_{l+})P_l^1 e^{i\varphi}$$

on the other hand, depends, in the static limit, on the linear combination

$$(5.11)\qquad C_2' = C_2 + \frac{C_1}{2M},$$

as can be seen from the relation

$$(5.12)\qquad f_{l-} - f_{l+} = \frac{2l+1}{2l(l+1)}\int_{-1}^{1}\mathrm{d}c(1-c^2)P_l' f_2\,,$$

and eq. (5.6).

We recall that by the discussion of the preceding section, C_1 and C_2 are related to the vector part of the charge distribution radius and anomalous magnetic moment, rexpectively. C_2' corresponds therefore to the total magnetic moment:

$$\mu_{\text{anom}} + \frac{e}{2M}\,.$$

It is interesting to note that, in so far as the terms depending on the resonance are concerned, the non-spin-flip amplitude is related in the static limit only to the charge distribution radius of the nucleon whereas the spin-flip amplitude is connected only to its total magnetic moment.

Evaluating (2.13) for P and D waves we find that the terms to be added onto the CGLN expressions for f_{P_1}, f_{P_3}, f_{D_3}, f_{D_5} are

$$(5.13)\qquad \begin{cases} f_{P_1}^{(\pi\pi)} = -\dfrac{3}{2}\dfrac{M}{W}\begin{pmatrix}2\\-1\end{pmatrix}\dfrac{1}{t_r}\,[\omega C_1 F_1 + q^2 C_2'(F_0 - F_2)]\,, \\[2ex] f_{P_3}^{(\pi\pi)} = -\dfrac{3}{2}\dfrac{M}{W}\begin{pmatrix}2\\-1\end{pmatrix}\dfrac{1}{t_r}\left[\omega C_1 F_1 - \dfrac{q^2}{2}\,C_2'(F_0 - F_2)\right], \\[2ex] f_{D_3}^{(\pi\pi)} = -\dfrac{3}{4}\dfrac{M}{W}\begin{pmatrix}2\\-1\end{pmatrix}\dfrac{1}{t_r}\,[\omega C_1(3F_2 - F_0) + 3q^2 C_2'(F_1 - F_3)]\,, \\[2ex] f_{D_5}^{(\pi\pi)} = -\dfrac{3}{4}\dfrac{M}{W}\begin{pmatrix}2\\-1\end{pmatrix}\dfrac{1}{t_r}\,[\omega C_1(3F_2 - F_0) - 2q^2 C_2'(F_1 - F_3)]\,. \end{cases}$$

We must still evaluate the effect on f_s of the extra constants $C_A^+ \ldots$ introduced in Section **2** when passing from the Mandelstam representation to the one-dimensional Cini-Fubini form. (The effect on the $f_{P_{\frac{1}{2}}}$ amplitude is only a non-static correction and constants have no effect on the other amplitudes.) One easily verifies that these constants simply add to f_s a term of the form

$$(5.14)\qquad \varkappa + \begin{pmatrix}2\\-1\end{pmatrix}\beta\omega\,.$$

This correction is of exactly the same form as the CGLN contribution (5.3),

As for the $P_{\frac{3}{2},\frac{3}{2}}$ equation, our additional term is small in the region of the resonance itself and hence the resonance solution given in Ref. (6) will be modified simply by the addition of a small real part.

6. – Comparison with experiment and conclusions.

We have postulated a simple possible model for the effect of the pion-pion interaction on the pion-nucleon scattering amplitude. However a direct comparison of the phase-shift predictions of this model with experiment is not very fruitful because of the large uncertainties involved in the phase-shift analysis of the experimental data.

The best established low energy results apart from the existence of the $P_{\frac{3}{2},\frac{3}{2}}$ resonance are the values of the S-wave scattering lengths. Those quantities, however, are implicitly very dependent on the core contribution to the scattering amplitude, a fact which is reflected in our having taken the high energy contributions to our dispersive integrals as arbitrary constants. These arbitrary constants give contributions to the S-wave scattering amplitude of the same form as the CHEW, GOLDBERGER, LOW and NAMBU terms, namely the expression (5.14). These terms by themselves give an adequate description of the scattering lengths. However, at higher energies the experimental data cannot be adequately explained by the simple dependence given in (5.14). Using our model up to an energy of about $q = 1.5\mu$ enables us to fit all the S-wave data and gives us a value of the « width » Γ of our resonance. Fitting the data with $t_r = 22.4\mu^2$ gives $C_1 \sim -.58$ which corresponds to a value of $\Gamma \sim 2.4\mu^2$; positive, as it must be if our postulate of a resonance is correct. Note that Γ is not the conventional width of the resonance but that with our resonance form (3.11) the energy difference between the points where the resonance reaches half its maximum value is given by $\Gamma/\sqrt{t_r}$.

With this value of t_r and the value of $C_1 = -.58$ the P and D wave threshold behaviour as calculated from (5.13) is shown in the table. If one allows for the uncertainties in $F_1^{\mathcal{N}}$ and $F_2^{\mathcal{N}}$ in the determination of t_r from the isovector parts of the nucleon form factors, then t_r could very well be $15\mu^2$

TABLE I. – *Table of threshold values for P and D waves.*

Term	π-π contribution		Chew term	Total		Exp.
	$t_r = 22.4$	$t_r = 15$		$t_r = 22.4$	$t_r = 15$	
$f^{\frac{1}{2}}_{P_{\frac{1}{2}}}/q^2$	.046	.049	$-.14$	$-.094$	$-.091$	$-.038 \pm .038$
$f^{\frac{1}{2}}_{P_{\frac{3}{2}}}/q^2$	$-.016$	$-.013$	$-.035$	$-.051$	$-.048$	$-.039 \pm .022$
$f^{\frac{3}{2}}_{P_{\frac{1}{2}}}/q^2$	$-.023$	$-.025$	$-.035$	$-.058$	$-.060$	$-.044 \pm .005$
$f^{\frac{3}{2}}_{P_{\frac{3}{2}}}/q^2$	.008	.007	.213	.221	.220	$.234 \pm .019$
$f^{\frac{1}{2}}_{D_{\frac{3}{2}}}/q^4$	.0013	.0020	$-.0019$	$-.0006$	$+.0001$	—
$f^{\frac{3}{2}}_{D_{\frac{3}{2}}}/q^4$	$-.0007$	$-.0010$	.0013	$+.0006$	$+.0003$	—
$f^{\frac{5}{2}}_{D_{\frac{5}{2}}}/q^4$	$-.0005$	$-.0007$	.0029	$+.0024$	$+.0022$	—
$f^{\frac{3}{2}}_{D_{\frac{5}{2}}}/q^4$	.0003	.0004	$-.0065$	$-.0062$	$-.0061$	—

instead of $22.4\mu^2$. The values of the P and D waves at threshold corresponding to $t_r = 15\mu^2$ are therefore given too. We also give the contribution from the CHEW *et al.* terms as calculated from (5.4) and (5.5) and compare the total with the experimental results (taken from the 1958 Annual International Conference on High Energy Physics at CERN).

While the theoretical numbers quoted in the table are not in exact agreement with the experimental numbers one must remember that the contribution from the π-π interaction may be varied by varying C_1. The above calculation of C_1 is only reliable as an order of magnitude estimate, since the inclusion of the S wave rescattering corrections in eq. (3.8) could have a significant effect at this energy.

One feature which is not brought out by just inspecting the threshold behaviour of the partial waves is the energy variation of the π-π contribution and of the Chew term. One finds in fact that the energy variation of the π-π contribution is stronger than that of the Chew term and therefore at higher energies the π-π term becomes comparable or larger than the Chew term and determines to a large extent the variation of the phase shifts with energy.

One encouraging feature is the fact that we are able to make the D_{13} phase shift positive at low energies. Also, it is the D_{13} phase shift to which the π-π interaction gives the largest contribution. The C.G.L.N. term alone is negative and so would seem to imply a repulsive interaction for this partial wave whereas experimentally it resonates around 600 MeV.

Of course more extensive calculations must still be done and a direct comparison of theoretical and experimental phase shifts is probably not the best way to put the theory to a severe test. For in analysing an experimental cross-section into partial waves one usually arrives at phase shifts with large uncertainties on them and whose value may depend on the assumed values of other partial waves *e.g.* the D waves. On the other hand, the theory presented here gives simultaneously definite values for S, P and D waves. A better procedure for comparing theory and experiment is therefore to compare directly the differential cross-sections on which the experimental errors are rather small. Such a programme is at present in progress.

In conclusion we would like to remark that it is amusing that one can probably reach an approximation to low energy pion-nucleon scattering identical to the one presented here by considering a model in which both the (3,3) resonance and the π-π, $J=1$, $T=1$ resonance are replaced by isobars having the corresponding masses, spins and isospins. Of course the formulation presented here is much more general since it allows for the insertion of experimental data on π-π scattering in all spin and isospin states when such information becomes available.

* * *

We wish to thank Prof. S. FUBINI for many helpful discussions during the course of this work. We are also indebted to Mr. W. KLEIN for numerical computations.

RIASSUNTO (*)

Dalle proprietà analitiche dell'ampiezza dello scattering pione-nucleone postulate da Mandelstam, deriviamo una relazione fissa di dispersione del trasporto di momento che ha per variabile l'energia, che dovrebbe essere valida a basse energie. Questa formulazione ci permette di valutare l'effetto di una risonanza di scattering di due pioni sullo scattering pione-nucleone. Con una opportuna scelta dei parametri di risonanza pione-pione possiamo approssimare sia gli spostamenti di fase sperimentali pione-nucleone sia i fattori di forma elettromagnetici del nucleone.

(*) *Traduzione a cura della Redazione.*

PAPER 60

Theory of Strong Interactions*

J. J. Sakurai

The Enrico Fermi Institute for Nuclear Studies and the Department of Physics, The University of Chicago, Chicago, Illinois

> "There is a large experimental program on production of *K* particles by nuclear collisions and by photons, scattering, and interactions of those mesons with nuclei, etc. But just between us theoretical physicists: What do we do with all these data? We can't do anything. We are facing a very serious problem. . . . Perhaps the results of all experiments will produce some idiotic surprises, and some dope will be able to calculate everything from some simple rule. What we are doing can be compared with those complicated models invented to explain the hydrogen spectra which turned out to satisfy very simple regularities."
>
> R. P. Feynman

All the symmetry models of strong interactions which have been proposed up to the present are devoid of deep physical foundations. It is suggested that, instead of postulating artificial "higher" symmetries which must be broken anyway within the realm of strong interactions, we take the *existing exact* symmetries of strong interactions more seriously than before and exploit them to the utmost limit. A new theory of strong interactions is proposed on this basis.

Following Yang and Mills we require that the gauge transformations that are associated with the three "internal" conservation laws—baryon conservation, hypercharge conservation, and isospin conservation—be "consistent with the local field concept that underlies the usual physical theories." In analogy with electromagnetism there emerge three kinds of couplings such that in each case a massive vector field is coupled linearly to the conserved current in question. Each of the three fundamental couplings is characterized by a single universal constant. Since, as Pais has shown, there are no other internal symmetries that are exact, and since any successful theory must be simple, there are no other fundamental strong couplings. Parity conservation in strong interactions follows as the direct consequence of parity conservation of the three fundamental vector couplings. The three vector couplings give rise to corresponding current-current interactions. Yukawa-type couplings of pions and *K* particles to baryons are "phenomenological," and may arise, for instance, out of four-baryon current-current interactions along the lines suggested by Fermi and Yang. All the successful features of Chew–Low type

* This work was supported by the U. S. Atomic Energy Commission.

meson theories and of relativistic dispersion relations can, in principle, be in accordance with the theory whereas none of the predictions based on relativistic Yukawa-type Lagrangians are meaningful unless ω/M is considerably less than unity.

Simple and direct experimental tests of the theory should be looked for in those phenomena in which phenomenological Yukawa-type couplings are likely to play unimportant roles. The fundamental isospin current coupling in the static limit gives rise to a short-range repulsion (attraction) between two particles whenever the isospins are parallel (antiparallel). Thus the low-energy s-wave πN interaction should be repulsive in the $T = \frac{3}{2}$ state and attractive in the $T = \frac{1}{2}$ state in agreement with observation. In $\pi\Sigma$ s-wave scattering the $T = 0$ state is strongly attractive, and there definitely exists the possibility of an s-wave resonance at energies of the order of the $K^- p$ threshold, while the $T = 1$ $\pi\Sigma$ phase shift is likely to remain small; using the K matrix formalism of Dalitz and Tuan, we might be able to compare the "ideal" phase shifts derived in this manner with the "actual" phase shifts deduced from $K^- p$ reactions. It is expected that the two-pion system exhibits a resonant behavior in the $T = 1$ (p-wave) state in agreement with the conjecture of Frazer and Fulco based on the electromagnetic structure of the nucleon. The three pion system is expected to exhibit two $T = 0, J = 1$ resonances. It is conjectured that the two $T = \frac{1}{2}$ and one $T = \frac{3}{2}$ "higher rsonances" in the πN interactions may be due to the two $T = 0$ 3π resonances and the one $T = 1$ 2π resonance predicted by the theory. Multiple pion production is expected at all energies to be more frequent than that predicted on the basis of statistical considerations. The fundamental hypercharge current coupling gives rise to a short-range repulsion (attraction) between two charge-doublet particles when their hypercharges are like (opposite). If the isospin current coupling is effectively weaker than the hypercharge current coupling, the KN "potential" should be repulsive and the $\bar{K}N$ "potential" should be attractive, and the charge exchange scattering of K^+ and K^- should be relatively rare, at least in s states. All these features seem to be in agreement with current experiments. Conditions for the validity of Pais' doublet approximation are discussed. The theory offers a possible explanation for the long-standing problem as to why associated production cross sections are small and K^- cross sections are large. The empirical fact that the ratio of $(K\bar{K}2N)$ to $(K\Lambda N) + (K\Sigma N)$ in NN collisions seems to be about twenty to thirty times larger than simple statistical considerations indicate is not surprising. The fundamental baryonic current coupling gives rise to a short-range repulsion for baryon-baryon interactions and an attraction for baryon-antibaryon interactions. There should be effects similar to those expected from "repulsive cores" for all angular momentum and parity states in both the $T = 1$ and $T = 0$ NN interactions at short distances though the $T = 1$ state may be more repulsive. A simple Thomas-type calculation gives rise to a spin-orbit force of the right sign with not unreasonable order of magnitude. The ΛN and ΣN interactions at short distances should be somewhat less repulsive than the NN interactions. Annihilation cross sections in $N\bar{N}$ collisions are expected to be large even in Bev regions in contrast to the predictions of Ball and Chew. The observed large pion multiplicity in $N\bar{N}$ annihilations is not mysterious. It is possible to invent a reasonable mechanism which makes the reaction $p + \bar{p} \rightarrow \pi^+ + \pi^-$ very rare, as recently observed. Fermi–Landau–Heisenberg type theories of high energy collisions are not expected to hold in relativistic NN collisions; instead the theory offers a theoretical justification for the "two-fire-ball model" of high-energy jets previously proposed on purely phenomenological grounds.

Because of the strong short-range attraction between a baryon and antibaryon there exists a mechanism for a baryon-antibaryon pair to form a meson. The dynamical basis of the Fermi–Yang–Sakata–Okun model as well as that of the Goldhaber–Christy model follows naturally from the theory; all the *ad hoc* assumptions that must be made in order that the compound models work at all can be explained from first principles. It is suggested that one should not ask which elementary particles are "more elementary than others," and which compound model is right, but rather characterize each particle only by its internal properties such as total hypercharge and mean-square baryonic radius. Although the fundamental couplings of the theory are highly symmetric and universal, it is possible for the three couplings *alone* to account for the observed mass spectrum. The theory can explain, in a trivial manner, why there are no "elementary" particles with baryon number greater than unity provided that the baryonic current coupling is sufficiently strong. The question of whether or not an $|S| = 2$ meson exists is a dynamical one (not a group-theoretic one) that depends on the strength of the hypercharge current coupling. A possible reason for the nonexistence of a $\pi^{0\prime}$ (charge-singlet, nonstrange boson) is given. The theory realizes Pais' principles of economy of constants and of a hierarchy of interactions in a natural and elegant manner.

It is conjectured that there exists a deep connection between the law of conservation of fermions and the universal V-A weak coupling. In the absence of strong and electromagnetic interactions, baryonic charge, hypercharge, and electric charge all disappear, and only the sign of γ_5 can distinguish a fermion from an antifermion, the fermionic charge being diagonalized by γ_5; hence $1 + \gamma_5$ appears naturally in weak interactions. Parity conservation in strong interactions, parity conservation in electromagnetic interactions, parity nonconservation in weak interactions can all be understood from the *single common* principle of generalized gauge invariance. It appears that in the future ultimate theory of elementary particles all elementary particle interactions will be manifestations of the five fundamental vector-type couplings corresponding to the five conservation laws of "internal attributes"—baryonic charge, hypercharge, isospin, electric charge, and fermionic charge. Gravity and cosmology are briefly discussed; it is estimated that the Compton wavelength of the graviton is of the order of 10^8 light years.

It is suggested that every conceivable experimental attempt be made to detect directly quantum manifestations of the vector fields introduced in the theory, especially by studying Q values of pions in various combinations in $N\bar{N}$ annihilations and in multiple pion production.

PAPER 61

ELECTRON SCATTERING FROM THE PROTON*

F. Bumiller, M. Croissiaux,† and R. Hofstadter
Department of Physics and High-Energy Physics Laboratory, Stanford University, Stanford, California
(Received August 25, 1960)

We have recently put into operation a new large double-focusing magnetic spectrometer capable of analyzing electrons or other singly-charged particles up to a momentum value of 1000 Mev/c. This spectrometer is of the 180° type previously used in this laboratory and has a mean radius of curvature of 72 in. We have employed this spectrometer in electron-scattering work on the proton between incident electron energies of 650 Mev and 900 Mev and between scattering angles of 45° and 145°. A typical value of the solid angle employed in detecting electrons is 5.6×10^{-3} steradian. The higher energies (> 650 Mev) have been realized by virtue of the recent extension in the length of the Stanford linear accelerator.

The 72-in. spectrometer forms part of a two-magnet system; the second part is the 36-in. spectrometer described previously.[1] Figure 1 is a schematic drawing of the two spectrometers in a position in which they are 120° apart. Both spectrometers are arranged so that they can be rotated independently about a common scattering center. We have taken data simultaneously with both spectrometers, usually employing the 36-in. magnet at large angles, e.g., up to 145°. The 36-in. spectrometer can handle scattered electrons only up to 500 Mev/c without excessive deterioration of focusing and we have used the 36-in. spectrometer in these experiments only in the very safe region below 370 Mev/c. Such a procedure limits, and has limited in the past, the ability of this spectrometer in obtaining scattering data at high energies and small angles,[1,2] i.e., in those circumstances where the energy of the scattered electron is high.

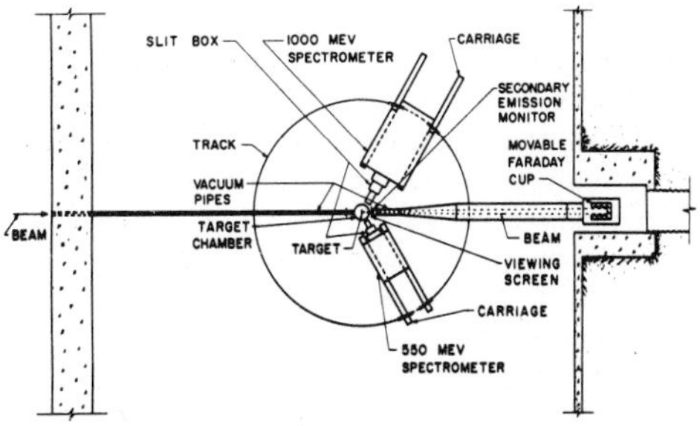

FIG. 1. The double spectrometer system used in these experiments.

We have begun to carry out a series of experiments on the proton at various energies and angles with these spectrometers. In both instruments we used Čerenkov counters as detectors. In. Fig. 2(a) we show a typical electron-scattering

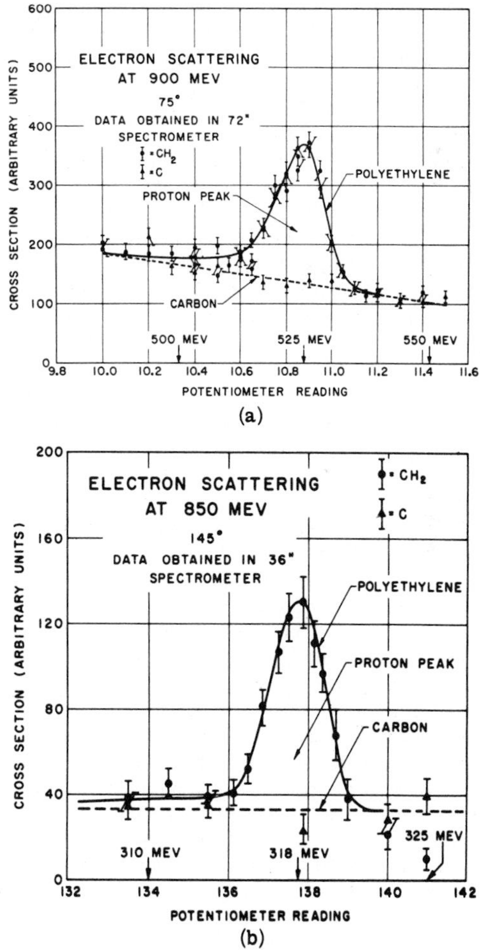

FIG. 2. (a) Electron-scattering peak obtained with a 0.237-in. polyethylene target at an incident energy of 900 Mev and a scattering angle of 75°. The target was at 45° with respect to the incident beam. (b) Same except parameters are 850 Mev, 145°, 36-in. spectrometer, and target at 0°.

peak obtained with the 72-in. spectrometer at an incident energy of 900 Mev and a scattering angle of 75°. The target material was polyethylene and we have subtracted the carbon background in analyzing the data to obtain the proton-scattering peak. The carbon data were obtained in the same run with a separate graphite target. In Fig. 2(b) we show a corresponding peak obtained in the 36-in. spectrometer at 850 Mev and 145°.

The cross sections obtained in this work are absolute cross sections and are based on the readings of the Faraday cup shown in Fig. 1 which gives the number of electrons in the main beam. The secondary emission monitor was an adjunct used as a monitor for the 72-in. spectrometer and was calibrated during each run with reference to the Faraday cup. The Faraday cup was the same unit used in previous experiments.[2] In our present experiments the vacuum pipe leading to the Faraday cup was not used.

It is difficult at the present time to estimate the errors associated with our absolute cross sections. The main uncertainty is the detection efficiency of our Čerenkov counters. These counters have been tested carefully but it is still possible that a 10% or smaller error remains in our efficiency measurements. Our efficiency measurements differ very little from 100% and we have therefore used this figure as the detector efficiency. Statistical errors are usually small compared with possible systematic errors and perhaps a measure of our errors should be the differences between individual measurements made under the same conditions of energy and angle. These differences are always less than ±10%. Another small source of uncertainty is the value of the dispersion constant of the 72-in. spectrometer. We have measured the dispersion constant to an accuracy of about 5%.

Our results are presented in Table I and include standard radiative corrections.[1] In addition to the cross sections in the Table we give the values of the square of the momentum transfer. In many cases we have given a single value as an average of several measured cross sections. As a general rule we believe our results are accurate to about ±10% because of the aforementioned possible errors. Relatively speaking, errors are probably less than ±5%. Our interpretation of the above results will be given in an accompanying paper.[3]

We understand that the Cornell group[4] is investigating the same electron-scattering problem.

Table I. Summary of results.

E (Mev)	θ (deg)	q^2 (fermi^{-2})	$(d\sigma/d\Omega)\times 10^{33}$ (cm^2/sr)
597	60°	6.96	67.9
597	90°	11.20	8.76
597	120°	14.06	2.65
650	135°	16.97	1.51
700	60°	9.16	38.0
700	75°	12.01	11.2
700	135°	18.90	0.955
700	145°	19.43	0.778
750	45°	6.86	136
750	75°	13.45	10.0
750	90°	16.06	4.08
750	135°	20.86	0.728
750	141.5°	21.24	0.735
750	145°	21.42	0.580
775	135°	21.86	0.644
800	45°	7.70	104
800	60°	11.53	23.5
800	75°	14.93	8.19
800	90°	17.75	2.99
800	120°	21.64	0.888
800	135°	22.86	0.605
800	145°	23.44	0.360
850	45°	8.59	80.6
850	60°	12.77	17.8
850	75°	16.46	5.62
850	120°	23.60	0.711
850	135°	24.88	0.509
850	145°	25.50	0.371
875	40°	7.56	127
875	45°	9.05	82.0
875	60°	13.42	15.7
875	145°	26.54	0.376
900	45°	9.51	61.5
900	60°	14.06	14.3
900	75°	18.03	5.35
900	90°	21.24	2.09
900	145°	27.58	0.347

Unfortunately we have no firm data of that group to compare with our results.

We wish to acknowledge most gratefully the cheerful cooperation and assistance we have received from D. Aitken, P. Auvil, C. Buchanan, G. Burleson, B. Chambers, H. Collard, E. Dally, P. Gram, T. Janssens, M. Ryneveld, and W. Wadensweiler.

*This work was supported in part by the Office of Naval Research and the U. S. Atomic Energy Commission, and by the U. S. Air Force, through the Office of Scientific Research of the Air Research and Development Command.

†Visitor from University of Strasbourg, Strasbourg, France.

[1]E. E. Chambers and R. Hofstadter, Phys. Rev. 103, 1454 (1956).

[2]R. Herman and R. Hofstadter, High-Energy Electron Scattering Tables (Stanford University Press, Stanford, California, 1960), and the work of F. Bumiller and R. Hofstadter shown in Fig. 8 of this reference.

[3]R. Hofstadter, F. Bumiller, and M. Croissiaux, following Letter [Phys. Rev. Letters 5, 263 (1960)].

[4]K. Berkelman and J. Cassels (private communication).

PAPER 62

SPLITTING OF THE PROTON FORM FACTORS AND DIFFRACTION IN THE PROTON*

R. Hofstadter, F. Bumiller, and M. Croissiaux†
Department of Physics and High-Energy Physics Laboratory, Stanford University, Stanford, California
(Received August 25, 1960)

Electron-scattering studies of the proton obtained in the last few years have been summarized recently.[1] The measurements showed that the proton form factors (F_1, F_2) were less than unity, implying a finite structure, and lay in a region in which they were approximately equal to each other at momentum transfers (q) as high as $q^2 = 9.3$ in units of squared inverse fermis. At this value of the momentum transfer the measured ratio was $F_1/F_2 = 1.23 \pm 0.20$.[2] The experiments were confined to angles larger than 60° at the highest energies then obtainable (650 Mev) because of the limitation imposed by the energy-handling ability of the 36-in. spectrometer. It was therefore not possible to solve for F_1 and F_2 separately at values of $q^2 \geq 9.3$. Several independent experiments[2,3] indicated that the F_1 values were slightly greater than the F_2 values at the same momentum transfer, but for simplicity and ease of calculation, in the past, the ratio of form factors was usually taken to be unity.

We have now succeeded in splitting apart the two proton form factors. Because of the great interest in the proton form factors and because our data appear to be internally consistent, we wish to present in this paper some conclusions drawn from the experimental results given in the accompanying paper.[4]

Our procedure has been to solve for the separate form factors (F_1, F_2) at conditions lying between $7.7 \leq q^2 \leq 25$ by choosing a pair of experimentally measured cross sections at the same value of q^2 but at different correlated values of energy and angle. We have used the method of intersecting ellipses[5] to find the form factors.

Table I shows the values selected and the form factors found by combining the results. In a few cases, indicated by asterisks, we have used older data and combined the older values with the newly-measured cross section at the same value of q^2. In two cases (866 Mev, 75°; 675

Table I. Form factors F_1 and F_2.

q^2 (f^{-2})	E_1 (Mev)	θ_1 (deg)	$(d\sigma/d\Omega)_1$ (cm^2/sr)	E_2 (Mev)	θ_2 (deg)	$(d\sigma/d\Omega)_2$ (cm^2/sr)	F_1	F_2
7.70	800	45°	1.04×10^{-31}	400	124°	*1.06×10^{-32}	0.520	0.490
9.16	700	60°	3.80×10^{-32}	464	135°	*6.26×10^{-33}	0.500	0.420
11.50	800	60°	2.35×10^{-32}	500	135°	*4.18×10^{-33}	0.451	0.341
14.06	900	60°	1.43×10^{-32}	597	120°	2.65×10^{-33}	0.423	0.214
16.97	866	75°	5.56×10^{-33}	650	135°	1.51×10^{-33}	0.430	0.160
18.03	900	75°	5.35×10^{-33}	675	135°	1.23×10^{-33}	0.451	0.108
21.24	900	90°	2.09×10^{-33}	750	141.5°	7.35×10^{-34}	0.405	0.087

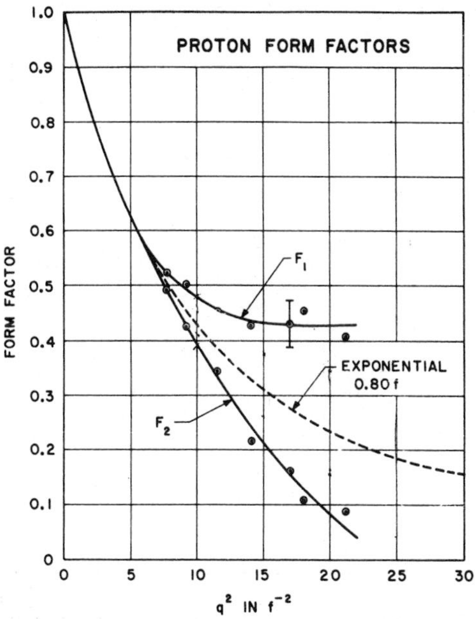

FIG. 1. The proton form factors obtained in Table I, plotted against q^2. F_2 may be approaching a diffraction zero.

Mev, 135°) we have interpolated between two newly-measured results in order to obtain properly matched pairs of cross sections.

The form factor results now show the behavior plotted in Fig. 1. The dashed line is the form factor corresponding to the exponential model and $F_1 = F_2$. Apparently our new F_2, which is seen to approach zero, indicates qualitatively that the Pauli magnetic moment cloud is a "soft," spread-out distribution. On the other hand, the constancy of F_1 suggests qualitatively that the Dirac electric/magnetic cloud has a small, perhaps point-like, core.

The form factors found in the above manner were then put back into the well-known Rosenbluth Eq. (40) of reference 1:

$$d\sigma/d\Omega = \sigma_{NS}\{a_{11}F_1^{\,2} + a_{12}F_1F_2 + a_{22}F_2^{\,2}\}, \quad (1)$$

where the values of the coefficients a_{11}, a_{12}, and a_{22} are taken from the tables[1] at the appropriate energies and angles. When this is done we obtain the results shown in Fig. 2. Notice that in Fig. 2(c) the cross section appears to be going through a diffraction dip, so characteristic of electron-scattering studies on heavier nuclei. The experimental data indeed show this diffraction dip and we believe that this is the first time diffraction has been observed in the proton.

Within experimental error the new experimental results appear to be in agreement with the split form factor curves. It is very interesting to observe that the new form factors account for an increase of the cross section above the exponential case at small angles, merge approximately with the exponential case at 120°, and drift below the exponential case at the large angles 135° and 145°. This is what the experiments appear to indicate and the result is a rather complicated pattern of cross sections which the form factors must satisfy. The experimental data appear to fit the calculated curves for separate form factors absolutely as well as relatively.

The data are in excellent agreement with the earlier experimental results.[1] The measurements of a proton root-mean-square radius appear to remain undisturbed because those measurements were made at low q values. However, we are aware that at higher values of q^2 the conclusions about the neutron's form factors may be influenced slightly.[1,6] This question is now under investigation by R. Herman and the authors. It may be pointed out that the inelastic electron-scattering studies on the deuteron should perhaps yield new information on the F_1 form factor of the neutron when combined with these results. It is interesting to speculate on whether the proton's F_2 factor rises again after approaching zero at about $q^2 \cong 24$ or whether it becomes negative at that point. In our analysis we assumed $F_2 \cong 0$ at $q^2 > 24$.

By use of these results new information on F_2 of the neutron should result from a study of the deuteron's elastic scattering at large angles.

We wish to thank Mr. Francis Lewis for his help in making some of the calculations with intersecting ellipses.

---

*This work was supported in part by the Office of Naval Research and the U. S. Atomic Energy Commission, and by the U. S. Air Force, through the Office of Scientific Research of the Air Research and Development Command.

†Visitor from University of Strasbourg, Strasbourg, France.

[1]R. Herman and R. Hofstadter, High-Energy Electron Scattering Tables (Stanford University Press, Stanford, California, 1960).

[2]F. Bumiller and R. Hofstadter; see Fig. 8, p. 28,

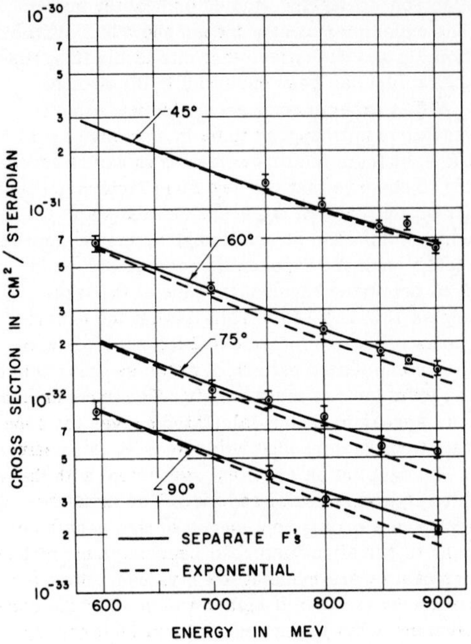

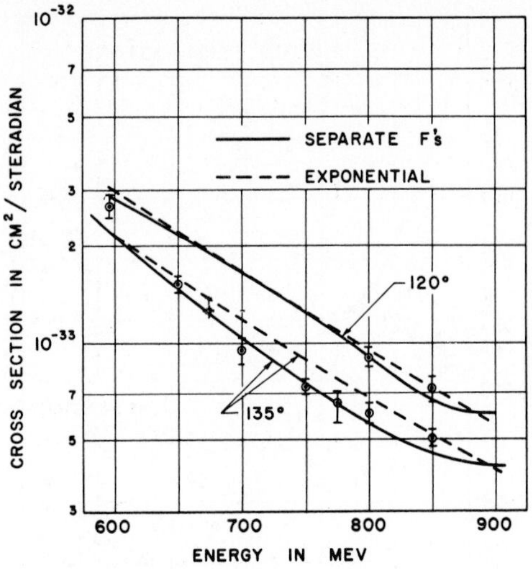

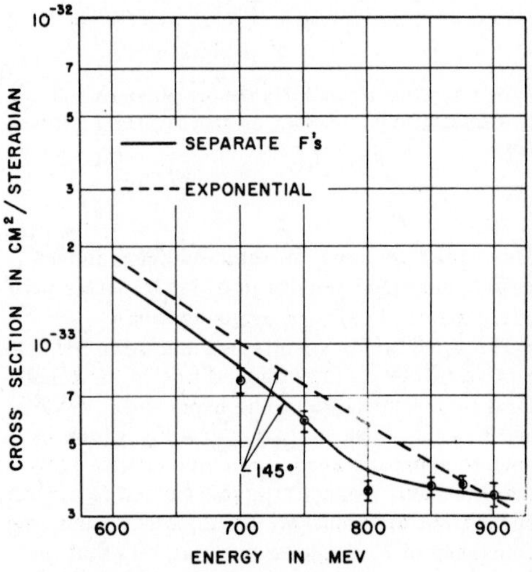

FIG. 2. Comparison of observed and calculated cross sections. The experimental points are shown by hollow circles. The dashed line refers to the case $F_1 = F_2$ and corresponds to the form factors deduced from the old exponential model.[1] The solid line is obtained from Eq. (1) and the newly-obtained form factors of Table I and Fig. 1.

of reference 1.

[3]E. E. Chambers and R. Hofstadter, Phys. Rev. 103, 454 (1956).

[4]F. Bumiller, M. Croissiaux, and R. Hofstadter, preceding Letter [Phys. Rev. Letters 5, 261 (1960)].

[5]R. Hofstadter, Ninth Annual International Conference on High-Energy Physics, Kiev, July, 1959 (unpublished). See also reference 1, pp. 30-32.

[6]R. Hofstadter, F. Bumiller, and M. R. Yearian, Revs. Modern Phys. 30, 482 (1958).

SCATTERING OF HIGH-ENERGY ELECTRONS BY PROTONS

By PROF. R. R. WILSON, DR. K. BERKELMAN, PROF. J. M. CASSELS*, F.R.S., and DR. D. N. OLSON

Laboratory of Nuclear Studies, Cornell University, Ithaca, N.Y.

THE elastic scattering of electrons by protons is described[1] by the Rosenbluth formula (lengths will be expressed in fermis, and $\hbar = c = 1$. For momenta $1 f^{-1} = 197$ MeV./c.):

$$\frac{d\sigma}{d\Omega} = \frac{\alpha^2}{4E^2}\frac{\cos^2\theta/2}{\sin^4\theta/2}\left[1 + \left(\frac{2E}{M}\right)\sin^2\theta/2\right]^{-1}$$

$$\left\{F_1{}^2 + \frac{q^2}{4M^2}\left[2(F_1 + \varkappa F_2)^2\tan^2\frac{\theta}{2} + \varkappa^2 F_2{}^2\right]\right\} \qquad (1)$$

where $\frac{d\sigma}{d\Omega}$ is the laboratory differential cross-section, α is the fine structure constant, E is the laboratory energy of the incident electron, θ is the laboratory angle of scattering, M is the proton mass, $q^2 = 4E^2 \sin^2\theta/2[1 + (2E/M)\sin^2\theta/2]^{-1}$ is the square of the four-momentum transfer, and $\varkappa = 1{\cdot}79$ is the anomalous magnetic moment of the proton in nuclear magnetons. The form factors F_1 and F_2 are associated respectively with the Dirac and Pauli interactions of the proton with an electromagnetic field.

The formula, of course, relies on the validity of conventional quantum electrodynamics, and also on the absence of fourth-order processes in which two photons are exchanged between the electron and the physical nucleon. Both assumptions are expected to be valid in the conditions of the experiment described here, although the second one may well break down at energies not much greater[2].

For convenience a cross-section $\frac{d\sigma'}{d\Omega}$, loosely referred

* Now at the Chadwick Laboratory, University of Liverpool.

to as the 'point proton cross-section', may be defined by writing $F_1 = F_2 = 1$ in the formula; then experimental results can be expressed in terms of $F^2(q^2,\theta)$, where:

$$\frac{d\sigma}{d\Omega} = F^2(q^2,\theta)\,\frac{d\sigma'}{d\Omega} \tag{2}$$

Clearly F can be expressed in terms of F_1 and F_2 as required.

Hofstadter *et al.*[3], using electrons with energies up to 650 MeV. from the Stanford linac, have studied the scattering at 75° ($q^2 \lesssim 11 f^{-2}$) and 135° ($q^2 \lesssim 17 f^{-2}$). Their results are well fitted by writing:

$$F = F_1 = F_2 = (1 + 0{\cdot}0533\, q^2)^{-2} \tag{3}$$

A recent letter by Hand[4], who also used the Stanford linac, reports measurements at 135° for $q^2 \approx 26 f^{-2}$. These results are also consistent with equation (3).

This article reports an investigation of the scattering in which q^2 ranged up to $25 f^{-2}$ at 66° and at 112°. As will be seen, the results at the higher angle agree with Hand's. At the lower angle, on the other hand, a variation of F^2 with θ is revealed which can only mean that F_1 and F_2 are not equal.

Apparatus and Procedure

Figs. 1 and 2 show vertical and horizontal views of the general layout and of the counter telescope. The electron beam of the Cornell synchrotron spiralled inwards at the peak of the magnetic cycle, as a result of controlled decrease of the radiofrequency accelerating voltage. For periods of about 1 msec., repeated 30 times per sec., the electrons bombarded polyethylene or carbon targets in a scattering chamber located in one of the straight sections. The targets were in the form of rods about 1/16 in. square, disposed horizontally in the median plane of the synchrotron at an angle of 45° to the beam direction. The tips of the targets were 1·1 cm. inside the normal equilibrium orbit of the beam. Discoloration of the polyethylene showed that the targets were bombarded at distances up to 1/16 in. back from the tips.

A totally absorbing ion chamber, or quantameter[5], integrated absolutely the bremsstrahlung emitted from the target. Knowledge of the radiation-length of the target materials at the various electron energies gives directly the effective product of the target thickness and the incident electron charge, which is the quantity required for cross-section calculations. It was evident that on the average the electrons traversed the target about ten times before being finally lost from the synchrotron.

Photographs were taken of the bremsstrahlung spot immediately in front of the ion chamber. Usually these showed a clean spot about 1/4 in. in diameter, which checked that electrons were not hitting objects, other than the targets, in or near the scattering chamber. In the early stages of the experiment a second diffuse spot was sometimes caused by electrons hitting a beam-detecting device at the upstream entrance to the chamber; this improper mode of operation was associated with incorrect monitoring and low measured cross-sections. The trouble was eliminated by adjustment of the in-phase correction coils which steer the synchrotron beam at high energies.

Scattered electrons, or recoil protons, left the scattering chamber through a 0·005 in. 'Mylar' window and were then deflected magnetically by a single quadrupole lens. This produced vertical focusing of the particles passing over or under a central obstacle 3·7 in. high, made of lead and copper. The momentum window of the spectrometer was defined by this obstacle and by the plastic scintillator A, the maximum height of which was 1/8 in. In vertical section this scintillator had the shape of a truncated diamond, in order to obtain the best possible bias curve for the pulses.

The quadrupole lens was of course defocusing horizontally, and therefore scintillator A was made 8 in. wide. In a typical run the collected particles were emitted at semi-horizontal angles up to 0·97°, measured at the target with respect to the central ray; the total solid angle collected by the spectrometer was 4·41 millisteradians.

The momenta of the particles varied with the horizontal angle of emission, an effect which was only appreciable for recoil protons. To compensate for it, scintillator A was turned through a small angle (for example, 18° at 1,205 MeV.) round its vertical axis, counterclockwise as seen from above.

For a point target on the axis the theoretical curve of detection efficiency versus magnetic field gradient, for a fixed momentum particle, was trapezoidal in shape. It had an almost flat top and a typical full width of 3·1 per cent at half-efficiency. In practice the resolution curve was smeared by the finite height of the target and various multiple scattering processes, especially for recoil protons. However, the area under the peak should not be seriously changed by these

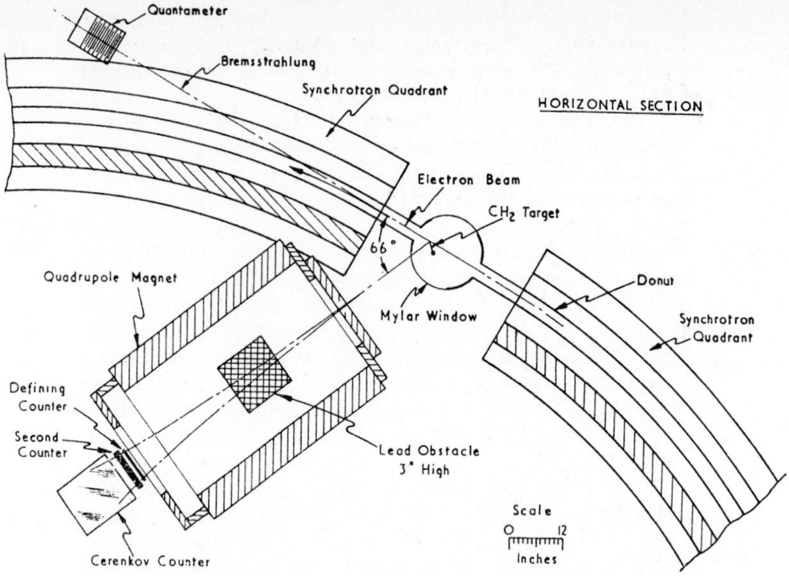

Fig. 1. Plan view of the apparatus described in the text

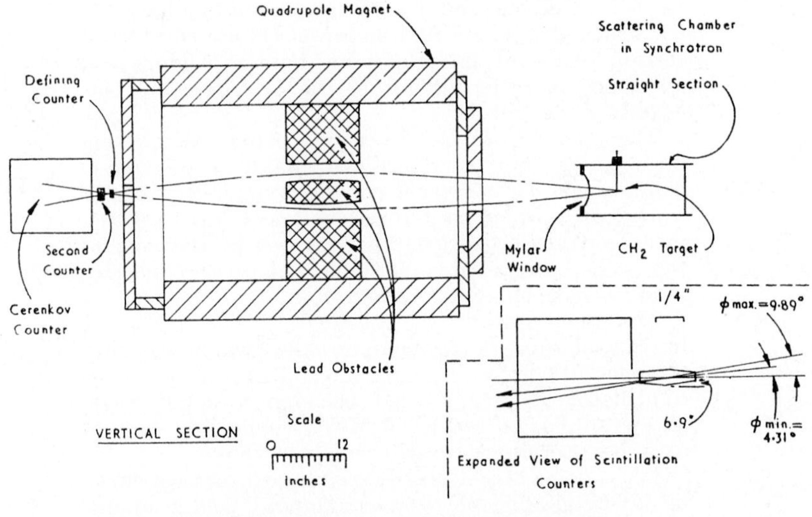

Fig. 2. Side view of the target, spectrometer, and counter telescope. The inset shows an enlarged view of the two scintillation counters

effects, and so the cross-sections were computed by integrating peaks in the experimental counting-rate as a function of magnetic field gradient. Actually the voltage across a shunt in series with the exciting coils of the magnet was used as the independent variable, and the areas multiplied by an appropriate constant. At the highest momenta the field gradients were not quite proportional to the existing currents, and a differential correction ($\gtrsim 9$ per cent) was made for this.

The procedure just outlined was used for (*a*) the 66° scattering of 587, 684, 781, 879 and 1,034 MeV. electrons, (*b*) the 112° scattering of 320 and 761 MeV. electrons, and (*c*) the protons recoiling at 66° from the scattering of electrons with energies of 684, 781, 982, 1,034, 1,173 and 1,205 MeV.

The counting rate was measured only in the region of the peak for (*d*) the 66° scattering of 982, 1,085, 1,173, and 1,215 MeV. electrons, and (*e*) the 112° scattering of 909 MeV. electrons. The corresponding cross-sections were evaluated using the line shape established in the full sets of measurements.

The other two counters in the telescope were used to reduce backgrounds. Counter *C* was inoperative when the comparatively slow recoil protons were being detected, and the bias on the plastic scintillator counter *B* was raised so that relativistic particles were not detected. Coincidences between counters *A* and *B* were required, the effective pulse widths being about 0·5 μsec.

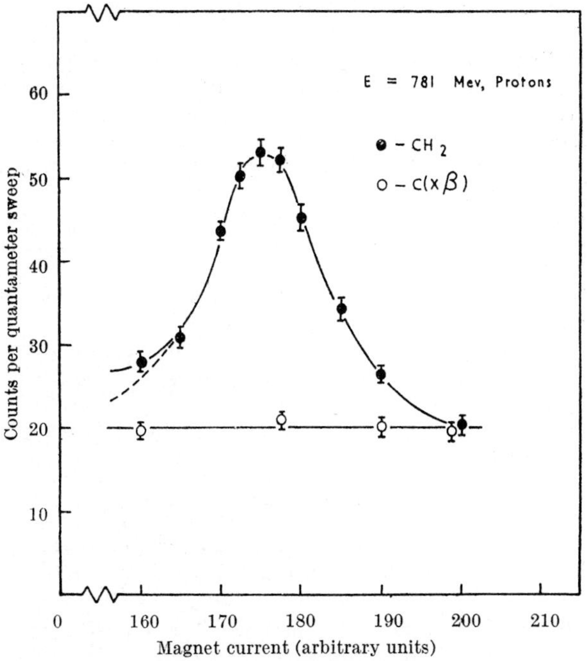

Fig. 3. The counting-rate as a function of magnet current; protons recoiling at 66° from collisions of 781-MeV. incident electrons

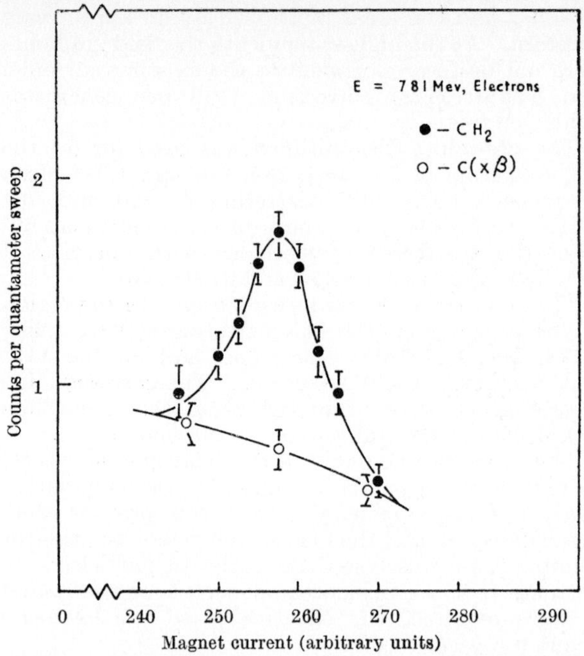

Fig. 4. The counting-rate as a function of magnet current; electrons scattered at 66° from collisions of 781-MeV. incident electrons

When electrons were being detected the bias on counter B was lowered, and counter C was brought into operation. This was a lead glass total absorption Čerenkov detector, which produced recognizably large pulses when the desired electrons arrived. Triple coincidences between counters A, B and C were required, the effective width of the mixed pulses being about 20 ns. for A, 200 ns. for C, and 0·7 μs. for B. Each triple coincidence event opened an electronic gate, allowing the output from counter C to reach a pulse-height analyser.

At all times the electronic equipment was gated by a 4 ms. pulse locked to the peak of the magnetic cycle of the synchrotron. This reduced corrections for cosmic ray events ($\lesssim$ 10 per cent, but usually negligible).

Results

Figs. 3 and 4 show respectively the recoil proton and the scattered electron peaks observed at 66° from 781-MeV. incident electrons. The ordinates are the coincidence counts observed per 'sweep' of the quantameter (1 sweep $= 4{\cdot}97 \times 10^{12}$ MeV.), and the abscissæ are the voltages in the spectrometer shunt.

The counting-rate as a function of the magnet current after subtraction of the rate from carbon

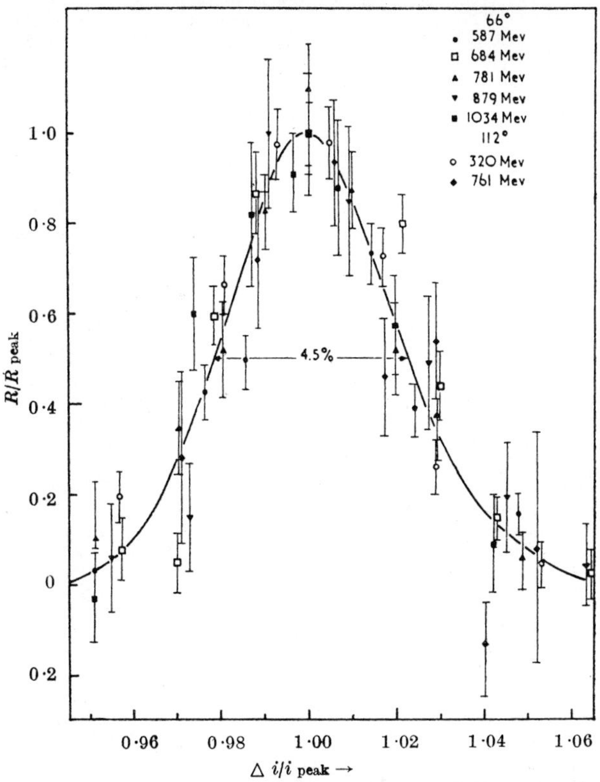

Fig. 5. Line shape of the peaks caused by elastically scattered electrons

The carbon target results have been multiplied by a normalizing factor $\beta = 0{\cdot}89$, which equalizes the effects of the carbon nuclei in the two target materials. Rather clean elastic peaks are revealed in both figures, although there is a small inelastic tail in the proton distribution. Fig. 5 shows the line shapes observed in all the complete sets of electron measurements, before correction for saturation.

It was found that the height of a peak decreased slowly if a given polyethylene target was bombarded for a long time. Presumably this was due to ejection of the hydrogen from the target, an effect probably correlated with a brownish discoloration which also appeared. The polyethylene targets were changed every few hours and a suitable correction for ageing was established and applied ($\lesssim$ 3 per cent).

Finally, the usual radiation correction ($\lesssim$ 13 per cent) was applied to allow for the emission of bremsstrahlung in the electron-proton scattering process.

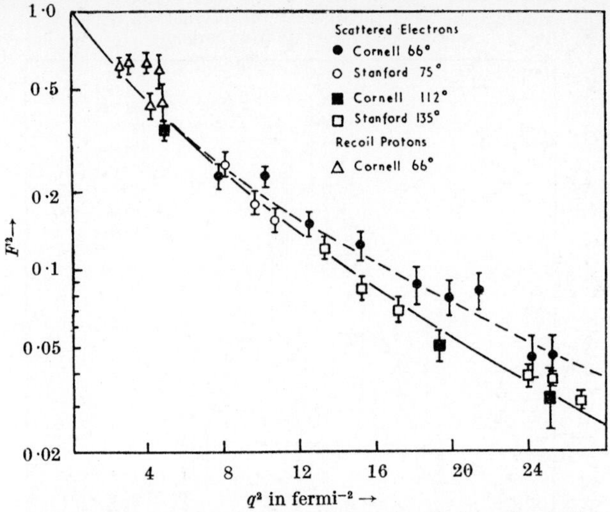

Fig. 6. Experimental results, including Stanford results at high q^2. The full line is given by the formula $F^2 = (1+0{\cdot}0533\ q^2)^{-4}$, while the dashed line is fitted to the 66° experimental points at high q^2

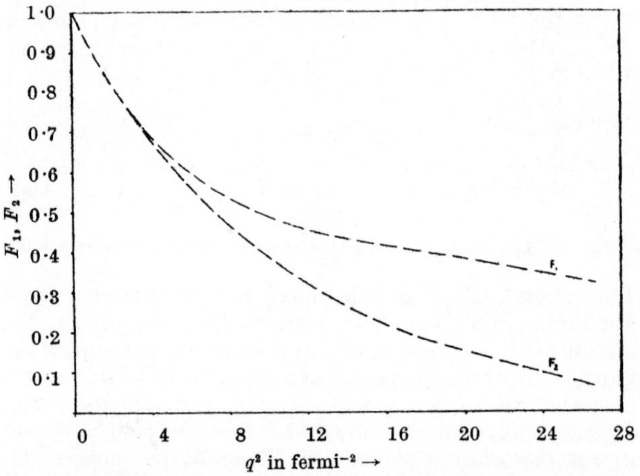

Fig. 7. The individual form factors required to reproduce the full line of Fig. 6 at 135°, and the dashed line of Fig. 6 at 66°

The results, expressed as a plot of F^2 against q^2, are shown in Fig. 6. For comparison some of the results of Hofstadter *et al.* are also shown, together with those of Hand.

Discussion

The results of the present experiment clearly agree well with the Stanford data wherever they overlap, that is for $q^2 \lesssim 11\, f^{-2}$ when $\theta < 90°$, and for $q^2 \lesssim 26 f^{-2}$ when $\theta > 90°$. Often the form factors at low q^2 are expanded in the static approximation :

$$F_{1,2} = 1 - \frac{1}{6}\, a_{1,2}^2\, q^2 + \ . \ . \ . \tag{4}$$

where $a_{1,2}$ are the root mean square radii of the charge and the anomalous magnetic moment of the proton. Thus no change is indicated in the conclusion of Hofstadter *et al.* that these radii are about $0{\cdot}8\ f$. It should be noted, however, that equation (4) is subject to relativistic and dynamic corrections of the order of q^2/M^2, so that the exact physical significance of this line of interpretation is not very clear.

At high values of q^2 the points for $\theta < 90°$ (circles and dashed line in Fig. 6) flatten out[6] and lie consistently higher than the points for $\theta > 90°$ (squares and full line in Fig. 6). This behaviour indicates that F_1 and F_2 are not equal, and in fact an average of the points near $q^2 = 20$ gives $\frac{F_2}{F_1} = 0{\cdot}37 \begin{matrix} +\,0{\cdot}17 \\ -\,0{\cdot}14 \end{matrix}$. Fig. 7 shows the individual values of F_1 and F_2 which would give the dashed and full lines of Fig. 6 at angles of 66° and 135° respectively. The two form factors must behave in this general fashion, although at present their values have clearly not been determined with precision. (This conclusion was reported by one of us (R. R. W.) to the Tenth Annual Rochester Conference on High Energy Physics (August 25–September 1, 1960). A subsequent paper by Prof. R. Hofstadter included a similar deduction on the basis of recent work at Stanford.)

The flattening out of F_1 at $q^2 \approx 12\ f^{-2}$ must be associated with the inner structure of the proton, at radii of the order of $0{\cdot}3\,f$. The charge density in this region may be expected to include contributions from virtual states containing nucleon–antinucleon pairs, kaons and multiple pions. It is likely to be some time before these various effects are disentangled with any certainty.

The most promising line of theoretical attack is based on the dispersion theory[7,8] of the isotopic scalar and vector parts of the nucleon form factors. Unfortunately there are no general theorems relating the neutron and proton form factors, so that data on electron–neutron scattering at high q^2, for both large and small angles, are needed before further progress can be made.

We are indebted to Dr. P. C. Stein and Mr. D. Edwards for help in taking readings, and to Mr. A. Contogouris for helpful discussions on theoretical matters. Mr. P. D. O'Neill gave valuable help with numerical computations. The co-operation of the synchrotron crew is gratefully acknowledged.

This work was supported by the Office of Naval Research and the U.S. Atomic Energy Commission.

[1] Rosenbluth, M. N., *Phys. Rev.*, **79**, 615 (1950).

[2] Drell, S. D., and Fubini, S., *Phys. Rev.*, **113**, 741 (1959).

[3] Hofstadter, R., Bumiller, F., and Yearian, M. R., *Rev. Mod. Phys.*, **30**, 482 (1958).

[4] Hand, L. N., *Phys. Rev. Letters*, **5**, 168 (1960).

[5] Wilson, R. R., *Nuclear Instr.*, **1**, 101 (1957).

[6] Berkelman, K., Cassels, J. M., and Wilson, R. R., *Bull. Amer. Phys. Soc.*, II, **5**, 282 (1960).

[7] Chew, G. F., Karplus, R., Gasiorowicz, S., and Zachariasen, F., *Phys. Rev.*, **110**, 265 (1958).

[8] Federbush, P., Goldberger, M. L., and Treiman, S. B., *Phys. Rev.*, **112**, 642 (1958).

PAPER 64

ELECTROMAGNETIC PROPERTIES OF THE PROTON AND NEUTRON*

D. N. Olson, H. F. Schopper,† and R. R. Wilson
Laboratory of Nuclear Studies, Cornell University, Ithaca, New York
(Received February 15, 1961)

Measurements of electron-proton scattering made at Cornell[1] and Stanford[2] below 1000 Mev have shown that F_{1p} and F_{2p}, the electric and magnetic form factors of the proton, are not equal; indeed that F_{2p} is nearly zero for values of q, the momentum-energy transfer, of about 5 fermi^{-1}, while F_{1p} remains in the vicinity of 0.4—all this is indicative of a core of charge of about 0.4 e.

New measurements of scattering cross sections from hydrogen and deuterium at higher values of q appear to permit us to determine the extent and charge of this core of the nucleon and also to deduce similar properties of the surrounding mesonic cloud. The Cornell 1.3-Bev electron synchrotron has been used in extending our earlier measurements in exactly the manner described in Nature.[1] The new results are shown in Table I and Figs. 1 and 3. It is of striking physical significance that the cross section falls so low at 1.2 Bev, i.e., to 10^{-34} cm^2/sr.

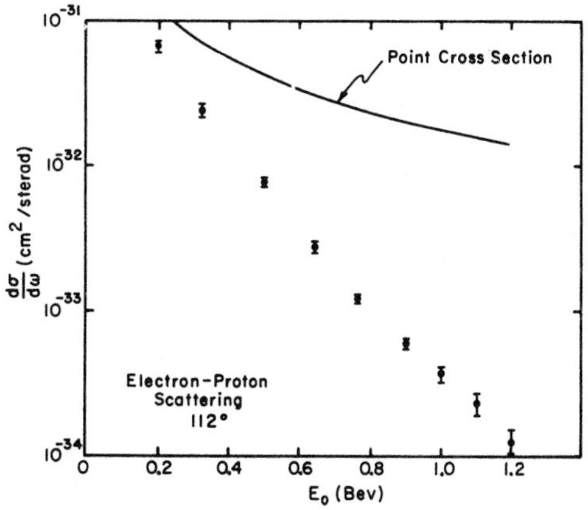

FIG. 1. Experimental results for electron-proton scattering at 112°.

Now one of the simplest models of the nucleon has a point core of charge $+\frac{1}{2}e$ surrounded by an extended mesonic cloud of $+\frac{1}{2}e$ for the proton or $-\frac{1}{2}e$ for the neutron. Indeed, some aspects of such a model are reflected in the experimental data, but the model departs significantly from the facts at a number of points. In the first place, from Foldy's interpretation of neutron scattering by atomic electrons[3] we know that the rms radius of the charge distribution of the neutron is zero and this implies that at $q \approx 0$, $F_{1n} \lesssim 0.002q^2$; the above picture implies that $F_{1n} = \frac{1}{6}(0.8)^2 q^2$, q^2 being measured in fermi^{-2}. In the second place,

Table I. Experimental results. Columns 2 and 3 give the experimentally determined cross sections and peak cross sections for electrons of incident energy E_0 scattered through an angle of 112°. Radiative corrections have been applied. In order to calculate the integrated deuteron cross sections, allowance must be made for electrons which do not scatter into the detection channel because of internal motion of the nucleons in the deuteron. Calculating the energy spread of scattered electrons using the impulse approximation and including the resolution of the apparatus as determined from electron-proton scattering, we obtain the values for $\Delta E/E$ listed in column 4. Then, subtracting the proton cross section from column 2, we arrive at the integrated cross section for electron-neutron scattering given in the last column.

E_0 (Mev)	$(d\sigma/d\omega)_p$ (10^{-32} cm^2/sr)	$(d^2\sigma/dE\,d\omega)_d$ (10^{-33} cm^2/Mev sr)	$\Delta E/E$	$(d\sigma/d\omega)_d$ (10^{-32} cm^2/sr)	$(d\sigma/d\omega)_n$ (10^{-32} cm^2/sr)
200	6.6 ±0.6	2.30 ±0.33	0.154	5.35 ±0.77	-1.2 ±1.2
325	2.40 ±0.25	0.85 ±0.076	0.133	2.49 ±0.23	0.09 ±0.34
502	0.76 ±0.06	0.250 ±0.016	0.112	0.78 ±0.11	0.15 ±0.12
640	0.270 ±0.023				
761	0.119 ±0.008	0.034 ±0.008	0.093	0.114 ±0.027	0.005 ±0.030
900	0.059 ±0.006				
1000	0.037 ±0.005	0.0158 ±0.0028	0.080	0.051 ±0.009	0.014 ±0.010
1100	0.023 ±0.004				
1200	0.0123 ±0.0025	0.0059 ±0.0028	0.074	0.019 ±0.009	0.007 ±0.009

the form factor F_{1p} should approach 0.5 for large values of q^2; in fact, it seems to be falling below 0.4. Nevertheless, we have interpreted our experiment in the spirit of this very simple model; to fit the facts we have found it necessary to assign a radius of about 0.2 f to the core and to put a small part of the positive charge of the core in an extensive cloud that is the same for neutron and proton.

If we assume that Rosenbluth's formula is still valid at our energies, i.e.,

$$\frac{d\sigma}{d\omega}=\frac{e^4}{4E^2}\,\frac{\cos^2(\theta/2)}{\sin^4(\theta/2)}\left[1+\left(\frac{2E}{M}\right)\sin^2(\theta/2)\right]^{-1}$$

$$\times\left\{F_1{}^2+\frac{q^2}{4M}\left[2(F_1+kF_2)^2\tan(\theta/2)+k^2F_2{}^2\right]\right\}, \quad (1)$$

where E is the incident electron energy, θ the laboratory angle, M the nucleon mass, and k the anomalous magnetic moment, then we want to find the form factors F_1 and F_2 which are functions of q^2, and for this at least two measurements of $d\sigma/d\omega$ at the same q value but at different angles are necessary. The data have been resolved in this manner for values of $q^2<25\ \mathrm{f}^{-2}$ where cross sections have been measured at 112° and 66°, and the values of F_1 and F_2 that have been obtained are plotted in Fig. 2. At values of $q^2>25$ we have only the data at 112°; at smaller angles the large values of q^2 cannot be reached with our available energy nor can we easily go to larger angles for then the counting rate becomes prohibitively small. We are preparing new experimental equipment, however, to do just this.

On the other hand, by measuring electron-deuteron scattering, we have been able to infer values of F_1 and F_2 for both the proton and neutron as follows: Equation (1) can be rewritten in the form

$$d\sigma/d\omega=(a_{11}F_1{}^2+a_{12}F_1F_2+a_{22}F_2{}^2)\sigma_{ns}, \quad (2)$$

so that we may use the values of the constants and σ_{ns}, the point "no-spin" electric cross section, which have been conveniently tabulated.[4] Thus an ellipse is obtained for a particular value of the cross section when F_2 is plotted against F_1. Such an ellipse is shown in Fig. 2 for the highest energy measured ($q^2=37$). Depending on the value of F_2, F_1 can take on values between plus and minus 0.3. Thus it may be that our

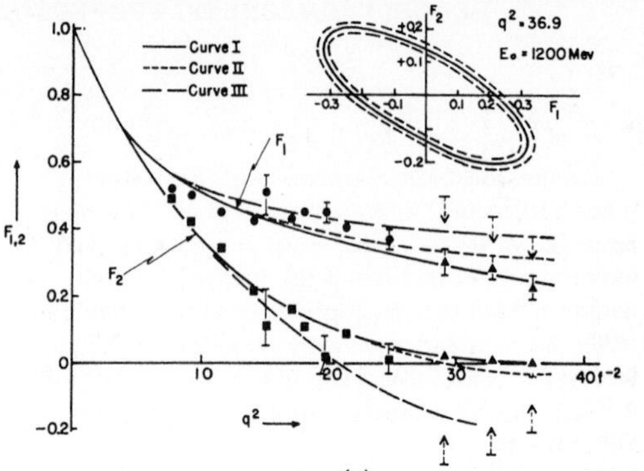

(a)

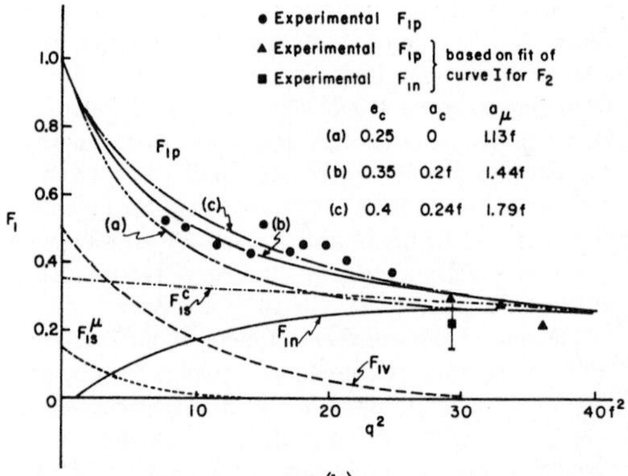

(b)

FIG. 2. (a) Experimentally determined form factors for the proton, as functions of the momentum transfer q. Circles (●) are used for the form factor F_{1p} and squares (■) for the magnetic form factor F_{2p} as determined from measurements at two different scattering angles (points with flags: Cornell data; points without flags: Stanford data). For $q^2>25$, only measurements at 112° were performed (Fig. 1). These determine ellipses in the F_1-F_2 plane, as shown in the insertion, from which the extreme values of F_{1p} and F_{2p} can be inferred. These are shown by the arrows but are not, of course, simultaneously realized. Assuming that F_{2p} is given by curves I, II, or III, one can derive respective values for F_{1p}. The results presented in Fig. 3 exclude curves II and III, so that curve I (▲) gives the proper values for F_{1p} and F_{2p}. (b) F_1 can be decomposed into partial form factors according to Eqs. (3) and (4). Three fits using the core charges and radii given in the insertion are shown. The experimental data are best reproduced by case (b). Only for this case are the partial form factors displayed. F_{1n} computed by using them is also included in the figure.

measured cross section, $\sim 10^{-34}$ cm^2/sr, is small because of destructive interference between large values of a positive F_{1p} and a negative F_{2p}. In the case of the neutron, however, the magnetic form factor would be just reversed so that the interference should then be constructive and a large value of the cross section would result. That the magnetic form factors of the proton and neutron are very nearly equal and opposite follows from the fact that the anomalous magnetic moments are equal and opposite to within 5 %.[5] The curves of Fig. 3 show the ratio of neutron and proton cross sections based on calculations using expression (2) for the neutron cross section with various assumptions for F_2, but assuming that F_1 is due to a core and is the same for neutron and proton—essentially true for $q^2 > 25$. The experimental points, obtained by replacing our CH_2 targets with CD_2, using the peak value method,[4] and then making the appropriate subtractions, are also shown. They are consistent with curves having values of $F_{2p} = 0 \pm 0.03$. We conclude, therefore, that $F_{2p} \sim 0$ and is, in fact, given as a function of q^2 by Curve I of Fig. 2. This can then be used to obtain the corresponding values of F_{1p} from ellipses similar to that of Fig. 2 but corresponding to measurements at $q^2 = 28.7$ and 32.7. These are plotted in Fig. 2. Curve II of Fig. 3 and the corresponding curve of Fig. 2(a) indicate the accuracy of

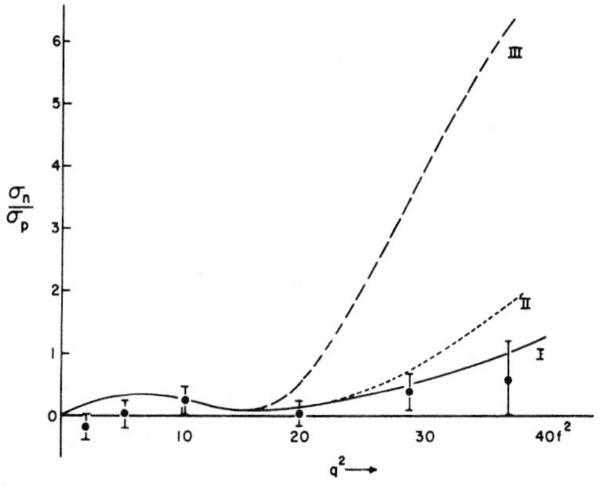

FIG. 3. The ratio of the neutron and proton cross sections as a function of the momentum transfer q. Curves I, II, and III were calculated with form factors F_{1p}, and $F_{2p} = F_{2n}$ given by the curves I, II, and III in Fig. 2(a), and with F_{1n} from Fig. 2(b). The experimental points were computed from the data in Table I.

this procedure, i.e., about ± 0.03 in the value of F_{2p} and ± 0.05 in F_{1p}. Note the pronounced minimum in the curve of electron-neutron scattering at $q^2 \approx 15$ f^{-2}, i.e., about 700 Mev.

Now let us see how the simple core model must be changed to conform with these form factors. We will separate each form factor into an isoscalar and an isovector partial form factor—the vector part changing its sign when we change from a proton to a neutron, the scalar part remaining unchanged. We can write

$$F_{1p} = F_{1S} + F_{1V}, \quad F_{1n} = F_{1S} - F_{1V}, \tag{3}$$

$$F_{2p} = F_{2S} + F_{2V}, \quad F_{2n} = F_{2S} - F_{2V}. \tag{4}$$

As the charges of the proton and the neutron are different, F_1 must consist of an isoscalar and an isovector part. F_2, on the other hand, will be determined predominantly by F_{2V} as the anomalous magnetic moments of proton and neutron agree within 5 %. We believe that the experiments are not accurate enough to allow the detection of an F_{2S} contribution of the order of a few percent and therefore we assume $F_{2S} = 0$.[5] Then in order to get a vanishing rms radius for the neutron charge distribution, F_1 has to be decomposed in at least three terms. We shall write F_{1S} as a sum of two terms and shall associate $F_{1S}{}^c$, the term with the smaller radius, with a core, the other one $F_{1S}{}^\mu$ with a cloud. It will be shown that all experimental results can be reproduced without assuming that F_{1V} has a core, too. Again, however, we cannot definitely exclude such a core because of experimental uncertainties. With each form factor we can associate a charge, i.e., the value of the form factor at $q = 0$, and for $F_{1S}{}^c$, $F_{1S}{}^\mu$, and F_{1V} we have, respectively, e_c, e_μ, and e_V. The charge on the proton requires that $e_c + e_\mu + e_V = 1$, and that of the neutron requires that $e_c + e_\mu - e_V = 0$; from this it follows that $e_c + e_\mu = \frac{1}{2}$ and that $e_V = \frac{1}{2}$, a unit charge being that of the electron, of course. We can also write some relations for the mean square radii associated with each of the above charge distributions, i.e.,

$$a_p{}^2 = e_c a_c{}^2 + e_\mu a_\mu{}^2 + e_V a_V{}^2 = (0.8\ \text{f})^2, \tag{5}$$

and

$$a_n{}^2 = e_c a_c^2 + e_\mu a_\mu{}^2 - e_V a_V{}^2 = 0, \tag{6}$$

where a_p and a_n are the measured rms radii of charge already determined at low q^2. It follows that

$$e_c a_c^2 + e_\mu a_\mu^2 = \tfrac{1}{2} a_p^2, \tag{7}$$

and hence that $a_V = a_p$.

The core model implies that $a_c^2 \ll a_\mu^2$ in which case (7) gives $a_\mu^2 = a_p^2/2e_\mu$. We are left with the problem of determining e_μ and e_c. This we do by fitting our experimental curve of F_{1p} at very large values of q^2, i.e., between 20 and 37, at which place both F_{1S}^μ and F_V have become small compared to F_{1S}^c. For example, let us assume most simply that the core is a point charge; then, quite independently of what we choose for the form of F_S^μ or F_V, we obtain $e_c \approx 0.25$ and it follows that $a_\mu = 1.1$. However, such an assumption does not give a good fit of the experimental data. See curve (a) of Fig. 2(b). We can do better if we assume an extended distribution for the core charge—for simplicity a Gaussian form is used. Now although we know that $a_V = a_p = 0.8$ f, we do not know the shape of the charge distribution. We assume rather arbitrarily the same Gaussian shape that fits F_{2V}. This becomes quite negligible for $q^2 > 25$ f^{-2} where only the form factor of the core remains and which we then fit in this region. We could arbitrarily make $e_c \approx 0.5$; then a_c would be 0.37 f, but the fit at intermediate values of q^2 would be poor. The best fit gives $e_c = 0.35 \pm 0.1$ and $a_c = 0.2 \pm 0.1$ f. This choice determines that $e_\mu = 0.15 \pm 0.1$ and $a_\mu = 1.4 \pm 0.4$ f. (See Table II.) The corresponding partial form factors are plotted in Fig. 2(b) together with the total form factor for the neutron and proton given by (3). It should be emphasized that the model leaves only one free parameter, i.e., e_c, if a point core is assumed, and only two parameters for an extended core. The shapes of the distributions can also be considered as free parameters, but we have found by trial that our results are insensitive to whether Gaussian or exponential forms are used. Yukawa-type distributions give somewhat different results, but such distributions have a built-in core. However, the spirit of our approach and underlying it has been the core model; hence, we have avoided, but by no means dismissed, Yukawa distributions.[6]

Table II. Parameters giving the best fit to all experimental data with $F_i = e_i \exp(-a_i^2 q^2/6)$.

$e_c = 0.35 \pm 0.1$	$a_c = 0.2 \pm 0.1$ f
$e_\mu = 0.15 \pm 0.1$	$a_\mu = 1.44 \pm 0.5$ f
$e_{1V} = 0.5$	$a_{1V} = 0.8$ f
$e_{2V} = 1.0$	$a_{2V} = 0.8$ f

The core form factor and its range seem quite reasonable, but the reason for the long-range isoscalar charge form factor, F_{1S}^μ, is not so obvious. If F_{1V} is due to two-meson processes, then F_{1S}^μ may be due to three-meson processes[5] but why, except for a very strong resonance, should this have a longer range? Again, it may have its origin in some obscure one-meson process. Is it possible that F_{1S}^μ is of electromagnetic origin, i.e., is the meson cloud polarized by the core charge? The sign of the effect is right, although the Coulomb forces would seem to be too weak.

Taking the Fourier transforms of the form factors, one can compute the charge distributions of the proton and neutron. These are plotted in Fig. 4. Of course, these distributions and the form factors themselves will be changed by relativistic effects which have not been taken into account.[7] Also, by choosing somewhat different models one might obtain somewhat different parameters. We believe, however, that the charge distributions shown in Fig. 4 give a qualitative picture of the nucleons. Its main features are a positive core for both particles with a charge of about 30% and a radius of approxi-

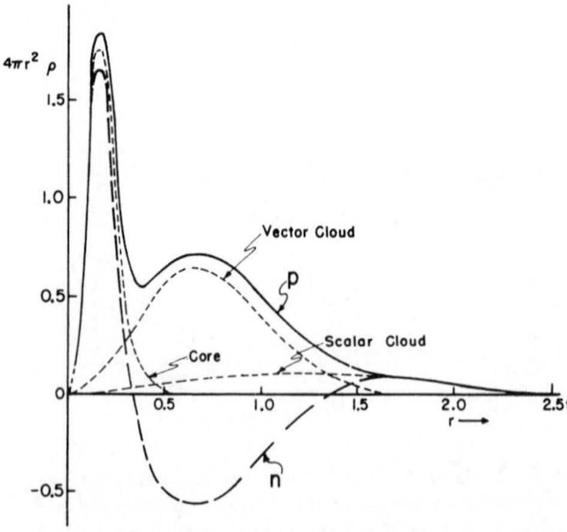

FIG. 4. Charge distribution for the proton and the neutron implied by the form factors shown for the fit (b) in Fig. 2(b).

mately the nucleon Compton wavelength. The proton core is surrounded by a positive cloud, the neutron by a negative one. The neutron has in addition a positive shell at its outside that contains a few percent of the elementary charge. The distributions of the anomalous magnetic moments are spread out with rms radii of about 0.8 f and it is not necessary, with present accuracy, to assign a magnetic core.[8]

*Supported by joint contract of the Office of Naval Research and the U. S. Atomic Energy Commission.

†On leave from Technische Hochschule, Karlsruhe, Germany.

[1]R. Wilson, K. Berkelman, J. Cassels, and D. Olson, Nature 188, 94 (1960).

[2]F. Bumiller, M. Croissiaux, and R. Hofstadter, Phys. Rev. Letters 5, 261 (1960).

[3]L. L. Foldy, Revs. Modern Phys. 30, 471 (1958).

[4]R. Herman and R. Hofstadter, High-Energy Electron Scattering Tables (Stanford University Press, Stanford, California, 1960).

[5]P. Federbush, M. Goldberger, and S. Treiman, Phys. Rev. 112, 642 (1958). They point out that $F_{2S}(0)/F_{2V}(0) = (\mu_p - \mu_n)/(\mu_p + \mu_n) = 0.03$.

[6]Unfortunately, there is not much information on the shape of the form factors from meson theory. From dispersion relations one can derive a Yukawa or Clementel-Villi type form factor according to whether one uses unsubtracted or subtracted dispersion relations [J. Bowcock, W. N. Cottingham, and D. Lurié, Phys. Rev. Letters 5, 386 (1960)]. In these calculations the π-π resonance was approximated by a δ function. A. Stanghellini [Nuovo cimento 18, 1258 (1960)] implies that a wider resonance allows for quite different shapes of form factors.

[7]F. Ernst, R. Sachs, and K. Wali, Phys. Rev. 119, 1105 (1960). They suggest that the charge and magnetic moments are determined by $F_{ch} = F_1 - (q^2/2M)F_2$ and $F_{mag} = (1/2M)F_1 + F_2$.

[8]Our results were presented at the New York meeting of the American Physical Society: R. R. Wilson, Bull. Am. Phys. Soc. 6, 35 (1961); D. N. Olson, H. F. Schopper, and R. R. Wilson, Bull. Am. Phys. Soc. 6, 63 (1961). At the same meeting the Stanford group also presented new measurements of electron-deuteron scattering that allowed the determination of F_{1n} and F_{2n} at $q^2 < 20$. As nearly as we could determine, their results were quite consistent with our curves of F_{1n} and F_{2n}, but perhaps our interpretations in terms of isoscalar and isovector form factors differed.

PAPER 65

DIRAC AND PAULI FORM FACTORS OF THE NEUTRON*

R. Hofstadter and C. de Vries†
Stanford University, Stanford, California

and

Robert Herman
Research Laboratories, General Motors Corporation, Warren, Michigan
(Received February 15, 1961)

Recent work on electron scattering at Stanford[1-3] has shown that the electromagnetic form factors of the proton were split apart at large values of the momentum transfer (q) and the detailed behavior of the Dirac (F_{1p}) and Pauli (F_{2p}) form factors was reported. These studies showed also that F_{2p} is approaching zero and that the electron-proton scattering cross section exhibits a diffraction dip at $q^2 \cong 25$ f^{-2} which is associated with the behavior of F_{2p} at that value of the momentum transfer. Some information concerning the proton form factors has also been reported by the Cornell group.[4] The information in references 1-3 was used by Herman and Hofstadter,[5] who deduced values of the Dirac and Pauli form factors of the neutron (F_{1n} and F_{2n}, respectively) from the above data by making the assumption that $F_{2n} = F_{2p}$ which was known from earlier measurements[6,7] to be roughly true at low values of q^2. In this way the work of reference 5 showed that $F_{1n} \neq 0$. Although there is an ambiguity in the sign of F_{1n}, Herman and Hofstadter chose the negative sign because it has been commonly accepted that the charge cloud of the neutron is due primarily to the presence of negative mesons. The chief result of the present communication is the independent experimental determination of the two form factors of the neutron (F_{1n}, F_{2n}) and a verification that $F_{1n} \neq 0$. In another communication[8] we attempt to resolve the ambiguity of sign in F_{1n}.

The above results were obtained by combining measurements of the inelastic electron scattering cross section of the deuteron at two sets of values of energy (E) and angle (θ) of the scattered electron for the same value of q^2. In essence this method is the same as the method of intersecting ellipses used in determining F_{1p} and F_{2p} of the proton.[9,10] The application of this method to the neutron was given in reference 9. This method of determining F_{1n} and F_{2n} eliminates many errors. In the present work the modified Jankus theory of electrodisintegration of the deuteron was used to evaluate F_{1n} and F_{2n} from the value of the cross section at the peak of the inelastic continuum.[6,11,12] The modified Jankus theory was employed in an extended form provided by Goldberg[13] which takes account of finite nonzero values of F_{1n}. Calculations made by Durand[14] show that the modified Jankus theory[10] is quite accurate at the peak of the inelastic continuum.

In all cases the measurement of the deuteron peak was accompanied by a corresponding measurement of the cross section of the proton peak. This procedure minimizes many possible experimental errors. Thus, an absolute cross section of the deuteron peak could be obtained by using the absolute data in references 1-3. Radiative corrections were calculated for the deuteron and proton peaks by Sobottka's method[7] and the magnitude of the radiative correction applied in finding the final value of the deuteron cross section was nearly always small and constant: ~10%. Furthermore, the differences in the corrections for the interaction in the final state[12] were estimated and found to be <~4% when calculated for the two members of the deuteron cross-section pair. The final-state corrections were not applied in the above evaluation of the deuteron cross sections since they are small (<~4%) and not particularly well known at the present time. Improved calculations of these interactions are now in progress.[15]

In Fig. 1 we show a pair of deuteron inelastic peaks at a value of $q^2 = 16.7$ f^{-2} with the accompanying proton peaks. The data were taken with targets of liquid hydrogen and liquid deuterium with the new 72-in. magnetic spectrometer.[1-3] We present in Table I the values of the deuteron

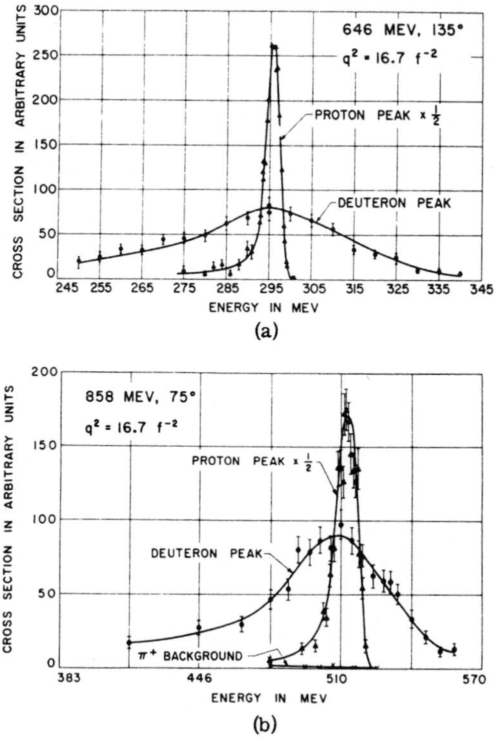

FIG. 1. A pair of deuteron inelastic continua is shown for $q^2 \cong 16.7$ f^{-2}, along with the comparison proton peaks used for absolute calibration. The very small π^+ background at 858 Mev and 75° was measured in order to estimate the π^- background under the deuteron peak (see references 7 and 11).

Table I. Experimental electron-deuteron scattering cross sections.[a]

q^2 (f^{-2})	E_0 (Mev)	θ^0	$(d^2\sigma/d\Omega dE)_{max}\times 10^{34}$ (cm²/sr Mev)
5.1	300	135	8.32*
	500	60	35.9*
7.0	362	135	4.6**
	600	60	17.8*
8.6	414	135	3.07**
	675	60	11.1
9.1	429	135	2.65**
	700	60	8.9
11.5	500	136	1.59
	800	60	5.44
14.7	590	135	0.82
	850	67.5	2.6
16.7	646	135	0.51
	858	75	1.31
18.0	675	135	0.46
	900	75	1.32
21.0	750	141.5	0.25
	900	90	0.53

[a]The experimental cross-section values with one asterisk have been taken from Sobottka, reference 7. Those with two asterisks have been interpolated by using Sobottka's values for $\theta = 135°$.

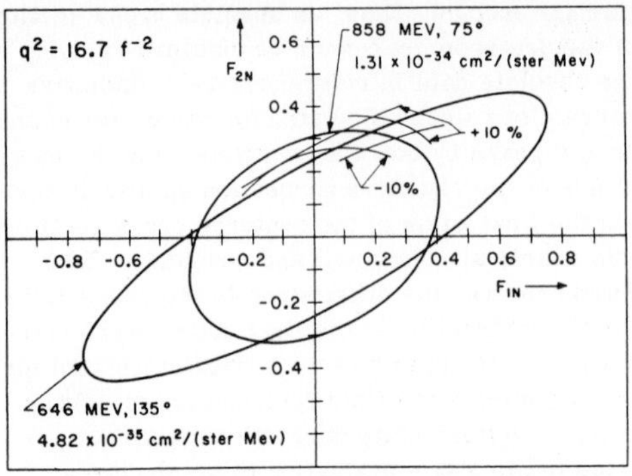

FIG. 2. An example of intersecting ellipses according to the modified Jankus theory for the pair 858 Mev, 75° and 646 Mev, 135° at $q^2 \cong 16.7\ f^{-2}$. Note the effect that would be caused by ±10% experimental errors in the deuteron cross section. The value of the cross section at 646 Mev and 135° used in the text is slightly different from the value used in this example and is 5.1×10^{-35} cm²/(sr Mev).

cross sections obtained in the above manner.

The convenient method of intersecting ellipses used in obtaining the form factors of the neutron is illustrated in Fig. 2 at $q^2=16.7\ f^{-2}$. The effect of possible errors in the measurement of the deuteron cross sections is also shown in the figure. The errors in the neutron form factors arising from all sources other than possible systematic errors are believed to be approximately of the order of the spread in the final values. The errors in the deuteron cross section are believed to be less than about ± 10%.

In studying the neutron problem, one finds four possible intersections of ellipses for a given value of q^2 which determine the F_{1n}, F_{2n} pair. Of these we have chosen the one set which seems to be physically reasonable. This set is given in Table II together with the known proton form factors.[1-3] Further details concerning the other possible solutions will be described subsequently. It should be noted that in all cases $F_{2n} \neq F_{2p}$ although at small values of q^2 the assumption of equality used in reference 5 is satisfied approximately.

From the chosen set of values of F_{1p}, F_{1n}, F_{2p}, F_{2n}, we may now form the corresponding set of values of the isotopic form factors which are defined as follows:

$$F_{1S}=F_{1p}+F_{1n}, \tag{1}$$

$$F_{1V}=F_{1p}-F_{1n}, \tag{2}$$

$$F_{2S}=[1.79F_{2p}-1.91F_{2n}]/(-0.12), \tag{3}$$

$$F_{2V}=[1.79F_{2p}+1.91F_{2n}]/(3.70). \tag{4}$$

The experimental values of the isotopic form factors as defined above are given in Table II. We observe that F_{1V} and F_{2V} are quite similar to each other while F_{1S} has a different behavior. F_{2S} is the least well-known isotopic form factor since it is associated with the small difference between the absolute values of F_{2p} and F_{2n}. We are investigating the possible errors in the values of the isotopic form factors but believe that the errors are not large enough to change the basic pattern of behavior exhibited in Table II.

We wish to thank C. Buchanan, F. W. Bunker, B. Chambers, H. Collard, and E. Dally for their help in this experiment. Our special appreciation is due Donald W. Aitken who helped us considerably during the early stages of this work. Finally we wish to acknowledge a number of valuable discussions with Dr. A. Goldberg and

Table II. Proton, neutron, and isotopic form factors.[a]

q^2 (f^{-2})	(1) F_{1p}	(2) F_{2p}	(3) F_{1n}	(4) F_{2n}	(5) F_{1S}	(6) F_{2S}	(7) F_{1V}	(8) F_{2V}
0	1.00	1.00	0.00	1.00	1.00	1.00	1.00	1.00
5	0.62	0.62	0.04	0.70	0.66	1.9	0.58	0.66
10	0.48	0.39	0.11	0.51	0.59	2.2	0.37	0.45
15	0.43	0.21	0.17	0.38	0.60	3.0	0.26	0.30
20	0.42	0.08	0.19	0.32	0.61	3.9	0.23	0.20

[a]The entries in columns (3)-(4) represent smoothed values taken from curves through the experimental data of this communication. Columns (5)-(8) are the result of calculations using Eqs. (1)-(4). The results for the other sets of intersections will be discussed in a forthcoming paper.

Dr. M. R. Yearian.

---

*This material was presented as a post-deadline paper at the New York Meeting of the American Physical Society, February 1-4, 1961. This work was supported in part by the Office of Naval Research and the U. S. Atomic Energy Commission and by the U. S. Air Force, through the Office of Scientific Research of the Air Research and Development Command.

†On leave from Institute of Nuclear Research, Amsterdam, The Netherlands.

[1]R. Hofstadter, F. Bumiller, and M. Croissiaux, Proceedings of the 1960 Annual International Conference on High-Energy Physics at Rochester (Interscience Publishers, New York, 1960), p. 762.

[2]F. Bumiller, M. Croissiaux, and R. Hofstadter, Phys. Rev. Letters 5, 261 (1960).

[3]R. Hofstadter, F. Bumiller, and M. Croissiaux, Phys. Rev. Letters 5, 263 (1960).

[4]K. Berkelman, J. M. Cassels, D. N. Olson, and R. R. Wilson, reference 1, p. 757. See also R. R. Wilson, K. Berkelman, J. M. Cassels, and D. N. Olson, Nature 188, 94 (1960).

[5]R. Herman and R. Hofstadter, reference 1, p. 767.

[6]M. R. Yearian and R. Hofstadter, Phys. Rev. 110, 552 (1958); 111, 934 (1958).

[7]S. Sobottka, Phys. Rev. 118, 831 (1960).

[8]R. Hofstadter and R. Herman, following Letter [Phys. Rev. Letters 6, 293 (1961)].

[9]R. Hofstadter, Ninth Annual International Conference on High-Energy Physics, Kiev, July, 1959 (to be published).

[10]R. Herman and R. Hofstadter, High-Energy Electron Scattering Tables (Stanford University Press, Stanford, California, 1960).

[11]R. Hofstadter, F. Bumiller, and M. R. Yearian, Revs. Modern Phys. 30, 482 (1958).

[12]V. Jankus, thesis, Stanford University, 1956 (unpublished); Phys. Rev. 102, 1586 (1956).

[13]A. Goldberg (private communication).

[14]L. Durand, III, Phys. Rev. 115, 1020 (1959). See also reference 10, pp. 48-49.

[15]B. Bosco (private communication).

PAPER 66

ELECTRIC AND MAGNETIC STRUCTURE OF THE PROTON AND NEUTRON*

Robert Hofstadter
Stanford University, Stanford, California

and

Robert Herman
Research Laboratories, General Motors Corporation, Warren, Michigan
(Received February 15, 1961)

We attempt to present in this paper a unified interpretation of the presently known experimental data on the electromagnetic form factors of two fundamental particles: the proton and the neutron. As we shall show, this interpretation is fully consistent with the idea that the two particles are two different aspects of a single entity—the nucleon. The third component of the isotopic spin of the nucleon is then used to distinguish between the two fundamental particles. The new experimental material on the neutron form factors,[1] which now completes a block of information on the proton[2] and neutron, has served as the stimulus for the attempted explanation.

We would like to explain the main features of the experimental behavior of the Dirac form factors (F_{1p}, F_{1n}) and Pauli form factors (F_{2p}, F_{2n}) of the proton (p) and neutron (n) as functions of the momentum-transfer invariant (q^2). We propose to do this in a well-known way[3] by expressing each proton and neutron form factor as a sum of a scalar and vector contribution. This decomposition is rooted in the idea that the scalar and vector form factors are simpler and more basic than those of either the proton or neutron. Accordingly we make the following definitions, which are standard except perhaps for the normalizing constants:

$$F_{1S} = F_{1p} + F_{1n}, \tag{1}$$

$$F_{1V} = F_{1p} - F_{1n}, \tag{2}$$

$$F_{2S} = [1.79F_{2p} + (-1.91)F_{2n}]/(-0.12), \tag{3}$$

$$F_{2V} = [1.79F_{2p} - (-1.91)F_{2n}]/(3.70). \tag{4}$$

This choice of normalization has the advantage that at $q = 0$ all four isotopic form factors take on the value of unity.

We shall now attempt to find the four isotopic form factors from the experimental information given in Hofstadter et al.[1,2] for the values of

F_{1p}, F_{1n}, F_{2p}, F_{2n}. A comprehensive, though approximate, fit to all the experimental data can be represented by the following expressions for the fundamental isotopic form factors:

$$F_{1S} = 0.44 + \frac{0.56}{1+0.214q^2}, \quad (5)$$

$$F_{1V} = -0.20 + \frac{1.20}{1+0.10q^2}, \quad (6)$$

$$F_{2V} = -0.20 + \frac{1.20}{1+0.10q^2}, \quad (7)$$

$$F_{2S} = 4.0 + \frac{-3.0}{1+0.214q^2}. \quad (8)$$

These results have very few independent fitting parameters. The independent parameters of Eqs. (5), (6), and (7) are only 0.44, -0.20, and a root-mean-square radius, $a = 0.85\times10^{-13}$ cm. All other numerical values in these equations are determined, once the above choice is made. The rms radius is obtained from the coefficient $(-\frac{1}{6}a^2)$ of q^2 in the expansion of F_{1S}, F_{1V}, and F_{2V} in powers of q^2. The quantity F_{2S} in Eq. (8) requires the additional fitting parameter 4.0. F_{2S} is the least well-known quantity of the set of isotopic form factors, and we regard both its values and its form as somewhat indeterminate at the present time.

Equations (5) to (8) are remarkably simple and have the same fundamental structure, namely, the Clementel-Villi (C-V) form.[4-6] It is very satisfactory that this simple C-V form is also suggested by the dispersion relations idea[7] that the approximate nucleon form factor is just the result of a pole plus a constant representing the core of a nucleon. The Fourier transform of the C-V form factor is a delta function at the center of the distribution ($r = 0$) plus a Yukawa cloud. Thus the spatial interpretation of Eqs. (5) to (8) is very clear: Each form factor corresponds to a distribution in space of a simple Yukawa cloud and a point-like core. (Our present experiments are not capable of distinguishing between a point core and a core of radius comparable to a nucleon Compton wavelength.) Though we are aware that the spatial transform is not a completely consistent relativistic concept, we believe that the density distributions so obtained are approximately correct and correspond, at the same time, to dispersion theory models.[3]

We may solve Eqs. (1)-(4) for F_{1p}, F_{1n}, F_{2p}, and F_{2n} and substitute the values of F_{1S}, F_{1V}, F_{2V}, and F_{2S} given in Eqs. (5)-(8). Thus we obtain

$$F_{1p} = 0.12 + \frac{0.28}{1+0.214q^2} + \frac{0.60}{1+0.10q^2}, \quad (9)$$

$$F_{1n} = 0.32 + \frac{0.28}{1+0.214q^2} - \frac{0.60}{1+0.10q^2}, \quad (10)$$

$$F_{2p} = -0.34 + \frac{0.10}{1+0.214q^2} + \frac{1.24}{1+0.10q^2}, \quad (11)$$

$$F_{2n} = -0.068 - \frac{0.094}{1+0.214q^2} + \frac{1.16}{1+0.10q^2}. \quad (12)$$

Graphical representations of these equations are given by the solid lines in Fig. 1. Experimental points of references 1 and 2 are also

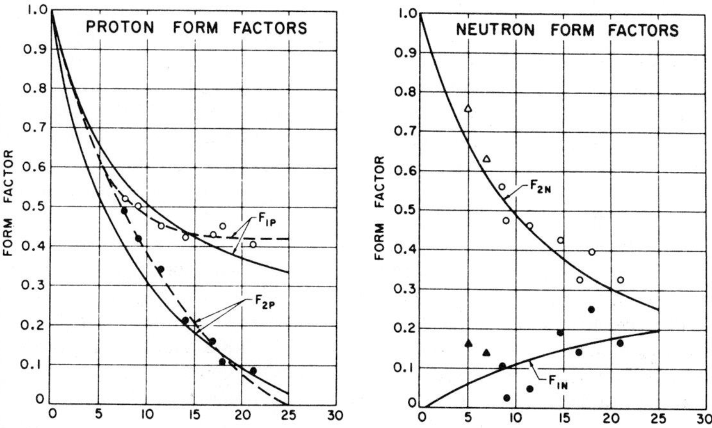

FIG. 1. The experimental points of references 1 and 2 together with theoretical curves (solid lines) representing Eqs. (9)-(12). Below $q^2 \cong 7$ no points are shown but the theoretical curves are in good agreement with previously published cross sections.[5] The dashed lines refer to the empirical curves given in reference 2. An improved fitting of the data at $q^2 \geq 7$ by the method of least squares is now in progress and can be carried through with slight adjustments of the constants in Eqs. (5)-(8). The solid and hollow triangles refer to the neutron data of Sobottka.[8]

given in the figures. Even though a best adjustment of the free parameters has not yet been made, the fit between experiment and theory is already satisfactory over the entire range of values of q^2 and embraces all the measurable quantities F_{1p}, F_{1n}, F_{2p}, and F_{2n}. The largest departures from the curves correspond to the points of Sobottka[8] which we have analyzed, but which were measured at an earlier time when our spectrometer was not stabilized by magnetic flux-coil methods.

The coefficients of q^2 in the expressions (9)-(12) give immediately the rms radii of the Dirac and Pauli charge and magnetic moment distributions in the proton and neutron. We find that

$$a_{1p}=0.85 \text{ f};\quad a_{1n}=0.00 \text{ f};$$

$$a_{2p}=0.94 \text{ f};\quad a_{2n}=0.76 \text{ f}. \tag{13}$$

These radii are consistent with known facts about these distributions. We note the important point that the root-mean-square radius of the neutron is zero, in agreement with the measurements of Fermi, Rabi, Hughes, Havens, and their collaborators on the neutron-electron interaction.[9] The rms magnetic radius of the neutron is nearly the same as that of the proton. One of the conditions employed in finding the parameters of Eqs. (5)-(8) was that $a_{1n}=0$. Thus the long-standing problem of a small or zero neutron charge radius and a normal magnetic radius seems to be resolved.

The splitting of F_{1p} and F_{2p} at small values of q^2 is perfectly in accord with known data on the proton cross sections, as may easily be verified by substituting such form factors into the Rosenbluth formula.

The choice of positive sign for values of F_{1n} was required for the above set of isotopic form factors. If negative values of F_{1n} are taken for the intersections of reference 1, a different set of isotopic form factors is obtained which seems difficult to understand in any simple way.[7,10] It is possible, in principle, to find the sign of F_{1n} relative to F_{1p} by making elastic scattering measurements in the deuteron. The present experimental evidence[11,12] is not definitive on the question. If the relativistic correction of Blankenbecler[13] is employed together with the results of references 11 or 12, the choice of F_{1n} should be positive, as we have suggested. But the experimental errors do not permit a definite decision on this point.

We now find the Fourier spatial transforms of Eqs. (9) and (10) and present the results graphically in Fig. 2. It may be seen from Eqs. (9) and (10) that the neutron charge distribution is obtained from that of the proton essentially by flipping over one of the two Yukawa clouds. Thus the neutron and proton charge clouds are in a partial sense mirror images of each other. The fact that the cores are different (0.12 for the proton, 0.32 for the neutron) is probably a consequence of the inexact nature of our approximation. It seems quite likely that the higher order terms in Eqs. (9) and (10), which are omitted in our analysis, might account for the actual differences between F_{1V} and F_{2V} which we ignored in our approximate choice of isotopic form factors. Such higher order terms may well restore full symmetry between neutron and proton.

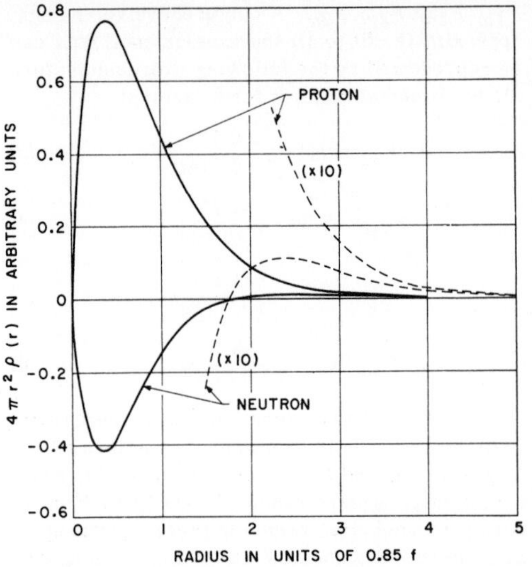

FIG. 2. The proton and neutron charge density distributions given by the Fourier transforms of Eqs. (9) and (10). The expressions for the spatial transforms are given in reference 6. The delta functions at the origin are omitted in this figure.

The magnetic moments of proton and neutron are found from the combinations $(F_{1p}+1.79F_{2p})$ and $(F_{1n}-1.91F_{2n})$, and have the approximate mirror symmetry expected of them. The details of the magnetic moment clouds will be presented in a subsequent communication.

We call attention particularly to the prediction that the neutron charge cloud has a positive outer fringe.[14] The positive sign of F_{1n} is connected with the positive outer cloud. It would be interesting to seek other experimental evidence on the sign of the outer cloud.

We also note the fact that the ranges of the component Yukawa charge clouds in the proton (or in the neutron) are different. The vector cloud has a range of approximately 0.32 fermi and the scalar cloud a range of approximately 0.47 fermi. Thus, this evidence indicates that the three-pion resonance has a lower energy than the two-pion resonance.[7,15] An improved adjustment of the constants in Eqs. (5)-(8) might change this quantitative relationship between the two resonances.

If the above considerations prove to be true, the scheme of construction of proton and neutron is simpler than might have been expected. Furthermore, the internal consistency of the results suggests that the techniques of quantum electrodynamics are still valid at distances whose values lie between a nucleon Compton wavelength and a pion Compton wavelength.

We would like to offer our special thanks to Professor S. Fubini of the University of Padua for his important suggestion to choose positive F_{1n} values and for his illuminating comments on the dispersion-theoretic aspects of the C-V form factors. We also appreciate his gracious encouragement during the course of analysis of the form factors. We wish to thank Professor L. I. Schiff also for similar suggestions and for his warm and constant encouragement during the course of this work. We are grateful to Professor G. Breit for his kind critical comments. Finally we wish to express our appreciation to Mrs. Penny Bakey Seligman and Dr. Denos Gazis for their generous assistance with some of the calculations.

*This material was presented as a post-deadline paper at the New York Meeting of the American Physical Society, February 1-4, 1961. This work was supported in part by the Office of Naval Research and the U. S. Atomic Energy Commission and by the U. S. Air Force, through the Office of Scientific Research of the Air Research and Development Command.

[1]R. Hofstadter, C. de Vries, and R. Herman, preceding Letter [Phys. Rev. Letters 6, 290 (1961)].

[2]R. Hofstadter, F. Bumiller, and M. Croissiaux, Phys. Rev. Letters 5, 263 (1960).

[3]G. F. Chew, R. Karplus, S. Gasiorowicz, and F. Zachariasen, Phys. Rev. 110, 265 (1958); also P. Federbush, M. L. Goldberger, and S. B. Treiman, Phys. Rev. 112, 642 (1958); S. D. Drell, 1958 Annual International Conference on High-Energy Physics at CERN, edited by B. Ferretti (CERN Scientific Information Service, Geneva, 1958), pp. 20-33, and other references contained in these articles.

[4]E. Clementel and C. Villi, Nuovo cimento 4, 1207 (1956).

[5]R. Hofstadter, F. Bumiller, and M. R. Yearian, Revs. Modern Phys. 30, 482 (1958).

[6]R. Herman and R. Hofstadter, High-Energy Electron Scattering Tables (Stanford University Press, Stanford, California, 1960).

[7]S. Fubini (private communication).

[8]S. Sobottka, Phys. Rev. 118, 831 (1960).

[9]For references to the neutron-electron work see especially p. 487 and the references given in R. Hofstadter, S. Bumiller, and M. R. Yearian, Revs. Modern Phys. 30, 482 (1958).

[10]L. I. Schiff (private communication).

[11]J. A. McIntyre and G. R. Burleson, Phys. Rev. 112, 2077 (1958).

[12]J. I. Friedman, H. W. Kendall, and P. A. M. Gram, III, Phys. Rev. 120, 992 (1960).

[13]R. Blankenbecler (private communication).

[14]A similar conclusion was arrived at by D. N. Olson, H. F. Schopper, and R. R. Wilson, Bull. Am. Phys. Soc. 6, 35, 63 (1961), who made the assumption that $F_{2n}=F_{2p}$ at large values of q^2. Our measurements are not in agreement with this assumption for either choice of sign of F_{1n}.

[15]W. R. Frazer and J. R. Fulco, Phys. Rev. 117, 1609 (1960).

PAPER 67

EXPERIMENTAL RESULTS ON THE π-π CROSS SECTION*

Jerry A. Anderson, Vo X. Bang, Philip G. Burke, D. Duane Carmony, and Norbert Schmitz†
Lawrence Radiation Laboratory, University of California, Berkeley, California
(Received March 2, 1961)

At the 1960 Rochester Conference,[1] we reported our first experimental results on the π-π cross section, which we obtained by applying the Chew-Low extrapolation method[2] to about 700 π-p inelastic scatterings. These events were analyzed in photographs taken with the Alvarez 72-inch hydrogen bubble chamber, which was exposed to a 1.03-Bev/c π^- beam at the Bevatron. We now have a total of 1275 inelastic events with the proton stopping in the chamber. In this paper we will use the notation, the selection and evaluation criteria, and the extrapolation procedures which have been discussed in reference 1.

Figure 1 shows our experimental distributions,

$$F(p^2, \omega^2) = (p^2+1)^2 \partial^2\sigma(p^2, \omega^2)/\partial p^2 \partial\omega^2,$$

as functions of the four-momentum transfer p^2

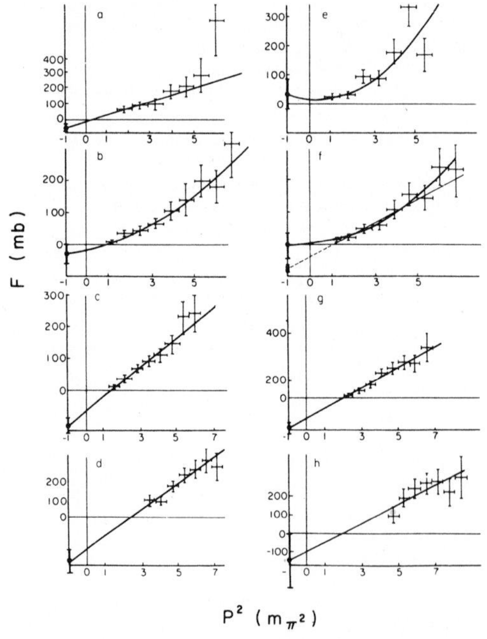

FIG. 1. Extrapolation curves $F(p^2, \omega^2)$ at fixed ω^2. (a) $\omega^2 = 5$ to $8.2\ m_\pi^2$; (b) $\omega^2 = 11$ to 13.7; (c) $\omega^2 = 16.5$ to 19.2; (d) $\omega^2 = 22$ to 24.7; (e) $\omega^2 = 8.2$ to 11; (f) $\omega^2 = 13.7$ to 16.5; (g) $\omega^2 = 19.2$ to 22; (h) $\omega^2 = 24.7$ to 27.5.

for eight different intervals of ω^2, the invariant mass of the di-pion. We express p^2 and ω^2 in units of the pion mass squared. Fitting polynomials in (p^2+1) of several orders through these data, we obtain results as follows.

1. Whereas at the time of the Rochester Conference a first-order polynomial adequately fitted the data for all the intervals of ω^2, we find that a χ^2 test now reveals the necessity of a quadratic fit for the low-ω^2 intervals. In the higher ω^2 intervals, although we have more events than at the lower ω^2 intervals, the linear fits are still exceedingly good. We therefore take the linear values for the extrapolation π-π cross section at the higher energy.

2. Also at the time of the Rochester Conference some of the fitted curves had the unphysical feature that they went negative in the physical region. This was possible because we do not have events right up to the edge of the physical region. Since we now require quadratic fits for the lower ω^2 intervals, this difficulty has been removed in all cases except for the lowest ω^2 interval (5.5 to 7.8 m_π^2). For this interval only we had to apply a constraint forcing the fitted curve to go through the end of the physical region. We then find that a linear curve with this added constraint gives a good fit. In all other intervals the fitted curve remains positive in the physical region without this constraint.

In order to get some information about the π-π interaction from a very small number of events, Bonsignori and Selleri[3-5] have made the assumption that formula (3.13) of reference 2 (which is exactly correct only at the pole $p^2 = -1$) approximately describes the p^2 dependence at the beginning of the physical region. With this assumption an average π-π cross section has been determined. The assumption means that all other contributions to the amplitude for single-pion production (p^2 dependence of the vertex functions of the single-pion exchange diagram, exchanges of 3, 5, or more pions, and production by collision of the pion with the nucleon core rather than with the cloud) have been neglected in comparison with the single-pion exchange at the pole. With our present statistics we are able to check the assumption of Bonsignori and Selleri. If it were justified, it should be possible [as one can see from (3.12) in reference 2] to fit the experimental distributions (or the first part of them) of Fig. 1 by a straight line passing through zero for $p^2=0$. Our data show that this is not possible. Thus, nonpole terms are important and an extrapolation requiring a large number of events is necessary to extract the pole term.

Frazer and Fulco[6] could explain the vector part of the electromagnetic structure of the nucleon assuming a strong π-π resonance in the $T=J=1$ state at $\omega^2=11$. The π^--π^0 amplitude is 50% isotopic spin 1 and 50% isotopic spin 2. We find no evidence for a π-π resonance of the width and location predicted in reference 6.

Our data do show a rise in the π-π cross section starting at $\omega^2=17$, reaching a value of the order of 200 mb at $\omega^2=20$ to 22. (See Fig. 2.) However, one must remember that it is just in this region of ω^2 that our extrapolation distance begins to get larger, making the extrapolation procedure less conclusive. We are now scanning film obtained at 1.275 Bev/c incident momentum in order to reduce the extrapolation distance in this region. Also, for ω^2 greater than 9, we have a background of events coming from the reaction $\pi^-+p\rightarrow\pi^-+p+2\pi^0$. These events do not have a pole at $p^2=-1$, but come from a branch cut. We are eliminating this background by means of a kinematical fit.

On the other hand, Bowcock et al.[7] found on a later analysis of the nucleon electromagnetic structure and the low-energy pion-nucleon phase shifts that the Frazer-Fulco resonance should be shifted to about $\omega_{res}^2=22$. This is consistent with our present results. If we assume that our data peak at $\omega^2=20$ to 22 (our incident energy is insufficient to examine the high-energy side of the peak), then the height is in accord with $(2J+1)4\pi ƛ^2 \sin^2\delta_1$ for a p-state resonance—that is, $\sin^2\delta_1=1$. Our half-width (obtained from the low-energy side) is approximately $5m_\pi^2$. Of course, our data do not rule out a nonresonant rise in the cross section composed of s, p, d, f, $\cdots$ states which just happens to satisfy $12\pi ƛ^2$ at $\omega^2=20$ to 22. We are currently evaluating the differential cross section in the region $\omega^2=20$. We hope to resolve this experimental ambiguity in the very near future.

We would like to thank Professor Luis W. Alvarez for his great interest and encouragement throughout the experiment. It is a pleasure to thank Professor Frank S. Crawford, Jr., who designed the beam, as well as Professor Arthur H. Rosenfeld and other members of the Alvarez group, for many interesting and stimulating discussions. We are indebted to Professor Goeffrey F. Chew and to Dr. James S. Ball for several discussions on the theoretical aspects and to Dr. Herbert M. Steiner for useful comments. Finally, we want to thank our scanners for their help in finding and analyzing the events.

*This work was performed under the auspices of the

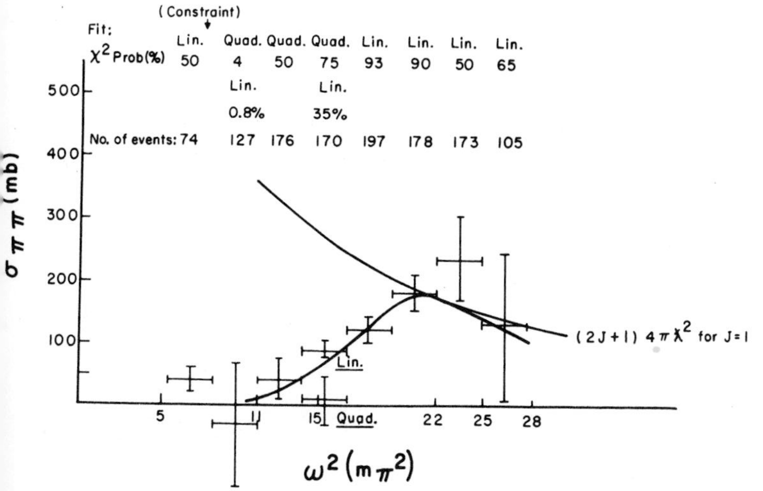

FIG. 2. The π^--π^0 cross section as a function of the total di-pion mass squared as determined by the Chew-Low method. Also shown are the maximum height of a p-state resonance and the shape of the Frazer-Fulco resonance [W. R. Frazer and J. R. Fulco, Phys. Rev. Letters 2, 367 (1959), Eq. (10)], assuming the parameters $v_r=3.5$, $\Gamma=0.3$.

U. S. Atomic Energy Commission.

†Now at the Max-Planck-Institut für Physik und Astrophysik, München, Germany.

[1]J. A. Anderson, P. G. Burke, D. D. Carmony, and N. Schmitz, in Proceedings of the 1960 Annual International Conference on High-Energy Physics at Rochester (Interscience Publishers, Inc., New York, 1960), p. 58.

[2]G. F. Chew and F. E. Low, Phys. Rev. 113, 1640 (1959).

[3]V. Alles-Borelli, S. Bergio, E. Perez-Ferreira, and P. Waloschek, Nuovo cimento 14, 211 (1959).

[4]I. Derado and N. Schmitz, Phys. Rev. 118, 309 (1960).

[5]F. Bonsignori and F. Selleri, Nuovo cimento 15, 465 (1960).

[6]W. R. Frazer and J. R. Fulco, Phys. Rev. 117, 1609 (1960).

[7]F. J. Bowcock, W. N. Cottingham, and D. Lurié, Phys. Rev. Letters 5, 386 (1960).

PAPER 68

ELECTROMAGNETIC FORM FACTORS OF THE NUCLEON AND PION-PION INTERACTION

S. Bergia and A. Stanghellini
Istituto di Fisica dell' Università di Bologna, Bologna, Italy

S. Fubini
Istituto di Fisica dell' Università di Padova, Padova, Italy and CERN, Geneva, Switzerland

and

C. Villi
Instituto di Fisica dell' Università di Parma, Parma, Italy
(Received March 13, 1961)

We wish to propose a simple model for the electromagnetic structure of the nucleon, based on dispersion theory and on a strong pion-pion interaction. The model is a synthesis of several theoretical ideas proposed by Frazer and Fulco,[1] Nambu,[2] and Chew.[3]

Let us first of all summarize some general properties of the nucleon form factors. We write the interaction of the nucleon with the electromagnetic field in the form:

$$\langle p'|j_\mu|p\rangle A_\mu = i\bar{u}(p')[G_1(t)\gamma_\mu + G_2(t)\sigma_{\mu\nu}k_\nu]u(p)A_\mu, \qquad (1)$$

where p', p, and k are the four-momenta of the final nucleon, initial nucleon, and photon, respectively, and $t=k^2=(p'-p)^2$. The G_i still are operators in the isospin space:

$$G_i = G_i^S + G_i^V \tau_3,$$

and so

$$G_i^p = G_i^S + G_i^V; \quad G_i^n = G_i^S - G_i^V.$$

As is well known, the separation into the isoscalar and the isovector current is very useful because only an even number of pions contribute to G^V and an odd number to G^S. At $t=0$ the G_i functions tend to the static charge and magnetic moment of the nucleon:

$$G_1^p(0) = e, \quad G_1^n(0) = 0,$$

$$G_2^p(0) = \mu_p = eg_p/2M, \quad G_2^n(0) = \mu_n = eg_n/2M,$$

$$G_1^S(0) = G_1^V(0) = e/2,$$

$$G_2^S(0) = (\mu_p + \mu_n)/2 = eg_S/2M,$$

$$G_2^V(0) = (\mu_p - \mu_n)/2 = eg_V/2M,$$

$$g_p = 1.79, \quad g_n = -1.91,$$

$$g_S = -0.06, \quad g_V = 1.85, \qquad (2)$$

The functions $G(t)$ are related to the usual Hofstadter form factors $F(t)$ by the following definitions:

$$G_i^{p,n}(t) = G_i^{p,n}(0)F_i^{p,n}(t). \qquad (3)$$

Dispersion theory allows one to write the different functions $G(t)$ in the following form[4]:

$$G(t) = \frac{1}{\pi}\int_0^\infty \frac{g(t')}{t'-t}dt'. \qquad (4)$$

The spectral functions $g(t)$ are of fundamental theoretical importance because they are related to the weight with which the different many-particle states contribute to the nucleon form factors. Therefore, if there is no bound state formed by pions, $g(t)$ will be different from zero only for t larger than $4m_\pi^2$ for the vector part and $9m_\pi^2$ for the scalar part.

If there is no strong correlation between the pions, $g(t)$ is related just to the statistical weight of the many-particle state with c.m. energy $E=\sqrt{t}$ and therefore will be a smoothly increasing function of t starting from zero.

If on the other hand, there is a strong correlation between the pions, due to a resonance with an energy E_R, the spectral function will exhibit a maximum for $t=t_R=E_R^2$. This result was first shown by Frazer and Fulco[1] and is schematically illustrated in Fig. 1.

Therefore, in a model without a strong pion-pion correlation the spectral function $g(t)$ will be dominated by the large values of t and $G(t)$ will have little dependence on t. The discrepancy of this model from the experimental data is discussed by Drell.[5]

On the other hand, a strong-correlation model leads to a rapid variation of $G(t)$ as suggested by experiment. Since for observable values of t ($t \leq 0$) the dispersion denominator in Eq. (4) is always positive, if the resonance state has a reasonable width ($<\frac{1}{2}m_\pi$), its effect can be well approximated by means of $\alpha/(t_R-t)$, where t_R is the resonance position and α is the area under the resonance curve.

Let us now discuss briefly the experimental results for the nucleon form factors at low momentum transfers. For $-t<10m_\pi^2$ the nucleon form factors were roughly given as follows:

$$F_1^{\,p}(t) \simeq F_2^{\,p}(t) \simeq F_2^{\,n}(t) \equiv F(t),$$

$$F_1^{\,n}(t) \simeq 0. \qquad (5)$$

Many different analytic functions were proposed for $F(t)$ but a particularly good fit was obtained either with an exponential form or with the form proposed by Clementel and Villi[6]:

$$F(t) = 0.2 + \frac{1.2}{1-(t/22m_\pi^2)}. \qquad (6)$$

From our theoretical point of view, it is very difficult to understand an exponential form factor; on the other hand, the Clementel-Villi model can be naturally understood on the basis

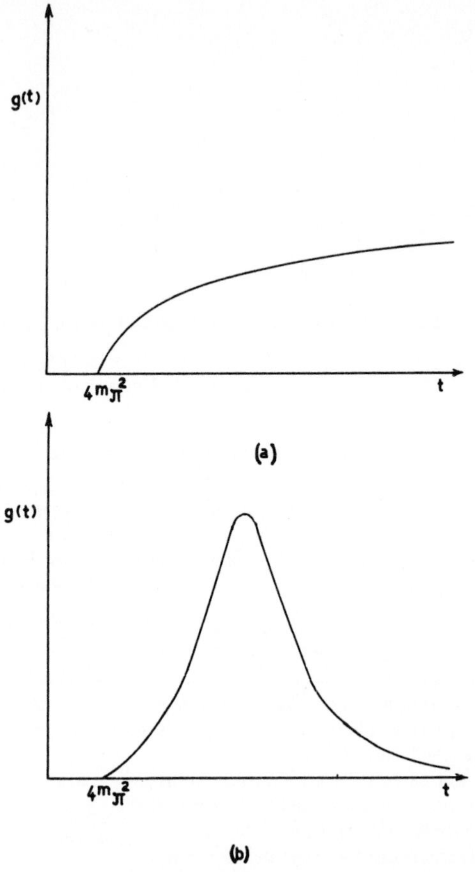

FIG. 1. Schematic representations of $g(t)$ in arbitrary scale. (a) Uncorrelated pions; (b) strong pion-pion resonance.

of a resonant state of energy $4.7m_\pi$. The constant term appearing in Eq. (6) represents the total contribution of the higher t states which in the low-momentum-transfer region is approximately constant. Thus Eqs. (5) and (6) indicate that it is possible to interpret both isovector form factors $F_1^{\,V}$ and $F_2^{\,V}$ by means of the approximate form, which has a pole at $t_R \simeq 22m_\pi^2$:

$$G_1^{\,V} \simeq \frac{e}{2}\left(-0.2 + \frac{1.2}{1-(t/22m_\pi^2)}\right),$$

$$G_2^{\,V} \simeq \frac{eg_V}{2M}\left(-0.2 + \frac{1.2}{1-(t/22m_\pi^2)}\right). \qquad (7)$$

By taking this attitude, the resonant state at $E_R \simeq 4.7m_\pi$ will be attributed to a $T=1$, $J=1$ two-pion state.

Such a resonant state, at this energy, has been observed in different experiments[7] on pion production by pions, and its parameters, deduced from Eq. (7), have been used[8] to explain satisfactorily the low-energy behavior of the pion-nucleon scattering phase shifts.

The isoscalar charge form factor $G_1^S(t)$ must be of the same order of magnitude of $G_1^V(t)$, in order to give a vanishing neutron charge distribution. This means that we have to expect important low-t contributions to the isoscalar form factors. The isoscalar magnetic form factor is experimentally very small and little is known about its energy variation.

The recent[9] experimental data on electron-proton scattering at larger values of the momentum transfer stress the need of having an important low-mass contribution to the isoscalar charge form factor. It is found that the charge form factor of the proton (Fig. 2) deviates strongly from Eq. (7) and it would be impossible to fit it with any reasonable form with only one pole.

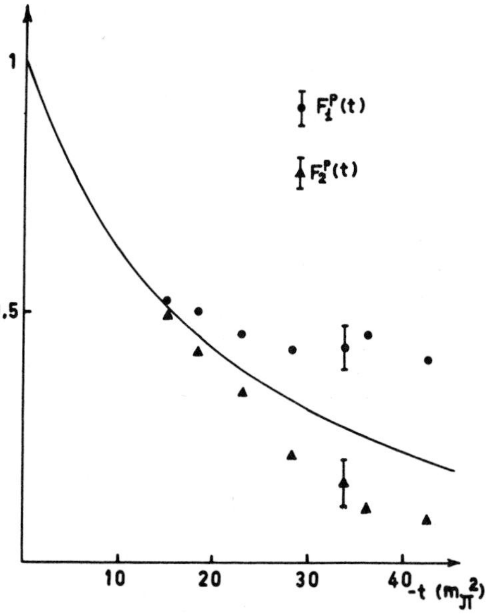

FIG. 2. Proton form factors at high momentum transfer (from reference 9). The solid line represents the Clementel and Villi model [in Eq. (6)].

A reasonable extension of the preceding ideas is to assume that G_1^V is still approximately given by Eq. (7) with the pole at $t_V \simeq 22m_\pi^2$, which is the value suggested by other experimental information. In this manner the flattening of G_1^p will be essentially due to the effect of G_1^S. Thus G_1^S must be composed of an almost constant part and a part which goes to zero much faster than G_1^V. This means that the charge form factor of the neutron will be positive at large values of t. This result seems to be confirmed by recent experiments on the neutron.[10]

If we tentatively attribute an average mass to the decreasing part of G_1^S, we have something like $8m_\pi^2$, certainly less than $22m_\pi^2$. This shows that it would be very difficult to explain the rapid variation of G_1^S on the basis of a simple statistical formula for $g_1^S(t)$, since the spectral integral will only start at $9m_\pi^2$. We thus expect the existence of a $T=0$, $J=1$ three-pion resonance (or bound state if $t_S < 9m_\pi^2$). The magnetic isoscalar part must also have a pole at the same position of t_S, but the present experimental information about it is certainly not enough to allow detection of its effects.

From the preceding discussion we expect expressions for G_1^S which have similar form to those for G_1^V. This leads to the following general form for the nucleon form factors:

$$G_1^V = \frac{e}{2}\left[(1-a_V) + \frac{a_V}{1-(t/t_V)}\right],$$

$$G_1^S = \frac{e}{2}\left[(1-a_S) + \frac{a_S}{1-(t/t_S)}\right],$$

$$G_2^V = \frac{eg_V}{2M}\left[(1-b_V) + \frac{b_V}{1-(t/t_V)}\right],$$

$$G_2^S = \frac{eg_S}{2M}\left[(1-b_S) + \frac{b_S}{1-(t/t_S)}\right], \qquad (8)$$

where t_V and t_S represent the position of the isovector and isoscalar unstable particles, respectively.

The residues of the poles a_V, b_V, a_S, b_S are connected with the constants appearing in similar terms giving the effect of pion-pion interaction in π-N scattering, N-N scattering, and photoproduction.[7,11] The validity of the present model can thus be checked by trying a general fit of many different sets of experimental data using the same phenomenological parameters.

One of the best known experimental properties of the form factors is that the mean charge radius of the neutron is zero. This leads to

$$a_S/t_S \simeq a_V/t_V = a. \tag{9}$$

As a consequence we have

$$G_1^{\,p} = e\left[1 + \frac{a}{2}\left(\frac{t_S}{t_S - t} + \frac{t_V}{t_V - t}\right)t\right];$$

$$G_1^{\,n} = -e\,\frac{a}{2}\left(\frac{t_V}{t_V - t} - \frac{t_S}{t_S - t}\right)t. \tag{10}$$

This means that we have in our model five independent parameters (a, t_V, t_S, b_S, and b_V), for one of which (t_V) we know the approximate value from independent experiments.

Some preliminary determinations[10,12] of the parameters contained in Eq. (8), using information from the proton and neutron form factors, confirm the validity of the present model. We wish to stress a very important consequence of the fact that t_S turns out to be smaller than t_V. From Eq. (10) one sees that the outer part of the charge distribution of the neutron is positive in contrast with what one would obtain on the basis of a model without strong pion-pion interaction.[13]

It is not surprising that, in a strong $T=1$ pion-pion interaction model, the three-pion state has a mass lower than the two-pion state. The existence of a resonance in a $T=1$, $J=1$ two-pion state forces the three-pion state to be in a $T=0$, $J=1$ state in which all the three pions are two-by-two resonating in a $T=1$, $J=1$ state.[3] Moreover the $T=0$, $J=1$ three-pion state is a completely saturated unit because if we add an extra pion it will be in a $T=0$ or 2 state with respect to the others. So, if we believe that there is a strong attraction in the $T=1$ state only, we can expect that the four-, five-, etc., pion states are not strongly correlated at low energy.

The possibility of detecting experimentally the $T=0$ unstable particle (which we shall denote by ρ) is discussed in references 2 and 3. A very interesting possibility is to identify it with the $T=0$ particle observed by Abashian et al.,[14] who find $t_S \simeq 5$. The choice $J=1$ for ρ was suggested by Chew[15] in order to explain the small effect of this particle in the decay spectrum of the K meson.

The spin of ρ together with the small available phase space would make the decay probability $K \to \rho + \pi$ very small but not impossible to detect.

On the other hand, preliminary[10,12] estimates show that a value $t_S \simeq 5$ is not incompatible with the experimental data on the form factors. There also seems to be some indication in favor of $t_S \simeq 5$ coming from the theoretical analysis of the electromagnetic form factor of the α particle.[16]

Another important indication coming from the qualitative determination of the parameters of Eq. (8) is that large constant terms are needed; in other words, the two- and three-pion resonating states are not sufficient to describe the nucleon completely.

One could take two attitudes: The first is that the dispersion relations make sense only in the subtracted version and the necessary constant terms are not linked to any observable effect; the second point of view is that the form factors tend to zero for $t \to \infty$ and the constants represent contributions of high-energy states. Such contributions, which are approximately constant at low momentum transfer, will show their t dependence as the momentum transfer increases. Being in favor of the second point of view (at least so far as the magnetic form factor is concerned), we are convinced that our knowledge of the nucleon structure is still incomplete and that higher energy electron-nucleon scattering will be of great importance in clarifying the many-particle contributions to the nucleon structure.

We wish to thank Professor R. Hofstadter for having communicated to us his results prior to publication. At the time part of this investigation was carried out, one of us (S.F.) was visiting the Department of Physics of Stanford University. He wishes to express his most sincere thanks for the very kind hospitality extended to him and to acknowledge the very illuminating discussions he had on this subject with Professor L. Schiff and Professor R. Hofstadter.

---

[1]W. R. Frazer and J. R. Fulco, Phys. Rev. Letters 2, 365 (1959); Phys. Rev. 117, 1609 (1960).

[2]Y. Nambu, Phys. Rev. 106, 1366 (1957).

[3]G. F. Chew, Phys. Rev. Letters 4, 142 (1960).

[4]This form is valid if no subtractions are needed; otherwise we have

$$G(t) = G(0) + \frac{t}{\pi}\int_0^\infty \frac{g(t')}{t'(t'-t)}\,dt'.$$

[5]S. D. Drell, Proceedings of the Seventh Annual Rochester Conference on High-Energy Nuclear Physics

(Interscience Publishers, New York, 1957), p. 27.
[6]E. Clementel and C. Villi, Nuovo cimento 4, 1207 (1958).
[7]E. Pickup, F. Ayer, and E. O. Salant, Phys. Rev. Letters 4, 474 (1960); J. G. Rushbrooke and D. Radojičić, Phys. Rev. Letters 5, 567 (1960).
[8]J. Bowcock, W. N. Cottingham, and D. Lurié, Phys. Rev. Letters 5, 386 (1960).
[9]R. Hofstadter, F. Bumiller, and M. Croissiaux, Phys. Rev. Letters 5, 263 (1960).
[10]R. Hofstadter, C. de Vries, and R. Herman, Phys. Rev. Letters 6, 290 (1961); R. Hofstadter and R. Herman, Phys. Rev. Letters 6, 293 (1961).
[11]M. Cini, Proceedings of the Ninth Annual Rochester Conference on High-Energy Nuclear Physics (Interscience Publishers, New York, 1959); F. Fubini, Proceedings of the Conference on Strong Interactions, Berkeley, California, 1960 [Revs. Modern Phys. (to be published)].
[12]S. Bergia and A. Stanghellini (to be published).
[13]L. I. Schiff, Revs. Modern Phys. 30, 462 (1958).
[14]A. Abashian, N. E. Booth, and K. M. Crowe, Phys. Rev. Letters 5, 258 (1960).
[15]G. F. Chew, Proceedings of the Berkeley Conference on Strong Interactions, Berkeley, California, 1960 [Revs. Modern Phys. (to be published)]. We thank Professor M. Baldo-Ceolin and G. Quareni for a very illuminating discussion on this point.
[16]L. Bertocchi, C. Ceolin, and M. Tonin (private communication).

PAPER 69

PION-PION INTERACTION IN PION PRODUCTION BY π^+-p COLLISIONS*

D. Stonehill, C. Baltay, H. Courant, W. Fickinger, E. C. Fowler,
H. Kraybill, J. Sandweiss, J. Sanford,† and H. Taft

Yale University, New Haven, Connecticut and Brookhaven National Laboratory, Upton, New York

(Received May 12, 1961)

Since the first conjectures[1] that rise in the total π^--p cross section between 300 and 600 Mev might be caused by a pion-pion interaction, this subject has received considerable attention. Theoretical analysis[2] of high-energy electron scattering on protons and neutrons has predicted a resonance in the pion-pion interaction at a total di-pion energy (ω) of 4 to 5 pion masses, with isotopic spin and angular momentum both equal to one. Several analyses of π^--p experiments[3] in the 1-Bev energy range have tended to confirm this prediction, and application[4] of the Chew-Low method has indicated a steep rise in the pion-pion cross section above $\omega = 4$. Recent work[5] with 1.9-Bev π^--p collisions shows a peak in the pion-pion interaction at $\omega \sim 5.5$. We report here evidence of pion-pion interaction in π^+-p collisions at three separate energies, which show striking effects attributable to a pion-pion resonance with ω of about 5.5 pion masses.

The data presented are results of a systematic study of pion-proton reactions at kinetic energies of 910 Mev, 1090 Mev, and 1260 Mev, which is still in progress. Photographs taken at the Cosmotron in the Brookhaven 20-inch hydrogen bubble chamber have been scanned for all interactions. All two-pronged collisions have been measured on a projection microscope of the Franckenstein type and have been processed by the Yale spatial reconstruction and kinematical fitting programs on the IBM 704 of the New York University Computing Center. Each possible identification assigned by the computation has been compared by a physicist with other information (including ionization densities) available from the photographs, to establish the final identification. Cross sections for the various reactions, based upon the first compilation of these events, are shown in Table I.

The influence of pion-pion interaction will appear most readily in the single pion production processes: $\pi^+ + p \to p + \pi^+ + \pi^0$ and $\pi^+ + p \to n + \pi^+ + \pi^+$. Accordingly, the Q value of the two outgoing pions (that is, the kinetic energy of their relative motion in their mutual center of momentum) has been computed for each individual occurrence of single pion production. The distribution of Q values at each energy is shown in Fig. 1. This figure includes all identified events, without additional selection.

In the reaction $\pi^+ + p \to p + \pi^+ + \pi^0$, a definite peak appears at each energy in the Q-value region of 400-500 Mev, extending well above the number of events to be expected from a uniform momentum-space distribution of secondary particles. The peaks also extend well above the distribution to

Table I. π^+-p **cross sections (in mb) at 910-Mev, 1090-Mev, and 1260-Mev kinetic energy.**

	910 Mev	1090 Mev	1260 Mev
σ_{total}	24.5 ± 1.3	30.1 ± 1.6	40.3 ± 2.2
σ_{elastic}	10.3 ± 0.9	12.6 ± 1.1	16.5 ± 1.4
$\sigma(p\pi^+\pi^0)$	10.4 ± 0.9	10.8 ± 1.0	11.9 ± 1.2
$\sigma(n\pi^+\pi^+)$	2.6 ± 0.4	2.5 ± 0.5	4.6 ± 0.7
$\sigma_{\text{multiple }\pi\text{ prod.}}$	1.3 ± 0.3	3.9 ± 0.6	6.9 ± 0.9
$\sigma(\Sigma\text{-}K)$	$0.034^{+0.018}_{-0.012}$	0.25 ± 0.02	0.42 ± 0.07

624

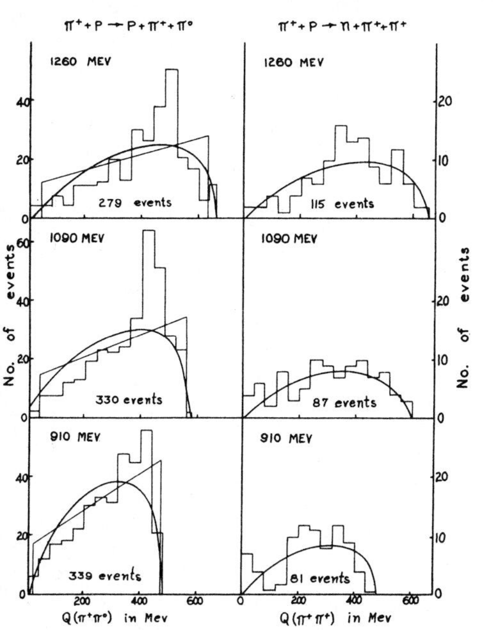

FIG. 1. Distribution of pion-pion Q values (that is, kinetic energy of the two outgoing pions in their mutual center-of-momentum system) for the reactions $\pi^+ + p \to p + \pi^+ + \pi^0$ and $\pi^+ + p \to n + \pi^+ + \pi^+$ at 910-Mev, 1090-Mev, and 1260-Mev laboratory kinetic energy of the incident pion. The curved lines are the Q distribution resulting from uniform distribution of the secondary particles in momentum space. The straight lines give the Q distribution resulting from isotropic decay of a pion-proton isobar of unique mass 1230 Mev.

be expected from isotropic decay of the $\frac{3}{2}$-$\frac{3}{2}$ pion-nucleon isobar, which is known to influence this reaction.[6]

In the pion-pion Q distributions for $\pi^+ + p \to n + \pi^+ + \pi^+$, on the other hand, no peaks appear in the region 400 to 500 Mev. (There may be a peak for the 1260-Mev pion energy in the vicinity of 350 Mev, but this is not statistically certain.)

Now, two π^+ mesons can only have a total isotopic spin of 2, whereas the π^+-π^0 combination contains isotopic spin values of 1 and 2. Therefore, a resonance in the $I = 1$ state can only appear in the $p\pi^+\pi^0$ reaction. On the other hand, if charge independence is assumed, a resonance in the $I = 2$ state should appear 80% as $n\pi^+\pi^+$ reactions and 20% as $p\pi^+\pi^0$. We conclude that the interaction responsible for the observed peaks is overwhelming in the state $I = 1$, and possibly not at all in the state $I = 2$. This is consistent both with theoretical predictions[1,2] and with the conclusions of Walker et al.[5]

At present, only an approximate estimate of the pion-pion resonance energy can be made from these data. At 910 Mev, the peak is attenuated and shifted to lower energies by the lack of available momentum space at higher Q values. The peak at 1090 Mev also seems to be about 50 Mev lower than at 1260 Mev. However, the data are not inconsistent with a single resonance with ω between 5.0 and 5.5, corresponding to a total dipion mass of 700 to 770 Mev. The full width at half maximum appears to be ~90 Mev. (The rms error in the determination of Q values is less than 10 Mev.)

We are pleased to acknowledge the considerable help we have received from the regular Brookhaven staff, especially at the Cosmotron and with the Bubble Chamber Group.

---

*This work was partially supported by the U. S. Atomic Energy Commission.

†Part of the work reported here was done by J. R. Sanford who held a National Science Foundation Cooperative Graduate Fellowship.

[1]R. Cool, O. Piccioni, and D. Clark, Phys. Rev. 103, 1082 (1956); F. J. Dyson, Phys. Rev. 99, 1037 (1955); G. Takeda, Phys. Rev. 100, 440 (1955).

[2]W. R. Frazer and J. R. Fulco, Phys. Rev. Letters 2, 365 (1959); J. Bowcock, W. N. Cottingham, and D. Lurié, Phys. Rev. Letters 5, 386 (1960); S. Bergia, A. Stanghellini, S. Fubini, and C. Villi, Phys. Rev. Letters 6, 367 (1961).

[3]I. Derado, Nuovo cimento 15, 853 (1960); F. Selleri, Nuovo cimento 16, 775 (1960); P. Carruthers and H. A. Bethe, Phys. Rev. Letters 4, 536 (1960); E. Pickup, F. Ayer, and E. O. Salant, Phys. Rev. Letters 5, 161 (1960); D. Robinson, B. Munir, E. Pickup, and E. Salant, Bull. Am. Phys. Soc. 6, 301 (1961).

[4]J. Anderson, V. Bang, P. Burke, D. Carmony, and N. Schmitz, Phys. Rev. Letters 6, 365 (1961).

[5]W. Walker, H. Fechter, R. March, D. Lyon, P. Satterblom, and A. Erwin, Bull. Am. Phys. Soc. 6, 311 (1961), and private communication from W. D. Walker.

[6]Private communication.

PAPER 70

EVIDENCE FOR A π-π RESONANCE IN THE $I=1$, $J=1$ STATE*

A. R. Erwin, R. March, W. D. Walker, and E. West
Brookhaven National Laboratory, Upton, New York and University of Wisconsin, Madison, Wisconsin
(Received May 11, 1961)

Since the earliest data became available on pion production by pions, certain features have been quite clear. The main feature which is strongly exhibited above energies of 1 Bev is that collisions are preferred in which there is a small momentum transfer to the nucleon.[1] This is shown by the nucleon angular distributions which are sharply peaked in the backward direction. These results suggest that large-impact-parameter collisions are important in such processes. The simplest process that could give rise to such collisions is a pion-pion collision with the target pion furnished in a virtual state by the nucleon. The quantitative aspects of such collisions have been discussed by a number of authors. Goebel, Chew and Low, and Salzman and Salzman[2] discussed means of extracting from the data the π-π cross section.

Holladay and Frazer and Fulco[3] deduced from electromagnetic data that indeed there must be a strong pion-pion interaction. In particular, Frazer and Fulco deduced that there probably was a resonance in the $I=1$, $J=1$ state. A qualitative set of π-p phase shifts in the 400-600 Mev[4] region were used by Bowcock et al.[5] to deduce an energy of about 660 Mev in the π-π system for the resonance. The work of Pickup et al.[6] showed an indication of a peak in the π-π spectrum at an energy of about 600 Mev.

The present experiment was designed to explore the π-π system up to an energy of about 1 Bev. The π^- beam was produced by the external proton beam No. 1 at the Cosmotron. A suitable set of quadrupole and bending magnets focussed the pion beam on a Hevimet slit about 10 ft from the Adair-

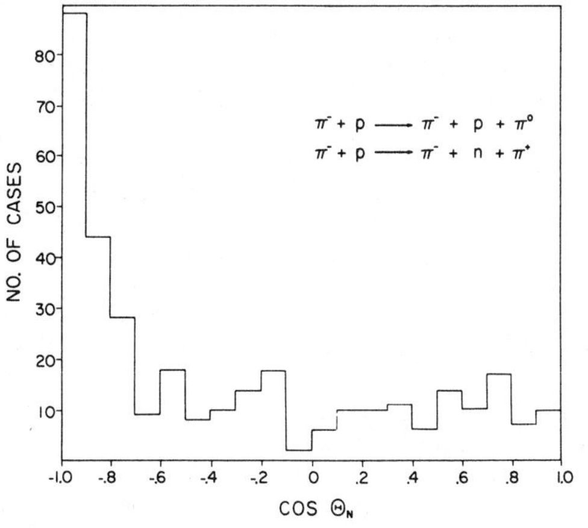

FIG. 1. The angular distribution of the nucleons from the processes $\pi^- + p \rightarrow \pi^- + \pi^0 + p$ and $\pi^- + p \rightarrow \pi^- + \pi^+ + n$.

Leipuner 14-in. H_2 bubble chamber. The pions were guided into the chamber by another bending magnet. The measured momentum was 1.89 ± 0.07 Bev/c.

Events selected for measurement were taken in a fiducial volume of the chamber. The forward-going track was required to be at least 10 cm long. Measurements were made on a digitized system and the output was analyzed by use of an IBM-704. The events were analyzed by means of a program based on the "Guts" routine written by members of the Alvarez bubble chamber group.

Figure 1 shows the combined angular distribution for the nucleons from the two processes, $\pi^- + p \rightarrow \pi^- + \pi^0 + p$ and $\pi^- + p \rightarrow \pi^- + \pi^+ + n$, which appear to be identical within statistics. The results indicate a large number of events with small momentum transfer to the nucleons.

We concentrate our interest on those events with small momentum transfer since these events satisfy the qualitative criterion of being examples of π-π collisions. Somewhat arbitrarily, we center our attention on cases in which the momentum transfer to the nucleon is less than 400 Mev/c. Table I gives the ratios of the three possible final states $\pi^-\pi^+n$, $\pi^-\pi^0p$, and $\pi^0\pi^0n$, assuming the π-π scattering to be dominated, respectively, by the $I = 0$, 1, 2 scattering states of the π-π system.

The experimental results in the last column indicate a strong domination by $I = 1$ state. For the $I = 1$ state the basic π-π scattering cross sections $\sigma(\pi^-\pi^0 \rightarrow \pi^-\pi^0)$ and $\sigma(\pi^-\pi^+ \rightarrow \pi^-\pi^+)$ are equal.

Table I. Ratios of final states.

	$I=0$	$I=1$	$I=2$	Experiment ($\Delta \leq 400$ Mev/c)
$\pi^-\pi^+n$	2	2	2/9	1.7 ± 0.3
$\pi^-\pi^0p$	0	1	1	1
$\pi^0\pi^0n$	1	0	4/9	$< 0.25 \pm 0.25$

The nucleon four-momentum transfer spectrum seems to be in qualitative agreement with the theory for the process in which a π is knocked out of the cloud. Figure 2 shows ideograms for the mass spectrum of the di-pions for cases with $\Delta \leq 400$ Mev/c and $\Delta > 400$ Mev/c, where Δ is the four-momentum transfer to the nucleon. The curve for $\Delta \leq 400$ Mev/c clearly shows a peak at 765 Mev/c. In the ideogram for $\Delta > 400$ Mev/c the peak is still present but seems to be smeared to higher values of the di-pion mass, m^*. One worries that diagrams other than the one involving

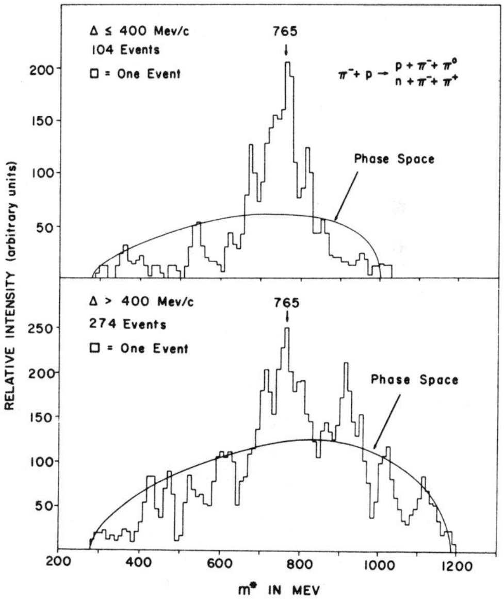

FIG. 2. The combined mass spectrum for the $\pi^-\pi^0$ and $\pi^-\pi^+$ system. The smooth curve is phase space as modified for the included momentum transfer and normalized to the number of events plotted. Events used in the upper distribution are not contained in the lower distribution.

one-pion exchange might be contributing to the observed peak in this m^* spectrum. In particular, an important contribution at lower energies comes from a diagram in which one of the π's rescatters off the nucleon and ends up in the 3-3 state with respect to the nucleon. If one restricts the data to cases with $\Delta \leq 400$ Mev/c this diagram does not seem to be very important, but if one takes cases with $\Delta > 400$ Mev/c many cases consistent with rescattering are found.

In order to deduce values of the π-π cross section, we use the formula[2]

$$\frac{d^2\sigma}{dm^* d\Delta^2} = \frac{3f^2}{\pi} \frac{\Delta^2}{(\Delta^2+1)^2}\left(\frac{m^*}{q_{iL}}\right)^2 K\bar{\sigma}_{\pi-\pi},$$

where $\bar{\sigma}_{\pi-\pi}$ is the mean of $\sigma(\pi^-\pi^0 \to \pi^-\pi^0)$ and $\sigma(\pi^-\pi^+ \to \pi^-\pi^+)$. In the above formula all momenta and energies are measured in units of pion masses. q_{iL} = momentum of the incoming pion measured in units of the pion mass. K = momentum of the pions in the di-pion center-of-mass system. Then

$$\delta\sigma = \frac{3f^2}{\pi}\left(\frac{m^*}{q_{iL}}\right)^2 K\bar{\sigma}_{\pi-\pi}\,\delta m^* \int_{\Delta_{\min}(m^*)}^{\Delta_{\max}} \frac{\Delta^2 d\Delta^2}{(\Delta^2+1)^2}.$$

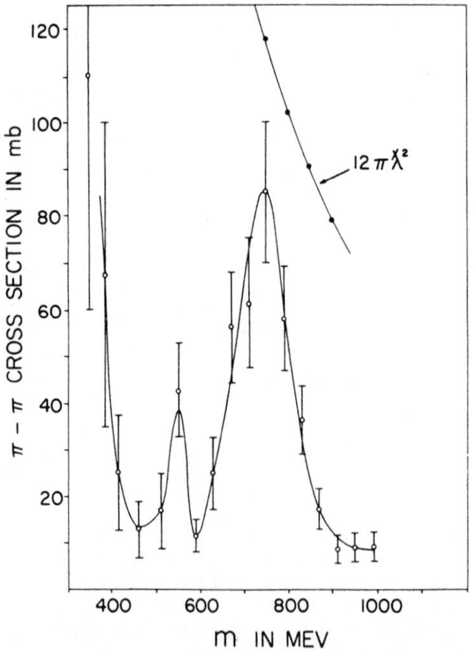

FIG. 3. The π-π cross section as deduced from cases with the four-momentum transfer less than 400 Mev/c.

The results of this calculation using the experimentally determined $\delta\sigma$'s are shown in Fig. 3. The results indicate a peak in the neighborhood of 750 Mev with a width of 150-200 Mev, which is about 3/4 of what it would be ($12\pi\lambda^2$) for a resonance in the $I=1$, $J=1$ state. Since this cross section was determined off the energy shell, it is difficult to estimate the effect of the interference of other diagrams and also the effect of line broadening.[7] Whether or not the other peak and the S-wave scattering indicated in Fig. 3 are real will have to await better statistics for verification.

We wish to acknowledge with gratitude the help and cooperation of R. K. Adair and L. Leipuner in the use of their bubble chamber, and to the latter also for his assistance in adapting the "Guts" routine to our use. We also acknowledge the help of J. Boyd, J. Bishop, P. Satterblom, R. P. Chen, C. Seaver, and K. Eggman in measuring, scanning, and tabulating. We were greatly aided by Dr. J. Ballam and Dr. H. Fechter in setting up the beam. We have had helpful conversations with Dr. R. K. Adair, Dr. C. J. Goebel, Dr. M. L. Good, and in particular Dr. G. Takeda.

---

*Work supported in part by the U. S. Atomic Energy Commission and Wisconsin Alumni Research Foundation.

[1]L. M. Eisberg, W. B. Fowler, R. M. Lea, W. D. Shephard, R. P. Shutt, A. M. Thorndike, and W. L. Whittemore, Phys. Rev. 97, 797 (1955); W. D. Walker and J. Crussard, Phys. Rev. 98, 1416 (1955).

[2]C. Goebel, Phys. Rev. Letters 1, 337 (1958); G. F. Chew and F. E. Low, Phys. Rev. 113, 1640 (1959); F. Salzman and G. Salzman, Phys. Rev. 120, 599 (1960).

[3]W. Holladay, Phys. Rev. 101, 1198 (1956); W. Frazer and J. Fulco, University of California Radiation Laboratory Report UCRL-8880, August, 1959 (unpublished).

[4]W. D. Walker, J. Davis, and W. D. Shephard, Phys. Rev. 118, 1612 (1960).

[5]J. Bowcock, N. Cottingham, and D. Lurie, Nuovo cimento 19, 142 (1961), and Phys. Rev. Letters 5, 386 (1960).

[6]E. Pickup, F. Ayer, and E. O. Salant, Phys. Rev. Letters 5, 161 (1960); Proceedings of the Tenth Annual International Conference on High-Energy Physics at Rochester (Interscience Publishers, Inc., New York, 1960); see also F. Bonsignori and F. Selleri, Nuovo cimento 15, 465 (1960).

[7]Deductions made by extrapolations seem to give different values of the cross section. Also the position of the maximum is not determined very well. J. A. Anderson, Vo. X. Bang, P. G. Burke, D. D. Carmony, and N. Schmitz, Phys. Rev. Letters 6, 365 (1961).

PAPER 71

INELASTIC ELECTRON-DEUTERON SCATTERING AND THE ELECTROMAGNETIC STRUCTURE OF THE NEUTRON*

Loyal Durand, III
Brookhaven National Laboratory, Upton, New York
(Received April 25, 1961; revised manuscript received May 11, 1961)

Recent experiments on elastic electron-proton scattering performed at Stanford[1] and Cornell[2] have provided detailed information on the behavior of the Dirac (charge) and anomalous magnetic moment form factors F_{1p} and F_{2p} of the proton for electron 4-momentum transfers up to $q^2 = 36\ \mathrm{f}^{-2}$. Corresponding information on the form factors F_{1n} and F_{2n} of the neutron has been obtained from studies of the cross section $d^2\sigma/(d\Omega_e dE_e')$ for the inelastic scattering of electrons from the deuteron, $e+d \to e+n+p$.[3-5] Analysis of the recent Stanford data on this process, using the theoretical cross section calculated by Jankus[6] with the modifications introduced by Hofstadter and others,[7] leads to two interesting conclusions. First, F_{2n} and F_{2p}, which were thought on the basis of earlier work to be approximately equal for $q^2 \leqslant 10\ \mathrm{f}^{-2}$,[5] were found to differ markedly for $q^2 \gtrsim 5\ \mathrm{f}^{-2}$,[4] reflecting a difference in the spatial distribution of the anomalous magnetic moment in the two nucleons. Second, the Dirac form factor of the neutron F_{1n} was found to differ from zero for $q^2 \gtrsim 5\ \mathrm{f}^{-2}$, this result providing the first evidence for an extended distribution of charge in the neutron.[4] The values of the form factors F_{1n} and F_{2n} obtained from Fig. 1 of Hofstadter and Herman[4] are given in Table I for representative values of q^2. The values of F_{1n} are also shown in Fig. 1.

We wish to report in the present Letter on the marked changes in the neutron form factors which result from a reanalysis of the Stanford data on inelastic electron-deuteron scattering[4] using a theoretical cross section obtained from a completely covariant theory.[8] This work, which extends considerably the semirelativistic theory given in a previous paper,[9] is based on the techniques of dispersion relations. Calculation of the cross section $d^2\sigma/(d\Omega_e dE_e')$ is especially simple in the region of the large peak which corresponds to the quasi-elastic scattering of the electron by a single nucleon. The dominant terms in the transition amplitude then arise from single-nucleon pole terms which can be calculated exactly. Retention of these pole terms alone would correspond to the replacement of the complete deuteron wave function in the nonrelativistic theory by its asymptotic form. The largest remaining terms arise at the quasi-elastic peak from anomalous regions in the dispersion relations. The spectral functions in these regions are closely related to the short-range parts of the nonrelativistic deuteron wave function. The proximity of the single-nucleon poles to the physical region for the transition results in a relatively weak dependence of the peak cross section on the high-mass regions of the spectral functions, or alternatively, on the short-range structure of the deuteron wave function. It is consequently a good approximation to use in the dispersion relations spectral functions calculated directly from a nonrelativistic model for the wave function. The denominators in the dispersion relations may nevertheless be retained in covariant form; the usual ambiguities[7,9] with respect to the kinematics and the relativistic treatment of the deuteron wave function are thereby eliminated. We may also remark that the nucleon form factors appear

Table I. Changes in the neutron form factors F_{1n} and F_{2n} which result from changes in the theoretical peak value of $d^2\sigma/(d\Omega_e dE_e')$. The form factors with the superscript J result from an analysis of the experimental cross sections[a] based on the modified Jankus theory.[b] The form factors without superscripts are obtained when the data are reanalyzed using the present theory. The calculations were based on the method of intersecting ellipses.[c] The tabulated values of the form factors denoted by asterisks correspond to the point of closest approach in those cases in which the ellipses failed to intersect.[d]

q^2 (f^{-2})	F_{1n}^J	F_{1n}	F_{2n}^J	F_{2n}
5.1	0.16	0.09	0.76	0.75
10.0	0.12	-0.09*	0.49	0.38*
11.5	0.03	-0.11*	0.46	0.34*
15.0	0.18	-0.08*	0.40	0.28*
18.0	0.25	-0.02	0.40	0.28
21.0	0.17	0.00	0.33	0.22

[a] See footnote 13.
[b] See reference 7.
[c] See reference 4.
[d] See footnote 14.

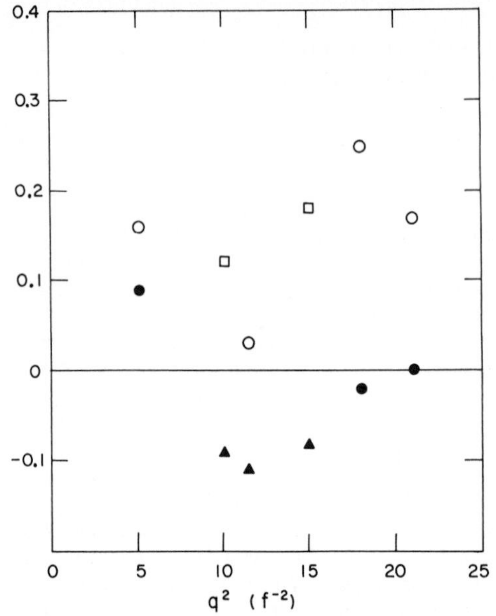

FIG. 1. Values of the Dirac form factor F_{1n} for the neutron obtained by analyzing the data of Hofstadter et al. (reference 4) by the method of intersecting ellipses using the modified Jankus result for $d^2\sigma/(d\Omega_e dE_e')$ (open circles) and the improved result of the present paper (solid circles). For the points indicated by open and solid squares, "experimental" cross sections were constructed using the smoothed values of the nucleon form factors given in Table I and footnote 13. The points indicated by solid triangles represent cases for which no intersection was obtained unless allowance was made for possible experimental errors. The uncertainty in these points is very large. It is expected that the tabulated values of F_{1n} for these points are too large in magnitude, $F_{1n} \approx 0$ being possible within the accuracy of the data.

naturally in the present theory, and are evaluated on the mass shell in the dominant pole terms. Off-mass-shell corrections have been estimated in the remaining expressions, and are thought to be small.

The cross section $d^2\sigma/(d\Omega_e dE_e')$ is well represented in the neighborhood of the quasi-elastic peak by the approximate expression:

$$d^2\sigma/(d\Omega_e dE_e') = \sigma_{\rm Mott} m p \pi^{-1}(m/E)M(p,q)(G_n + G_p), \tag{1}$$

where

$$\sigma_{\rm Mott} = \tfrac{1}{4}\alpha^2 E_e^{-2}\sin^{-4}(\tfrac{1}{2}\theta)\cos^2(\tfrac{1}{2}\theta), \tag{2}$$

and

$$G_i = F_{1i}^{\,2} + (q^2/4m^2)\kappa_i^{\,2}F_{2i}^{\,2} + (q^2/2m^2)(F_{1i} + \kappa_i F_{2i})^2\tan^2(\tfrac{1}{2}\theta). \tag{3}$$

Here E_e is the energy of the incident electron, θ is the electron scattering angle in the laboratory system, m is the nucleon mass, κ_n and κ_p are the anomalous parts of the nucleon magnetic moments, and p is the momentum and E the energy of either of the outgoing nucleons in their center-of-mass system. The effects on the scattering of the structure of the deuteron are contained entirely in the function $M(p,q)$.

The cross section given in Eq. (1) neglects the following: (1) the effects of interactions between the outgoing nucleons; (2) scattering involving the D-state component of the deuteron wave function; (3) small corrections involving interference between scattering by the neutron and by the proton (< 0.5 % error); (4) the effects on the functions G_n and G_p of the initial Fermi momentum of the nucleons in the deuteron (< 0.5 % error). The effects of final-state interactions have been calculated[8] by the methods of reference 9 using approximate final-state wave functions matched to the neutron-proton scattering phase shifts of Bryan, Signell, and Marshak,[10] and are found to decrease the peak cross section by roughly 1.5-2.5 %, depending on q and θ. We have adopted as a reasonable approximation to these effects a uniform 2 % decrease of the peak cross section. The D-state component of the deuteron wave function scatters less efficiently than the S-state component, and the peak cross section is decreased by an additional 3 % for a large range of q when this effect is included. The function $M(p,q)$ may be shown to reduce for $q \gtrsim 1$ to the form (constant)$/p^2$ at the quasi-elastic peak. Evaluating the constant for a repulsive core wave function,[8] and incorporating the foregoing corrections, one then obtains for the peak value of $d^2\sigma/(d\Omega_e dE_e')$ only

$$[d^2\sigma/(d\Omega_e dE_e')]_{\rm peak} = \sigma_{\rm Mott}(4.57\times10^{-3})(1\pm0.05) \times (m^2/pE)(G_n + G_p). \tag{4}$$

The factor (1 ± 0.05) represents our estimate of the uncertainties in the theoretical cross section associated with the foregoing effects, with the contributions to the scattering of meson currents in the deuteron, and of off-mass-shell corrections to the form factors. This result is essentially equivalent in form to that given by Goldberg[11] as an approximation to his impulse-type calculations, but includes some additional corrections, and is furthermore free of the ambiguities attendant on the impulse approximation.

The results obtained from Eq. (4) differ from the peak value of the modified Jankus cross section[7] in three respects: (1) The value of the overall numerical factor 4.57×10^{-3} in Eq. (4) includes the corrections discussed above; (2) Eq. (4) contains a factor (m/E) originating in the three-body phase space which is absent in the Jankus cross section, and decreases the peak value significantly for large values of p; (3) the functions G_i are replaced in the modified Jankus cross section by functions G_i',

$$G_i' = G_i - (q^2/2m^2)F_{1i}^{\ 2} + O[(q^2/4m^2)^2].$$

The terms of order $(q^2/4m^2)^2$ in G_i' cannot be retained consistently in the nonrelativistic theory,[9] and should be omitted from the modified Jankus cross section. The appearance of the extra term $-(q^2/2m^2)F_{1i}^{\ 2}$ in G_i' may be traced to an incorrect modification of the Jankus theory intended to make the peak cross section reduce for large q^2 to a sum of Rosenbluth cross sections[12] for the scattering of electrons from free nucleons. The resulting errors in the theoretical value of $d^2\sigma/(d\Omega_e dE_e')$ are quite large, especially at small scattering angles.

The effect of the foregoing results on the values of the neutron form factors F_{1n} and F_{2n} determined from the Stanford electron scattering experiments, has been investigated by reanalyzing the experimental data of Hofstadter et al.[4] for representative values of q^2. The calculations were based on the theoretical expression for the peak value of the inelastic deuteron cross section $d^2\sigma/(d\Omega_e dE_e')$ given in Eq. (4). The function G_p which appears there was evaluated when possible using the Rosenbluth cross section for elastic electron-proton scattering,[12]

$$(d\sigma/d\Omega_e)_p = \sigma_{\text{Mott}}[1 + (2E_e/m)\sin^2(\tfrac{1}{2}\theta)]^{-1}G_p, \quad (5)$$

in conjunction with experimental values of the elastic scattering cross sections.[1] This result was combined with the experimental electron-deuteron scattering cross sections of Hofstadter et al.[4,13] using Eq. (4) to obtain the Rosenbluth factor G_n for the neutron. The values of F_{1n} and F_{2n} were determined by combining values of G_n corresponding to a fixed q^2, but different energies and scattering angles, using the method of intersecting ellipses.[7] For $q^2 = 10\ \text{f}^{-2}$ and $15\ \text{f}^{-2}$, values of $d^2\sigma/(d\Omega_e dE_e')$ and $(d\sigma/d\Omega_e)_p$ at properly matched energies and scattering angles were not available in the published data. In these cases we have constructed "experimental" cross sections using the Rosenbluth and the modified Jankus theories with smoothed values of the nucleon form factors taken from references 1 and 4.[13] Corrected values of the neutron form factors were then obtained by reanalyzing these "data" using the corrected theoretical cross section of Eq. (4). We note finally that the ellipses failed in three cases [$q^2 = 10$, 11.5, and $15\ \text{f}^{-2}$] to intersect unless allowance was made for possible errors in the cross sections.[14] In these cases, we have determined rough values of F_{1n} and F_{2n} by choosing as the "intersection" the midpoint of the region of closest approach. It is expected from an examination of the effects of possible experimental errors that the value of F_{2n} so determined is slightly too small, and that of F_{1n}, considerably too negative. $F_{1n} \approx 0$ would be consistent with the data within the possible errors.

The results of this analysis are summarized in Table I. The corrected values of F_{1n} are in addition plotted in Fig. 1 along with the values obtained by Hofstadter et al.[4] using the modified Jankus theory. The changes in F_{1n} are quite striking. The results of Hofstadter et al.[4] suggested that this form factor was a positive increasing function for $q^2 \geq 5\ \text{f}^{-2}$, with a value $F_{1n} \approx 0.2$ for $q^2 = 20\ \text{f}^{-2}$. The present results favor small or zero values of F_{1n} over the entire range of q^2 which was considered. This result, if substantiated by the analysis of newer experimental data,[15] would indicate that the outer structure of the neutron is more nearly neutral than has been supposed.[3,4] The changes in F_{2n} are less striking, but range up to 30% for large values of q^2, and bring this form factor closer in magnitude to F_{2p}. A detailed analysis of the relevant data will be necessary before the variation of the neutron form factors with increasing q^2 can be specified with any assurance. We wish in particular to emphasize that the corrected values of F_{1n} and F_{2n} given in Table I are quite sensitive to changes in the cross sections $d^2\sigma/(d\Omega_e dE_e')$ and $(d\sigma/d\Omega_e)_p$, and may be altered when the results of recent experiments are analyzed.[15]

The author would like to thank Professor R. R. Wilson, Professor R. Hofstadter, Dr. R. Herman, and Dr. C. deVries for valuable discussions with regard to the electron-deuteron scattering experiments, and I. Cole and E. Windschauer for computational assistance.

*Work performed under the auspices of the U. S. Atomic Energy Commission.

[1]F. Bumiller, M. Croissiaux, and R. Hofstadter, Phys. Rev. Letters 5, 261 (1960); R. Hofstadter, F. Bumiller, and M. Croissiaux, Phys. Rev. Letters 5, 263 (1960).

[2]R. R. Wilson, K. Berkelman, J. M. Cassels, and D. N. Olson, Nature 188, 94 (1960).

[3]D. N. Olson, H. F. Schopper, and R. R. Wilson, Phys. Rev. Letters 6, 286 (1961).

[4]R. Hofstadter, C. deVries, and R. Herman, Phys. Rev. Letters 6, 290 (1961); R. Hofstadter and R. Herman, Phys. Rev. Letters 6, 293 (1961).

[5]M. R. Yearian and R. Hofstadter, Phys. Rev. 110, 552 (1958); 111, 934 (1958). S. Sobottka, Phys. Rev. 118, 831 (1960).

[6]V. Z. Jankus, Phys. Rev. 102, 1586 (1956).

[7]R. Herman and R. Hofstadter, High-Energy Electron Scattering Tables (Stanford University Press, Stanford, California, 1960), pp. 40-45. The modified Jankus cross section as given in this reference does not include the effects of a nonvanishing Dirac form factor F_{1n} for the neutron, but the necessary modifications are easily made.

[8]L. Durand, III, Phys. Rev. (to be published).

[9]L. Durand, III, Phys. Rev. 115, 1020 (1959).

[10]P. S. Signell and R. E. Marshak, Phys. Rev. 106, 832 (1957); 109, 1229 (1958). P. S. Signell, R. Zinn, and R. E. Marshak, Phys. Rev. Letters 1, 416 (1958); R. A. Bryan, Bull. Am. Phys. Soc. 5, 35 (1960). The author is indebted to Dr. Bryan for supplying values for the neutron-proton scattering phase shifts.

[11]A. Goldberg, Phys. Rev. 112, 618 (1958). The principal advantage of the present procedure relative to the simple impulse approximation is the possibility of examining in detail such questions as the effects of binding on the current operators, the effects of final-state interactions and neutron-proton interference terms in the scattering, and of relativistic corrections involving the deuteron wave function.

[12]M. N. Rosenbluth, Phys. Rev. 79, 615 (1950).

[13]For $q^2 = 11.5$, 18.0, and 21.0 f^{-2}, we have used the experimental peak values of $d^2\sigma/(d\Omega_e dE_e')$ given by Hofstadter, deVries, and Herman[4] in conjunction with the experimental proton cross sections $(d\sigma/d\Omega_e)_p$ for the same scattering angles and energies given by Hofstadter, Bumiller, and Croissiaux.[1] For $q^2 = 5.1$, the values of $d^2\sigma/(d\Omega_e dE_e')$ interpolated from the data of Sobottka[5] by Hofstadter, deVries, and Herman[4] were combined with proton cross sections calculated from the exponential proton model of E. E. Chambers and R. Hofstadter [Phys. Rev. 103, 1454 (1956)]. This model was used by Sobottka to normalize his deuteron cross sections.[5] The cross sections for $q^2 = 10\ f^{-2}$ and 15 f^{-2} were calculated as described in the text, using smoothed values of the nucleon form factors taken from Fig. 1 of Hofstadter and Herman.[4] The values assumed for the neutron form factors $F_{1n}^{\ J}$ and $F_{2n}^{\ J}$ resulting from an analysis using the Jankus theory are given in Table I. The values assumed for the proton form factors are as follows: $q^2 = 10\ f^{-2}$, $F_{1p} = 0.48$, $F_{2p} = 0.39$; $q^2 = 15\ f^{-2}$, $F_{1p} = 0.43$, $F_{2p} = 0.21$.

[14]The failure of the ellipses to intersect indicates that the input data are not consistent with the theoretical form of $d^2\sigma/(d\Omega_e dE_e')$ given in Eq. (4). However, intersections could be obtained by changing either the large-angle or the small-angle deuteron cross section $d^2\sigma/(d\Omega_e dE_e')$ by 10% or less. An error in the cross sections of this magnitude is consistent with the estimated accuracy of the experiments.[1,4] Furthermore, such errors are undoubtedly present, as indicated by the deviation of the experimental values of G_n from the values calculated for the same q^2 and θ using neutron form factors taken from the smooth curve drawn through the points in reference 4. The deviations are of both signs, and range up to about 50% of G_n, but are generally smaller. Since scattering by the proton contributes on the order of $\frac{1}{2}-\frac{2}{3}$ of the peak deuteron cross section, depending on q^2 and θ, the corresponding errors in $d^2\sigma/(d\Omega_e dE_e')$ are reduced by factors of 2-3, and lie within the expected range. Conversely, it is clear that values obtained for G_n, hence, for the neutron form factors, can be changed significantly by rather small changes in the experimental values of $d^2\sigma/(d\Omega_e dE_e')$ and $(d\sigma/d\Omega_e)_p$.

[15]The Stanford group has recently extended its measurements of the inelastic electron-deuteron, and the elastic electron-proton scattering cross sections to a number of energies and scattering angles not previously considered, with the largest value of q^2 now 25 f^{-2}. Preliminary analyses at several of the new points suggest that F_{1n} may indeed be greater than zero, but somewhat smaller in magnitude than indicated in reference 4. [R. Hofstadter (private communication). The author is greatly indebted to Professor Hofstadter for a number of communications concerning the Stanford experiments.] The Cornell group has also extended considerably its measurements at larger values of q^2 [R. R. Wilson (private communication)].

PAPER 72

Radiative Corrections to Electron-Proton Scattering*

YUNG-SU TSAI
Institute of Theoretical Physics, Department of Physics, Stanford University, Stanford, California
(Received November 15, 1960)

The radiative corrections to the electron-proton scattering are calculated with the effects of the proton recoil taken into account. We assumed the experimental conditions of Hofstadter *et al.* at Stanford, namely only the final electrons are momentum-analyzed. The anisotropy in the maximum energy of photons which can be emitted and the radiation from the proton current are the two main effects due to the proton recoil, and both effects are considered. The mesonic effects in the two-photon exchange diagrams are not considered. Other than the uncertainty in the mesonic effects, our formula is good up to about 5 Bev.

I. INTRODUCTION

RECENTLY[1–4] the energy of the electron-proton scattering has been increased to around 1 Bev and within a few years the energy will probably go up to 5 Bev (Cambridge Machine) or 15 Bev (Stanford Monster). The purpose of this paper is to calculate the quantum electrodynamic parts of the radiative corrections which are applicable up to 5 Bev of the incident energy.

Schwinger[5] first calculated the radiative corrections to the potential scattering and he found that the cross section is altered by a factor $(1+\delta)$, where

$$\delta\approx\frac{-2\alpha}{\pi}\left\{\left(\ln\frac{E}{\Delta E}-\frac{13}{12}\right)\left(\ln\frac{-q^2}{m^2}-1\right)+\frac{17}{36}\right\}. \quad (I.1)$$

Here q is the four-momentum transfer, E is the energy of incident or scattered electrons (in the potential scattering they are identical), m is the rest mass of the electron, and ΔE is the maximum energy loss of the electron or the maximum energy of a photon which can be emitted (they are identical in the potential scattering). In the region $M^2\gg -q^2\gg m^2$, where M is the rest mass of the proton, Eq. (I.1) is a good approximation and has been used extensively by the experimentalists[6] in analyzing the data of the *e–p* scattering. However at high incident energy and large scattering angle, i.e., $-q^2\gtrsim M^2$, the incident energy (E_1) is no longer equal to the energy of the final electron (E_3) and the maximum energy loss of the electron ΔE is no longer equal to the maximum energy of a photon which can be emitted. In fact E_3 and E_1 are related by the formula

$$E_3=E_1/\eta, \quad (I.2)$$

where

$$\eta\equiv 1+E_1M^{-1}(1-\cos\theta). \quad (I.3)$$

For definiteness let us define the energy resolution ΔE as the experimental quantity shown in Fig. 1. Then from the energy-momentum conservation, it can be shown that the maximum energy of a photon which can be emitted along the direction of the final electron is ΔE, but in the direction of the incident electron it is $\eta^2\Delta E$. Thus Eq. (I.1) becomes quite ambiguous in the practical application at high energies because one does not know what to use for E and ΔE. Intuitively one would guess that Eq. (I.1) should be changed to

$$\delta\approx\frac{-2\alpha}{\pi}\left\{\left(\frac{1}{2}\ln\frac{E_1}{\eta^2\Delta E}+\frac{1}{2}\ln\frac{E_3}{\Delta E}-\frac{13}{12}\right)\times\left(\ln\frac{-q^2}{m^2}-1\right)+\frac{17}{36}\right\}. \quad (I.4)$$

It will be shown later that Eq. (I.4) is approximately true if one neglects the radiation by the proton current.

When $-q^2\gtrsim M^2$ the velocity of the recoil proton v_4 approaches the velocity of light, i.e., $\beta_4\equiv v_4/c\rightarrow 1$. Thus one would expect that in this case the radiation

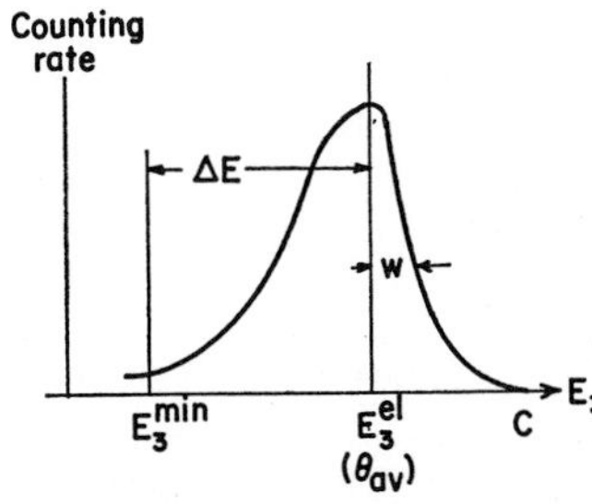

FIG. 1. A typical energy spectrum of the scattered electrons at a fixed angle. The point $E_3^{el}(\theta_{av})$ is chosen to be the energy of the elastically scattered electron at the center of the entrance slit. ΔE should be chosen such that $W\ll\Delta E\ll E_3(1+2E_1/M)^{-1}$. The widths W is caused by the energy spread in the incident beam and the finite width of the entrance slit. The curve should be integrated from E_3^{min} to C in order to compute the cross section.

* Supported in part by the U. S. Air Force through the Air Force Office of Scientific Research.

[1] R. Hofstadter and R. R. Wilson, *Proceedings of the Tenth Annual International Conference on High-Energy Physics at Rochester* (Interscience Publishers, Inc., New York, 1960).
[2] L. N. Hand, Phys. Rev. Letters **5**, 168 (1960).
[3] F. Bumiller, M. Croissiaux, and R. Hofstadter, Phys. Rev. Letters **5**, 261 (1960); **5**, 263 (1960).
[4] R. R. Wilson, K. Berkelman, and J. Cassels, Cornell University reprint (to be published).
[5] J. Schwinger, Phys. Rev. **76**, 760 (1949), Eq. (2.105).
[6] R. Hofstadter, Revs. Modern Phys. **28**, 214 (1956). Actually the energy of the scattered electron E_3 was used in E of Eq. (I.1) in this reference.

from the proton current would be no longer negligible. If one tries to calculate the bremsstrahlung from the proton current, one encounters the usual infrared divergence and thus one is forced to consider diagrams such as M_2, M_3, and M_6 in Fig. 2 in order to achieve the infrared cancellation. The exact calculation of M_2, M_3, and M_6 is not attempted in this paper since to do it one has to consider mesonic contributions from these diagrams such as carried out by Drell and Fubini.[7] We shall merely extract the infrared contributions from these diagrams using the technique developed by Yennie, Frautschi, and Suura.[8]

It has been emphasized by the present author[9] in a previous paper that in the calculation of the radiative corrections for any process a critical analysis of the experimental corrections for any process a critical analysis of the experimental conditions is necessary. We shall proceed to discuss our problem in the same spirit. The experimental conditions assumed are those of Hofstadter *et al.* at Stanford that electrons, after being scattered by a hydrogen target and going through an entrance slit, are momentum analyzed by a magnetic spectrometer and the recoil protons are left undetected.

The notation used is similar to that in reference 9. p_1 and p_3 represent the four-momenta of incident and scattered electrons, respectively. p_2 and p_4 are the four-momenta of initial and recoil protons, respectively. The metric chosen is such that $p_1\cdot p_2=E_1E_2-\mathbf{p}_1\cdot\mathbf{p}_2$. The units $\hbar=c=1$ and $e^2/4\pi=\alpha$ are used. $\not{p}$ represents $p_\mu\gamma_\mu$.

The infrared divergence is avoided by assuming that a photon has a small fictitious mass λ whenever we encounter integrations in which such divergence occurs. When the photon mass λ is used, it always appears in both the elastic and inelastic cross sections in the form[10]

$$K(p_i,p_j)\equiv(p_i\cdot p_j)\int_0^1\frac{dy}{p_y^2}\ln\frac{p_y^2}{\lambda^2}, \qquad \text{(I.5)}$$

where $p_y=p_iy+p_j(1-y)$. We shall call terms of this kind infrared terms. They always cancel out completely when elastic and inelastic cross sections are added together. Thus one does not have to integrate Eq. (I.5) explicitly. [In the matrix element of M_2 of Fig. 2, we shall see that the infrared terms have the form $K(p_i,-p_j)$ instead of $K(p_i,p_j)$. $K(p_i,-p_j)$ is complex. In our calculation only the real part of M_2 contributes to the cross section, and it can be shown[8] that

$$\operatorname{Re}K(p_i,-p_j)\approx K(p_i,p_j).]$$

Terms of order $m^2/-q^2$ compared with unity are neglected throughout in this paper. In the calculation of the contribution to the cross section by the radiation from the proton current one encounters a lot of Spence functions $\Phi(x)$. We shall neglect those Spence functions which are of order unity, e.g., $\Phi(1)$. This approximation causes an error of order $\alpha\approx1\%$ in the cross section.

In Secs. II and III elastic and inelastic scattering cross sections, respectively, are treated. The observable cross section is obtained by adding elastic and inelastic cross sections. In Sec. IV some numerical examples are given. In Sec. V some precautions to the practical applications of our formula are considered.

II. ELASTIC SCATTERING CROSS SECTION

The Feynman diagrams contributing to the elastic scattering cross section to order α^3 are shown in Fig. 2. The expression for the elastic scattering cross section can be written as[11]

$$d\sigma_{\text{elastic}}=(2\pi)^2\frac{E_1E_2}{[(p_1p_2)^2-m^2M^2]^{\frac{1}{2}}}\times\frac{1}{4}\int\delta(p_3+p_4-p_1-p_2)d^3p_3d^3p_4$$

$$\times\sum_{\text{spin}}[M_1{}^\dagger M_1+\sum_{i=2}^{6}2\operatorname{Re}(M_1{}^\dagger M_i)]. \qquad \text{(II.1)}$$

The first term in the square bracket of Eq. (II.1) represents the Rosenbluth cross section. The matrix

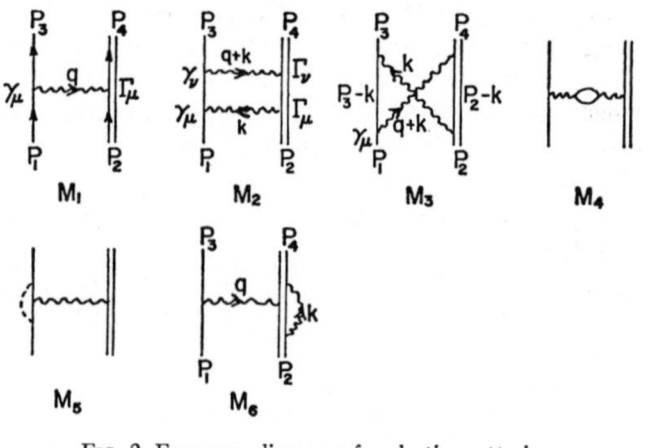

FIG. 2. Feynman diagrams for elastic scattering.

[7] S. D. Drell and S. Fubini, Phys. Rev. **113**, 741 (1959).

[8] D. R. Yennie, S. C. Frautschi, and H. Suura, Ann. Phys. (to be published). In addition to the problem of infrared divergence these authors also gave a general treatment of the recoil effects in the electron-proton scattering. The purpose of our paper is to derive a convenient formula which can be used readily by the experimentalists. Thus the present work and these authors' work are complementary to each other.

[9] Y. S. Tsai, Phys. Rev. **120**, 269 (1960), also *Proceedings of the Tenth Annual International Conference on High-Energy Physics at Rochester* (Interscience Publishers, New York, 1960).

[10] The notations for the infrared terms are improved in this paper. $-2K(p_1,p_3)/q^2$ corresponds to $\mu_2(q^2)$ in reference 9.

[11] Compare with Eq. (1) of reference 9.

element M_1 can be written as[12]

$$M_1=\frac{-i\alpha Z}{\pi}\frac{mM}{(E_1E_2E_3E_4)^{\frac{1}{2}}}\frac{1}{q^2}\bar{u}(p_3)\gamma_\mu u(p_1)\bar{u}(p_4)\Gamma_\mu(q^2)u(p_2),$$

where $q=(p_1-p_3)$,

$$\Gamma_\mu(q^2)=F_1(q^2)\gamma_\mu+\frac{\kappa}{2M}F_2(q^2)q\gamma_\mu, \quad \text{(II.2)}$$

and $\kappa=1.79$ is the Pauli magnetic moment of the proton. $F_1(q^2)$ and $F_2(q^2)$ are the electric and magnetic form factors, respectively, of the proton and are to be determined by the experiment. After averaging over the initial states and summing over the final states, one obtains the Rosenbluth cross section[13]:

$$\left(\frac{d\sigma}{d\Omega}\right)_{\text{Rosenbluth}}=\frac{r_0^2m^2Z^2}{4E_1^2\eta}\frac{\cos^2(\theta/2)}{\sin^4(\theta/2)}\times\left\{F_1^2-\frac{q^2}{4M^2}[2(F_1+\kappa F_2)^2\tan^2(\theta/2)+\kappa^2F_2^2]\right\}, \quad \text{(II.3)}$$

where $r_0=\alpha m^{-1}\sim2.82\times10^{-13}$ cm is the classical radius of an electron. For the vacuum polarization (M_4) and the electron vertex (M_5) diagrams, we can directly use the results of the electron-electron scattering calculation[14] and obtain

$$M_4=\frac{\alpha}{\pi}\left[\frac{-5}{9}+\frac{1}{3}\ln\left(\frac{-q^2}{m^2}\right)\right]M_1, \quad \text{(II.4)}$$

$$M_5=-\frac{\alpha}{2\pi}[K(p_1,p_3)-K(p_1,p_1)-\tfrac{3}{2}\ln(-q^2/m^2)+2]M_1, \quad \text{(II.5)}$$

where

$$K(p_i,p_j)=(p_i\cdot p_j)\int_0^1\frac{dy}{p_y^2}\ln\frac{p_y^2}{\lambda^2},\quad p_y=p_iy+p_j(1-y).$$

The terms $K(p_1,p_3)$ and $K(p_1,p_1)$ in Eq. (II.5) are infrared terms. It will be shown later that they cancel out completely with the similar terms in the inelastic cross section and therefore they need not be integrated explicitly.

As mentioned in the previous section, we shall merely extract the infrared terms from M_2, M_3, and M_6 and assume the noninfrared parts of these diagrams to be negligible. Let us consider the matrix element for M_2 as shown in Fig. 2. When either of the 4-momenta of the photon propagators approaches zero, i.e., $k\to0$ or $k+q\to0$, we have infrared divergence. Suppose $k\to0$, then Γ_μ in M_2 of Fig. 2 can be replaced by γ_μ, and we may write the matrix element for M_2 as

$$M_2=\frac{e^4}{(2\pi)^6}\frac{mMZ^2}{(E_1E_2E_3E_4)^{\frac{1}{2}}}\int d^4k\,\bar{u}(p_3)\gamma_\nu\frac{p_1+k+m}{k^2+2p_1\cdot k}\times\gamma_\mu u(p_1)\bar{u}(p_4)\Gamma_\nu\frac{p_2-k+M}{k^2-2k\cdot p_2}\gamma_\mu u(p_2)\times\frac{1}{(k^2-\lambda^2)[(k+q)^2-\lambda^2]}. \quad \text{(II.6)}$$

The infrared contribution from M_2 due to $k\to0$ is obtained by neglecting k in the numerator and in $(k+q)^2$, and we obtain

$$M_2'=\frac{i\alpha Z}{4\pi^3}\int\frac{4(p_1\cdot p_2)d^4k}{(k^2+2p_1\cdot k)(k^2-2k\cdot p_2)(k^2-\lambda^2)}M_1=\frac{-\alpha Z}{2\pi}K(p_2,-p_1)M_1. \quad \text{(II.7)}$$

Similarly the infrared contribution from M_2 due to $k+q\to0$ can be obtained by a substitution $k+q\to k$ in Eq. (II.6), and we have

$$M_2''=\frac{-\alpha Z}{2\pi}K(p_4,-p_3)M_1. \quad \text{(II.8)}$$

Thus we have accomplished the extraction of infrared terms from M_2. Neglecting the noninfrared terms in M_2, we obtain

$$M_2=M_2'+M_2''=\frac{-\alpha Z}{2\pi}M_1[K(p_2,-p_1)+K(p_4,-p_3)]. \quad \text{(II.9)}$$

$K(p_2,-p_1)$ and $K(p_4,-p_3)$ are complex. Only the real parts contribute to the cross section. It can be shown that[8]

$$\text{Re}\,K(p_i,P_j)=K(p_i,p_j)+\text{“negligible,”} \quad \text{(II.10)}$$

where "negligible" means the term of order unity. Using a similar method, one can extract the infrared terms from M_3. Neglecting the noninfrared terms in M_3, we get

$$M_3=\frac{\alpha Z}{2\pi}M_1[K(p_2,p_3)+K(p_4,p_1)]. \quad \text{(II.11)}$$

Similarly, for M_6 we have

$$M_6=\frac{-\alpha Z^2}{2\pi}M_1[K(p_2,p_4)-K(p_2,p_2)], \quad \text{(II.12)}$$

---

[12] Although we are primarily interested in the electron-proton scattering in this paper, our result can be used in the electron-nucleus scattering. The atomic number Z is kept here for this purpose. Also we shall see later that Z is a convenient quantity for identifying the contributions from various diagrams in the inelastic cross section. For electron-nucleus scattering the definitions of F_1, F_2, κ, and M should be appropriately changed.

[13] M. N. Rosenbluth, Phys. Rev. 79, 615 (1950).

[14] See Eqs. (5) and (6) of reference 9.

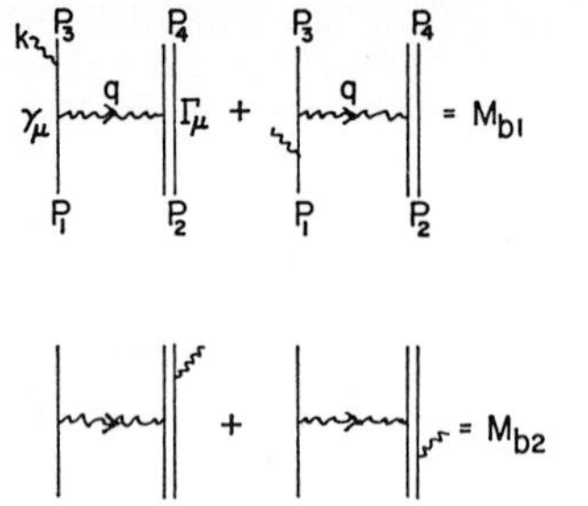

FIG. 3. Feynman diagrams for inelastic scattering.

where the term $K(p_2,p_2)$ was introduced by the renormalization of M_6 and represents the infrared term of the electromagnetic proton self-energy. [Compare Eq. (II.12) with Eq. (II.5).]

Substituting expressions for the matrix elements in Eq. (II.1), we obtain the elastic scattering cross section

$$\left(\frac{d\sigma}{d\Omega}\right)_{\text{elastic}}=\left(\frac{d\sigma}{d\Omega}\right)_{\text{Rosenbluth}}\bigg\{1+\frac{\alpha}{\pi}[-K(p_1,p_3)$$
$$+K(p_1,p_1)-ZK(p_2,p_1)-ZK(p_4,p_3)$$
$$+ZK(p_2,p_3)+ZK(p_4,p_1)$$
$$-Z^2K(p_2,p_4)+Z^2K(p_2,p_2)]$$
$$+\frac{\alpha}{\pi}\left[\frac{-28}{9}+\frac{13}{6}\ln\frac{-q^2}{m^2}\right]\bigg\}. \quad \text{(II.13)}$$

III. INELASTIC CROSS SECTION

The Feynman diagrams for the matrix elements contributing to the inelastic cross section to order α^3 are shown in Fig. 3. Since we are interested only in the soft photon emissions, the vertex function connecting the real photon k and the proton current may be approximated by γ_ν. Thus the matrix elements M_{b1} and M_{b2} may be written as

$$M_{b1}=\frac{e^3}{(2\pi)^{7/2}}\frac{mMZ}{(2\omega E_1E_2E_3E_4)^{\frac{1}{2}}}\bar{u}(p_3)\bigg[e\frac{p_3+k+m}{2p_3\cdot k}\gamma_\mu$$
$$-\gamma_\mu\frac{p_1-k+m}{2p_1\cdot k}e\bigg]u(p_1)\bar{u}(p_4)\Gamma_\mu u(p_2)$$
$$\times[1/(p_1-p_3-k)^2], \quad \text{(III.1)}$$

$$M_{b2}=\frac{-e^3}{(2\pi)^{7/2}}\frac{mMZ^2}{(2\omega E_1E_2E_3E_4)^{\frac{1}{2}}}\bar{u}(p_3)\gamma_\mu u(p_1)$$
$$\times\bar{u}(p_4)\bigg[e\frac{p_4+k+M}{2p_4\cdot k}\Gamma_\mu$$
$$-\Gamma_\mu\frac{p_2-k+M}{2p_2\cdot k}e\bigg]\frac{u(P_2)}{(p_1-p_3)^2}. \quad \text{(III.2)}$$

We shall neglect the k's in the numerators of the above equations and in the term (p_1-p_3-k) in Eq. (III.1). The experimental conditions under which this approximation is valid will be discussed in detail in Appendix A. Here we simply state the result:

$$\Delta E(1+2E_1/M)\ll E_3. \quad \text{(III.3)}$$

With this approximation we may write

$$M_{b1}+M_{b2}\approx\frac{i}{\pi^2}\left(\frac{\alpha}{2}\right)^{\frac{1}{2}}M_1\frac{1}{(2\omega)^{\frac{1}{2}}}$$
$$\times\left[\frac{p_3\cdot e}{p_3\cdot k}-\frac{p_1\cdot e}{p_1\cdot k}-\frac{Zp_4\cdot e}{p_4\cdot k}+\frac{Zp_2\cdot e}{p_2\cdot k}\right]. \quad \text{(III.4)}$$

The inelastic scattering cross section can be calculated by using the formula

$$d\sigma_b=(2\pi)^2\frac{E_1E_2}{[(p_1\cdot p_2)^2-m^2M^2]^{\frac{1}{2}}}\frac{1}{4}\int d^3p_3d^3p_4d^3k$$
$$\times\delta(p_3+p_4+k-p_1-p_2)$$
$$\times\sum_{\text{spin}}(M_{b1}^\dagger+M_{b2}^\dagger)(M_{b1}+M_{b2}). \quad \text{(III.5)}$$

In the above formula, one has to perform the integration

$$A=\int\frac{d^3p_3}{E_3}\int\frac{d^3k}{2\omega}\int\frac{d^3p_4}{E_4}\delta(p_3+p_4+k-p_1-p_2)\chi^2, \quad \text{(III.6)}$$

where

$$\chi^2=\left[\frac{p_3}{p_3\cdot k}-\frac{p_1}{p_1\cdot k}-\frac{Zp_4}{p_4\cdot k}+\frac{Zp_2}{p_2\cdot k}\right]^2. \quad \text{(III.7)}$$

The range of this integration is determined by the experimental conditions. One can perform this integration in any coordinate system provided the experimental conditions are transformed into those in the coordinate system in which the integration is carried out.[15] The procedure we shall use here is somewhat involved. In Stanford experiments k and p_4 are undetected and for p_3 the entrance slit and the spectrometer determine the angular range $(\theta_{\min},\theta_{\max})$ and the energy range $E_3>E_3^{\min}$, respectively. This experimental condition is shown in Fig. 4. The curve AD corresponds to the energy-angle relation of the elastically scattered electron obtained from Eq. (I.2). Only the electrons which are scattered into the area $ABCD$ are detected. As mentioned in the introduction, due to the recoil effect the maximum energy of a photon which can be emitted is very anisotropic. Very roughly speaking, the maximum energy of a photon which can be emitted in the forward direction is much larger than the maximum energy of a photon which can be emitted in the backward direction when there is a big recoil. Thus

[15] For choice of the coordinate system when Eq. (III.3) is not satisfied see Sec. VII.c of reference 9.

one has to perform the k integration in Eq. (III.6) in a very elongated ellipsoidal volume. We avoid doing this by choosing a special Lorentz frame in which this ellipsoid becomes a sphere and do the k integration in this frame. We then transform everything back into the laboratory system and use some other trick to do the p_3 integration. The p_4 integration is eliminated at the beginning by using the δ function. We will show more precisely in the following how this is done.

We first perform the p_4 integration by using the δ function and obtain

$$A=\int\frac{d^3p_3}{E_3}\int\frac{d^3k}{\omega}S(E_4)\delta((t-k)^2-M^2)\chi^2, \quad \text{(III.8)}$$

where

$$t\equiv p_4+k+p_1+p_2-p_3, \quad \text{(III.9)}$$

and

$$S(y)=1,\quad y>0$$
$$=0,\quad y<0.$$

In the special frame[16] $\mathbf{p}_4+\mathbf{k}=0$ or $t=(t_0,0)$, the δ function in Eq. (III.8) is independent of the angle in which the photon is emitted. Thus we perform the photon integration in this special frame:

$$A=\int d\Omega\int_{E_{\min}}^{E_{\max}}p_3dE_3\frac{[(kt)^2-\lambda^2t^2]^{\frac{1}{2}}}{2t^2}\times S(t^2-t_{\min}{}^2)\int d\tilde{\Omega}_k\chi^2, \quad \text{(III.10)}$$

where

$$t_{\min}{}^2=M^2+2M\lambda+\lambda^2\approx M^2+2M\lambda, \quad \text{(III.11)}$$

and the tilde represents the quantity in the special frame. After the photon angular integration, we transform all the quantities in the special frame back into those of the laboratory system and perform the p_3 integration. For the p_3 integration we use the following trick. From Eq. (III.9) we obtain

$$x\equiv t^2-M^2=2m^2+2M(E_1-E_3)-2E_1E_3(1-\cos\theta). \quad \text{(III.12)}$$

Thus instead of integrating with respect to E_3 and θ, we can integrate with respect to x and θ. Equation (III.10) can then be written as

$$A=\int d\Omega\frac{E_3}{4M\eta}\int_{x_{\min}}^{x_{\max}}\frac{xdx}{2(x+M)^2}\int d\tilde{\Omega}_k\chi^2, \quad \text{(III.13)}$$

where $x_{\min}=2\lambda M$, which corresponds to the value of x along the curve CD in Fig. 4, and $x_{\max}$ is the value of x along BC. The infrared divergence occurs just under the curve AD. Since relatively few electrons are scattered near the curve BC, we may replace the curve BC by $B'C'$ where the curve $B'C'$ is obtained by

$$x=x_{\max}\equiv 2m^2+2M(E_1-E_3{}^{\min})-2E_1E_3{}^{\min}(1-\cos\theta_{\text{av}})\approx 2M\eta\Delta E, \quad \text{(III.14)}$$

where

$$\theta_{\text{av}}\equiv(\theta_{\max}+\theta_{\min})^{\frac{1}{2}},$$
$$\Delta E\equiv E_3{}^{\text{el}}(\theta_{\text{av}})-E_{\min}, \quad \text{(III.15)}$$

and

$$E_3{}^{\text{el}}(\theta_{\text{av}})=\frac{E_1}{1+E_1M^{-1}(1-\cos\theta_{\text{av}})}. \quad \text{(III.16)}$$

With this modification of the region of integration, $x_{\max}$ is now independent of θ, thus we can finally write

$$A=d\Omega\frac{E_3}{4M\eta}\int_{2M\lambda}^{2M\eta\Delta E}\frac{xdx}{2(x+M^2)}\int d\tilde{\Omega}_k\chi^2. \quad \text{(III.17)}$$

Using Eqs. (II.3), (III.5), and (III.17), we can express the inelastic scattering cross section as

$$\left(\frac{d\sigma}{d\Omega}\right)_b=-\left(\frac{d\sigma}{d\Omega}\right)_{\text{Rosenbluth}}\frac{\alpha}{8\pi^2}\int_{2\lambda M}^{2M\eta\Delta E}\frac{xdx}{2(x+m^2)}\times\int d\tilde{\Omega}_k\chi^2. \quad \text{(III.18)}$$

The photon angular integration can be carried out in the following way:[17]

$$\int d\tilde{\Omega}_k\frac{(p_i\cdot p_j)}{(p_i\cdot k)(p_j\cdot k)}=(p_i\cdot p_j)\int_0^1dy\int\frac{d\tilde{\Omega}_k}{(p_y\cdot k)^2}$$
$$=4\pi(p_i\cdot p_j)\int_0^1\frac{dy}{|\tilde{k}|^2p_y{}^2+\lambda^2E_y{}^2}$$
$$=4\pi(p_i\cdot p_j)\int_0^1\frac{t^2dy}{[(k\cdot t)^2-\lambda^2t^2]p_y{}^2+\lambda^2[(p_i\cdot t)y+(1-y)(p_j\cdot t)]^2}$$
$$=16\pi(p_i\cdot p_j)\int_0^1\frac{(x+M^2)dy}{(x^2-4\lambda^2M^2)p_y{}^2+4\lambda^2(p_j\cdot t)^2[1+y(p_i\cdot t-p_j\cdot t)(p_j\cdot t)^{-1}]^2}, \quad \text{(III.19)}$$

[16] This coordinate system is often used in the calculation of processes in which two of the three final particles are undetected; for example, $\mu\rightarrow e+\nu+\nu$ or $e+p\rightarrow e+p+\pi$.

[17] *Note added in proof.* Strictly speaking, this angular integration is incorrect when $i=j=4$, since $p_4\cdot k=(x-\lambda^2)/2$ and is independent of photon direction. However, it can be shown that the same result is obtained by using the correct method as long as one considers only the emission of a soft photon.

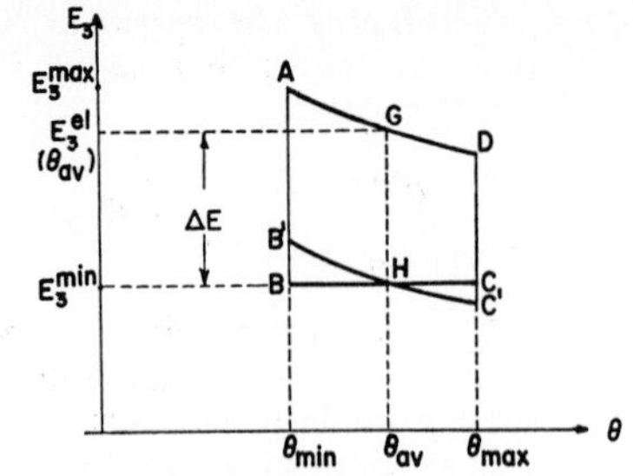

FIG. 4. θ_{min} and θ_{max} define the width of the entrance slit. E_3^{min} defines the spectrometer threshold. The curve AD corresponds to the elastic scattering. Only those electrons going into the area $ABCD$ are detected. We approximate the number of electrons going into the area $ABCD$ by the number of electrons going into the area $AB'C'C$.

where $p_y = p_i y + p_j(1-y)$. We have made the quantities in the special frame covariant by using $\tilde{\omega} = (k\cdot t)/(t^2)^{\frac{1}{2}}$, $\bar{E}_i = (p_i\cdot t)/(t^2)^{\frac{1}{2}}$, and $(k\cdot t) = \frac{1}{2}(x+\lambda^2)$. Notice that the quantities $(p\cdot t)$ in Eq. (III.19) are important only in the infrared limit and therefore we can replace t by p_4, and we can express them in terms of lab quantities as follows:

$$p_1\cdot t \rightarrow ME_3, \quad p_2\cdot t \rightarrow ME_4, \qquad p_3\cdot t \rightarrow ME_1, \quad p_4\cdot t \rightarrow M^2. \tag{III.20}$$

The integration with respect to x can be carried out easily and we obtain

$$\int_{2\lambda M}^{2M\eta\Delta E} \frac{xdx}{2(x+M^2)} \int d\tilde{\Omega}_k \frac{(p_i\cdot p_j)}{(p_i\cdot k)(p_j\cdot k)}$$
$$= 4\pi(p_j\cdot p_j)\int_0^1 \left\{ \ln\frac{p_y^2}{\lambda^2} - 2\ln\frac{(p_j\cdot t)}{M\eta\Delta E} - 2\ln[1+y(p_i\cdot t - p_j\cdot t)/(p_j\cdot t)] \right\} \frac{dy}{p_y^2}$$
$$= 4\pi K(p_i,p_j) - 8\pi(p_i\cdot p_j)\ln\frac{(p_j\cdot t)}{M\eta\Delta E}\int_0^1 \frac{dy}{p_y^2} - 8\pi(p_i\cdot p_j)\int_0^1 \frac{\ln[1+y(p_i\cdot t - p_j\cdot t)/(p_j\cdot t)]}{p_y^2}dy. \tag{III.21}$$

The first term is the infrared term and it cancels out completely with the similar term in the elastic scattering cross section. The integrations of the second and third terms are straightforward, the results are listed in Appendix B.

The observable cross section is obtained by adding elastic and inelastic scattering cross sections. We have

$$\frac{d\sigma}{d\Omega} = \left(\frac{d\sigma}{d\Omega}\right)_{\text{elastic}} + \left(\frac{d\sigma}{d\Omega}\right)_b \equiv \left(\frac{d\sigma}{d\Omega}\right)_{\text{Rosenbluth}}(1+\delta), \tag{III.22}$$

where

$$\delta = \frac{-\alpha}{\pi}\left\{ \frac{28}{9} - \frac{13}{6}\ln\left(\frac{-q^2}{m^2}\right) + \left(\ln\frac{-q^2}{m^2} - 1 + 2Z\ln\eta\right)\left(2\ln\frac{E_1}{\Delta E} - 3\ln\eta\right) - \Phi\left(\frac{E_3-E_1}{E_3}\right) - Z^2\ln\frac{E_4}{M} \right.$$
$$+ Z^2\ln\frac{M}{\eta\Delta E}\left(\frac{1}{\beta_4}\ln\frac{1+\beta_4}{1-\beta_4} - 2\right) + \frac{Z^2}{\beta_4}\left[\frac{1}{2}\ln\frac{1+\beta_4}{1-\beta_4}\ln\frac{E_4+M}{2M} - \Phi\left(-\left(\frac{E_4-M}{E_4+M}\right)^{\frac{1}{2}}\left(\frac{1+\beta_4}{1-\beta_4}\right)^{\frac{1}{2}}\right)\right]$$
$$+ Z\left[\Phi\left(-\frac{M-E_3}{E_1}\right) - \Phi\left(\frac{M(M-E_3)}{2E_3E_4-ME_1}\right) + \Phi\left(\frac{2E_3(M-E_3)}{2E_3E_4-ME_1}\right) + \ln\left|\frac{2E_3E_4-ME_1}{E_1(M-2E_3)}\right| \ln\left(\frac{M}{2E_3}\right)\right]$$
$$- Z\left[\Phi\left(-\frac{E_4-E_3}{E_3}\right) - \Phi\left(\frac{M(E_4-E_3)}{2E_1E_4-ME_3}\right) + \Phi\left(\frac{2E_1(E_4-E_3)}{2E_1E_4-ME_3}\right) + \ln\left|\frac{2E_1E_4-ME_3}{E_3(M-2E_1)}\right| \ln\left(\frac{M}{2E_1}\right)\right]$$
$$- Z\left[\Phi\left(-\frac{M-E_1}{E_1}\right) - \Phi\left(\frac{M-E_1}{E_1}\right) + \Phi\left(\frac{2(M-E_1)}{M}\right) + \ln\left|\frac{M}{2E_1-M}\right| \ln\left(\frac{M}{2E_1}\right)\right]$$
$$\left. + Z\left[\Phi\left(-\frac{M-E_3}{E_3}\right) - \Phi\left(\frac{M-E_3}{E_3}\right) + \Phi\left(\frac{2(M-E_3)}{M}\right) + \ln\left|\frac{M}{2E_3-M}\right| \ln\left(\frac{M}{2E_3}\right)\right]\right\}. \tag{III.23}$$

$\Phi(x)$ is the Spence function[18]

$$\Phi(x) = \int_0^x \frac{-\ln|1-y|dy}{y} \tag{III.24}$$

and β_4 is the ratio of the velocity of the recoil proton to that of light,

$$\beta_4 = (E_4^2 - M^2)^{\frac{1}{2}}/E_4, \quad E_4 = E_1 + M - E_3.$$

We have kept Z in our formula for convenience of discussion. Z is equal to $+1$ for $e^- + p$ scattering and is equal to -1 for $e^+ + p$ scattering. The terms proportional to Z come from the interference terms between

[18] K. Mitchell, Phil. Mag. 40, 351 (1949).

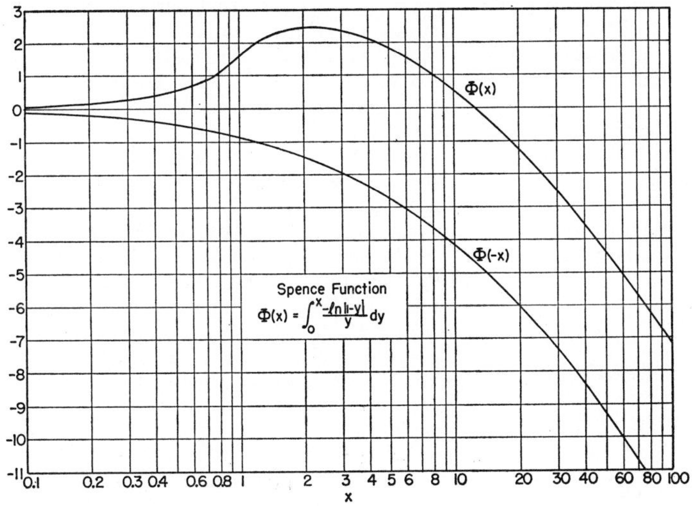

FIG. 5. Spence function $\Phi(x)$.

M_{b1} and M_{b2} and the terms proportional to Z^2 come from $M_{b2}^\dagger M_{b2}$. If we neglect the radiation from the proton current, i.e., letting $Z=0$ in Eq. (III.23), we obtain Eq. (I.4), except for a small term $\Phi[(E_3-E_1)/E_1]$, which we guessed on intuitive physical grounds. We notice that the radiation from the proton current increases (or decreases) the radiative corrections to e^-+p (or e^++p) scatterings.

IV. NUMERICAL EXAMPLES

Example A. Consider the radiative corrections under the following conditions[3]:

$E_1=900$ Mev, $\theta=145°$, $\eta=2.75$,

$E_3=327$ Mev, $E_4=1511$ Mev, $\Delta E=13.1$ Mev,

$\beta_4=0.783$ $q^2=-2M(E_1-E_3)=-1.075\times10^6$ Mev^2.

Equation (III.23) gives $\delta=-15\%$ for e^-+p and $\delta=-8.6\%$ for e^++p scatterings. If one neglects the radiation from protons, one gets from Eq. (I.4) $\delta=-11\%$.

Example B. Consider an example at a higher energy:

$E_1=5$ Bev, $E_3=500$ Mev, $\eta=10$, $\Delta E=10$ Mev, $\beta_4=0.975$.

Equation (III.23) gives $\delta=-21.0\%$ for e^-+p and $\delta=-9.9\%$ for e^++p scatterings. Equation (I.4) gives $\delta=-12.84\%$.

Notice in both examples given above that the condition (III.3) is satisfied.

V. PRACTICAL CONSIDERATIONS

In applying Eq. (III.23) to the actual analysis of data some precautions are necessary. When an electron beam is scattered by a liquid hydrogen target, the scattered electrons, after going through an entrance slit and the magnetic spectrometer, will have a typical energy spectrum shown in Fig. 1. The shape of this spectrum is in general due to (1) the energy spread of the incident beam, (2) the finite thickness of the target, (3) the finite width of the entrance slit, and (4) the radiative corrections which we have treated in this paper. The effect due to the finite thickness of the target is also a radiative phenomenon and thus one should be able to calculate it along lines similar to the present treatment. This effect may cause as much as 10% correction to the cross section at 900 Mev under typical experimental conditions.[19] The smearing of the energy spectrum due to the energy spread of the incident beam and the finite width of the entrance slit do not cause any appreciable trouble as long as ΔE is chosen sufficiently larger than the energy spread of the scattered electrons due to these two effects. Suppose the initial beam has an energy spread ΔE_1; then the energy spread of the scattered electron due to ΔE_1 can be calculated from Eq. (I.2):

$$(\partial E_3/\partial E_1)\Delta E_1=\Delta E_1\eta^{-2}. \quad \text{(V.1)}$$

Similarly the energy spread of E_3 due to the finite width of the entrance slit is

$$(\partial E_3/\partial\theta)\Delta\theta=(E_1^2/M\eta^2)\sin\theta d\theta. \quad \text{(V.2)}$$

Thus one should choose ΔE such that

$$\Delta E\gg\Delta E_1\eta^{-2}, \quad \text{(a)}$$

and

$$\Delta E>(E_3^2/M)\sin\theta\Delta\theta. \quad \text{(b)}$$

The condition (a) is necessary because the shape of the spectrum near $E_3^{\text{el}}(\theta_{\text{av}})$ is mainly due to the energy

[19] R. Hofstadter (private communication). See reference 6, Eq. (34). This formula needs a reexamination at energies with which we are concerned here.

spread of the incident beam, which has nothing to do with the radiative effect. Condition (b) is necessary because we have replaced the area of integration $ABCD$ by $AB'C'D$ in Fig. 4 in order to simplify the calculation. This approximation breaks down unless condition (b) is satisfied.[20] Experimentally these two conditions are equivalent to taking $\Delta E \gg W$, where W is the width of the spectrum to the right of $E_3^{\mathrm{el}}(\theta_{\mathrm{av}})$ as shown in Fig. 1.

Conditions (a) and (b) give a lower limit for ΔE. On the other hand ΔE should not be too large, otherwise condition (III.3) will not be satisfied.

VI. DISCUSSION

A. In this paper we have amply demonstrated the power of the technique of infrared extraction developed by Yennie *et al.*[8] We have assumed the noninfrared parts of the matrix elements M_2, M_3, and M_6 to be negligible. This has to be somehow justified. Drell and Fubini[7] have considered the mesonic contributions to M_2 and M_3, especially the resonance effect of the nucleon Compton scattering. They estimated the contribution on the cross section to be about 1% in the energy range ~1 Bev. It is very desirable to extend this kind of consideration to higher energies.[21] One could of course try to treat the proton as a structureless Dirac particle and calculate these matrix elements exactly and show that the noninfrared parts are indeed negligible.[22] However, in an electron-electron scattering[9] it was explicitly shown that the noninfrared parts of M_2+M_3 are negligible. Thus one would expect that this must also be true for $e+p$ scattering if protons are structureless. The order of magnitude of the contribution to the cross section from M_6 can be estimated by using Eq. (II.5) with m^2 replaced by M^2. It can be shown that even at $E_1 = 10$ Bev, and $E_3 = 500$ Mev, the contribution to the cross section from M_6 is only about +0.5%. Thus the neglect of the noninfrared parts of M_6 is probably justified up to about 10 Bev. In summary, our Eq. (III.23) is good up to about 1 Bev within ±2% of the cross section. (Of the 2% error, 1% is from the approximation used in our integration and 1% from the noninfrared parts of the contributions from $M_2+M_3+M_6$.) If one can prove that the noninfrared parts of M_2+M_3, especially the mesonic resonance effects, are negligible (±1%) even at higher energies, then our result is good up to about 5 Bev within 2% of the cross section.

B. In this paper we have considered the radiative corrections to the $e+p$ scattering when only the scattered electrons are detected. In part of the Cornell experiment[4] the recoil protons are detected instead of the scattered electrons. Our formula is not applicable under this experimental condition. Under this experimental condition, very hard photons can be emitted along the direction of the scattered electrons and thus one would expect the radiative corrections should be much smaller than the result of the present calculation.

VII. ACKNOWLEDGMENTS

The author is grateful to Professor S. D. Drell for suggestions and criticism of the manuscript. Discussions with Professor D. R. Yennie, Professor J. D. Bjorken, and Dr. S. C. Frautschi were helpful. The author wishes to express his thanks to Professor R. Hofstadter, Dr. E. B. Dally, and Dr. F. Bumiller for discussions on some experimental matters.

APPENDIX A

We have neglected the photon momentum k in the numerators of Eqs. (III. 1,2). We investigate here under what experimental conditions this procedure is justified. For this purpose it is necessary to consider everything in the center-of-mass system. (We denote the quantities in the c.m. system by a tilde in this section.) It is easily seen that for the above-mentioned approximation to be applicable, the maximum energy of a photon $\omega_{\max}$ which can be emitted in the c.m. system must be smaller than the momentum of all the particles. Thus in the center-of-mass system,

$$\tilde{\omega}_{\max} \ll \tilde{E}_1. \qquad \text{(A.1)}$$

To determine the value of $\omega_{\max}$ we transform experimental conditions as specified by Fig. 4 into those in the c.m. system. The result is plotted in Fig. 6. $\tilde{E}_1$ can be obtained by considering the invariant

$$p_1 \cdot p_2 = ME_1 \approx \tilde{E}_1\tilde{E}_2 + \tilde{E}_1^2 \approx \tilde{E}_1[(\tilde{E}_1^2+M^2)^{\frac{1}{2}} + \tilde{E}_1].$$

Hence

$$\tilde{E}_1 \approx E_1[1+(2E_1/M)]^{-\frac{1}{2}}. \qquad \text{(A.2)}$$

Similarly,

$$\tilde{E}_2 \approx (E_1+M)[1+(2E_1/M)]^{-\frac{1}{2}}. \qquad \text{(A.3)}$$

[20] In electron-electron scattering when one of the initial electrons is at rest, the extreme opposite condition to (*b*) was used. See reference 9, Sec. V.

[21] The noninfrared parts of M_2+M_3, including the mesonic effects, can be evaluated experimentally by comparing the cross sections of $e^+ + p$ with those of $e^- + p$ scatterings performed under identical experimental conditions. After applying the radiative corrections given by Eq. (III.23), the difference in two cross sections must be exactly twice the contributions from the noninfrared parts of M_2+M_3. (We assumed that the difference in the effects due to the finite target thickness for $e^- + p$ and $e^+ + p$ scatterings is negligible.) Such an experiment is being performed at Stanford by J. Pine and D. Yount.

[22] In this connection it is interesting to notice that McKinley and Feshbach have calculated the second Born approximation to the Coulomb scattering and found that the first Born cross section is altered by a factor $(1+\delta)$, where $\delta = Z\alpha\pi[\sin(\frac{1}{2}\theta) - \sin^2(\frac{1}{2}\theta)] \times \cos^{-2}(\frac{1}{2}\theta)$. In a later paper Dalitz confirmed this result. This correction is independent of energy and has different signs for $e^- + p$ $(Z=1)$ and $e^+ + p$ $(Z=-1)$ scatterings. At 145° this correction gives $\delta \approx 0.015Z$ and at smaller angles the correction is smaller. In view of the lack of exact calculation for the noninfrared parts of M_2+M_3, we may add this correction to Eq. (III.23) for practical analysis of the $e^\pm + p$ scatterings. See W. A. McKinley, Jr., and H. Feshbach, Phys. Rev. **74**, 1759 (1948); and R. H. Dalitz, Proc. Roy. Soc. (London) **A206**, 509 (1951).

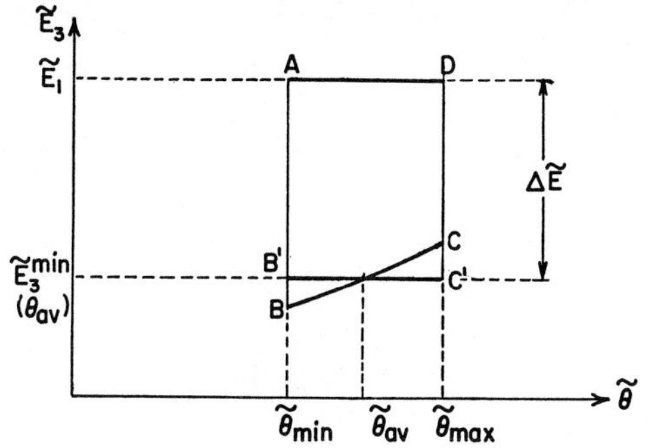

FIG. 6. Experimental conditions (Fig. 4) expressed in terms of quantities in the center-of-mass system.

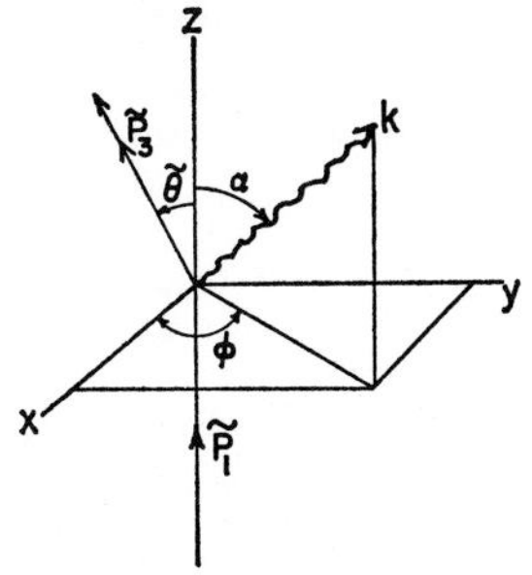

FIG. 7. The geometry for calculating the maximum energy of a photon which can be emitted in the center-of-mass system. p_3 is on the xz plane.

For the elastic scattering, $\tilde{E}_3=\tilde{E}_1$, which corresponds to the straight line AD in Fig. 6. The lower bound of $\tilde{E}_3$ can be obtained by considering the invariant

$$p_3\cdot p_2=ME_3^{\min}\approx\tilde{E}_3(\tilde{E}_2+\tilde{E}_1\cos\tilde{\theta}).$$

Hence,

$$\tilde{E}_3=ME_3^{\min}(\tilde{E}_2+\tilde{E}_1\cos\tilde{\theta})^{-1}, \quad (A.4)$$

which corresponds to the curve BC in Fig. 6. The relation between θ and $\tilde{\theta}$ can be obtained by considering the invariant

$$\frac{M^2(p_1\cdot p_3)}{(p_1\cdot p_2)(p_3\cdot p_2)}=(1-\cos\theta)=\frac{M^2(1-\cos\tilde{\theta})}{(\tilde{E}_1+\tilde{E}_2)(\tilde{E}_2+\tilde{E}_1\cos\tilde{\theta})}.$$

Hence,

$$\cos\tilde{\theta}=[(E_1+M)\cos\theta-E_1]\eta^{-1}M^{-1}, \quad (A.5)$$

and from this we obtain $\tilde{\theta}_{\min}$, $\tilde{\theta}_{\rm av}$, and $\tilde{\theta}_{\max}$ corresponding, respectively, to $\theta_{\min}$, $\theta_{\rm av}$, and $\theta_{\max}$ of Fig. 4. Using an argument similar to that in the discussion of Fig. 4, we may replace the area $ABCD$ by the area $AB'C'D$. The length DC' is defined as $\Delta\tilde{E}$. Then from Eqs. (A.2, 3, 4, 5) we have

$$\begin{aligned}\Delta\tilde{E}&=\tilde{E}_1-ME_3^{\min}(\tilde{E}_2+\tilde{E}_1\cos\tilde{\theta}_{\rm av})^{-1}\\&=\eta(1+2E_1M^{-1})^{-\frac{1}{2}}\Delta E.\end{aligned} \quad (A.6)$$

The maximum energy of a photon which can be emitted, $\omega_{\max}(\alpha,\varphi)$, can be calculated by using the equation $(p_1+p_2-p_3-k)^2=M^2$ and letting $\tilde{E}_3=\tilde{E}_3^{\min}$. We have then

$$\tilde{\omega}_{\max}(\alpha,\varphi)=\frac{\Delta\tilde{E}(M+2E_1)}{M+E_1+E_1(\cos\tilde{\theta}\cos\alpha+\sin\alpha\cos\varphi\sin\tilde{\theta})}, \quad (A.7)$$

where α and φ are defined in Fig. 7. If the photon $\tilde{k}$ is emitted along the direction of $\tilde{p}_1$, we have

$$\tilde{\omega}_{\max}(0,\varphi)=\Delta\tilde{E}\eta. \quad (A.8)$$

Similarly, along the $\tilde{p}_2$, $\tilde{p}_3$, and $\tilde{p}_4$ directions we have, respectively,

$$\tilde{\omega}_{\max}(\pi,\varphi)=\Delta\tilde{E}\frac{M+2E_1}{M+E_1(1-\cos\tilde{\theta})}<\Delta\tilde{E}(1+2E_1M^{-1}), \quad (A.9)$$

$$\tilde{\omega}_{\max}(\tilde{\theta},0)=\Delta\tilde{E}, \quad (A.10)$$

and

$$\tilde{\omega}_{\max}(\pi-\theta,\pi)=\Delta\tilde{E}\frac{M+2E_1}{M+E_1\sin^2\tilde{\theta}}<\Delta\tilde{E}(1+2E_1M^{-1}). \quad (A.11)$$

From Eqs. (A.6, 8, 9, 10 and 11) we have

$$\tilde{\omega}_{\max}<\eta(1+2E_1M^{-1})^{\frac{1}{2}}\Delta E. \quad (A.12)$$

Thus condition (A.1) can be written in terms of lab quantities [using Eq. (A.2)] as

$$\Delta E(1+2E_1M^{-1})\ll E_3. \quad (III.3)$$

This result is very important experimentally. In example B of Sec. IV, the maximum energy of a photon which can be emitted along the p_1 direction is $\Delta E\eta^2=1$ Bev in the lab system. Our consideration here shows that even in this case the approximation we used is not bad.

APPENDIX B

We list here the results of all the integrations which appeared in Eq. (III.21). The invariant products $(p_i\cdot t)$ in Eq. (III.21) are reduced to lab quantities by using Eqs. (III.20). Let us define

$$I_{i,j}\equiv\frac{-1}{8\pi}\int_{2\lambda M}^{2M\eta\Delta E}\frac{xdx}{2(x+M^2)}\int d\tilde{\Omega}_k\frac{(p_i\cdot p_j)}{(p_i\cdot k)(p_j\cdot k)}+\tfrac{1}{2}K(p,p_ip_j).$$

Then the following results can be obtained from Eq.

(III.21):

$$I_{1,1}=\ln\frac{E_1}{\eta^2\Delta E},\quad I_{2,2}=\ln\frac{E_4}{\eta\Delta E},$$

$$I_{3,3}=\ln\frac{E_3}{\Delta E},\quad I_{4,4}=\ln\frac{M}{\eta\Delta E},$$

$$2I_{1,3}=\left(\ln\frac{E_1}{\eta^2\Delta E}+\ln\frac{E_3}{\Delta E}\right)\ln\frac{-q^2}{m^2}-\Phi\left(\frac{E_3-E_1}{E_3}\right),$$

$$2I_{2,3}=\ln\frac{E_3}{\Delta E}\ln\frac{4E_3^2}{m^2}-\left[\Phi\left(-\frac{M-E_3}{E_1}\right)-\Phi\left(\frac{M(M-E_3)}{2E_3E_4-ME_1}\right)+\Phi\left(\frac{2E_3(M-E_3)}{2E_3E_4-ME_1}\right)+\ln\left|\frac{2E_3E_4-ME_1}{E_1(M-2E_3)}\right|\ln\frac{M}{2E_3}\right],$$

$$2I_{2,1}=\ln\frac{E_1}{\eta^2\Delta E}\ln\frac{4E_1^2}{m^2}-\left[\Phi\left(-\frac{E_4-E_3}{E_3}\right)-\Phi\left(\frac{M(E_4-E_3)}{2E_1E_4-ME_3}\right)+\Phi\left(\frac{2E_1(E_4-E_3)}{2E_1E_4-ME_3}\right)+\ln\left|\frac{2E_1E_4-ME_3}{E_3(M-2E_1)}\right|\ln\frac{M}{2E_1}\right],$$

$$2I_{4,1}=\ln\frac{E_1}{\eta^2\Delta E}\ln\frac{4E_3^2}{m^2}-\left[\Phi\left(-\frac{M-E_3}{E_3}\right)+\Phi\left(\frac{M-E_3}{E_3}\right)+\Phi\left(\frac{2(M-E_3)}{M}\right)+\ln\left|\frac{M}{2E_3-M}\right|\ln\frac{M}{2E_3}\right],$$

$$2I_{4,3}=\ln\frac{E_3}{\Delta E}\ln\frac{4E_1^2}{m^2}-\left[\Phi\left(-\frac{M-E_1}{E_1}\right)-\Phi\left(\frac{M-E_1}{E_1}\right)+\Phi\left(\frac{2(M-E_1)}{M}\right)+\ln\left|\frac{M}{2E_1-M}\right|\ln\frac{M}{2E_1}\right],$$

$$2I_{2,4}=\frac{1}{\beta_4}\ln\frac{1+\beta_4}{1-\beta_4}\ln\frac{M}{\eta\Delta E}+\frac{1}{\beta_4}\left[\frac{1}{2}\ln\frac{1+\beta_4}{1-\beta_4}\ln\frac{E_4+M}{M}-\Phi\left(-\left(\frac{E_4-M}{E_4+M}\right)^{\frac{1}{2}}\left(\frac{1+\beta_4}{1-\beta_4}\right)^{\frac{1}{2}}\right)\right].$$

The following identity was found to be useful in many of the above integrations:

$$\int_0^1\frac{\ln(1+cy)dy}{ay^2+by}=\frac{-1}{b}\left[\Phi(-c)-\Phi\left(\frac{a+b}{b-(a/c)}\right)+\Phi\left(\frac{1}{1-(a/bc)}\right)+\ln|(bc/a)-1|\ln\left(\frac{a+b}{b}\right)\right].$$

PAPER 73

SCATTERING OF Bev ELECTRONS BY HYDROGEN AND DEUTERIUM*

R. M. Littauer, H. F. Schopper,† and R. R. Wilson
Laboratory of Nuclear Studies, Cornell University, Ithaca, New York
(Received July 21, 1961)

At Cornell University, using the 1.3-Bev electron accelerator, measurements of the scattering of electrons by hydrogen and deuterium have been extended to new energies and angles. The cross section at 90° has been measured using the same equipment and procedure that were previously employed[1,2] at 66° and 112°. A new quadrupole magnet spectrometer of large solid angle has been placed at 45° or at 135° so that measurements could be made at two angles simultaneously. In Table I are shown the new results at 45°, 90°, and 135°, while all of the Cornell measurements are summarized in Fig. 1.

The hydrogen cross section, $d\sigma/d\Omega$, was determined in a straightforward manner. We have used the Schwinger correction for radiation. For the deuteron, the differential cross section $d^2\sigma/dE'd\Omega$ was measured at the energy where the electrons scattered from protons give an elastic peak. Then the total deuteron cross section, shown in Fig. 1, was calculated from this deuteron peak cross section using the impulse approximation as given by Goldberg.[3] Most recently, Durand[4] derived Goldberg's formula more rigorously and showed that it is accurate to within a few percent.

Table I. Differential cross sections for elastic scattering of electrons of energy E_0 by protons, and peak cross sections for scattering by deuterons. All parameters in the laboratory frame. Schwinger correction applied.

E_0	Proton $(d\sigma/d\Omega)\times 10^{32}$ (cm^2/sr)			Deuteron $(d^2\sigma/dE'd\Omega)\times 10^{33}$ (cm^2/Mev sr)		
(Mev)	45°	90°	135°	45°	90°	135°
317		6.04 ±0.24	1.21 ±0.08		2.14 ±0.14	0.623 ±0.080
387	92.5 ±4.0	3.61 ±0.15	0.790 ±0.031	31.2 ±2.0	1.29 ±0.05	0.307 ±0.026
407	81.0 ±1.9			31.2 ±0.7		
465		1.91 ±0.06	0.296 ±0.019		0.635 ±0.04	0.130 ±0.011
552	37.5 ±1.1			10.9 ±0.3		
565		0.815 ±0.08	···		0.330 ±0.03	···
600		0.99 ±0.03	0.178 ±0.008		0.333 ±0.015	0.0638 ±0.004
664	22.0 ±0.7			5.88 ±0.3		
720		0.388 ±0.017	0.0732 ±0.005		0.132 ±0.010	0.0248 ±0.0032
800	10.4 ±0.5			2.68 ±0.15		
836		0.212 ±0.01	0.0302 ±0.005		0.0448 ±0.003	0.0121 ±0.0026
941	6.63 ±0.3			1.39 ±0.06		
974		0.080 ±0.014	0.0272 ±0.004		0.0147 ±0.003	0.0083 ±0.0024
1050	4.68 ±0.2			0.76 ±0.04		
1136		0.0362 ±0.0028	0.0117 ±0.004		0.0107 ±0.003	0.0033 ±0.0015
1166	3.24 ±0.17			0.61 ±0.06		

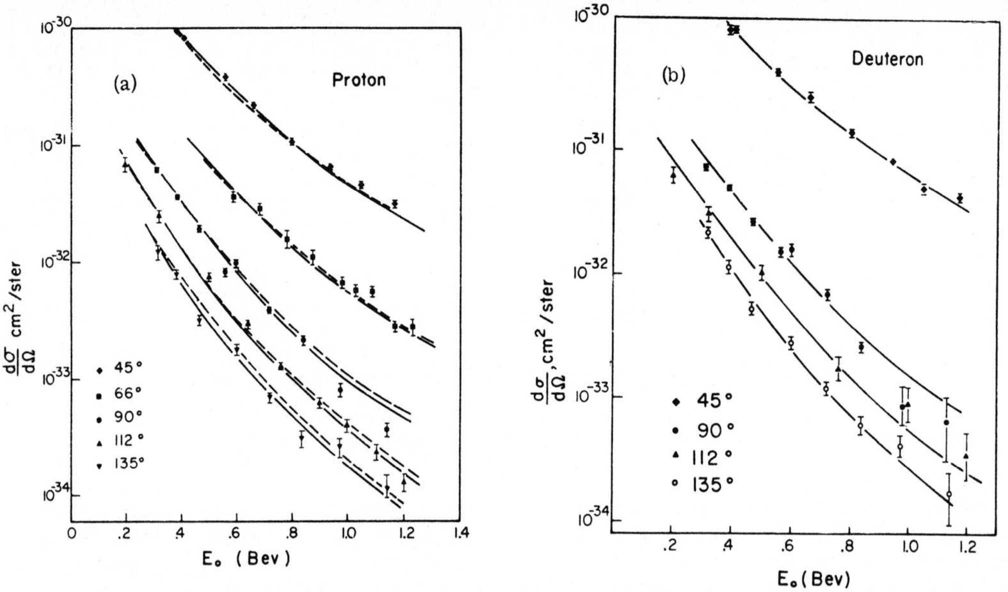

FIG. 1. Differential elastic scattering cross section for the proton (a) and the deuteron (b), as a function of incident electron energy and laboratory scattering angle. Full curves computed with core model, dashed curves according to Bergia et al. See R. M. Littauer et al., following Letter [Phys. Rev. Letters 7, 144 (1961)].

Figure 2 illustrates the determination of the electric form factors F_1 and the magnetic form factors F_2 by the intersecting ellipse method.[5] For a given value of q^2, the square of the momentum-energy transfer, one ellipse in the F_1-F_2 plane is determined by a measurement of the cross section at a par-

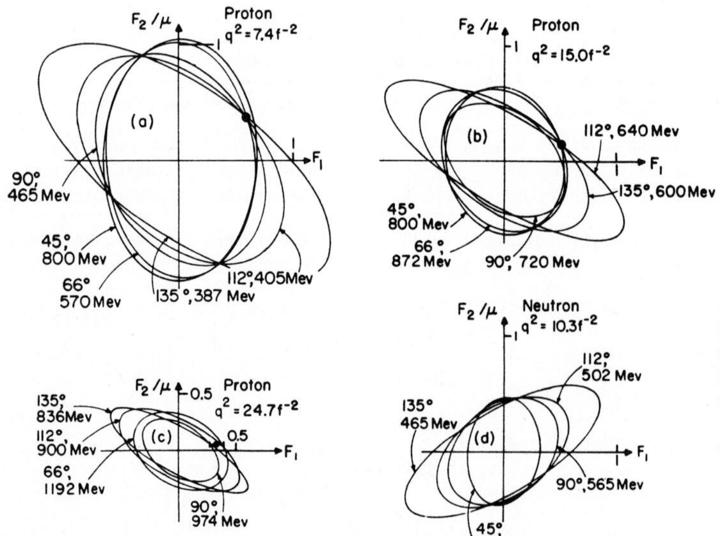

FIG. 2. Determination of F_1 and F_2 by the method of intersecting ellipses. Examples for the proton at $q^2=7.4$ f^{-2} (a), 15.0 f^{-2} (b), and 24.7 f^{-2} (c); for the neutron at $q^2=10.3$ f^{-2} (d). In each case the abscissa is F_1, the ordinate F_2/μ.

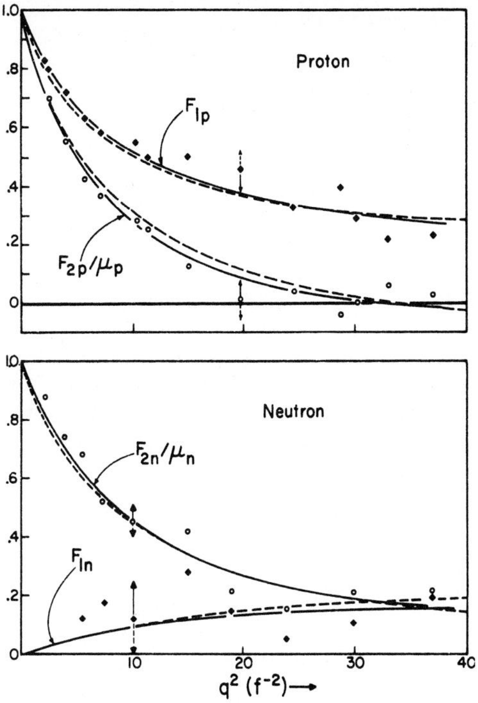

FIG. 3. Electric and magnetic form factors for the proton and neutron. The points are obtained by the intersecting-ellipse method; thus, errors for F_1 and F_2 are not independent. Typical acceptable deviations are indicated, in correlated senses, by the solid and broken arrows. The solid curve shows a fit to the data by the core model, the dashed curve by the Clementel-Villi form.

ticular angle. Other measurements at different angles but at the same q^2 determine other ellipses. (The form factors are presumed to be functions of q^2 only.) The intersections[6] give specific values of F_1 and F_2 which have been plotted against q^2 in Fig. 3.

In our previous measurements of the scattering from deuterium we had results at but one angle; hence, in analyzing our data we necessarily made the assumption that $F_{2n} = -F_{2p}$. This assumption, of course, is now no longer made in finding the results shown in Fig. 3; we find, in agreement with the recent Stanford measurements,[7] that $-F_{2n}$ becomes larger than F_{2p} especially at high values of q^2, where F_{2p} is small or might even go negative while $-F_{2n}$ is still positive. These new values of F_{2n} do not seriously change our previously deduced values of F_{1p} (by less than the statistical error), but they do indicate that it is necessary to assign a small negative magnetic moment to the core of the proton and neutron which gives rise to a small isoscalar part of the magnetic form factors.

Our values of F_{1n}/μ_n are positive and between 0.1 and 0.2, in agreement with the earlier Stanford results[7] calculated with a modified Jankus theory.[8,5] This disagrees, however, with the reinterpretation of the Stanford results by Durand,[4] which yields values of F_{1n}/μ_n that are small or may even go negative.

---

*Supported in part by joint contract of Office of Naval Research and the U. S. Atomic Energy Commission.

†On leave from the Technische Hochschule Karlsruhe, Germany.

[1]R. Wilson, K. Berkelman, J. Cassels, and D. Olson, Nature 188, 94 (1960).

[2]D. N. Olson, H. F. Schopper, and R. R. Wilson, Phys. Rev. Letters 6, 286 (1961).

[3]A. Goldberg, Phys. Rev. 112, 618 (1958).

[4]L. Durand, III, Phys. Rev. Letters 6, 631 (1961); and to be published.

[5]R. Herman and R. Hofstadter, High-Energy Electron Scattering Tables (Stanford University Press, Stanford, California, 1960).

[6]It can be shown that if there were no experimental errors all ellipses for a certain q value would intersect in the same four points. The question is which intersection gives the right values for F_1 and F_2. Two of these intersections are reflections of the other two in the origin and can be eliminated since they imply only a trivially different normalization. The choice between the remaining two intersections cannot be made on the basis of the experimental results alone. However, it is evident that F_{1p} has to be positive since F_{1p} approaches +1 for $q \to 0$. Furthermore, one expects that the charge in the proton and neutron core has the same sign, which implies that F_{1n} has the same sign as F_{1p}, i.e., positive.

[7]R. Hofstadter and R. Herman, Phys. Rev. Letters 6, 293 (1961).

[8]V. Z. Jankus, Phys. Rev. 102, 1589 (1956).

PAPER 74

STRUCTURE OF THE PROTON AND NEUTRON*

R. M. Littauer, H. F. Schopper,† and R. R. Wilson
Laboratory of Nuclear Studies, Cornell University, Ithaca, New York
(Received July 3, 1961; revised manuscript received July 21, 1961)

We have previously analyzed our data[1] to show that the proton and neutron have a common core of positive charge of about $0.35e$, whose radius might be about 0.2 fermi. This core is surrounded by a meson cloud of radius 0.8 f, with an average charge which changes from $+0.5e$ for the proton to $-0.5e$ for the neutron. Additionally, we found it necessary to postulate another cloud, the same for the neutron and proton, with a positive charge of $0.15e$ and an rms radius of about 1.4 f, thus extending out beyond the meson cloud. These clouds of charge take on meaning in the simple A model of the nucleon put forward by Bergia, Stanghellini, Fubini, and Villi,[2] referred to herein as BSFV. Their model is based on dispersion theory and on a two-pion interaction similar to that used by Frazer and Fulco.[3] In this model they identify the meson cloud with a $T=1$, $J=1$ two-pion resonant state while the extended cloud might correspond to a three-meson resonant state, most probably with $T=0$ and $J=1$. Our new measurements,[4] when examined in the light of the above model of the nucleon, imply that the resonant energy of the two-pion state is $4.0\,m_\pi$ and that of the three-pion state is $2.9\,m_\pi$.

Let us now analyze our form factors into isoscalar and isovector partial form factors[5]:

$$F_{1p}=F_{1S}+F_{1V};\quad F_{1n}=F_{1S}-F_{1V},$$
$$F_{2p}=F_{2S}+F_{2V};\quad F_{2n}=F_{2S}-F_{2V}. \tag{1}$$

In making our simple core model analysis, we got a vanishing rms radius for the neutron charge distribution by resolving the isoscalar form factor F_{1S} of Eq. (1) further into two terms, i.e., $F_{1S}=F_{1S}^{\text{core}}+F_{1S}^{\text{cl}}$, where we associated F_{1S}^{core}, the term with the smaller radius, with the core of the nucleon, and F_{1S}^{cl}, with an extended cloud. Our new results can best be fitted by partial form factors corresponding to exponential density distributions. Partial form factors of Gaussian or other shape without a singularity give a worse fit. We write therefore

$$F_{1S}=e_S^{\text{core}}(1+a_{S,\text{core}}^2q^2/12)^{-2}+e_S^{\text{cl}}(1+a_{S,\text{cl}}^2q^2/12)^{-2},$$
$$F_{1V}=e_V(1+a_V^2q^2/12)^{-2}, \tag{2}$$

where the a's are the rms radii of the respective charge distributions. In order to obtain the right total charges and rms radii for the proton and neutron, the following conditions must hold:

$$e_S^{\text{core}}+e_S^{\text{cl}}+e_V=1,$$
$$e_S^{\text{core}}+e_S^{\text{cl}}-e_V=0,$$
$$e_S^{\text{core}}a_{S,\text{core}}^2+e_S^{\text{cl}}a_{S,\text{cl}}^2+e_Va_V^2=a_p^2,$$
$$e_S^{\text{core}}a_{S,\text{core}}^2+e_S^{\text{cl}}a_{S,\text{cl}}^2-e_Va_V^2=a_n^2. \tag{3}$$

Assuming that $a_{S,\text{core}}^2 \ll a_{S,\text{cl}}^2$ and because $a_n^2=0$, one obtains

$$e_V=\tfrac{1}{2},\quad e_S^{\text{core}}+e_S^{\text{cl}}=\tfrac{1}{2},$$
$$a_V^2=2e_S^{\text{cl}}a_{S,\text{cl}}^2=a_p^2. \tag{4}$$

These conditions restrict the six adjustable parameters so that only two are left to fit the experimental data at higher q values, e.g., e_S^{core} and $a_{S,\text{core}}$.

To describe our newly determined magnetic form factors, we now assign partial magnetic moments μ_S^{core}, μ_S^{cl}, μ_V to the same core and clouds that we have used to describe the charge distributions and we write

$$F_{2S}=\mu_S^{\text{core}}(1+b_{S,\text{core}}^2q^2/12)^{-2}+\mu_S^{\text{cl}}(1+b_{S,\text{cl}}^2q^2/12)^{-2},$$
$$F_{2V}=\mu_V(1+b_V^2q^2/12)^{-2}, \tag{5}$$

where $b_{s,\,\text{core}}$, $b_{s,\,\text{cl}}$, and b_v are the rms radii of the partial form factors for the magnetic moment and all magnetic moments are measured in nuclear magnetons (nm).

In exactly the same manner as for the partial electric charges, we can infer the conditions

$$\mu_s^{\text{core}} + \mu_s^{\text{cl}} + \mu_v = \mu_p = 1.793 \text{ nm},$$

$$\mu_s^{\text{core}} + \mu_s^{\text{cl}} - \mu_v = \mu_n = -1.913 \text{ nm},$$

$$\mu_s^{\text{core}} b_{s,\,\text{core}}^2 + \mu_s^{\text{cl}} b_{s,\,\text{cl}}^2 + \mu_v b_v^2 = \mu_p b_p^2,$$

$$\mu_s^{\text{core}} b_{s,\,\text{core}}^2 + \mu_s^{\text{cl}} b_{s,\,\text{cl}}^2 - \mu_v b_v^2 = \mu_n b_n^2. \tag{6}$$

From these one readily obtains with $b_{s,\,\text{core}}^2 \ll b_{s,\,\text{cl}}^2$:

$$\mu_v = 1,$$

$$\mu_s^{\text{core}} + \mu_s^{\text{cl}} = (\mu_p + \mu_n)/2 = -0.060 \text{ nm}, \tag{7}$$

$$2\mu_s^{\text{cl}} b_{s,\,\text{cl}}^2 = \mu_p b_p^2 + \mu_n b_n^2,$$

$$2\mu_v b_v^2 = \mu_p b_p^2 - \mu_n b_n^2. \tag{8}$$

A consequence of these conditions is again that only two parameters, e.g., μ_s^{core} and $b_{s,\,\text{core}}$, are left to fit the data at high q values, if b_p^2 and b_n^2 are obtained from the slope of the form factors at small q values.

Table I. Best-fit parameters for core model with exponential density distributions. See text for definition of symbols.

e_s^{core}	= 0.25	$a_{s,\text{core}}$	= 0.2 f
e_s^{cl}	= 0.25	$a_{s,\text{cl}}$	= 1.13 f
e_v	= 0.5	a_v	= 0.80 f
μ_s^{core}	= -0.22	$b_{s,\text{core}}$	undetermined
μ_s^{cl}	= 0.16	$b_{s,\text{cl}}$	= 1.30 f
μ_v	= 1.853	b_v	= 0.89 f
a_p	= 0.80 f	b_p	= 0.98 f
a_n	= 0	b_n	= 0.79 f

At large values of q^2, the effect of the extensive isoscalar cloud will be negligible and we can fit the core parameters. A point moment of -0.19 nm would give a satisfactory fit, but let us ascribe to the core, arbitrarily, the same rms radius of 0.2 f which fits the charge core. In this case, the core moment must be -0.22 nm. In order to make the static moments correct, we must then ascribe a magnetic moment of +0.16 nm to the extended isoscalar cloud so that the total isoscalar moment $= \frac{1}{2}(\mu_p + \mu_n) = -0.060$ nm, as required by (7).

Table I summarizes the parameters we have found for the partial form factors; these are plotted in Fig. 1, and the corresponding spatial distributions are shown in Fig. 2.

The qualitative result then of these new measurements is that we find it necessary to attribute a magnetic moment of negative sign to the charge core that our previous measurement had revealed. It is not unreasonable that the angular momentum of the meson cloud be unity; then necessarily the core will have a spin of $-\frac{1}{2}$, which might rather

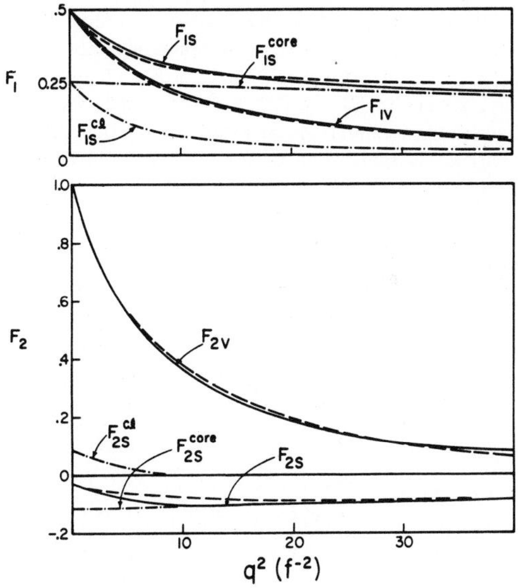

FIG. 1. Partial form factors for F_1 and F_2. Each form factor is resolved into isoscalar and isovector parts, whose sum and difference give, respectively, the neutron and proton form factors. The solid curves indicate the fit according to the core model, where the scalar partial form factors have been further split into terms corresponding to a core and an extended cloud, each of exponential distribution. The dashed curves indicate the best fit obtained by the Clementel-Villi form.

naturally give rise to the negative magnetic moment—for example, by dissolution of the core into a $K^+\Lambda$ system in direct analogy to pion emission. It is also perhaps significant that the radius of the extended isoscalar cloud of magnetic moment comes out so close to that of the isoscalar charge cloud—also true of the isovector clouds.

BSFV have proposed aesthetically simple form factors for the nucleon based on the model already referred to above. In our notation their form factors are

$$F_2^{\,v} = \tfrac{1}{2}\left[(1-\alpha_v) + \frac{\alpha_v}{1+q^2/q_v^2}\right], \quad F_2^{\,v} = 1.853\left[(1-\beta_v) + \frac{\beta_v}{1+q^2/q_v^2}\right], \tag{9}$$

$$F_1^{\,s} = \tfrac{1}{2}\left[(1-\alpha_s) + \frac{\alpha_s}{1+q^2/q_s^2}\right], \quad F_2^{\,s} = -0.060\left[(1-\beta_s) + \frac{\beta_s}{1+q^2/q_s^2}\right], \tag{10}$$

where one minus the constants α or β give the fraction of the charge or magnetic moment in a point core, and α_s or α_v give the corresponding fraction in a Yukawa meson cloud of mean square radius $6/q_s^2$ or $6/q_v^2$. It appears that BSFV have, not unreasonably, assumed that the radii of the Yukawa clouds that appear in F_1 and F_2 are the same. They show that the radius of the Yukawa part of the isovector partial form factor is due to a $T=1$, $J=1$ two-pion resonant state with the resonance at q_v, while the isoscalar radius will correspond to a three-meson resonant state, most probably with $T=0$, $J=1$, at q_s. The six parameters in (9) and (10) are reduced to five because the experimental requirement that the neutron charge radius is zero leads to the relation

$$a_s/q_s^{\,2} = a_v/q_v^{\,2}. \tag{11}$$

Table II gives values of the five independent parameters that best fit our data plus the rms radii of the neutron and proton. The same parameters have also been determined at Stanford[6] and their values in our nomenclature are shown for com-

Table II. Parameters for best fit according to BSFV[a] form.

	Cornell	Stanford
α_v	1.10	1.20
β_v	1.14	1.20
α_s	0.58	0.56
β_s	-1.5	-3.0
a_v	0.85 f	0.77 f
a_s	1.16 f	1.13 f
a_p	0.88 f	0.85 f
b_p	0.95 f	0.94 f
b_n	0.87 f	0.76 f
$q_v^{\,2}$	$8.3\ \text{f}^{-2} = 16(m_\pi/c)^2$	$10\ \text{f}^{-2} = 19.6(m_\pi/c)^2$
$q_s^{\,2}$	$4.4\ \text{f}^{-2} = 8.5(m_\pi/c)^2$	$4.7\ \text{f}^{-2} = 9(m_\pi/c)^2$

[a]See reference 2.

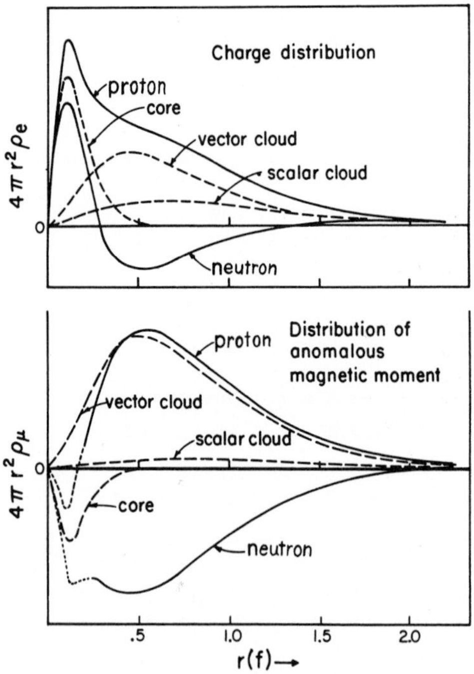

FIG. 2. Spatial distribution of charge and anomalous magnetic moment for proton and neutron, according to the core model.

parison; the general agreement is good. Slight discrepancies arise mainly because our experimental values for F_{2p} at high q^2 values are close to zero whereas an extrapolation of the Stanford form factors gives negative values. Our experiments indicate also a somewhat smaller difference between F_{2p} and F_{2n}.

The experimental data are fit equally well by the BSFV form factors or by those following from our simple core model (see Fig. 1 and the curves in the preceding Letter[4]).

According to the interpretation of BSFV, our values of q_v and q_s would imply that the resonant energy of the two-pion state is $4.0\,m_\pi$ and that of the three-pion state is $2.9\,m_\pi$.

---

*Supported in part by joint contract of Office of Naval Research and the U. S. Atomic Energy Commission.

†On leave from the Technische Hochschule Karlsruhe, Germany.

[1]D. N. Olson, H. F. Schopper, and R. R. Wilson, Phys. Rev. Letters 6, 286 (1961).

[2]S. Bergia, A. Stanghellini, S. Fubini, and C. Villi, Phys. Rev. Letters 6, 367 (1961).

[3]W. Frazer and J. Fulco, Phys. Rev. 117, 1609 (1960).

[4]R. M. Littauer, H. F. Schopper, and R. R. Wilson, preceding Letter [Phys. Rev. Letters 7, 141 (1961)].

[5]Our normalization, following BSFV, is such that the value of the form factor at $q^2=0$ gives either the static charge or magnetic moment as the case may be. Thus F_1 normalizes to unity or zero for the proton or neutron, and F_2 normalizes to the appropriate anomalous magnetic moment measured in nuclear magnetons. The Rosenbluth scattering formula then must be written in the form

$$\frac{d\sigma}{d\Omega}=\sigma_0\left\{F_1^{\,2}+\frac{q^2}{4M^2}\left[2(F_1+F_2)^2\tan^2(\theta/2)+F_2^{\,2}\right]\right\},$$

i.e., the different proton and neutron cross sections result directly from inserting the different values of F_1 and F_2 that are given by (1). We can speak of a partial charge or a partial magnetic moment whose value is given by the value of the corresponding partial form factor at $q^2=0$, the total charge or moment being the sum of the partial charges or partial moments.

[6]R. Hofstadter and R. Herman, Phys. Rev. Letters 6, 293 (1961); see, however, the reinterpretation of some of these results by L. Durand, III, Phys. Rev. Letters 6, 631 (1961).

PAPER 75

EVIDENCE FOR A $T=0$ THREE-PION RESONANCE*

B. C. Maglić, L. W. Alvarez, A. H. Rosenfeld, and M. L. Stevenson
Lawrence Radiation Laboratory and Department of Physics, University of California, Berkeley, California
(Received August 14, 1961)

The existence of a heavy neutral meson with $T=0$ and $J=1^-$ was predicted by Nambu[1] in an attempt to explain the electromagnetic form factors of the proton and neutron. Chew[2] has pointed out that such a vector meson should exist on dynamical grounds as a three-pion resonance or a bound state. Such a particle is also expected in the vector meson theory of Sakurai[3] and, as a member of an octet of mesons, according to the unitary symmetry theory[4]; and for other reasons.[5] We will refer to it as ω.

Previous searches[6] for ω have primarily been confined to the mass region $m_\omega < 3\mu$, with μ = the pion mass, where only the following radiative decay modes are allowed: $\omega \to \pi^0+\gamma$, $\omega \to 2\pi^0+\gamma$, and $\omega \to \pi^+ + \pi^- + \gamma$. The ω cannot decay into two pions.

The present search was made assuming $m_\omega > 3m_\pi$, where the decay

$$\omega \to \pi^+ + \pi^- + \pi^0 \tag{1}$$

is possible.[7] We have searched for such a 3-pion decay mode by studying the effective mass distribution of triplets of pions in the reaction

$$\bar{p}+p \to \pi^+ + \pi^+ + \pi^- + \pi^- + \pi^0. \tag{2}$$

We have measured 2500 four-prong events produced by antiprotons of 1.61 Bev/c in the 72-inch hydrogen bubble chamber.[8] The c.m. energy is 2.29 Bev. Upon fitting these 2500 four-prong events by using our kinematics program KICK, 800 four-prong events had a $\chi^2 \leqslant 6.5$ for hypothesis (2) and would not fit the hypothesis that no π^0 was produced (610 of these 800 had a $\chi^2 < 2.5$).

The 800 four-prong events must have some small contamination of events in which two π^0's were produced, but inspection of the "missing mass" distribution convinces us that it is <7%. Other tests confirm this low contamination. For example, the angular distribution of the π^0 is symmetric within statistics, and the momentum of the π^0 resembles the momentum distribution of the charged pions.

We have evaluated the 3-body effective mass,

$$M_3 = [(E_1+E_2+E_3)^2 - (\vec{P}_1+\vec{P}_2+\vec{P}_3)^2]^{1/2}, \tag{3}$$

for each pion triplet in Reaction (2). Each of the 800 four-prong events yields ten such quantities corresponding to the following charge states:

$$|Q|=0:\ \pi^+\pi^-\pi^0\ (800\times 4 \text{ combinations}), \tag{4}$$

$$|Q|=1:\ \pi^\pm\pi^\pm\pi^\pm\ (800\times 4 \text{ combinations}), \tag{4'}$$

and

$$|Q|=2:\ \pi^\pm\pi^\pm\pi^0\ (800\times 2 \text{ combinations}). \tag{4''}$$

For each value of M_3 as given by Eq. (4) we can calculate an uncertainty δM_3, by using the variance-covariance matrix of the fitted track variables, which is evaluated by KICK. By using these δM_3 we have formed the resolution function of M_3, and find that it has a half-width at half-maximum, $\Gamma_{resol}/2$, equal to 8.7 Mev. However, our input errors to KICK allow only for Coulomb scattering and estimated measurement accuracy, and do not account for optical distortion and unknown systematic errors. For example, our distributions have the correct shape but are too wide by a scale factor of about 2. This suggests that our average input error is too small by about $\sqrt{2}$. Hence, our estimate of δM_3 must be increased by about $\sqrt{2}$, and of $\Gamma_{resol}/2$ to 12 Mev. We chose 20-Mev histogram intervals for plotting our M_3 distribution.

In Fig. 1 we have plotted the M_3 distributions for the 800 Reactions (2). Distributions 1(A) and 1(B) are for charge combinations $|Q|=1$ and 2, respectively. The solid curves are an approximation to phase space.

The neutral M_3 distribution, 1(C), shows a peak centered at 787 Mev that contains 93 pion triplets above the phase-space estimate of 98. To contrast the difference between the neutral M_3 distribution and that for $|Q|>1$, we have replotted at the bottom of Fig. 1 both the neutral distribution and $\frac{2}{3}$ the sum of the $|Q|=1$ and $|Q|=2$ distributions.

Figure 2 shows the M_3 spectra with phase space subtracted. The absence of the peak in the $|Q|>0$ distributions determines the isotopic spin of the resonance,

$$T_\omega = 0.$$

The χ^2 distribution of the events in the "peak region" was compared with the χ^2 distribution of the events in the adjacent "control region," ranging from $M_3 \geqslant 820$ to $M_3 < 900$ Mev. These distributions agree with each other, which indicates that the events in the peak are genuine, rather than being caused by some unknown background reaction which was misinterpreted as Reaction

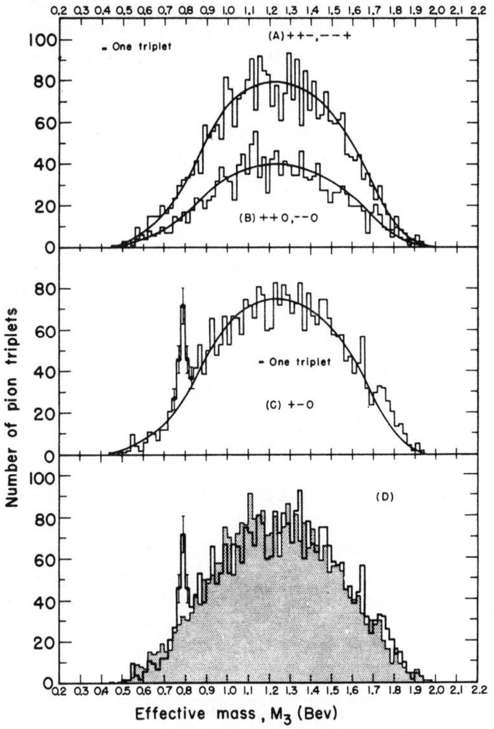

FIG. 1. Number of pion triplets versus effective mass (M_3) of the triplets for reaction $\bar{p}+p\rightarrow 2\pi^+ + 2\pi^- + \pi^0$. (A) is the distribution for the combination (4′), $|Q|=1$; (B) is for the combination (4″), $|Q|=2$; and (C) for (4), $Q=0$, with 3200, 1600, and 3200 triplets, respectively. Full width of one interval is 20 Mev. In (D), the combined distributions (A) and (B) (shaded area) are contrasted with distribution (C) (heavy line).

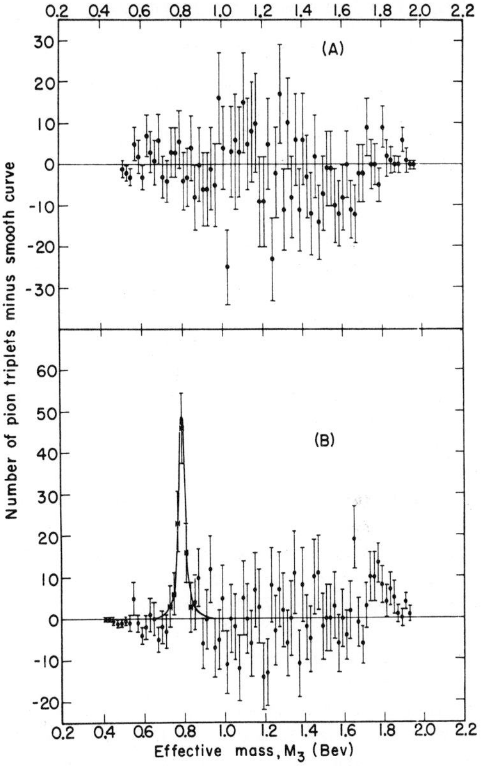

FIG. 2. (A) M_3 spectrum of the pion triplets in the combined distributions 1(A) and 1(B), with the smooth curve subtracted. (B) M_3 spectrum of the neutral pion triplets in distribution 1(C), again with the smooth background subtracted; a resonance curve is drawn through the peak at 787 Mev with $\Gamma/2=15$ Mev. The error flags are $\sqrt{N}$, where N is the total number of triplets per 20-Mev interval before subtraction of the smooth background curve.

(2). The missing-mass distributions in the two regions also agree with each other, thus supporting the above conclusion.

The peak in Fig. 2(B) appears to have a half-width $\Gamma/2<15$ Mev. This is so close to our resolution, $\Gamma_{\text{resol}}/2$, of 12 Mev that we cannot unfold it without further study and at present can only conclude that

$$M_\omega = 787 \text{ Mev},$$

and

$$\Gamma/2<15 \text{ Mev}. \quad (5)$$

By using the uncertainty principle, we see that this half-width implies a mean life $\tau>4\times10^{-23}$ sec. Our ω's are produced with a typical c.m. momentum of 800 Mev/c, so that in a mean life they travel farther than 13 f.

We now assume that the ω peak is real, and want to estimate how many ω mesons it contains. As shown in Fig. 1(C), 191 triplets have M_3 values between 740 and 820 Mev. (We call this the "peak region.") However, these 191 triplets come from only 170 different four-prong events [i.e., 21 Reactions (2) have two values of M_3 in the peak region]. We use the charged M_3 distribution to estimate the background in the interval as 98 triplets, and then calculate a production of 83 ± 16 ω mesons out of 800 Reactions (2); i.e.,

$(10\pm 2)\%$ of Reactions (2) proceed via

$$\bar{p}+p\rightarrow\pi^{+}+\pi^{-}+\omega. \quad (6)$$

Among the same 800 five-pion events, we have searched for—and found—the $T=J=1$ pion-pion resonance (ρ meson).[9] We found that approximately 30% of them proceed via

$$\bar{p}+p\rightarrow 2\pi+\rho. \quad (7)$$

We have checked whether there is any correlation between the observed ρ mesons and the ω mesons. For each triplet inside the peak region, $740\leq M_3 < 820$ Mev, we have evaluated the effective mass of the remaining $\pi^+\pi^-$ doublet, M_2. The M_2 distribution is consistent with a continuum, starting from about 300 Mev, that has $(10\pm 2)\%$ of the doublets with values of M_2 in the region of ρ, which we took to be 750 ± 50 Mev. There is no evidence that the ω and the ρ are produced in association.

Although the masses of ω and ρ differ by only 35 Mev, we believe that they cannot be the same particle, because of their different widths (the $\Gamma/2$ for ρ being 40 Mev), isotopic spin, and G-conjugation parity—which forbids $2\pi\rightarrow 3\pi$.

In referring to the $T=0$ 3π resonance as ω, we have tacitly supposed that it is in fact a vector state with $J=1^-$. However, the spin and parity must be decided by experiment. Even if we assume the spin is <2, there are left three possibilities which are listed in Table I. A $T=0$ state of three pions must be antisymmetric in all pairs; hence all three pions must have different charges, i.e., $\pi^0\pi^0\pi^0$ is forbidden. The matrix element of the $\pi^+\pi^-\pi^0$ state is conveniently analyzed in terms of a single pion plus a di-pion. The pions of the di-pion are assigned momentum $\vec{P}$ and angular momentum $\vec{L}$ (in the di-pion rest frame). Then another pair of variables, $\vec{p}$ and $\vec{l}$, describe the remaining pion in the 3π rest frame. Because the state is antisymmetric in any pair, $\vec{L}$ must be odd; henceforth, we assume $L=1$. Then if $l=0$ we have a $J=1^-$ (i.e., vector) matrix element, as listed on the bottom line of Table I. Since three pions are involved, there is an intrinsic parity of $(-1)^3$, so that the corresponding "meson" is not V, but A.

If $l=1$, the matrix element can be 1+ (axial) or 0+ (scalar) corresponding, respectively, to a vector meson (ω) or a pseudoscalar (PS) meson.

Do we have enough data to distinguish between totally antisymmetric A vs S vs V matrix elements? It is convenient to make a Dalitz plot[10] [Fig. 3(D) for the peak region events, 3(A) for the control region events] that displays the threefold symmetry of three pions in an antisymmetric state. Unit area on a Dalitz plot is proportional to the corresponding Lorentz-invariant phase space, so that the density of plotted points is proportional to the square of the matrix element. It is easily shown that the size of the figure is proportional to $T_1+T_2+T_3=Q=m_\omega-(2m_{\pi^\pm}+m_{\pi^0})$.[11] Because of the finite width of the peak and the control regions, Q varies from event to event, so we use normalized variables, T_i/Q. The antisymmetry allows the plot to be folded about any median, so that in Figs. 3(C) and 3(B) all the data have been concentrated into $\frac{1}{6}$ of the plot area; the statistical distribution of the events is then more evident.

All three competing matrix elements, being antisymmetric, must vanish where any two pions "touch" in momentum space. If two pions touch, the third must have its maximum kinetic energy [regions (d), (f), and (b) on the plot]. The resonance region points [Figs. 3(C) and 3(D)] seem to show the required depopulation at points (d), (f), and (b).

More evident, however, on the plot is the fact that near $p=0$ [points (a), (c), and (e)] the density of peak-region points is only one half of that on the control plot. This is all the more suggestive when it is remembered that even the peak-region data contain only $(43\pm 7)\%$ resonance events. This depopulation at $p=0$ suggests an angular momen-

Table I. Possible three-pion resonances with $T=0$, $J\leq 1$.

"Meson" Type, $\vec{J}$	$\vec{l}$, $\vec{L}$	Matrix element Type, $\vec{J}$	Simple example	Vanishes at:
V, 1-	1, 1	A, 1+	$E_-(\vec{p}_0\times\vec{p}_+)+E_0(\vec{p}_+\times\vec{p}_-)+E_+(\vec{p}_-\times\vec{p}_0)$	whole boundary
PS, 0-	1, 1	S, 0+	$(E_--E_0)(E_0-E_+)(E_+-E_-)$	$a,c,e+b,d,f$
A, 1+	0, 1	V, 1-	$E_-(\vec{p}_0-\vec{p}_+)+E_0(\vec{p}_+-\vec{p}_-)+E_+(\vec{p}_--\vec{p}_0)$	b,d,f only

FIG. 3. (A): Dalitz plot of 171 triplets from the control region ($820 \leq M_3 < 900$); (B): folded control region plot; (D): Dalitz plot for 191 triplets in the peak region, 43 ± 7% of which are due to ω mesons; (C) folded peak region plot. T_+, T_-, and T_0 are kinetic energies of the π^+, π^-, and π^0, respectively.

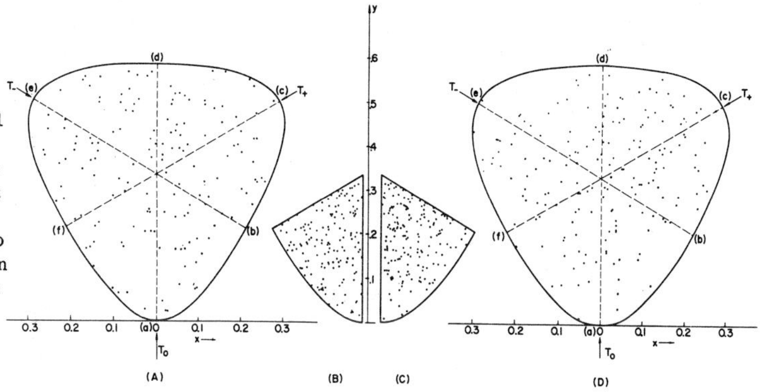

tum barrier ($l > 0$) and constitutes mild evidence against a V matrix element (A meson).

The two stronger remaining candidates have A vs S matrix elements. The dashed lines in Fig. 3(D), as well as the two straight lines of the folded distribution in Fig. 3(C), correspond to equal energies of two pions. The scalar matrix element (S) of Table I vanishes when any two pions have the same energy, and therefore would require depopulation along these lines. This is not observed. An A matrix element has terms in $\vec{p}_i \times \vec{p}_j$, which vanish for collinear pions. The boundary of the plot represents collinearity, and seems indeed to be depopulated; although clearly more statistics and more detailed analysis such as investigation of polarization and alignment are needed.

We conclude that the data fit the qualitative criteria for an axial vector matrix element (ω meson); there is reasonable evidence against both an A meson and a PS meson.

The film used in this measurement was obtained in collaboration with J. Button, P. Eberhard, G. Kalbfleisch, J. Lannutti, G. Lynch, and N. H. Xuong; and this experiment would not have been possible without their help. It is a pleasure to thank Professor Murray Gell-Mann for his theoretical discussions. We wish to acknowledge the active participation of C. Tate, L. Champomier, A. Hussain, C. Rinfleisch, and F. Richards in the final stages of this experiment.

---

*Work done under the auspices of the U. S. Atomic Energy Commission.

[1]Y. Nambu, Phys. Rev. 106, 1366 (1957). See also S. Bergia, A. Stanghellini, S. Fubini, and C. Villi, Phys. Rev. Letters 6, 367 (1961); R. Blankenbecler and J. Tarski (to be published); G. Chew, R. Karplus S. Gasiorowicz, and F. Zachariasen, Phys. Rev. 110, 265 (1958); P. Federbush, M. Goldberger, and S. Treiman, Phys. Rev. 112, 642 (1958).

[2]G. F. Chew, Phys. Rev. Letters 4, 142 (1960). See also V. de Alfaro and B. Vitale, Phys. Rev. Letters 7, 72 (1961).

[3]J. Sakurai, Ann. Phys. 11, 1 (1960); Nuovo cimento 16, 388 (1960). See also V. I. Ogievetski and I. V. Polubarinov, Dubna Report D-676, 1961, submitted to J. Exptl. Theoret. Phys. (U.S.S.R.) for publication.

[4]M. Ikeda, S. Ogawa, and Y. Ohnuki, Progr. Theoret. Phys. (Kyoto) 22, 715 (1959); see also Y. Ohnuki, in Proceedings of the 1960 Annual International Conference on High-Energy Physics at Rochester (Interscience Publishers, Inc., New York, 1960); Y. Yamaguchi, Progr. Theoret. Phys. (Kyoto), Suppl. No. 11 (1959); J. Wess, Nuovo cimento 15, 52 (1960); Y. Neeman, Nuclear Phys. (to be published); A. Salam and J. C. Ward, Nuovo cimento (to be published); M. Gell-Mann (to be published); M. Gell-Mann and F. Zachariasen, Phys. Rev. (to be published).

[5]S. Sawada and M. Yonezawa, Progr. Theoret. Phys. (Kyoto) 22, 610 (1959). A somewhat similar particle was predicted by M. Johnson and E. Teller, Phys. Rev. 98, 783 (1955); H. Duerr and E. Teller, Phys. Rev. 101, 494 (1956); E. Teller, Proceedings of the Sixth Annual Rochester Conference on High-Energy Physics, 1956 (Interscience Publishers, New York, 1956); H. Duerr, Phys. Rev. 103, 469 (1956).

[6]A. Alberigi, C. Bernardini, R. Querzoli, G. Salvini, A. Silverman, and G. Stoppini (reported by G. Bernardini), in Ninth Annual International Conference on High-Energy Physics at Kiev, July, 1959 (Academy of Science U.S.S.R., Moscow, 1960), Vol. 1, p. 42; R. Gomez, H. Burkhardt, M. Daybell, H. Ruderman, M. Sands, and R. Talman, Phys. Rev. Letters 5, 170 (1960). A. Abashian, N. Booth, and K. Crowe, Phys. Rev. Letters 5, 258 (1960); 7, 35 (1961). J. Button, P. Eberhard, G. R. Kalbfleisch, J. Lannutti, S. Limentani, G. Lynch, B. Maglić, M. L. Stevenson, and N. H. Xuong (reported by F. Solmitz), in Proceedings of the 1960 Annual International Conference on High-Energy Physics at Rochester (Interscience Publishers, Inc., New York, 1960), p. 166; K. Berkelman, G. Cortellessa, and A. Reale, Phys. Rev. Letters 6, 234 (1961).

E. Pickup, F. Ayer, and E. O. Salant, Phys. Rev. Letters 5, 161 (1960); J. G. Rushbrooke and D. Radojčić, Phys. Rev. Letters 5, 567 (1960); J. Anderson, V. Bang, P. Burke, D. Carmony, and N. Schmitz, Phys. Rev. Letters 6, 365 (1961); A. R. Erwin, R. March, W. D. Walker, and E. West, Phys. Rev. Letters 6, 628 (1961); D. Stonehill, C. Baltay, H. Courant, and N. H. Xuong, Phys. Rev. 121, 1788 (1961).

[7]According to G. Sudarshan (University of Rochester, private communication) m_ω is expected to be within the limits $m_\rho < m_\omega < m_\rho + m_\pi$, where $m_\rho = 750$ Mev is the mass of the $T = J = 1$ $\pi\pi$ resonance.

[8]J. Button, P. Eberhard, G. R. Kalbfleisch, J. E. Lannutti, G. R. Lynch, B. C. Maglić, M. L. Stevenson, and N. H. Xuong, Phys. Rev. 121, 1788 (1961).

[9]M. L. Stevenson, G. R. Kalbfleisch, B. C. Maglić, and A. H. Rosenfeld, Lawrence Radiation Laboratory Report UCRL-9814 (to be published). For previous evidence see: I. Derado, Nuovo cimento 15, 853 (1961); W. Fickinger, E. C. Fowler, H. Kraybill, J. Sandweiss, J. Sanford, and H. Taft, Phys. Rev. Letters 6, 624 (1961).

[10]R. Dalitz, Phil. Mag. 44, 1068 (1953). See also E. Fabri, Nuovo cimento 11, 479 (1954).

[11]Specifically, Q equals the height of the exscribed triangle.

PAPER 76*

π-π RESONANCE IN π^--p INTERACTIONS AT 1.25 Bev*

E. Pickup,† D. K. Robinson, and E. O. Salant
Brookhaven National Laboratory, Upton, New York
(Received August 14, 1961)

It has become apparent that π-π interactions are important in π-p collisions in the Bev region. Several experiments on single-pion production[1-6] have shown that there is an excess of nucleons at low laboratory kinetic energies over that which would be expected on a statistical or isobar theory. Goebel[7] has pointed out that such an excess would be indicative of a π-π interaction. Fraser and Fulco[8] showed that a π-π resonance in an $I=1$, $J=1$ state could explain features of electron-nucleon scattering, and suggested a resonance at $w^2 \simeq 10\mu^2$, where w is the total energy of the two pions in the π-π rest frame, and μ is the pion rest mass ($w = Q + 2\mu$). Later calculations[9] suggested that the resonance was at $w^2 \simeq 22\mu^2$. Indications of a π-π resonance in π-p interactions have been obtained in several experiments,[5,6,10-12] but the results were limited by low incident pion energies, or by statistics. With the higher statistics available in the present work, strong evidence is obtained for a π-π resonance in an $I=1$ state.

As part of a study of π-p interactions, using the bubble chamber technique, we have measured 4000 π^--p events at 1.25-Bev incident pion energy. 968 events of the type

$$\pi^- + p \rightarrow \pi^- + \pi^+ + n, \qquad (1)$$

and 566 of the type

$$\pi^- + p \rightarrow \pi^- + \pi^0 + p, \qquad (2)$$

have been identified using the GUTS kinematic fitting program, and ionization density measurements.

Comparison of the pion momentum spectra with the predictions of the extended isobar model[13] indicate that pion production through isobar formation is not the dominant process at this energy.

*See page 686 of this volume for corrections and addenda.

The nucleons from both reactions are produced predominantly backward in the c.m. system, and thus are peaked at low laboratory kinetic energies. Figures 1(a) and (b) show the nucleon laboratory kinetic energy, T, for reactions (1) and (2), respectively. The curves in Fig. 1 were computed assuming a constant π-π cross section, $\sigma_{\pi-\pi}$, from the equation given by Chew and Low[14]:

$$\frac{\partial^2\sigma}{\partial\Delta^2\partial w^2} \xrightarrow[\Delta^2\to-\mu^2]{} \frac{f^2}{2\pi}\frac{\Delta^2/\mu^2}{(\Delta^2+\mu^2)^2}\frac{w}{q_{1L}}(\tfrac{1}{4}w^2-\mu^2)^{1/2}\sigma_{\pi-\pi}, \quad (3)$$

where Δ is the four-momentum transfer to the nucleon ($\Delta^2=2MT$), f^2 is the renormalized pion coupling constant and q_{1L} is the laboratory momentum of the incident pion. The theoretical curves are normalized to the total numbers of events in the histograms. The theoretical and experimental distributions seem to agree at low momentum transfers, but the histograms are more sharply peaked than would be expected.[15]

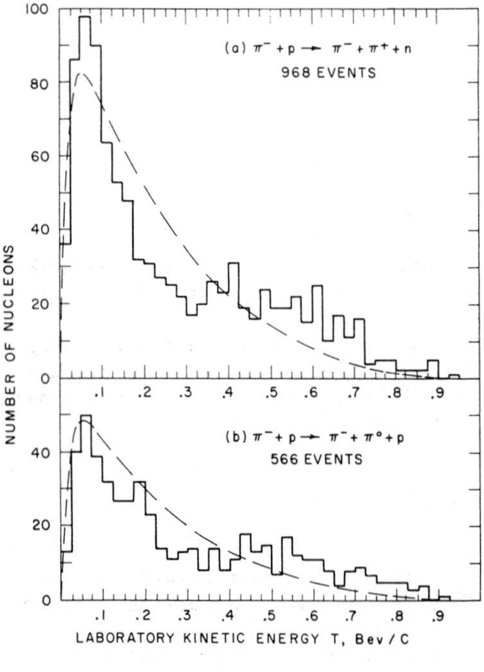

FIG. 1. Histogram of nucleon laboratory kinetic energies. The curve was calculated from the Chew-Low equation, for constant $\sigma_{\pi-\pi}$.

There is also a group of high-momentum-transfer events, not expected on a one-pion exchange model.

Figure 2 shows Q values for π^--π^+ and π^--π^0 systems, and also the prediction of the statistical model. The isobar prediction is similar to the latter. Both histograms exhibit well-defined peaks at the same Q value. The agreement in position of the two Q peaks suggests that the same π-π resonance state is dominant in both reactions. It follows, therefore, that isotopic spin $I=0$ is excluded for this state.

The branching ratio for reactions (1) and (2), $R=\sigma(2)/\sigma(1)=0.585\pm0.031$, and the ratio, $R_{\pi-\pi}$, for events in the $Q_{\pi-\pi}$ peaks (400 Mev $< Q_{\pi-\pi} <$ 550 Mev), is 0.50 ± 0.04. The one-pion exchange model predicts that $R_{\pi-\pi}=\frac{1}{2}$ for a π-π interaction

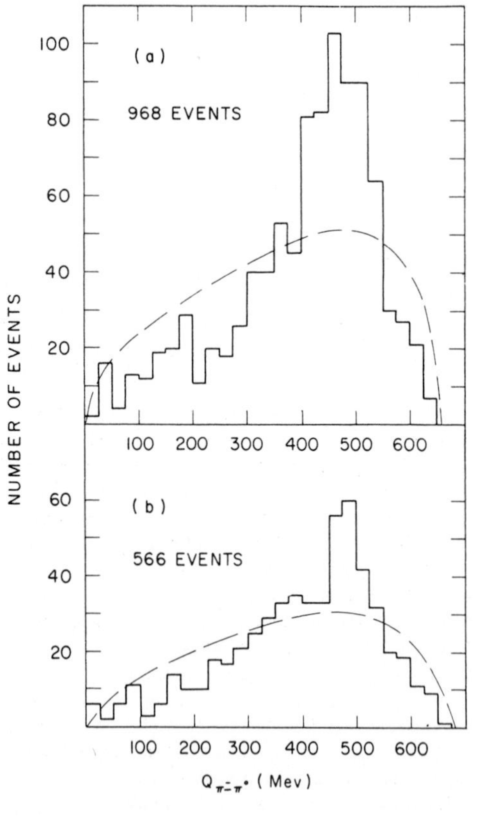

FIG. 2. Q-value distributions for π-π system for all events, for (a) $\pi^-+p\to\pi^-+\pi^++n$, (b) $\pi^-+p\to\pi^-+\pi^0+p$; the dashed curves are from statistical theory.

in a pure $I=1$ state, and $\frac{9}{2}$ for $I=2$. The model is more likely to be valid if we select events with small Δ^2. Restricting the selection of events in the Q peak to those with $\Delta^2<10\mu^2$, or $T<104$ Mev, we obtain $R_{\pi-\pi}=0.42\pm0.06$. The data are in agreement with the predictions of the model for $I=1$. This state is further suggested by the Yale π^+-p experiment at 1.26 Bev,[11] by comparing the π^+-π^0 and π^+-π^+ Q distributions.

The π-π cross section, as a function of w^2, was calculated by integrating Eq. (3) up to $\Delta^2=10\mu^2$, assuming this equation to be valid in the physical region. Comparison of the experimental and theoretical distributions in Fig. 1 indicates that this may be a reliable procedure for small Δ^2.[16] Figure 3 shows $\sigma_{\pi-\pi}$ obtained in this way, for the combined events from reactions (1) and (2). The background on the low-energy side of the resonance is associated with both reactions. This would seem to eliminate a pure $I=0$ low-energy effect. We obtain $\sigma_{\pi-\pi}=95$ mb at the peak, $w^2=29\mu^2$ ($Q=475\pm10$ Mev). The full width at half maximum is 130 Mev. These values, and the values determined at 1.74 Bev by Erwin et al.[12] agree within statistics. This agreement between results at two quite different energies implies that there is, indeed, a resonance, π^*, in the π-π system.

The decay angle, δ, between the direction of the π^- in the rest frame of π^* and the c.m. direction of π^*, was calculated. In Figs. 4(a) and (b) the distributions of events in the Q peaks show backward-forward symmetry, but a marked departure from isotropy. Restricting the selection to events with small Δ^2 shows that the anisotropy is mainly associated with such events. For events outside the Q peak, the asymmetries observed in both reactions (1) and (2) are consistent with some $(\frac{3}{2},\frac{3}{2})$ π-p isobar formation.

To investigate angular momentum states involved in the π^* resonance, the angle, α, between the direction of the π^- in the rest frame of π^* and the direction of the incident pion, was calculated. Events were selected in which π^* was emitted closely parallel or antiparallel to the incident pion direction ($|\cos\theta|\geq0.9$).[17] Provided that the Adair analysis[18] holds for this selection, and for a short-lived resonant state, the π^- angular distribution is expected to be a relatively simple function of the angular momentum state J ($a+b\cos^2\alpha$ for $J=1$). The distributions are shown in Figs. 4(c) and (d). That in 4(c), at least, is suggestive of $J=1$, rather than larger J values which would give higher powers of $\cos^2\alpha$. The distribution in 4(c)

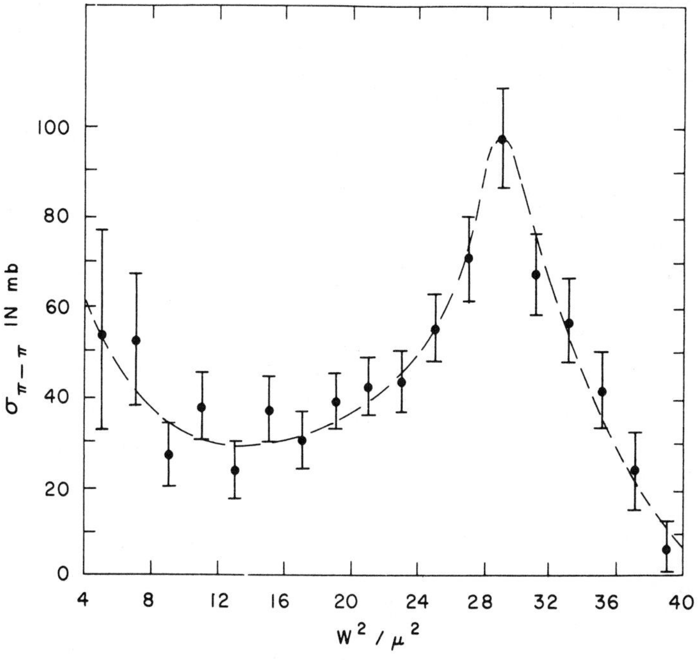

FIG. 3. Variation of cross section, $\sigma_{\pi-\pi}$ with energy, w, for the π-π system for events with $\Delta^2<10\mu^2$. The dashed curve is a free curve drawn through the points. μ = rest mass of charged pion.

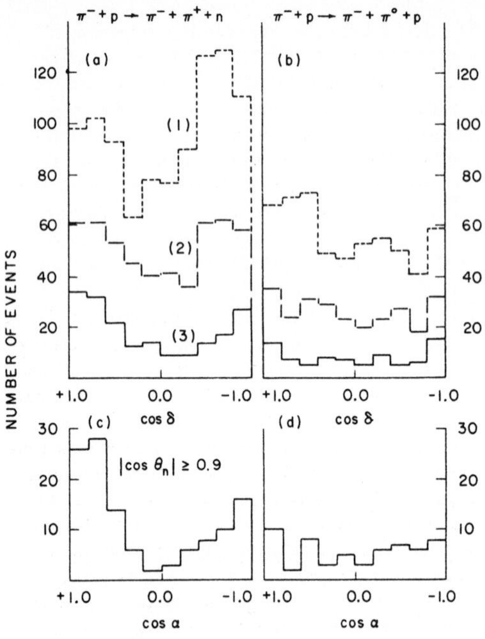

FIG. 4. Angular distributions for the π-π system. (a) and (b) show decay angles δ of π^- in π^* rest frame, relative to c.m. direction of π^*: (1) All events (dotted); (2) events with 400 Mev $\leq Q_{\pi-\pi} \leq$ 550 Mev (dashed); (3) events from (2) with $\Delta^2 < 10\mu^2$ (solid). (c) and (d) show decay angles α of π^- in π^* rest frame, relative to incident pion direction, for events with $|\cos\theta| \geq 0.9$, where θ = c.m. angle of π^*.

shows some asymmetry (backward/forward ratio = 43/76), which may indicate interference from another state.

We wish to thank the BNL bubble chamber group, the Yale group who set up the beam, and our efficient team of scanners.

*Work was performed under the auspices of the U. S. Atomic Energy Commission.

†On leave of absence from the National Research Council, Ottawa, Ontario, Canada.

[1]F. Bonsignori and F. Selleri, Nuovo cimento 15, 465 (1960).

[2]I. Derado, Nuovo cimento 15, 853 (1960).

[3]E. Pickup, D. K. Robinson, and E. O. Salant, Proceedings of the Tenth Annual International Rochester Conference on High-Energy Physics (Interscience Publishers, Inc., New York, 1960), p. 72.

[4]J. G. Rushbrooke and D. Radojičić, Phys. Rev. Letters 5, 567 (1960).

[5]D. K. Robinson, B. Munir, E. Pickup, and E. O. Salant, Bull. Am. Phys. Soc. 6, 301 (1961).

[6]E. Pickup, F. Ayer, and E. O. Salant, Phys. Rev. Letters 4, 474 (1960).

[7]C. Goebel, Phys. Rev. Letters 1, 337 (1958).

[8]W. R. Frazer and J. R. Fulco, Phys. Rev. Letters 2, 365 (1959); Phys. Rev. 117, 1609 (1960).

[9]J. Bowcock, W. N. Cottingham, and D. Lurié, Phys. Rev. Letters 5, 386 (1960).

[10]J. A. Anderson, V. X. Bang, P. G. Burke, D. D. Carmony, and N. Schmitz, Phys. Rev. Letters 6, 365 (1961).

[11]D. Stonehill, C. Baltay, H. Courant, W. Fickinger, E. C. Fowler, H. Kraybill, J. Sandweiss, J. Sanford, and H. Taft, Phys. Rev. Letters 6, 624 (1961).

[12]A. R. Erwin, R. March, W. D. Walker, and E. West, Phys. Rev. Letters 6, 628 (1961).

[13]R. M. Sternheimer and S. J. Lindenbaum, Phys. Rev. 123, 333 (1961).

[14]G. F. Chew and F. E. Low, Phys. Rev. 113, 1640 (1959).

[15]Substitution of a resonant form for $\sigma_{\pi-\pi}$ in Eq. (3) would not significantly change the shape of the theoretical curve.

[16]Similar calculations for pion production in p-p collisions at 2 Bev give absolute $np\pi^+$ cross sections in approximate agreement with experiment for small momentum transfers [W. J. Fickinger, E. Pickup, D. K. Robinson, and E. O. Salant, following Letter, Phys. Rev. Letters 7, 196 (1961)]. Also, in p-p collisions at 2 Bev, a test of the Chew-Low method by extrapolation into the unphysical region [similar to the test made at 3 Bev by G. A. Smith, H. Courant, E. Fowler, H. Kraybill, J. Sandweiss, and H. Taft, Phys. Rev. Letters 5, 571 (1961)] gave good results [W. J. Fickinger, E. Pickup, D. K. Robinson, and E. O. Salant (to be published)].

[17]It should be noted that this selection of events is approximately equivalent to selecting events with very small Δ^2 [Figs. 4(a), (b)].

[18]R. K. Adair, Phys. Rev. 100, 1540 (1955).

PAPER 77*

Electromagnetic Form Factors of the Proton*

F. Bumiller, M. Croissiaux,† E. Dally,‡ and R. Hofstadter
Department of Physics and High-Energy Physics Laboratory, Stanford University, Stanford, California

(Received July 20, 1961)

This paper reports experimental findings on the Dirac (F_1) and Pauli (F_2) form factors of the proton. The form factors have been obtained by using the Rosenbluth formula and the method of intersecting ellipses in analyzing the elastic electron-proton scattering cross sections. A range of energies covering the interval 200–1000 Mev for the incident electrons is explored. Scattering angles vary from 35° to 145°. Values as high as $q^2 \cong 31$ f^{-2} (q = energy-momentum transfer) are investigated, but form factors can be reliably determined only up to about $q^2 = 25$ f^{-2}. Splitting of the form factors is confirmed. The newly measured data are in good agreement with earlier Stanford data on the form factors and also with the predictions of a recent theoretical model of the proton. Consistency in determining the values of the form factors at different energies and angles gives support to the techniques of quantum electrodynamics up to $q^2 \cong 25$ f^{-2}. At the extreme conditions of this experiment (975 Mev, 145°) the behavior of the form factors may be exhibiting some anomaly.

I. INTRODUCTION

Since early 1955,[1] electron-scattering studies of the proton have been in progress at Stanford University when it was first shown that the proton is a structure more complicated than a point-charge and point-magnetic-moment. A summary of the findings on the proton made up to early 1960 was included in a recent book on electron-scattering tables.[2]

More recently an extension of the investigation to higher incident electron energies revealed important new features about the electromagnetic form factors of the proton which will now be sketched briefly in order to permit an understanding of the subject material of this paper.

The initial measurements[1,2] on the proton's Dirac (F_1) and Pauli (F_2) form factors showed that F_1 and F_2 were appreciably smaller than unity. This fact alone implied finite structure of the proton. The form factors (F_1,F_2) were found to lie in a region in which they were approximately equal to each other at energy-momentum transfers (q) less than $q^2 = 9.3$ f^{-2}. At this value of q^2 the measured ratio was $F_1/F_2 = 1.23 \pm 0.20$.[3] The value of this ratio was also in agreement with earlier measurements[4] of the quantity F_1/F_2. The early experiments were restricted to an angular range larger than 60° at the highest energies then available (~650 Mev) from the Stanford linear accelerator. They were also restricted because of the limitation imposed by the energy-handling ability of the 36-in. spectrometer used at that time. Under these conditions, the accuracy of the experiments did not allow a determination of F_1 and F_2 separately at $q^2 > 9.3$ f^{-2}. Although the experiments cited[3,4] did indeed show that F_1 was slightly larger than F_2 at the same momentum transfer, the F_1/F_2 ratio was sufficiently close to unity so that for simplicity and for ease of calculation in most problems, the two form factors were usually taken to be equal to each other.

Recently the splitting of F_1 and F_2 was established at higher energies.[5–8] In the past year we have endeavored to increase the accuracy of our earlier results.[5–7] This paper reports the results of such an effort. We have also wished to compare our results with a theoretical model of the proton.[9] We shall see that the experimental proton results are in excellent agreement with that model.

II. EXPERIMENTAL METHOD

The basic idea of our method rests on a supposition which is in fact required by arguments of relativistic invariance, that each form factor is a function only of q^2. In this event one may solve for F_1 and F_2 by the "method of intersecting ellipses."[10,11]

In this method a measurement of a differential electron-proton scattering cross section at a given energy and angle (E_1, θ_1, respectively) determines, according to the Rosenbluth formula, Eq. (1), an ellipse in the F_1, F_2 plane. If a second measurement of a cross section

* This work was supported in part by the Office of Naval Research and the U. S. Atomic Energy Commission and by the U. S. Air Force, through the Office of Scientific Research of the Air Research and Development Command.

† Now at the Centre de Recherches Nucléaires, Strasbourg, France.

‡ Now at the Department of Physics, University of Zurich, Zurich, Switzerland.

[1] R. Hofstadter and R. W. McAllister, Phys. Rev. **98**, 217 (1955).

[2] R. Herman and R. Hofstadter, *High-Energy Electron-Scattering Tables* (Stanford University Press, Stanford, California, 1960).

[3] F. Bumiller and R. Hofstadter: See Fig. 8, p. 28, of reference 2.

[4] E. E. Chambers and R. Hofstadter, Phys. Rev. **103**, 1454 (1956).

[5] R. Hofstadter, F. Bumiller, and M. Croissiaux, *Proceedings of the 1960 Annual International Conference on High-Energy Physics at Rochester* (Interscience Publishers, Inc., New York, 1960), pp. 762–766.

[6] F. Bumiller, M. Croissiaux, and R. Hofstadter, Phys. Rev. Letters **5**, 261 (1960).

[7] R. Hofstadter, F. Bumiller, and M. Croissiaux, Phys. Rev. Letters **5**, 263 (1960).

[8] K. Berkelman, J. M. Cassels, D. N. Olson, and R. R. Wilson, *Proceedings of the 1960 Annual International Conference on High-Energy Physics at Rochester* (Interscience Publishers, Inc., New York, 1960), p. 757 ff. Cf. the account of this Rochester Conference paper subsequently published in Nature **188**, 94 (1960).

[9] R. Hofstadter and R. Herman, Phys. Rev. Letters **6**, 293 (1961).

[10] R. Hofstadter, *Ninth Annual International Conference on High-Energy Physics, Kiev, July, 1959 Plenary Session* IV, (Academy of Science, U.S.S.R., 1960), pp. 355-374.

[11] See reference 2, pp. 30–32 and Fig. 9.

* *See page 686 of this volume for corrections and addenda.*

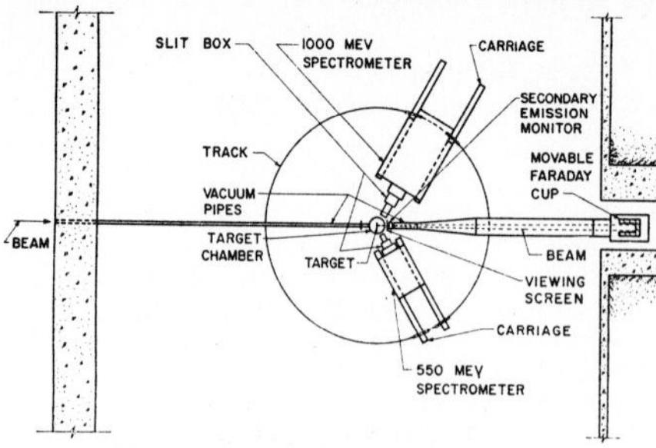

FIG. 1. This figure provides a schematic diagram of the experimental electron-scattering area, and shows the target chamber, the two spectrometers, the Faraday cup, the vacuum pipes, and other important parts of the apparatus. The track on which the spectrometers roll has an approximate radius of 13.5 ft.

is made at (E_2,θ_2) such that q^2 is the same as in the first measurement, a second ellipse can be determined. The requirement that the actual values of F_1 and F_2 be functions only of q^2 serves to determine the form factors at the point of intersection of the two ellipses. A third or fourth (etc.) measurement can also be used and if consistent determinations of F_1 and F_2 are obtained within experimental error, the Rosenbluth theory can be said to be confirmed and the values of F_1 and F_2 would be definitely established. Such consistency has been found in our measurements below $q^2 \leqslant 25\ \mathrm{f}^{-2}$, but a determination of F_1 and F_2 at our very highest values of q^2 ($\cong 30\ \mathrm{f}^{-2}$) needs further discussion.

Two ellipses will intersect in four points in the F_1, F_2 plane. It is easy to see that the normalization of the electric charge and the static magnetic moment of the proton serve to define only the set in the first quadrant with values: $F_1(0)=+1.0$; $F_2(0)=+1.0$.

In the above manner we employ the following formulas:

$$\frac{d\sigma}{d\Omega}=\sigma_{\mathrm{NS}}\left\{F_1^2(q^2)+\frac{\hbar^2q^2}{4M^2c^2}\left[2\{F_1(q^2)+KF_2(q^2)\}^2\times\tan^2\frac{\theta}{2}+K^2F_2^2(q^2)\right]\right\}, \quad (1)$$

where

$$\sigma_{\mathrm{NS}}=\left(\frac{e^2}{2E}\right)^2\frac{\cos^2(\theta/2)}{\sin^4(\theta/2)}\frac{1}{[1+(2E/Mc^2)\sin^2(\theta/2)]}, \quad (2)$$

and

$$q=\frac{(2E/\hbar c)\sin(\theta/2)}{[1+(2E/Mc^2)\sin^2(\theta/2)]^{\frac{1}{2}}}, \quad (3)$$

where the symbols have their usual significance and K has the numerical value of 1.79.

We may then write

$$d\sigma/d\Omega=\sigma_{\mathrm{NS}}[a_{11}F_1^2+a_{12}F_1F_2+a_{22}F_2^2], \quad (4)$$

where

$$a_{11}=1+(\hbar^2q^2/2M^2c^2)\tan^2(\theta/2), \quad (5)$$

$$a_{12}=(\hbar^2q^2K/M^2c^2)\tan^2(\theta/2), \quad (6)$$

$$a_{22}=(\hbar^2q^2K^2/2M^2c^2)[\tan^2(\theta/2)+\tfrac{1}{2}]. \quad (7)$$

Values of σ_{NS}, a_{11}, a_{12}, and a_{22} may be found from the tables of reference 2 and the ellipses can be plotted according to Eq. (4). It is thus necessary to find the experimental values of the cross section $d\sigma/d\Omega$ at many settings of energy E and scattering angle θ.

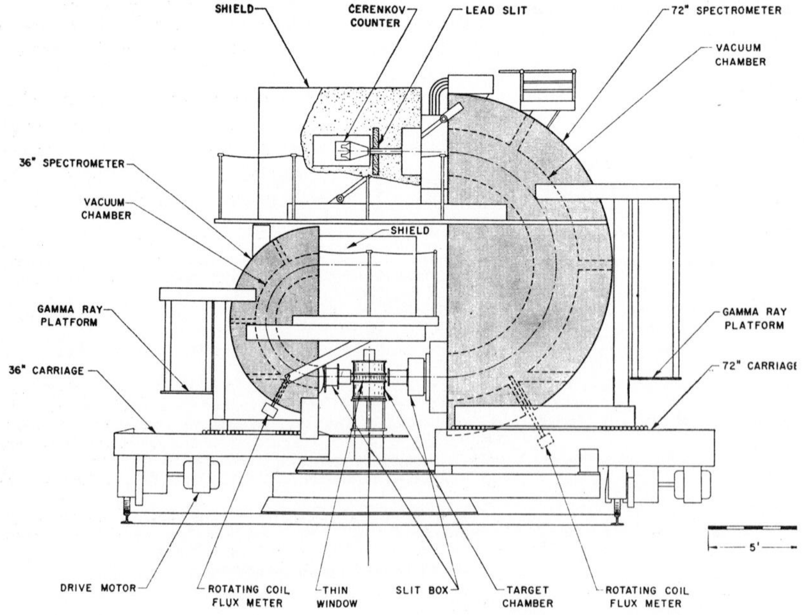

FIG. 2. This figure shows a side view of the spectrometers, target assembly, counters and shields, and other parts of the apparatus. The weight of the 72-in. spectrometer and the massive counter shield is in the neighborhood of 200 tons. The pulsed nature of the beam of the linear accelerator makes it necessary to use such a massive shield.

III. MEASUREMENTS OF ELASTIC CROSS SECTIONS

Most of the cross sections reported in this paper are entirely new and have been determined over a period of the last year. Some of the cross sections were recalculated from older published work[3,5,6] using new and better determinations of spectrometer characteristics and also new values of the radiative corrections.

All measurements given in this paper are absolute cross sections and were measured with the apparatus described in references 5–7 and also more thoroughly in reference 12. Figures 1 and 2 provide, respectively, schematic drawings of the experimental area and the double spectrometer system. The rotating coil flux meters, which are very important components of the two spectrometers, have been described briefly[13] and will be discussed subsequently in more detail.[14]

With such apparatus, which includes a Faraday cup for absolute normalization of the incident electron beam, we have taken 150 elastic scattering curves of appearance comparable with those shown in Figs. 3 and 4. The two elastic peaks chosen in Figs. 3 and 4 illustrate the quality of the small-angle and large-angle determinations. It is to be noted that the target material was polyethylene (CH_2). The carbon backgrounds were taken separately using graphite targets. The carbon background points have been fitted by least-squares analyses of the data.

In obtaining absolute data, various quantities and properties of the apparatus have to be determined with fair precision. For example, the momentum calibration of the magnetic spectrometer must be known, as well as the dispersion (number of inches per percent spread of momentum) at the exit slit of the spectrometer. Slit openings, target thickness, target density, etc., must all be determined with accuracy. A moving polyethylene target was used to prevent depletion of the hydrogen content through bombardment and heating of the target. It must also be known that the Faraday cup does not miss some of the beam which spreads after leaving the target. "Thick" target effects must be avoided in order to insure good geometry of the rays entering the spectrometer. One must also be sure that the entrance slits that are used are not too large so that parts of the electron trajectories do not hit the walls of the spectrometer or pass through a region in which the magnetic focusing properties are unsatisfactory.

The electron trajectories in the spectrometer were studied ("optics" study) by placing a fluorescent screen in the focal region of the spectrometer and viewing the

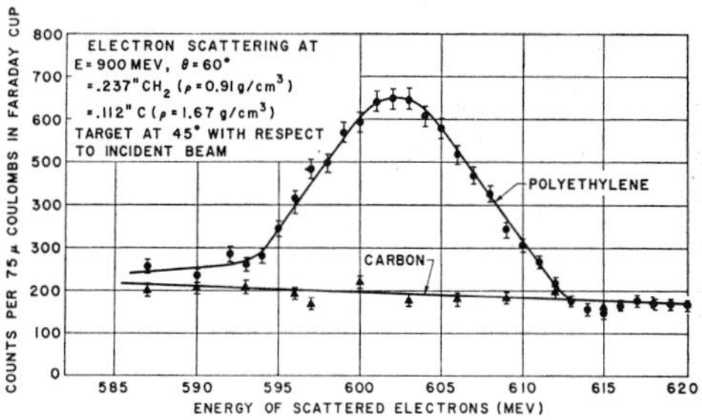

FIG. 3. An electron scattering peak observed at 60° from a polyethylene target at an incident energy of 900 Mev. This curve was taken with the 72-in. spectrometer and illustrates the quality of runs taken at the small angles. The value of the abscissa gives the directly-measured energy of the scattered electrons. The ordinate is proportional to the differential cross section in cm^2/sr Mev.

screen remotely with a television system. For this purpose the linear accelerator beam was led directly into the spectrometer, which was set at the zero degree setting of the scattering angle. A small deflecting magnet placed in front of the spectrometer bent the beam up down to simulate the entrance conditions of scattered electrons. The spectrometer scattering angle was varied slightly from zero to take care of the horizontal dimension. In the optics study, the angle of inclination of the focal plane, the movement of the focus with target position, the depth of focus, the energy calibration, the dispersion, etc., were investigated in detail.

It is further necessary to know the efficiency of the Čerenkov detector in order to be certain that any loss in this counter is recognized and allowed for. The Čerenkov counter efficiency was investigated with the help of a multi-channel analyzer and its pulse distributions examined during almost every run, and we believe the efficiency is so close to 100% that we have arbitrarily taken 100% as its efficiency. A Lucite Čerenkov counter and two different liquid Čerenkov counters were used in the efficiency studies and in the measurements and no discrepancies among the counters were

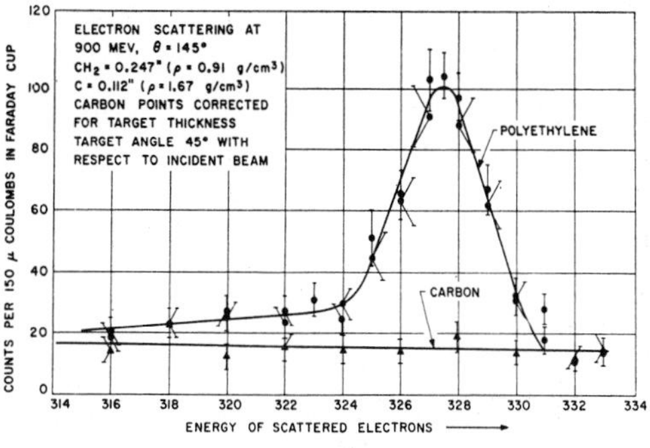

FIG. 4. This figure is similar to Fig. 3 but shows the quality of peaks taken at large angles, in this case, 145° at an incident energy of 900 Mev.

[12] R. Hofstadter, F. Bumiller, B. R. Chambers, and M. Croissiaux, *Proceedings of an International Conference on Instrumentation for High-Energy Physics* (Interscience Publishers, Inc., New York, 1961) pp. 310–315.

[13] F. Bumiller, J. F. Oeser, and E. B. Dally, *Proceedings of an International Conference on Instrumentation for High-Energy Physics* (Interscience Publishers, Inc., New York, 1961) pp. 308–309.

[14] F. Bumiller and J. F. Oeser (to be published).

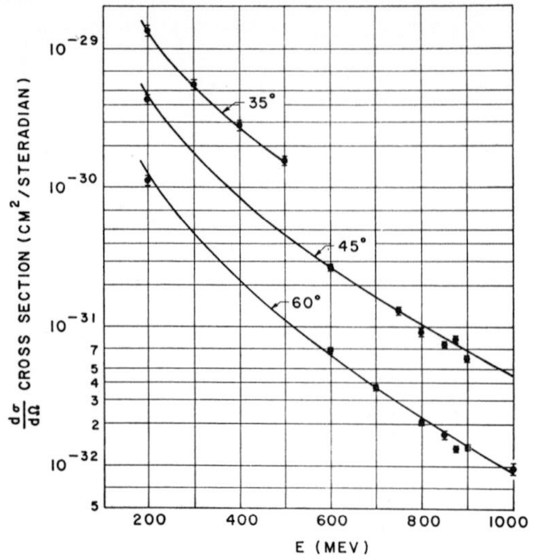

FIG. 5. The elastic electron-proton scattering cross sections in the range 35° to 60°. The experimental points are shown with appropriate error bars and correspond to the values in the sixth column of Table I. The solid line refers to the calculated cross sections (last column of Table I) using the form factors found in these experiments.

noted. All the above matters, and others not mentioned, have been studied in detail too great to be reproduced here. Various errors introduced at all stages in the measurements have been investigated and, e.g., such matters as the widths at half-maximum of the experimental peaks are thought to be understood. As a result of such considerations we present in the Appendix a discussion of some of their actual numerical values.

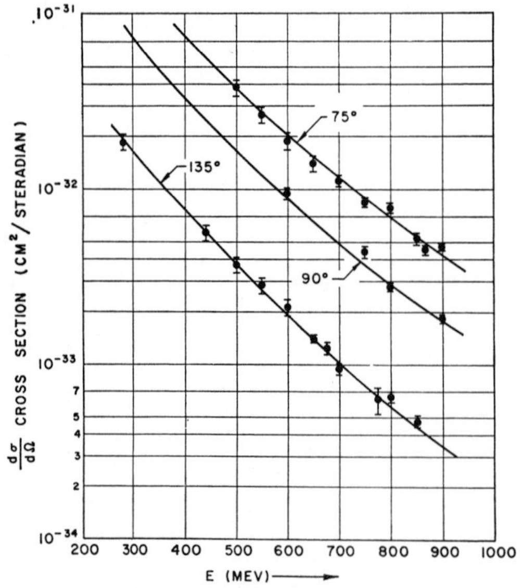

FIG. 6. This figure is similar to Fig. 5 and corresponds to the angular range 75° to 135°.

Since the elastic peaks are measured usually over a range extending only to energies 5% or less below the value at the peak, it is necessary to make radiative corrections for the area under the tail of the curve which is not examined. Such radiative corrections have been applied regularly in the past. Recently, an improved calculation has been made by Sobottka[15,16] which allows for the recoil of the struck proton. An even more accurate calculation has been carried out by Tsai.[17] Since the two calculations agree quite closely, we have chosen the simpler Sobottka correction to use with our data. Typical values of the radiative corrections including straggling are 30% at large angles (~135°) for a "ΔE" interval equal to the half-width and 25% at a small angle (~60°). We have usually used values of ΔE equal to the half-widths, since the polyethylene-carbon subtraction procedure involves a relatively large error in the tails of the proton curves beyond a few percent below the peak. The radiative corrections are, however, not sensitive to either angle or energy. As will be shown below, this implies that only very small errors in F_1 and F_2 can result from possible larger errors in the values of the radiative corrections. Thus the choice between the Sobottka calculation or the Tsai calculation has negligible influence on the form factors. This is also true whether one uses ΔE intervals of 1% or 5% consistently.

When the radiative corrections as well as other known corrections are applied to the data, we obtain the final results for the experimentally measured elastic cross sections shown in Table I. The results given in Table I are also shown in Figs. 5, 6, and 7 and appropriate error bars are attached to each experimental point. Although 150 individual peaks were measured, a number of determinations at the same energy and angle have been combined together to give a weighted mean cross section. Therefore Figs. 5, 6, and 7 show only 58 measured points.

A comparison of these results with those given in references 5, 6, and 7 shows that the earlier results were correct within experimental errors quoted in those references. However, certain small systematic differences can be observed: The newer small-angle measurements are generally a bit lower than the older ones. This is a direct consequence of new and improved knowledge of the energy calibration and dispersion properties of the 72-in. spectrometer. The new large-angle measurements are generally in good agreement with the older measurements but a little higher on the average.

We wish to call particular attention to the high-energy results at 145° shown in Fig. 7. The cross sec-

[15] S. Sobottka, Phys. Rev. **118**, 831 (1960).
[16] S. Sobottka, thesis, Stanford University, 1960 (unpublished).
[17] Y.-S. Tsai, Phys. Rev. **122**, 1898 (1961). Note that straggling corrections are not calculated in this paper.

TABLE I. Experimental elastic cross sections and other pertinent data.

E (Mev)	θ (degree)	q^2 (f^{-2})	% radiative correction	%ΔE used in rad. corr.	$(d\sigma/d\Omega)_{exp}$ (10^{-32} cm²/sr)	Possible error	Possible error in %	$(d\sigma/d\Omega)_{calc}$[a] (10^{-32} cm²/sr)
200	35	0.358	15.0	4.5	1340	110	8.2	1330
	45	0.566	15.0	4.5	430	35	8.2	452
	60	0.928	16.0	4.5	113	9	8.0	126
280	135	4.42	17.0	4.5	1.86	0.18	9.7	1.88
300	35	0.790	16.0	4.5	550	44	8.0	538
400	35	1.38	16.0	4.5	281	23	8.2	271
440	135	9.38	18.0	4.5	0.565	0.056	10.0	0.585
500	35	2.12	17.0	4.5	156	12	7.7	153
	75	6.82	18.0	4.5	3.80	0.38	10.0	3.79
	135	11.48	17.0	4.5	0.370	0.037	10.0	0.380
550	75	8.03	18.0	4.5	2.65	0.26	10.0	2.76
	135	13.26	17.0	4.5	0.285	0.029	10.0	0.270
600	45	4.56	27.6	1.46	26.5	1.4	5.3	26.4
	60	7.00	25.9	1.87	6.70	0.41	6.1	6.19
	75	9.30	16.0	4.5	1.88	0.19	10.0	2.06
	90	11.28	28.9	1.57	0.944	0.071	7.5	0.878
	135	15.09	30.5	1.12	0.212	0.023	10.8	0.188
	145	15.55	30.3	1.09	0.141	0.022	15.6	0.155
650	75	10.63	19.0	4.5	1.40	0.14	10.0	1.56
	135	16.97	29.3	1.34	0.140	0.007	5.0	0.138
675	135	17.93	30.6	1.22	0.123	0.009	7.3	0.120
700	60	9.17	27.5	1.76	3.62	0.16	4.4	3.63
	75	12.01	25.8	2.01	1.12	0.074	6.6	1.18
	135	18.9	30.3	1.23	0.940	0.072	7.6	0.102
	145	19.42	29.0	1.35	0.0747	0.0032	4.3	0.0851
750	45	6.86	25.6	1.94	13.0	0.92	7.1	13.2
	75	13.45	26.3	1.93	0.839	0.049	5.8	0.910
	90	16.06	26.1	2.15	0.439	0.034	7.7	0.368
	145	21.42	30.4	1.15	0.0643	0.0039	6.1	0.0650
775	135	21.83	30.6	1.19	0.0630	0.0109	17.3	0.0675
	145	22.42	31.3	1.06	0.0616	0.0069	11.2	0.0560
800	45	7.70	25.4	2.12	9.12	0.65	7.1	10.3
	60	11.52	25.5	2.08	2.07	0.08	3.9	2.24
	75	14.93	23.8	2.37	0.782	0.052	6.6	0.684
	90	17.74	27.0	1.91	0.277	0.012	4.3	0.287
	135	22.85	27.6	1.51	0.0655	0.0043	6.6	0.0593
	145	23.44	30.2	1.18	0.0513	0.0031	6.0	0.0485
825	145	24.44	29.2	1.28	0.0425	0.0054	12.7	0.0450
835	145	24.86	30.0	1.20	0.0447	0.0026	5.8	0.0395
850	45	8.59	25.1	2.21	7.47	0.26	3.5	8.30
	60	12.77	26.7	1.90	1.68	0.12	7.1	1.75
	75	16.46	24.5	2.38	0.520	0.037	7.1	0.545
	135	24.88	26.6	1.56	0.470	0.031	6.6	0.450
	145	25.50	29.8	1.19	0.338	0.026	7.7	0.368
866	75	16.93	26.6	1.97	0.452	0.028	6.2	0.500
875	45	9.05	23.7	2.49	8.15	0.47	5.8	7.45
	60	13.42	26.4	2.05	1.34	0.058	4.3	1.57
	145	26.50	31.2	1.16	0.0315	0.0025	7.9	0.0320
900	45	9.51	25.8	2.14	5.92	0.33	5.6	6.70
	60	14.06	27.0	1.96	1.37	0.057	4.2	1.39
	75	18.02	24.8	2.36	0.470	0.017	3.6	0.429
	90	21.24	27.1	2.00	0.183	0.010	5.5	0.179
	145	27.57	27.6	1.45	0.0296	0.0020	6.7	0.0269
925	145	28.62	30.4	1.13	0.0269	0.0024	8.9	0.0246
950	145	29.68	29.3	1.26	0.0269	0.0044	16.3	0.0212
975	95	24.90	29.2	1.68	0.100	0.008	8.0	0.098
	145	30.78	30.8	1.07	0.0265	0.0033	12.4	0.0185
1000	60	16.75	24.8	2.41	0.957	0.081	8.5	0.896

[a] Refer to the definition in Sec. IV.

tions above 875 Mev show a flattening which was already noted in references 5, 6, and 7. We shall return to this matter in the subsequent discussion.

IV. PROTON FORM FACTORS

The absolute cross sections given in Table I and in Figs. 5, 6, and 7 can now be used to calculate the electromagnetic form factors of the proton as indicated in Sec. II. We show in Figs. 8 and 9 two examples in which several ellipses intersect in a common region. There are no examples among all our cases for $q^2 \leqslant 25$ which fail to give intersections. We have employed the following procedure in making the computations for the proton ellipses:

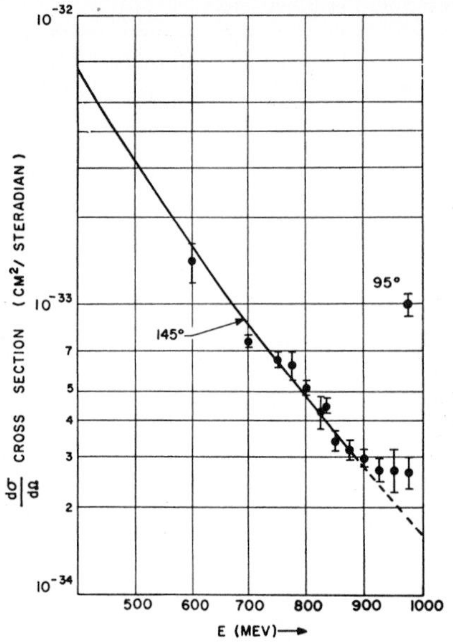

FIG. 7. This figure is similar to Fig. 5 and corresponds to the scattering angle 145°. A single point at 95° is also shown.

We have first passed smooth curves through the experimental points of Figs. 5, 6, and 7, so that at each angle we have a definite behavior of the cross sections. [In one case where we have an isolated point (975 Mev, 95°), the appropriate cross section was used with another member of a pair to find the corresponding values of F_1 and F_2.] Then we can select pairs of values

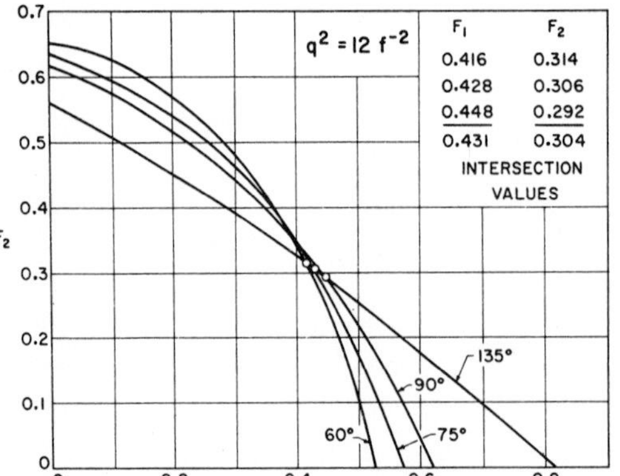

FIG. 8. This figure shows sections of elliptical arcs in the F_1, F_2 plane corresponding to the measured cross sections at the appropriate experimental conditions. The useful intersections are indicated by small circles. Note the relatively sharp intersections of small-angle and large-angle ellipses. Neighboring angles give less well determined intersections for a given experimental accuracy. "Average" intersections can be found from such plots and determine average values of F_1 and F_2. The figures for determining the averages are shown in the inset.

(E_1,θ_1), (E_2,θ_2) from which to find intersections. As explained previously,[10,11] a small-angle cross-section ellipse intersects sharply and cleanly with an ellipse corresponding to a large-angle cross section and this type of intersection has naturally been accorded the greatest weight in our form factor analysis. When two cross sections at nearby angles are studied the intersection develops into a near-tangency and the F_1, F_2 determination can involve large errors. This behavior may be seen in Figs. 8 and 9. In Fig. 10 we illustrate the effect of experimental errors on the determination of the form factors corresponding to possible errors of $\pm 10\%$ in the cross sections. Figure 10 also shows that if the error in the cross section at the two points is in the same direction, the resulting form factor error is very small. This explains why many possible errors which are in the same direction for small and large angles have a

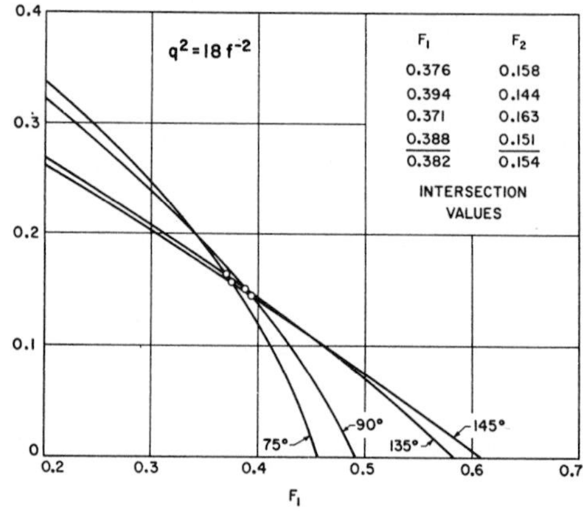

FIG. 9. This figure is similar to Fig. 8 and shows the quality of the intersections found in these experiments.

tendency to cancel out. Such would be the case for radiative corrections.

We chose eleven values of q^2 and determined at each value of q^2 the mean values of F_1 and F_2 formed by the many intersections of the corresponding ellipses. These F_1, F_2 values are then plotted, with their experimental errors, as a function of q^2, and a smooth curve can be drawn through the points. From the two form-factor curves we can then calculate a "trial" set of cross sections according to Eq. (4). By inspection we may note where the "trial" cross sections deviate most from the experiment. A little familiarity with this type of calculation immediately shows how one can get an improved fit to the data. By adjusting the F_1, F_2 vs q^2 curves a little up or down, one may obtain a second trial set of form factors and cross sections, and we may continue in the same manner. This process converges very rapidly so that within the present experimental error there is no further point in refining the fit. This second set of form factors is the set from which we calculated cross sections labeled $(d\sigma/d\Omega)_{calc}$. Table I, last column, gives this set of cross sections, which furnishes a "smoothed" set of experimental cross sections.

A "final" pair of form factor curves is shown in Fig. 11. The error bars attached to the points represent, in our best judgment, the limits of errors of the small-angle and large-angle intersections of ellipses. These limits of errors are definitely smaller than those obtainable from intersections corresponding to neighboring scattering angles. We believe that it is unrealistic, considering the present accuracy of the experiments, to give significant weight to the intersections corresponding to neighboring scattering angles.

Table II presents the numerical values of the form factors found in the above manner and shown in Fig. 11. Figure 11 and Table II are, in an important sense, the end products of this experiment.

The values of the proton form factors found from the data of this paper are in good agreement with those presented earlier[5–7] and lie within the experimental error

TABLE II. Proton form factors.[a]

q^2 in f^{-2}	F_1	$\pm\Delta F_1$	F_2	$\pm\Delta F_2$
4	0.702	0.013	0.597	0.011
6	0.602	0.009	0.487	0.009
8	0.523	0.015	0.440	0.012
10	0.491	0.019	0.343	0.013
12	0.431	0.017	0.304	0.012
14	0.396	0.017	0.261	0.011
16	0.387	0.014	0.202	0.013
18	0.382	0.012	0.154	0.010
20	0.364	0.016	0.133	0.018
22	0.350	0.006	0.100	0.008
25	0.333	0.008	0.070	0.010

[a] The errors in ΔF_1 and ΔF_2 may be approximately twice as large as given in this table, provided they are correlated. See the relevant remarks in the legend to Fig. 11.

illustrated in Fig. 1 of reference 7. In the case of the present data the curve for F_2 is apparently not about to pass through zero at $q^2=25$ f^{-2} but may do so at a larger value of q^2. In the case of F_1 the new behavior at large q^2 indicates a small but definite negative slope at $q^2\simeq 25$ f^{-2} and a horizontal tangent is probably no longer likely in this region.

The question naturally arises whether these new results for $F_1(q^2)$ modify the older value of the rms radius of the electric charge distribution, which was measured as 0.80±0.04 f by Hofstadter *et al.*[18] or the single determination of McAllister[19] which was 0.71±0.12 f. Although we have made no special effort to measure an rms radius by concentrating on low values of q^2, an investigation of the slope of the present F_1 curve at the low values of q^2 shows that the rms radius is 0.75±0.05 f, in reasonable agreement with the above values.

[18] R. Hofstadter, F. Bumiller, and M. R. Yearian, Revs. Modern Phys. 30, 482 (1958).

[19] R. W. McAllister, thesis, Stanford University, 1960 (unpublished).

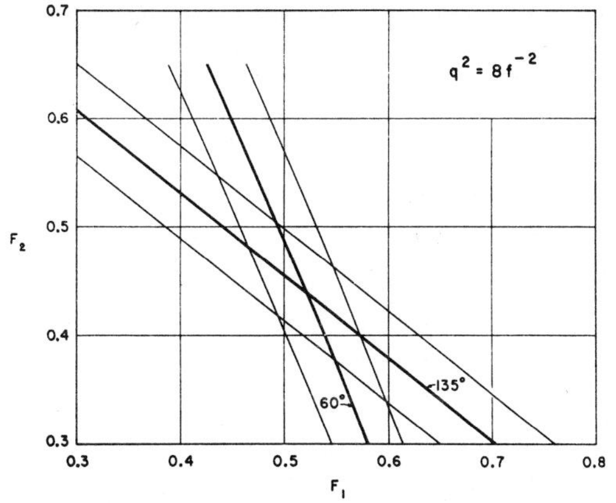

FIG. 10. This figure shows the effect of experimental errors ±10% in the cross sections on the determinations of F_1 and F_2. Note the wide variations in the form factors if the errors have opposite signs and the smaller variations if the two errors have the same sign.

It is a remarkable fact that the experimental cross sections are very close, at all values of q^2, to the well-known "exponential" form factor behavior.[2,4,18]

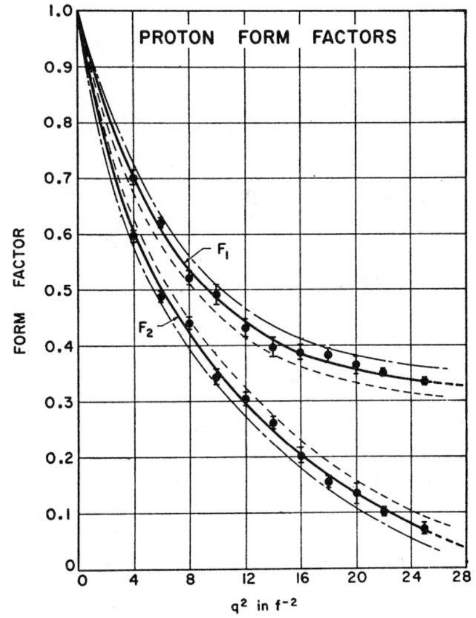

FIG. 11. This figure shows the form factors, and their errors, as found in these experiments. The corresponding values of F_1 and F_2 are also given in Table II. These same form factors have been used in the calculation of the last column of Table I. It will be noted that two dashed curves lie between the F_1, F_2 central-value solid lines. If the error limits are correlated so that they move in opposite directions, as indicated by the dashed limits, the corresponding cross sections will remain consistent with experiment. A similar statement holds for the two dot-dashed curves lying outside the F_1, F_2 central-value solid lines. Though we have not studied the correlated error question in detail we feel that the dashed and dot-dashed curves give reasonable representations of the present error limits of F_1 and F_2. Further work on errors is in progress.

The rms magnetic radius is not as well known as the electric radius, but a rough evaluation of the slope of the $F_2(q^2)$ vs q^2 curve indicates that the rms magnetic radius is 0.97 ± 0.10 f. An experiment is now in progress to try to improve the latter value.

V. INTERNAL CONSISTENCY OF THE DATA

As previously remarked, a consistent behavior of all intersections of the proton ellipses would lead to unique values of F_1 and F_2, within, of course, experimental error. Up to values of $q^2\cong25$ f^{-2}, wherever we have been able to test this question, we have observed unique values of F_1 and F_2, that is, consistency of the experiment with Rosenbluth theory. In the region between $q^2\cong25$ and 31 f^{-2}, that is, at large angles ($\cong145°$) and high energies, we do not have the ability to form intersections using higher-energy-smaller-angle data of our own, and so we cannot test the validity of the theory in this region. However, the flattening-off of the data at $\theta=145°$ between 875 and 975 Mev suggests that something strange is happening here. This flattening has been observed on several occasions. Our form-factor analysis (Table II and Fig. 11) gives the dashed behavior in the region >875 Mev in Fig. 7. We observe the rather large deviations between experiment and a continuation of "theory" in this region.

At the Washington meeting of the American Physical Society in April, 1961, we called attention to the observation that the flattening observed in these experiments at $(d\sigma/d\Omega)\cong2.7\times10^{-34}$ cm^2/sr, and in particular the point at 975 Mev and 145° ($q^2\cong30.7$ f^{-2}), is barely consistent, if not inconsistent, with a cross-section value taken from some recent measurements reported by the Cornell group[20] at 112° and ~1050 Mev between two measured points at 1000 Mev and 1100 Mev. That is, no real intersection is obtained for our 975-Mev ellipse and the Cornell ellipse. Any failure of this kind in finding consistency in the form factors would imply either: (a) some correction to the Rosenbluth formula Eq. (1) is needed, such as, e.g., one due to two-photon-virtual-exchanges, or (b) a breakdown of quantum electrodynamics, or (c) some errors in the experimental determinations. Since the flattening occurs at the extreme limits of our experimental measurements it is certainly possible that our results in this region are open to error. We do not think that this is the case because we performed various independent tests to check these results. It is to be noted that the points in the flattened region were *not* used at all in our form factor determinations. It may also still be true that the flattening represents a diffraction effect (where F_2 may go through zero) but we cannot tell that this is so at the present time. More accurate experimentation is desirable to check consistency of the proton form factors at many different values of q^2.

[20] D. N. Olson, H. F. Schopper, and R. R. Wilson, Phys. Rev. Letters **6**, 286 (1961).

VI. SIGNIFICANCE OF THE FINDINGS

Our investigation of the proton's form factors has been motivated by the desire to find a self-consistent set of values of F_1 and F_2 which gives a complete description of the behavior of an electron with the proton at the corresponding interaction vertex. For a Dirac particle of spin $\frac{1}{2}$, these two form factors are adequate to describe the interaction, as has been shown by many authors. We believe we have succeeded in our aim at least as far as $q^2\cong25$ f^{-2}. Thus the phenomenological form factors F_1, F_2 are now known in the range $0\leqslant q^2\leq25$ f^{-2} with fair accuracy. In many respects this goal has now been perhaps sufficiently well achieved at this stage of development of "fundamental" particle theory.

On the other hand, it seems likely that at least the outer parts of the electromagnetic structure of the proton are describable in terms of a more or less standard geometrical picture. Furthermore, we believe that there is definite heuristic value in having ideas about a geometrical model of a proton.

Such a model was proposed recently[9,21] in terms of a dispersion-relations suggestion for simple types of nucleon form factors associated with pion-pion interactions. Isotopic scalar and isotopic vector form factors were deduced from both experimental proton and neutron[22] form factors. The presently-determined form factors are sufficiently close to those used in the formulation of the model[9] that we have no reason, on the score of proton form factors, to alter the model or the conclusions of Hofstadter and Herman.[9]

VIII. CONCLUSIONS

(1) The splitting of the proton form factors has been confirmed.

(2) The qualitative behavior of F_1 and F_2 as functions of q^2 has been determined in the range $0\leq q^2\leq25$ f^{-2}.

(3) Good consistency in the determination of proton form factors has been found in the range $0\leq q^2\leq25$ f^{-2}. This finding serves as a support for the validity of quantum electrodynamics up to this value of q^2. Thus it is probable that quantum electrodynamics is valid at distances lying between the nucleon and pion Compton wavelengths.

(4) Some evidence for a partial breakdown in the self-consistency of the proton form factors may have been uncovered at large scattering angles (145°) at $q^2\cong30$ f^{-2}.

(5) In the range $0\leq q^2\leq25$ f^{-2} the proton form factors are in agreement with the proposed nucleon models of Hofstadter and Herman,[9] although the present results alone do not require such a model.

(6) The present results for the rms electric radius of

[21] S. Bergia, A. Stanghellini, S. Fubini, and C. Villi, Phys. Rev. Letters **6**, 367 (1961).

[22] R. Hofstadter, C. deVries, and R. Herman, Phys. Rev. Letters **6**, 290 (1961).

the proton are in reasonable agreement with the older results.[18,19]

ACKNOWLEDGMENTS

We wish to acknowledge with thanks the enthusiastic support we have had from the following members of the staff of the High-Energy Physics Laboratory: H. Dahl, G. Gilbert, C. Olson, M. Ryneveld, L. Towle, P. Wilson, and E. Wright. We are especially thankful to Mr. T. Janssens who gave us a great deal of help in using the method of intersecting ellipses. One of us (M. Croissiaux) wishes to acknowledge the kind support of Professor S. Gorodetzky and the Centre National de la Recherche Scientifique (France) in permitting him to work at Stanford University.

APPENDIX. ERRORS IN THE CROSS SECTIONS

A. The errors in part A appear in all cross sections.

(1) Incident energy in absolute units: ±0.5%.

(2) Scattering angle, θ: ±0.1°. The errors in the cross sections vary from ≈1.3% at $\theta=35°$ to ≈0.2% at $\theta=145°$.

(3) Incident beam integration: ±3%. The beam integration is influenced by errors in the Faraday cup, involving the measured voltage produced by the integrated charge, the value of the integration capacitor, and the automatic shutoff mechanism.

(4) Number of protons in the target: ±1.5%. This number depends on the density of the target material, the target thickness and uniformity, and the target angle.

(5) Solid angle: ±0.5%. Here we consider only the possible errors in the settings of the slits and their mean distances from the target. Slit openings permissible for satisfactory "optical" performance of the spectrometers have been determined experimentally.

(6) Dispersion: ±1%.

(7) Energy calibration of the spectrometers in absolute units: ±0.5%.

(8) Radiative corrections: ±2%.

B. The integrated number of counts under an elastic peak is influenced by the carbon subtraction. For example, the relevant numbers for two individual cross-section curves are:

	900 Mev, 60°	900 Mev, 145°
CH_2 counts	9726	432
C counts	4370	110
H counts	5356±119	322±23

and lead to pure statistical errors of these numbers which are 2.22% and 7.14%, respectively. Most cross sections were measured more than once. In the determination of an average cross section, the error in the proton counts was used as a weight factor.

C. Although we believe that the items given in parts A and B contain all accountable errors, we found in many cases that the error in the average exceeded that predicted by pure statistical arguments. Probable sources of this behavior are instabilities in the counting electronics and in the widths of the elastic peaks under those conditions when a spectrometer field control was not available. We therefore combined the mean error of the average with the statistical errors from parts A and B and this is the error given in Table I.

PAPER 78

EVIDENCE FOR A THREE-PION RESONANCE NEAR 550 Mev*

A. Pevsner, R. Kraemer, M. Nussbaum, C. Richardson, P. Schlein, R. Strand, and T. Toohig
The Johns Hopkins University, Baltimore, Maryland

and

M. Block, A. Engler, R. Gessaroli, and C. Meltzer
Northwestern University, Evanston, Illinois
(Received November 10, 1961)

A study has been under way of multipion resonances in $\pi^+ + d$ reactions observed in the Lawrence Radiation Laboratory 72-in. bubble chamber exposed to a 1.23-Bev/c pion beam from the Bevatron. A preliminary report on this research was given at the Aix-en-Provence Conference on Elementary Particles[1] where the existence of the ω^0 meson reported by the Berkeley group[2] was confirmed. Since then these data have been substantially increased, although the experiment is still in progress. The existence of a second neutral 3-pion resonance with a mass of approximately 550 Mev is indicated by this larger sample of events.

Many authors[3] have speculated on the existence of neutral, strongly interacting bosons of mass of the order of 3-4 m_π, in order to fit the data for nucleon form factors obtained from electron scattering experiments. These bosons could be readily identified experimentally in the reaction

$$\pi^+ + d \rightarrow p + p + X^0. \qquad (1)$$

In order to observe the possible decay mode,

$$X^0 \rightarrow \pi^+ + \pi^- + \pi^0, \qquad (2)$$

we consider the reaction

$$\pi^+ + d \rightarrow p + p + \pi^+ + \pi^- + \pi^0. \qquad (3)$$

Only events where both protons are visible and at least one proton stops in the chamber with a range less than 15 cm were accepted for analysis.[4]

The events were measured with a digitized microscope and reconstructed by the Berkeley PANG program. A kinematic fit[5] was obtained for the assumed π^0 using the KICK program, and the effective mass of the fitted 3-pion system was then calculated. In order to check the identification of the π^0, we have calculated the missing neutral mass for events which fit our criteria. An ideogram[6] for this missing neutral mass is given in Fig. 1 for the first 199 of our events.

Figure 2 is a histogram of the effective mass of the 3-pion system for our 233 events. An average mass uncertainty on a given event is ~±20 Mev. The large peak near 770 Mev is clearly identifiable as the ω^0. Another large peak in the 3-pion mass plot of Fig. 2 is seen near 550 Mev, which strongly suggests the existence of a second 3-pion resonance (or particle). We shall hereafter refer to this particle as η.

In order to estimate the number of events in this peak which are reasonably due to the η particle, we make the following interpretation of our data. We believe the impulse approximation is reasonably valid because of the loose structure of the deuteron. Thus the basic reaction we are looking at is

$$\pi^+ + n \rightarrow p + X^0, \qquad (4a)$$

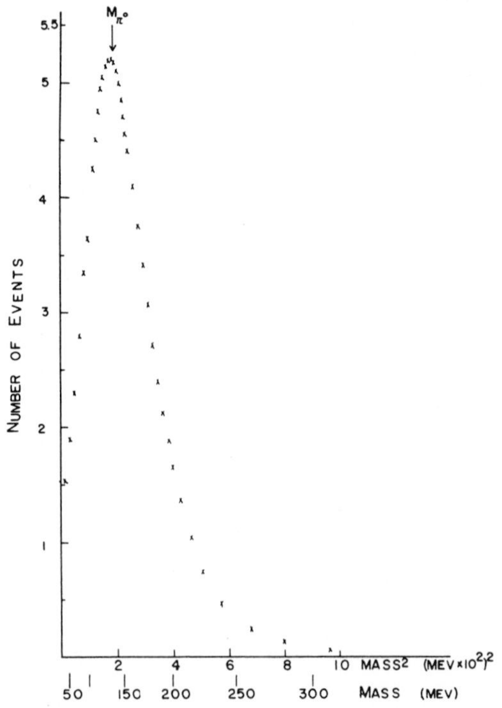

FIG. 1. Ideogram of the missing mass in the reaction ($\pi^+ + d \rightarrow p + p + \pi^+ + \pi^- +$ missing mass) for 199 events which meet the selection criteria.

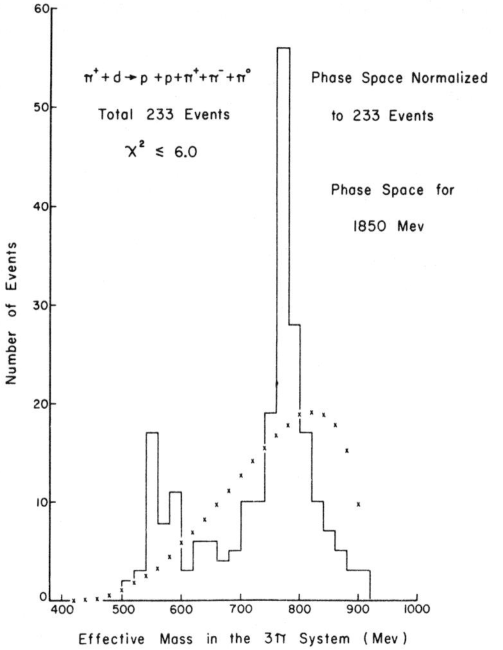

FIG. 2. Histogram of the effective mass of the three-pion system for 233 events.

where

$$X^0 \to \pi^+ + \pi^- + \pi^0. \quad (4b)$$

We have calculated the Lorentz-invariant phase space[7] for the 3-pion mass from the background reaction to (4a), i.e.,

$$\pi^+ + n \to p + \pi^+ + \pi^- + \pi^0, \quad (5)$$

using the experimental average of the total energy in the p-3π center-of-mass system (1850 Mev). This curve, normalized to the total number of events, is plotted in Fig. 2.

Clearly, because of the presence of the ω^0 particle at 770 Mev, such a normalization of phase space yields a gross overestimate of events expected near 550 Mev. Between 540 and 600 Mev there are 36 events in the experimental distribution, whereas the overestimated phase space would account for 12.

An analysis of the data, which takes into account the spread in errors on the individual events on the histogram, gives a mass of approximately 764 Mev with a half-width at half maximum of ≤ 20 Mev for the ω^0 and a mass of ~546 Mev with a half-width at half maximum of ≤ 25 Mev for the η.

An attempt is being made to determine the isotopic spin for both peaks by studing the reaction

$$\pi^+ + d \to p + \pi^+ + \pi^+ + \pi^- + n. \quad (6)$$

Only 61 events were found in an analysis of one-half the film represented by Fig. 2. The low yield is probably indicative of the lack of any resonance in the isotopic spin states 1 and 2. This is in accord with the Berkeley assignment of $T = 0$ to the ω^0.

A search for the $\pi^0 + \gamma$ decay mode of the ω^0 and η is being carried out by a study of events of the type

$$\pi^+ + d \to p + p + \text{(neutrals)}. \quad (7)$$

The results will be available shortly.

The proton form factor F_{1p} obtained from electron scattering experiments[8] cannot be fitted using only the ω^0 and ρ particles.[9] However, a three-pion resonance of mass $\leq 4m\pi$ having $T = 0$ and spin 1^- would make a fit to the data possible.[10] With the film on hand we expect to more than double our statistics, so that a determination of the isotopic spin and spin of the η may be possible to see whether it fits these theories.

The authors wish to thank Dr. Luis Alvarez, Dr. Edwin McMillan, Dr. Frank Crawford, and the staff of the Lawrence Radiation Laboratory for their cooperation and for the facilities which made this experiment possible. We also wish to thank Dr. Walter Selove of the University of Pennsylvania and Dr. Leon Madansky and Dr. Gordon Feldman of The Johns Hopkins University for helpful discussions, and Dr. A. Rosenfeld, Dr. P. Berge, and Mr. R. Harvey of the Lawrence Radiation Laboratory, Mrs. Doris Ellis of The Johns Hopkins University, and Dr. David Onley and Mr. Arthur Kovacs of Duke University, for their invaluable help with the computer programs.

---

*Work supported by the U. S. Air Force Office of Scientific Research, the National Science Foundation, and Office of Naval Research.

[1]A. Pevsner, R. Kraemer, M. Nussbaum, P. Schlein, T. Toohig, M. Block, A. Kovacs, and C. Meltzer, Proceedings of the 1961 Conference on Elementary Particles, Aix-en-Provence (to be published).

[2]B. Maglić, L. Alvarez, A. Rosenfeld, and M. L. Stevenson, Phys. Rev. Letters 7, 178 (1961).

[3]Y. Nambu, Phys. Rev. 106, 1366 (1957); G. F. Chew, Phys. Rev. Letters 4, 142 (1960); J. J. Sakurai, Ann. Phys. 11, 1 (1960); S. Bergia, A. Stanghellini, S. Fubini, and C. Villi, Phys. Rev. Letters 6, 367 (1961).

[4]In a sample representing one-fourth of the film reported here, the requirement that one of the protons had to stop with a range ≤ 15 cm was removed. The results agree within statistics with those reported here.

[5]Events were accepted for analysis which fit the following criteria: (a) $\chi^2 \leq 6$ for the hypothesis $\pi^+ + d \rightarrow p + p + \pi^+ + \pi^- + \pi^0$. (b) $\chi^2 \geq 25$ for the hypothesis $\pi^+ + d \rightarrow p + p + \pi^+ + \pi^-$. (c) If the nonstopping proton had a momentum ≥ 700 Mev/c, where it becomes difficult to differentiate a proton from a π^+ by ionization in this chamber, then the χ^2 had to be greater than 15 for the hypothesis $\pi^+ + d \rightarrow p + n + \pi^+ + \pi^+ + \pi^-$, which is another background reaction under these circumstances.

[6]The ideogram was calculated in units of mass squared since our experimental errors are Gaussian in this representation. Each event was given a constant-area Gaussian distribution.

[7]M. M. Block, Phys. Rev. 101, 796 (1956); P. Srivastava and G. Sudarshan, Phys. Rev. 110, 765 (1958).

[8]R. Hofstadter and R. Herman, Phys. Rev. Letters 6, 293 (1961); R. M. Littauer, H. F. Schopper, and R. R. Wilson, Phys. Rev. Letters 7, 141 (1961).

[9]S. Fubini, Proceedings of the 1961 Conference on Elementary Particles, Aix-en-Provence (to be published); P. T. Matthews, ibid.; G. Breit, Proc. Natl. Acad. Sci. U. S. 46, 746 (1960); Y. Fujii, Progr. Theoret. Phys. (Kyoto) 21, 232 (1959).

[10]G. Feldman, T. Fulton, and K. C. Wali (private communication); see also J. Sakurai, Phys. Rev. Letters 7, 355 (1961).

PAPER 79

ELECTROMAGNETIC STRUCTURE OF PIONS AND NUCLEONS

S. FUBINI

Istituto di Fisica dell'Università Padova (Italy)

CERN - Geneva (Switzerland)

INTRODUCTION -

Giving a report on the electromagnetic structure of pions and nucleons is at the same time very pleasant and rather dangerous. It is very pleasant since in the last year very important progress both experimental and theoretical has been achieved, on the other side many questions are still open and I have to take the risk that some of the things I am going to say might soon become out of date.

In the first part of my talk I shall recall the definitions of the form factors, their connection with different kinds of experiments and those general properties which can be rigorously deducted from theory and that will constitute the basis of the subsequent phenomenological treatment.

Part two deals with the different theoretical approximations which are necessary to extract the form factors from experiment especially in the case of unstable particles like the neutron and the pion.

Finally, in Part three I shall discuss the recent phenomenological attempts to understand the nucleon form factors and to correlate those data with the ones coming from different experiments.

In the preparation of this talk I had much help from Dr. A. Stanghellini to whom I wish to express my most sincere thanks.

I - GENERAL PROPERTIES

1 - ELECTRON SCATTERING -

Let us consider elastic electron scattering by a nucleon or a pion. Since the electron interacts only electromagnetically, the scattering matrix will depend on the exchange of one or many photons between the electron and the nucleon (pion).

The approximation of keeping only the one photon exchange term is well justified at the energies and momentum transfers reached in the present experiments, the evaluation of the two photon exchange contribution will be discussed in part II.

The one photon exchange graph is represented in figure 1 :

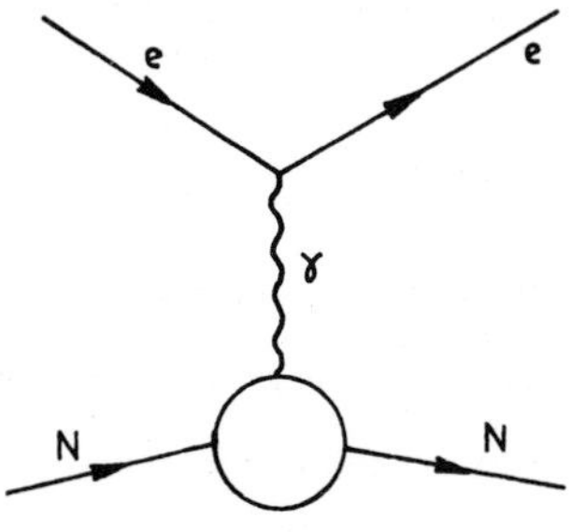

Figure 1

It gives the (eN) scattering amplitude as the product of the electron-photon vertex function, of the photon propagator and of the nucleon-photon vertex function :

$$\langle e_2 N_2 | T | e_1 N_1 \rangle = \frac{(\bar{u}_2 \gamma_\mu u_1) \langle N_2 | J_\mu | N_1 \rangle}{k^2} \tag{I.1}$$

where u_2 and u_1 are the initial and final electron spinors and :

$$k^2 = (e_1 - e_2)^2 = (N_2 - N_1)^2 = t \tag{I.2}$$

is the four momentum transfer between electron and nucleon.

The only unknown of the problem depending in an essential manner on the strong interactions responsible for the complicated structure of the nucleon is the photon-nucleon vertex $\langle N_2 | J_\mu | N_1 \rangle$ which represents the expectation value of the electromagnetic current in the physical nucleon state.

Invariance under Lorentz transformations and under time and space inversions allows to express the photon-nucleon vertex in terms of two functions of the momentum transfer t as follows :

$$\langle N_2 | J_\mu | N_1 \rangle = i \bar{v}_2 \, [G_1(t) \gamma_\mu + G_2(t) \sigma_{\mu\nu} k_\nu] v_1 \tag{I.3}$$

where v_1 and v_2 are the initial and final nucleon spinors.

The form factors G_i are still operators in the isotopic spin space. One defines the isovector and isoscalar form factors as follows :

$$G_i = G_i^S + G_i^V \tau_3 \tag{I.4}$$

and so the proton and neutron form factors are given by :

$$\begin{cases} G_i^P = G_i^S + G_i^V \\ G_i^N = G_i^S - G_i^V \end{cases} \tag{I.5}$$

From Eqs. (I.1) and (I.3) one obtains immediately the well-known expression for the electron-nucleon scattering cross-sections :

$$\sigma_n = \frac{\sigma_N^0}{l^2} \left[G_1^2 + \frac{t}{2 M^2} (G_1 + 2 M G_2)^2 \, tg^2 \frac{\vartheta}{2} + 4 M^2 G_2^2 \right] \tag{I.6}$$

where σ_N^0 is the cross-section due to a point nucleon.

This is the Rosenbluth formula giving the (eN) cross-section in terms of the nucleon form factors. We wish to point out that the fact that the cross-section, which depends both on the electron energy and angle, is given in terms of two functions of one single variable, gives a very strong restriction implying, e.g. that the results of three different experiments with the same value of the momentum transfer must depend only on two numbers.

This restriction depends essentially on the fact that only one particle is exchanged between electron and nucleon. The two photon exchange corrections will depend both on the electron energy and angle and so by making several measurements at different energies but at the same t one has a way of testing experimentally the validity of the one photon exchange approximation. For the electron-pion scattering matrix element one has a formula analogous to (I.1) which will now contain the pion-photon vertex function. Using the same invariance arguments of the nucleon case one can write :

$$\langle \pi_1 | J_\mu | \pi_2 \rangle = \frac{(\pi_1 + \pi_2)_\mu}{(4 \pi_1^0 \pi_2^0)^{1/2}} G_\pi(t) \, T_3 \tag{I.7}$$

where π_1 and π_2 are the initial and final pion momenta (and π_1^0, π_2^0 their time components), $G_\pi(t)$ is the electromagnetic form factor of the pion and T_3 is the third component of the isospin of the pion. Eq. (I.7) shows that the π^0 has no electromagnetic structure unlike the neutron. This important difference depends on the fact that the π^0 is a self-charge conjugate particle (on the other hand the K_0 like the neutron would have electromagnetic structure).

The electron-pion scattering cross-section is given by :

$$\sigma_{l\pi} = \frac{\sigma^{o}_{\pi}}{1^2} G^2_{\pi}(t) \tag{I.8}$$

where σ^{o}_{π} is the cross-section due to a point pion charge distribution. At zero momentum transfer the functions $G_{i}(t)$ tend to the well-known limits given by the nucleon and pion total charge and of the nucleon anomalous magnetic moment :

$$G^{P}_1(O) = e, \qquad G^{N}_1(O) = 0, \qquad G^{\pi}_1(O) = e$$

$$G^{P}_2(O) = e\frac{g'_P}{2M} \qquad\qquad G^{N}_2(O) = \frac{eg_N}{2M}$$

$$G^{s}_1(O) = G^{v}_1(O) = \frac{e}{2} \tag{I.9}$$

$$G^{s}_2(O) = \frac{eg_s}{2M} \qquad\qquad G^{v}_2(O) = \frac{eg_v}{2M}$$

One often finds in the literature the form factors $F_v(t)$ normalized as follows :

$$G_2(t) = G_2(O)\ F_2(t)$$

$$G^{P}_1(t) = G_1(O)\ F^{P}_1(t) \tag{I.10}$$

$$G^{N}_1(t) = e\ F^{N}_1(t)$$

2 - THE FORM FACTORS FOR TIME-LIKE MOMENTUM TRANSFERS -

Until now we have considered the determination of the form factors from electron scattering. In this case the photon four momentum k, being the difference of the initial and final electron momenta, will always be space-like and thus (•) $t < 0$. The possibility of determining experimentally the form factors for positive values of t is given by the reactions :

$$e^- + e^+ \begin{cases} \nearrow \pi^- + \pi^+ \\ \searrow N + \overline{N} \end{cases}$$

The many interesting possibilities given by (e^-e^+) reactions have been studied in detail by R. Gatto and N. Cabibbo.

In the case of the e^-e^+ reactions the virtual photon momentum is the <u>sum</u> of the electron and positron momenta and will therefore be time-like, the momentum transfer t will now be positive and larger than $4m^2_{\pi}$, $4M^2_N$ for the $(\pi^-\pi^+)$ and $(N\overline{N})$ cases.

In the one photon exchange approximation these reactions will be represented by the same graphs as in figure 1 but viewed from the reverse side. Now our matrix elements will depend on the $\langle O|J_{\mu}|\pi^-\pi^+\rangle$, $\langle O|J_{\mu}|N\overline{N}\rangle$ vertex functions. Expressions for them can be obtained by applying trivial changes to Eqs. (I.3), (I.7).

$$\langle O|J_{\mu}|\pi^-\pi^+\rangle = \frac{(\pi_- - \pi_+)_{\mu}}{(4\pi^{o}_{-}\pi^{o}_{+})^{\frac{1}{2}}} G_{\pi}(t) \tag{I.11}$$

$$\left.\begin{matrix} \langle O|J_{\mu}|P\overline{P}\rangle \\ \langle O|J_{\mu}|n\bar{n}\rangle \end{matrix}\right\} = i(\bar{v}_{\bar{N}}[G^{(P,n)}_1(t)\gamma_{\mu} + G^{(P,n)}_2(t)\ \sigma_{\mu\nu}k_{\nu}]v_N) \tag{I.12}$$

where now $k = e_+ + e_-$. The cross-sections for the $(e^- + e^+ \longrightarrow \pi^- + \pi^+)$ reaction is given by (see Cabibbo and Gatto) :

(•) We use a metric for which $t = k^2_o - k^2$.

$$\frac{d\sigma_{\pi^-\pi^+}}{d\cos\vartheta} = \frac{\pi}{16}\frac{\beta^3}{E^2}\left|G_\pi(t)\right|^2 \sin^2\vartheta \qquad (I.13)$$

where $E = \sqrt{\frac{t}{4}}$ $\beta = \sqrt{\frac{t-4}{t}}$.

There is an important difference between the form factors as defined in the space-like or time-like region : the form factors appearing in electron scattering are always real (both positive and negative) whereas in the time-like region the form factors will in general be complex, the imaginary part depending on the interaction between the two particles in the final state. More precisely, using invariance under time reversal, one can obtain for the imaginary part of the pion vertex the following expression :

$$\text{Im} < 0 \mid J_\mu \mid \pi^-\pi^+ > = \Sigma_\alpha < 0 \mid J_\mu \mid \alpha >< \alpha \mid T^+ \mid \pi^-\pi^+ > \qquad (I.14)$$

where α are all states with nucleon number zero and total $J = 1$ (since the current is a vector operator) and T^+ is the scattering matrix. An analogous expression can be obtained for the $N\bar{N}$ final state.

Eq. (I.14) means that for a given energy the imaginary part of the electromagnetic form factor of the pion is large only when there is a large pion-pion interaction for $J = 1$ at that energy. For values of $t < 16\ m_\pi^2$; below the threshold for production of 4 pions Eq. (I.14) takes a particularly simple form :

$$\text{Im}\ F_\pi(t) = F_\pi(t)\ e^{-i\delta_1} \sin\delta_1 \qquad (I.15)$$

This means that $F_\pi(t)$ will be given by a real quantity multiplied by $e^{i\delta_1}$ or equivalently :

$$\text{Im}\ F_\pi(t) = \text{Re}\ F_\pi(t)\ \text{tg}\,\delta_1 \qquad (I.15')$$

where δ_1 is the $T = J = 1$ pion-pion phase shift.

An equation analogous to Eq. (I.14) can be written in the nucleon case. Its direct use is not so simple and illuminating since in $N\bar{N}$ annihilation kinematics allows the production of states from 2 to 13 pions ! This equation however will be very useful when analytically continued for values of $t \ll 4\ M^2$. This will be discussed in detail in connection with the dispersion relations. The use of the final state theorem has shown the connection of the form factors in the time-like region with pion-pion interaction. I wish here to recall a very important symmetry property of the pion-pion system which will be useful in the study of form factors.

It is well-known that the π° is a self charge conjugate particle so that :

$$C\,\pi^\circ = \pi^\circ$$

If we introduce the real pion fields π_1 and π_2 related to π^+ and π^- by :

$$\pi^+ = \pi_1 + i\pi_2$$

$$\pi^- = \pi_1 - i\pi_2$$

we have :

$$C\pi^\circ = \pi^\circ, \quad C\,\pi_1 = \pi_1, \quad C\,\pi_2 = -\pi_2 \qquad (I.16)$$

We are looking for a transformation under which all three kinds of pions transform in the same manner. Let us consider the charge symmetry operator :

$$S = e^{i\pi\,\tau_2} \qquad (I.17)$$

representing a rotation of 180° around the y axis in the isotopic spin space. We have :

$$S\pi^\circ = -\pi^\circ, \quad S\pi_1 = -\pi_1, \quad S\,\pi_2 = \pi_2 \qquad (I.18)$$

So that if one considers the product of both transformations ;

$$G = CS \qquad (I.19)$$

one has for all three kinds of pions :

$$G \pi_i = - \pi_i \tag{I.20}$$

The pion state is an eigenstate of G corresponding to eigenvalue -1 (*). Invariance under G tells us that an initial state with an even (odd) number of pions must always lead to an even (odd) number of pions in the final state.

Let us now apply G invariance to electromagnetic transitions. On the basis of the behaviour in isospin space, the electromagnetic current operator can be separated into two parts :

$$J_\mu = J_\mu^S + J_\mu^V \tag{I.21}$$

where J^S behaves like an isoscalar and J^V like the third component of an isovector. Since J_μ is odd under charge conjugation we have the following properties under G transformation.

$$G J_\mu^S G^{-1} = - J_\mu^S$$
$$G J_\mu^V G^{-1} = - J_\mu^V \tag{I.22}$$

Eq. (I.21) shows that the isoscalar current must always be coupled to an odd number of pions and the isovector current to an even number. This explains for example why the current appearing in the pion form factor is only isovector (recall the operator T_3 in the expression (I.7) for the $(\pi\pi\gamma)$ vertex function).

3 - DISPERSION RELATIONS FOR THE FORM FACTORS -

I wish now to discuss the connection between the form factors defined in the space-like and in the time-like regions. The general principles of quantum field theory tell us that since those form factors depend on the same $(NN\gamma)$, $(\pi\pi\gamma)$ vertex functions, the two kinds of reactions $e\pi \longrightarrow e\pi$ and $e + \bar{e} \longrightarrow \pi + \pi$ lead to the values of the same functions in the intervals $-\infty < t < 0$, $4m^2 < t < +\infty$ respectively. Since the regions defined by the two kinds of experiments are separated by the gap $(0 - 4m^2)$ the statement that we have to deal with the same function is still rather academic unless we do not give a well-defined procedure to connect directly the data we can obtain in both regions.

Such a procedure is given by the use of dispersion relations which allow to continue analytically from one region to the other.

Let us first consider the simpler case : the pion form factor. It is possible to prove, starting from the general principles of quantum field theory, that G (t) is an analytic function of t whose only singularity is a cut on the real axis from $4m^2$ to $+\infty$. Moreover perturbation theory suggests that for $t \longrightarrow \infty$ G (t) does not behave worst than a constant. Thus applying the Cauchy theorem to the function $\frac{G(t)}{t}$ (the denominator t is to ensure convergence at infinity) to the contour drawn in figure 2 we obtain for G (t) the following representation valid for any complex value of t.

$$\frac{G_\pi(t)}{t} = \frac{G_\pi(O)}{t} + \frac{1}{\pi} \int_{4m_\pi^2}^{\infty} \frac{g_\pi(t')}{t'(t' - t)} dt'$$

where the real function g (t') represents the discontinuity of G (t) along the cut.

Using the low energy limit given by Eq. (I.9) we obtain :

$$G_\pi(t) = e + \frac{t}{\pi} \int_{4m_\pi^2}^{\infty} \frac{g_\pi(t')}{t'(t' - t)} dt' \tag{I.23}$$

If t is on the positive real axis on the integration path, the physical interpretation of Eq. (I.23) is well-known : by taking $t = t_0 \pm i\eta$ where η is a small positive number, one obtains $G_\pi(t)$ and $G^*_\pi(t)$ respectively.

(*) For the nucleon the situation is of course much more complicated : under C $P \longrightarrow \bar{P}$ and under S $P \longrightarrow N$ so that G transforms $P \longrightarrow \bar{N}$.

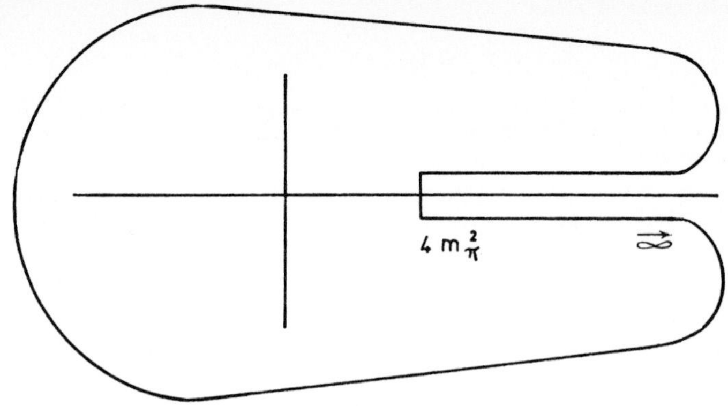

Figure 2

This leads immediately to :

$$g_\pi(t) = \frac{G_\pi(t) - G_\pi^*(t)}{2i} = \text{Im } G_\pi(t) \qquad (I.24)$$

Eqs. (I.23) and (I.24) give the relation between form factors for space-like and time-like momentum transfers.

The spectral function $g_\pi(t) = \text{Im } G_\pi(t)$ can in principle be obtained starting from (e^+e^-) experiments, its knowledge allows to obtain an unambiguous prediction on the form factors for space-like t. Recalling the expressions (I.14) and (I.15) for g (t) given by the final state theorem one can see the close connection between the electromagnetic form factors of the pion and pion-pion interaction.

If low energy pion-pion interactions were unimportant one would expect $g_\pi(t')$ to be small for low t'. Because of the double denominator in Eq. (I.23) this would cause the dispersion integral to be small. In other words, with a small pion-pion interaction we would ewpect $G_\pi(t) \approx e$ for $|t| < M^2$. On the other hand, it will be shown in the next section that the recently discovered $T = J = 1$ $\pi - \pi$ resonance causes a rapid variation of the form factors for low values of t. In the case of the nucleon form factors the situation is more complicated. Let us first of all write down explicitly the expression for the imaginary analogous to Eq. (I.14) fiven by the final state theorem :

$$\text{Im} < 0 \,|\, J_\mu \,|\, N\bar{N} > \; = \; \Sigma_\alpha < 0 \,|\, J_\mu \,|\, \alpha > < \alpha \,|\, T^+ \,|\, N\bar{N} > \qquad (I.25)$$

Eq. (I.25) has only a direct physical meaning for $t \geqslant 4M^2$ which is the minimum mass for a physical $N\bar{N}$ state. However, the lightest state which has the right quantum number to contribute to the sum in Eq. (I.25) is the two pion state with a minimum mass $4m^2$.

This fact strongly suggests that the imaginary parts of the form factors are actually different from zero for $t > 4m^2$. This is well illustrated in figure 3 which shows the graphs in which two pions are exchanged between the $N\bar{N}$ system and the photon.

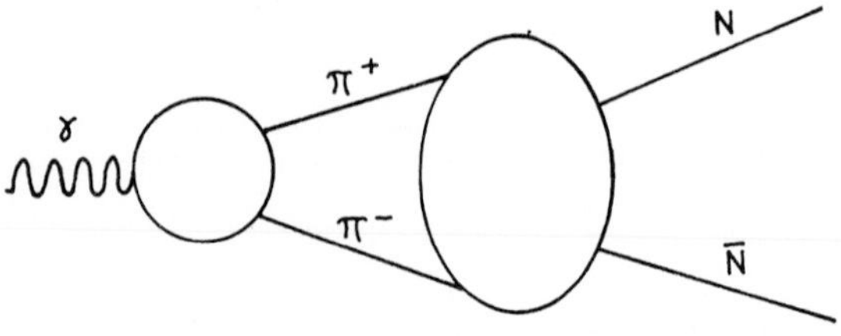

Figure 3

The two blubs in figure 3 represent the $<0|J_\mu|\pi^+\pi^->$ and $<\pi^+\pi^-|T^+|N\bar{N}>$ matrix elements in Eq. (I.25).

If we now try to write down dispersion relations analogous to Eq. (I.23) one expects the integration on t' to start at $4m^2$ not at $4M^2$. One indeed obtains :

$$G_v^{1,2}(t) = G_v^{1,2}(O) + \frac{t}{\pi}\int_{4m_\pi^2}^{\infty} \frac{g_v^{1,2}(t')}{t'(t'-t)}\,dt' \qquad (I.26)$$

$$G_s^{1,2}(t) = G_s^{1,2}(O) + \frac{t}{\pi}\int_{9m_\pi^2}^{\infty} \frac{g_s^{1,2}(t')}{t'(t'-t)}\,dt' \qquad (I.27)$$

The lowest limits in Eqs. (26) and (27) are $4m^2$ and $9m^2$ respectively. This is due to the fact that, as discussed in Section 2., the isovector current is coupled to an even number of pions (and so can lead to the 2π state), and the isoscalar current is coupled to an odd number (and so the lowest mass state is the three pion state).

The dispersion relations for the nucleon form factors have therefore the big difficulty that the spectral functions $g_v(t)$ $g_s(t)$ are not directly connected with experiment in the interval $t < 4m^2$. In this same interval (called "unphysical region") the unitarity relation (I.25) cannot be used unless one does not obtain a theoretical prescription which gives it a meaning and which allows to compute matrix elements of the type $<\pi^+\pi^-|N\bar{N}>$ for $t < 4M^2$. This is indeed possible by means of the Mandelstam representation and will be discussed in the next section.

The appearance of such large unphysical regions has not yet allowed a derivation of Eqs. (I.26) and (I.27) from quantum field theory. However, one has verified their validity to all orders of perturbation theory.

II - THE DERIVATION OF THE FORM FACTORS FROM EXPERIMENT

Before explaining the specific models which have been recently proposed for the form factors, I wish to discuss the methods and theoretical approximations which are necessary in order to extract the different form factors from experiment.

First of all one has to consider the limits of validity of the simple one photon exchange approximation. Secondly, since the neutron and pion are unstable particles the determination of their form factors cannot be made directly by electron scattering but one has to use more complicated phenomena like (eD) interactions and electron production of pions so that we need some kind of a theory for these phenomena.

1 - TWO PHOTON EXCHANGE CONTRIBUTIONS -

The graph giving the two photon exchange contribution to electron scattering is shown in figure 4 where the lower blub represents Compton effect of virtual photons on the nucleon.

Of course, the graph representing two photon exchange is of order e^4 in the electromagnetic coupling constant whereas the leading one photon term is of order e^2. So the first correction to the Rosenbluth formula for e scattering comes from the interference between the two photon and the one photon contributions to the scattering matrix.

Let us now consider in some detail the graph in figure 4 : unlike the one photon term which contains only real form factors the two photon term will have both a real and an imaginary part.

The imaginary part will be related through unitarity to inelastic electron nucleon scattering :

$$\mathrm{Im} <e'N'|T|eN> = \Sigma <e'N'|T^+|e''N''\ \text{pions}> \times <e''N''\ \text{pions}|T|eN> \qquad (II.1)$$

This means that the imaginary part will have a large enhancement factor coming from resonant pion-nucleon intermediate states in Eq. (II.1). On the other hand, the real part of the amplitude will be related to the imaginary part by a dispersion relation : it will therefore change of sign passing through zero at the energies for which the different resonances are produced.

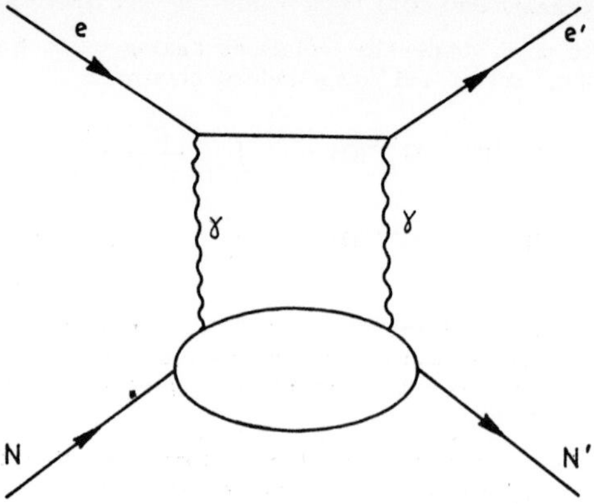

Figure 4

Now we have already seen that the first correction to the Rosenbluth cross-section comes from interference between e^2 and e^4 terms. The e^2 term being real, it does only interfere with the real part of the e^4 term which is not enhanced by any resonance.

This effect together with the $\frac{1}{137}$ factor make the corrections to the Rosenbluth formula less than 1 % in the region of experimental interest.

2 - THE DEUTERON AS A SOURCE OF INFORMATION ABOUT THE NEUTRON -

Since neutron targets are not easily available the main source of information about the neutron comes from the use of deuteron targets which due to the small binding energy B and to the corresponding large spread of the wave function is a very good source of quasi-free neutrons.

The first reactions one looks at is :

$$e + D \longrightarrow P + N + e \tag{II.2}$$

or equivalently :

$$(\gamma) + D \longrightarrow P + N \tag{II.2'}$$

where (γ) indicates the virtual photon exchanged between the electron and the deuteron. The experiments are usually carried out by looking only at the spectrum of the recoil electron for a fixed value of the scattering angle. This means, according to (II.2'), that one determines experimentally the four momentum k_o, $\vec{k}$ (in the lab. system) of the virtual photon but one does not observe the P and N in the "final" state.

The process in which we are particularly interested is the one in which one of the nucleons (for example the neutron) interacts directly with the virtual photon whereas the other particle plays the role of a spectator. Therefore, one has to select the appropriate kinematical circumstance to reveal such a quasi-free particle scattering. This is obtained by considering that the virtual nucleon in the deuteron (N) can be considered as a particle having total energy M-B and narrow momentum distribution of width $\sqrt{M\,B}$. One has in the continuum a quasi-elastic peak corresponding to the reaction :

$$(\gamma) + (N) \longrightarrow N$$

The position of the peak will be given by :

$$(M - B + k_o)^2 - \vec{k}^2 = M^2$$

or equivalently :

$$k_o = B - \frac{t}{2M} \tag{II.3}$$

with a width of the order of $\sqrt{MB}$. The electron deuteron cross-section on the peak can be simply determined by means of impulse approximation. Indeed, for large enough values of t, the wavelength of the virtual photon is small as compared with the deuteron size and thus one can write the total cross-section as the incoherent sum of a proton and a neutron contribution. One obtains :

$$\frac{d^2\sigma}{d\Omega_e dE'_e} = C\,(\sigma_p + \sigma_n) \tag{II.4}$$

where C is a coefficient depending on the kinematical variables and on the deuteron wave function and σ_p and σ_N are the free proton and neutron cross-sections given by the corresponding Rosenbluth formulae. Eq. (II.4) has been first obtained by Goldberg and is now the basis of the derivations of the neutron cross-section from experiment.

However, the Goldberg derivation makes use of non-relativistic quantum mechanics, in this framework the distinction between three dimensional and four dimensional momentum transfers and between electric and magnetic effects is rather ambiguous. Thus one had some doubts on the reliability of Eq. (II.4) which only recently has become the basis of the determination of the neutron form factor.

Therefore, it seems instructive to discuss the interpretation, due to Durand, of Eq. (II.5) using relativistic Feynman graphs.

The graphs shown in figure 5 represent the contribution from the quasi-free proton and neutron to the deuteron cross-section :

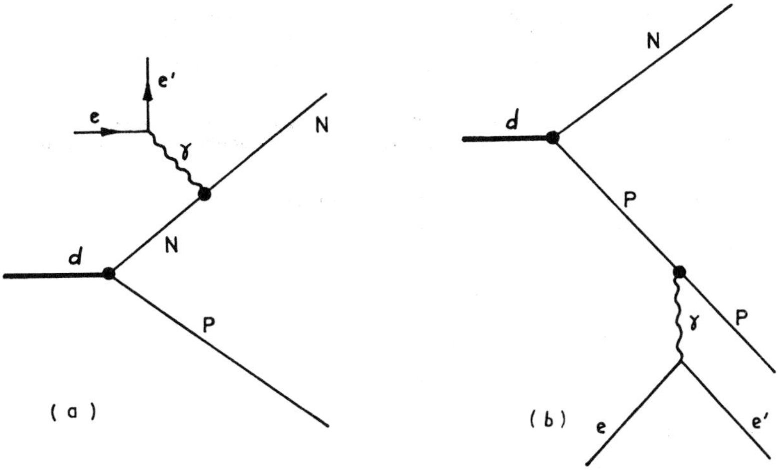

Figure 5

The complete expressions of the matrix elements corresponding to graphs (a) and (b) are given in the paper by Durand. They contain the product of three terms :

1/ the (DPN) vertex function whose size depends on the asymptotic normalization constant of the deuteron wave function N,

2/ the nucleon propagator containing denominators :

$$D_n = (d-p)^2 - M^2, \qquad D_p = (d-n)^2 - M^2 \tag{II.5}$$

for graphs (a) and (b) respectively (d p n are the deuteron and the final proton and neutron four momenta).

3/ the (γPP) and (γNN) vertex functions containing the usual combination of the G_1 G_2 form factors.

The appearance of the two denominators D_n and D_p in the expression for the matrix elements is of the utmost importance and determines the main features of quasi-elastic scattering. Indeed, in the laboratory system we can simply write :

$$\frac{1}{2 M_d} D_{p,n} = -\left(\frac{B}{2} + T_{n,p}\right) \qquad \text{(II.6)}$$

where Tp,n are the kinetic energy of the final nucleons related by energy conservation.

$$T_p + T_n = k_o - B \qquad \text{(II.7)}$$

This equation shows that the two matrix elements will vary very rapidly with T_p, T_n and become very large in narrow regions of the phase space around $T_p \sim 0$. In other words : scattering by a quasi-free nucleon will be most important when the other "spectator" nucleon comes out with a small recoil.

The above discussion shows that for k_o sufficiently large the interference effect between proton and neutron is quite small since the regions of importance of the two graphs are very different and well separated. Therefore, the deuteron cross-section is simply given in terms of proton and neutron cross-sections :

$$\frac{\partial^3\sigma}{\partial k\, \partial k_o \partial T_p} = \left[\frac{\sigma_n}{\left(T_p + \frac{B}{2}\right)^2} + \frac{\sigma_p}{\left(T_n + \frac{B}{2}\right)^2}\right] \times \text{const} \qquad \text{(II.8)}$$

Equation (II.8) shows that the best procedure to measure the neutron form factors is to select these events corresponding to small proton recoils. This has not yet been done and one has, for the moment, to rely on the comparison with experiment of the cross-section integrated on all final nucleon states.

The integration will, of course, be made between T_{min} and T_{max} (functions of t and k_o) which are the maximum and minimum values of the nucleon kinetic energy allowed by the kinematics of the problem.

Now Eq. (II.8) shows that quasi-elastic scattering is important only in a limited range of values of T_p i.e., for $T_p < B$ and $T_N < B$. This means that we shall have a narrow maximum in the cross-section when k_o and t are related in such a manner that the range of integration extends between 0 and $k_o - \frac{B}{2}$ and therefore covers completely the two important regions $T_p < B$ $T_N < B$. This maximum corresponds to the position of the quasi-elastic peak in the spectrum of the recoil electron. The peak relation between k_o and t is immediately given by energy momentum conservation :

$$k_o - B = \sqrt{M^2 + \vec{k}^2} - M$$

which coincides with Eq. (II.3).

Now, integrating Eq. (II.8) between 0 and k_o - B one obtains the expression of the peak cross-section which coincides with the Goldberg formula (•).

The foregoing has made it clear that the range of applicability of the simple Goldberg formula is limited to large (> 15 μ^2) values of t. For smaller values of t the approximation of summing the free proton and neutron effects becomes less accurate and may introduce considerable errors in the determination of nucleon form factors. In particular one important correction comes from the effect of final state P N interaction. A very elegant method of dealing with those corrections has been recently developped by B. Bosco. Consider the transition matrix element M (E) to a final P N state

----

(•) Actually the relativistic derivation of the constant C appearing in Goldberg formula is made by multiplying the nucleon propagator by the damping factor : $\frac{T_o}{T + T_o}$ which simulates the effect of the inner part of the deuteron wave function given by Hulthen model.

with a well-defined angular momentum J and energy E and let us call $M_0(E)$ the same matrix element computed without final state corrections.

Bosco's analysis is based on the following properties :

1/ M(E) satisfies the final state theorem $\text{Im}\, M(E) = \text{Re}\, M(E)\, \text{tg}\,\delta$ (δ being the nucleon phase shift),

2/ M(E) has simple analytic properties deduced for a general class of potential models,

3/ for large values of E $M(E) \longrightarrow M_0(E)$.

These properties allow to obtain a linear integral equation whose solution is an expression of the matrix element M(E) depending directly on the experimental NN phase shifts. The final state corrections turn out to be rather large (around 15 %) and give very important changes in the determination of the form factors for small t.

The result of Bosco shows very clearly that at small values of t simple models are not adequate to describe the whole situation. It is very important in the future to consider very carefully other possible corrections like the ones due to interference effects.

Finally, I wish to mention elastic eD scattering as a source of information on the coherent combination of proton and neutron amplitude.

The interest in elastic deuteron scattering lies in the fact that only the isoscalar form factors appear. The difficulty of theoretical interpretation of these data is due to the fact that quasi-free nucleon effects are summed coherently with other effects (for example of meson currents) which are quite difficult to evaluate.

3 - ELECTRON PRODUCTION OF PIONS -

A source of information on the neutron and electron form factors is given by inelastic electron nucleon scattering, in particular with the production of one pion.

The study of electron-production of pions as a method to obtain the electromagnetic form factors has been started by Fubini, Nambu and Wataghin using the dispersion method.

However, the techniques used in this first investigation are rather crude (since they were based on a $\frac{1}{M}$ expansion) and allow only a first determination of the isovector form factor of the nucleon.

An improved calculation of electron production has been recently carried out by P. Dennery. This calculation is completely covariant and makes use of the Cini-Fubini approximation to the Mandelstam representation. The result of Dennery can be simply illustrated by means of the following relativistic graphs.

The entire electroproduction amplitude is given by the sum of the graphs drawn in figure 6. Let us discuss separately each contribution :

a) the graphs represent the usual nucleon pole terms : they contain the $(NN\gamma)$ vertex function which is given in terms of the four nucleon form factors,

b) the graph represents the direct interaction of the photon with the virtual pion. It contains the $(\pi\pi\gamma)$ vertex function i.e., the electromagnetic form factor of the pion,

c) the graphs represent the effect of the excitation of the (33) resonant state N^*. They contain the $(N^*N\gamma)$ vertex function. This vertex function can be analyzed (using the general invariance arguments) in terms of three new form factors G_{N^*}.

Of course, the excitation of the $\frac{3}{2}$ N^* state requires that the photon behaves as an isovector.

So the first step in Dennery's work is to express the whole amplitude in terms of the five pion and nucleon form factors and of the three G_{N^*} related to the excitation of the isobaric state. The second step is to note that, since the (33) resonant state is composed of pion and nucleon, the G_{N^*} will be linear combinations of G_π and G_N in the same manner as the deuteron form factor is a linear combination of the proton and neutron ones. This determination can be carried out by means of the dispersion method by imposing the consistency of the dispersion relations with unitarity.

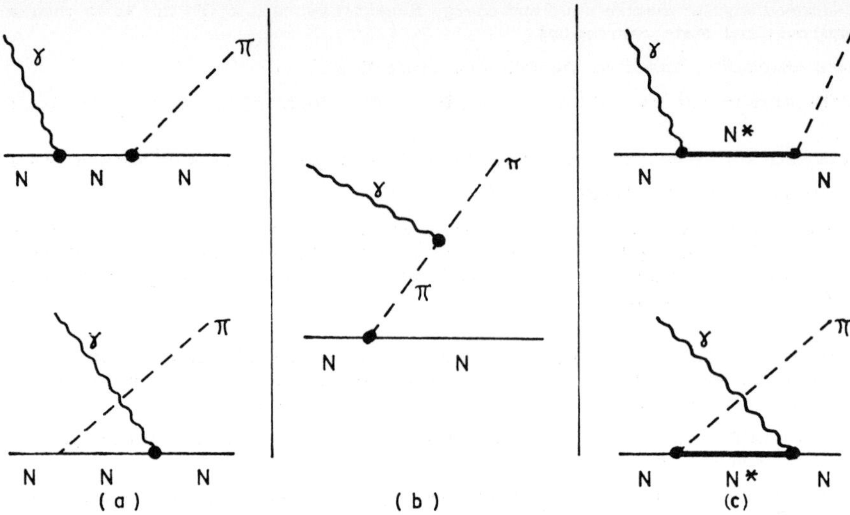

Figure 6

This combination of analyticity and unitarity gives rise to an integral equation whose solution allows to evaluate the three G_{N^*}.

Therefore, it is hoped that Dennery's work will offer a powerful tool for the determination of the form factor. His expression for the matrix elements although simple in principle, is algebraically rather involved because of the unpleasant fact that the N has spin 1/2 the photon spin 1 and the N* spin 3/2 . Numerical calculation of the different cross-sections are now in progress.

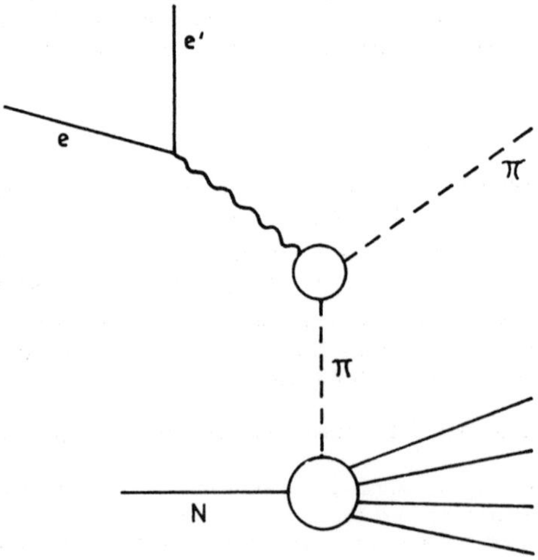

Figure 7

We have seen that electron-production of mesons offers in principle a way of determining $G_\pi(t)$. The practical determination of $G_\pi(t)$ is rather difficult because (due to the appearance of γ_5 in the πN vertex) the graph (b) gives a small contribution to the total production cross-section.

As pointed out by Drell the effect of direct electron pion interaction will become much more important in reactions in which several pions are produced. The situation is illustrated in figure 7. In the lowest vertex many pions are produced in the interaction between the virtual pion and the target nucleon. This effect enhances the contribution of the peripheral graph of figure 1. Fokion Hadjioannou at Stanford has investigated this process in detail and found for an initial energy of 10 GeV, a reasonably large cross-section for the process. The competing diagrams turn out to be sufficiently small not to interfere with the determination of G_π.

III - THEORETICAL MODELS FOR THE NUCLEON FORM FACTORS

The theoretical attempts to understand the nucleon form factors have followed two different points of view. The first one is to try to compute directly the expectation value of the electromagnetic current in the physical nucleon state starting from a field theoretical Hamiltonian.

The main difficulty of these approaches is that reliable methods of computation are not available when perturbation theory fails. The attempt in this direction which has had a certain amount of success is the one based on the static Hamiltonian of Chew and Low [1]. Using only two parameters the coupling constant and the cut-off (whose values were already determined from π N scattering) one has obtained a rough agreement with the magnetic structure of the nucleon, whereas the model failed completely in explaining the charge structure of the neutron. In later investigations, the validity of the static approximation as applied to the nucleon structure has been questioned because the recoil corrections have been found to be large and going in the wrong direction [2], [3].

The second, more recent, point of view has been based on the use of dispersion relations. Its aim is more modest in the sense that what one tries to do is to obtain sufficiently simple expressions for the form factors in terms of a few parameters and to connect those parameters with the ones appearing in the theory of different phenomena like π-π, π-N and N-N scattering. The general philosophy of this approach will be discussed by Matthews and I Shall discuss here only the specific application to the nucleon form factors.

The first dispersion calculations were performed in a scheme in which one assumed no pion-pion correlation. The values of the spectral functions g(t) obtained in such a manner were much too small in the low t region and so they excluded any possibility of agreement with experiment. Even by performing two subtractions the disagreement between theory and experiment was still very large. Therefore one becomes convinced that some of the starting hypothesis had to be changed, in particular Frazer and Fulco have shown that the introduction of a strong pion-pion interaction could enhance the spectral function in such a manner that theory can become consistent with experimental data.

The results I am going to discuss are based on the idea of a strong correlation between pions. This idea has received in the last few months several experimental confirmations.

1 - THE FORM FACTOR OF THE PION -

Let us first discuss briefly the application of dispersion methods to the pion form factor [2], [4].

We recall from part I that $G_\pi(t)$ could be written in the spectral form :

$$\mathrm{Re}\, G_\pi(t) = e + \frac{t}{\pi} \int_{4m_\pi^2}^{\infty} \frac{\mathrm{Im}\, G_\pi(t')}{t'(t'-t)}\, dt' \qquad \text{(III. 1)}$$

for those values of t for which only the 2π contribution is important (i.e., when $\pi\pi$ scattering is mainly elastic).

$$\mathrm{Im}\, G_\pi(t) = \mathrm{Re}\, G_\pi(t)\ \mathrm{tg}\,\delta_1 \qquad \text{(III. 2)}$$

In the "two pion approximation" one can therefore write :

$$\text{Re}\, G_\pi(t) = e + \frac{t}{\pi} \int_{4m_\pi^2}^{\infty} \frac{\text{Re}\, G_\pi(t')\text{tg}\,\delta(t')}{t'(t'-t)}\, dt' \qquad \text{(III. 3)}$$

The integral equation (III. 3) is of a well-known type and its general solution has been given by Omnès [5]. The application of Omnes' method to Eq. (III. 3) gives, in the no-subtraction philosophy :

$$G_\pi(t) = e \exp\left[\frac{t}{\pi} \int_{4m_\pi^2}^{\infty} \frac{\delta(t')}{t'(t'-t-i\eta)}\, dt'\right] \qquad \text{(III. 4)}$$

Eq. (III. 4) solves in principle the problem of the pion form factors in the two pion approximation. This solution requires a rather good knowledge of the T = J = 1 pion-pion phase shift which is at present not yet available. If one approximates the pion-pion amplitude by means of a simple Breit-Wigner resonance formula :

$$e^{i\delta}\sin\delta = \frac{\Gamma k^3}{(t_v - t) - i\Gamma k^3} \qquad \text{(III. 5)}$$

then a simple approximation to Eq. (III. 4) is :

$$G_\pi(t) = C\,\frac{e^{i\delta}\sin\delta}{k^3} \qquad \text{(III. 6)}$$

where the constant C is approximately given by the condition $G(O) = e$

$$C \cong \frac{e\Gamma}{t_v} \qquad \text{(III. 6')}$$

The general trend of the real and imaginary parts of $G_\pi(t)$ in the case of a π-π resonance is sketched in figure 8.

Figure 8 shows clearly the physical situation. The most interesting features of the pion form factors are exhibited in the time-like region whereas in the space-like region one merely sees the decrease of a Breit-Wigner resonance.

We wish to stress the very qualitative character of Eqs. (III. 4) and (III. 5) : we now know that the position of the π-π resonance is for $t \cong 3\ m^2$ in a region in which the 4 pion channel is already open so that the validity of the two pion approximation may be questioned, especially for Eq. (III. 6'). There is, however, one important feature which is model independent, i.e. the spectral function is mainly concentrated in the π-π resonance region. This feature already allows to obtain a general form for $G_\pi(t)$ valid in the space-like region. Since for t space-like we are very far from the resonance position, a simple approximation is obtained by applying the mean value theorem.

$$G_\pi(t) = e + \frac{Bt}{t - t_v} = e\left(1 - a + \frac{a}{1 - \frac{t}{t_v}}\right) \qquad \text{(III. 7)}$$

where :

$$B \cong \int \frac{g_v(t')\, dt'}{t'}.$$

The corrections due to the widths of the resonance are of order $(\Gamma/t_v)^2$ and therefore amount to a few percents.

Unfortunately the simple formulae obtained in this section refer to a process for which experimental data are not yet available. Many of our difficulties come from the fact that many of the processes which are simple from the theoretical standpoint are difficult from the experimental one and vice-versa.

2 - THE FORM FACTORS OF THE NUCLEON -

In section I.3 we have seen that the isovector form factors of the nucleon can be written in the spectral form :

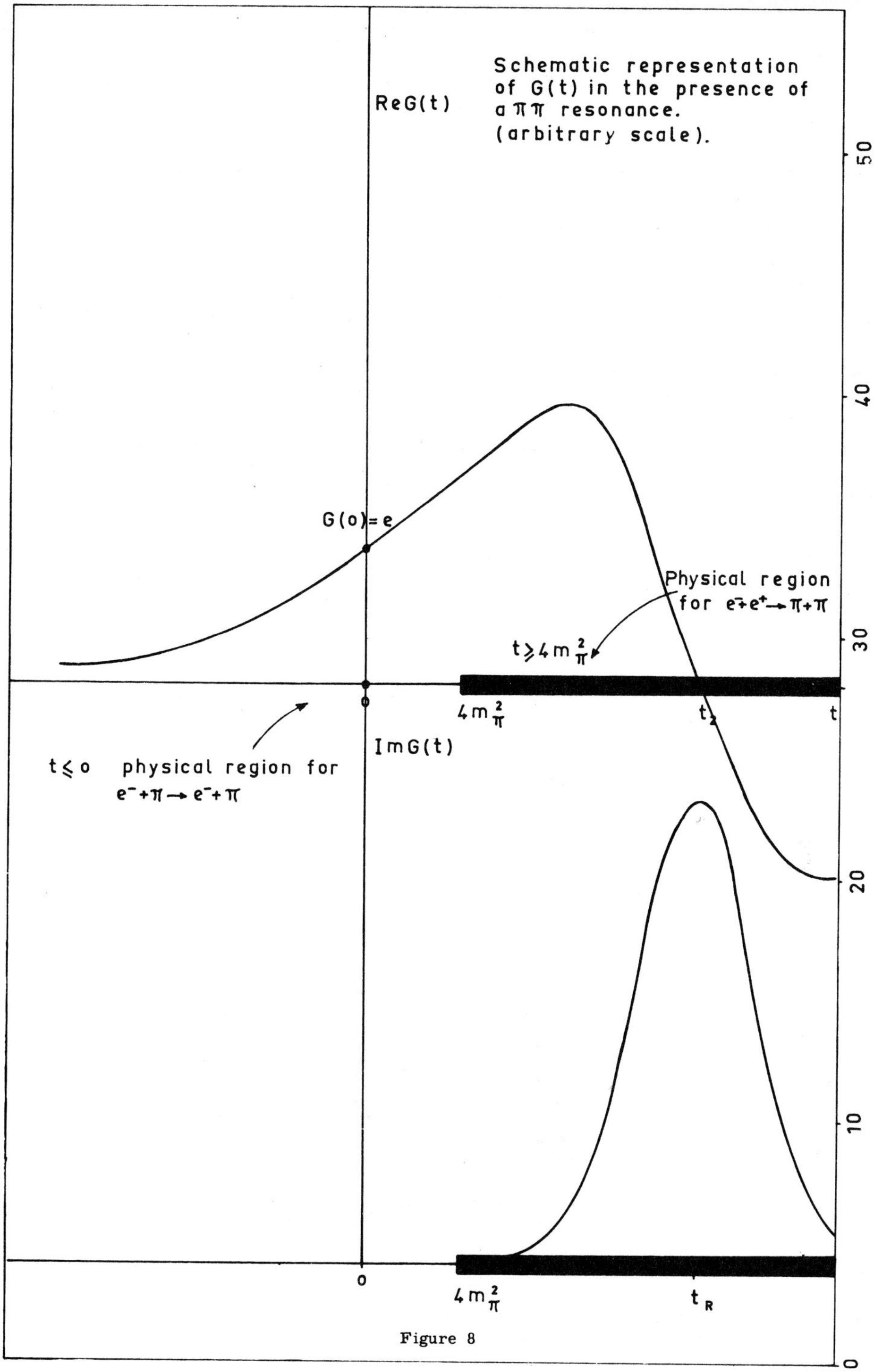
Schematic representation
of G(t) in the presence of
a ππ resonance.
(arbitrary scale).
ReG(t)
G(o)=e
Physical region
for e⁻+e⁺→π+π
t≥4m²π
0
4m²π
t₂
t
ImG(t)
t≤o physical region for
e⁻+π→e⁻+π
0
4m²π
tR
50
40
30
20
10
0

Figure 8

$$G_v^{1,2}(t) = G_v^{1,2}(O) + \frac{t}{\pi} \int_{4m_\pi^2}^{\infty} \frac{g_v^{1,2}(t')}{t'(t'-t)} dt' \qquad \text{(III. 8)}$$

and that the spectral functions were related through unitarity to the sum :

$$\sum_\alpha < O | J_\mu | \alpha > < \alpha | T^+ | N\bar{N} >.$$

In the region where the two pion contribution is the dominant one, the spectral function $g_v(t)$ depends from the product of two terms :

a) the $< O|J_\mu|\pi\pi >$ vertex function which has been studied in section 1.

b) the $< \pi\pi | T^+ | N\bar{N} >$ amplitude.

We have already seen that this amplitude appears for a $(N\bar{N})$ energy t much lower than the physical threshold for the process. Therefore we actually need a theoretical procedure which allows to give a meaning to such an amplitude.

This procedure is given in principle by the Mandelstam representation [6] which allows to continue analytically the scattering amplitude from the physical region to the unphysical values of energy and angle.

I am not going to discuss here the mathematical details of the derivation of this amplitude and its use in connection with the calculation of $g_v(t)$ which can be found in the paper by Frazer and Fulco [4] but only report on the main physical results which are intuitively very simple. (See figure 9).

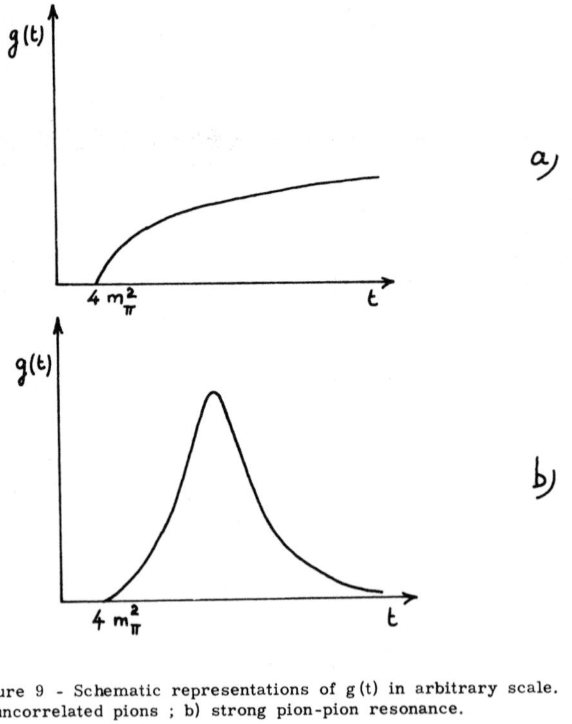

Figure 9 - Schematic representations of g (t) in arbitrary scale.
a) uncorrelated pions ; b) strong pion-pion resonance.

Without π-π interaction the spectral function is a smoothly varying function of t starting from zero at $t = 4\,m^2$. On the other hand, in the presence of a strong pion-pion resonance at $t = t_v$ the spectral function will exhibit a maximum at $t = t_R$ (as in the case of the pion form factor).

This is intuitively clear since $g_v(t)$ represents the weight with which the different two pion states contribute to the nucleon structure. Therefore a strong π-π correlation will concentrate the weight function in the resonance region.

Thus, in the case of a strong π-π interaction, we can write as for Eq. (III.7) :

$$G_v^{1,2}(t) = G_v(O)\left[(1 - a_v^{1,2}) + \frac{a_v^{1,2}\, t_v}{t_v - t} \right] \tag{III.9}$$

Eq. (III.9) has first been proposed by Clementel and Villi [7] and used in comparison with the early experiment on electromagnetic structure of the proton with a value $t_v = 23\ m_\pi^2$. This was interpreted by Bowcock, Cottingham and Lurié [8] in terms of a dipion mass of $\sim 4.7\ m_\pi$ not far from the recent experimental value of $5.4\ m_\pi$ found in pion production.

Let us now discuss the isoscalar part of the form factors. In this case the spectral representation is :

$$G_s(t) = G_s(O) + \frac{t}{\pi} \int_{9m_\pi^2}^{\infty} \frac{g_s(t')}{t'(t' - t)}\, dt' \tag{III.10}$$

As already discussed in part I, the first contributor to $g_s(t)$ will be the three pion state. This contribution is the product of two terms :

a) the $(\gamma 3\pi)$ vertex $\langle O | J_\mu | \pi\pi\pi \rangle$

b) the $\langle \pi\pi\pi | T^+ | N\bar{N} \rangle$ matrix element.

The treatment of the isoscalar form factor is thus much more complicated than in the isovector case. However, some of the qualitative features are the same as in the isovector case.

If there exists a strong correlation between three pions the spectral function will exhibit a maximum at the resonance position t_s, otherwise it will be a smooth function of t.

The present experimental evidence suggests a strong concentration of the spectral function in the low t region ; one was therefore led to assume also the existence of a 3π resonance and to write :

$$G_s^{1,2}(t) = G_s(O)\left[(1 - a_s^{1,2}) + \frac{a_s^{1,2}\, t_s}{t_s - t} \right] \tag{III.11}$$

The three pion resonance t_s is the translation in the dispersion language of the neutral vector meson suggested in 1957 by Nambu [9], [10] in order to explain the apparent lack of neutron charge structure at that time.

Eqs. (9) and (10) constitute a well-defined model for the four nucleon form factors [11] . It contains six parameters : the positions of the two resonances and the four constants representing the effect of these resonances in the electromagnetic structure of the nucleon. These constants are related through theory to similar constants giving the effect of pion-pion interaction in different phenomena like πN and NN scattering.

So we have arrived to a stage that, although we are still far from a fundamental understanding of the nucleon structure, we have a very simple description of both proton and neutron structure and we can correlate the (eN) scattering experiments with other experiments in pion physics.

3 - THE PION-PION RESONANCES -

The model described in the last section requires the existence of two metastable particles :

a) a T = 1 J = 1 two π resonance,

b) a T = 0 J = 1 three π resonance.

The experimental fits of Eqs. (III.9) and (III.10) made both at Stanford [12] an d at Cornell [13] were giving for the masses of these resonances the following values :

$$t_s \sim 10\ m_\pi^2 \qquad\qquad t_v \sim 20\ m_\pi^2$$

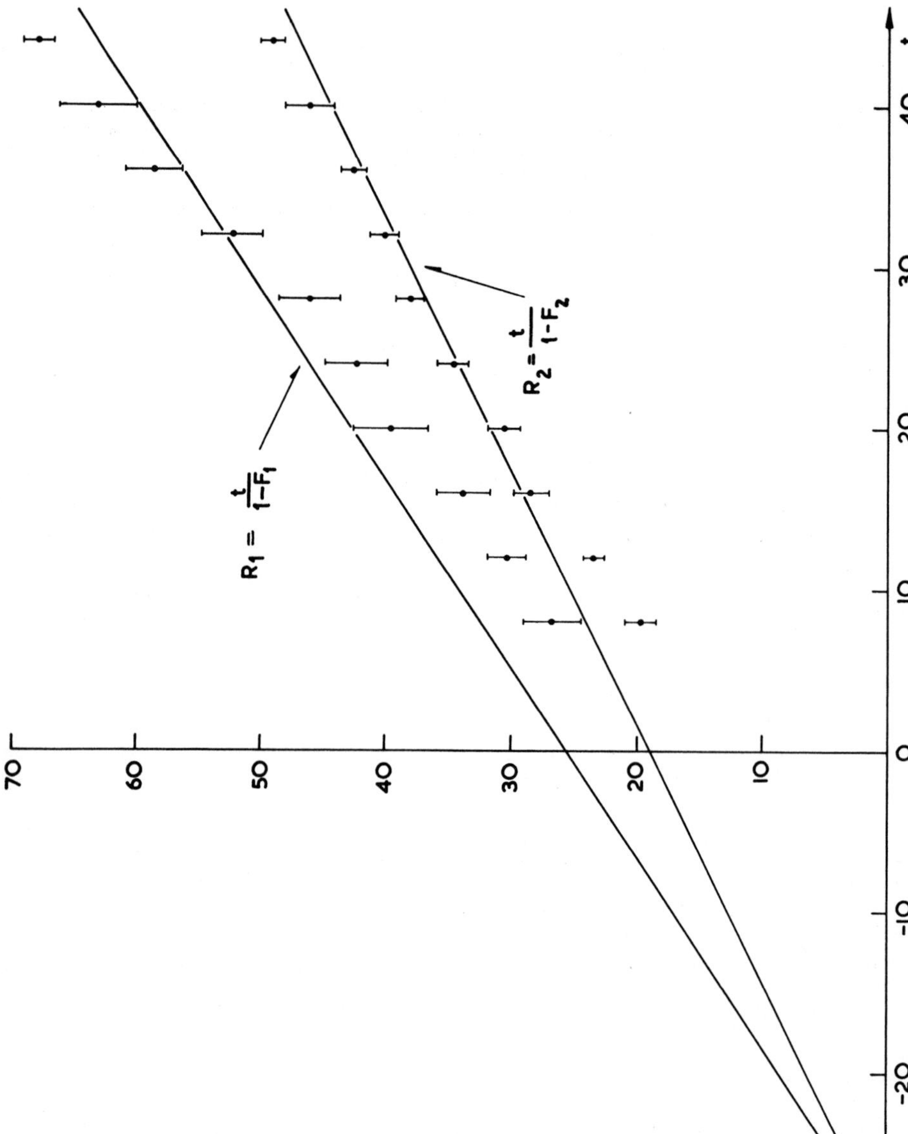

$R_1 = \frac{t}{1-F_1}$
$R_2 = \frac{t}{1-F_2}$
t
-30
-20
-10
0
10
20
30
40
10
20
30
40
50
60
70

Figure 10

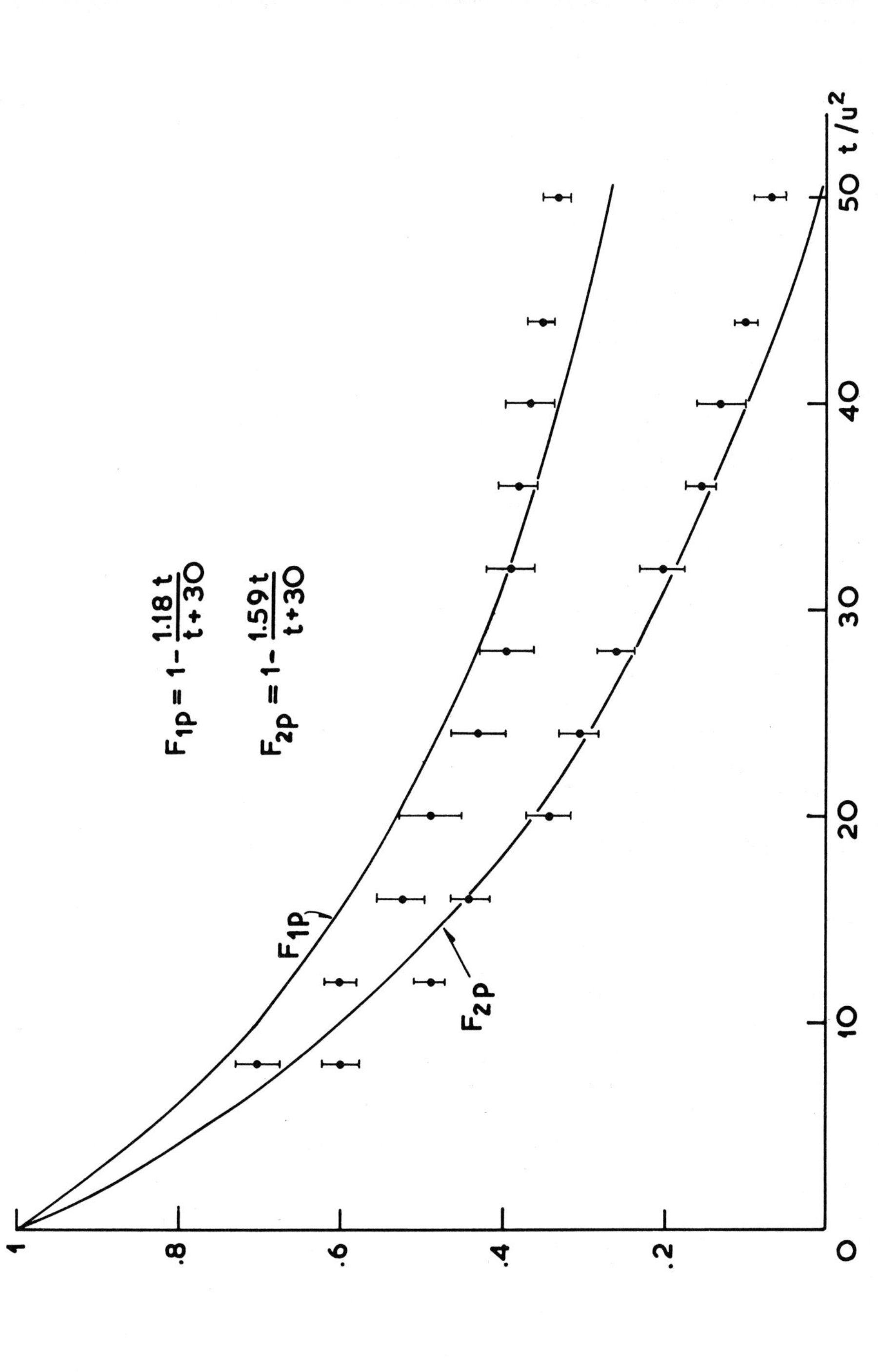
$F_{1p} = 1 - \frac{1.18\,t}{t+30}$
$F_{2p} = 1 - \frac{1.59\,t}{t+30}$
F_{1p}
F_{2p}
1
.8
.6
.4
.2
0
10
20
30
40
50
t/u^2

Figure 11

A statistical analysis performed by Bergia and Stanghellini [14] shows that the acceptable values of t_s and t_v can very between rather wide limits.

Very recently direct evidence for the existence of pion pion resonances was found.

First of all a T = 1 π - π resonance has been found in $\pi + N \longrightarrow \pi + \pi + N$ experiments both at Wisconsin [15] and at Bologna, Saclay and Orsay [16]. An angular distribution analysis [16] gives strong evidence in favour of J = 1. The mass of the particle is 5.4 m_π, i.e., $t_v = 29\ m_\pi^2$ which is certainly compatible with the results of the analysis of the isovector form factor.

Secondly a 3π resonance of T = 0 has been recently discovered in two different experiments [17], [18] with a mass slightly larger than the one of the two-pion resonance.

In this case the experimental result is very far from the prediction coming from the analysis of the form factor. In order to give an idea of the discrepancy, Figures 10 and 11 show the comparison with experiment of an attempt of fit taking $t_s \sim 32\ m_\pi^2$ as suggested by the recently found 3π resonance. This comparison shows that even if the 3π resonance recently found will turn out to have J = 1, the electromagnetic structure of the nucleon still needs a significantly lower mass contribution to the isoscalar spectral functions.

It is very difficult to make any prediction on the issue of future experiments, I wish, however, to recall that there exists another low energy T = 0 effect which in my opinion is not yet understood. I am referring to the He_3 recoil experiment in P + D reaction [19]. The bump found in the recoil spectrum of He_3 was first interpreted as a T = 0 J = 1 state. This interpretation was then dismissed on the basis of the experimental width and on arguments based on the K meson decay [20]. I wish to point out that the interpretation now favoured on the basis of a T = 0 J = 0 low energy π - π interaction (with a scattering length of $a = 2.5 \frac{1}{m_\pi}$) gives also rise to very serious difficulties.

First of all it is very hard to understand why such a strong $\pi\pi$ correlation at threshold does not strongly perturb the decay spectrum of the τ meson [21] which shows a rather small variation from phase space.

Another difficulty of such a large scattering length has been pointed out by C. Ceolin and R. Stroffolini [22].

If one tries to compute the effect of π - π interaction with $a = 2.5 \frac{1}{m_\pi}$ on $\pi + N \longrightarrow \pi + \pi + N$ one finds a production cross-section which is about twenty times larger than the experimental ones. The situation is illustrated in figure 12, which shows that $a_s > 1$ is inconsistent with production data.

So both interpretations of the He_3 recoil experiment are, in my opinion, equally unsatisfactory and maybe the ABC particle might still be considered as a possible candidate for the T = 0 J = 1 role.

4 - CONCLUSIONS -

We have seen that the situation concerning the electromagnetic structure of the nucleon, although still unsettled, is certainly very interesting.

We have now a general model which tries to interpret both proton and neutron structures in terms of a unique physical phenomenon : strong interaction between bosons.

Such a strong interaction has now been revealed experimentally with features which are not very far from the ones that were guessed on the basis of the interpretation of form factors.

Now the main theoretical problem for the future is to study and correlate between themselves the different features of the vector particles and to predict other possible higher resonances which might have an effect on the inner structure of the nucleon.

Very interesting work on this programme is now in progress, but since it still is in a rather preliminary stage, I shall only refer to the main features. There are two independent and complementary lines of thought. The first one interprets the vector unstable particles as resonant state due to some kind of pion-pion force. Dispersion methods have been applied both to study the 3π resonance in terms of the 2π (R. Blankenbecler and J. Tarski) or the 2π resonance in terms of the 3π (R. Blankenbecler). These calculations also give predictions about the existence of higher resonances. A potential calculation has been performed by L. Schiff, the parameters of the π - π force are extracted from the experimental information about the dipion. It is then shown that this attraction leads to a three pion quasi-bound state with the right quantum numbers.

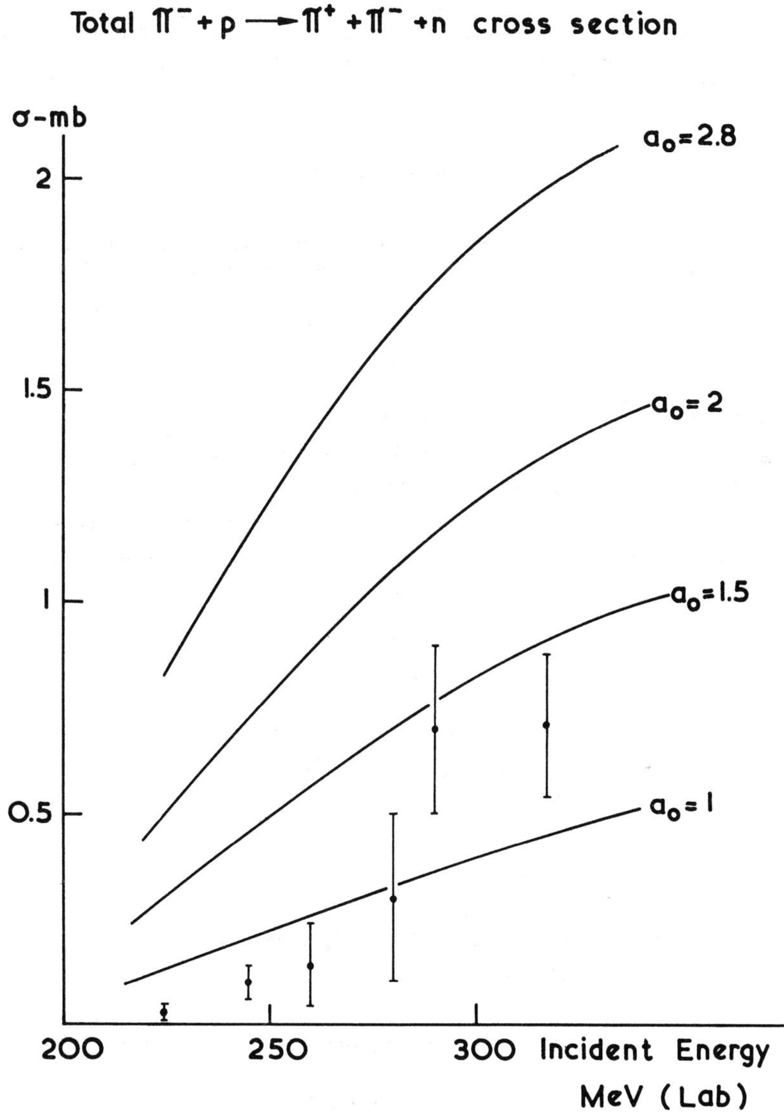
Total π⁻ + p ⟶ π⁺ + π⁻ + n cross section
σ-mb
2
1.5
1
0.5
a₀=2.8
a₀= 2
a₀=1.5
a₀= 1
200
250
300
Incident Energy
MeV (Lab)

Figure 12

The second approach, followed by Sakurai [23] and Gell-Mann and Zachariasen gives to the vector particles a more fundamental role in elementary particle physics.

The vector particles can be considered as "heavy photons" and interact with current which (as the electromagnetic current) are conserved, namely the currents related to conservation of baryon charge and hypercharge. One difficulty is that the possible experimental tests of this theory refer to vector mesons having zero momentum and zero total energy. The vector particles experimentally found until now have such a large mass so that we are very far from the limit in which the test of the theory can be done.

REFERENCES

A general treatment of the different problems related to nucleon structure can be found in S.D. Drell and F. Zachariasen "Electromagnetic structure of nucleons", Oxford University Press, 1961.

Part I.

M.N. ROSENBLUTH - Phys. Rev. 79, 615 (1950).

CHEW, KARPLUS, GASIOROWICZ and ZACHARIASEN - Phys. Rev. 110, 265 (1958).

FEDERBUSH, GOLDBERGER and TREIMAN - Phys. Rev. 112, 642 (1958).

D. YENNIE, M. LEVY and D. RAVENHALL - Rev. Mod. Phys. 29, 144 (1957).

N. CABIBBO and R. GATTO - Phys. Rev. Letters 4, 313 (1960), Nuovo Cimento 20, 184 (1961).

Part II.

(Sect. 1) :

S. DRELL and M. RUDERMAN - Phys. Rev. 106, 561 (1957).

S. DRELL and S. FUBINI - Phys. Rev. 113, 741 (1959).

(Sect. 2) :

V.Z. JANKUS - Phys. Rev. 102, 1586 (1956).

R. BLANKENBECKLER - Phys. Rev. 111, 1684 (1958).

L. DURAND III - Phys. Rev. 115, 1020 (1959) - 123, 1393 (1961).

A. GOLDBERG - Phys. Rev. 112, 618 (1958).

B. BOSCO - Phys. Rev. 123, 1072 (1961).

and "A Phenomenological Approach to Electrodisintegration of Deuteron", Stanford University, preprint.

G.F. CHEW and F. LOW - Phys. Rev. 113, 1640 (1959).

(Sect. 3) :

S. FUBINI, Y. NAMBU and V. WATAGHIN - Phys. Rev. 111, 329 (1958).

BLANKENBECKLER, GARTENHAUS, HUFF and NAMBU - Nuovo Cimento 17, 775 (1960).

P. DENNERY - (CERN preprint).

[1] H. MIYAZAWA - Phys. Rev. 101, 1564 (1956),
S. FUBINI - Nuovo Cimento 3, 1425 (1956),
F. ZACHARIASEN - Phys. Rev. 102, 295 (1956),
BLOKINTSEV, BARASHENKOV, BARBASHEV - JETP 36, 1145 (1959),
S. TREIMAN and R. SACHS - Phys. Rev. 103, 435 (1956).

[2] FEDERBUSH, GOLDBERGER, TREIMAN - Phys. Rev. 112, 642 (1958).

[3] J.D. WALECKA - Nuovo Cimento 11, 821 (1959).

[4] N. FRAZER and J. FULCO - Phys. Rev. Letters 2, 365 (1959), Phys. Rev. 115, 1763 (1959), 117, 1609 (1960).

[5] R. OMNES - Nuovo Cimento 8, 316 (1958).

[6] S. MANDELSTAM - Phys. Rev. 112, 1344 (1958) - 115, 1741, 1752 (1959).

[7] E. CLEMENTEL and C. VILLI - Nuovo Cimento 4, 1207 (1956).

[8] BOWCOCK, COTTINGHAM, LURIE-- Phys. Rev. Letters 5, 386 (1960).

[9] Y. NAMBU - Phys. Rev. 106, 1366 (1957).

[10] G.F. CHEW - Phys. Rev. Letters 4, 142 (1960).

[11] BERGIA, FUBINI, STANGHELLINI and VILLI - Phys. Rev. Letters 6, 367 (1961).

[12] R. HOFSTADTER and R. HERMAN - Phys. Rev. Letters 6, 293 (1961).

[13] LITTAUER, SCHOPPER and WILSON - Phys. Rev. Letters 7, 141-144 (1961).

[14] S. BERGIA, A. STANGHELLINI - Nuovo Cimento 21, 155 (1961).

[15] A.R. ERWIN, R. MARCH, W.D. WALKER and E. WEST - Phys. Rev. Letters 6, 628, (1961), D. STONEHILL, C. BALTAY, H. COURANT, W. FICKINGER, E.C. FOWLER, H. KRAYBILL, J. SANDWEISS, J. SANFORD and H. TAFT - Phys. Rev. Letters 6, 624 (1961), E. PICKUP, D.K. ROBINSON and E.V. SALANT - Phys. Rev. Letters 7, 192 (1961).

[16] Collaboration Saclay - Orsay - Bari - Bologne - This conference, Session F Vol. 1, p. 257.

[17] MAGLIC, ALVAREZ, ROSENFELD and STEVENSON - Phys. Rev. Letters (to be published).

[18] A. PEVSNER, R. KRAEMER, M. NUSSBAUM, P. SCHLEIN, T. TOOHIG, M. BLOCH, A. KOVACS, C. MELTZER - this conférence, Session F, Vol. 1, p. 277.

[19] A. ABASHIAN, N.E. BOOTH, K.M. CROWE - Phys. Rev. Letters 7, 35 (1961).

[20] R. SACHS and SAKITA - Phys. Rev. Letters 6, 306 (1961).

[21] N. KHURI and S.B. TEEIMAN - Phys. Rev. 119, 1115 (1960).

[22] C. CEOLIN and R. STROFFOLINI - Nuovo Cimento (to be published).

[23] J.J. SAKURAI - Annals of Physics 11, 1 (1960).

PAPER 80

SCALAR NUCLEON FORM FACTOR $F_1^n + F_1^p$ *

Norman K. Glendenning and Gustav Kramer†
Lawrence Radiation Laboratory, University of California, Berkeley, California
(Received October 23, 1961)

All meson-theoretic derivations of nucleon-nucleon potentials agree that the outer region should behave like the one-pion exchange potential (OPEP). The inner region cannot be calculated unambiguously, however, and is therefore usually treated phenomenologically.

The modification of the inner region in such a way as to fit the low-energy n-p data is the subject of a forthcoming work.[1] There we discovered that the integrals that enter the deuteron electromagnetic form factor G^2 are very insensitive to the inner region of the potential for $q \lesssim 3\ \mathrm{f}^{-1}$, and are therefore determined by the well-established OPEP tail. This fact can be used to extract the sum of the neutron and proton charge form factors $F_1^p + F_1^n$ with practically no uncertainty arising from our imperfect knowledge of the n-p force. The sum $F_1^p + F_1^n$ is obtained from the expression[2]

$$G_{\mathrm{exp}}^2 = (F_1^p + F_1^n)^2 (G_0^2 + G_2^2) + [2\tan^2(\theta/2) + 1] G_{\mathrm{mag}}^2, \qquad (1)$$

where G_0, G_2, G_{mag} are, respectively, the contributions from the spherical and quadrupole charge distributions and the magnetic moment.[3] In addition to F_1^p and F_1^n, G_{mag} contains also the magnetic parts of the nucleon form factors F_2^p and F_2^n. Since G_{mag} is almost everywhere at least two orders of magnitude less than $G_0^2 + G_2^2$, its value will effect at most the third figure of $F_1^p + F_1^n$ (except at large angles, which we avoid). Since the already published neutron form factors of Hofstadter et al.[4] should allow us to compute G_{mag} to at least one significant figure, we shall use the published values of the nucleon form factors in G_{mag}.

We have used the experimental cross section for elastic electron-deuteron scattering of Friedman, Kendall, and Gram[5] to find $G_{\mathrm{exp}}^2 = (d\sigma/d\Omega)_{\mathrm{exp}}/(d\sigma/d\Omega)_0$, where $(d\sigma/d\Omega)_0$ is the cross section for electron scattering from a spinless point charge.

Drawing a smooth curve through a recent experimental measurement[6] of the proton charge form factor F_1^p, we obtained values for this quantity which we subtracted from our value of $F_1^p + F_1^n$ to get the neutron charge form factor. Our results are tabulated in Table I. The upper and lower limit on $F_1^n + F_1^p$ come both from the experimental uncertainty in G_{exp}^2 and the slight uncertainty in the integrals appearing on the right side of Eq. (1) arising from our imperfect knowledge of the nucleon force at small distances.

As can be seen from the table, it is consistent with the existent data to say that the neutron charge form factor F_1^n is zero, at least up to a momentum transfer $q = 3\ \mathrm{f}^{-1}$. However, most of the data suggest a very small negative value of the form factor.

Our results do not agree with those of the Stan-

Table I. Upper and lower limits on the scalar nucleon form factor $F_1^n + F_1^p$ and the neutron form factor F_1^n deduced from the experimental proton and deuteron form factors F_1^p and G are shown. We obtain F_1^p by drawing a smooth curve through the experimental points of reference 6.

q (f^{-1})	θ (deg)	G^2 exp	$F_1^n + F_1^p$ Lower	$F_1^n + F_1^p$ Upper	F_1^p exp	F_1^n Lower	F_1^n Upper
0.99	60.0	0.266 ±0.025	0.781	0.877	0.901	-0.120	-0.024
1.07	70.0	0.241 ±0.023	0.789	0.890	0.889	-0.100	0.001
1.36	90.0	0.151 ±0.015	0.779	0.897	0.839	-0.060	0.058
1.51	105.0	0.101 ±0.009	0.716	0.824	0.809	-0.093	0.015
1.79	43.0	0.0496 ±0.0048	0.638	0.751	0.748	-0.110	0.003
1.99	48.5	0.0290 ±0.0027	0.574	0.685	0.706	-0.132	-0.021
2.22	55.0	0.0225 ±0.0022	0.610	0.744	0.658	-0.048	0.086
2.41	61.0	0.0107 ±0.0009	0.489	0.600	0.619	-0.130	-0.019
2.61	67.5	0.00733 ±0.00077	0.467	0.598	0.578	-0.111	0.020
2.82	75.0	0.00422 ±0.00042	0.413	0.537	0.538	-0.125	-0.001

ford[4] and Cornell[7] groups who analyzed the inelastic (deuteron breakup) process. However, no analysis of the inelastic process to date has accounted for the presence of the D state in the deuteron, nor all of the final-state interactions, except in a rough manner.[2,8]

There is some uncertainty introduced into our results by unknown relativistic and meson-current effects. Nevertheless we feel that these effects will be small in the region of low momentum transfer considered here.[9]

---

*Work supported by the U. S. Atomic Energy Commission.

†On leave from the University of Heidelberg, Heidelberg, Germany.

[1]N. K. Glendenning and G. Kramer, Lawrence Radiation Laboratory Report UCRL-9904 (to be published). The potentials were required to yield the deuteron binding energy and quadrupole moment and give a scattering phase shift at zero energy consistent with the known scattering length. In addition, the phase shifts at higher energies were calculated and they agree roughly with the analysis of the experimental data at 95 Mev by M. H. MacGregor, Phys. Rev. 123, 2154 (1961), and with two of the solutions in the energy range up to 300 Mev of M. H. Hull, K. E. Lassila, H. M. Ruppel, F. A. McDonald, and G. Breit, Phys. Rev. 122, 1606 (1961).

[2]V. Z. Jankus, Phys. Rev. 102, 1586 (1956).

[3]R. Hofstadter, Ann. Rev. Nuclear Sci. 7, 231 (1957).

[4]R. Hofstadter, C. de Vries, and R. Herman, Phys. Rev. Letters 6, 290 (1961); R. Hofstadter and R. Herman, Phys. Rev. Letters 6, 293 (1961). We used Eqs. (9) through (12) in the second of these references.

[5]J. I. Friedman, H. W. Kendall, and P. A. M. Gram, Phys. Rev. 120, 992 (1960).

[6]F. Bumiller, H. Croissiaux, E. Dally, and R. Hofstadter, Phys. Rev. 124, 1623 (1961).

[7]D. N. Olson, H. F. Schopper, and R. R. Wilson, Phys. Rev. Letters 6, 286 (1961). R. M. Littauer, H. F. Schopper, and R. R. Wilson, Phys. Rev. Letters 6, 141 (1961); 6, 144 (1961).

[8]L. Durand, III, Phys. Rev. Letters 6, 631 (1961); Phys. Rev. 123, 1393 (1961).

[9]R. Blankenbecler, thesis, Stanford University, 1958 (unpublished), has studied relativistic corrections, using a simplified model of the deuteron (two bosons, one of which is charged, bound by a separable potential). In this model the corrections can give rise to a 25 to 30% reduction in the cross section at $q = 3\ \mathrm{f}^{-1}$ which would mean that the scalar charge form factor would be larger by as much as 15%. Whether the corrections would be as large in a realistic model is not clear. However, suppose that this is the correction that obtains at $q = 3\ \mathrm{f}^{-1}$. Then if we applied a correction that is 15% at $q = 3\ \mathrm{f}^{-1}$ and goes linearly to zero as $q \to 0$, the limits we place on F_1^n would lie one above and one below the zero value for all values of q listed in our table except at $q = 2.2\ \mathrm{f}^{-1}$, where both limits are positive.

PAPER 81*

NEUTRON FORM FACTORS AND NUCLEON STRUCTURE*

C. de Vries† and R. Hofstadter
Department of Physics and High-Energy Physics Laboratory, Stanford University, Stanford, California

and

Robert Herman
Research Laboratories, General Motors Corporation; Warren, Michigan
(Received March 26, 1962)

Last year new information on the Dirac and Pauli form factors of the neutron was reported.[1-3] A theoretical model based on the existence of two resonances involving pions was proposed by Bergia, Stanghellini, Fubini, and Villi[4]; which was consistent with the Clementel-Villi expressions for the form factors. From a different point of view, an attempt to fit the experimental neutron and proton form factor material in terms of Yukawa clouds with different ranges and delta functions was made by Hofstadter and Herman.[2] As is well known, the Clementel-Villi model is equivalent to the latter interpretation. Therefore the two models are identical in all practical aspects. An important feature of each model was that it gave a neutron rms electric radius of zero and values of the proton rms radii and neutron magnetic radius in agreement with experiment. The Cornell group[5] has confirmed the form factor data and the model of nucleon structure as given in references 1 and 2.

We now wish to present a concise version of our recent results. In summary we find that while the idea of the nucleon models proposed above[1,2,4] appears to be quite satisfactory, the numerical values of the parameters involved require certain changes. Thus the numerical values of the parameters we are now reporting differ from those of the previous Stanford results, and noting the above-mentioned agreement of

*See page 686 of this volume for corrections and addenda.

Stanford and Cornell results, the new values also differ from the Cornell results.

The differences between the older and the present results are ascribed to the following sources: (a) more precise and more abundant Stanford electron scattering measurements on hydrogen[6] and deuterium[7]; (b) an improved theory for inelastic electron scattering by the deuteron, given by Durand.[8]

The new cross sections (item a) agree very well with the older experimental data.[1,9,10] Because they are more numerous these new cross sections yield much more information concerning the quasi-elastic scattering peak of the deuteron as a function of scattering angle (60, 75, 90, 120, and 135 degrees) than the older data. The new data include values of the four-momentum transfer, q^2, lying between 3.0 and 22 F^{-2}. (1 F $\equiv 10^{-13}$ cm.)

The theory mentioned under item (b) gives a formula for the quasi-elastic peak cross section which is in good agreement with the impulse approximation results of Goldberg.[11] The main effect of using the Durand-Goldberg formula for the peak of the deuteron inelastic cross section curve, instead of using the result of the Jankus theory,[12] as modified in reference 10, is to depress the results for F_{1n} toward lower values.[8] Whereas the earlier indications obtained from using the modified Jankus theory gave positive values of F_{1n}, we now find numerical values of F_{1n} close to zero or perhaps slightly negative throughout the region of q^2 under consideration.[13] The new values of F_{2n} are slightly lower than reported before but are still higher than those of F_{2p}.

Since a full account of the experiments will be given in a subsequent article, we merely show in Fig. 1 typical results of the actual measurements. In this figure we have plotted the ratio of the elastic scattering cross section of the proton to the cross section at the peak of the inelastic deuteron spectrum for different scattering angles as a function of q^2. The experimental points have been corrected for radiative effects[14] but not for the influence of the interaction in the final state. The straight lines in Fig. 1 were obtained by weighted least-squares fitting of the data. Smoothed ratio values obtained in this way were used in the subsequent analysis.

Neutron cross sections have been obtained from the combination of these ratios and the absolute proton cross sections by using the appropriate formula given by Durand.[8] For the absolute proton cross sections we have used two separate sets of form factors: (1) the central values for F_{1p} and F_{2p} as published in reference 6, which are the solid lines in the upper part of Fig. 2, and (2) the central values (dashed lines in Fig. 2) which follow from a kind of analysis somewhat different from that discussed in reference 6. This analysis will be described subsequently. Because of the correlation of errors which is qualitatively indicated by the direction of the arrows in the top part of Fig. 2, the absolute cross sections calculated from the two sets of proton form factors are not significantly different, and, of course, both sets agree with experiment within experimental errors.

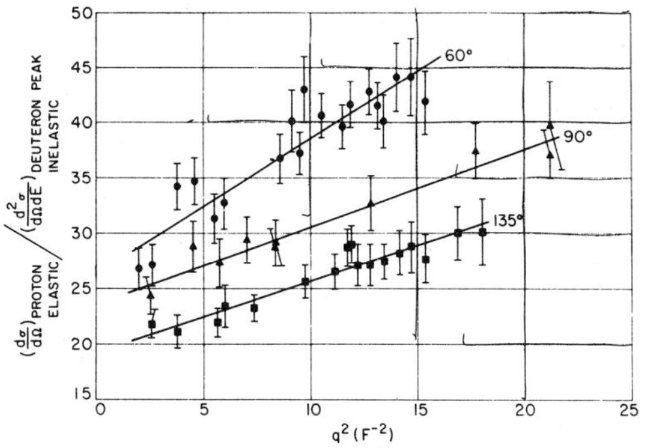

FIG. 1. This figure shows examples of the experimental ratios of the differential proton cross section to the doubly-differential peak deuteron cross section at various angles, as a function of q^2. The straight lines were obtained by weighted least-squares fittings of the data. Measurements have also been made at 75 and 120 degrees (see reference 7) but are not shown here.

Considering the present Stanford information on proton cross sections it is difficult to prefer one set of central values over the other. More precise determinations of the absolute proton cross sections are now being made. However, for the present we have carried along both sets of central values for F_{1p} and F_{2p}, together with their individual error assignments.

The results for the neutron form factors have been plotted in the lower part of Fig. 2. (Note the comment about the other solutions in footnote 13.) The vertical widths of the bands are associated mainly with the errors in the proton form factors and to a lesser extent with the experimental errors of the ratio measurements. The arrows in the neutron bands correspond, therefore, qualitatively to the correlated errors in the proton form factors.

It can be seen that at, say, $q^2 \geq 8\ \mathrm{F}^{-2}$, F_{1n} tends to be slightly negative, while at lower q^2 values this form factor appears to have positive values. In the low-q^2 region we have also plotted the results of Glendenning and Kramer[15] on the analysis of the elastic deuteron scattering results of Friedman, Kendall, and Gram.[16] The same trend was previously indicated by Schiff[17] who analyzed the elastic deuteron results of McIntyre.[18] Because we have neglected the corrections for the final-state interaction in our inelastic data, we feel that our present positive values for F_{1n} at low q^2 are not inconsistent with the Glendenning results.[15] We should note that the final-state interaction has very little influence on the form factors of the neutron at values of $q^2 \geq 8\ \mathrm{F}^{-2}$. Therefore the dotted curves have been drawn so as to combine the results of the present work in the higher q^2 region with the data from the elastic scattering from the deuteron. The corresponding changes in the neutron magnetic form factor, F_{2n}, are also indicated by dotted curves.

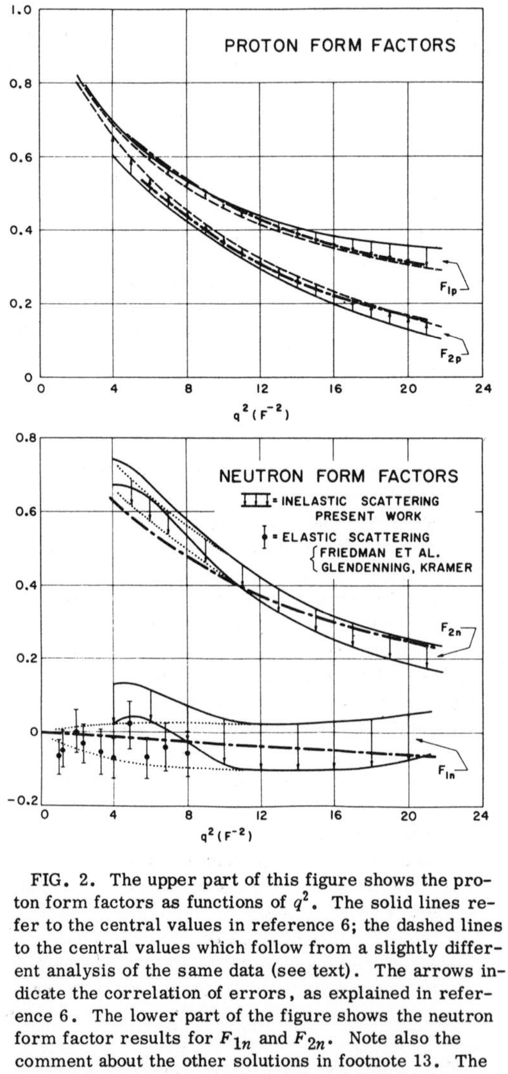

FIG. 2. The upper part of this figure shows the proton form factors as functions of q^2. The solid lines refer to the central values in reference 6; the dashed lines to the central values which follow from a slightly different analysis of the same data (see text). The arrows indicate the correlation of errors, as explained in reference 6. The lower part of the figure shows the neutron form factor results for F_{1n} and F_{2n}. Note also the comment about the other solutions in footnote 13. The neutron form factors are expected to lie in the bands indicated. The points with error bars for F_{1n} refer to a recent analysis made by Glendenning and Kramer.[15] The dotted curves are drawn as a compromise between the trend indicated by the Glendenning points and the trend of the inelastic data of the present work in the higher q^2 region. The heavy dashed-dotted curves are the results of the theoretical fit described in the text.

Experimental values of the isotopic form factors can now be obtained from proton and neutron form factors using the definitions and normalizations of reference 2. In an attempt to fit those experimental form factors we have used the theoretical form of form factors as proposed by Bergia et al.[4] and Hofstadter and Herman[2]:

$$F_{1S} = \frac{s_1}{1+2.04\,q^2/M_S^{\,2}} + 1 - s_1,$$

$$F_{2S} = \frac{s_2}{1+2.04\,q^2/M_S^{\,2}} + 1 - s_2,$$

$$F_{1V} = \frac{v_1}{1+2.04\,q^2/M_V^{\,2}} + 1 - v_1,$$

$$F_{2V} = \frac{v_2}{1+2.04\,q^2/M_V^{\,2}} + 1 - v_2. \qquad (1)$$

These form factors are based on dispersion theory and strong pion-pion interactions and have the well-known Clementel-Villi form. In Eq. (1) q^2 is given in F^{-2} and $M_S^{\,2}$ and $M_V^{\,2}$ are given in units of $m_\pi^{\,2}$. It can be shown that the following relations between the parameters apply:

$$s_1/M_S^{\,2} = v_1/M_V^{\,2} = a_{1p}^{\,2}/12.24,$$

$$v_2/M_V^{\,2} = 0.0406(a_{2p}^{\,2} + a_{2n}^{\,2}),$$

$$s_2/M_S^{\,2} = -1.22\,a_{2p}^{\,2} + 1.30\,a_{2n}^{\,2}, \qquad (2)$$

where a_{1p}, a_{2p}, and a_{2n} are the rms radii of the proton charge and proton and neutron magnetic moment distributions, respectively.

Before giving the results of the fitting procedure we wish to make the following remarks: (a) If only one two-pion state and one three-pion state are responsible for the behavior of the vector and scalar form factors, respectively, then the form of Eq. (1) is justified approximately. In this event we should use the numerical values 28 and 32 for M_V^2 and M_S^2, respectively, because these values are well established (ρ meson and ω meson).[19] (b) If there is more than one two-pion state and/or more than one three-pion state (perhaps the ζ meson and η meson[20]; see, however, Bastien et al.[21]), then the general form of the isotopic form factors should contain explicit contributions from each of the appropriate resonances. It can be shown, in that case, however, that the simple form of Eq. (1) is still a good first approximation and the fit to the data will then yield "effective" mass values.

The result of the fitting procedure is indicated in Table I, where the numerical values of the parameters with their error assignments are given. The best fit to all the form factors is obtained for a value of $a_{1p} = 0.79$ F, which is in excellent agreement with the precise determination of this quantity by Lehmann, Taylor, and Wilson[22] ($a_{1p} = 0.785 \pm 0.04$ F) and also with earlier determinations,[6,23] and a value of $a_{2p}^2 + a_{2n}^2 = 1.50\ \text{F}^2$, also in agreement with earlier work.[6,10] These results correspond to values of $M_V^2 = 18\, m_\pi^2$ and $M_S^2 = 23 \times m_\pi^2$. The fits to the experimental material using these parameters are shown in Fig. 2 (dashed-dotted lines).

It may be of interest to note that a good fit to F_{1V} can be obtained with the ρ-particle mass ($M_V^2 = 28\, m_\pi^2$), but only if $a_{1p} \sim 0.69$ F. For this low value of the rms radius of the charge distribution of the proton, a fit to F_{1S} can be obtained by using a value of $M_S^2 \sim 40\, m_\pi^2$, but the fit is poor.

With respect to the numerical values given in the table we may draw the following conclusions: (1) The constants ($1 - s_1$, $1 - v_1$, $1 - v_2$) take on rather small values; this fact supports the usefulness of the analysis we have made. (2) It does not seem possible to fit the data by using only the known ρ meson and ω meson. Our data indicate that both for the isovector and isoscalar form factor, at least one other heavy meson is needed. The required masses would have to be smaller than $28\, m_\pi^2$ and $32\, m_\pi^2$, respectively. (See also Fubini[24] for relevant remarks.) (3) Since F_{2S} is related to the difference of the nearly equal anomalous magnetic moments of the nucleons, it is very difficult to measure this quantity accurately and the only conclusion one can draw is that it is of the order of unity or slightly greater than unity. (4) If M_S^2 is larger than M_V^2, which is favored by our data, then the outer region of the neutron exhibits a slight negative charge density, but of course the accurate behavior at small q^2 must still be determined. (5) The experimental data indicate that F_{1n} is approximately zero. From Table I it can be seen that a good fit for this condition corresponds to $M_S^2 = M_V^2 \sim (19 \pm 3) \times m_\pi^2$ for $a_{1p} = 0.79 \mp 0.03$ F. The theoretical significance of $F_{1n} \equiv 0$ would be very great.

As already indicated, the results reported here do not agree with the data of the Cornell group.[5]

Table I. Parameter fits to the isotopic form factors.

Best fit	Typical other fits	
$a_{1p} = 0.79$ F	$a_{1p} = 0.75$ F	$a_{1p} = 0.83$ F
$a_{2p}^2 + a_{2n}^2 = 1.50\ \text{F}^2$		
$M_V^2 = (18 \pm 2) m_\pi^2$	$M_V^2 = (21 \pm 3) m_\pi^2$	$M_V^2 = (15 \pm 2) m_\pi^2$
$V_1 = 0.92 \pm 0.10$		
$M_S^2 = (23 \pm 3) m_\pi^2$	$M_S^2 = (29 \pm 3) m_\pi^2$	$M_S^2 = (23 \pm 3) m_\pi^2$
$s_1 = 1.17 \pm 0.15$		
$v_2 = 1.10$		
$s_2 = -0.5$		

We believe this is mainly due to small systematic differences in the absolute proton cross sections. Work is now in progress at Stanford to redetermine absolute proton and neutron data, using improved techniques. We hope that this proposed work will clarify the present situation.

We wish to thank Dr. Sol Krasner and Mr. Carol Crannell for their help with numerous calculations. We also wish to thank other members of the electron-scattering group at Stanford for their assistance with the experiments. We wish to acknowledge with thanks the many discussions we have had with Dr. B. Bosco regarding the final-state interactions in the deuteron.

---

*This material was presented in a contributed paper at the New York meeting of the American Physical Society, January 26, 1962. This work was supported in part by the Office of Naval Research and the U. S. Atomic Energy Commission and by the U. S. Air Force, through the Office of Scientific Research and Development Command.

†On leave from Institute of Nuclear Research, Amsterdam, Holland.

[1]R. Hofstadter, C. de Vries, and R. Herman, Phys. Rev. Letters 6, 290 (1961).

[2]R. Hofstadter and R. Herman, Phys. Rev. Letters 6, 293 (1961).

[3]D. N. Olson, H. F. Schopper, and R. R. Wilson, Phys. Rev. Letters 6, 286 (1961).

[4]S. Bergia, A. Stanghellini, S. Fubini, and C. Villi, Phys. Rev. Letters 6, 367 (1961); S. Bergia and A. Stanghellini, Nuovo cimento 21, 155 (1961).

[5]R. M. Littauer, H. F. Schopper, and R. R. Wilson, Phys. Rev. Letters 7, 141 (1961).

[6]F. Bumiller, M. Croissiaux, E. Dally, and R. Hofstadter, Phys. Rev. 124, 1623 (1961).

[7]A preliminary version of the present data was given at the Aix-en-Provence meeting in September, 1961 [Proceedings of the Aix-en-Provence International Conference on Elementary Particles, 1961 (C.E.N. Saclay, France, 1961), Vol. 1, p. 121].

[8]L. Durand, III, Phys. Rev. Letters 6, 631 (1961); Phys. Rev. 123, 1393 (1961).

[9]S. Sobottka, Phys. Rev. 118, 831 (1960); thesis, Stanford University, 1960 (unpublished).

[10]M. R. Yearian and R. Hofstadter, Phys. Rev. 110, 552 (1958); 111, 934 (1958).

[11]A. Goldberg, Phys. Rev. 112, 618 (1958).

[12]V. Z. Jankus, Phys. Rev. 102, 1586 (1956).

[13]There are two possible sets of solutions for F_{1n} (and F_{2n}) which led in the earlier work to positive and negative values. In the present work the solution plotted in Fig. 2 corresponds to the older positive solution. The second solution now gives even more negative values for F_{1n} than the values of Fig. 2. We will present the second solution in a forthcoming article. At the present time we consider only the first solution and we refer the reader to references 2 and 7 for the reasons why we have taken the present solution more seriously.

[14]The radiative corrections to the cross section of the elastic proton peak and to the height of the inelastic deuteron peak have been calculated with the formulas of Sobottka.[9] Uncertainties in these corrections will probably cancel in forming the ratios of Fig. 1 of the present paper. We have investigated the influence of the Tsai radiative correction [Phys. Rev. 122, 1898 (1961)] on the absolute cross section of reference 6 in place of that given by Sobottka.[9] If Tsai's radiative correction had been applied, the absolute cross sections given in reference 6 would probably have been a few percent higher than reported. Since the differences between Tsai and Sobottka results are almost independent of scattering angle, for constant q^2, the numerical values of the form factors are insensitive to whichever of the two corrections is chosen for the radiative effects.

[15]N. K. Glendenning and G. Kramer, Phys. Rev. Letters 7, 471 (1961).

[16]J. I. Friedman, H. W. Kendall, and P. A. M. Gram, Phys. Rev. 120, 992 (1960).

[17]L. I. Schiff, Revs. Modern Phys. 30, 462 (1958).

[18]J. A. McIntyre and S. Dhar, Phys. Rev. 106, 1074 (1957).

[19]A. Erwin, R. March, W. Walker, and E. West, Phys. Rev. Letters 6, 628 (1961); B. Maglić, L. Alvarez, A. Rosenfeld, and M. Stevenson, Phys. Rev. Letters 7, 178 (1961).

[20]A. Pevsner, R. Kraemer, M. Nussbaum, C. Richardson, P. Schlein, R. Strand, T. Toohig, M. Block, A. Engler, R. Gessaroli, and C. Meltzer, Phys. Rev. Letters 7, 421 (1961); R. Barloutaud, J. Heughebaert, A. Leveque, J. Meyer, and R. Omnes, Phys. Rev. Letters 8, 32 (1962).

[21]P. L. Bastien, J. Peter Berge, O. I. Dahl, M. Ferro-Luzzi, D. H. Miller, J. J. Murray, A. H. Rosenfeld, and M. B. Watson, Phys. Rev. Letters 8, 114, 302(E) (1962).

[22]P. Lehman, R. Taylor, and R. R. Wilson (to be published); R. R. Wilson (private communication).

[23]R. Hofstadter, F. Bumiller, and M. R. Yearian, Revs. Modern Phys. 30, 482 (1958); R. W. McAllister, thesis, Stanford University, 1960 (unpublished).

[24]S. Fubini, Proceedings of the Aix-en-Provence International Conference on Elementary Particles, 1961 (C.E.N. Saclay, France, 1961), Vol. 2, p. 33.

PAPER 82*

U12. Mu-Mesonic X-Ray Energies.* C. S. JOHNSON, E. P. HINCKS,† AND H. L. ANDERSON, *The University of Chicago.*—Precise measurements of μ-mesonic K x-rays have been made using a NaI scintillation-crystal spectrometer. The energies were determined for 20 elements with atomic numbers ranging from $Z=12$ (Mg) to $Z=50$ (Sn). These energies have been calculated by Ford and Wills based on a nuclear-charge distribution chosen by them to give a good fit to the Stanford electron-scattering experiments. Our measurements showed that many of their values were too low. The discrepancy amounted to 2.5% in the case of $Z=20$ (Ca) and diminished to zero for values of Z approaching $Z=12$ (Mg) and $Z=30$ (Zn). A more recent analysis of the electron-scattering experiments by Crannell *et al.* showed in the case of $Z=20$ (Ca) a root-mean-square radius for their nuclear-charge distribution which was appreciably smaller than that of Ford and Wills. This brings the $K\alpha$ energy values much closer to our measurements. The value of the K μ-mesonic x-ray measurements in confirming the nuclear-charge distributions obtained from electron-scattering measurements is emphasized by these results. Residual discrepancies in the energies may be an indication of other nuclear interaction effects.

* Work supported by the Office of Naval Research.
† Present address: Division of Pure Physics, National Research Council of Canada, Ottawa, Ontario, Canada.

See page 686 of this volume for corrections and addenda.

PAPER 83

Mu-Mesonic Atom Studies of Ti, Fe, Co, Zn, Tl, Pb, Bi[†]

W. FRATI[‡] and J. RAINWATER Columbia University, New York, New York

Since the original studies of the 2p-1s mu-mesonic x-rays by Fitch and Rainwater, we have at various times attempted to improve the precision of these results with respect to the 2p-1s transitions, and study the 3d-2p transitions for elements near Z=82. In this paper we report new results for these transitions which we believe to be an order of magnitude superior to the earlier studies and which complete our objective. The improved results are due largely to technological improvements during this interval: (1) Cyclotron improvements, including greatly improved shielding against unwanted background, improved muon beam intensity and purity, and a stretching of production time by a factor of 10 in time during the 1/60-sec cycle period. (2) An improved x-ray detector consisting of a 3" x 3" NaI high resolution crystal surrounded by a large NaI annulus in anticoincidence to minimize the contribution of all but the full-energy peaks. (3) The use of two 100-channel Penco PHA's in parallel with one registering the pulse spectrum of a lower energy "reference γ-ray" present at all times, and the other recording the x-ray spectrum or the spectrum of a calibration γ source of essentially the same energy as the x-rays. This permitted correction of drift effects to about 0.1%. The 3d-2p calibration source was the Na^{24} 2.7535-Mev γ-ray. The 2p-1s calibration source was a fast neutron irradiated circulating water target which gave a (6.134 $\pm$ 0.006) Mev γ-ray in a transition from a known excited state of O^{16} following β-decay of N^{16}. The x-ray curves were χ^2 fitted in terms of the calibration line position and shape using the energy shift for one line, the relative weighting and splitting of the fine structure lines, and two background function constants as adjustable parameters. The results and their net uncertainties are listed in the tables and compared with predicted values computed by Ford and Wills (L.A.M.S.-2387) using nuclear size and shape parameters which fit the Stanford high-energy electron scattering. Alternate Bi values are given (*) based on parameters which seem to us to be more reasonable theoretically. Special measurements looking for capture γ-rays showed only a 2.6-Mev γ-ray for Bi which mainly alters the 3d-2p relative weighting W of the fine structure lines from the expected 0.50 to a measured 0.59. The expected W is obtained for the Pb 2p-1s transition but the large W=0.97 for Tl is believed to be due to a mixing of states due to the near equality of the 2p splitting and the spacing of the Tl $d_{3/2}$ first excited nuclear state from the ground $s_{1/2}$ state. The agreement of the level positions and the fine structure splitting with the computed values is regarded as very satisfactory. The results clearly exclude other than spin 1/2 for the muon if one also uses the experimentally well established result that the muon g factor is almost exactly 2.

RESULTS: The numbers in parentheses indicate the uncertainty in the final digit of the preceding number. Energies are in Mev. W is the ratio of the intensities involving the $2p_{1/2}$ to those involving the $2p_{3/2}$ states.

Element	$E(2p_{3/2}-1s)$		Δ_{2p}		W	$E(3d_{5/2}-2p_{3/2})-0.1\Delta_{3d}$		$\Delta_{2p}-0.9\Delta_{3d}$		W
	Exp	Theo	Exp	Theo	Exp	Exp	Theo	Exp	Theo	Exp
Tl(81)	5.930(11)	6.001(50)	0.1876(43)	0.1843	0.97(9)	2.458(5)	2.452	0.146(5)	0.1475	0.53(3)
Pb(82)	5.990(11)	6.025(50)	0.1859(60)	0.188	0.49(7)	2.498(4)	2.502	0.147(4)	0.1494	0.51(2)
Bi(83)	6.053(9)	5.995(50)	0.1895(42)	0.188	0.75(5)	2.555(4)	2.538	0.148(4)	0.1478	0.59(2)
Bi*		6.047(50)		0.191			2.550		0.151	

Element	Z	2p-1s Exp	2p-1s Theo	Calibrating Source	and Energy
Ti	22	0.9247(25)	0.9198(3)	Cs^{137}	0.6616
Ti	22	0.925(15)		Mn^{56}	0.845
Fe	26	1.2555(24)	1.2393(6)	Na^{22}	1.2736
Cu	29	1.5082(40)	1.4965(7)	Na^{24}	1.3679
Cu	29	1.5064(44)		Na^{22}	1.2736
Zn	30	1.5869(45)	1.5865(8)	Na^{22}	1.2736

† Submitted for publication in the Physical Review (1962) as a full-length paper.

‡ Present: University of Pennsylvania, Philadelphia, Pa.

CORRECTIONS AND ADDENDA

(the page numbers are those that have been added for this volume)

Paper 1

page 32

Equation at the top: Insert a minus sign after the equals sign

Eq. (1): Insert a minus sign after the opening square bracket

page 33

Equation in the middle of the page: Insert a minus sign after the opening square bracket

Paper 8

page 97

Eq. (5), first line, left-hand term: Insert a minus sign after the equals sign

Paper 32

page 217

Eq. (10), next to last line: Should read

$$-\frac{(z_1 - z)}{(z_1 + z)}\left[\frac{Q_0(z)}{z} - \frac{Q_0(z_1)}{z_1}\right]$$

Eq. (10), last line: Should read

$$\times\left(\frac{2}{3}\mu_p\mu_n\right)\cdots$$

Paper 33

page 223

Figure 2: For $\vec{p}_1 - \vec{p}_0 = \vec{q}$ read $\vec{p}_1 - \vec{p}_0 = \hbar\vec{q}$

Figure 2 legend: For $\mathbf{q}$ read $\hbar\mathbf{q}$

Eq. (18): For a read a^2

page 231

Eq. (31): For $\frac{17}{12}$ read $\frac{17}{72}$

Ref. 54: For Asjkin read Ashkin

page 240

1st col., line 20: For $(F < 1)$ read $(F_2 < 1)$

1st col., line 21: For $(F_2 < 1)$ read $(F_1 < 1)$

page 241

1st col., line 24: For $\times 10^{-26}$ cm^2 read $\times 10^{26}$ cm^2

page 258

1st col., line 23: For Figure 52 read Figure 53

page 259

Table VI, $_3Li^7$, col. (10): For 1.19 read 1.91

Paper 35

page 276

2nd col., line 26: The sentence should read "Thus, the discrepancy of Fig. 4 results only from the S-state charge distribution of the deuteron."

Paper 40

page 312

1st col., 1st eq.: the symbol α was omitted from the expression on the right-hand side

1st col., Eq. (16): For 0.58 read 0.51

Paper 42

page 329

Eq. 66: Add t after the parenthesis $(E_0 - E)$

page 330

Eq. 70: Change the minus sign after the equals sign to a plus sign

Eq. 71: Delete the e before the integral

Eq. 74: For e^4 read e^2

Eq. 76: For 2 read 4 (after the minus sign)

Paper 44

page 415

Figure 1: A statement was omitted that the decrease to zero of the left-hand peak on the low-energy side arises from a cutoff of the Cerenkov counter and not from a true decrease of the number of scattered electrons.

Paper 48

The authors wish to add the following addendum to their article.

The cross section for large-angle bremsstrahlung is given very accurately by the formula below (proof not given), which amplifies and replaces Eq. (13) (page 456) of the article:

$$\frac{d^2\sigma}{d\Omega dE_2} = \frac{t_0 f(x_1)}{k_1}\left(\frac{dk_1}{dE_2}\right)\frac{d\sigma}{d\Omega}(E_1 - k_1) + \frac{t_0 f(x_2)}{k_2}\ \frac{d\sigma}{d\Omega}(E_1) \tag{1}$$

where the electron may be considered to radiate a photon spectrum, per radiation length, given by

$$f(x) \equiv \frac{1}{2}[1 + x^2] \tag{2}$$

in traversing an equivalent radiator of

$$t_0 = \frac{1}{137\pi}\ [\ln(q^\mu q_\mu/\mu^2) - 1] \tag{3}$$

radiation lengths.

Strong photon-electron angular correlations produce two distinct kinematic cases:

$$\begin{aligned} E_1 - k_1 = E_1 \cdot x_1 &= \frac{E_2}{1 - \frac{E_2}{M}(1 - \cos\theta)} \qquad (\mathbf{k}_1 \parallel \text{beam}) \\ E_2 + k_2 = E_2/x_2 &= \frac{E_1}{1 + \frac{E_1}{M}(1 - \cos\theta)} \qquad (\mathbf{k}_2 \parallel \text{scattered electron}) \end{aligned} \tag{4}$$

$$\frac{dk_1}{dE_2} = \left[1 - \frac{E_2}{M}(1 - \cos\theta)\right]^{-2}$$

The cross section given by (1) has been compared numerically with the quantum mechanically correct result of Berg and Lindner [R. A. Berg and C. N.

Lindner, *Phys. Rev.*, **112**, 2072 (1958)], which takes into account the physical properties of the proton. The agreement is ≈ 1 to 2 per cent for

$$x_1, x_2 \lesssim 0.6$$

and for all energies up to 5 Bev.

This formula is much easier to compute than the Berg-Lindner formula, especially if a table of elastic scattering cross sections is available.

Paper 58

page 536

5th line under Eq. (2): should read;

. . . in the second $\kappa = 12 m_\pi c/\hbar$, $q^2\kappa = 2.85 \times 10^6$ Mev.

8th line from bottom: should read:

. . . has values 1180, 295, 20, 1.5 Mev . . . .

Paper 70

page 608

Footnote 3 should contain an additional reference to G. F. Chew and S. Mandelstam, *Phys. Rev.*, **119**, 467 (1960).

At the end of the text there should be an additional footnote: [8] It is possible that the effects of large S-wave π-π scattering have been observed by A. Abashian, N. E. Booth, and K. M. Crowe, *Phys. Rev. Letters*, **5**, 258 (1960).

Paper 76

page 637

Owing to a computational error, the mean value of the $\pi^-\pi^\circ$ and $\pi^-\pi^+$ cross sections at the maximum of the resonance was incorrectly stated as $\sigma_{\pi-\pi} = 95$ mb. The correct value is 65.0 ± 7.5 mb. The values of the ordinate in Fig. 3 should be multiplied by 0.68.

Paper 77

page 643

Table I, col. 6, line 43: For 0.470 read 0.0470
Table I, col. 6, line 44: For 0.338 read 0.0338
Table I, col. 9, line 43: For 0.450 read 0.0450
Table I, col. 9, line 44: For 0.368 read 0.0368

Paper 81

page 679

The authors wish to point out that in Table 1 the value of v_2 is incorrectly given as 1.10. The quantity v_2 should have the value 1.15. The corresponding value of $a_{2p}^2 + a_{2n}^2$ should be 1.57 fermi^2 instead of 1.50 fermi^2. No conclusions, data, or figures are altered by these corrections.

2nd col., line 32: $M_S^2 = M_V^2 \sim (19 \pm 3)m_\pi^2$ should read
$M_S^2 = M_V^2 \sim (20 \pm 3)m_\pi^2$.

Table I, 3rd col., last entry: $M_S^2 = (23 \pm 3)m_\pi^2$ should read
$M_S^2 = (20 \pm 3)m_\pi^2$.

page 680

1st col., line 7: Mr. Carol Crannell should read Mrs. Carol Crannell.
Ref. 22: R. R. Wilson should read R. Wilson.

Paper 82

The authors have done additional work ("Mu-Mesonic X-Ray Energies and Nuclear Radii for Fourteen Elements from $Z = 12$ to $Z = 50$," to be published) which has been abstracted in the following remarks. I wish to thank Dr. H. L. Anderson for providing me with the following material before publication.

"The results have been interpreted to give a measure of the extent of the nuclear charge $R_e = (5\overline{r^2}/3)^{1/2}$ based on a Dirac theory of the μ-mesonic atom, correcting for the vacuum polarization but taking other possible perturbing effects (e.g., nuclear polarization) to be small. The $2p - 1s$ transition energy depends essentially on the second moment of the charge distribution, somewhat independently of the detail of the shape. The radius R_e refers to a sphere of uniform charge distribution having this value of $\overline{r^2}$. Our values of $r_0 = R_e/A^{1/3}$ are within $(1.22 \pm 0.02) \times 10^{-13}$ cm for all nine of our elements between $A = 35$ (Cl) and $A = 119$ (Sn). There is general, but not detailed, agreement with the radii that have been deduced from the Stanford electron scattering experiments."

NAME INDEX

(the page numbers are those that have been added for this volume)

The index includes names of persons who are authors of articles reproduced in this volume or who have been mentioned in the section called "Comments on the Reprints."

Alff, C., 25
Allton, E. A., 18, 452
Amaldi, E., 5
Alvarez, L. W., 27, 630
Anderson, H. L., 30, 681
Anderson, J. A., 25, 596
Avakov, G. V., 5
Ayer, F., 21
Backenstoss, G., 30
Baltay, C., 25, 604
Bang, V. X., 25, 596
Baranger, E. U., 9
Barber, W. C., 14
Barloutoud, R., 28
Barnes, K. J., 15
Bartlett, J. H., 3
Bastien, P. L., 28
Berge, J. P., 28
Bergia, S., 25, 599
Berkelman, K., 23, 573
Berley, D., 25
Berthold, F., 14
Bethe, H. A., 21
Block, M., 28, 648
Bonsignori, F., 21
Bosco, B., 26
Bowcock, J., 21, 543
Breit, G., 15, 21, 535
Brenner, S., 10
Brix, P., 30
Brown, G. E., 10
Brugger, H., 25
Bumiller, F., 17, 22, 28, 424, 567, 570, 639
Burke, P. G., 25, 596
Burleson, G. R., 5, 13
Carmony, D. D., 25, 28, 596
Carruthers, P., 21
Cassels, J. M., 23, 573
Chambers, E. E., 13, 261
Chew, G. F., 17, 440
Clementel, E., 14, 279
Colley, D., 25
Condon, E. U., 4
Cottingham, W. N., 21, 543
Courant, H., 25, 604
Crannell, H., 14
Croissiaux, M., 22, 28, 567, 570, 639
Crouch, M. F., 12, 210
Dahl, O. I., 28
Dally, E., 28, 639
De Vries, C., 23, 29, 588, 676
Dee, P. I., 4
Derado, I., 20, 524
Dhar, S., 13
Dirac, P. A. M., 3, 31
Downs, B. W., 15, 309
Drell, S. D., 5, 17, 19, 492
Drickey, D. J., 13, 29
Durand, L., III, 12, 18, 26, 29, 609
Ehrenberg, H. F., 16, 19, 414, 504
Elton, L. R. B., 5, 10, 13, 94
Engfer, R., 30
Engler, A., 28, 648
Ernst, F. J., 15
Erwin, A. R., 26, 606